Energy Conversion Factors

Selected from *Physics Today*, February 1964; recommended by National Academy of Sciences – National Research Council.

	FORMULA	FACTOR	
Thermochemical calorie	$\mathrm{cal_{th}}$	4.1840	joules
Electron volt	eV	1.60210×10^{-19}	joule $(\mathrm{eV})^{-1}$
ENERGY ASSOCIATED WITH			
unified atomic mass unit	c^2/N_Ae	9.31478×10^8	$\mathrm{eV}\text{-}\mathrm{u}^{-1}$
proton mass	$m_\mathrm{p}c^2/e$	9.38256×10^8	$\mathrm{eV}\text{-}m_\mathrm{p}{}^{-1}$
neutron mass	$m_\mathrm{n}c^2/e$	9.39550×10^8	$\mathrm{eV}\text{-}m_\mathrm{n}{}^{-1}$
electron mass	$m_\mathrm{e}c^2/e$	5.11006×10^5	$\mathrm{eV}\text{-}m_\mathrm{e}{}^{-1}$
cycle	e/h	2.41804×10^{14}	$\mathrm{Hz}(\mathrm{eV})^{-1}$
wavelength	ch/e	1.23981×10^{-6}	eV-m
°K	e/k	1.16049×10^4	$°\mathrm{K}(\mathrm{eV})^{-1}$

Introduction to

NUCLEAR PHYSICS

HARALD A. ENGE

Massachusetts Institute of Technology

ADDISON-WESLEY PUBLISHING COMPANY, INC., Reading, Massachusetts, U.S.A.

ADDISON-WESLEY (CANADA) LIMITED, Don Mills, Ontario

This book is in the Addison-Wesley Series in Physics

Printed in the United States of America

Library of Congress Catalog Card No. 66-21268

ISBN 0-201-01870-5
JKLMNOPQ-AL-898765

ADDISON-WESLEY PUBLISHING COMPANY
READING, MASSACHUSETTS · Menlo Park, California
London · Amsterdam · Sydney

ADDISON-WESLEY (CANADA) LIMITED
DON MILLS, ONTARIO

Preface

The main parts of this book have been developed from lecture notes for a course in Introduction to Nuclear Physics that I have given at Massachusetts Institute of Technology for a number of years. Prerequisite for this subject is a one-term course in atomic physics with wave mechanics. Some knowledge of elementary wave mechanics is therefore necessary for the full understanding of the major parts of this book. For those readers who feel uncertain about their proficiency in this subject, a brief review is given in Appendix 1.

It is difficult to define the level of this book as a third-year, fourth-year, or graduate text. Any student who has studied mechanics, electricity and magnetism, and elementary wave mechanics is ready for it. The students taking the course at Massachusetts Institute of Technology are indeed from the third and fourth year, as well as from the graduate school.

The book covers what I feel are the most important areas of nuclear-structure physics, or low-energy nuclear physics. Only one chapter out of fifteen has been devoted to the exciting field of elementary-particle physics, and one chapter covers nuclear energy. There are several reasons why elementary-particle physics or high-energy physics has not been covered more extensively in this book. The most obvious one is that it is not my own field of specialization, and in experimental nuclear physics, the low- and high-energy fields are pretty much separated now. Another reason is that the elementary-particle field is in a period of rapid development such that what is written now is very soon outdated. It is my hope that a specialist in the high-energy field will write an accompanying text.

In the organization of the material in this book, no attention whatsoever has been paid to the historical development of the subject. The experiments selected as examples are practically always typical, good, recent experiments rather than historical firsts. In each chapter, covering a given topic, the experimental facts are usually presented first. Thereafter, a theory is developed for this topic, and finally, experimental results and theory are compared. In this way, I hope to impress upon the student the fact that physics is an experimental science. Partly for reasons of mathematical complexity, theories of modern physics are most often derived by use of a number of approximations. Sometimes these theories can describe the physical processes with amazing precision, relatively speaking. Sometimes there is hardly any resemblance at all between the experimental facts and the theoretical results, and it becomes a matter of judgment whether the theoretical exercise has proved anything or not. Naturally, I have selected for this elementary text only simple, straightforward theories which have enjoyed a reasonable measure of success.

For a one-semester course, I have taken the material for my lectures mostly from Chapters 1, 2, 3, 6, 9, 10, 11, 13, and 15. The other chapters can be left out almost completely without loss of continuity.

Some of the problems given at the end of each chapter are marked with an asterisk. These are intended for use as "term problems"; that is, they require a considerable amount of work on the part of the student. Many of them have several sets of numerical parameters to be used. The instructor can then give one set to each student.

A number of people have helped in various phases of the development of this book. Without comparison, the person to whom I owe the greatest debt of gratitude is Mrs. Mary E. White, secretary, typist, language teacher, proofreader, indexer, and librarian and researcher for table material. My sincere thanks also go to Mr. James E. Spencer and Mrs. Helen J. Young for valuable help, particularly in the assimilation of the material for the Table of Nuclides (Appendix 6). Corrections and suggestions received from Professor H. A. Medicus, Professor P. R. Bevington, and Mr. K. Endre Toth have been extremely helpful. Finally, a project such as this, which has to be carried out mostly evenings and on weekends, becomes a family project. The encouragement and help received from my wife and boys are greatly appreciated.

H.A.E.

Winchester, Massachusetts
May 1966

Contents

PART 3 Properties of Stable Nuclei, Nuclear Models

Chapter 4 Masses and Relative Abundances of Atomic Species

Chapter 5 Nuclear Moments

Chapter 6 Nuclear Models

PART 1

Introduction

1 Brief Discussion of Nuclear Properties

1–1 *Objectives of Studying Nuclear Physics*

Rutherford established the fact that the atom consists of a nucleus surrounded by electrons. The diameter of the atom is roughly 10^{-8} cm, and that of the nucleus is of the order of 10^{-12} cm. Atomic dimensions are already much too small for direct visual observations, even if the most powerful microscopes are used. However, we can still "study" the atom or the nucleus by indirect methods. These involve performing certain experiments from which we obtain data that we can see or hear and arranging each experiment so that the observed data must have some bearing on what goes on inside the atom or the nucleus.

The principal aim of nuclear physics studies is, then, by the aid of such indirect data, to understand how the nucleus is constructed and specifically to find the answers to the following questions.

(1) What are the building blocks of the nuclei?

(2) How do they move relative to each other?

(3) What is the law or laws governing the forces holding a nucleus together?

The answer to the first of these questions has long been known: the building blocks are neutrons and protons, each of which, however, has its own internal structure. Nuclear physics proper, also called low-energy nuclear physics or nuclear-structure physics, concerns itself with the questions of nuclear forces and nuclear structure. High-energy nuclear physics, or elementary-particle physics, deals with the particles of physics, their interactions, and their structure.

The expressions and concepts used in nuclear physics are mostly borrowed from macroscopic physics. We try to picture nucleons (protons and neutrons) moving around each other, subject to forces acting between them. This may be a very clumsy approach to the problem, but man is a creature who has not been provided with the proper senses to observe directly what is going on inside the nucleus. We shall continue to use borrowed expressions such as velocity, force, potential energy, etc., but we must always keep an open mind, and be very critical in using these classical concepts in nuclear physics.

Newton's laws are the accepted physical laws for describing motion of macroscopic particles at low and medium velocities. As amended by Einstein and others, these laws work for high velocities as well. By macroscopic particles, we mean particles with diameters of, say, more than 10^{-4} cm. Wave mechanics has had spectacular success in describing atomic and molecular phenomena which involve systems with diameters of the order of 10^{-8} cm. An important question now is: Can we extrapolate the proved validity of the wave-mechanics methods from atomic dimensions to the realm of the nucleus? The linear dimensions, as we have mentioned, decrease approximately by a factor of 10^4. Even more spectacular, perhaps, than the difference in linear dimensions is the difference in measurable *energy densities* between the macroscopic, atomic, and nuclear systems. A steel bar (or spring) under elastic tension may have a recoverable ("macroscopic") energy content of about 10^6 joules/m^3. The binding energy of all the electrons in heavy-element atoms amounts to about 10^{16} joules/m^3 of atomic matter (ordinary matter). The binding energy of the nucleons in an atomic nucleus amounts to about 10^{32} joules/m^3 of nuclear matter.

The answer to the question of whether or not wave mechanics can properly describe all important nuclear phenomena cannot yet be given with conviction. As we shall see later in this text, wave mechanics has been very successful, at least in some cases. In other instances, the extreme mathematical complexities of the problem make it difficult to decide whether it is the right approach.

In the following chapters we shall describe certain selected experiments in nuclear physics and try to understand, by means of elementary theories, how these experiments can further our understanding of nuclear forces and of nuclear structure. These experiments can be classified roughly as follows:

(1) measurement of static (unchanging) properties of nuclei, including measurements of size, mass, angular momentum, magnetic dipole moment, electric quadrupole moment, etc.;

(2) disintegration studies of radioactive nuclei (self-inflicted changes);

(3) studies of reactions of transmutation (forced changes).

This introductory chapter contains brief discussions of these topics to give the reader a quick glance at the subject matter that will be covered in the text and to introduce some of the terminology that will be used. On one topic, the size of nuclei, there is no further discussion in the text, and the treatment in this chapter is therefore somewhat more detailed than a mere introduction to concepts would warrant.

1–2 Nomenclature

Two nuclei with identical numbers of protons, Z, and identical numbers of neutrons, N, belong to the same nuclear species. A nuclear species is called a *nuclide*. It is identified by its chemical symbol and a superscript indicating the total number of nucleons, $A = Z + N$. Sometimes the number of protons (implied by the chemical symbol) is given as a subscript in front of the symbol. Examples are given in Table 1–1. Nuclides with identical Z are called *isotopes*,

Table 1–1

Symbol	Element	Z	N	A
C^{12} or $_6C^{12}$	Carbon	6	6	12
C^{13} or $_6C^{13}$	Carbon	6	7	13
Kr^{86} or $_{36}Kr^{86}$	Krypton	36	50	86
Hg^{192} or $_{80}Hg^{192}$	Mercury	80	112	192

a term which is often incorrectly used instead of "nuclide." For instance, Hg^{192} is often called a "radioactive isotope." It is a radioactive nuclide. Nuclides with identical A are called *isobars;* those with identical N are called *isotones.* Finally, an excited state (Section 1–12) of a given nuclide may be relatively long-lived, so that its decay time is directly observable. Such an excited state is called an *isomeric* (or metastable) state, and thus two nuclei of the same species but in different energy states, of which at least one is metastable, are called *isomers.*

1–3 The Nuclear Radius

Nucleons in the nucleus are confined to an approximately spherically symmetric structure. It is customary to talk about a nuclear radius, although a sharp spherical wall with a large density of nucleons everywhere inside and zero density outside does not exist.

The most direct studies of the density of nucleons in nuclei have been made by Hofstadter and coworkers at Stanford University.* The method is one of high-energy (e.g., 183 MeV) electron scattering or diffraction. Figure 1–1 shows the experimental arrangement in schematical form. The electron beam from a linear accelerator is momentum-analyzed and steered into a scattering chamber by two deflecting magnets.† In the center of the scattering chamber, the beam passes through a thin foil of the scattering material, for instance gold. Electrons scattered by deflections in the electric fields of the nuclei in the foil may pass through a thin window in the scattering chamber, a short distance through air, and thereafter through another window into the vacuum system of a magnetic spectrometer. The latter instrument momentum-analyzes the scattered electrons so that only elastic events in the target foil are recorded. The spectrometer can rotate about an axis through the target so that the intensity of scattered electrons can be observed as a function of the scattering angle θ.

---

* See, for instance, R. Hofstadter, H. R. Fechter, and J. A. McIntyre, *Phys. Rev.* **92,** 978 (1953) and B. D. Hahn, D. G. Ravenhall, and R. Hofstadter, *Phys. Rev.* **101,** 1131 (1956). See also various papers in *Rev. Mod. Phys.* **30,** 142–584 (1958).

† Magnetic focusing of ion beams is discussed in Appendix 2.

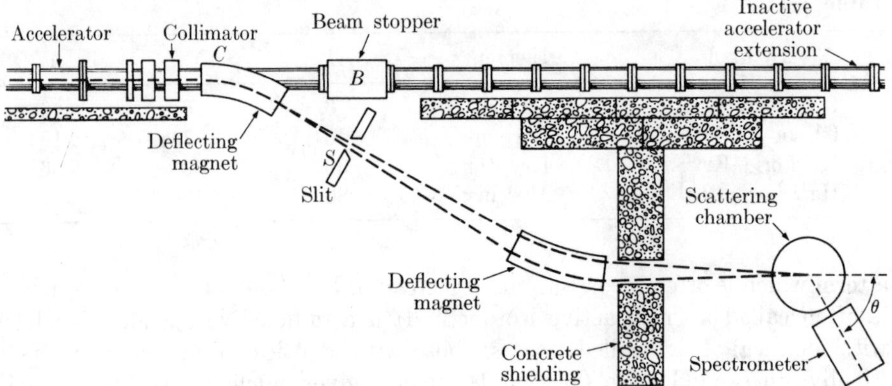

Fig. 1–1. Apparatus used by Hofstadter and coworkers for high-energy electron-scattering experiments of nuclei. (From R. Hofstadter *et al., op. cit.*)

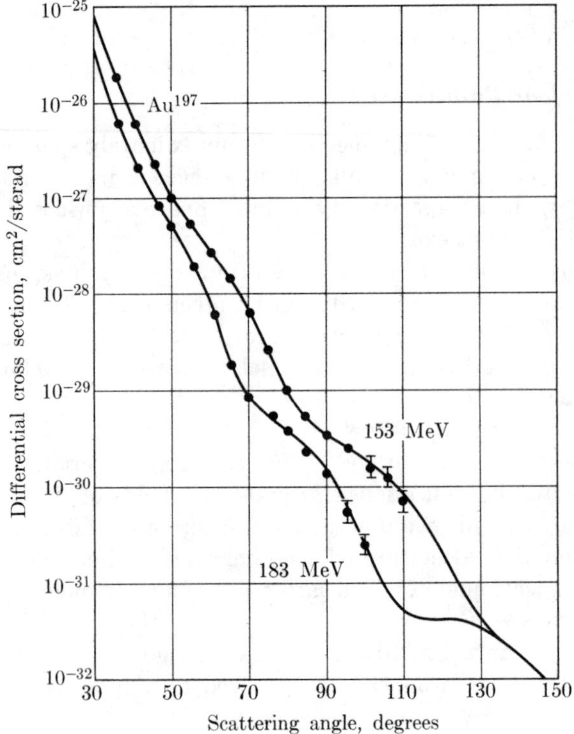

Fig. 1–2. Results of electron-scattering experiments performed on gold. (From B. Hahn *et al., op. cit.*)

Figure 1–2 shows two typical angular distributions for electrons elastically scattered by gold. The intensity falls off very rapidly for increasing angle θ, as does the intensity of alpha particles in a Rutherford-type experiment. The accurate analysis of electron-nucleus scattering is more complex than the analysis of Rutherford scattering, which is treated in all elementary texts on atomic physics. We shall not go into the details of electron-nucleus scattering here, but will simply point out that the attractive potential produced by the positive charge of the nucleus changes the momentum and hence the wavelength of the electrons. Therefore the electron-scattering process is very similar to the diffraction of light waves moving through media of different indexes of refraction, n. In this analogy, the nucleus can be thought of as a crystal ball, and it is well known from optics that light passing such an obstacle will leave a pattern of minima and maxima on a screen behind it (see Problem 1–2). The small wiggles in the angular distributions of Fig. 1–2 are reminiscent of such a diffraction pattern, but they are not quite so pronounced. The reason for this, as mentioned earlier, is that the nucleus does not have a sharp surface.

Hofstadter *et al.* assumed that the density of charge (protons) in the nucleus is distributed according to the formula

$$\rho = \frac{\rho_1}{1 + e^{(r-R_e)/z_1}}, \tag{1–1}$$

where ρ_1 is the density at small values of the radius r, R_e is the value of r that gives $\rho = \rho_1/2$, and z_1 is a measure of the surface thickness. The scattering data on gold and other elements were analyzed in terms of scattering potentials produced by spherically symmetric charge clouds of the form given in Eq. (1–1). In these analyses, the radius R_e and the thickness parameter z_1 were treated as adjustable parameters. The solid lines of Fig. 1–2 are examples of the results of such analyses for the best choice of R_e and z_1. The agreement between theory and experiment is very impressive, and the analyses provide relatively accurate determinations of R_e and z_1. Typical charge distributions found in some nuclides are illustrated in Fig. 1–3. Figure 1–3(a) shows the electric-charge density, i.e., plots of Eq. (1–1) with the best-fit values of R_e and z_1, and with ρ_1 chosen to give the correct total charge z_e. In Fig. 1–3(b) the *nucleon density* is calculated on the assumption that the distribution of nuclear matter is the same as the distribution of nuclear charge (protons). The number of nucleons in the nuclei studied ranges from 40 to 209. As illustrated by the examples in Fig. 1–3, it was found that the central parts of all these nuclei are of approximately the same density. We can therefore draw the important conclusion that *aside from surface effects, the density of nuclear matter is the same in all nuclei.* The experimental data are not accurate enough to yield the exact shape of the curves given in Fig. 1–3, particularly in the transition region, since functions similar to, but different from, Eq. (1–1) can give equally good fits. However, the data definitely indicate that the surface has a certain thickness. Hofstadter *et al.* define the thickness t as the distance between the points at 10 and 90%

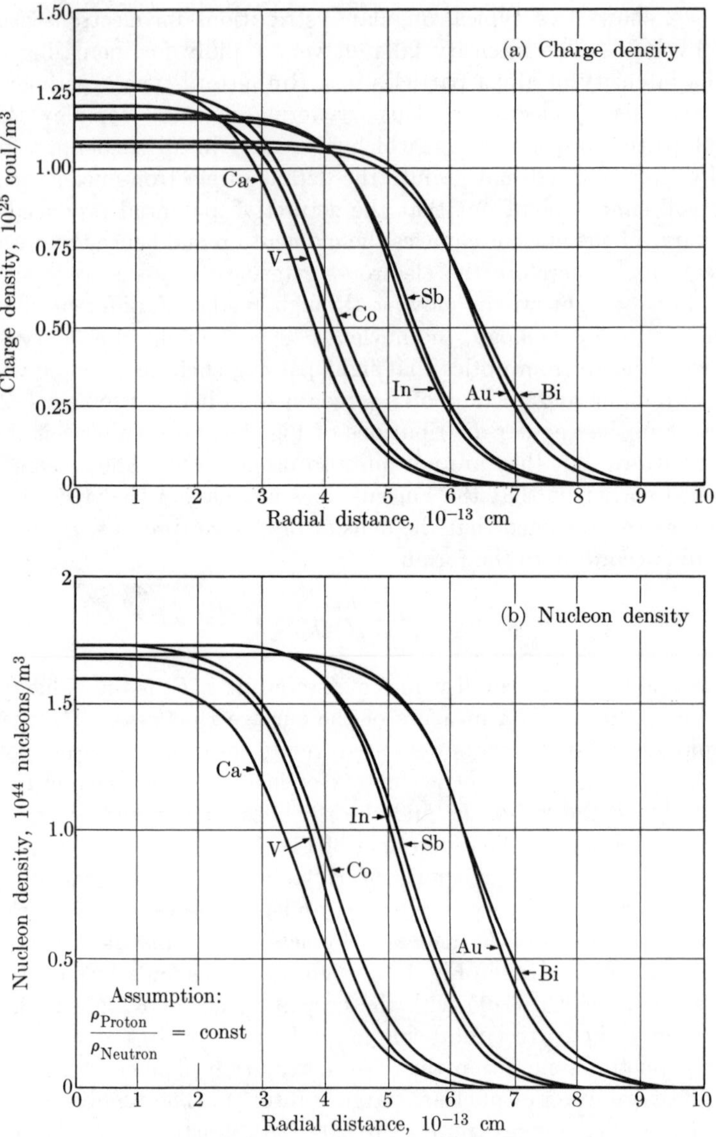

Fig. 1–3. Charge density and nucleon density as determined by high-energy electron scattering. (From B. Hahn *et al.*, *op. cit.*)

of maximum density. In terms of the thickness parameter z_1 of Eq. (1–1), it is then $t = 4z_1 \ln 3$, and the experimental results indicate that it is approximately the same for all nuclei and equal to

$$t = (2.4 \pm 0.3) \times 10^{-15}\ \mathrm{m}.$$

The distance from the center to the point at 50% of maximum density, called the *mean electromagnetic radius* R_e of the nucleus, is found to vary with nucleon number A as

$$R_e = (1.07 \pm 0.02)A^{1/3} \times 10^{-15}\ \mathrm{m} = 1.07A^{1/3}\ \mathrm{F}. \tag{1–2}$$

In nuclear physics it is customary to measure linear dimensions in fermis: $1\ \mathrm{F} = 10^{-15}\ \mathrm{m}$.

Other nuclei studied by the Stanford group exhibit diffraction patterns that indicate deviations from spherical symmetry. These deviations are expressed quantitatively through the *quadrupole moment*, which is discussed briefly in Section 1–8.

Other types of experiments give slightly higher values than Eq. (1–2) for the nuclear radius. However, all experiments indicate that the radius is approximately proportional to $A^{1/3}$. This is, of course, consistent with the observation made above that the density of nuclear matter is the same for all nuclei. Two examples of other types of experiments that yield information about the nuclear radius are (1) fast neutron scattering and (2) lifetime measurements of alpha-radioactive nuclei (Chapter 10). These experimental data may be analyzed in terms of a simplified model in which an attractive nuclear potential extends to a sharp radius R. They then yield approximately the following value for the *nuclear potential radius:*

$$R = 1.4A^{1/3} \times 10^{-15}\ \mathrm{m} = 1.4A^{1/3}\ \mathrm{F}. \tag{1–3}$$

The nuclear potential radius, as defined above, should not be expected to be exactly equal to the mean electromagnetic radius. The two results, Eqs. (1–2) and (1–3), are compatible.

1–4 Nuclear Mass and Binding Energy

The nucleus contains about 99.975% of the mass of an atom. A table of nuclear masses can be made from an atomic-mass table by subtracting the electron masses (with due consideration of the mass reduction associated with the atomic binding energies when accuracy warrants this). However, except for the nuclear "particles," which are ionized hydrogen, helium, or heavier atoms, *atomic*, rather than nuclear masses, are almost always used in nuclear physics. Often it makes no difference which of the two is used, because the number of electrons cancels out in most equations involving masses (e.g., nuclear-reaction energies). In many cases, the presence of the atomic electrons should not be neglected, because they directly take part in the nuclear processes considered (e.g., electron capture, internal conversion).

The International Union of Pure and Applied Physics (IUPAP) on September 8, 1960 adopted a new mass scale based on C^{12} to replace the old scale, based on O^{16}. The mass of one unit (symbol u for *unified mass unit*) equals one-twelfth of the mass of the neutral unexcited atom consisting of a C^{12} nucleus and six electrons. The choice of a unit for atomic masses other than the one used for macroscopic bodies (the kilogram) is justified by the convenient magnitudes of the atomic masses on this scale and by the extremely high degree of accuracy (Chapter 4) which can be achieved in measuring atomic masses relative to each other and particularly relative to C^{12}. In kilograms, the unified mass unit is

$$1\ \mathrm{u} = \frac{10^{-3}}{N_A} = \frac{10^{-3}}{6.02252 \times 10^{23}} = 1.66043 \times 10^{-27}\ \mathrm{kg},$$

where N_A is the new Avogadro number. The energy equivalent in joules of the mass unit is

$$E = mc^2 = 1.66043 \times 10^{-27} \times (2.997925 \times 10^8)^2 = 1.492232 \times 10^{-10}\ \mathrm{J}.$$

The energy unit *electron volt* (eV) is equal to the energy acquired by a particle of charge $e = 1.60210 \times 10^{-19}$ coul when it is accelerated through a potential of 1 V. This is equal to 1.60210×10^{-19} J. Hence the energy equivalent of the atomic mass-unit is

$$E = mc^2/e = 9.31480 \times 10^8\ \mathrm{eV} = 931.480\ \mathrm{MeV}.$$

The rest mass and energy equivalent of the particles (ions) encountered in low-energy nuclear physics are listed in Table 1–2. The rest masses for some examples of atomic species are listed in Table 1–3 of Section 1–6. Table 1–3 also lists the binding energies of the nuclei, that is, the energy that is released when the appropriate numbers of protons and neutrons are combined to form the nucleus. The binding energy (BE) can be calculated as the reduction in mass times the square of the velocity of light,

$$\mathrm{BE} = [Zm_{\mathrm{p}} + (A - Z)m_{\mathrm{n}} - {}_Zm^A]c^2, \tag{1–4}$$

where Z is the number of protons, $A - Z$ is the number of neutrons, and m_{p}, m_{n}, and ${}_Zm^A$ are the rest masses of the proton, neutron, and the final nucleus, respectively. Note that the binding energy is a positive quantity.

Table 1–3 also gives the total *atomic* binding energy, that is, the energy that is released when the nucleus combines with Z electrons to form a neutral atom. Clearly, the atomic binding energy is quite small compared with the nuclear

Table 1–2. Mass and energy equivalent of nuclear particles

	u	m_0c^2, MeV
Electron	5.48597×10^{-4}	0.511007
Neutron	1.008665	939.551
Proton	1.007277	938.258
Deuteron	2.013554	1875.585
Triton	3.015501	2808.879
$(He^3)^{++}$	3.014933	2808.350
Alpha particle	4.001506	3727.323

binding energy. We can therefore, without appreciable error, compute the nuclear binding energy as

$$\mathrm{BE} = [ZM_{\mathrm{H}} + (A - Z)M_{\mathrm{n}} - {}_ZM^A]c^2, \tag{1–5}$$

where the M's represent *atomic* masses. For the neutron, of course, the mass is the same as above. What Eq. (1–5) actually expresses is the energy that will have to be removed when Z hydrogen atoms and $A - Z$ neutrons form the neutral atom ${}_ZM^A$ in its nuclear and atomic ground state. Since the electron rest masses cancel in Eq. (1–5) and since the atomic binding energies are very small, Eq. (1–5) can be used instead of Eq. (1–4) to compute the nuclear binding energies.

1–5 Angular Momentum

Qualitatively, we can picture a nucleus as consisting of nucleons moving about the center of mass in certain orbits ("independent-particle model"). Protons and neutrons have the same intrinsic-spin quantum number as the electron, $s = \frac{1}{2}$, and their orbital angular momenta have integral quantum numbers, just as in atomic physics. *The resulting total angular-momentum quantum number J is therefore integral for nuclei with even A and half-integral for nuclei with odd A.* As in atomic physics, the square of the total angular momentum is given by the formula

$$p_J^2 = J(J + 1)\hbar^2, \tag{1–6}$$

where $\hbar = 1.05450 \times 10^{-34}$ joule-sec.

The total angular-momentum quantum number J is often called the "spin" of the nucleus, especially by atomic physicists, who, incidentally, use the symbol I. In this text, J will be referred to as the *angular momentum,* and the term "spin" will be reserved for the intrinsic spin of the neutron or proton. Some examples of ground-state angular momenta of nuclei are given in Table 1–3.

If the component of the angular-momentum vector can be measured along any particular direction (the direction of a magnetic field or of a beam of particles, for instance), such a measurement can give only one of the following results: $-J\hbar$, $(-J+1)\hbar, \ldots, J\hbar$. For the theoretical treatment of any problem involving the angular momentum, the z-axis is oriented so that it coincides with the direction of the magnetic field or the beam of particles. The z-component of the total angular momentum is then $p_{Jz} = m_J\hbar$, where $m_J = -J, -J+1, \ldots$, or J. The number of orientations that the angular-momentum vector can have relative to a fixed axis is readily seen to be $2J+1$.

Experimenters spend more combined effort on the measurement of angular momenta of nuclear states than on the measurement of any other parameter of nuclear physics. This is because energy, angular momentum, and parity (see next section) are the most readily measurable parameters of the wave function for a given state and are also the most important ones for aiding the theorist in developing nuclear theories. The experimental methods used for measuring ground-state angular momenta are described in Chapter 5. For the ground states of even Z, even N nuclei, it has been found without exception that $J = 0$. The angular momenta and parities of excited states are deduced from disintegration and reaction data (Chapters 9, 10, 11, and 13).

1–6 Parity and Symmetry

Parity is a concept of great importance in atomic and nuclear physics, but with no counterpart in classical physics. It is a property of the wave function describing a quantum-mechanical system. A wave function representing a single particle is said to have positive (even) parity if it does not change sign by reflection through the origin, and negative (odd) parity if it does change sign. Thus

$$\psi(x, y, z) = \psi(-x, -y, -z), \qquad \text{for positive parity,}$$

$$\psi(x, y, z) = -\psi(-x, -y, -z), \qquad \text{for negative parity.}$$

A wave function describing many particles can be written as a product of individual-particle wave functions or as a sum of such products. The parity of the whole system is then obviously the product of the parities of the single-particle wave functions. Since $|\psi|^2$ is symmetric whether the parity is positive or negative, the mass density and the charge density of nuclei are always symmetric.

In nuclear processes, as in classical physics, total energy, momentum, and angular momentum are conserved. In addition, parity is also normally conserved. However, since the publication of the famous theoretical work of Lee and Yang* on this subject, several experiments have demonstrated that parity is not conserved in certain processes (see Section 11–8).

---

* T. D. Lee and C. N. Yang, *Phys. Rev.* **104,** 254 (1956); *Phys. Rev.* **105,** 1671 (1957).

The parity of a nuclear state is often indicated by a superscript + or − on the angular momentum J as illustrated by the examples in Table 1–3. In this table the proton has been assigned positive parity. This is merely a convention in nuclear-structure theory where the nucleons are treated as point particles; in elementary-particle research, however, it has deeper significance. The neutron also has positive parity.

Another significant concept in atomic and nuclear physics is that of symmetry. One simple solution of Schrödinger's equation for two identical noninteracting particles moving in the same potential is

$$\psi_{nk} = \psi_n(1)\psi_k(2), \tag{1–7}$$

where ψ_n and ψ_k are two solutions of the same one-body wave equation, and 1 and 2 represent the coordinates of particles 1 and 2. However, the wave function ψ_{nk} is not an acceptable function for two identical particles because it implies that we can label the particles and observe which particle is in state n and which is in state k. We can avoid this difficulty by writing the wave function in either one of the two following forms, both of which are solutions of Schrödinger's equation if Eq. (1–7) is a solution:

$$\psi_S = (1/\sqrt{2})[\psi_n(1)\psi_k(2) + \psi_n(2)\psi_k(1)], \tag{1–8a}$$

$$\psi_A = (1/\sqrt{2})[\psi_n(1)\psi_k(2) - \psi_n(2)\psi_k(1)]. \tag{1–8b}$$

The probability density $|\psi|^2$ is symmetric when labels 1 and 2 are interchanged in both equations. Therefore both represent acceptable solutions of the two-body problem. The wave function ψ_S is symmetric, and ψ_A is antisymmetric; that is, ψ_A changes sign when labels 1 and 2 are interchanged and ψ_S does not. When the two particles possess an intrinsic spin s, Eqs. (1–8) must be multiplied by appropriate spin functions.

It can be shown, in general, that symmetry is conserved,* but no theoretical principle can be invoked to show that functions with one kind of symmetry only are the appropriate ones for a given kind of particle. However, experimental evidence clearly shows that the total wave function for a system of particles having half-integral internal angular momentum (fermions) is antisymmetric in the exchange of any pair of particles. Conversely, the total wave function for a system of particles having integral internal angular momentum (bosons) is symmetric in the exchange of any pair.

The antisymmetric wave functions for fermions are consistent with the Pauli exclusion principle, which states that no more than one particle can have the same set of quantum numbers (including the quantum number describing its

---

* See, for instance, R. M. Eisberg, *Fundamentals of Modern Physics*, New York: John Wiley and Sons, 1962, p. 365.

Table 1–3. Examples of atomic masses, binding energies, nuclear angular momenta and parities, magnetic dipole moments, and electric quadrupole moments

Nuclide	Atomic mass, u	Nuclear binding energy, MeV	Atomic binding energy, MeV	Nuclear angular momentum and parity	Nuclear magnetic moment, nm	Nuclear electric quadrupole moment, 10^{-24} cm^2	$\Delta R/R$
$_1H^1$	1.007825	–	0.000014	$\frac{1}{2}^+$	+2.79275	–	–
$_1H^2$	2.014102	2.225	0.000014	1^+	+0.85735	+0.00282	0.04*
$_2He^4$	4.002603	28.295	0.000079	0^+	0	0	0
$_3Li^7$	7.016004	39.244	0.00019	$\frac{3}{2}^-$	+3.2564	−0.04	?
$_8O^{16}$	15.994916	127.617	0.0020	0^+	0	0	0
$_{17}Cl^{35}$	34.968851	298.20	0.012	$\frac{3}{2}^+$	+0.8218	−0.0790	−0.032
$_{26}Fe^{57}$	56.935398	499.90	0.034	$\frac{1}{2}^-$	0.05	0	0
$_{71}Lu^{176}$	175.942660	1417.97	0.37	7^-	+3.180	+8.0	0.26
$_{92}U^{235}$	235.043915	1783.17	0.69	$\frac{7}{2}^-$	−0.35	±4.1	±0.083

*For the deuteron, a radius $R = 2.4$ F has been used. Equation (1–2) yields 1.35 F, but this formula is not applicable for a two-nucleon system.

spin direction). For the nucleus, where we are dealing with two kinds of particles with half-integral spin, the exclusion principle operates within each group of particles, but does not prevent a neutron and a proton from having the same set of quantum numbers. Expressed differently, the wave function can be symmetric or antisymmetric in the exchange of the two particles. The symmetry of nuclear wave functions in proton-neutron exchange and an associated quantum number, the *isospin*, are discussed in Section 6–7.

1–7 Magnetic Dipole Moment

The magnetic dipole moment set up by a plane current loop is $\mu_1 = iS$, where i is the current and S is the area of the loop. A revolving spinless particle with electric charge e therefore sets up a magnetic dipole moment which is equal to the number of revolutions per second times the charge times the area enclosed by the orbit. For a circular loop we find that

$$\mu_1 = (ev/2\pi r)\pi r^2 = evr/2,$$

where v is the velocity of the particle and r is the radius of the orbit. The orbital angular momentum of this particle is $p_l = mvr$. The ratio of the magnetic dipole moment to the angular momentum is called the *gyromagnetic ratio*. It is

$$\gamma = \mu_1/p_l = e/2m. \tag{1–9}$$

This relationship will obviously hold also for components of the two vectors μ_1 and p_l in any direction, for instance in the direction of a magnetic field. From quantum mechanics, we know that the component of the mechanical moment p_l along a defined direction (z-direction) is $m_l\hbar$, where m_l is a positive or negative integer or zero. Therefore, for the z-component of the magnetic dipole moment, we obtain

$$\mu_{1z} = (e\hbar/2m)m_l. \tag{1–10}$$

This expression yields the correct result for the z-component of the magnetic dipole moment that is due to orbital motion of electrons in an atom. It is believed to give the correct result also for the orbital motion of protons in a nucleus. The mass in the denominator of Eq. (1–10) should then be the proton mass m_{p}. In order to have a convenient scale for magnetic dipole moments, we introduce the nuclear magneton defined by

$$1 \text{ nuclear magneton (nm) } \frac{e\hbar}{2m_{\text{p}}} = 5.0505 \times 10^{-27} \text{ J-m}^2/\text{Wb.}^*$$

On this scale, clearly, the z-component of the magnetic dipole moment resulting from orbital motion of a proton is just m_l nuclear magnetons.

---

* The Bohr magneton used in atomic physics has the value $m_{\text{p}}/m_0 = 1836.12$ nuclear magnetons (m_0 is the electron mass).

The magnetic dipole moment can be calculated classically in the same fashion as above for a body spinning about its own axis. If we make the assumption that the distribution of charge in the body is the same as the distribution of mass (not necessarily true), we get the same result as in Eq. (1–10). For a body without charge, of course, we get no magnetic dipole moment. On this basis, for the electron, proton, and neutron we expect to find one-half Bohr magneton, one-half nuclear magneton, and zero, respectively, since the z-component of the intrinsic spin is one-half in all cases. Experimentally, for these z-components we find:

Electron, -1.001145358 Bohr magnetons;

Proton, 2.79275 nuclear magnetons;

Neutron, -1.9135 nuclear magnetons.

The value of the magnetic dipole moment for the electron is accounted for by modern theories (quantum electrodynamics). However, the values of the proton and neutron magnetic dipole moments have yet to be explained. The negative signs indicate that the directions of the angular momentum vector and the magnetic dipole moment vector are opposite.

The total magnetic dipole moment for a nucleus is the sum of the moments associated with the spins of the protons and neutrons and the moments associated with the orbital motion of the proton. Since the z-component of the magnetic dipole moment is the only component observable (through its interaction with a magnetic field), by convention we take the expression *the magnetic (dipole) moment* for a nucleus to mean the maximum z-component or

$$\mu \equiv \mu_{1z} \quad \text{in the state where} \quad m_J = J.$$

The magnetic dipole moments for the nuclei in Table 1–3 are given in column 6 of the table.

1–8 Electric Quadrupole Moment

The electric dipole moment for an assembly of charges can be defined as

$$\mathbf{p}_E = \int_N \mathbf{r}\rho \, d\tau, \tag{1–11}$$

where ρ is the charge density, $d\tau$ the volume element, and the integration is carried out over the charged system (nucleus N). An electric dipole moment is zero for atoms and nuclei in stationary states. This is a consequence of the symmetry of nuclei about the center of mass; in other words, it is a consequence of the definite parity of the nuclear states. However this symmetry does not need to be spherical; there is nothing precluding the nucleus from assuming the shape of an ellipsoid of rotation, for instance. Indeed, most nuclei do assume approximately such a shape, and the deviation from spherical symmetry is expressed by a quantity called the *electric quadrupole moment.* This concept can best be introduced in the following manner.

Assume that an electric potential $U(x, y, z)$ can be defined in a region of space surrounding the origin of the coordinate system (x, y, z). We place a nucleus having a charge density $\rho(x, y, z)$ with its center of mass (charge center) at the origin. To calculate the total electrostatic energy resulting from the interaction between U and ρ, we expand the electric potential U in a Taylor series of x, y, and z. The interaction energy can then be expressed as

$$
\begin{aligned}
E = \int U(x, y, z)\rho\, d\tau &= U(0) \int \rho\, d\tau \\
&+ \left(\frac{\partial U}{\partial x}\right)_0 \int x\rho\, d\tau + \left(\frac{\partial U}{\partial y}\right)_0 \int y\rho\, d\tau + \left(\frac{\partial U}{\partial z}\right)_0 \int z\rho\, d\tau \\
&+ \frac{1}{2}\left(\frac{\partial^2 U}{\partial x^2}\right)_0 \int x^2\rho\, d\tau + \frac{1}{2}\left(\frac{\partial^2 U}{\partial y^2}\right)_0 \int y^2\rho\, d\tau + \frac{1}{2}\left(\frac{\partial^2 U}{\partial z^2}\right)_0 \int z^2\rho\, d\tau \\
&+ \left(\frac{\partial^2 U}{\partial x\, \partial y}\right)_0 \int xy\rho\, d\tau + \left(\frac{\partial^2 U}{\partial x\, \partial z}\right)_0 \int xz\rho\, d\tau + \left(\frac{\partial^2 U}{\partial y\, \partial z}\right)_0 \int yz\rho\, d\tau \\
&+ \text{higher-order terms.}
\end{aligned} \tag{1-12}
$$

The first line gives simply the interaction energy of a point charge (monopole) in the field $U(0)$. The second line gives the energy of a dipole with its x-, y-, and z-components in the electric field with components $-\partial U/\partial x$, etc. The six terms on the next two lines are quadrupole terms with the six integrals defining six cartesian components of the quadrupole moment. Not all these terms are linearly independent, however, and for an ellipsoid of rotation, a single quadrupole moment suffices to describe the interaction. Let us show this.

First, because of symmetry, the three integrals involving the cross products xy, xz, and yz vanish. Second, when the z-axis is the symmetry axis, the integral over y^2 gives the same result as the integral over x^2. We can therefore write, for the quadrupole interaction energy,

$$
\Delta E_2 = \frac{1}{2}\left(\frac{\partial^2 U}{\partial z^2}\right)_0 \int z^2\rho\, d\tau + \frac{1}{2}\left(\frac{\partial^2 U}{\partial x^2} + \frac{\partial^2 U}{\partial y^2}\right)_0 \int \frac{x^2 + y^2}{2}\, \rho\, d\tau.
$$

Now, from Laplace's equation, we have

$$
\frac{\partial^2 U}{\partial x^2} + \frac{\partial^2 U}{\partial y^2} = -\frac{\partial^2 U}{\partial z^2}\cdot
$$

By substituting this and $r^2 = x^2 + y^2 + z^2$, we obtain

$$
\Delta E_2 = \frac{1}{4}\left(\frac{\partial^2 U}{\partial z^2}\right)_0 \int (3z^2 - r^2)\rho\, d\tau = \frac{eQ}{4}\left(\frac{\partial^2 U}{\partial z^2}\right)_0, \tag{1-13}
$$

where the quadrupole moment Q is defined as

$$Q = (1/e) \int (3z^2 - r^2)\rho \, d\tau. \tag{1–14}$$

According to Eq. (1–14), the expression will give $Q = 0$ for a spherically symmetric charge distribution. A charge distribution stretched in the z-direction (prolate) will give a positive quadrupole moment, and an oblate distribution will give a negative quadrupole moment. Since the expression is divided by the electronic charge, the dimension of the quadrupole moment is that of an area which, in nuclear physics, is measured in barns (1 barn $= 10^{-24}$ cm^2).

In a quantum-mechanical definition of the quadrupole moment (Section 9–4), the charge density ρ is replaced by the probability density $|\psi|^2$, and the expression is summed over all the protons. In principle, these calculations are simple and directly yield the quadrupole moment referred to the z-axis. In classical or semiclassical calculations, one must consider the fact that the nuclear symmetry axis is not, in general, the space-fixed z-axis to which measured quadrupole moments are referred. Let us assume that the J-axis can be regarded as a symmetry axis, or at least that the time average of the charge distribution has a rotational symmetry about the J-axis. We can then define a quadrupole moment Q_J given by Eq. (1–14) with the z-direction along the J-vector. The angle θ between this vector and the space-fixed z-axis in the state for which $m_J = J$ is given by

$$\cos \theta = J/\sqrt{J(J+1)} = \sqrt{J/(J+1)}$$

(not applicable for $J = 0$, of course). It can be shown by simple classical calculations (Problem 1–7) that the relationship between Q_J and the observed quadrupole moment Q, which relates to the space-fixed z-axis in the state $m_J = J$, is

$$Q = \frac{J - \frac{1}{2}}{J + 1} Q_J. \tag{1–15}$$

This shows that a nucleus with $J = \frac{1}{2}$ has a zero quadrupole moment with reference to a space-fixed axis. The same is true for a nucleus with $J = 0$ for which there are no constraints on the orientation, and therefore the time-averaged charge distribution is symmetric.

If we picture the nucleus as a uniformly charged ellipsoid of rotation with the symmetry axis along the J-vector, the quadrupole moment referred to this axis will be (see Problem 1–8)

$$Q_J = \tfrac{2}{5}Z(a^2 - b^2) \approx \tfrac{6}{5}ZR^2(\Delta R/R). \tag{1–16}$$

Here, Z is the element number, R is the average nuclear radius, a and b are the major and minor half-axes, and ΔR is the deviation from average in the direction of the symmetry axis. As we will discuss further in Section 6–8, the nuclear symmetry axis is never quite aligned with the J-vector so that Q_J, the time-averaged quadrupole moment in the J-direction, is smaller than the *intrinsic* quadrupole moment Q_{int} referred to the symmetry axis.

The largest quadrupole moments measured (for example, Lu^{176} and Er^{167}) represent deviations from spherical symmetry of $\Delta R/R \approx 25$ to 30%. Table 1–3 gives examples of some experimentally determined quadrupole moments and the corresponding values of $\Delta R/R$.

1–9 Nuclear-Disintegration Processes

The most important nuclear-disintegration processes are described very briefly below. The purpose here is mainly to introduce the terminology. More detailed treatments of these processes are presented in Chapters 9, 10, and 11.

Figure 1–4 illustrates the various kinds of breakup or disintegration processes that radioactive (unstable) nuclei may undergo. The nucleus is represented as an assembly of protons and neutrons, a proton being indicated by a cross, and a neutron by an open circle.

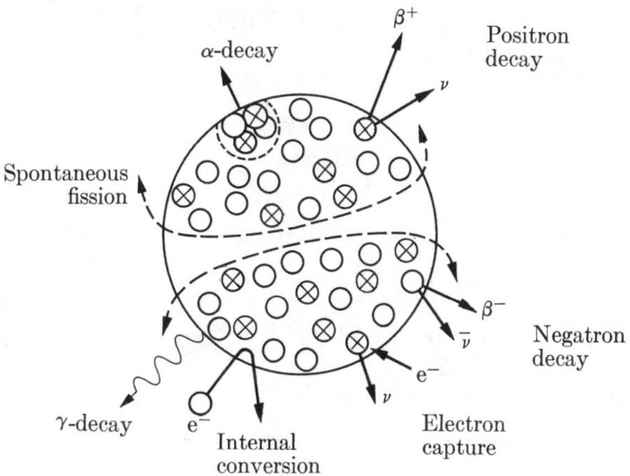

Fig. 1–4. Nuclear decay modes.

(*a*) *Alpha disintegration.* All nuclei heavier than lead are unstable. Some of them disintegrate by alpha emission. As indicated in the diagram, this means that two protons and two neutrons leave the nucleus together in an assembly called the alpha particle, which is identical to the He^4 nucleus. The reason that such an assembly, rather than a single particle, leaves the nucleus will be made clear in Chapter 10, "Alpha Decay."

(*b*) *Spontaneous fission.* Some heavy nuclei may decay by spontaneous fission. This means that the nucleus breaks up into two or possibly three large fragments plus some neutrons. The large fragments form new nuclei which are radioactive and decay in a chain of beta disintegrations toward stable nuclei in the intermediate-mass range.

(*c*) *Beta disintegration.* A less drastic change of the nucleus takes place in the beta-disintegration process. In a β^- process, a neutron in the nucleus changes into a proton, while a negative electron and an antineutrino simultaneously are created and emitted. In a β^+ process, a proton changes into a neutron, while a positron and a neutrino are created. The positron is a particle of the same mass and spin as an electron but with positive charge. The neutrino and antineutrino are particles with zero rest mass and spin of 1/2. In both the β^- and the β^+ processes, the disintegration energy is supplied through a change in the rest energy and binding energy of the nucleon that is converted, and also, to some extent, through a change in the binding of other nucleons. The energy is expended mostly as rest energy and kinetic energy of the created particles. The beta particle and the neutrino carry away almost all the disintegration energy. The residual nucleus will, in general, recoil slightly so that conservation of momentum is observed, but because of the comparatively large mass of the nucleus, the recoil energy is usually negligible.

A positron-emitting nuclide can also decay by capturing one of the orbital electrons of the atom and simultaneously emitting a neutrino. The neutrino in this case has to carry away all the disintegration energy with the exception of the small recoil energy of the nucleus.

(*d*) *Gamma emission.* Nuclei, as well as atoms, can exist only in certain quantum states (Section 1–12), each characterized by its eigenvalues for energy, angular momentum, and parity. De-excitation of these states down to the ground state can take place by gamma emission. A gamma ray is a photon (electromagnetic quantum) with energy $h\nu$ and momentum $h\nu/c$, just like the photon we encountered in atomic physics. There is no principal difference between an atomic photon, an x-ray quantum, and a gamma quantum, except perhaps for the wavelength. The difference in notation has historic reasons and serves the useful purpose of revealing the origin of the electromagnetic quantum. In competition with gamma emission there is a process called *internal conversion*, in which the energy is given to an atomic electron (e.g., K-electron) which thereby is expelled (Section 9–9).

All disintegration processes are characterized by the energy released in the process and the speed of the process in addition to the type of particles or quanta emitted. The parameter most often used for describing the speed is the half-life, $t_{1/2}$, which is defined as the time it takes for half the members of a large sample of unstable nuclei of a given kind to decay. The radioactive decay law and the relationship between the half-life and other parameters describing the speed of the disintegration process are described in Section 8–2.

1–10 Chart of Nuclides and Domains of Instabilities

A convenient way to present miscellaneous data concerning the nuclides is offered by the Chart of the Nuclides, or Segrè chart, in which each nucleus is represented by a unit square in a plot of Z vs. N. A small part of such a chart

SYMBOLS

RADIATIONS AND DECAY

α	alpha particle
β^-	negative electron
β^+	positron
γ	gamma ray
n	neutron
p	proton
ε	electron capture
IT	isomeric transition
D	radiation delayed
SF	spontaneous fission
E	disintegration energy

TIME

μs	microseconds (10^{-6}s)
s	seconds
m	minutes
h	hours
d	days
y	years

Z																	
11	Na 22.9898 σ.53										Na 20 0.4s β^+ (α > 2) E15	Na 21 3/+ 23s β^+2.50,·· γ.35 E3.52	Na 22 3+ 2.58y β^+.54,··, ε γ1.28 σ 90,000 E2.84	Na 23 3/+ 100 σ(40 + 13) 22.98977	Na 24 4+ 0.02s IT.47 / 15.0h β^-1.39,·· γ2.75, 1.37,·· E5.52	Na 25 5/+ 60s β^-3.8, 2.8,·· γ.98, .58, .40, 1.61,·· E3.8	Na 26 1.0s β^-6.7,·· γ1.83,·· E8.5
10	Ne 20.183 σ.26								Ne 17 0.69s β^+>5 (p 2.3, 3.8, 4.6, 4.9, 5.1)	Ne 18 1.46s β^+3.42, 2.37 γ1.04 E4.4	Ne 19 1/+ 18s β^+2.23 E3.25	Ne 20 90.92 19.99244	Ne 21 3/+ 0.257 σ100 20.99395	Ne 22 8.82 σ .036 21.99138	Ne 23 38s β^-4.4, 3.9,·· γ.44, 1.65 E4.4	Ne 24 3.38m β^-1.98, 1.10 γ.47, .88 E2.45	
9	F 18.9984 σ.010								F 16 ~10^{-19}s p.81 16.01171	F 17 66s β^+1.74 E2.76	F 18 1+ 110m β^+.65, ε E1.67	F 19 1/+ 100 σ.010 18.99840	F 20 11s β^-5.40 γ1.63 E7.03	F 21 4.6s β^-4.0, 5.4,·· γ.35, 1.38 E5.7		14	
8	O 15.9994 σ<.0002							O 14 71s β^+1.81, 4.14 γ2.31 E5.15	O 15 1/− 124s β^+1.74 noγ E2.76	O 16 99.759 σ <.0002 15.99491	O 17 5/+ 0.037 σ nα 2 16.99914	O 18 0.204 σ.0002 17.99916	O 19 5/+ 29s β^-3.25, 4.60 γ.20, 1.36,·· E4.81	O 20 14s β^-2.69 γ1.06 E3.8			
7	N 14.0067 σ 1.9						N 12 1+ 0.011s β^+16.4 (3α ~4) E17.6	N 13 1/− 10.0m β^+1.19 E2.22	N 14 1+ 99.63 σ_{np} 1.8 σ.008 14.00307	N 15 1/− 0.37 σ.00002 15.00011	N 16 2− 7.35s β^-4.3, 10.4,·· γ6.13, 7.12 (α1.7) E10.4	N 17 4.14s β^-3.3, 4.1, 2.7–8.7 (n 1.2, .43) γ.87,·· E8.7		12			
6	C 12.01115 σ.0037					C 10 19s β^+1.9,·· γ.72, 1.04 E3.6	C 11 3/− 20.5m β^+.96 noγ E1.98	C 12 98.89 σ.0037 12.00000	C 13 1/− 1.11 σ.0009 13.00335	C 14 5730y β^-.156 noγ σ<10^{-6} E.156	C 15 1/+ 2.25s β^-4.5, 9.77 γ5.30 E9.77	C 16 0.74s β^- (n) E8.0					
5	B 10.811 σ 759				B 8 0.78s β^+1.4 (2α3) E18	B 9 ≥3×10^{-19}s p, (2α) 9.01333	B 10 3+ 19.78 $\sigma_{n\alpha}$3840 σ.5 10.01294	B 11 3/− 80.22 σ < .05 11.00931	B 12 1+ 0.020s β^-13.4, 9.0 γ4.4 (α.2) E13.4	B 13 3/− 0.019s β^-13.4, 9.7 γ3.68 E13.4		10					
4	Be 9.0122 σ.009			Be 6 ≳4×10^{-21}s p, α, Li^5 6.0198	Be 7 3/− 53d ε γ.48 σ_{np} 5400 E.86	Be 8 ~3×10^{-16}s 2α.09 8.00531	Be 9 3/− 100 σ.009 9.01219	Be 10 2.7×10^6y β^-.56 noγ E.56	Be 11 13.6s β^-11.5, 9.3,·· γ2.12, 6.8, 4.6–8.0 E11.5								
3	Li 6.939 σ 71			Li 5 3/− ~10^{-21}s p, α 5.0125	Li 6 1+ 7.42 $\sigma_{n\alpha}$950 σ.031 6.01513	Li 7 3/− 92.58 σ.036 7.01601	Li 8 2+ 0.85s β^-13 (2α3) E16.0	Li 9 0.17s β^-11, 13 (n, 2α) E14		8							
2	He 4.0026 σ.007		He 3 1/+ 0.00013 σ_{np}5327 3.01603	He 4 ~100 σ0 4.00260	He 5 3/− 2×10^{-21}s n, α 5.0123	He 6 0.81s β^-3.51 noγ E3.51	He 7 ~50μs β^-~10,·· γ.5										
1	H 1.00797 σ.33	H 1 1/+ 99.985 σ.33 1.007825	H 2 1+ 0.015 σ.00057 2.01410	H 3 1/+ 12.26y β^-.0181 noγ E.0181		4		6									
			n 1 1/+ 12m β^-.78 E.78 1.008665		3												
			1	2													

Z ↑   N →

Chemical Element

H 1.00797 σ.33	— Symbol — Atomic Weight (Carbon-12 Scale) — Thermal Neutron Absorption Cross Section in Barns

Naturally Occurring or Otherwise Available but Radioactive

Symbol, Mass Number — Half-Life — Thermal Neutron Capture Cross Section in Barns —	C 14 5730y β^-.156 noγ σ<10^{-6} E.156	} Modes of Decay — Disintegration Energy in Mev

Artificially Radioactive

Modes of Decay, Radiation and Energy in Mev; ( ) Indicate Radiations from Short-Lived Daughter {	N 16 2− 7.35s β^-4.3, 10.4,·· γ6.13, 7.12 (α1.7) E10.4	— Symbol, Mass Number, J^π — Half-Life — Disintegration Energy in Mev

Two Isomeric States Both Radioactive

Disintegration Energy in Mev — Radioactive Upper Isomer	Na 24 4+ 0.02s IT.47 / 15.0h β^-1.39,·· γ2.75, 1.37,·· E5.52	— Symbol, Mass Number, J^π — Half Lives, ? Indicates Uncertainty Modes of Decay and Energy in Mev in Order of Intensity; ·· Indicates Additional Low Intensity Transitions; – Indicates Several Energies Included Disintegration Energy in Mev Radioactive Lower Isomer

Stable

Percent Abundance — Mass (Carbon-12 Scale) —	Ne 22 8.82 σ .036 21.99138	— Even Z, Even N Nuclides Have $J^\pi = 0^+$ — Symbol, Mass Number — Thermal Neutron Activation Cross Section in Barns

Figure 1-5

is shown in Fig. 1–5. The section is reproduced by permission from a complete chart covering all known nuclides and kept up to date by the Knolls Atomic Power Laboratory.* In these charts isotopes are arranged in horizontal lines and isotones in vertical lines, so that isobars fall along diagonals with slope −1. As can be seen from the section of the chart shown in Fig. 1–5, the stable and long-lived light nuclei occupy a band centered on the line $Z = N$. The nuclides below this band are β^- unstable, and the nuclides above are β^+ unstable. The beta unstable nuclides decay in chains along an isobar line toward the nearest stable nuclide in the band.

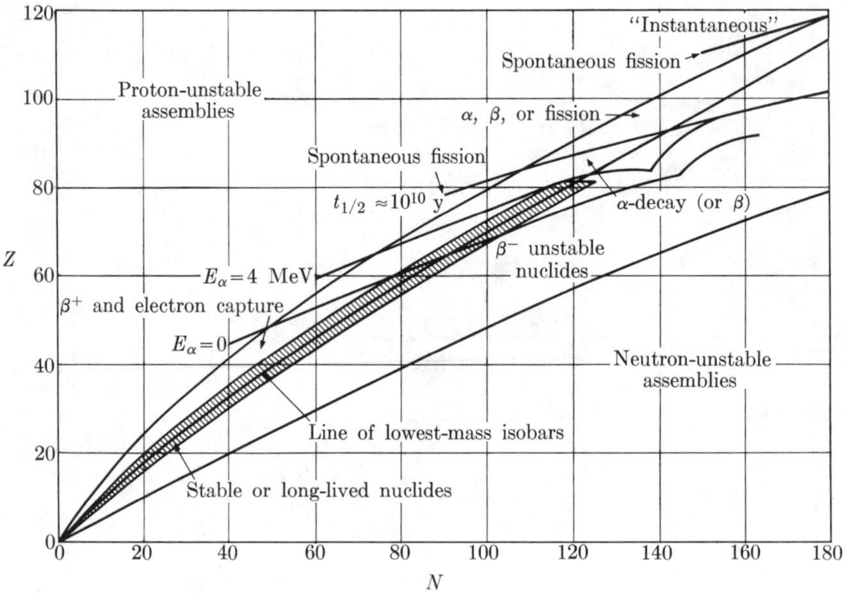

Fig. 1–6. General arrangement of the Chart of Nuclides with lines of stability against various break-up modes.

Figure 1–6 shows the general layout of the complete Chart of Nuclides without any details. We see how the band of stable nuclides curves away from the line $Z = N$ for heavier nuclides. The same curvature is reflected on the two lines indicating the limits of dynamical stability of assemblies of neutrons and protons. An assembly of nucleons that is so unstable that it will emit a neutron or a proton will decay so rapidly, by emitting the kind of nucleon of which there is an excess, that it does not deserve to be called a nucleus. Neutron-unstable assemblies have lifetimes of the order of 10^{-21} to 10^{-20} s, whereas proton-unstable assemblies may stay together for a slightly longer time. The limits of neutron and proton instability shown in Fig. 1–6 have been calculated from

* Operated by the General Electric Company for the United States Atomic Energy Commission.

the semiempirical mass formula discussed in Section 4–6, since very few experimental data exist for systems that far removed from the band of stable nuclides. Also shown in Fig. 1–6 are two lines intended to outline the area of alpha instability. All nuclides above the zero-energy line, aside from minor local fluctuations that are not brought out in this figure, are actually alpha unstable. However, because of the Coulomb-barrier penetration factor (see Chapter 10), nuclides with an available energy of less than 4 MeV for alpha decay have extremely long half-lives, and for practical purposes most of them can be regarded as stable. Finally, in Fig. 1–6, an area of nuclides is indicated that may decay by spontaneous fission when the beta and alpha half-lives are sufficiently long. The fission process is discussed in Section 14–1.

1–11 Nuclear Reactions

Much information is gained about the structure of nuclei by studying the radioactive disintegrations mentioned above. Another method of gaining such information is to study the effect on the nuclei of bombardment by a beam of particles or gamma rays. In Fig. 1–7, a particle or gamma ray is entering a target nucleus, and subsequently the same particle or another particle or gamma ray is leaving the nucleus. The initial condition for a nuclear reaction is usually well defined experimentally; that is, the type of target nucleus and the energy and type of bombarding particles are given. In general, however, there are a number of possible end results of the reaction.

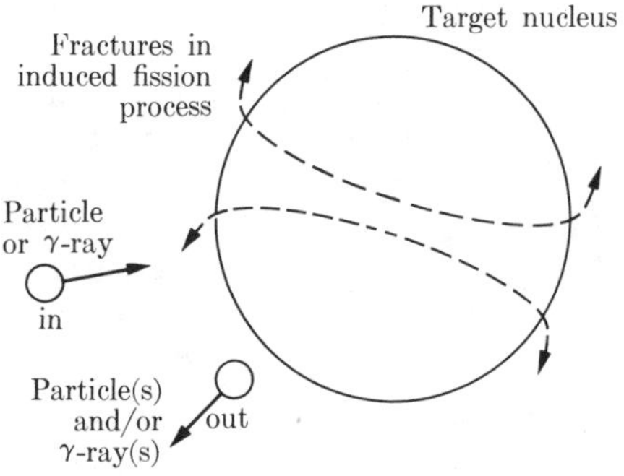

Fig. 1–7. Nuclear reactions.

There are many ways of classifying nuclear reactions. The following classification is one that is natural for the experimenter. When we go deeper into the details of the reactions (Chapter 13), we shall subdivide these classes and, to some extent, also classify the reactions along other lines.

(*a*) *Nuclear-particle reactions and scattering.* A nuclear particle in this connection means a nucleon (neutron or proton) or one of the nuclei of light atoms (for example, deuteron, alpha particle, etc.). A beam of charged particles with energy high enough to overcome the electrostatic repulsion of the nucleus can be produced in a positive-ion accelerator (for example, a Van de Graaff generator or a cyclotron). Neutrons are produced in a nuclear reactor or as secondary particles in a nuclear reaction.

In nuclear-particle reactions, a particle in the incident beam may come close enough to one of the nuclei in the target so that it interacts with its nucleons, or it may even penetrate into the target nucleus. The same particle or the same kind of particle may subsequently be expelled from the nucleus. In this case, the process is called *scattering*. If a different kind of particle or more than one particle is emitted from the nucleus, the process is called a *reaction of transmutation*, since the *residual* nucleus has been transmuted into a different nuclear species. Both in a scattering process and in a reaction of transmutation, the residual nucleus may be left in an excited state (Section 1–12). Usually, it then decays to the ground state through the emission of one or more gamma rays. Typical examples of nuclear-particle reactions and scattering processes are:

$$\begin{array}{lcccccccc} \text{Target} & + & \text{Incident particle} & = & \text{Residual nucleus} & + & \text{Emitted particle}, \\ \mathrm{Mg}^{26} & + & \mathrm{p} & = & \mathrm{Mg}^{26} & + & \mathrm{p}, \\ \mathrm{Mg}^{26} & + & \mathrm{p} & = & \mathrm{Na}^{23} & + & \alpha. \end{array}$$

The first of these two processes, the $\mathrm{Mg}^{26}(\mathrm{p}, \mathrm{p})\mathrm{Mg}^{26}$ process, for brevity, is an elastic scattering event if Mg^{26} is left in its ground state, and an inelastic scattering event if it is left in an excited state. The second process, $\mathrm{Mg}^{26}(\mathrm{p}, \alpha)\mathrm{Na}^{23}$ is a reaction of transmutation. Note that in the equations above the total number of protons as well as the total number of neutrons always balances between the two sides.

(*b*) *Radiative capture.* A low-energy neutron or proton may be captured by a nucleus which thereby is transformed into a residual nucleus in a highly excited state. Instead of expelling the incident particle again (scattering), the residual nucleus may decay to the ground state and rid itself of the binding energy of the particle by the emission of one or more gamma rays. This is called radiative capture. A typical example is

$$\mathrm{Mg}^{26} + \mathrm{p} \rightarrow \mathrm{Al}^{27} + \gamma.$$

(*c*) *Photodisintegration.* In the photodisintegration process, the target nucleus is bombarded by electromagnetic radiation. If the quantum energy is high enough, one or more particles may be liberated. An example is

$$\mathrm{Al}^{27} + \gamma \rightarrow \mathrm{Mg}^{26} + \mathrm{p}.$$

Radiative capture and photodisintegration are inverse processes. However, the experimental techniques involved in the study of these two processes are very different.

(*d*) *Induced fission.* On capturing a particle, a heavy nucleus may undergo a more violent transformation, namely, induced fission, which is virtually a nuclear explosion. The process that is responsible for most of the mass-to-energy transformation in the uranium reactor is

$$_{92}U^{235} + n\ (\text{slow}) \rightarrow X + Y + \nu\ \text{neutrons}.$$

The target nucleus absorbs a slow neutron and breaks up into two large fragments X and Y (for instance, $_{54}Xe^{140}$ and $_{38}Sr^{93}$) and a few neutrons. The free neutrons can be slowed down and, in turn, induce new fission events (chain reaction).

1–12 Energy Levels

Experimental studies of radioactive-disintegration processes and of nuclear reactions are important partly because the *mechanism* of breakup or reaction can be described theoretically, and therefore observed facts related to this mechanism constitute one important testing ground for various theories. Perhaps more important is the information that is gained about *excited states* of nuclei through these experimental studies. The experimentally determined energy-level diagrams of nuclei represent another testing ground for nuclear theories. We recall that Niels Bohr* based his theory of the atom on similar atomic data. Nuclear physicists have not as yet been quite so successful, but some progress has been made. The most spectacular agreements between experimentally determined nuclear levels and theoretical predictions have been demonstrated in a theoretical work by Niels Bohr's son, A. Bohr,† in cooperation with B. Mottelson (cf. Section 6–9).

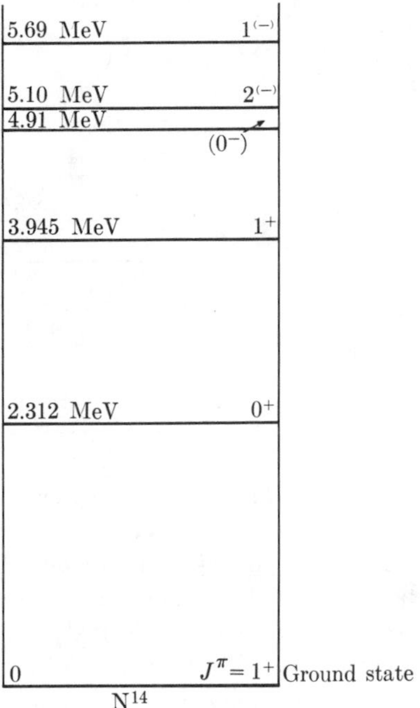

Fig. 1–8. The first few excited states of the nuclide $_7N^{14}$. (From T. Lauritsen and Fay Ajzenberg-Selove, "Energy Levels of Light Nuclei," *Nuclear Data Sheets*, 1962. Reproduced by permission.)

An example of an energy-level diagram including excitation energies, angular momenta, and parities is shown in Fig. 1–8. Most of the information given in the figure has been obtained from nuclear-reaction studies.

---

* N. Bohr, *Phil. Mag.* (London) **26,** 1 (1913).

† A. Bohr, *Dan. Mat. Fys. Medd.* **27,** Nr. 16 (1953).

1–13 Mirror Nuclei

When two nuclides have the same number of nucleons, and the number of protons in one of them equals the number of neutrons in the other, these two nuclides constitute a mirror pair. Examples are ${}_3Li^7$-${}_4Be^7$, ${}_4Be^9$-${}_5B^9$, ${}_5B^{11}$-${}_6C^{11}$, and ${}_6C^{13}$-${}_7N^{13}$. The energy-level diagrams for the two nuclei of a mirror pair have been found experimentally to be very similar. As an example, Fig. 1–9 shows the lower parts of the energy-level diagrams of C^{13} and N^{13}. The proton-rich N^{13} is heavier than C^{13} by the mass equivalent of 2.22 MeV (atomic-mass difference), and N^{13} decays into C^{13} by positron emission. As we shall see, the mass difference can be ascribed to the larger electrostatic potential of N^{13} which has more charge than C^{13} packed into approximately the same nuclear volume.

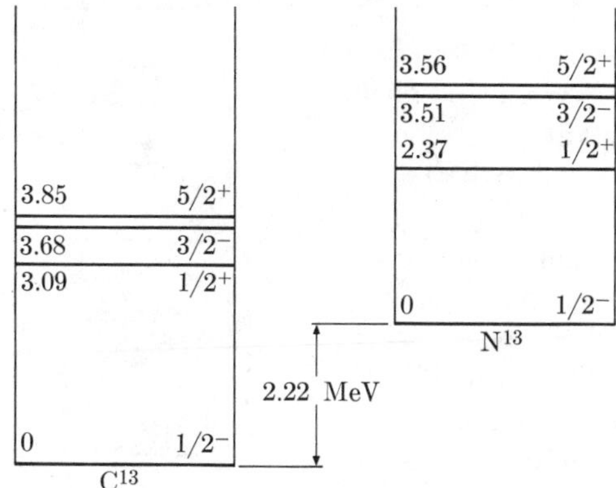

Fig. 1–9. Energy-level diagram for the mirror pair C^{13}-N^{13}.

As is discussed in more detail in Chapter 3, there are strong reasons for believing that the nuclear forces proper are charge independent and that contributions from the relatively weak electromagnetic forces are additive. This means that aside from the difference in electromagnetic interaction, the forces holding the nucleons together in a nucleus are the same between a pair of neutrons as between a pair of protons or between a neutron-proton pair, subject to the restrictions on possible relative states imposed by the Pauli exclusion principle. The similarity of the energy-level diagrams of mirror nuclei is only one of several observations supporting this contention. Indeed, from this similarity we can only conclude that the proton-proton force equals the neutron-neutron force, and no conclusion can be drawn about the neutron-proton force.

The relatively weak magnetic interactions can be neglected so that the only electromagnetic force of moderate importance in a nucleus is the Coulomb force. For Z protons uniformly distributed inside a spherical volume of radius R, one finds that the total electrostatic energy is

$$E_c = \frac{3}{5}\,\frac{Z(Z-1)e^2}{4\pi\epsilon_0 R}\,. \tag{1–17}$$

By taking the difference in E_c between a nucleus with Z protons and one with $Z - 1$ protons, one finds the difference in Coulomb energy between the members of a mirror pair. Including also the slight mass difference between the neutron and the proton and an electron, we obtain

$$\Delta E_c = \frac{6}{5}\frac{(Z - \frac{1}{2})e^2}{4\pi\epsilon_0 R} - (m_n - m_H)c^2$$
$$= 1.15(Z - \tfrac{1}{2})A^{-1/3} - 0.78 \text{ MeV}. \tag{1–18}$$

For the C^{13}-N^{13} pair, this formula gives $\Delta E_c = 2.40$ MeV, whereas the average difference for the four levels in Fig. 1–9 is 1.92 MeV, and the difference between individual levels fluctuates a few tenths of 1 MeV. Of course, the actual nuclei are not uniformly charged spheres, as was assumed in the derivation of Eq. (1–18). A higher accuracy should therefore not be expected.

For the "sharp cutoff" nuclear radius, we used $R = 1.5A^{1/3}$ F in Eq. (1–18). This seems to yield the most consistent results for the Coulomb energy differences between mirror nuclei and may actually be regarded as another measurement of the nuclear radius. Our theory is much too simple, however, and the results of high-energy electron scattering (Section 1–3) are much more reliable.

PROBLEMS

1–1. Using Eq. (1–2), calculate the approximate density in kg/m^3 and metric ton/mm^3 of nuclear matter (1 metric ton = 1000 kg).

1–2. The Fraunhofer diffraction pattern behind a circular obstacle of diameter D is a series of dark rings with angular spacing $\Delta\theta \approx \lambda/D$. Using the de Broglie wavelength $\lambda = h/p$ for 183-MeV electrons, check whether this simple model applied to electron-nuclear scattering qualitatively predicts the distance between wiggles in Fig. 1–2.

1–3. Calculate the latent nuclear-energy content in joules in 1 kg of heavy water, assuming that all deuterium atoms can be fused to form He^4.

1–4. Calculate the latent fission energy content in 1 kg of $_{92}U^{235}$, assuming that all atoms are split by the typical fission reaction mentioned in the text (mass of $_{54}Xe^{140} = 139.919$; $_{38}Sr^{93} = 92.915$).

1–5. Find the energy difference in joules between the two possible states of a proton in a magnetic field of $B = 1$ Wb/m^2. What is the frequency of a photon that has the energy required to cause a transition between these two states (spin flip)?

1–6. Calculate the electric quadrupole moment (Eq. 1–14) of a charge of magnitude Ze distributed over a ring of radius R and with axis along (a) the z-axis, (b) the x-axis.

1–7. Prove Eq. (1–15). *Hint:* Calculate the contribution to the quadrupole moment Q with respect to the z-axis from a thin ring of radius r about the J-axis (symmetry axis) and with a center a distance a from the origin. The contribution to Q_J from such a ring is, of course,

$$[3a^2 - (a^2 + r^2)] \int \rho \, d\tau.$$

1–8. Prove Eq. (1–16), assuming that the ellipsoid has a sharp boundary and that R is the radius of a sphere with the same volume as the ellipsoid.

1–9. Starting with $m = m_0/\sqrt{1 - \beta^2}$ and $p = mv$, show that $(mc^2)^2 = (m_0c^2)^2 + (pc)^2$ and that the radius ρ of a particle's orbit in a magnetic field B is given by

$$B\rho = \frac{3.334}{z} \sqrt{2m_0c^2T + T^2} \text{ kilogauss-cm,}$$

where the kinetic energy T and the rest energy m_0c^2 are measured in MeV, and z is the number of elementary charges carried by the particle.

1–10. Show that the wavelength of a photon is

$$\frac{0.0124}{E(\text{MeV})} \times 10^{-8} \text{ cm.}$$

1–11. Use the uncertainty principle to estimate the minimum kinetic energy in MeV of a nucleon confined to a cube of sides $\Delta x = \Delta y = \Delta z = 2$ F.

PART 2

The Nuclear Two-Body Problem

2 The Deuteron

2–1 Introduction

Theoretical atomic physics was born in 1913 when Niels Bohr introduced his theory of the hydrogen atom. This was essentially a solution of the atomic two-body problem. An accurate description of the electrostatic force acting between the particles was known from macroscopic measurements, but the mechanics of the atomic systems was unclear. The mechanics of atomic problems, as developed by Bohr, was greatly refined later by Schrödinger and Heisenberg when they introduced their wave-mechanical theories in 1926.

In nuclear physics, the situation is somewhat different in that the nuclear forces are inaccessible to direct macroscopic observations. However, wave mechanics has been applied with some success, at least in some areas of nuclear physics. We may therefore try to use the principles of wave mechanics on nuclear problems and then, by comparison with experimental data, hope to find a consistent description of the nuclear forces acting between two or more bodies in terms of relative separations, spin orientations, and so forth. The simplest system to analyze, obviously, is the system consisting of only two nucleons.

Two different types of experimental data exist for two-nucleon systems. One set consists of the result of a study of the only existing bound nuclear two-body system, the deuteron. In atomic physics, the success of wave mechanics or any other theory is measured in terms of the ability of the theory to produce exactly the energies of the observed excited states. Unfortunately, the deuteron possesses only one single bound level, the ground state. The experimentally determined static properties of the deuteron that can be used for testing theories are therefore essentially only the energy of the ground state, its angular momentum, parity, electric quadrupole moment, and magnetic dipole moment, and also some measurements on the size of the deuteron by high-energy electron scattering.

Another type of experimental data on the two-nucleon system arises from studies of the scattering of one nucleon by another. In practice, this means that a beam of nucleons hits a target of nucleons, and collision probabilities, angular distributions, etc., are measured. Since it is not practical to make a neutron target, the experiments are limited to so-called neutron-proton scattering and proton-proton scattering.

Theoretical work performed by several authors on existing experimental scattering data and data on the static properties of the deuteron have yielded several semiphenomenological descriptions of the forces acting between two nucleons. These descriptions are fairly consistent but all are very complicated. The results of one of these works are quoted in Section 3–11.

2–2 The Deuteron; Experimental Data

(*a*) *Binding energy of the deuteron.* The binding energy of the deuteron is given in Table 1–3 as 2.225 MeV. This number is an average of a large number of direct and indirect determinations obtained by atomic-mass measurements and nuclear-reaction data. There are essentially two direct methods for the measurement of the deuteron binding energy. One comprises the measurement of the energy of the gamma ray given off when a proton and a neutron combine to form the deuteron (n-p capture). The other method consists of measuring the energy of the gamma radiation that will break the bond between the neutron and the proton (photodisintegration).

We will here describe an n-p capture experiment performed at the nuclear reactor at the Massachusetts Institute of Technology.* The experimental arrangement is shown in Fig. 2–1(a). Slow neutrons (energy less than 1 eV) from the reactor are hitting a hydrogen-containing target. Some of these neutrons are captured by protons in the target to form deuterons. The energy of the capture gamma rays is measured by the use of a quartz-crystal spectrograph, which is essentially the same type of instrument as used extensively in x-ray work. It utilizes the principle of Bragg reflection, illustrated in Fig. 2–1(b). The Bragg reflection law is derived from the fact that path lengths from a wavefront in the incident beam to a wavefront in the reflected (diffracted) beam are equal or differ by a whole number of wavelengths. The law is

$$\theta_1 = \theta_2 \ (= \theta), \qquad 2d \sin \theta = n\lambda, \tag{2–1}$$

where λ is the wavelength of the radiation and n is the order number of the reflection. Only first-order reflections ($n = 1$) are considered here.

Figure 2–1(c) illustrates the focusing principle of the spectrograph. A photographic plate, used as a recorder, is bent to a radius of curvature of 3 m. The crystal is bent to a radius of curvature of 6 m so that the lattice planes are pointing toward the point β, the midpoint of the photographic plate. The Bragg condition, Eq. (2–1), can be fulfilled for a few selected rays of the incident beam (position I), namely those that hit one of the planes of the crystal at a

* A. H. Kazi, N. C. Rasmussen, and H. Mark, *Phys. Rev.* **123,** 1310 (1961).

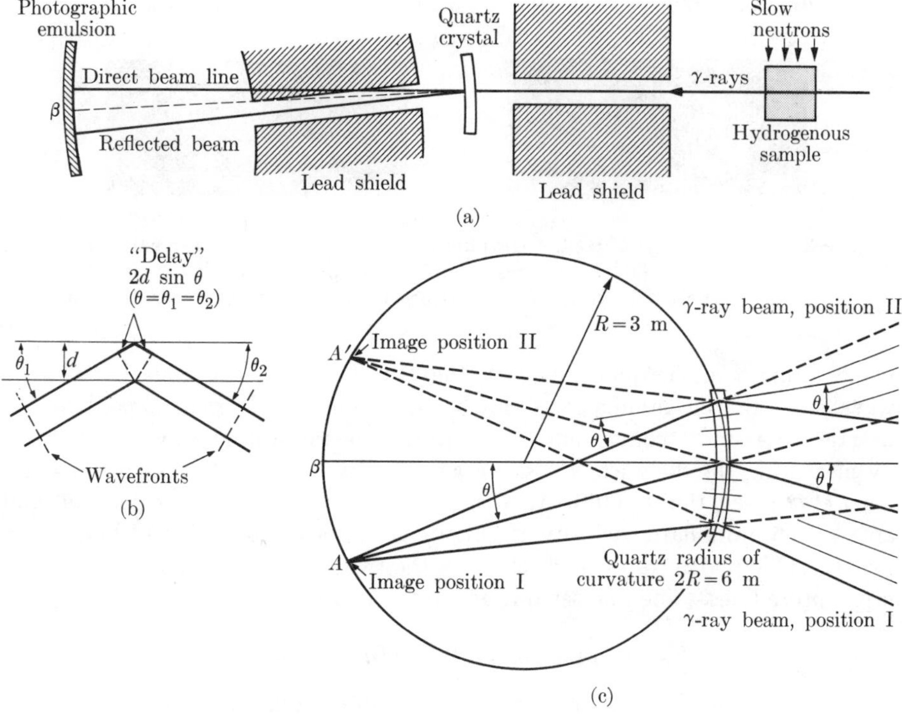

Fig. 2–1. Neutron-proton capture experiment. (a) Setup at nuclear reactor; (b) Bragg reflection; (c) focusing action of bent crystal.

glancing angle θ. First-order reflection will send such a ray through point A, no matter from which part of the crystal it is reflected.

The entire apparatus can be rotated about an axis through the center of the crystal. Another exposure can then be taken with the incident beam hitting the crystal from the other side of the lattice planes in such a manner that another first-order image is found at point A' (beam position II). The distance along the photographic plate from the blackened line at A in the emulsion to the other line at A' yields the Bragg angle,

$$\theta = AA'/4R.$$

The gamma-ray energy in electron volts can be found by use of the Bragg relationship, Eq. (2–1), as follows:

$$E_\gamma = \frac{h\nu}{e} = \frac{hc}{e\lambda} = \frac{hc}{2ed\sin\theta} \approx \frac{2Rhc}{(AA')ed} = \frac{\text{const}}{AA'}.$$

Since R can be measured accurately and the spacing d between the lattice

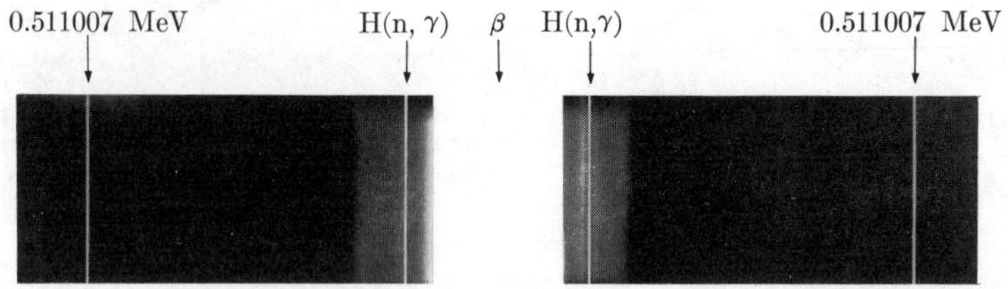

Fig. 2–2. Reproduction of a photographic plate showing the two n-p capture gamma lines and the two 0.511007-MeV lines. The central part, was shielded by lead (Fig. 2-1) to prevent the direct beam from hitting it. (Courtesy of N. C. Rasmussen.)

planes utilized in the quartz crystal (the 310 planes) is accurately known, the wavelength of the gamma rays can be determined with great precision. In practice, it is more convenient to determine the calibration constant $2Rhc/ed$ by measuring the distance AA' for a gamma ray of accurately known energy. Kazi *et al.* used the 0.511007-MeV gamma rays emitted when a positron and an electron annihilate each other. Figure 2–2 is a reproduction of one of the photographic plates (retouched) showing the two annihilation lines and the two n-p capture lines. The line separations in the two pairs are

$$AA' = 12.1406 \text{ cm for 0.511007-MeV radiation;}$$

$$AA' = 2.7890 \text{ cm for n-p capture radiation.}$$

From this we calculate

$$E_\gamma = 0.511007(12.1406/2.7890) = 2.2244 \text{ MeV}.$$

Since $\sin\theta$ has been approximated by the angle θ in the above calculation, a small correction must be applied to the calculated value of E_γ. However this amounts to only 0.1 keV.

Because the gamma ray carries a small, but significant, momentum, $h\nu/c$, the deuteron recoils slightly. The total energy released is therefore $E_B = E_\gamma + E_{\text{recoil}}$. Since the recoiling-deuteron momentum is equal to the gamma-ray momentum, one finds, for the recoil energy,

$$E_{\text{recoil}} = \frac{p^2}{2m} = \frac{E_\gamma^2}{2mc^2} = \frac{2.225^2}{2 \times 1875} = 1.3 \times 10^{-3} \text{ MeV}.$$

After applying this small correction to the energy of the observed gamma ray, we get $E_B = 2.2256$ MeV for the binding energy of the deuteron. The experimental uncertainty of the above measurement is about ± 1.5 keV.

(*b*) *Angular momentum and parity.* The angular momentum of a nuclear ground state can be determined by a number of optical, radiofrequency, and microwave methods, some of which will be discussed in Chapter 5. In the case of the deuteron, the angular momentum has been determined as $J = 1$.

The parity of a nuclear state cannot be measured directly. It can be determined indirectly by studies of nuclear disintegrations and reactions for which certain rules of parity changes exist. In Section 2–3, we will see that an even-parity wave function for the deuteron gives the most plausible theoretical image of this nucleus. All pertinent nuclear-reaction data corroborate this result.

(c) *Magnetic dipole moment.* The ratio of the magnetic dipole moment of the deuteron to that of the proton has been measured to an accuracy of about 5 parts in 10^8 by a magnetic resonance-absorption method.* This method of measuring magnetic dipole moments is described in Section 5–7. Briefly, radiofrequency techniques are used to measure the frequency, or quantum energy, needed to flip over a nucleus with its magnetic moment in a magnetic field. The result of the measurement referred to above is

$$\mu_{\rm d}/\mu_{\rm p} = 0.307012192 \pm 0.000000015.$$

By use of the same resonance-absorption method, and other methods, an absolute determination of the magnetic moment for a proton has been obtained. The value given in Table 1–3 is a weighted average of the results of these measurements. Combined with the ratio above, this gives, for the magnetic dipole moment of the deuteron, $\mu_{\rm d} = 0.857393$ nuclear magneton (nm).

(d) *Electric quadrupole moment.* A radiofrequency molecular-beam method (Section 5–6) has been employed† to determine the quadrupole moment of the deuteron as $Q = 0.00282$ barn.

(e) *Radius of the deuteron.* In Section 1–3, we discussed briefly the fairly precise measurements of the radii of complex nuclei carried out by Hofstadter and coworkers at Stanford University. Their method, high-energy electron scattering (diffraction), has also been employed to study the distribution of electric charge in the proton‡ and in the deuteron.§ The results for the deuteron have been compared with theoretical predictions based on a wave-mechanical image of this nucleus. One of the conclusions that can be drawn from this study is that the deuteron has a root-mean-square electromagnetic radius of approximately 2.1 F. The rms radius for the proton is approximately 0.8 F.

---

* T. F. Wimett, *Phys. Rev.* **91,** 499 (A) (1953).

† H. G. Kolsky, T. E. Phipps, Jr., N. F. Ramsey, and H. B. Silsbee, *Phys. Rev.* **87,** 395 (1952); recalculated by E. P. Auffray, *Phys. Rev. Letters* **6,** 120 (1961).

‡ E. E. Chambers and R. Hofstadter, *Phys. Rev.* **103,** 1454 (1956).

§ J. A. McIntyre and R. Hofstadter, *Phys. Rev.* **98,** 158 (1955); J. A. McIntyre and G. R. Burleson, *Phys. Rev.* **112,** 2077 (1958); and J. R. Friedman, H. W. Kendall, and P. A. M. Gram, *Phys. Rev.* **120,** 992 (1960).

2–3 *Simple Theory of the Deuteron*

We will now try to apply the methods of quantum mechanics in an effort to obtain a theoretical description of the deuteron. The objective is to learn something about the nuclear forces by requiring that theoretically predicted quantities agree with experimentally observed ones. In the center-of-mass system, the Schrödinger equation for the two-body problem is (Eq. A1–59)

$$-\frac{\hbar^2}{2m}\nabla^2\psi + V\psi = E\psi, \tag{2–2}$$

where m is the reduced mass

$$m = \frac{m_1 m_2}{m_1 + m_2}, \tag{2–3}$$

V is the potential describing the forces acting between the two bodies, and E is the total energy of the system. For the ground state of the deuteron, the energy is

$$E = -E_B = -2.225 \text{ MeV}.$$

The potential V is an unknown function of the separation between the two particles and possibly also of other variables. It is our aim with these calculations to throw some light on this function. For simplicity, let us start by assuming that the potential is a function only of the separation between the two particles, $V = V(r)$. This is an assumption that we will actually have to give up later. When the potential is spherically symmetric, we know that

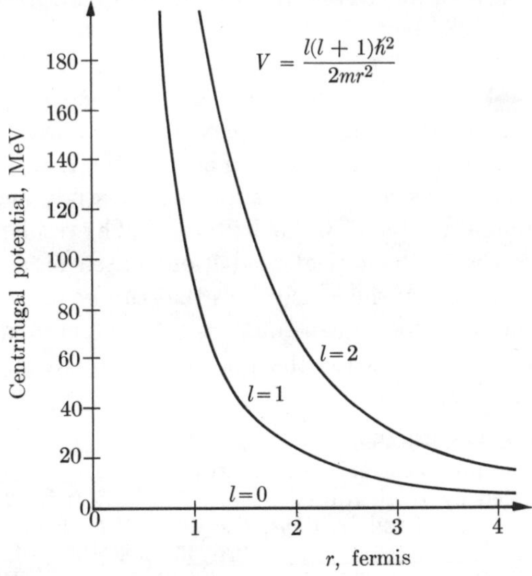

Fig. 2–3. Centrifugal potential for neutron-proton system.

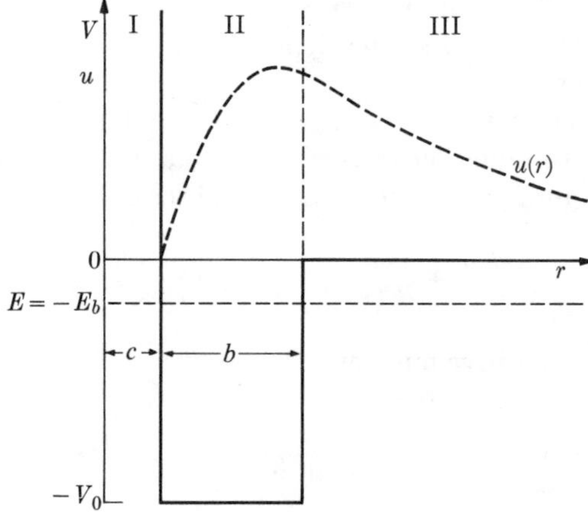

Fig. 2-4. Simplified neutron-proton potential and deuteron radial wave function.

the wave equation can be separated and that the solutions can be written in the following way:

$$\psi = (u_l/r)Y_{lm}(\theta, \phi). \qquad (2\text{-}4)$$

Here, $Y_{lm}(\theta, \phi)$ is a spherical harmonic function, and u_l is the solution of the radial wave equation

$$\frac{d^2u_l}{dr^2} + \frac{2m}{\hbar^2}\left[E - V - \frac{l(l+1)\hbar^2}{2mr^2}\right]u_l = 0. \qquad (2\text{-}5)$$

The last term in the brackets appears as a straight addition to the actual potential V. It is called the *centrifugal potential* because its derivative with respect to r is equal to the classical centrifugal force when the angular momentum is $[l(l+1)]^{1/2}\hbar$. In Fig. 2-3 the centrifugal potential is plotted vs. r for the deuteron problem for $l = 0$, 1, and 2. The effect of the centrifugal potential is obviously to force the particles apart. To achieve binding, we need an attractive, or negative, potential V that will more than compensate for the repulsive centrifugal potential, at least over a certain range of the particle separation r. Clearly, this is most easily accomplished in the $l = 0$ state. For any two-body system with a spherically symmetric potential, the lowest quantum-mechanical state is therefore always an $l = 0$ state (an S-state).

The potential function that gives the simplest solution of Schrödinger's equation is the square well (Fig. 2-4). The "hard core" (infinitely high) potential for $r < c$ effectively prevents the particles from getting closer to each other than the distance c. From scattering studies and from the study of nuclear structure, we have reasons to believe that the neutron-proton potential actually contains such a hard core. We have no reason to believe that the attractive part of the actual potential is of the square-well type; the only justification for trying the square-well potential here is its simplicity. In the following, the core radius c, the width b, and the depth V_0 of the well will be treated as adjustable parameters.

Since the wave function must be zero in region I (Fig. 2–4), it suffices to solve the radial wave equation in regions II and III. In region II, we can write the equation (for $l = 0$), dropping the subscript on u:

$$\frac{d^2u}{dr^2} + \frac{2m}{\hbar^2}[V_0 - E_B]u = 0, \tag{2-6}$$

where V_0 and E_B are positive numbers. The solution of this equation satisfying the boundary condition $u = 0$ at $r = c$ is*

$$u_{\text{II}} = A \sin K(r - c), \tag{2-7}$$

where A is a normalization constant and

$$K = (1/\hbar)\sqrt{2m(V_0 - E_B)}. \tag{2-8}$$

In region III the radial equation takes the form

$$\frac{d^2u}{dr^2} - \frac{2m}{\hbar^2} E_B u = 0. \tag{2-9}$$

The solution of this equation that satisfies the boundary condition $u = 0$ at $r = \infty$ is

$$u_{\text{III}} = Be^{-\kappa r}, \tag{2-10}$$

where B is a normalization constant and

$$\kappa = (1/\hbar)\sqrt{2mE_B}. \tag{2-11}$$

The complete wave functions in region II and III are given by Eq. (2–4) with the spherical harmonic for $l = 0$ being $Y_{0,0} = (4\pi)^{-1/2}$ and with u_0 equal to u_{II} or u_{III} respectively. In the following we will work with the radial wave functions only. By matching u_{II} with u_{III} at the boundary between the two regions, we obviously also match the total wave functions ψ_{II} and ψ_{III}. When we later normalize u, again, the total wave function will be normalized, and finally, when we calculate expectation values, the angular part will integrate out automatically and the r in the denominator of Eq. (2–4) will, when squared, cancel the r^2 in the volume element. We are therefore justified in using one-dimensional wave functions.

---

* Ordinarily, we also require that the first-order derivatives of the wave function shall be continuous (corresponding to finite second-order derivatives). In this case, since the potential becomes infinite for $r \lessgtr c$, d^2u/dr^2 is also allowed to become infinite without violating Schrödinger's equation.

Equations (2–7) and (2–10) now have to be matched at the boundary $r = c + b$ in such a way that both the function u itself and its first derivative are continuous across the boundary. This is the only way in which Schrödinger's equation (2–6) can also be satisfied at that point. These boundary requirements (with $r = c + b$) yield

$$\begin{aligned} AK \cos Kb &= -\kappa B e^{-\kappa(c+b)}, \\ A \sin Kb &= \quad B e^{-\kappa(c+b)}. \end{aligned} \tag{2–12}$$

Since at the moment we are not interested in the normalization constants A and B, we divide the two equations by each other and obtain

$$K \cot Kb = -\kappa. \tag{2–13}$$

Equation (2–13) implicitly relates the binding energy E_B of the two-nucleon system to the width b and depth V_0 of the assumed square-well potential. The core radius c does not enter into the equation. Since E_B has been measured, Eq. (2–13) gives one relationship between the two unknown parameters V_0 and b. Therefore, to determine these parameters we must find another equation connecting them; that is, we have to make use of another pertinent experimental result. By means of an example we will first attempt to illustrate the orders of magnitudes of V_0 and b.

We assume, quite arbitrarily, that the well depth is $V_0 = 40$ MeV, and we proceed to solve Eq. (2–13) for the width b. A general formula for a wave number measured in inverse fermis is

$$|k| = (1/\hbar)\sqrt{2m|T|} = 0.2187\sqrt{m|T|}\ \mathrm{F}^{-1}, \tag{2–14}$$

where m is measured in mass units (u) and the kinetic energy T is measured in MeV. For the two-nucleon problem, where the reduced mass is $m = 0.504$ u, the formula becomes

$$k = 0.1555\sqrt{|T|}\ \mathrm{F}^{-1}. \tag{2–15}$$

With numerical values inserted, we get for the wave numbers $K = 0.955\ \mathrm{F}^{-1}$ and $\kappa = 0.232\ \mathrm{F}^{-1}$, so that Eq. (2–13) yields

$$b = \frac{1}{K}\,\mathrm{arccot}\left(-\frac{\kappa}{K}\right) = \frac{1}{0.955}\,\mathrm{arccot}\,(-0.243) = 1.895\ \mathrm{F}.$$

Since the arccot function is cyclic, there are actually infinitely many values of b that satisfy this equation. However, a ground-state wave function always has the longest possible wavelength (see Fig. 2–4). This corresponds to an angle Kb in the second quadrant.

Obviously, we can choose any positive wave number K or well depth V_0 and then solve Eq. (2–13) for b. A curve showing this functional relationship

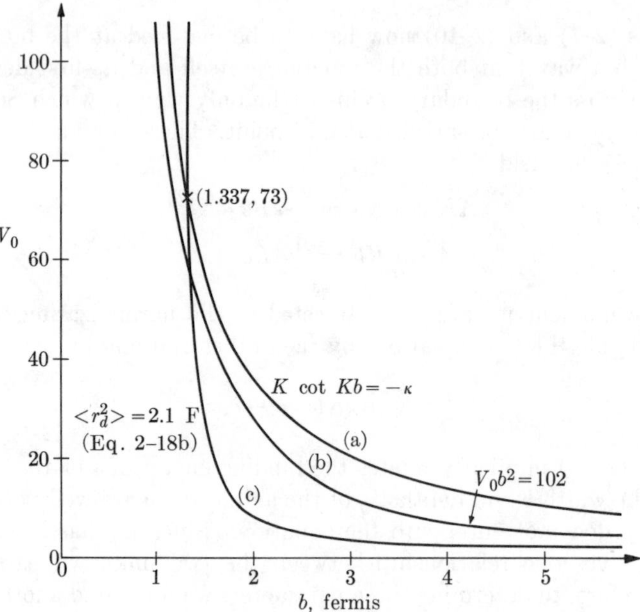

Fig. 2–5. Potential-well depth vs. well width (a) which gives correct binding energy for the deuteron, (b) which barely binds a neutron to a proton, and (c) which gives correct size of deuteron.

between V_0 and b is plotted in Fig. 2–5. As indicated by this curve, a square well of any width can be adjusted in depth so that it gives the correct binding energy for the deuteron.

It should be emphasized again at this point that the square-well potential is unrealistic and was chosen because of the simplicity of the ensuing analysis. However, we can make a similar analysis for any other reasonable potential shape, and we will then find a relationship similar to Eq. (2–13) between a characteristic width parameter and a characteristic depth parameter for this type of well.

2–4 *Normalization of the Deuteron Wave Function; Root-Mean-Square Radius*

In the previous section the normalizing constants A and B were left undetermined, since the relationship between well depth and width is independent of them. Here we will determine these constants and use the normalized wave function in calculating the rms radius of the deuteron. The normalizing condition applied to the radial wave function, Eqs. (2–7) and (2–10), yields

$$A^2 \int_c^{c+b} \sin^2 K(r - c)\, dr + B^2 \int_{c+b}^{\infty} e^{-2\kappa r}\, dr = 1.$$

The first integral is solved by putting

$$\sin^2 K(r - c) = \tfrac{1}{2}[1 - \cos 2K(r - c)],$$

and the second integral is straightforward. The solution is

$$\frac{A^2}{2}\left[b - \frac{1}{2K}\sin 2Kb\right] + \frac{B^2}{2\kappa}e^{-2\kappa(c+b)} = 1.$$

By combining this equation with the last of Eqs. (2–12) and with Eq. (2–13), we obtain

$$A^2 = \frac{2\kappa}{1 + \kappa b}, \tag{2–16}$$

$$B^2 = \frac{2\kappa\,(\sin^2 Kb)e^{2\kappa(c+b)}}{1 + \kappa b}. \tag{2–17}$$

To compare the theoretically predicted size of the deuteron with the rms electromagnetic radius observed by McIntyre *et al.* (Section 2–2), we compute the average of the square of the proton to center-of-mass distance. This distance is half the separation r between the proton and the neutron, so that the average of its square is*

$$\langle r_{\mathrm{d}}^2\rangle = (A^2/4)\int_c^{c+b} r^2 \sin^2 K(r - c)\,dr + (B^2/4)\int_{c+b}^{\infty} r^2 e^{-2\kappa r}\,dr.$$

Both these integrals can be solved by partial integrations. The normalization constants A^2 and B^2 are inserted from Eqs. (2–16) and (2–17), and the trigonometric functions are replaced by simple functions of κ and K by using Eq. (2–13). After some algebra, we obtain

$$\langle r_{\mathrm{d}}^2\rangle = \frac{1}{8\kappa^2} - \frac{1}{8K^2} + \frac{(2c + b)(1 + \kappa b)}{8\kappa} + \frac{c^2}{4} - \frac{\kappa b^3}{24(1 + \kappa b)}. \tag{2–18a}$$

The rms radius as expressed by Eq. (2–18a) is a function of c and b. The wave number κ is given, and we have used the matching equation (2–13) to eliminate K except in the second term which has been left as is because of the transcendental form of Eq. (2–13). The term $1/8K^2$ is relatively small for reasonable values of V_0.

In Eq. (2–18a) we have treated the proton as a point charge, which it is not. It can readily be shown, however, that if the charge density in the proton is spherically symmetric, the effect of this distributed charge on the rms radius of the deuteron can be accounted for by adding the square of the rms proton radius to Eq. (2–18a). The proof of this statement is left for Problem 2–4. Equation

---

* We use the angle brackets $\langle\ \rangle$ to denote average value.

(2–18a) now takes the form

$$\langle r_{\rm d}^2\rangle = \frac{1}{8\kappa^2} - \frac{1}{8K^2} + \frac{(2c+b)(1+\kappa b)}{8\kappa} + \frac{c^2}{4} - \frac{\kappa b^3}{24(1+\kappa b)} + \langle r_{\rm p}^2\rangle. \quad (2\text{–}18\text{b})$$

In Section 2–3 we arbitrarily chose the well depth $V_0 = 40$ MeV, corresponding to $K = 0.955\ \mathrm{F}^{-1}$, and determined the width of the well as $b = 1.895$ F by using Eq. (2–13). We now insert the same parameters, including $\kappa = 0.232\ \mathrm{F}^{-1}$, into Eq. (2–18b), together with $c = 0.4$ F as suggested from high-energy scattering (Section 3–10, Problem 3–7) and $\langle r_{\rm p}^2\rangle^{1/2} = 0.8$ F (see Section 2–2). We then obtain for the rms radius of the deuteron

$$\langle r_{\rm d}^2\rangle^{1/2} = 2.22\ \mathrm{F},$$

which is quite close to the value 2.1 F measured by McIntyre *et al.*

Another way of treating Eq. (2–18b) is as follows. If we accept the values of the rms radii as determined from electron scattering and the repulsive core parameter as suggested from high-energy scattering, then Eq. (2–18b) provides another relationship between V_0 and b which can be used, together with Eq. (2–13), to determine these parameters. Figure 2–5 shows a plot of $V_0 = f(b)$, as determined from Eq. (2–18b) for $c = 0.4$ F and $\langle r_{\rm p}\rangle^{1/2} = 0.8$ F. We see that a square well with $V_0 = 73$ MeV and $b = 1.337$ F is consistent with both the binding energy of the deuteron and the size of the deuteron as determined from electron scattering. A word of caution is in order here, however. The dominant term in Eq. (2–18b) is the first term, which depends on the binding energy only. The rms radius is not very sensitive to changes in b, which, conversely, means that b is very sensitive to an uncertainty in $\langle r_{\rm d}^2\rangle$. Specifically, a change of 0.1 F in $\langle r_{\rm d}^2\rangle^{1/2}$ will shift the curve in Fig. 2–5 by about 0.5 F. The square-well parameters given above should therefore be taken with a grain of salt.

2–5 *Spin Dependence of Nuclear Forces*

In the previous two sections, we have seen that the observed size and binding energy of the deuteron are consistent with a quantum-mechanical image of this nucleus based on an attractive potential of specified width and depth. We now proceed to compare the other experimental observations on the deuteron listed in Section 2–2 with the predictions of our simple theory.

One of the observations is that the total angular momentum of the deuteron in its ground state is $J = 1$. If the concept of an S-state is correct, this indicates a total intrinsic spin of $S = 1$ (proton and neutron spin vectors are parallel). In spectroscopic terminology, this is called a triplet state, which is designated $^3\mathrm{S}_1$. If the nuclear forces were spin-independent, one should expect to observe a singlet state, $^1\mathrm{S}_0$, with the same energy. This is not the case. As a matter of fact, *no bound state with $J = 0$ has been found in the deuteron!* This indicates

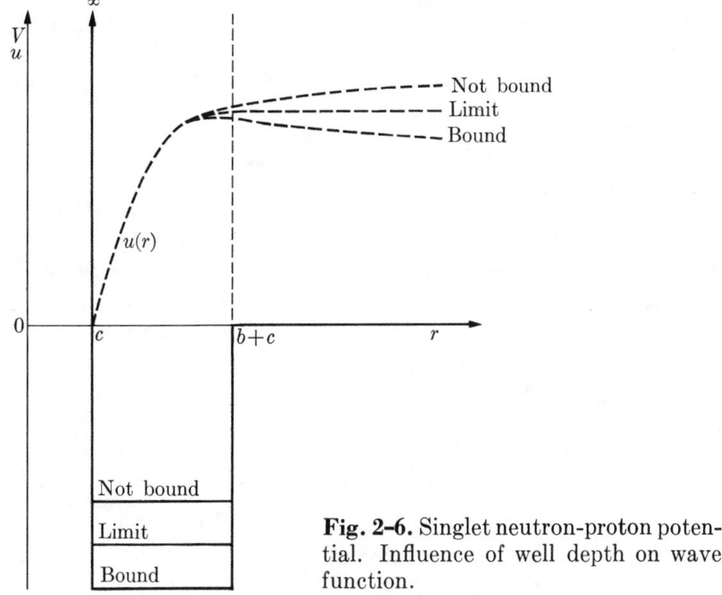

Fig. 2–6. Singlet neutron-proton potential. Influence of well depth on wave function.

that the neutron-proton force is stronger when the spins are parallel than when they are antiparallel; however, it does not mean that the antiparallel or singlet force is zero.

On the basis of our square-well potential, we can readily calculate what the maximum well depth can be for a given well width for a two-nucleon force that does not produce a bound state. The situation is illustrated in Fig. 2–6. We assume a spherically symmetric potential and consider the S-state for which Eq. (2–6) applies. A bound state will then again have a wave function outside the well of the form of Eq. (2–10). In the limit of zero binding energy, Eq. (2–10) becomes a constant. This can be matched with a sinusoidal wave function inside the well, in which the argument of the sine function goes from 0 to $\pi/2$. In the limit, we therefore obtain the following relationship between the internal wave number and the well width:

$$Kb = \pi/2. \tag{2–19}$$

Since the binding energy in the limit is equal to zero, we have $V_0 = T$. By combining Eqs. (2–15) and (2–19), we then obtain

$$V_{0s}b^2 \leq 102 \text{ MeV-F}^2. \tag{2–20}$$

This limiting value of the singlet potential well depth, V_{0s}, is plotted vs. the width b in Fig. 2–5. For any well shape other than the square well, there exists a relationship between depth and width similar to Eq. (2–20) for the limit of zero binding energy.

From the observation that a bound state with $J = 0$ does not exist, we do not actually know whether there is an attractive singlet potential at all. However, we shall see in the next chapter that the singlet force is indeed almost strong enough to produce a bound state.

2-6 Tensor Forces

Further means of testing whether our simple theory of the deuteron is qualitatively correct are provided by the observed magnetic dipole moment and electric quadrupole moment. Since, according to our theory, the proton has no orbital angular momentum, only magnetic moments associated with the proton and neutron spins contribute to the total magnetic dipole moment. In the case considered, the resultant magnetic moment is simply the sum of the dipole moments of the neutron and the proton. The situation is as follows:

Proton	2.79275 nm
Neutron	−1.91350 nm
Deuteron expected	0.87925 nm
Deuteron observed	0.85735 nm
Discrepancy	0.02190 nm, or $2\frac{1}{2}\%$.

The discrepancy of $2\frac{1}{2}\%$ is quite a bit larger than the experimental uncertainties. Of course, it may be that the magnetic dipole moment of the proton is slightly affected by the presence of the neutron and vice versa. In other words, the simple addition may not be strictly correct. Another possibility is that a relativistically correct theory (which ours is not) would give a different result.* However, we have other conclusive evidence that our image of the deuteron as a pure S-state is not correct. This is provided by the observed electric quadrupole moment of the deuteron. For an S-state, the quadrupole moment is $Q = 0$, since the wave function is spherically symmetric. The observed positive quadrupole moment is an indication that the probability density for the particles is stretched in the direction of the spin vector. In other words, the spin vectors of the particles are more often found lined up one after the other, rather than side by side.

We shall first give a qualitative discussion of a possible form of the deuteron wave function that is consistent with a quadrupole moment of the observed magnitude. Next, we shall see how our image of the nuclear forces will have to change in order to produce such a wave function.

Any function in space that satisfies the requirements of continuity and finiteness imposed on wave functions can be constructed as a sum of spherical harmonic functions with r-dependent coefficients. Other mathematical functions

---

* R. G. Sachs, *Nuclear Theory*, Reading, Mass.: Addison-Wesley Publishing Company, 1953, p. 42.

could be used; however, the spherical harmonic functions are the most suitable for wave-function expansions, since each of these is a solution of the angular part of Schrödinger's equation. Each of the r-dependent coefficients must individually be a solution of the radial wave-equation, and each term in the expansion must be multiplied with the proper spin function. Finally, we require that each term must yield the same values for the total angular momentum and parity when these quantities are conserved.

For the deuteron, the principal element of the total wave function presumably is the $^3S_1$ state discussed above. The only other state in which two particles give the same total angular momentum and parity is the $^3D_1$ state ($l = 2$, $S = 1$, and $J = 1$). A P-state ($l = 1$) and an F-state ($l = 3$) would give the wrong parity, and a G-state ($l = 4$) can only give a minimum total angular momentum of three units when the total spin is $S = 1$. We conclude that the total wave function of the deuteron must have the form

$$\psi = a_S\psi_S + a_D\psi_D, \tag{2–21}$$

where ψ_S and ψ_D are normalized wave functions with total angular momentum $J = 1$. The total wave function is normalized by requiring that the coefficients a_S and a_D satisfy the relationships

$$a_S^2 + a_D^2 = 1. \tag{2–22}$$

Equation (2–21) can be interpreted as describing a situation in which the deuteron is in an S-state part of the time and in a D-state part of the time. When it jumps from one state to another, the total spin has to flip over in order to conserve the total angular momentum.

The wave function ψ, defined by Eq. (2–21), clearly is not spherically symmetric, and the asymmetry of the $l = 2$ spherical harmonic functions contained in ψ_D is of a quadrupole type. The exact value of a_D that produces a quadrupole moment in agreement with the experimental value depends on the radial part of the function ψ_D. This again depends on the details of the r-dependence of the neutron-proton potential. Values of the D-state probability $p_D = a_D^2$ in the range 3 to 6% have been obtained from calculations on different potential shapes.*

The magnetic dipole moment can also be computed for the deuteron in the mixed state (Eq. 2–21). The theoretical value will, of course, depend on a_D, and it is found that a D-state probability $a_D^2 = 3.9\%$ produces the small perturbation necessary to bring the computed dipole moment into agreement with the observed one. This result is independent of the shape of the nuclear potential. However, because of other uncertainties (relativistic corrections and meson

---

* For example, H. Feshbach and J. Schwinger, *Phys. Rev.* **84**, 194 (1951).

currents), the magnetic dipole moment calculations are not considered so reliable as the quadrupole moment calculations.

Since the mixed deuteron state with $a_D^2 \approx 4\%$ produces an electric quadrupole moment and a magnetic dipole moment, both in qualitative agreement with observations, we are led to believe that this represents the correct image of the deuteron. What type of neutron-proton potential will produce this mixed state as the lowest quantum state remains to be investigated. Clearly, the potential cannot be spherically symmetric, since this produces a pure S-state (Section 2–3). The positive quadrupole moment indicates that the two nucleons prefer to line up their spin vectors one after the other rather than side by side. In the formal calculations, one therefore introduces, in addition to a dominant spherically symmetric potential, a so-called *tensor potential*, which is a function of the angles between the spin vectors of the neutron and the proton and the radius vector r separating them. Figure 2–7 shows qualitatively when the tensor potential is attractive and when it is repulsive.

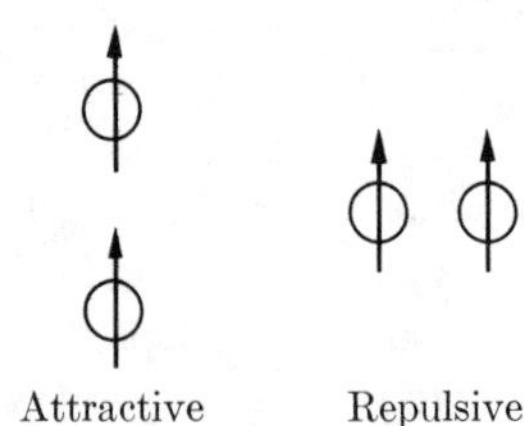

Fig. 2–7. Tensor part of the neutron-proton potential, qualitatively.

The radial dependence of the tensor potential may not necessarily be the same as the spherically symmetric part of the potential, also called the *central potential.* We may try a square-well type radial dependence for both. This gives five well parameters to be determined, namely the repulsive-core parameter c and V_{0C}, b_C, V_{0T}, and b_T, where the subscript C stands for central and the subscript T for tensor. The experimental information on the static properties of the deuteron is not sufficient to determine these parameters, let alone the actual shape of $V(r)$, if we drop the square-well assumption. Additional experimental information is needed, and it appears that this can be obtained by a study of nucleon-nucleon scattering phenomena.

PROBLEMS

2–1. Use one more term in the expansion for $\sin\theta$ to estimate the error introduced by replacing $\sin\theta$ with θ in the formula for E_γ on p. 33, for the numerical example discussed in the text.

2–2. Assume that the line-to-line distance AA' in the MIT curved-crystal spectrograph can be determined to ± 0.01 mm. If this is the principal uncertainty in the determination of the gamma-ray energy, what are the uncertainties in keV when $E_\gamma = 100$ keV, 500 keV, and 2000 keV? At what energy is it necessary to use a second term in the expansion of $\sin\theta$ (p. 33)?

2–3. Prove Eqs. (2–16), (2–17), and (2–18a). [Note the proof of (2–18a) is quite time consuming.]

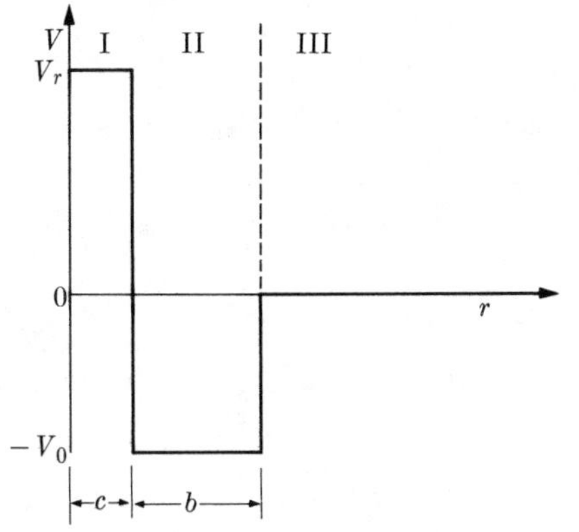

Figure 2-8

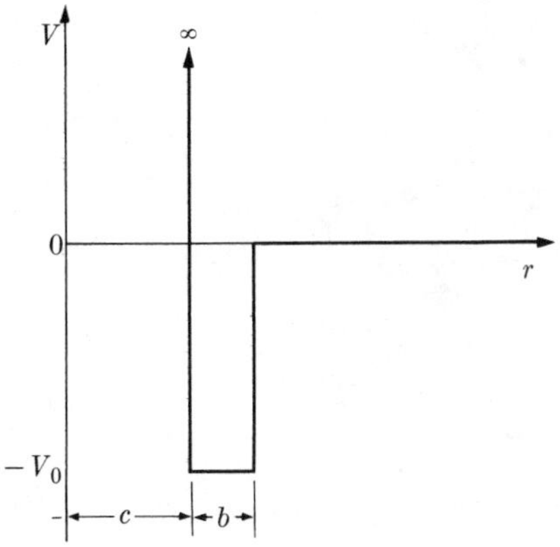

Figure 2-9

2–4. Prove the statement preceding Eq. (2–18b).

2–5. Assume that the deuteron wave function is given by Eqs. (2–7) and (2–10) with potential-well parameters as given on p. 42 (c = 0.4 F, V_0 = 73 MeV, and b = 1.337 F). What fraction of the time do the neutron and the proton spend outside the range of their forces ($r > b + c$)?

2–6. If, in the treatment of the deuteron problem, we omit the repulsive core ($c = 0$), the boundary condition at the origin becomes $u = 0$ at $r = 0$. Why?

2–7. Assume that a central potential with an r-dependence, as given in Fig. 2–8, binds the neutron and the proton together to form the deuteron. Solve the radial $l = 0$ wave equation for the three regions. (Use a hyperbolic sine function in region I, a sine function with phase shift in region II, and an exponential in region III.) Apply the boundary conditions at $r = 0$ and $r = \infty$ and match the wave functions at the two other boundaries to obtain two equations between c and b, relevant wave numbers, and the phase angle for the wave function in region II.

2–8. A spinless particle of mass m is bound to an infinitely heavy "sticky" sphere. The potential is as shown in Fig. 2–9. The well is very deep and narrow ($b \to 0$). Find an expression for the well depth V_0 needed to bind the particle in a state with orbital angular momentum l. Take $E_B \approx 0$.

*2–9. Solve the radial wave equation for $l \neq 0$ for the deuteron problem and calculate the well depth needed to bind the two particles together with $E = -2.225$ MeV and l = 0, 1, and 2. Use c = 0, and b = 1.0, 1.2, 1.4, 1.6, 1.8 F (choose one). Solve the problem by using Bessel functions (see Chapter 6) or by numerical integration.

3 Nucleon-Nucleon Scattering

3–1 Introduction

The most straightforward method of studying the interactions between submicroscopic particles is to perform scattering experiments, in which a beam of particles passes through a target containing other particles (atoms). A classical example is Rutherford's experiments with alpha-particle beams directed onto thin metallic foils. In this chapter, we study in some detail the scattering of neutrons or protons as they pass through a target which contains protons. These types of experiments are called neutron-proton and proton-proton scattering experiments, respectively.

The kinematics of a neutron-proton collision or scattering event is illustrated in Fig. 3–1(a). In the laboratory system, a neutron comes in from the left with velocity v_0 and hits a proton at rest. For the sake of simplicity, we use the

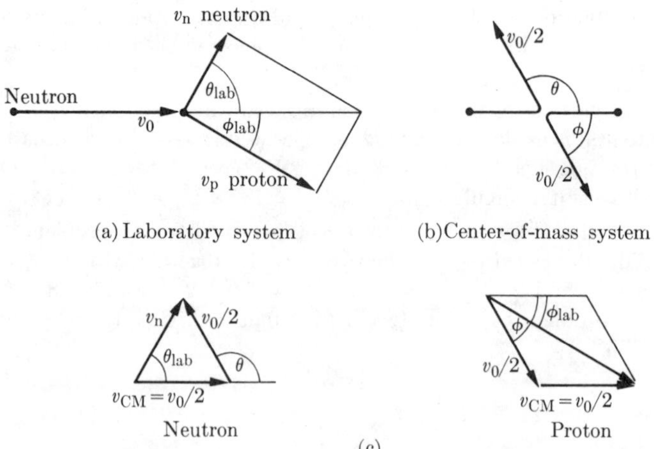

Fig. 3–1. Neutron-proton scattering in laboratory and center-of-mass systems.

classical formulas of dynamics and regard the neutron mass as equal to the proton mass. Both particles will then have a velocity $v_0/2$ in the center-of-mass system. Conservation of energy and momentum for an elastic event requires that both particles also have a velocity $v_0/2$ after the collision in the center-of-mass system. This is illustrated in Fig. 3–1(b). The *scattering angle* for the neutron is θ_{lab} in the laboratory system and θ in the center-of-mass system. The recoil angles for the proton are ϕ_{lab} and ϕ, respectively. If any one of these four angles is known, the others can be found as follows. First, the vector diagrams in Fig. 3–1(c) show that the relationships between θ and θ_{lab} and between ϕ and ϕ_{lab} are simply

$$\theta = 2\theta_{\text{lab}}, \qquad \phi = 2\phi_{\text{lab}}. \tag{3–1}$$

Since the sum of the neutron angle and the proton angle in the center-of-mass system is 180 degrees, it follows from Eqs. (3–1) that the sum of the corresponding angles in the laboratory system is 90 degrees. It is clear from this discussion and from the vector diagrams in Fig. 3–1 that all angles and velocities involved in a neutron-proton collision can be completely determined by the observation of the direction of one of the particles after the collision. The energy and the direction of the incoming neutron beam are assumed to be known.

The kinetic energy in the laboratory system is (classically) $\frac{1}{2}mv_0^2$ and the total kinetic energy in the center-of-mass system is $2 \times \frac{1}{2}m(v_0/2)^2 = \frac{1}{4}mv_0^2$. The relationship between the total kinetic energies in the center-of-mass and laboratory systems is therefore

$$E = \tfrac{1}{2}E_{\text{lab}}. \tag{3–2}$$

3–2 Scattering Cross Sections

In the study of nucleon-nucleon scattering, as well as other subjects in nuclear physics, we continuously compare theoretical and experimental results. For nucleon-nucleon scattering, a convenient meeting ground for theory and experiment is the scattering cross section. The concept of a scattering cross section, in general, can best be understood by studying Fig. 3–2. The large square in Fig. 3–2(a) represents a thin target, and the small rectangle, A, in the center

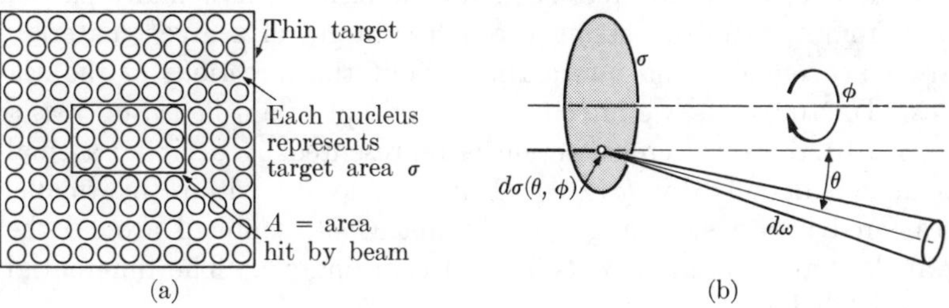

Fig. 3–2. Illustration of (a) scattering cross section and (b) differential cross section.

represents the area hit by the beam of incoming particles. Each little circle represents a nucleus (a proton, for instance). Each nucleus represents a target area σ, called the *cross section*. If the center of the particle hits within this area, a scattering event takes place. If the particle hits outside the circled areas, it goes through the target undeflected. The cross section, σ, represented by a circle in Fig. 3–2, should not, in general, be understood to mean the size of the nucleus. Neither should it be thought of as a sharply defined area, but if the centers of the particle and the nucleus come as close to each other as the radius of the circle, *on the average*, a scattering event takes place.

When a particle passes through a thin target, the probability for a scattering event is

$$\text{Probability for scattering} = \frac{\text{blocked area in beam}}{\text{beam area}},$$
$$-\frac{dN}{N} = \frac{(nA\,dx)\sigma}{A} = n\sigma\,dx. \tag{3–3}$$

Here, $-dN$ is the number of scattered particles, N is the number of incoming particles, n is the number of nuclei per unit volume of the target, dx is the thickness of the target, and A is the area of the target struck by the beam. If the target is so thin that the number of scattered particles is very small compared with the number of particles in the beam, Eq. (3–3) can be used directly. If the target is thicker, an integration has to be performed. The result is that the number of particles passing through the target undeflected is

$$N = N_0 e^{-n\sigma x}. \tag{3–4}$$

The total number of particles scattered by the target nuclei is

$$N_{\text{sc}} = N_0(1 - e^{-n\sigma x}). \tag{3–5}$$

When there are several isotopes of different cross sections present in the target, $n\sigma$ is replaced by $n_1\sigma_1 + n_2\sigma_2 + \cdots$ Experimentally, the cross section can be determined by measuring N_0 and either N or N_{sc}.

As seen above, the total cross section σ determines how many particles are scattered from a beam in passing through a target of a given material. The analysis, however, gives no information about the directions of the scattered particles. To study this, we introduce the concept of a *differential cross section*. In Fig. 3–2(b) the total cross section is represented by a circle; a small part of this circle is denoted by $d\sigma(\theta, \phi)$. If a particle hits within this smaller area, it is scattered into a solid angle $d\omega = \sin\theta\,d\theta\,d\phi$, centered around the scattering angle θ and the angle ϕ (spherical coordinates). The differential cross section is defined as

$$\text{Differential cross section} = \frac{d\sigma(\theta, \phi)}{d\omega}. \tag{3–6}$$

Following the discussion above, we find that the total number of particles scattered into a solid angle $\Delta\omega$ from a thin target $\Delta N_{sc}(\theta, \phi)$ is given by

$$\frac{\Delta N_{sc}(\theta, \phi)}{N_0} = nx \frac{d\sigma(\theta, \phi)}{d\omega} \Delta\omega. \tag{3–7}$$

The relationship between the differential cross section and the total cross section is simply

$$\sigma = \int_0^{2\pi} d\phi \int_0^{\pi} \frac{d\sigma(\theta, \phi)}{d\omega} \sin\theta \, d\theta. \tag{3–8a}$$

When the beam or the target is unpolarized, that is, when the spin directions are randomly distributed, the differential cross section is independent of ϕ, and we can then integrate over ϕ to obtain

$$\sigma = 2\pi \int_0^{\pi} \frac{d\sigma(\theta)}{d\omega} \sin\theta \, d\theta. \tag{3–8b}$$

3–3 *Experimental Data on Low-Energy Neutron-Proton Scattering*

For the rest of this chapter the discussion of nucleon-nucleon scattering is divided into two parts: low-energy and high-energy scattering. The dividing line is somewhat arbitrarily drawn at 15-MeV beam energy (laboratory system). Below this energy, for n-p scattering, the differential cross section in the center-of-mass system is practically isotropic (independent of angle) for reasons that will be discussed in the next section. It suffices, therefore, to measure the total scattering cross section.

As an example of a careful n-p cross-section determination, we shall discuss briefly an experiment performed by Storrs and Frisch.* Figure 3–3 is a sketch illustrating the principle of operation of their experimental setup. Neutrons of laboratory energy 1.315 MeV were produced through a nuclear reaction in a lithium target by a beam of protons from a Van de Graaff generator (Section

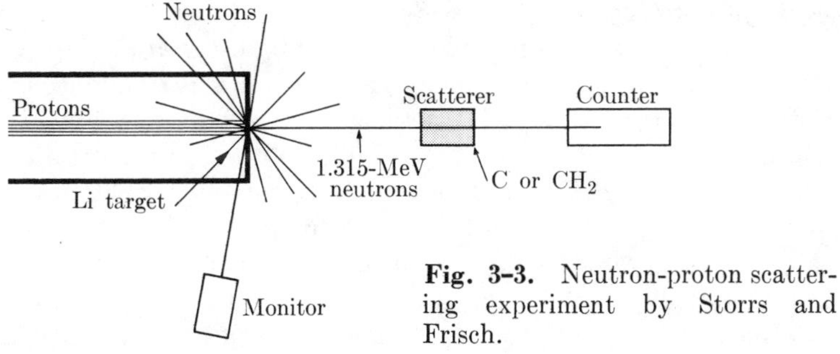

Fig. 3–3. Neutron-proton scattering experiment by Storrs and Frisch.

* C. I. Storrs and D. H. Frisch, *Phys. Rev.* **95**, 1252 (1954).

12–2). The neutrons were emitted in all directions from the lithium target. Some of them were detected by a counter, called the monitor, which was used to determine the length of exposure. Another counter was oriented so that it recorded only a narrow pencil of neutrons emitted in the forward direction. This pencil of neutrons could be intercepted by a scatterer which, in this experiment, was either a cylinder of polyethylene (CH_2) or graphite (C). The number of neutron counts in the second detector was recorded with and without the scatterer for a given number of counts in the monitor. For carbon, the cross section σ_C could be determined directly from Eq. (3–4), when N and N_0 were the number of counts registered in the neutron counter with and without the graphite scatterer. For polyethylene, the sum $n_C\sigma_C + n_H\sigma_H$ was obtained, where n_C and n_H are the concentrations of carbon atoms and hydrogen atoms. By subtracting the contribution from carbon, the hydrogen cross section was found. Several measurements were performed with scatterers of various lengths. The averages of all cross-section determinations with all corrections applied are

$$\sigma_C = (2.192 \pm 0.020) \times 10^{-24}\ \text{cm}^2,$$

and

$$\sigma_H = (3.675 \pm 0.020) \times 10^{-24}\ \text{cm}^2.$$

The hydrogen cross section σ_H is a measure of the probability of removing a neutron from the beam by collision with hydrogen atoms. Aside from n-p scattering, other possible processes are n-p capture, which leads to the formation of a deuteron, and neutron-electron scattering. The former process is of some significance only at thermal energies, and the latter process is negligible at all energies. The measured neutron-hydrogen cross section at 1.315 MeV is therefore regarded as a measurement of the n-p scattering cross section. The scattering experiment performed by Storrs and Frisch is described in considerable detail in the original paper. The reader is advised to study this paper to get a feeling for the care with which an experiment of this kind must be carried out in order to obtain results of one-percent accuracy.

The experiment described above gives only one point on a curve of the neutron-proton scattering cross section versus energy. A large number of similar measurements have been made covering the range from 0.01 eV to 300 MeV. Of course, the techniques employed vary somewhat from one end of the energy spectrum to the other. Of particular interest in the present discussion are measurements in the region 0.01 to 1000 eV. No primary source of neutrons produces beams of sufficiently low uniform energy to yield meaningful measurements in this range without further energy selection. Such energy selection can best be obtained with the so-called time-of-flight technique. The source can be pulsed electronically, or in the case of a nuclear reactor, by means of a rotating shutter, so as to produce short bursts of neutrons. The kinetic energies of the neutrons recorded by a counter are then determined by an electronic measurement of the velocity, or actually the flight time, from source to detector.

The most extensive measurements of the n-p scattering cross section in the low-energy part of the spectrum have been performed by Melkonian* and by Rainwater *et al.*† The neutron source in both cases was the pulsed cyclotron at Columbia University. This machine delivers short bursts of deuterons to a beryllium target in which the neutrons are produced by a nuclear reaction. The results of Melkonian's measurement are plotted in Fig. 3–4, together with results at higher energies, mostly taken from a review paper by R. K. Adair.‡

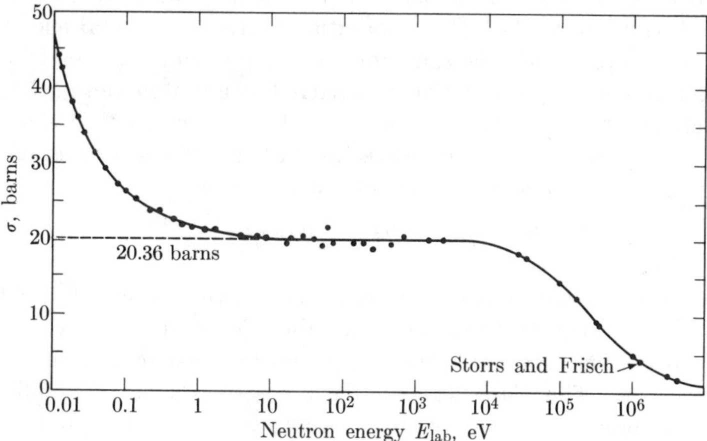

Fig. 3–4. Total n-p scattering cross section vs. neutron energy.

In the theory of the neutron-proton scattering developed in the next section, the proton will be assumed to be free and at rest. At neutron energies above a few electron volts, protons bound in the hydrogen atom in any solid, liquid, or gas can be assumed to be free and at rest, for the purpose of these calculations. A sharp increase in the n-p cross section below 1 eV (Fig. 3–4) is explained by the fact that the proton, strictly speaking, is neither completely free nor at rest. For this part of the energy spectrum the scatterer was H_2 gas, which has a dissociation energy of 4.5 eV/molecule. Below this energy, therefore, one must actually consider the whole hydrogen molecule as the target, rather than a single proton. In particular, the target mass is approximately twice the mass of the neutron; moreover, the molecule moves about with an average kinetic energy $\frac{3}{2}kT = 0.025$ eV, and this in effect increases the target area of the proton for slow-moving neutrons. The n-p scattering cross section for protons that are free and at rest is expected from theory to be as indicated by the dashed line.

---

* E. Melkonian, *Phys. Rev.* **76,** 1750 (1949).

† L. J. Rainwater, W. W. Havens, J. R. Dunning, and C. S. Wu, *Phys. Rev.* **73,** 733 (1948).

‡ R. K. Adair, *Rev. Mod. Phys.* **22,** 249 (1950).

3-4 *Partial Wave Analysis of* n-p *Scattering*

In this section and in the next, we shall treat theoretically the interaction between a beam of neutrons and a single proton at rest. More specifically, we shall attempt to compute the n-p scattering cross section as a function of neutron energy.

The quantum-mechanical problem dealing with a collision in the center-of-mass system between two particles of mass M is equivalent to the problem of a collision between a particle of mass $\frac{1}{2}M$ and a fixed scattering center. (See Appendix 1, Section A1–11.) The separation vector r, the total energy E, and the potential energy V are the same for the two problems. In the following we will think in terms of a neutron that is scattered by a proton, but in the formulas we are actually working with a spinless, reduced-mass particle that is being scattered by a fixed center. The wave function describing a beam of particles moving in the z-direction with constant momentum is

$$\psi_{\text{in}} = e^{ikz} = e^{ikr\cos\theta}, \tag{3–9}$$

with an appropriate normalizing constant. The wave function (Eq. 3–9) represents one particle per unit volume, since the square of the wave function is equal to unity. The flux is v particles per unit area per second, where v is the particle velocity. The plane wave actually describes a beam of infinite cross section. In practice, of course, the beam cross section is limited, but the dimensions are always very large compared with the range of nuclear forces. The relationship between the wave number k and the total energy is, as usual,

$$k = (1/\hbar)\sqrt{2mE}, \tag{3–10}$$

where m is the reduced mass, equal to $\frac{1}{2}M$. Equation (3–9) describes a beam of particles that is undisturbed by the scattering center.

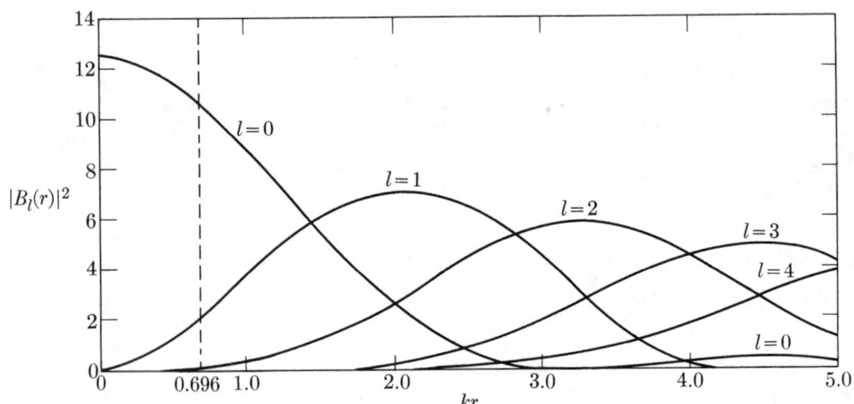

Fig. 3-5. Coefficients $|B_l(r)|^2$ in plane-wave expansion.

The wave function (Eq. 3–9) can be expanded into a series in terms of spherical harmonic functions. This is a purely mathematical rearrangement akin to the familiar Fourier expansion of periodic functions. The result is

$$\psi_{\text{in}} = e^{ikr\cos\theta} = \sum_{l=0}^{l=\infty} B_l(r)\,Y_{l,0}(\theta). \tag{3–11}$$

Each term in the expansion, labeled with an l-value, represents a solution of the Schrödinger equation in spherical coordinates for constant potential energy and with the scattering center as origin. The l-value, as usual, signifies the orbital angular momentum of the system. The expansion, therefore, classifies the particles in the beam according to their angular momenta. The radial functions $B_l(r)$ can be expressed in terms of spherical Bessel functions $j_l(kr)$ as follows:*

$$B_l(r) = i^l\sqrt{4\pi(2l+1)}\,j_l(kr).$$

The square of the coefficients $B_l(r)$ is plotted in Fig. 3–5 for $l = 0$ through 4. This gives the r-dependence of the probability density for each partial wave in expression (3–11). The square of the spherical harmonic function, $Y_{l,0}^2(\theta)$, giving the angular dependence of the probability density, is plotted in Fig. 3–6 (again for $l = 0$ through 4). The wave function (Eq. 3–11) describing a parallel beam of particles moving with constant momentum will be modified by the forces acting on the particles from the scattering center. We will imagine that these forces can be "turned on," and we will then study the resulting changes in the wave function (Eq. 3–11).

The particular way of expressing the wave function for the incoming particles in terms of *partial waves*, as the terms in Eq. (3–11) are called, has great advantages. First, since angular momentum is conserved in the scattering process,

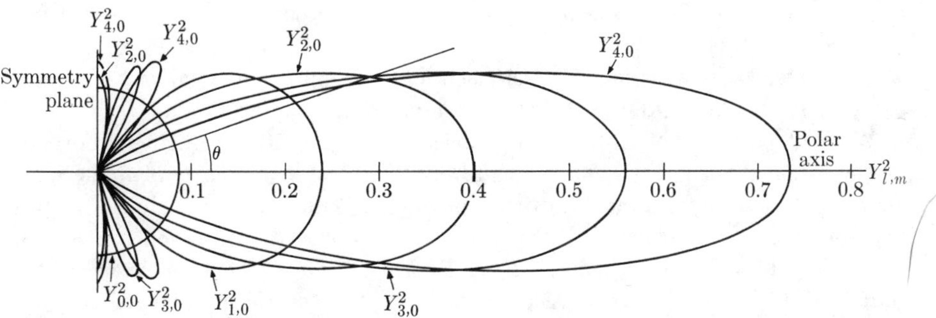

Fig. 3–6. Polar diagram of the functions $Y_{l,0}^2\ (\theta)$.

---

* For details, see Section 6–2 and J. M. Blatt and V. F. Weisskopf, *Theoretical Nuclear Physics*, New York: John Wiley and Sons, 1952, p. 784.

l does not change, except, as will be explained later, when there can be an exchange of orbital and spin angular momentum (by the tensor force). Second, the number of partial waves that are affected by the forces from the scattering center is severely limited. In particular at low energies, it will be sufficient to study the first ($l = 0$) term in the expansion, because at low energies the only particles that come close to the scattering center are those with $l = 0$. The higher the l-value (angular momentum), the larger the impact parameter has to be for a particle with given linear momentum. We can readily calculate the classical impact parameter needed to give such a particle an angular momentum $p_l = [l(l+1)]^{1/2}\hbar$, and then see whether this impact parameter puts the particle outside the presumed range of the nuclear forces of about 2 F.

However, for a quantitative discussion it is better to use a quantum-mechanical argument. As an example, let us consider a neutron with a laboratory energy of 10 MeV (center-of-mass energy, 5 MeV). According to Eq. (2–15), the corresponding wave number is $k = 0.348\ \mathrm{F}^{-1}$. If we assume that the nuclear forces have a range of approximately $r_f = 2$ F, the product kr_f is 0.696. This value is indicated in Fig. 3–5. Clearly, the probability that the distance between the two particles is at any time less than 2 F is extremely small, except in the $l = 0$ and $l = 1$ partial waves. The $l = 1$ density is also quite small at this point, but not entirely negligible. However, it turns out (Section 3–11) that the interactions are much weaker in odd l-states than in even l-states. For energies less than about 10 MeV, it is therefore sufficient to study the effect of the forces from the scattering center on the partial wave with $l = 0$.

The $l = 0$ part of the undisturbed wave function (Eq. 3–11) is

$$\psi_0 = B_0(r)Y_{0,0}(\theta) = \frac{\sin kr}{kr} = \frac{e^{ikr} - e^{-ikr}}{2ikr}. \tag{3–12}$$

Substitution of this solution into the radial wave equation with $l = 0$ and $V = 0$ shows that it is indeed a solution of the Schrödinger equation for a free particle. When we multiply ψ_0 by the time-dependent part of the wave function, $e^{-i\omega t}$, we see that the term e^{-ikr} represents an incoming spherical wave (moving toward the origin), and e^{ikr} represents an outgoing spherical wave.

When the interaction in the form of a scattering potential in the neighborhood of the origin is turned on, nothing can happen to the incoming part of the wave function at distances larger than the range of the nuclear force, that is, before the wave reaches the scattering potential. However, the outgoing part of the wave may be affected. Again, *outside the range of the scattering potential*, the *amplitude* of the outgoing wave is unchanged; that is, the number of particles moving away from the scattering center must equal the number of particles moving toward the center, assuming that no absorption takes place. The only possible change in the wave is therefore a change of phase. We will assume that such a change of phase takes place in the outgoing part of the wave, and we will divide the rest of this discussion into two parts. First, we will investigate what effect the phase change has on the total wave function outside the scattering potential. Next, we will discuss how the phase shift is caused by the scattering potential. For reasons that will become apparent later, we denote the phase shift experienced by the outgoing wave by $2\delta_0$. We then proceed to determine the effect of the phase shift on the part of the wave that is outside the range of the scattering potential. Instead of Eq. (3–12), we get, for the $l = 0$ part of the plane wave,

$$\psi_0 = \frac{e^{i(kr+2\delta_0)} - e^{-ikr}}{2ikr} = e^{i\delta_0} \frac{\sin (kr + \delta_0)}{kr}. \tag{3–13}$$

Of course, this function is also an $l = 0$ solution of Schrödinger's equation for a free particle (outside the scattering potential). We can find the new total wave function for the scattering problem outside the scattering potential by adding to the original plane wave e^{ikz} the difference between Eqs. (3–13) and (3–12). Since the two e^{-ikr} terms cancel each other, we obtain

$$\psi = e^{ikz} + \frac{e^{i(kr+2\delta_0)} - e^{ikr}}{2ikr} = e^{ikz} + \frac{e^{i(kr+\delta_0)}}{kr} \sin \delta_0. \tag{3–14}$$

The second term in the last expression represents a wave of amplitude $(\sin \delta_0)/kr$, moving away from the scattering center.* The number of particles carried by this wave per second is found by integrating the flux over a sphere of radius r enclosing the scattering center. We obtain

$$N_{\text{sc}} = \left(\frac{\sin \delta_0}{kr}\right)^2 4\pi r^2 v = \frac{4\pi \sin^2 \delta_0}{k^2} v, \tag{3–15}$$

where v is the velocity of the particles.

The scattering cross section is equal to the total flux of scattered particles divided by the flux v of particles per unit area in the incident beam:

$$\sigma_0 = \frac{N_{\text{sc}}}{\text{flux}} = \frac{4\pi \sin^2 \delta_0}{k^2}. \tag{3–16}$$

This shows that the cross section is closely related to the phase shift experienced by the outgoing part of the wave because of the interaction with the scattering potential. The analysis here is carried through only for $l = 0$ scattering

---

* It may appear as though the second term in Eq. (3–14) describes particles moving out from the scattering center without removing any particles from the incident beam represented by the term e^{ikz}. This is not true, however. A closer analysis reveals that the second term, by interference with the first term, actually removes particles from the part of the beam that has passed the scattering center.

(S-scattering). At higher energies, higher orbital angular momentum waves also have to be considered. It can be shown* that the total cross section can be written as a sum of partial cross sections, one for each l-value. The partial cross sections are

$$\sigma_l = \frac{4\pi(2l+1)\sin^2\delta_l}{k^2}. \tag{3-17}$$

The last term in Eq. (3–14), which represents the scattered $l = 0$ particles, is spherically symmetric. Hence, in the center-of-mass system, the flux of $l = 0$ neutrons out from the scattering center is isotropic. Therefore the differential cross section for $l = 0$ scattering is

$$\frac{d\sigma_0}{d\Omega} = \frac{\sigma_0}{4\pi} = \frac{\sin^2\delta_0}{k^2}. \tag{3-18}$$

To find the differential cross section in the laboratory system, we use the relationship (Eq. 3–1) $\theta = 2\theta_{\text{lab}}$. In the center-of-mass system, the solid angle between two cones with half-angles θ and $\theta + d\theta$ is

$$d\Omega = 2\pi \sin\theta\, d\theta = 8\pi \sin\theta_{\text{lab}} \cos\theta_{\text{lab}}\, d\theta_{\text{lab}},$$

and in the laboratory system, it is

$$d\Omega_{\text{lab}} = 2\pi \sin\theta_{\text{lab}}\, d\theta_{\text{lab}}.$$

The differential cross section in the laboratory system, therefore, is

$$\begin{aligned} \frac{d\sigma_0}{d\Omega_{\text{lab}}} &= \frac{d\sigma_0}{d\Omega}\frac{d\Omega}{d\Omega_{\text{lab}}} = \frac{\sigma_0}{\pi}\cos\theta_{\text{lab}} \qquad &\text{for}\quad 0 < \theta_{\text{lab}} < \frac{\pi}{2}, \\ \frac{d\sigma_0}{d\Omega_{\text{lab}}} &= 0 &\text{for}\quad \frac{\pi}{2} < \theta_{\text{lab}} < \pi. \end{aligned} \tag{3-19}$$

The total cross section is the same in both systems.

3–5 *Determination of the Phase Shift* δ_0

In the preceding section we carried out a wave-mechanical analysis of scattering in the region outside the range of the scattering potential and showed that the cross section is related to a change of phase in the outgoing part of the wave (Eq. 3–16). We will now attempt to determine the phase shift δ_0 for low-energy n-p scattering by also solving Schrödinger's equation in the region where the interaction between the two particles takes place. The analysis of the deuteron

---

* R. H. Dicke and J. P. Wittke, *Introduction to Quantum Mechanics*, Reading, Mass.: Addison-Wesley Publishing Company, 1960.

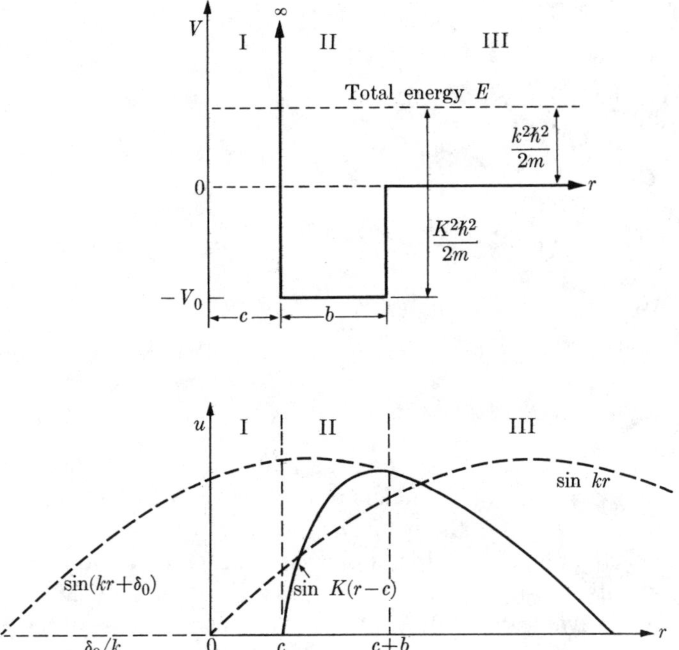

Fig. 3-7. Square-well n-p potential and the radial wave function u for n-p scattering.

problem (Chapter 2) has shed some light on the strength of the potential which acts between the neutron and the proton when their spins are parallel (triplet potential). We do not, however, know anything about the strength of the interaction when the spins of the two particles are antiparallel (singlet potential), except that it is not strong enough to produce a bound state in the deuteron. The two particles can collide in the antiparallel state, as well as in the parallel state, so that both situations have to be considered. For simplicity, let us again assume that in both cases the potential can be represented by a repulsive-core square well (Fig. 3-7). For the singlet case, the well is presumably shallower and/or narrower than the triplet well, or it may even be repulsive. However, this does not affect the method of solution of the wave-mechanical problem.

In region II of Fig. 3-7, the radial part of the $l = 0$ wave function must satisfy the radial wave equation

$$\frac{d^2u}{dr^2} + \frac{2m}{\hbar^2}(V_0 + E)u = 0. \tag{3-20}$$

The boundary condition at $r = c$ is $u = 0$, so that the solution is obviously

$$u_{\text{II}} = A \sin K(r - c), \tag{3-21}$$

where the wave number

$$K = (1/\hbar)\sqrt{2m(V_0 + E)}. \tag{3–22}$$

In region III, the radial wave equation is

$$\frac{d^2u}{dr^2} + \frac{2m}{\hbar^2} Eu = 0. \tag{3–23}$$

The solution of this equation is

$$u_{\text{III}} = B \sin (kr + \delta_0) \tag{3–24}$$

in accordance with Eq. (3–13). Here the wave number is

$$k = (1/\hbar)\sqrt{2mE}. \tag{3–25}$$

The wave function in region III must be matched with the one in region II at the boundary $r = c + b$. To make both the wave function and its first-order derivative continuous across the boundary, we may write two equations similar to Eqs. (2–12) and thereafter divide one into the other to eliminate the normalizing constants. We see that this whole procedure is equivalent to a matching of logarithmic derivatives $(1/u)(du/dr)$ of the two functions at the boundary. By doing this, we obtain

$$K \cot Kb = k \cot [k(c + b) + \delta_0]. \tag{3–26}$$

If the parameters of the square well (V_0, c, and b) are given, the phase shift δ_0 can be computed from Eq. (3–26) as a function of the energy E. This has been done for the well parameters arrived at in Section 2–4 ($V_0 = 73.3$ MeV, $c = 0.4$ F, $b = 1.337$ F). The resulting cross sections, computed from Eqs.

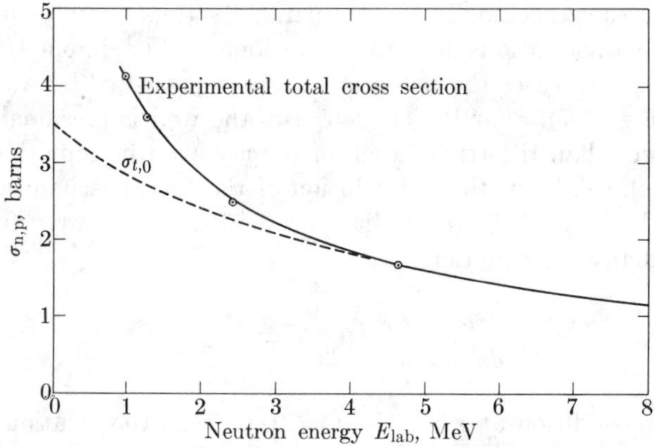

Fig. 3–8. Measured and calculated n-p scattering cross section vs. neutron energy.

(3–16) and (3–26), have been plotted in Fig. 3–8 (the curve marked $\sigma_{t,0}$). This curve represents the theoretical n-p scattering cross section in the triplet case, since it is the triplet well parameters we have used. We see that there is good agreement between $\sigma_{t,0}$ and the experimental points at energies above 5 MeV. Could it be, then, that the singlet and triplet cross sections are approximately equal in this energy range but are radically different at lower energies? If so, the singlet cross section must be much larger than the triplet cross section in this range so that a weighted average will match the experimental curve. Either this must prove to be the case, or our approach is totally wrong. We have, of course, tested only one potential well, a square well, with depth and width fixed by deuteron data. However, it turns out that the low-energy n-p cross section is very insensitive to changes in the well shape, provided the well gives the correct binding energy for the deuteron (Section 3–7).

In the preceding analysis we neglected the tensor force that was introduced in Section 2–6. However, it can be shown* that the tensor force has a less than one-percent effect on the neutron-proton cross section at energies below 10 MeV.

3–6 Singlet and Triplet Potentials

According to our classical notions, the spins of two colliding nucleons should tend to be antiparallel in half of the events and parallel in the other half. The quantum-mechanical prediction for the neutron-proton system is as follows. The total spin vector S of the system is quantized in the same fashion as in the stationary state (the deuteron). The total spin quantum number is $S = 0$ in the singlet state and $S = 1$ in the triplet state. The triplet state, as indicated by the notation, has therefore three substates with different spatial orientations of the spin vector, whereas the singlet state has only one substate. The occurrence of each substate is equally probable so that the average total $l = 0$ cross section is

$$\sigma_0 = \tfrac{3}{4}\sigma_{t,0} + \tfrac{1}{4}\sigma_{s,0}. \tag{3–27}$$

The subscript t stands for triplet, and s for singlet.

We can clarify the above result somewhat by studying Fig. 3–9. The four equally probable combinations of orientations of $s = \frac{1}{2}$ particles are shown at the left. The z-components of these particles are quantized, so that each particle has only two possible states. In cases (a) and (d) the z-components of the spins add up to 1 and -1, so that these cases clearly represent substates of $S = 1$. In cases (b) and (c), the z-components add up to zero, but because the spin vectors are not aligned with the z-axis, it is possible for the total spin to be $S = 1$ as well as $S = 0$. Half of the cases (b) and (c) will therefore result in a singlet state, the other half in a triplet state with zero z-component. The net result is that the chance of forming a singlet state is only one in four.

---

* Blatt and Weisskopf, *op. cit.*, p. 110.

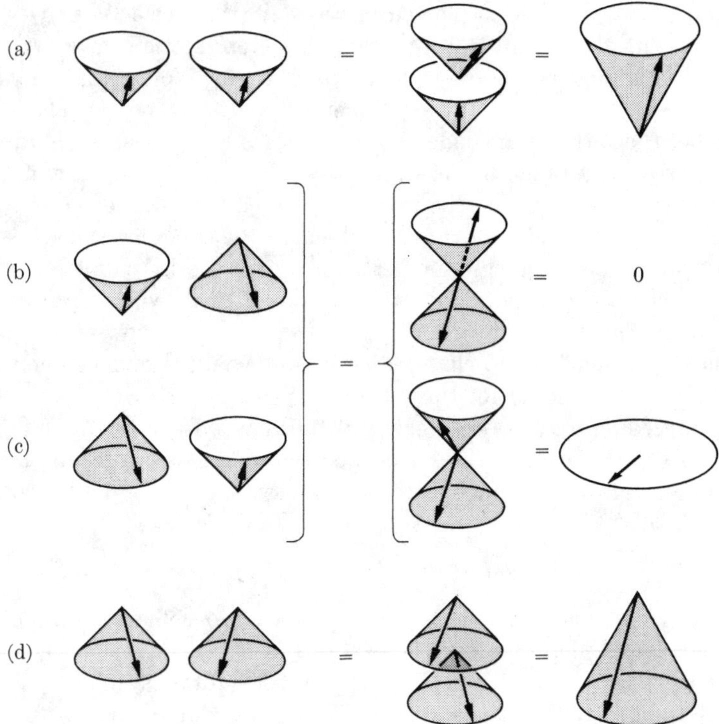

Fig. 3–9. Two spins $s = \frac{1}{2}$ can combine in four different ways. Three of these yield triplet spin states, and one yields a singlet spin state.

We shall first discuss the situation in the limit of zero energy, since certain slow-neutron experiments that have been performed allow us to determine the individual cross sections $\sigma_{t,0}$ and $\sigma_{s,0}$, not just their weighted average. The results of these measurements are discussed briefly below. We shall begin by introducing a new concept, the *scattering length a*.

The situation in the limit of zero energy is illustrated in Fig. 3–10. When the neutron energy, and therefore the wave number k in region III, approaches zero, the sine curve representing the radial wave function u degenerates into a straight line. Two cases are shown in the figure. In Case 1 the well is sufficiently deep and wide so that the wave function u at the boundary $r = c + b$ has a negative slope. The straight-line wave function outside intersects the axis at a point a positive distance a_1 from the origin. This distance is called the scattering length. In Case 2 the slope at the boundary is positive, and the scattering length a_2 is negative. The relation between the scattering length and the phase shift is (compare Figs. 3–7 and 3–10):

$$\text{Case 1:} \qquad \delta_{01} = \pi - a_1 k, \qquad \text{Case 2:} \qquad \delta_{02} = -a_2 k.$$

In both cases, the cross section (Eq. 3–16) for "zero" energy is

$$\sigma_0 = \frac{4\pi \sin^2 \delta_0}{k^2} = 4\pi a^2 \qquad (k \to 0). \tag{3–28}$$

In terms of the triplet scattering length a_t and the singlet scattering length a_s, the total cross section Eq. (3–27) becomes

$$\sigma = 3\pi a_t^2 + \pi a_s^2. \tag{3–29}$$

The experimental value of the total cross section for slow neutrons is 20.36 barns (Fig. 3–4). To determine the values of a_t and a_s, we need another equation, that is, another type of measurement, also at low energy.

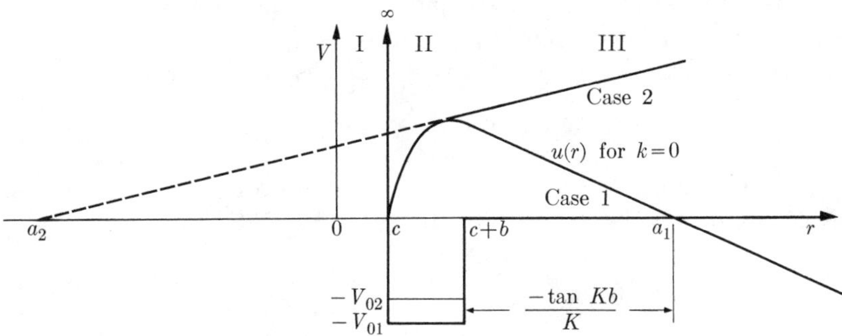

Fig. 3–10. Radial wave function u in the limit of zero neutron energy. Case 1 (potential $-V_{01}$ binding) gives positive scattering length; Case 2, negative (potential $-V_{02}$ nonbinding).

Certain other experiments give the value of a weighted sum of a_t and a_s. These are all various forms of coherent scattering experiments in which more than one proton interacts with the neutron. The amplitude of the scattered wave from a single proton is proportional to $(\sin \delta_0)/k = a$ (see Eq. 3–14). Equation (3–28) essentially expresses the fact that the scattering cross section is proportional to the square of the amplitude of the outgoing scattered wave. When several scattering centers are arranged in a disorderly manner and therefore are acting incoherently, the number of scattered neutrons in a given direction is proportional to the number of scattering centers. In other words, the squares of the amplitudes add. When the scattering centers are arranged as in a crystal, however, diffraction phenomena take place. Averaged over all angles, the number of scattered particles is still the same, but the distribution is no longer uniform. In directions where constructive interference takes place, the wave amplitudes, that is, the scattering lengths, rather than the squares, add algebraically. This is analogous to the diffraction of x-rays by a crystal. The average scattering length for coherent scattering from hydrogen with spin directions randomly distributed is

$$a_c = \tfrac{1}{4}(3a_t + a_s). \tag{3–30}$$

The most accurate measurement of this quantity has been made by Burgy, Ringo, and Hughes* through total reflection of slow neutrons from a liquid hydrocarbon target. They report a value for the coherent scattering length of $a_c = -1.89$ F. Simultaneous solution of Eqs. (3–29) and (3–30) for the given experimental values of σ_0 and a_c yields

$$a_t = 5.38 \text{ F}, \qquad a_s = -23.7 \text{ F}.$$

The definition of the scattering length and the discussion so far are not limited to any particular potential shape. We now turn to the square well again and ask whether the values of the scattering lengths above are consistent with the strength of the neutron-proton interaction indicated by the study of the deuteron. For the square well the scattering length is (see Fig. 3–10)

$$a = c + b - K^{-1} \tan Kb, \tag{3–31}$$

where the wave number K is given by Eq. (3–22) with $E = 0$. Inserting the values $V_0 = 73$ MeV, $b = 1.337$ F, and $c = 0.4$ F (Section 2–4), we obtain

$$a_t = 0.400 + 1.337 - \frac{\tan 1.775}{1.329} = 5.382 \text{ F},$$

in agreement with the observed value. We conclude that a repulsive-core square-well triplet potential can, with a wave-mechanical theory, correctly give the deuteron binding energy, the size of the deuteron, and the "zero" energy triplet n-p scattering cross section. Since it may be argued that we have used three adjustable parameters, V_0, b, and c, to fit three experimental results, the agreement is not so surprising, and we may expect that other well shapes may give equally good agreements. A more crucial test of our theories will result from a study of the low-energy n-p cross section as it varies with increasing energy. This subject is discussed in the next section. First, a few words about the singlet n-p force are in order.

The singlet scattering length is negative, indicating that at $E = 0$ the wave function u does not quite reach a maximum inside the well. This, of course, is in agreement with the observation made in Section 2–5 that no singlet bound state of the neutron-proton system exists. If we assume, quite arbitrarily, that the repulsive core and well width are the same for the singlet force as for the triplet force, then we can calculate the well depth V_{0s} by inserting $a_s = -23.7$ F into Eq. (3–31). The result is $V_{0s} = 54.7$ MeV, whereas Eq. (2–20) gives 57 MeV for the minimum well depth that will produce binding when the width is $b = 1.337$ F.

---

* M. T. Burgy, G. R. Ringo, and D. F. Hughes, *Phys. Rev.* **84,** 1160 (1951).

3–7 *Effective-Range Theory*

Having dealt with the "zero-energy" case, we now return to the variation of the n-p cross section with energy in the range 0 to 15 MeV. The partial cross sections for singlet and triplet n-p scattering are given by Eq. (3–16), in which the phase shift δ_0 in the square-well case can be found by Eq. (3–26). For a differently shaped well it can be found by a similar procedure. To calculate the phase shift for various well shapes, except in simple cases, one must perform numerical integrations which are, of course, tedious. However, it turns out that it is possible to expand the quantity $\cot \delta_0$ in a simple power series of k, and that this will greatly simplify the procedure of computing phase shifts. In the energy range considered, two terms in the power series suffice; the first term contains the scattering length, and the second term contains a quantity called the *effective range*, to be defined below.

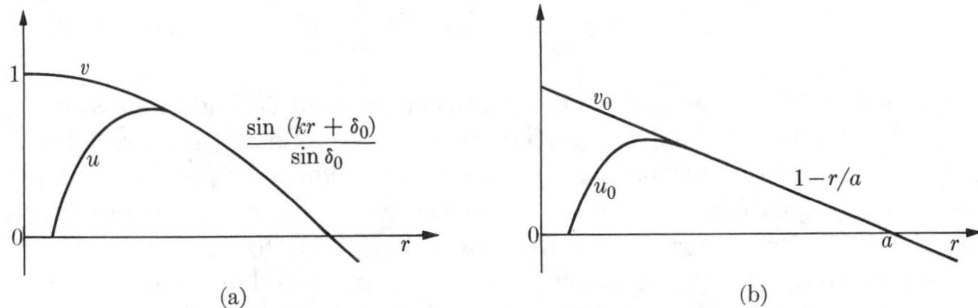

Fig. 3–11. Radial wave functions in the effective-range theory.

In developing the effective-range theory, we use the notation shown in Fig. 3–11(a). The radial wave function u is, as before, a solution of the radial wave equation for $l = 0$ inside and outside the potential well. A new function v is defined as follows: v is identical with u outside the potential well and extrapolates the behavior of u to the origin, unaffected by the nuclear potential. Both functions u and v are normalized in such a way that $v = 1$ for $r = 0$. Thus,

$$v = \frac{\sin (kr + \delta_0)}{\sin \delta_0}. \tag{3–32}$$

This particular normalization will give the formulas a neater appearance, and, as usual, the energy considerations are independent of the normalization constant. The situation at zero energy is shown in Fig. 3–11(b).

The functions u and u_0 are solutions of the radial wave equation:

$$-\frac{\hbar^2}{2m}\frac{d^2u}{dr^2} + Vu = Eu,$$

$$-\frac{\hbar^2}{2m}\frac{d^2u_0}{dr^2} + Vu_0 = 0.$$

On multiplying the first equation by u_0 and the second by u and subtracting, we obtain

$$(d/dr)(uu_0' - u_0u') = k^2uu_0, \tag{3-33}$$

where k is the wave number as defined by Eq. (3–10) and the primes indicate first-order derivatives with respect to r. The functions v and v_0 are solutions of the radial wave equation with constant potential. Proceeding as above, we get the following relationship between v and v_0:

$$(d/dr)(vv_0' - v_0v') = k^2vv_0. \tag{3-34}$$

We now subtract (3–33) from (3–34) and integrate over r from zero to infinity, or to a point outside the well. Then, since $v = u$ and $v_0 = u_0$ outside the well, and since $v = v_0 = 1$ and $u = u_0 = 0$ for $r = 0$, we obtain

$$-(v_0' - v')_{r=0} = k \cot \delta_0 + \frac{1}{a} = k^2 \int_0^\infty (vv_0 - uu_0)\, dr. \tag{3-35}$$

Equation (3–35) is exact. We can use it to compute cot δ_0, and by substituting δ_0 into Eq. (3–16), we find the partial cross section. So far, the procedure is hardly any simpler than the one described in Section 3–5, since the integral in Eq. (3–35) apparently has to be solved for each value of the energy E considered. However, as can be surmised from Fig. 3–11, for moderate energies we can, without introducing serious errors, replace v and u by v_0 and u_0 in Eq. (3–35). The integral on the right-hand side then takes the simple form

$$\tfrac{1}{2}r_0 = \int_0^\infty (v_0^2 - u_0^2)\, dr. \tag{3-36}$$

The parameter r_0 is defined by Eq. (3–36); it is called the *effective range* of the nuclear potential. The factor $\frac{1}{2}$ is included in the definition, because this makes r_0 approximately equal to the radius for which the potential becomes small. (For the square well, $r_0 \approx b + c$.) This justifies the name "effective range" for r_0. The effective range depends on the width of the nuclear potential well, but it is independent of energy. By substituting r_0 into Eq. (3–35), we obtain

$$\cot \delta_0 = -1/ka + \tfrac{1}{2}r_0k. \tag{3-37}$$

This gives the phase shift δ_0 in the so-called *shape-independent approximation* which is valid for low energies. Combined with Eq. (3–16) it yields the cross section

$$\sigma_0 = \frac{4\pi a^2}{[1 - \frac{1}{2}ar_0k^2]^2 + a^2k^2}\cdot \tag{3-38}$$

Equation (3–38) shows that to the approximation implied by the step from Eq. (3–35) to Eq. (3–36), the partial scattering cross section depends only on two constants, the scattering length a and the effective range of the nuclear potential r_0. It can be shown that the errors introduced into the calculation by the approximation are much smaller than the experimental uncertainties for the neutron-proton cross sections in the 0- to 15-MeV range.

Since the total cross section is a weighted sum of the singlet and triplet partial cross sections (Eq. 3–27), there are four constant parameters that enter into the complete expression, namely, a_t, a_s, r_{0t}, and r_{0s}. The scattering lengths for both singlet and triplet scattering, a_s and a_t, are determined from the very low-energy experiments, as described in Section 3–6. The triplet effective range r_{0t} can be determined through the additional information we have about the triplet forces in the binding energy of the deuteron. To show the connection between a_t, r_{0t}, and the wave number κ which expresses the deuteron binding energy (Eq. 2–11), we go through a derivation similar to the one leading to Eq. (3–35). The function u is now the deuteron radial wave function and the function v is the external deuteron wave function $v = e^{-\kappa r}$ extrapolated into the origin and normalized so that $v = 1$ for $r = 0$. Instead of Eq. (3–35), we then get

$$-\kappa + \frac{1}{a_t} = -\kappa^2 \int_0^\infty (vv_0 - uu_0)\,dr. \tag{3–39}$$

Again we replace the integral on the right-hand side with the integral in Eq. (3–36) and obtain

$$-\kappa + 1/a_t = -\tfrac{1}{2}r_{0t}\kappa^2.$$

This gives the following equation for the effective range:

$$r_{0t} = \frac{2}{\kappa^2}\left(\kappa - \frac{1}{a_t}\right). \tag{3–40}$$

With $\kappa = 0.232\ \mathrm{F}^{-1}$ and $a_t = 5.38$ F, we obtain $r_{0t} = 1.70$ F.

With a_t, a_s, and r_{0t} determined from very low-energy and deuteron data, we have only one more parameter, r_{0s}, that can be adjusted to fit all the data in the range 10 eV to 10 MeV. If we choose to fit the point on the curve determined by Storrs and Frisch exactly, the singlet effective range needs to be $r_{0s} =$ 2.4 F. With all constants inserted, we get the following numerical formula for the n-p cross section in the 10-eV to 15-MeV range:

$$\sigma_0 = \frac{2.73}{[1 - 0.0553\ E_\mathrm{n}]^2 + 0.350\ E_\mathrm{n}} + \frac{17.63}{[1 + 0.344\ E_\mathrm{n}]^2 + 6.80\ E_\mathrm{n}}\ \text{barns}. \tag{3–41}$$

The neutron energy E_n is the laboratory energy in MeV.

Equation (3–41) is plotted in Fig. 3–12, together with experimental points. The agreement between theory and experiment is spectacular and represents a convincing demonstration of the success of wave mechanics in this area of nuclear physics.

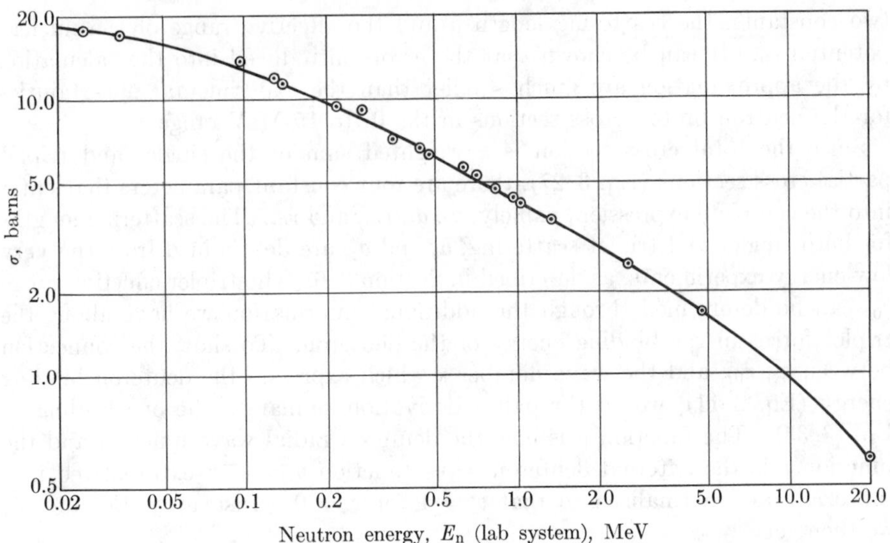

Fig. 3-12. Total cross section for n-p scattering. Theoretical curve based on a_t = 5.38 F, a_s = −23.7 F, r_{0t} = 1.70 F, r_{0s} = 2.40 F. Experimental points from a review paper by R. K. Adair, *Rev. Mod. Phys.* **22,** 249 (1950).

3–8 *Example of Proton-Proton Scattering at Low Energies*

Proton beams are now available with energies from zero to far into the BeV region. Very accurate measurements of p-p scattering cross sections have been performed, especially at low energies, but also in the higher-energy regions. In this section, we are going to discuss proton-proton scattering in the 0- to 10-MeV region. Most of the high-quality data collected in this region have been obtained by the use of the accurately controllable beams of Van de Graaff accelerators.

Since both scatterer and scattered particles are charged, Coulomb-field scattering is observed in addition to the scattering arising from nuclear forces. The large small-angle cross section (well known from the Rutherford scattering formula) makes it impractical to work with total cross sections. What is usually measured in a p-p scattering experiment is therefore the differential scattering cross section as a function of the scattering angle.

As an example of the many accurate measurements that have been performed, we will here describe the experiments of Knecht *et al.** with Van de Graaff beams of energies 1.397, 1.855, and 2.425 MeV. Figure 3–13 shows the principles of operation of the scattering chamber used by these authors. The chamber

---

* D. J. Knecht, S. Messelt, E. D. Berners, and L. C. Northcliffe, *Phys. Rev.* **114,** 550 (1959).

contains H_2 gas, which continuously streams into the chamber through a system of purifiers. The gas leaks out of the chamber again through the small openings of the beam collimator, and the volumes between each opening (slit) are connected to pumping systems in order to maintain a low pressure in the high-vacuum system of the generator. The main beam strikes a beam collector or Faraday cup which is connected to a current integrator. The total charge collected determines the number of protons N_0 that have passed through the target gas in a given exposure. Scattered protons passing through slits S_1 and S_2 are detected by a counter. This counter and the slits can be rotated about the center of the target chamber, so that the number of scattered particles N_{sc} can be measured as a function of scattering angle θ_{lab}.

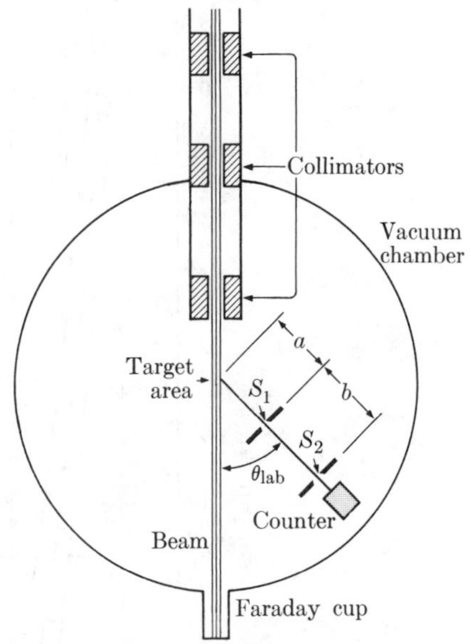

Fig. 3–13. Scattering chamber for p-p experiment. [From D. J. Knecht *et al.*, *Phys. Rev.* **114**, 550 (1959)].

The differential cross section for proton-proton scattering is determined by use of Eq. (3–7). The target thickness x entering into this formula is defined by the slit openings S_1 and S_2, the angle θ_{lab}, and other geometric parameters. It is approximately equal to $x = (a + b)S_1/b \sin \theta_{lab}$. The solid angle subtended by the counter, as seen from the target region, is approximately $\Delta\omega = (\text{area of } S_2)/(a + b)^2$. The number of scatterers n per unit volume is determined by measuring the pressure and temperature of the gas in the target chamber.

Since theoretical scattering cross sections are calculated in the center-of-mass system, it is customary to transform the measured cross sections to center-of-mass coordinates. The method is outlined in Section 3–4, and the transformation formula is*

$$\frac{d\sigma(\theta)}{d\omega} = \frac{1}{4 \cos \theta_{lab}} \left(\frac{d\sigma(\theta_{lab})}{d\omega}\right)_{lab}. \tag{3–42}$$

The proton-proton differential cross sections determined by Knecht *et al.*, as outlined briefly above, are plotted in Fig. 3–14. The experimental uncertainties are of the order of $\pm 0.2\%$ and are less than an amount corresponding

* To the accuracy of the described experiment, the relationship $\theta = 2\theta_{lab}$, on which Eq. (3–42) is based, is only approximately true. In the laboratory system, the masses of the two protons are not strictly equal, because one is moving and the other is at rest. This will affect the argument leading to the equation $\theta = 2\theta_{lab}$.

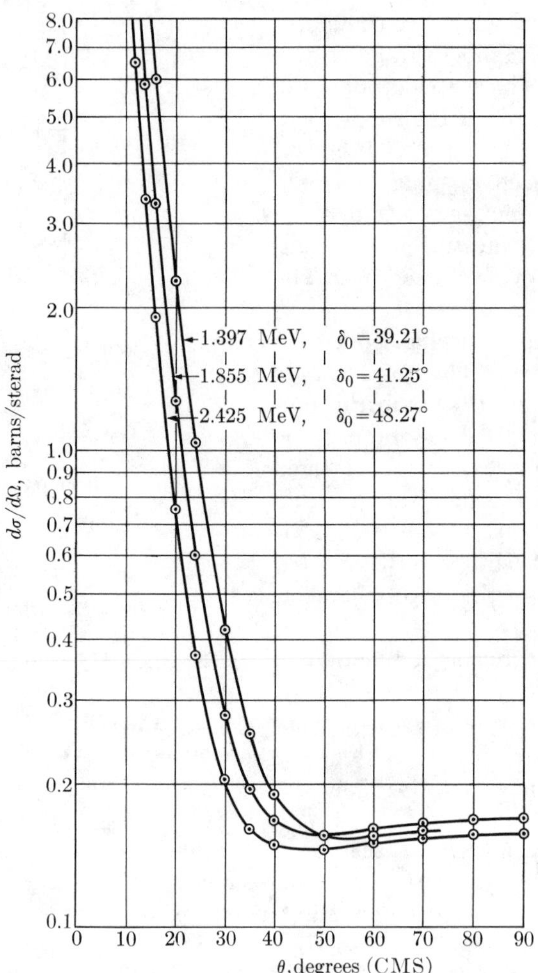

Fig. 3–14. Theoretical and experimental p-p cross sections at three energies (from data given by D. J. Knecht *et al.*).

to the diameter of the circles in Fig. 3–14. The curves drawn between the points in Fig. 3–14 represent theoretical cross sections. The mathematics of the theory for proton-proton scattering is considerably more complicated than for neutron-proton scattering; hence, only an outline of this theory is given below.

3–9 *Theory of Proton-Proton Scattering at Low Energies*

All evidence accumulated so far indicates that the nuclear forces are independent of the charge of the nucleons; however there are two important sources of difference between neutron-proton scattering and proton-proton scattering. One is the existence of the Coulomb force; this adds a long-range potential-energy term to the Schrödinger equation. The other arises from the fact that the scatterer and scattered particles are identical. This leads to the exclusion of certain angular-momentum states because of the operation of Pauli's principle. Specifically, for $l = 0$ scattering, the triplet state is excluded, and the only case we have to consider is the singlet state (antiparallel spins). The fact that the two particles are identical also has another effect. Since a recorder cannot distinguish between the scatterer and the scattered particle, it is impossible to distinguish between a small-angle scattering event and a large-angle scattering event (Fig. 3–15). In the theory, this fact is taken into account by adding the wave in the direction $\pi - \theta$ to the outgoing wave in the direction θ.

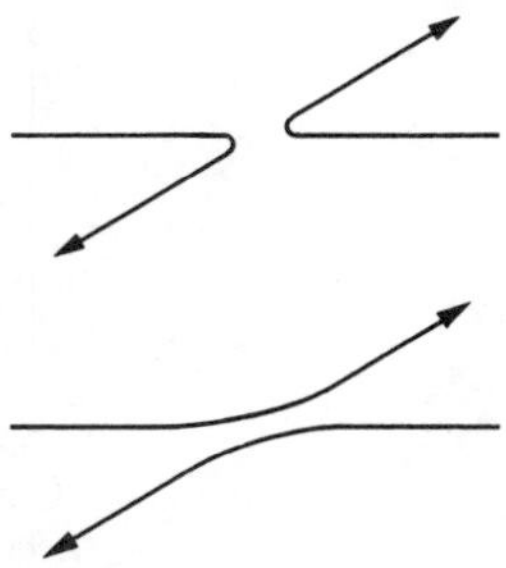

Fig. 3–15. Two indistinguishable p-p scattering events.

Figure 3–16 shows a potential-energy diagram for p-p scattering, in which the nuclear part of the potential has been represented as a square well and a repulsive core. The width and depth of the well are such that they fit the low-energy n-p singlet-scattering data. The diagram is to scale, and the total energy lines represent the energies used by Knecht *et al.* The radial wave equation for this problem is

$$\frac{d^2u}{dr^2} + \frac{2m}{\hbar^2}\left[E - V_N(r) - \frac{e^2}{4\pi\epsilon_0 r} - \frac{l(l+1)\hbar^2}{2mr^2}\right]u = 0, \tag{3–43}$$

where $V_N(r)$ is the square-well nuclear potential. Note that the Coulomb potential decreases with increasing r as r^{-1}, in contrast to the centrifugal potential which decreases as r^{-2}. This is significant. If we attempt to use the plane-wave expansion given in Section 3–4, we find that this "infinite" range Coulomb potential gives infinite phase shifts for all partial waves. Therefore the analytic approach used for neutron-proton scattering has to be modified for proton-proton scattering. The theory is fairly complicated, and only the result can be given here. For low energies, the nuclear potential will affect only the $l = 0$ partial wave, but the Coulomb field also produces higher l-value scattering. However, since the Coulomb potential is known, this part of the cross section can be computed. The resulting formula for the low-energy p-p differential cross section is

$$\begin{aligned}\frac{d\sigma(\theta)}{d\omega} = {} & \frac{\eta^2}{4k^2}\left[\frac{1}{\sin^4\theta/2} + \frac{1}{\cos^4\theta/2} - \frac{\cos(\eta\ln\tan^2\theta/2)}{\sin^2\theta/2\cos^2\theta/2}\right] + \Delta_{vp} \\ & - \frac{\eta\sin\delta_0}{2k^2}\left[\frac{\cos(\delta_0 + \eta\ln\sin^2\theta/2)}{\sin^2\theta/2} + \frac{\cos(\delta_0 + \eta\ln\cos^2\theta/2)}{\cos^2\theta/2}\right] \\ & + \frac{\sin^2\delta_0}{k^2}.\end{aligned} \tag{3–44}$$

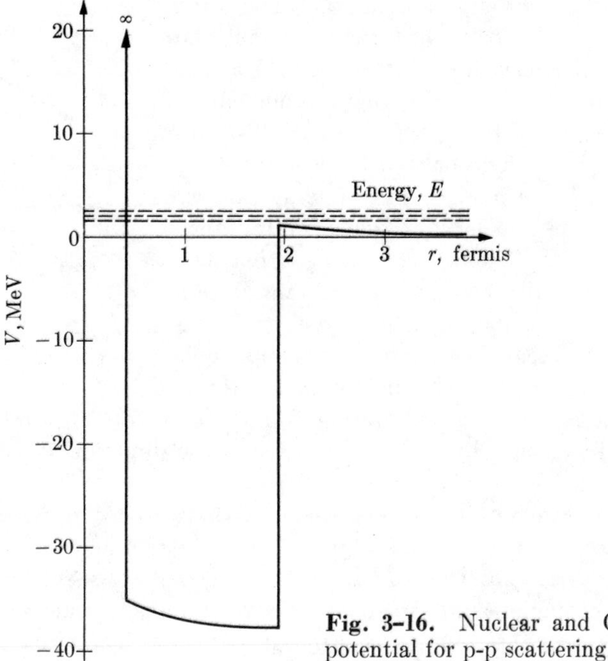

Fig. 3–16. Nuclear and Coulomb potential for p-p scattering.

The various quantities are: $\eta = e^2/4\pi\epsilon_0\hbar v$, $k^2 = 2mE/\hbar^2$, v = relative velocity of the two particles, E = total energy in the center-of-mass system, $m = M_p/2$ = reduced mass, δ_0 = phase shift for $l = 0$ nuclear scattering, and Δ_{vp} = correction for vacuum polarization.

The term Δ_{vp} is a small correction which arises from the polarizability of vacuum. According to Dirac's theory of the electron, which is still illustrative, although it may be outdated, vacuum is permeated by electrons in negative energy states. All states are filled, and the electrons are not normally detectable before they are brought up in a positive state. Then, in addition to the observed electron, the unoccupied state is observable as an electron "hole" or positron. However, in the presence of a strong electrostatic field the wave functions of the negative energy states are distorted, and a polarizing effect results. This distorts the field at small distances from the proton, so that the r^{-2} law does not hold. At large distances, there is no observable effect. The correction term Δ_{vp} in the cross-section formula (Eq. 3–44) is of the order of a few tenths of a percent for the energies considered. One of the important results of the accurate measurement of Knecht *et al.* is that good agreement between theory and experiment can only be obtained when Δ_{vp} is included. Their experiments therefore constitute another demonstration of the polarizability of vacuum.*

* Another example of the effect of vacuum polarization is the famous Lamb shift of hydrogen energy levels. Part of the observed shift is due to vacuum polarization.

Equation (3–44) contains only one adjustable parameter, the S-wave phase shift δ_0. For a given energy it must be possible to fit the observed cross sections at all angles for a single value of this parameter. The three curves given in Fig. 3–14 have been calculated by the use of Eq. (3–44) with the three values of δ_0 indicated in the figure. The remarkable agreement between experiment and theory is another great tribute to wave mechanics. It is particularly interesting that the theory correctly predicts the destructive interference between Mott (Coulomb field) scattering and nuclear scattering. This interference is most pronounced at the minima in the curves around 50 degrees.

The phase shift δ_0 in Eq. (3–44) should not be compared directly with the neutron-proton phase shift at the same energy. However, the theory permits a calculation of the nuclear potential parameters from a knowledge of δ_0. The results of such calculations support the contention that the proton-proton nuclear potential acting in the singlet S-state is equal to the neutron-proton singlet S-potential, or very closely so. A small difference is ascribed to differences in the magnetic moments.

We can now summarize the most important results that have been obtained from a study of low-energy nucleon-nucleon scattering and of the deuteron:

(1) The assumption of charge independence of nuclear forces is supported.

(2) The nuclear forces are spin-dependent (singlet and triplet forces). They also depend on the relative orientation of spin and displacement vector (tensor force).

(3) Analysis of the deuteron (binding energy) and of low-energy nucleon-nucleon scattering yields information about the width and the depth of the nuclear potential, but no details about the shape of the potential. Some more detailed information of this kind, for instance a clear indication of the existence of a repulsive core, can be obtained from a more detailed study of high-energy electron scattering on the deuteron.* More complete information about the nuclear forces, particularly the forces acting in higher orbital momentum states, can be obtained from high-energy nucleon-nucleon scattering experiments. A review of such high-energy data and their interpretation is given below.

3–10 High-Energy Nucleon-Nucleon Scattering

From the preceding sections, we have learned that wave mechanics is quite successful in describing low-energy nucleon-nucleon scattering phenomena. The analysis has given us some information about the strength of the nucleon-nucleon interactions, but no details about the distance dependence. Encouraged by the success so far, we now turn to higher energy scattering, that is, shorter wavelength scattering, in the hope of unveiling some of the details of the nuclear

* J. R. Friedman, H. W. Kendall, and P. A. M. Gram, *Phys. Rev.* **120,** 992 (1960). The shape of the angular distributions of electrons scattered from deuterium may be explained in terms of a "hole" in the center of the deuteron. There are other possible explanations.

potential. The meeting ground between experiment and theory is a set of phase shifts for the various angular momentum states in which the two particles do interact. In low-energy proton-proton scattering, because of the action of the exclusion principle, we are dealing with only one such state, and in low-energy neutron-proton scattering, we are dealing with two states, one singlet S-state and one degenerate triplet S-state. For each value of l greater than zero there are four n-p states, one singlet and three members of a triplet, but in the p-p case the exclusion principle allows only one or three states, depending on whether l is even or odd. At a given energy, we need sufficient experimental information to determine the phase shift for each of these states. In addition, if tensor forces are present, we need to introduce some so-called mixing parameters that connect, for instance, the $^3S_1$-state and the $^3D_1$-state. Thus the net result is that in the case of n-p scattering at a given energy, we need sufficient information to determine $(5l_{\text{max}} + 1)$ parameters (phase shifts and mixing parameters). Here l_{max} is the maximum l-value (taken as odd) that must be considered for the energy used. For p-p scattering, the number of parameters is $(5l_{\text{max}} + 3)/2$. For instance, if $l_{\text{max}} = 3$, we need to determine fourteen phase shifts and two mixing parameters for n-p scattering, and eight phase shifts and one mixing parameter for p-p scattering.

The experimental information that is most readily available is the angular distribution, i.e., the differential cross section as a function of the angle. Yang* and Wolfenstein† have shown that the neutron-proton differential cross section can be written as

$$\frac{d\sigma(\theta)}{d\Omega} = \sum_{n=0}^{2l_{\text{max}}} A_n Y_{n,0}(\theta). \tag{3–45}$$

The number of terms in this sum is $2l_{\text{max}} + 1$, and hence this is the maximum number of parameters, A_n, that can be determined from an n-p angular-distribution measurement. In proton-proton scattering, the angular distribution is symmetric around 90 degrees, so that only even n spherical harmonics enter into Eq. (3–45). The number of coefficients A_n that is obtained from p-p differential cross-section measurements is therefore only $l_{\text{max}} + 1$. Clearly, then, in both cases the angular-distribution measurements at a given energy do not yield enough information to determine the phase shifts and mixing parameters at that energy. We therefore have to look for additional information. Such information can be obtained from polarization experiments, that is, measurements of spin directions of the scattered particles.

In the simplest type of polarization experiment, one attempts to measure the spin direction of the scattered particle after a scattering event, or, more precisely, the percentage of particles with spin "up" and the percentage with spin "down" relative to the plane of the scattering event. To detect the polariza-

* C. N. Yang, *Phys. Rev.* **74,** 764 (1948).
† L. Wolfenstein, *Phys. Rev.* **75,** 1664 (1949).

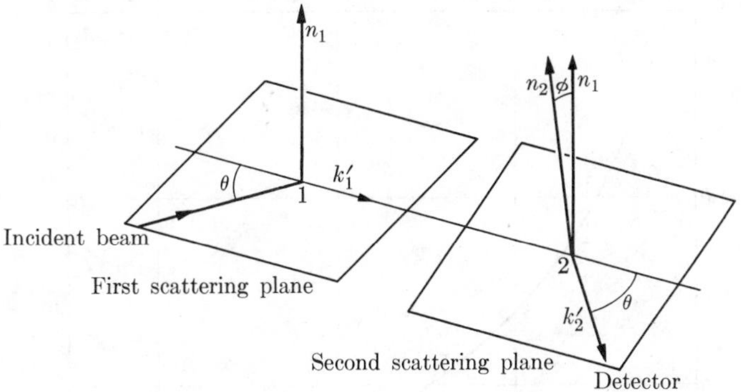

Fig. 3–17. Double-scattering experiment to measure polarization.

tion, one needs to let the particle scatter a second time. The geometry of such a double-scattering experiment is shown in Fig. 3–17. The apparatus is set up so that the scattering angle θ is the same in both events. The direction of the particle before and after each scattering event defines a scattering plane for that event. The vectors $\mathbf{n}_1$ and $\mathbf{n}_2$ in Fig. 3–17 are unit vectors normal to the scattering planes. The second scattering plane forms an angle ϕ with the first scattering plane, as shown. The two angles θ and ϕ are experimental parameters, determined by the relative orientation of the two targets and the counter equipment. Polarization is now defined in the following way. An unpolarized beam, i.e., a beam in which the spin directions are randomly distributed, falls on target 1. After scattering, the spin directions of the scattered particles may not be randomly distributed any longer; the polarization measures the amount of ordering of the spin directions along the normal $\mathbf{n}_1$ to the scattering plane. For a proton or a neutron, where the maximum spin component is equal to $\frac{1}{2}$, the polarization is defined as

$$P \equiv 2\langle S_n \rangle, \tag{3–46}$$

where $\langle S_n \rangle$ signifies the average spin component in the direction $\mathbf{n}_1$. This definition gives $P = \pm 1$ for 100% alignment.

It can be shown that*, for a given scattering angle θ, the intensity of the particles emerging from the second scattering center depends on the angle θ, in the following fashion:

$$I_2(\theta, \phi) = I_2\left(\theta, \frac{\pi}{2}\right)(1 + P_1 P_2 \cos \phi). \tag{3–47}$$

Here $P_1 = P_1(\theta)$ is the polarization of the particles emerging at an angle θ after the first scattering event, and $P_2 = P_2(\theta)$ is the polarization which would result from the second scattering event if the incoming beam on the second

---

* Wolfenstein, *loc. cit.*

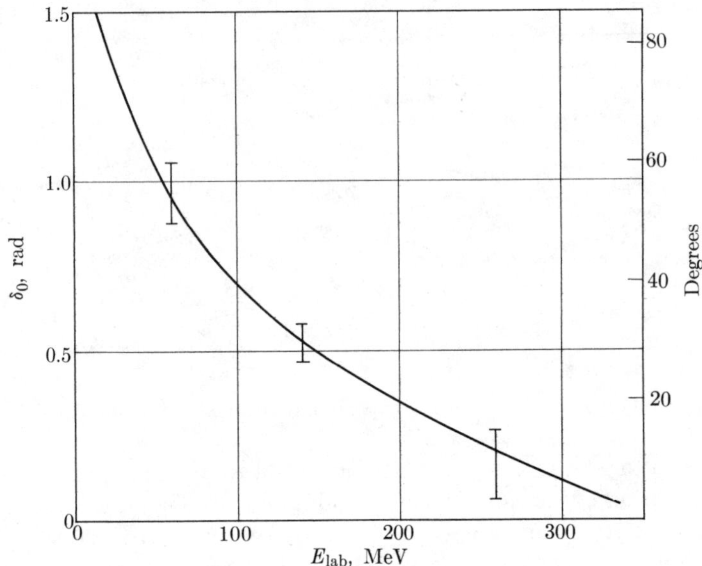

Fig. 3-18. The triplet phase shift δ_0 for the $l = 0$ state vs. neutron energy E_{lab}. (From M. H. Hull, Jr. *et al.**)

scattering center were unpolarized. When the scattering targets and the scattering angle θ in the two events are identical, we get $P_1 = P_2$ and therefore

$$I_2(\theta, \phi) = I_2\left(\theta, \frac{\pi}{2}\right)(1 + P^2 \cos \phi). \tag{3-48}$$

For a given energy and a given scattering angle θ, it is clear that it is possible to determine the polarization by measuring the intensity at two values of ϕ (for example, $\phi = 0$ and $\phi = \pi/2$).

In order to measure the polarization parameter $P(\theta)$, one has to carry out a double-scattering experiment, as outlined above. A large number of such experiments have been performed, both for n-p scattering and p-p scattering in the general range of energies from 80 to 300 MeV. Some triple-scattering experiments have also been performed. In a triple-scattering experiment, one can, among other things, determine to what extent a beam of particles that gets polarized in the first scattering event will be depolarized in the second event. The third scattering event finally detects the residual polarization.

All available neutron-proton and proton-proton scattering data have been analyzed on an electronic computer by Breit *et al.** at Yale University. The

---

* For p-p data: G. Breit, M. H. Hull, Jr., K. Lassila, and K. D. Pyatt, *Phys. Rev.* **120,** 2227 (1960); and for n-p data: M. H. Hull, Jr., K. E. Lassila, H. M. Ruppel, F. A. McDonald, and G. Breit, *Phys. Rev.* **122,** 1606 (1961).

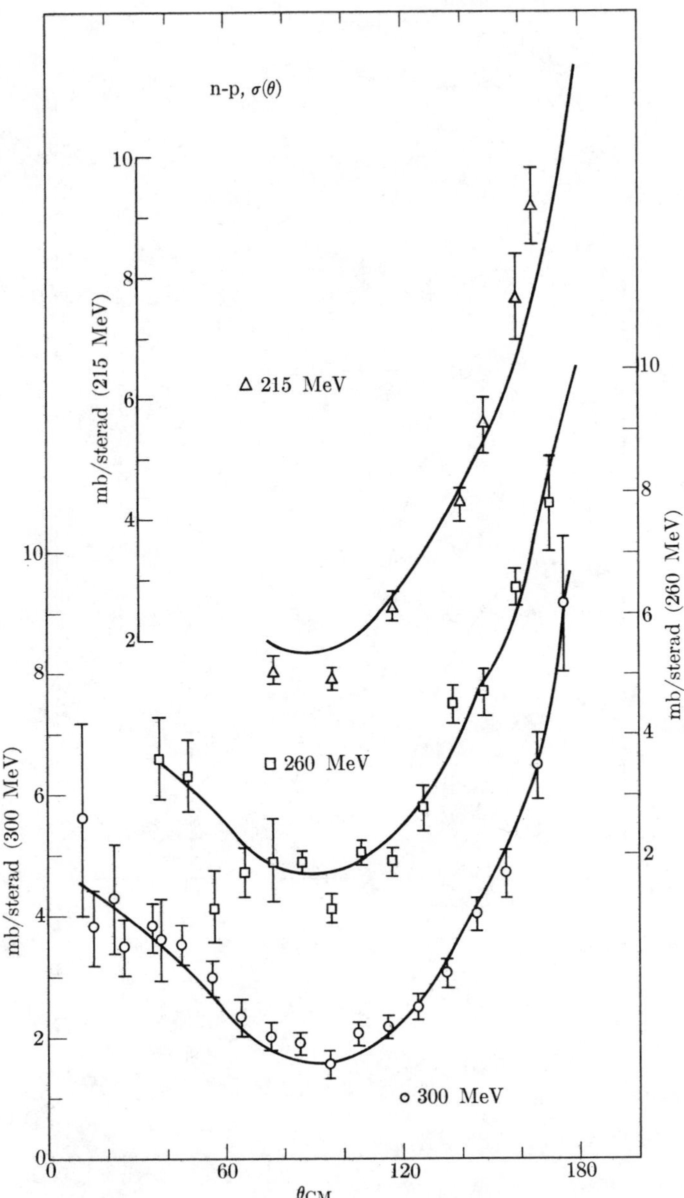

Fig. 3–19. Neutron-proton differential cross sections at 215, 260, and 300 MeV, measured and calculated from Breit's phase parameters. (From M. H. Hull, Jr. *et al.*, *op. cit.*)

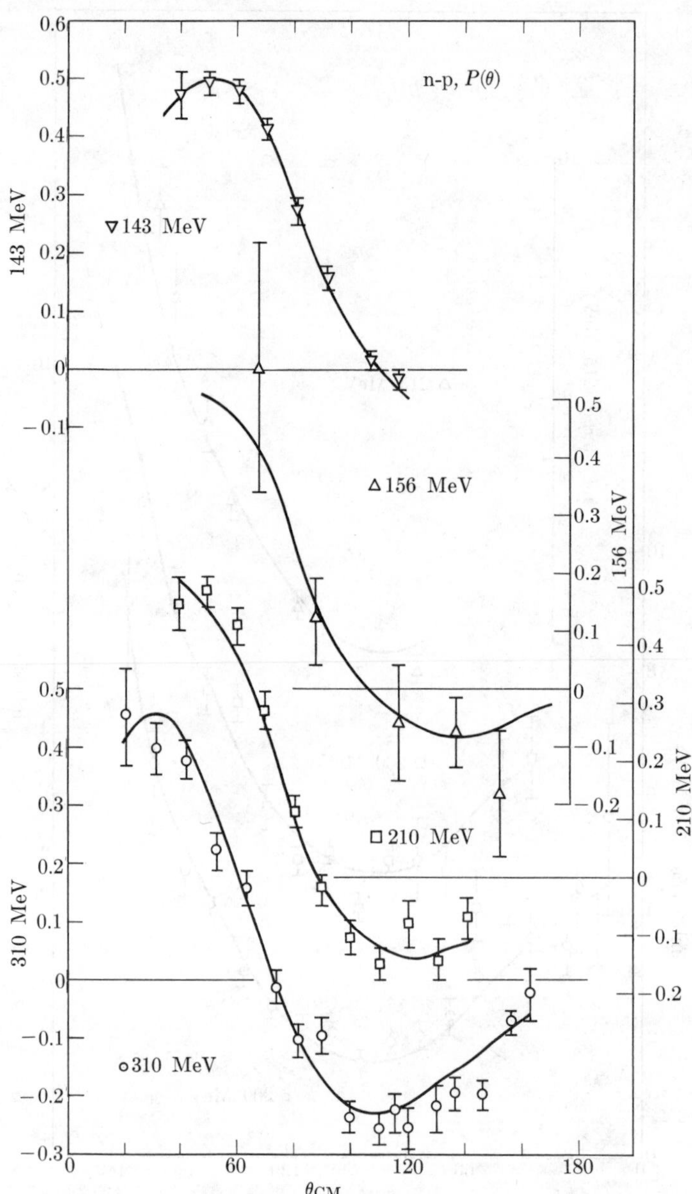

Fig. 3-20. Neutron-proton polarization $P(\theta)$ vs. scattering angle θ_{CM} at neutron energies E_{lab} = 143, 156, 210, and 310 MeV. The curves are calculated from Breit's phase parameters. (From M. H. Hull, Jr. *et al., op. cit.*)

object of the analysis was to obtain a set of phase parameters, each of which would be a smooth function of the energy. Figure 3–18 shows, as an example, the $^3S_1$ phase-shift as a function of neutron energy for the "best" solution. There are corresponding curves, not shown, which are calculated for triplet and singlet states up to the $^3G_5$-state. Charge independence of nuclear forces has been assumed, and the n-p data have been used to determine the phase parameters for states where p-p scattering is excluded.

As seen from Fig. 3–18, the $^3S_1$ phase-shift curve, extrapolated slightly beyond the range of the actual data, reaches zero at about 350 MeV. A simple model potential with a repulsive core followed by an attractive well, as illustrated by the square well, leads to such a result (Problem 3–7). This evidence, as well as the evidence from electron-scattering experiments on the deuteron, strongly supports the contention that a hard core must be part of the description of a nucleon-nucleon potential.

Some of the experimental data that have been used in the phase-shift determinations are shown in Figs. 3–19 and 3–20, together with the theoretical curves calculated from the final choice of phase shifts. The overall agreement for the two examples chosen, as well as for a host of others, is remarkably good. The conclusion that can be drawn from this is that it appears to be possible to use the method of partial wave analysis with a suitable choice of phase parameters to describe correctly all quantities observed in nucleon-nucleon scattering. The next step is to find a consistent description of a nucleon-nucleon potential which will produce these phase parameters, including their variation with energy. One approach to this problem is outlined in the next section.

3–11 Meson Theory of Nuclear Forces

It is now generally accepted that the nuclear forces are produced by a meson field which is similar in origin to electromagnetic fields but is of much shorter range. Yukawa* pointed out that the short range is consistent with a field carried by field quanta with a rest mass different from zero, contrary to the electromagnetic field which is carried by photons of zero rest mass. Yukawa's arguments, greatly simplified, are approximately as follows.

Electromagnetic fields obey a wave equation that can be derived from Maxwell's equations. For instance, the scalar electric potential U in free space obeys the well-known wave equation

$$\left(\nabla^2 - \frac{1}{c^2}\frac{\partial^2}{\partial t^2}\right)U = 0. \tag{3–49}$$

For a static field, we have $\nabla^2 U = 0$ (Laplace's equation) in free space or $\nabla^2 U = -\rho/\epsilon_0$ (Poisson's equation) in the presence of charges. By integrating

* H. Yukawa, *Proc. Phys. Math. Soc. Japan* **17,** 48 (1935).

these equations we find the static solution

$$U = \frac{q}{4\pi\epsilon_0 r} \tag{3-50}$$

for the scalar potential at a distance r from a point charge q.

According to modern theories, the electromagnetic field is carried by virtual photons which are continuously emitted and absorbed by the charged particles. In accordance with this view, we can regard Eq. (3–49) for the scalar potential and the equivalent equation for the electromagnetic vector potential as quantum-mechanical wave equations for the photon fields. In complete analogy with Schrödinger's equation, the electromagnetic wave equations of the form (3–49) can be derived by substituting the operator for momentum square, $-\hbar^2 \nabla^2$, and the energy operator, $-\hbar i\, \partial/\partial t$, into the equation

$$-p^2 + \frac{1}{c^2} E^2 = 0. \tag{3-51}$$

This equation, of course, is the correct relationship between momentum and energy for a particle of zero rest mass. The corresponding equation for a particle with rest mass m different from zero is

$$-p^2 - m^2c^2 + \frac{1}{c^2} E^2 = 0. \tag{3-52}$$

If we make the same substitution as above, we obtain

$$\left(\nabla^2 - \frac{m^2c^2}{\hbar^2} - \frac{1}{c^2}\frac{\partial^2}{\partial t^2}\right)\Phi = 0. \tag{3-53}$$

Equation (3–53), which is the correct wave equation for a spinless relativistic particle, is regarded as the equation for a scalar meson field Φ. We separate out time exactly as we do for Schrödinger's equation (see Appendix 1), and we obtain a time-independent wave equation for the meson field for total energy $E = 0$ (binding energy equals rest energy),

$$(\nabla^2 - \mu^2)\phi = 0, \tag{3-54}$$

where

$$\mu = mc/\hbar. \tag{3-55}$$

An acceptable spherically symmetric solution of Eq. (3–54) is

$$\phi = g\frac{e^{-\mu r}}{r}, \tag{3-56}$$

where g is an undetermined constant which plays the same role as the charge q in the electrostatic case, i.e., it depends on a "source" at the origin.

In the electrostatic case, the mechanical potential resulting from the interaction between two charges q is $qU = q^2/4\pi\epsilon_0 r$. This interaction results from the continuous transmission of virtual photons between the two charges. By analogy, for nuclear forces, the mechanical potential resulting from the interaction between two nucleons of strength g is

$$V = g^2 \frac{e^{-\mu r}}{r}, \tag{3–57}$$

arising from the continuous transfer of virtual mesons of rest mass m between the two nucleons. The term "virtual" implies that the meson cannot be released from the nucleons unless an energy of at least mc^2 is supplied. The order of magnitude of the duration of an excursion of the meson Δt is given by the uncertainty relationship $\Delta t\, \Delta E \approx \hbar$, where $\Delta E = mc^2$. This gives, for the range of the force, $\Delta r \approx \Delta tc \approx \hbar/mc$, in agreement with Eqs. (3–55) and (3–56).

From the observed range of nuclear forces, we can estimate by Eqs. (3–56) and (3–55) that the mass of the field-carrying mesons must be of the order of 300 electron rest masses. The class of mesons that comes closest to this is the pi mesons or *pions*, of which there are three kinds: positive, negative, and neutral, all with intrinsic spin $s = 0$. The mass, about 270 rest masses, inserted into Eq. (3–55) yields $\mu = 0.70\ \mathrm{F}^{-1}$. The force field between two protons or between two neutrons can be carried only by a neutral pi meson, but the force between a proton and a neutron can also be carried by a charged pi meson. In the latter case, the charge will be transferred from one nucleon to the other, so that the neutron changes into a proton, and vice versa.

Another kind of particle, the *muon*, discovered before the pion, was originally thought to be Yukawa's particle. However, the muon or muons (+ or −) interact very weakly with nuclear matter and do not have a neutral member in the family. Furthermore, they are spin $\frac{1}{2}$ particles that cannot be transferred from any system without changing the angular momentum of the system.

In this brief outline of the meson theory of nuclear forces, we have not discussed several important factors. First, it has been observed that the pion has negative intrinsic parity; therefore it cannot be transferred from a neutron to a proton in an $l = 0$ state and still conserve parity. To conserve both angular momentum and parity, the only possible state for the pion is the $l = 1$ state. When it is created and transferred, the spin of the parent nucleon flips over so that the resulting spin is still $\frac{1}{2}$. If this is taken into account, it turns out that the force field between two nucleons in the triplet state is not spherically symmetric, as suggested by Eq. (3–57), but has an additional term which is just the tensor force discussed in Chapter 2.

The one-pion exchange potential (OPEP) discussed above is based on the transfer of a single meson from one nucleon to another. In an important extension of this theory, one also considers the *simultaneous* transfer of *two* pions. The mathematically complicated term describing the two-pion exchange potential (TPEP) has the general character of an exponential of the form $e^{-2\mu r}$.

The factor 2 causes the TPEP to decrease much more rapidly for increasing distance than the OPEP so that the term is unimportant beyond about 2 F.

In an analysis of the Breit phase parameters, Feshbach *et al.** have given convincing evidence that the nuclear forces are adequately described by the one- and two-pion exchange potentials for distances greater than approximately 0.7 F between the nucleons. When we are considering a scattering event, the authors argue that below a given distance r_0, the possibility for many-pion exchanges rapidly becomes much greater, and the interaction is, in general, so strong that the wave function from this point on and toward $r = 0$ is practically independent of the bombarding energy. However, it may depend on l, S, and J; that is, it may be different for all the various states considered. In the work of Feshbach *et al.* the logarithmic derivatives at r_0, as well as r_0, are regarded as adjustable but energy-independent parameters. The wave function outside r_0 (which is about 0.7 F) can then be fitted to the constant logarithmic derivative at r_0 for each of the states considered.

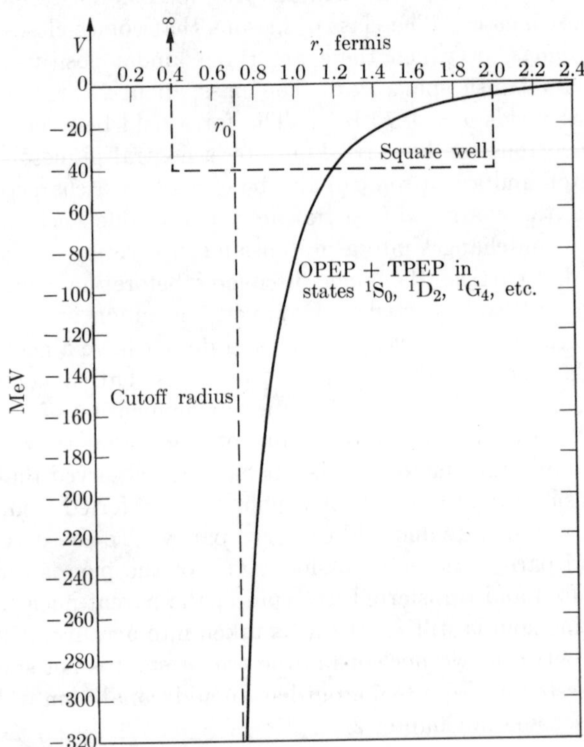

Fig. 3–21. Pion-exchange potential for singlet even l-states. A square well that fits low-energy singlet scattering data is shown for comparison (Courtesy of E. Lomon).

---

* H. Feshbach, E. Lomon, and A. Tubis, *Phys. Rev. Letters* **6**, 635 (1961).

Table 3–1. Comparison between experimental p-p scattering phase parameters and parameters derived from a pion-exchange potential with an energy-independent logarithmic derivative of the wave function at the cutoff radius $r_0 = 0.71$ F

State, JlS	Log derivative, $\frac{r_0}{\psi}\frac{d\psi}{dr}$	E_{lab}, MeV	Phase parameter, degrees: Predicted (Feshbach *et al.*)	Phase parameter, degrees: Experimental (Breit *et al.*)
000	1.1	95	24.2	23
		150	12.9	12.6
		210	2.8	4.3
		310	−10.9	− 7.8
011	−6.5	95	10.5	9.7
		150	3.9	3.5
		210	− 4.1	− 2.2
		310	−17	−11
111	15	95	−12.5	−13.5
		150	−16.7	−17.8
		210	−21.1	−21.8
		310	−28.1	−27.2
211	−0.193	95	11.6	11.6
		150	15.5	15.2
		210	17.5	17.4
		310	17.7	17.9
220	3.82	95	3.7	3.9
		150	5.9	5.8
		210	8.0	7.8
		310	10.5	10
231	−4.10	95	0.02	− 0.1
		150	0.27	0.05
		210	0.20	0.15
		310	− 0.84	0.2
331	100	95	− 1.5	− 1.7
		150	− 2.3	− 2.5
		210	− 2.9	− 3.3
		310	− 3.7	− 4.0
ϵ_2	−0.103	95	−13.8	−14
		150	−11.2	−11.2
		210	− 8.9	− 8.3
		310	− 5.8	− 6.6

Figure 3–21 shows, as an example, the combined one-pion and two-pion exchange potential for singlet states with even l-values ($^1S_0$, $^1D_2$, $^1G_4$, etc.). For comparison, a square-well potential is also shown, which fits the singlet scattering length $a_s = -23.7$ F and effective range $r_{0s} = 2.4$ F when the repulsive-core parameter has been arbitrarily chosen as $c = 0.4$ F (Section 3–7).

The cutoff radius r_0 is not, of course, synonymous with a repulsive-core parameter. In fact, for the particular potential considered in Fig. 3–21, the logarithmic derivative at $r = r_0$ indicates that the potential still is attractive in part of the region $r < r_0$.

Table 3–1 gives, again as an example, the phase parameters calculated by Feshbach *et al.* and the experimental (Breit) phase parameters (Section 3–10) for p-p scattering in the range 95 to 310 MeV. The various states are labeled with their J-, l-, and S-values, and a parameter describing the tensor-force coupling between the $^3P_2$- and $^3F_2$-states is labeled ϵ_2. The low-energy p-p scattering data have also been included in the adjustment leading to the parameters of Table 3–1. The adjustable parameters include the cutoff radius r_0, the logarithmic derivatives for the various partial waves at that radius, and also three parameters which determine the strength of various terms of the pion-exchange potential. The agreement between the observed and predicted phase parameters is, in general, quite good; the differences are only of the order of magnitude of the uncertainties of the experimental data. For the states which are excluded in p-p scattering by the uncertainty principle, n-p data have been used, and a similar set of logarithmic derivatives has been obtained.

The boundary-adjustment calculations of Feshbach *et al.* described above constitute one of a number of possible approaches to the determination of nuclear-force parameters. Several of these approaches have met with a limited measure of success, and the work is continuing to improve the agreement and to deepen our understanding of the pion-exchange potential. It can be said with confidence at this time that the meson theory of nuclear forces is here to stay.

PROBLEMS

3–1. A particle of mass M and initial velocity V_0 is scattered by a lighter particle of mass m at rest. Find the maximum angle θ_{lab} at which the scattered particle can be observed and the maximum angle ϕ_{lab} at which the recoiling lighter particle can be observed. (Use a vector diagram in the center-of-mass system.)

3–2. The differential cross section (lab) for a given scattering process is $d\sigma/d\omega = a + b\cos^2\theta$. (a) What is the total cross section? (b) A counter mounted 10 cm from the target at $\theta = 60°$ has an effective area of 0.1 cm^2. The target thickness is 10^{-4} cm and the number of atoms per cm^3 in the target is 10^{22}. Assume that $a = 4.2 \times 10^{-28}$ cm^2/sterad, and $b = 2.4 \times 10^{-28}$ cm^2/sterad. What is the counting rate (counts per second) when the beam is 1 μa (protons)?

3–3. Referring to the neutron-proton scattering experiment of Storrs and Frisch, calculate the transmission ratios N/N_0 (Eq. 3–4) for scatterers of graphite and polyethylene 2.5 cm thick. (The densities are 2.25 gm/cm^3 and 0.95 gm/cm^3, respectively.)

3–4. Calculate the classical impact parameter necessary to give orbital angular momentum $l = 1$ in a neutron-proton scattering event when the neutron energy is $E_{\text{lab}} = 10$ MeV.

3–5. Show that Eq. (3–13) is a solution of Schrödinger's equation for $l = 0$ and $V = 0$.

3–6. The interaction between two identical (hypothetical) particles of mass M is given by a repulsive potential of the form shown in Fig. 3–22 (r is the particle separation). Solve the $l = 0$ radial wave equation for region I and region II. The total energy (center of mass) is $E < V_0$. Use the boundary condition $u(r) = 0$ at $r = 0$. Match the wave functions at the boundary to obtain an equation for the phase shift δ. Show that at low energies $E \approx 0$ and for $V_0 = \infty$ ("hard sphere") the scattering cross section is $\sigma = 4\pi R^2$.

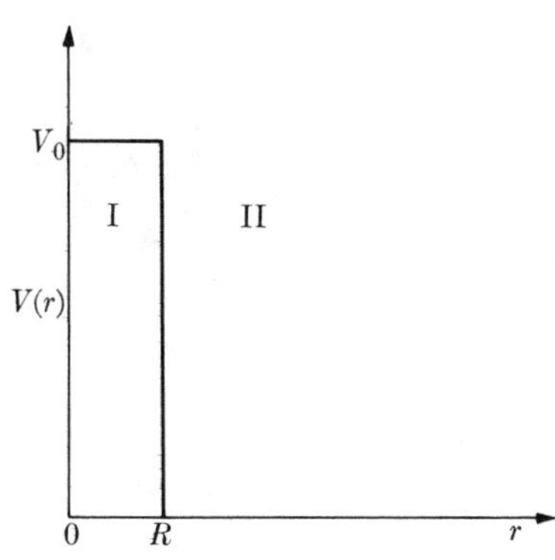

Figure 3–22

3–7. Matching $l = 0$ wave functions at the boundary $r = c + b$ of a square-well repulsive core potential for n-p scattering gives Eq. (3–26). Determine the repulsive core parameter c from the information that the triplet S phase shift is $\delta_0 = 0$ at $E_{\text{lab}} = 350$ MeV (Fig. 3–18). Use $V_0 = 73$ MeV and $b = 1.337$ F.

3–8. Go through the steps outlined on p. 67 to prove Eq. (3–40).

3–9. Determine r_{0s} from the experimental observation that $\sigma = 1.690$ barns at $E = 4.75$ MeV (lab). Use $a_t = 5.38$ F, $r_{0t} = 1.70$ F, and $a_s = -23.7$ F. Show that σ is not very sensitive to changes in r_{0s}.

3–10. (a) Calculate the triplet n-p scattering cross section at $E_n = 1$ MeV (lab) by using the exact equation (3–26) for δ_0. Well parameters are $c = 0.4$ F, $V_{0t} = 73.3$ MeV, and $b_t = 1.337$ F. (b) Calculate the same cross section as above using Eq. (3–38) with $a_t = 5.38$ F and $r_{0t} = 1.70$ F.

3–11. Prove Eq. (3–42).

3–12. Separate Eq. (3–53) to prove Eq. (3–54). Show that Eq. (3–56) is a solution of Eq. (3–54) and plot the one-pion exchange potential (Eq. 3–57) in the range $r = 1$ to 5 F for $g^2 = 0.087 m_\pi c^2$.

*3–13. Design an experiment to measure the p-p differential cross section at 10 MeV (lab). List the major equipment used. Draw a sketch of the scattering chamber. Give mechanical tolerances and tolerances on gas pressure, beam energy, etc., necessary for an accuracy of 0.1%.

PART 3

Properties of Stable Nuclei, Nuclear Models

4 Masses and Relative Abundances of Atomic Species

4–1 Introduction

Historically, the study of atomic masses has been of the greatest importance in the development of nuclear physics. As early as 1910 Soddy conjectured that the absence of simple numerical relationships between some, but not all, atomic masses indicated that some elements consisted of mixtures of atoms of different weights but similar chemical properties. In the following year Rutherford proposed the nuclear atom. In 1912, J. J. Thomson published the results of his now famous positive-ray experiment, which proved that ordinary neon gas consists of a mixture of atoms with different masses. In 1913 Soddy introduced the definition of *isotopes* as atoms with identical chemical properties but with different nuclear characteristics. Important progress in the realm of isotopes and atomic masses came in 1919 with the development by Aston of a real mass spectrograph. Aston's spectrograph employed both electrostatic and magnetic deflection, as did the spectrograph later developed by Mattauch. The accuracy of Aston's first instrument was rather poor compared with that of present-day devices. However, it sufficed to demonstrate that atomic masses could be expressed as integers (or near integers) when compared with each other, or that they were at least so close to integers that the discrepancy could be explained as a result of the loss of mass corresponding to the binding energy of the nucleus.

Mass spectroscopy continues to play an important role in nuclear physics because differences in masses between neighboring nuclides reflect differences in binding energies of the "last" nucleons. This is of direct theoretical interest and can also be used for predicting disintegration and reaction energies. Conversely, nuclear-reaction data and disintegration data can be used to construct an atomic-mass table. The fact that these different ways of determining atomic masses give consistent results provides a beautiful demonstration of Einstein's mass-energy equivalence principle.

4–2 Deflection-Type Mass Spectrographs and Spectrometers

In a deflection-type instrument for atomic-mass determination, the atoms to be studied are first ionized, then accelerated to several keV energy through an electrostatic potential, and finally deflected and focused by transverse electric

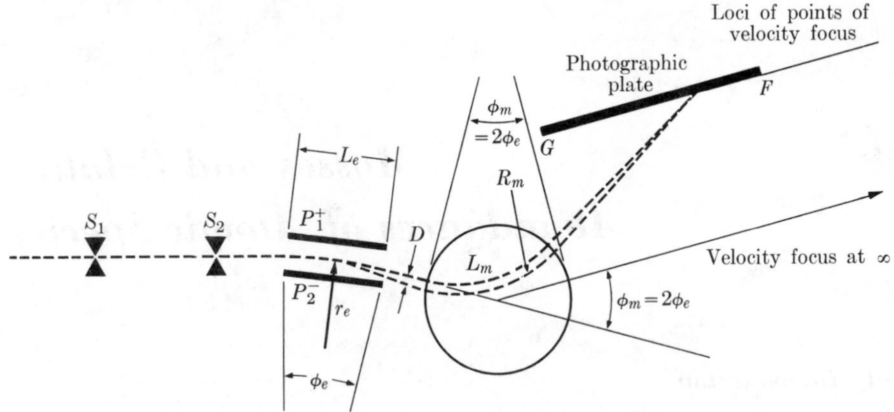

Fig. 4-1. Velocity-focusing principle of Aston's spectrograph.

and magnetic fields in succession. If all ions had exactly the same energy after being accelerated, it would suffice to deflect them by a magnetic field only. This would cause ions of different masses to take different paths and, hence, would result in the desired separation. However, since the ions are leaving the ion source with a small but still significant spread in energy, it is necessary either to select ions of a narrow range of energies or velocities or, better still, to introduce "velocity focusing." This means that ions of the *same mass* but *different velocity* can be deflected in such a way that they reach the same point on the recorder. This is accomplished by letting the ions pass first through an electrostatic deflector, that is, through a transverse electric field, and then through a suitable magnetic deflector. Both deflectors also have directional focusing properties, which means that ions diverging from a line source (a fine slit) can be brought to converge again to a line image on the recorder. A modern mass spectrograph has both velocity focusing and directional focusing.

When the detector in the instrument is a photographic plate, which permits a large part of the mass spectrum to be continuously recorded, the instrument is called a *spectrograph*. If the detector consists of a slit system and an electrode to which an ultrasensitive microammeter is connected, the instrument is called a *spectrometer*. The following paragraphs describe briefly various types of instruments which have all played an important role in the development of high-precision mass spectroscopy.

Aston* (1919) first introduced the concept of velocity focusing in a mass spectrograph. Figure 4–1 shows a diagram of the principal elements of Aston's first spectrograph. Ions from a discharge tube pass through two very narrow parallel slits, S_1 and S_2, and then through the electrostatic deflector, P_1 and P_2. The latter disperses the ions into an energy spectrum at position D. Thereafter the

* F. W. Aston, *Phil. Mag.* (*London*) **38,** 707 (1919).

ions are deflected magnetically and finally fall on the photographic plate GF. The principle of velocity focusing can best be illustrated by the following analysis: The angular deflection of an ion after passing through an electrostatic deflector of length L_e can be found by balancing the centrifugal force and the electrostatic force as follows:

$$mv^2/r_e = qE, \qquad \phi_e = L_e/r_e = qEL_e/mv^2. \tag{4–1a}$$

A similar analysis for the magnetic deflector yields

$$mv^2/r_m = qvB, \qquad \phi_m = L_m/r_m = qBL_m/mv. \tag{4–1b}$$

Differentiation of the expressions for the two angles with respect to the velocity and with respect to the mass yields

$$\frac{1}{\phi_e}\frac{d\phi_e}{dv} = \frac{2}{\phi_m}\frac{d\phi_m}{dv}, \tag{4–2}$$

$$\frac{1}{\phi_e}\frac{d\phi_e}{dm} = \frac{1}{\phi_m}\frac{d\phi_m}{dm}. \tag{4–3}$$

Equation (4–2) shows that the net velocity dispersion $d\phi_e/dv + d\phi_m/dv$ can be made equal to zero when ϕ_m is equal to $-2\phi_e$. Equation (4–3) shows that the net mass dispersion $d\phi_e/dm + d\phi_m/dm$ is then not equal to zero. The condition $\phi_m = -2\phi_e$ yields a net velocity dispersion equal to zero, and therefore ions emerging from the magnet have parallel paths. If the magnetic deflecting angle is made somewhat larger, that is $|\phi_m| > 2\phi_e$, the path of the ions will converge after the magnetic deflection, as shown in Fig. 4–1.

The preceding analysis is only correct when the magnitude of the magnetic deflecting angle ϕ_m does not depend on the amount of the preceding electrostatic deflection. This was approximately true in Aston's instrument (L_m constant), but it is not true in general. Another example is discussed below for which correct velocity focusing is accomplished with $\phi_e = 90°$ and $\phi_m = 60°$.

Aston's first instrument could separate isotopes with a mass difference of approximately 1%, and the masses could be determined to an accuracy of about 0.1%. The instrument did not directionally focus the ions to the extent that it produced an image of the entrance slit at the recorder. The ion beam passing through the slit system S_1 and S_2 had a divergence determined solely by the geometry of this system. The electrostatic and magnetic deflectors had weak focusing properties, which caused some reduction of this divergence, but not enough to produce an image on the recorder.

During the period 1935–1940, several instruments were completed that had directional focusing as well as velocity focusing. Some of these double-focusing instruments had both resolving power and accuracy that were 100 times better than the numbers quoted for Aston's first spectrograph. An example of such a

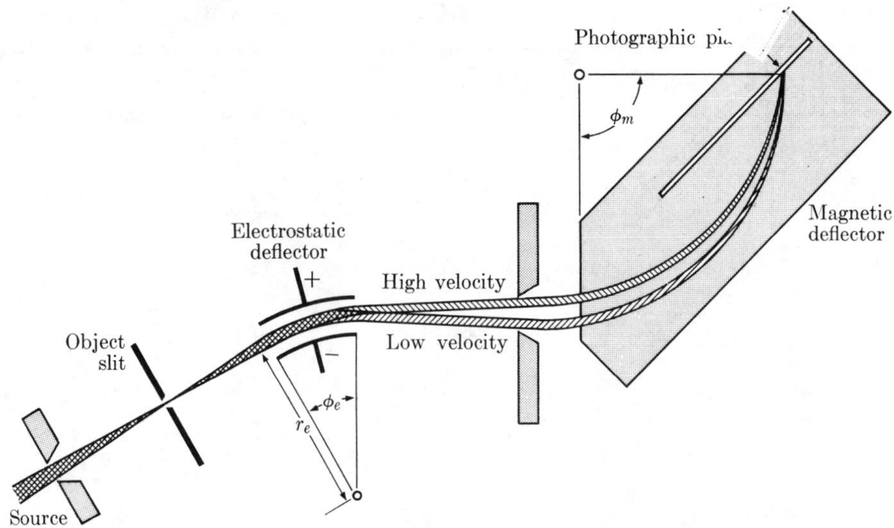

Fig. 4–2. Schematic diagram of a mass spectrograph (from Mattauch).

double-focusing instrument is one built by Mattauch,* shown in Fig. 4–2. The instrument has 31°50′ electric deflection, followed by 90° magnetic deflection. This spectrograph is double-focusing for all masses, and a very large mass spectrum can be recorded on the photographic plate simultaneously.

Aston's and Mattauch's instruments, as well as others,† used photographic plates as recorders; in other words, they were spectrographs. Dempster‡ and Nier§ both designed mass spectrometers with current collectors as recorders. Nier's instrument has been perfected over the years to the extent that it now can measure masses to an accuracy of about one part in a million. Figure 4–3 shows the principle of operation of this instrument. Positive ions are formed in the ion source by impact from electrons emitted by an incandescent filament. The ions are accelerated through a potential difference of approximately 40 kV and are focused on the object slit S_1, which is normally set to about 0.0005 in. The ions are deflected and directionally focused by the electrostatic analyzer in such a way that ions of the same *energy* will converge toward the same point at the position S_3. Ions of different energy will form an energy spectrum at position S_3. The ions are again directionally focused by the magnetic analyzer such that ions of the same *momentum* passing through the same point at S_3 will converge toward a point at position S_4. The electrostatic deflector disperses the ions

* J. Mattauch, *Phys. Rev.* **50,** 617 (1936).

† For example, K. T. Bainbridge, *Phys. Rev.* **40,** 130A (1935).

‡ A. J. Dempster, *Proc. Am. Phil. Soc.* **75,** 755 (1935).

§ A. O. Nier and T. R. Roberts, *Phys. Rev.* **81,** 507 (1951).

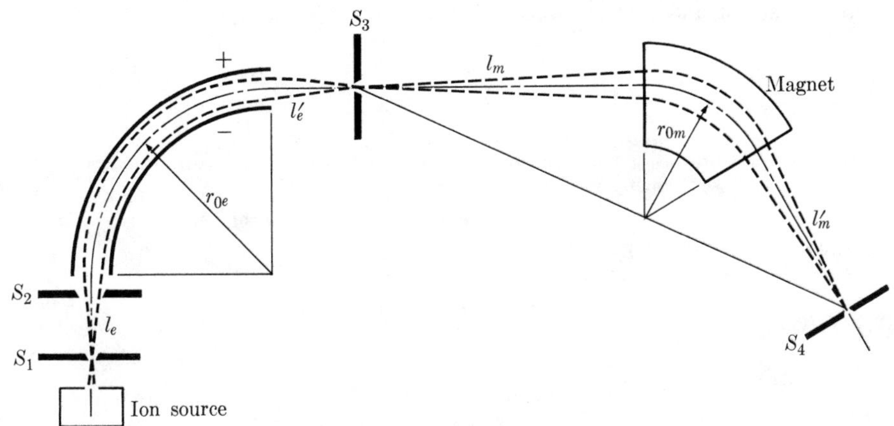

Fig. 4–3. Principle of operation of Nier's spectrograph.

according to their value of mv^2, and the magnetic deflector disperses them according to the value of mv. The dimensions of the deflectors and the slit distances are chosen so that the second velocity dispersion cancels the first but the total mass dispersion is nonzero. A mass spectrum is therefore produced at position S_4. The lateral position of the impact of a given ion at S_4 is to the first order independent of the velocity and the direction of the ion through slit S_1 and dependent only on the mass of the ion.

The focusing properties of the electrostatic analyzer and the magnetic analyzer are treated in Appendix 2. A summary of these directional-focusing properties and of the velocity-focusing properties for the combination of the two analyzers is given below. Only motion in the median plane is considered. Since there is virtually no force exerted on the particles in the vertical direction, the initial divergence of the ions will cause a point source to produce a vertical line image. In fact, the source, S_1, is also a vertical line.

The calculations in Appendix 2 are made for an electrostatic deflector, which is a sector of a cylindrical capacitor, and for a magnetic sector in which the central ray of the diverging beam enters and leaves normal to the field boundary. These calculations indicate that a beam diverging from a point at a distance l from the field boundary after being deflected through the sector converges toward a point at a distance l' from the exit field boundary. The relationship between l and l' is given by

$$\frac{1}{l + (1/k)\tan(kr_0\phi/2)} + \frac{1}{l' + (1/k)\tan(kr_0\phi/2)} = k\sin kr_0\phi, \tag{4–4}$$

where ϕ is the sector angle and r_0 is the orbit radius for the central ray. In form this is similar to the well-known optical lens equation $1/a + 1/b = 1/f$, where a is the object distance measured from the first principal plane and b is the image distance measured from the second principal plane. Comparison with Eq. (4–4) shows that the principal plane of the sectors must be a distance $(1/k)\tan(kr_0\phi/2)$ from the field boundaries inside the sector and that the focal length of the device is equal to

$$f = \frac{1}{k \sin kr_0\phi}. \tag{4–5}$$

In these expressions, the wave number k is equal to $k = \sqrt{2}/r_0$ for the electrostatic deflector and $k = 1/r_0$ for the magnetic deflector. It is also shown in Appendix 2 that the lateral displacement of the image of particles of different energy and momenta from the central ray image is

$$D' = d[1 - \cos kr_0\phi + kl' \sin kr_0\phi], \tag{4–6}$$

where

$$d = \frac{r_0}{2}\frac{\Delta T}{T} \quad \text{electrostatic sector,} \qquad \text{and} \qquad d = r_0 \frac{\Delta p}{p} \quad \text{magnetic sector.}$$

The numerical parameters for the Nier spectrometer are given below.

Electrostatic sector	Magnetic sector
$\phi_e = 90°$	$\phi_m = 60°$
$r_{0e} = 18.87$ cm	$r_{0m} = 15.24$ cm
$l_e = l'_e = 6.61$ cm	$l_m = 34.77$ cm
	$l'_m = 20.73$ cm

These sets of parameters satisfy the lens equation (4–4) for the electrostatic sector as well as for the magnetic sector. This means that particles diverging from slit S_1 will be directionally focused on slit S_3 by the electrostatic lens and then again directionally focused on slit S_4 by the magnetic lens (ray 1, Fig. 4–4). It remains to be demonstrated that particles of different velocities will be focused from slit S_1 to slit S_4. From Eq. (4–6) we find that the lateral displacement at position S_3 of a

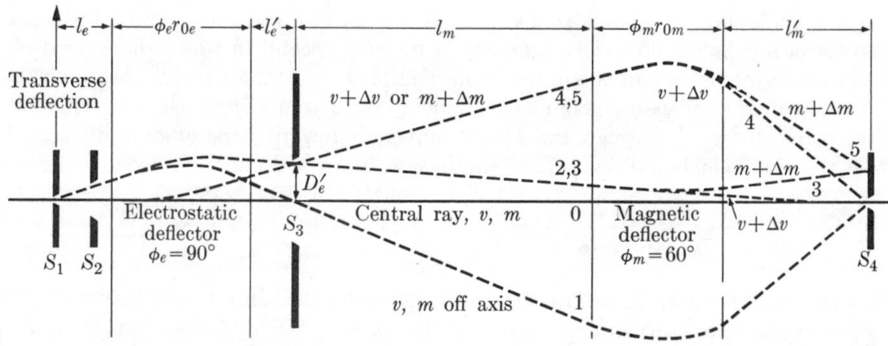

Fig. 4–4. Nier spectrograph with rays folded out to show focusing of particles with various masses and velocities.

particle with higher velocity than the central ray is (see Fig. 4-4, ray 4)

$$D'_e(v) = r_{0e}\,\frac{\Delta v}{v}\left[1 - \cos\sqrt{2}\phi_e + \frac{\sqrt{2}l'_e}{r_{0e}}\sin\sqrt{2}\phi_e\right].$$

Here $\Delta v/v$ is the fractional deviation of the velocity from the "central" velocity, defined for instance as the velocity for particles of a given mass focused to the midpoint of slit S_3. Equation (4-6) gives the displacement of the image point when the object point is on the center line. If l' is replaced by l, Eq. (4-6) can be taken to represent also the displacement of the object point from the center line when the image point is on the center line. For the magnetic lens, we get, for this reversed dispersion,*

$$D_m(v) = r_{0m}\,\frac{\Delta v}{v}\left[1 - \cos\phi_m + \frac{l_m}{r_{0m}}\sin\phi_m\right].$$

Velocity focusing is obviously obtained when $D'_e = D_m$, so that the velocity dispersion produced by the electrostatic sector is canceled by the magnetic sector. By inserting the numerical parameters given above into the two dispersion formulas, we will find that this condition is fulfilled.

If we now look at ions of different masses, the situation is clearly different. For the magnetic sector we find the reversed dispersion by replacing $\Delta v/v$ with $\Delta m/m$. For the electrostatic deflection, however, $\Delta v/v$ is replaced by $\Delta m/2m$. Therefore the mass dispersion for the two sectors does not balance, and the unbalance, as measured at position S_3, is

$$\Delta D(m) = \frac{r_{0m}}{2}\,\frac{\Delta m}{m}\left[1 - \cos\phi_m + \frac{l_m}{r_{0m}}\sin\phi_m\right].$$

To transfer the unbalance to position S_4 where the mass spectrum actually is measured, we multiply by the magnification of the magnetic sector. In any optical system this is the ratio of the image distance to the object distance, both distances being measured from the appropriate principal planes. The total magnetic dispersion of the Nier spectrometer is therefore

$$D(m) = \frac{r_{0m}}{2}\,\frac{\Delta m}{m}\left[1 - \cos\phi_m + \frac{l_m}{r_{0m}}\sin\phi_m\right]\frac{l'_m + r_{0m}\tan\phi_m/2}{l_m + r_{0m}\tan\phi_m/2}. \tag{4-7}$$

With numerical values inserted, this gives

$$D(m) = 13.3\,\frac{\Delta m}{m}\ \text{cm}.$$

To separate lines of mass difference Δm, with $\Delta m/m = 10^{-4}$ for instance, the opening of the exit slit S_4 needs to be smaller than 1.33×10^{-3} cm. This is indeed the order of magnitude of the slit openings used in the Nier spec-

---

* Imagine that the ions (ray 4, Fig. 4-4) run backward from S_4 to S_3 (with the magnetic field reversed).

trometer for S_1 and S_4. The slit system S_2 shown in Fig. 4–3 defines the angular acceptance of the spectrometer, and the slit system S_3 defines the velocity spread that is accepted for a given mass.

4–3 *The Doublet Method of Mass Spectroscopy*

Atomic masses are now measured by chemists, as well as by physicists, on a scale in which the mass of the C^{12} atom is exactly 12 units. The symbol for this new unified mass unit is u, whereas the symbol for the earlier physical unit based on the O^{16} scale was amu. A mass spectrograph or spectrometer can be calibrated by use of C^{12} ions, and the mass of other ions can be measured on this scale. However, this direct method of measuring the masses of atoms is not very accurate. The error involved in the measurement will, in general, be equal to a certain fraction, perhaps 0.01%, of the value of the mass measured. A much higher accuracy can be obtained by use of the so-called doublet method, in which the very small difference between two masses which are almost equal is measured. In the mass spectrometer, both ions are produced simultaneously in the ion source, and they appear as two nearby lines on the recorder slit or photographic plate.

In the Nier spectrometer, a slight change of the accelerating potential and a simultaneous change of the potential on the electrostatic deflector will switch the position of the image for a given mass on the detector. Or, to put it differently, ions with a different mass value will strike the detector. Assume that the potentials are changed by a fraction, δ, such that the energy of the ions following the central ray in the electrostatic deflector are changed from $p_0^2/2m_0$ to $p^2/2m$, where

$$\frac{p^2}{2m} = (1+\delta)\,\frac{p_0^2}{2m_0}\,.$$

For the particles that follow the central ray also in the magnetic deflector, we have $p = p_0$, so that we get

$$m = m_0/(1+\delta).$$

By making the change in electrostatic potentials intermittent and by adjusting its magnitude, two nearby mass lines can be brought to focus on the detector slits in rapid succession. In Nier's instrument, the output from the detector is displayed on an oscilloscope so that the two lines can be visually compared.

A typical example of a mass doublet measured with a Nier spectrometer is

$$C_{12}H_{16} - Gd^{160} = 198.05 \pm 0.09 \text{ mu} \qquad (1 \text{ millimass unit, mu} = 10^{-3} \text{ u}).$$

The stated uncertainty (± 0.09 mu) is about ± 1 part in 2200 of the measured difference but ± 1 part in 1.8 million of the total mass (≈ 160 u). Note that the chemical symbol stands for the mass of the neutral atom; the subscript is the chemical subscript indicating how many atoms there are in the molecule, and the superscript is, as usual, the mass number A of the isotope in question. The superscript is not used, for instance, on C (carbon) or H (hydrogen). The symbol simply indicates the most abundant isotope, C^{12} for carbon and H^1 for hydrogen. In the equation above, the atomic-mass number for the two molecules in question is the same, and therefore the difference in masses is only a fraction of a mass unit, usually measured in millimass units (mu) or micromass units (μu).

To determine the mass of Gd^{160} from the equation above, one needs to know the mass of hydrogen on the C^{12} scale. Hydrogen is regarded as a substandard because hydrocarbon ions can be produced with a great variety of mass numbers, and this provides a convenient scale for mass comparison with the doublet method. The mass of hydrogen can be determined by a number of different cycles. Consider, for instance, the following three doublet measurements:*

$$\begin{aligned} a &= CH_4 - O = 36381.5 \pm 0.9\ \mu u, \\ b &= C_4 - SO = 33016.4 \pm 1.3\ \mu u, \\ c &= O_2 - S = 17754.3 \pm 0.9\ \mu u. \end{aligned}$$

From this set of measurements, one can determine the masses of hydrogen, oxygen, and sulfur, which are all regarded as substandards. The mass of hydrogen, for instance, can be determined from the above measurement in the following way:

$$12H - C = 3a + c - b.$$

Since the mass of carbon is exactly equal to 12, we get for the mass of hydrogen

$$H = 1 + \tfrac{1}{12}(3a + c - b) = 1.0078235\ u.$$

The uncertainty of this number can be determined from the uncertainty quoted for the various measurements above. The quoted numbers are standard deviations or standard errors. According to the error theory, these errors combine so that the total error, or uncertainty, is equal to the square root of the sum of the squares of the contributions of the individual measurements. This yields

$$\text{Uncertainty} = \tfrac{1}{12}\sqrt{(3\Delta a)^2 + (\Delta b)^2 + (\Delta c)^2} \cong 0.3\ \mu u.$$

The accuracy quoted by Quisenberry *et al.* is therefore about 3 parts in 10 million.

Returning now to the measurement of the mass of Gd^{160}, we can use the number obtained for the hydrogen mass above and get for the mass of gadolinium:

$$Gd^{160} = 144 + 16 \times 1.0078235 - 0.19805 = 159.92713\ u.$$

---

* K. S. Quisenberry, T. T. Scolman, and A. O. Nier, *Phys. Rev.* **102,** 1071 (1956).

As mentioned earlier, it is possible to produce ions of molecules containing carbon, hydrogen, and possibly also oxygen in so many different combinations that virtually any mass number can be obtained. However, doublet measurements with these organic molecules as references have drawbacks because carbon also contains 1.11% C^{13}. By replacing a C^{12} atom and a hydrogen atom with a C^{13} atom in a hydrocarbon molecule or fragment, one obtains a molecule of the same mass number. At high mass numbers, these two ions are, relatively speaking, so close in mass that they are very hard to resolve. Only very recently have mass spectrometers been built with a resolving power sufficiently high to separate the C^{13} satellite from the main peak.*

As a supplementary technique Professor Nier's group and others have used the mass spectrometer to determine the mass differences between isotopes of the same element. Since these differences are of the order of one mass unit or more, the accuracy obtained in these measurements is not quite so high as for the true mass doublets. An example of a measurement of an isotopic doublet is*

$$\mathrm{Zr}^{92} - \mathrm{Zr}^{91} = 0.9993972 \text{ u} \pm 11.7\ \mu\text{u}$$

4-4 *The Mass Synchrometer*

Modern electronic techniques for measuring frequencies or time intervals are very highly developed, and a high degree of precision can be obtained in such measurements. It occurred to Goudsmit† that it would be possible to determine ion masses accurately by measuring the cyclotron frequency (number of revolutions per second) of the ions in a homogeneous magnetic field:

$$f_c = qB/2\pi m.$$

This quantity is, in the nonrelativistic approximation, independent of the velocity of the particles, so that velocity focusing is not needed in such an instrument.

An instrument was built at Brookhaven National Laboratory for measuring masses by this method. In the original instrument, the ions were emitted from an ion source in pulses, and the flight time spent in performing a certain number of revolutions or spirals was measured electronically. The instrument has been modified and much improved by L. G. Smith‡ and coworkers. The principle of operation is different in that a multiple of the cyclotron frequency is measured, rather than the flight time. A brief description of the modified instrument follows.

---

* See for instance: "Nuclidic Masses," *Proceedings of the Second International Conference on Nuclidic Masses*, Vienna, Austria, July 15–19, 1963, ed. by Walter H. Johnson, Jr., Vienna and New York: Springer-Verlag, 1964.

† S. Goudsmit, *Phys. Rev.* **74**, 622 (1948).

‡ L. G. Smith and C. C. Damm, *Rev. Sci. Instr.* **27**, 638 (1956).

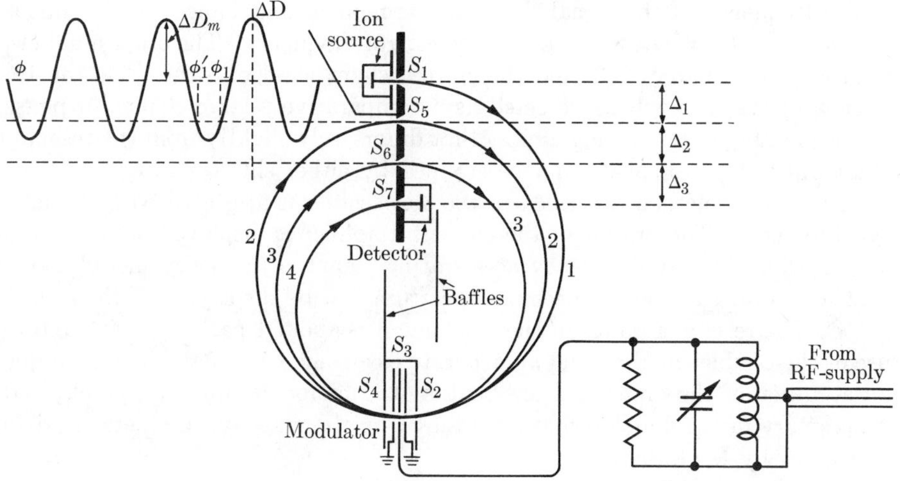

Fig. 4–5. Schematic diagram of the mass synchrometer. [From L. G. Smith and C. C. Damm, *Rev. Sci. Instr.* **27,** 638 (1956). Reproduced by permission.]

Figure 4–5 illustrates the principle of operation of the mass synchrometer. Ions are produced in the ion source by electron bombardment of the gas to be ionized. After extraction and acceleration to a suitable energy, some of the ions pass through the narrow slit S_1. Since the whole instrument is immersed in a magnetic field perpendicular to the plane of the paper, the ions will travel in circular orbits, and ions with a selected momentum, $mv = qB\rho$, will pass through slits S_2 to S_4. At this point the ions are given an impulse by a radiofrequency field; the sign and magnitude of this impulse will depend on the phase of the oscillations of the electric field at the moment the ions pass. After another 180-degree orbit, the ions are again at the plane of the slit S_1. The upper left of Fig. 4–5 shows the displacement of the ions measured from S_1 as a function of the time at which the ions passed slit S_3. Clearly, the ion which passes S_3 at such a time that it receives a positive impulse will travel with a larger radius of curvature and arrive at the plane of S_1 with a positive displacement. Other ions that pass through the slit S_2 at such a time that they receive a negative impulse will have a negative displacement when they arrive at the plane of S_1. Ions passing when the phase of the high-frequency oscillations is either ϕ_1 or ϕ_1' will get the (negative) impulse needed to pass through slit S_5. When these ions again come around to S_3, they will experience another change in momentum. If the frequency of oscillation of the accelerating voltage at position S_3 is a multiple of the cyclotron frequency of the ions, then the impulse the ions will receive the second time will be the same as the first time ($\Delta_2 = \Delta_1$). In such a case, the ions will also pass through slit S_6. After a third passage they will again have received the same reduction in momentum and then will pass through slit S_7. Behind this last slit is the current collector, which is connected to a very sensitive amplifier so that very feeble currents can be detected.

The frequency of the signal that imparts momentum changes to the ions at position S_3 is $f_0 = nf_c$, where f_c is the cyclotron frequency. The order number n used is approximately 200, and therefore a slight change in the cyclotron frequency of the ions will be detected as a comparatively large change in phase. Consequently, an ion having a mass that differs only slightly from the resonant mass will fall out of phase and be stopped by either slit S_6 or S_7.

The doublet method described in the last section is also used with the mass synchrometer. The output of the current amplifier is displayed on an oscilloscope, while the radiofrequency accelerating signal is frequency modulated so that a certain fraction of the mass spectrum can be displayed on the oscilloscope. The resolving power of the instrument is about 1 part in 20,000, and by use of the doublet method and an accurate electronic peak-matching technique, an accuracy of the order of a few tenths of a micromass unit can be claimed. A summary of the doublet values measured by the mass synchrometer is given in a paper by L. G. Smith.*

4–5 Atomic Masses from Nuclear-Reaction and Disintegration Data

Nuclear reactions and disintegration processes were briefly described in Sections 1–9 and 1–11; more detailed treatments of these processes are given in later chapters. At this point we will discuss briefly the relationship between nuclear-reaction energy measurements and atomic-mass differences.

Consider as an example the reaction mentioned in Section 1–11: $Mg^{26} + p = Na^{23} + \alpha$ [in shorter form, $Mg^{26}(p, \alpha)Na^{23}$]. Let us assume that the Na^{23} nucleus is left in its ground state after the reaction. In this case no energy is given off as gamma rays, and conservation of energy requires that

$$\text{Gain in kinetic energy} = \text{loss in rest energy.}$$

In a nuclear reaction, the gain in kinetic energy, or *Q-value* as it is called, is very often measured to an accuracy of $\Delta T \cong 5$ keV, or better. This corresponds to an uncertainty in the measurement of the mass change of

$$\Delta m = \Delta T/c^2 = 0.005/931 \simeq 5\ \mu\text{u}.$$

Returning now to the example mentioned above, we can write for the energy balance,

$$Q = (Mg^{26} + H^1)c^2 - (Na^{23} + He^4)c^2.$$

The nuclide symbol again refers to the mass of the neutral atom. Of course, the reaction takes place between nuclei, but the number of electrons attached to these nuclei before and after the reaction balances, and the change in atomic

* L. G. Smith, *Phys. Rev.* **111,** 1606 (1958).

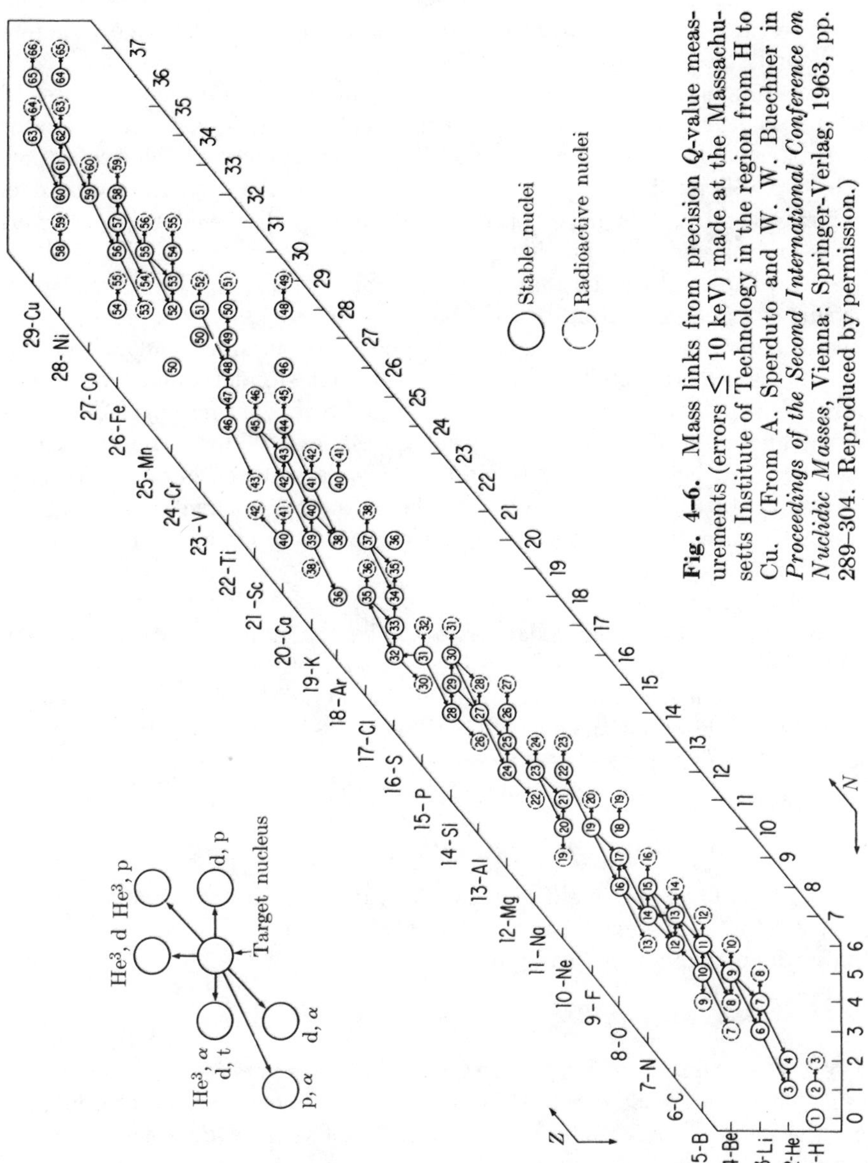

Fig. 4–6. Mass links from precision Q-value measurements (errors $\leq$ 10 keV) made at the Massachusetts Institute of Technology in the region from H to Cu. (From A. Sperduto and W. W. Buechner in *Proceedings of the Second International Conference on Nuclidic Masses*, Vienna: Springer-Verlag, 1963, pp. 289–304. Reproduced by permission.)

binding energy is insignificant. By performing measurements of Q-values with nuclear reactions linking C^{12} with the very light nuclei He^4, He^3, D^2, and H^1, it is possible to determine the masses of these light nuclei or particles through nuclear-reaction energy measurements alone. The masses of these particles then are regarded as substandards, and the Q-value equation above therefore links the mass of Mg^{26} to the mass of Na^{23}.

Figure 4–6 shows, as an example, a section of the chart of the nuclides in which the indicated mass links were determined by means of nuclear reactions or beta-disintegration measurements. These links are made not only between atoms that have stable nuclides, but also often between two atoms of which only one, the target, is stable. The mass-spectroscopic methods discussed in the previous sections can, of course, be applied only to stable or long-lived species, and the others, which constitute the majority of atomic species, can be reached only by means of reaction or disintegration data.

Masses determined from energy measurements are in agreement, within the limits of the experimental uncertainties, with masses determined by mass-spectroscopic methods. This fact is, of course, a direct confirmation of Einstein's mass-energy relationship. At present, the masses measured by means of nuclear-reaction data do not appear to be quite so accurate as the most exact mass-spectrometer data. This is not because the method is inherently inferior, but because no concentrated effort has lately been exerted toward reducing these uncertainties significantly.

A mass table for both stable and unstable species has been worked out by Mattauch *et al.** All available data obtained by the methods described in this and the two previous sections, as well as other methods, have been used as input data for a machine calculation involving least-square fits where redundancies exist. The tabulations include masses of some 1200 species, on the C^{12} scale.

4–6 The Semiempirical Mass Formula

A table of atomic masses might look exceedingly dull and uninteresting. However, it can reveal a great deal of information about nuclear structure. For instance, the total binding energy, defined as

$$\mathrm{BE} = [Z\mathrm{H}^1 + (A - Z)\mathrm{N}^1 - {}_ZM^A]c^2,$$

reflects the effects of the nuclear forces acting between the nucleons in the nucleus (Z, A) minus the effect of the repulsive forces between the protons and minus the insignificant atomic binding energy. The mass difference between neighbor nuclides in the chart of nuclear species (isotopes, isotones) reflects the binding energy of the last particle or particles. These effects can be studied

* J. H. E. Mattauch, W. Thiele, and A. W. Wapstra, *Nucl. Phys.* **67,** 1 (1965).

by means of the so-called semiempirical mass formulas, in which attempts are made to express the variation in mass (or in binding energy) in an analytic form. The first attempt to develop such a formula was made by Von Weizsäcker* in 1935.

We shall here try to construct a formula for the total energy of the nuclides as a number of terms that are functions of Z and A. A brief justification for each term will be given. The main term of the formula, aside from those giving the rest masses of the nucleons, is the so-called volume term. This term expresses the fact that the total binding energy is roughly proportional to the volume of the nucleus or to the total number of nucleons, A,

$$E_{\text{vol}} = -c_v A.$$

To justify this term, we recall that (1) the nuclear volume is approximately proportional to the number of nucleons (Section 1–3), and (2) since the nuclear forces are very short-range forces, each particle will "see" a certain number of neighbors around it, and the attractive forces from these neighbors will result in a binding energy which is approximately the same for all the particles inside the nuclear volume. The total binding energy is therefore nearly proportional to A.

The next important term is the Coulomb repulsion term, which equals the potential energy of Z protons packed together in a spherically symmetric assembly of mean radius $R = r_0 A^{1/3}$. For a spherical volume of uniform density, this energy is (Eq. 1–17)

$$E_{\text{Coulomb}} = \frac{3}{5}\,\frac{Z(Z-1)e^2}{4\pi\epsilon_0 R} = c_c Z(Z-1)A^{-1/3} \approx c_c Z^2 A^{1/3}.$$

In writing the volume energy term, we assumed that all nucleons are surrounded by other nucleons, as would be the case in infinite nuclear matter. In reality, of course, the nucleons on the surface of the nucleus will be attracted only by nucleons on one side. Hence there is a positive surface-energy term that is completely analogous to the surface energy of a liquid droplet. This is the effect that gives rise to surface tension. The surface energy of a nucleus is proportional to the area of the nucleus and can therefore be written

$$E_{\text{area}} = c_a A^{2/3}.$$

A study of masses of light nuclides reveals that the lightest member of a chain of isobars has approximately $Z \approx N$ (see also Fig. 1–5). For heavier nuclei, the most stable, or lowest-energy isobar, is one for which $Z < N$, but this deviation from symmetry is presumably caused by the relatively higher importance of the Coulomb energy term which is proportional to $Z(Z-1)$.

---

* C. F. Von Weizsäcker, *Z. Physik* **96**, 431 (1935).

The tendency of nuclei to be most stable for $Z = N$ is a result of the exclusion principle; the effect is called the symmetry effect. This effect can best be explained by reference to Fig. 4–7, which illustrates various single-particle quantum states that can be occupied by neutrons and protons. Each of these states is described by a wave function depending on spatial coordinates, and each can accommodate four nucleons, as shown. Some of the states may have the same energy, but this does not affect the outcome of the discussion below. Let us disregard for the moment the Coulomb repulsion between protons which is treated separately above, and let us assume that, as shown in Fig. 4–7, the state ψ_n is occupied by two protons, one with spin up and one with spin down, and that all lower states are occupied in the same manner. We can then add one more proton only by putting it into a higher energy state. However, we can add a neutron in state ψ_n. Therefore, of the two isobars found by adding either a proton or a neutron, the latter will in this case have the lowest energy. Clearly, the effect described favors isobars with $Z = N$; that is, there will be a term in the mass formula which increases with increasing value of $|Z - N|$. Empirically, it is found that the function

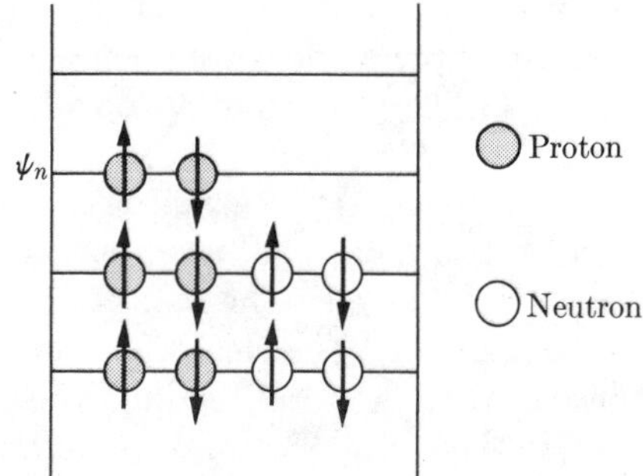

Fig. 4–7. Occupation of single-particle wave-mechanical states by protons (filled circles) and neutrons (open circles).

$$E_{\text{sym}} = c_s A^{-1}(N - Z)^2 = c_s A^{-1}(A - 2Z)^2$$

is a simple, although rather crude, approximation to the actual symmetry energy, which of course fluctuates wildly. (See also Problem 4–6.)

By adding all terms and including the mass of the constituent particles, we get for the total mass of the atoms with Z protons and $(A - Z)$ neutrons:

$$\begin{aligned} {}_Z M^A = ZM_{\text{p}} + (A - Z)M_{\text{n}} - c_v A + c_c Z(Z - 1)A^{-1/3} \\ + c_a A^{2/3} + c_s A^{-1}(A - 2Z)^2, \end{aligned} \tag{4–8}$$

where the units may be million electron volts or mass units, depending on the application.

This is the original form of the semiempirical mass formula. The coefficients c can be determined by using the method of least squares to compare the predictions of the formula and known mass values. The accuracy of the formula thus obtained is not overwhelming, but the discrepancies between observed mass values and predictions are always much smaller than the magnitude of any of the terms in Eq. (4–8). This fact indicates that the arguments used in the development of the formula are sound. To test this has been part of the objective of this exercise.

Another reason for developing a semiempirical mass formula is that if it is accurate enough, it can be used to predict masses, and therefore possible decay modes and decay energies of hitherto unexplored atoms. It turns out that a more sophisticated equation than (4–8) is needed for this application.

Seeger* has published very extensive tables of masses predicted by a modified formula. The new terms that have been included are designed to correct for the surface thickness (Section 1–3) and for nuclear shell effects (Chapter 6). Seeger's formula gives the *mass excess*, that is, the difference

$$\Delta M(Z, A) = {}_ZM^A - A,$$

or the energy equivalent of this difference in MeV. The complete formula for the mass excess in MeV for masses of *odd-A* atoms is

$$\begin{aligned}\Delta M_O(Z, A) = {} & 7.2887Z + 8.0713(A - Z) - \alpha A \\ & + 0.8076Z^2A^{-1/3}(1 - 0.7636Z^{-2/3} - 2.29A^{-2/3}) \\ & + \gamma A^{2/3} + (\beta - \eta A^{-1/3})A^{-1}[(A - 2Z)^2 + 2|A - 2Z|] - S_{jk}(N'Z').\end{aligned} \tag{4–9}$$

The last term in Eq. (4–9) is the shell correction term, which is a function of the parameters N' and Z', defined as

$$N' = \frac{N - N_j}{N_{j+1} - N_j}, \qquad Z' = \frac{Z - Z_k}{Z_{k+1} - Z_k}.$$

Here, N_j and Z_k are the magic numbers (see Section 6–3):

$$N_j, Z_k = 8, 20, 50, 82, 126, 184, \qquad \text{and} \qquad N_j \leq N < N_{j+1}, \qquad Z_k \leq Z < Z_{k+1}.$$

The function S_{jk} is thus different for the different intervals between magic numbers. The formula for S_{jk} is

$$\begin{aligned}S_{jk}(N', Z') = {} & \xi_j \sin N'\pi + \xi_k \sin Z'\pi + \nu_j \sin 2N'\pi + \nu_k \sin 2Z'\pi \\ & + (\phi_j + \phi_k)(\sin N'\pi)(\sin Z'\pi) + \chi.\end{aligned} \tag{4–10}$$

The adjustable constants in Eqs. (4–9) and (4–10) have been determined by the method of least squares. The constants in Eq. (4–9) are the same for the full range of masses listed from $A = 19$ to $A = 260$:

$$\alpha = 17.06 \text{ MeV}, \qquad \beta = 33.61 \text{ MeV}, \qquad \gamma = 25.00 \text{ MeV}, \qquad \eta = 59.54 \text{ MeV}.$$

The constants in Eq. (4–10) are given in Table 4–1 for the various intervals of Z and N.

---

* P. A. Seeger, *Nucl. Phys.* **25,** 1 (1961).

Table 4–1. The coefficients ξ, ν, ϕ, and χ, in MeV

$\leq Z$ or $N >$		ξ	ν	ϕ	χ
8	20	4.008	−0.428	−1.389	13.51
20	50	−0.508	2.331	−0.463	13.51
50	82	−7.636	0.496	1.950	13.51
82	126	−15.63	−2.284	10.67	13.51
126	184	−27.59	2.660	26.99	13.51

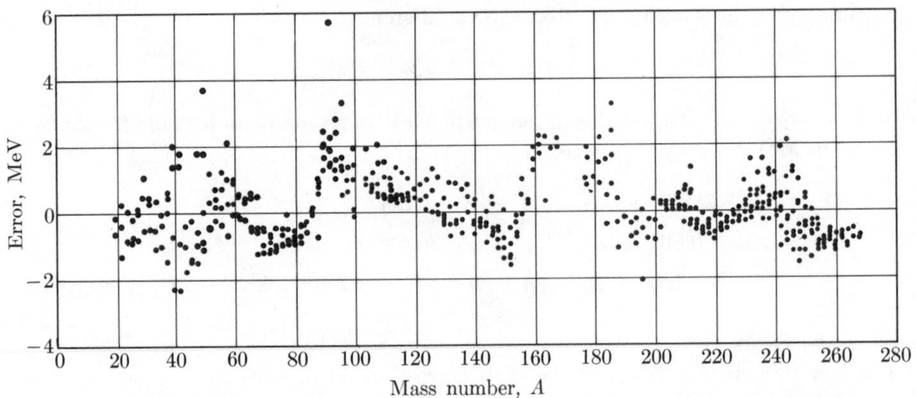

Fig. 4–8. Errors δ_i of 488 atomic-mass excesses for odd-mass atoms, calculated by the general mass law (Eq. 4-9) with the coefficients given in the text plotted vs. atomic-mass number A. [From P. A. Seeger, *Nucl. Phys.* **25,** 1 (1961).]

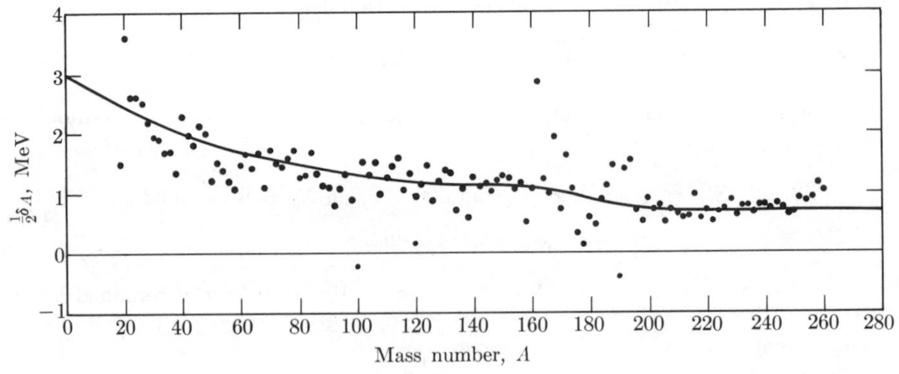

Fig. 4–9. The pairing energy term $\frac{1}{2}\delta_A$ as a function of A. The point for each even A is an average of $\pm$ $[\Delta M_{\text{exp}}(Z,A) - \Delta M_0(Z,A)]$ over those values of Z for which masses are known, taking the plus sign if Z is odd and the minus sign if Z is even. A total of 511 even masses were included in the calculation. [From P. A. Seeger, *Nucl. Phys.* **25,** 1 (1961).]

The error in prediction by Seeger's formula, as tested on 488 measured atomic-mass excesses, is plotted in Fig. 4–8 as a function of A. The standard deviation has been determined as $\sigma = 0.75$ MeV, which is quite good considering the fact that the total binding energy of heavy nuclei is about 1800 MeV.

For even-even atoms (Z even, N even) and odd-odd atoms, the formula (4–9) needs one more correction term arising from the pairing energy (Section 6–4). The final formula for the mass excess can then be written as

$$\Delta M(Z, A) = \Delta M_0(Z, A) + \begin{cases} +\frac{1}{2}\delta_A & \text{for odd-odd atoms,} \\ 0 & \text{for odd atoms,} \\ -\frac{1}{2}\delta_A & \text{for even-even atoms.} \end{cases}$$

Figure 4–9 shows a plot of the pairing energy $\frac{1}{2}\delta_A$, as determined by Seeger from a comparison between odd and even-even atoms and between odd and odd-odd atoms.

4–7 Relative Abundances of Atomic Species

The mass spectrometer can also be used to determine the relative abundances of the stable isotopes of an element. Since the ionization process in the ion source of the spectrometer is strictly an atomic process, the measured abundance ratio of ions produced reflects very accurately the actual abundance ratio of isotopes in the element. The resolving power of the instrument does not need to be so high as for a spectrometer used for precise mass determinations. Most important is that the instrument must be capable of separating the various isotopes of even the heaviest elements and recording their relative intensities with high precision.

The results of measurements of isotope abundance ratios are given in Appendix 6 for the various elements as they are found in the earth's crust. In a few elements, the abundance ratios may vary from sample to sample, depending on the origin of the material. The relative abundances of the stable isotopes of lead, as given in Appendix 6, apply to the element as formed during the evolution of our solar system. Different abundance ratios are found between the lead isotopes which appear as end products of radioactive decay chains in minerals containing uranium or thorium.

The measurements of abundance ratios can in some cases provide important clues to the age of the sample in which the element is found. Rubidium-containing minerals, for instance, can be used for such age determinations. The isotope Rb^{87} is unstable but has such an extremely long half-life (4.7×10^{10} years) that it has survived the time elapsed since the evolution of our solar system, and it is found free in nature. The decay product of Rb^{87} is Sr^{87}. In rubidium-containing minerals, therefore, Sr^{87} has a higher abundance relative to Sr^{86} than in minerals that do not contain rubidium. Measurements of the abundance ratios of the two strontium isotopes in a rubidium-containing and a nonrubidium-containing mineral can therefore be used to determine the age of the former.

A different time scale is provided by radioactive C^{14} used in the age determination of organic samples. Carbon-14 has a half-life of 5730 years and should therefore be completely extinct in the earth's crust and atmosphere. However, through the nuclear reaction $N^{14}(n, p)C^{14}$ initiated by cosmic radiation, a small amount of this isotope is continuously formed in the atmosphere. The equilibrium abundance in the earth's atmosphere was approximately 1.5×10^{-12}, as measured relative to C^{12} before the beginning of this century. From 1900 to 1954 the abundance ratio dropped because of increased contamination of the atmosphere with C^{12}, and from 1954 to 1964 the abundance ratio has increased by a factor of 2 because of nuclear testing. In living organisms, the atmospheric abundance ratio is found because a continuous exchange with the carbon in the atmosphere takes place. However, when the organism dies, such exchange stops, and the C^{14} in the dead organic material decays with a half-life of 5730 years. It is hardly feasible to measure abundance ratios as low as 10^{-12} with the mass spectrometer. However, since C^{14} is radioactive, very small amounts of this isotope can be measured by detecting the beta radiation given off in the decay and comparing the number of counts per second with the total mass of the material in the sample. This C^{14}-dating technique has been developed to a very high degree of accuracy by W. F. Libby* at the University of Chicago.

A study of the systematics of a table of element numbers Z and neutron numbers N for stable nuclides reveals many interesting facts. For instance, even numbers for Z and N are strongly favored, as illustrated in Table 4–2, which shows how 284 nuclides found in nature are distributed between elements of even Z and odd Z and between isotones of even N or odd N. All elements from hydrogen to uranium are included in this count, and for each element all isotopes that are sufficiently long-lived to be found in nature are also included. The four stable odd-odd nuclides are H^2, Li^6, B^{10}, and N^{14}, all in the light-element range. As is further discussed in Chapter 6, there is a strong tendency for two protons or for two neutrons to pair with each other in the nucleus. The energy released in the formation of such a pair is also mentioned in the previous section (Fig. 4–8). Nuclides with the same nucleon number A "communicate" with each other in the sense that those with greater atomic mass will decay by beta emission to lighter neighbors (Section 11–1). In an odd-odd nuclide, the mass number A is even, and the neighboring isobars are even-even nuclides. Hence, because of the pairing energy, the odd-odd nuclide is heavier than at least one of its neighbor isobars, except in the four cases mentioned where the symmetry energy outweighs the pairing-energy effect.

Another peculiarity worth mentioning with regard to the Z and N for stable nuclides is that for certain values (e.g., 20, 28, 50, 82) of Z, there are exceptionally many stable isotopes; for the same values of N, there are exceptionally many

---

* W. F. Libby, *Radiocarbon Dating*, 2nd edition. Chicago: University of Chicago Press, 1955.

Table 4–2. Number of β-stable and long-lived ($t_{1/2} > 10^9$ years) nuclides*

Z	N	β-stable	Long-lived
Even	Even	155	11
Even	Odd	53	3
Odd	Even	50	3
Odd	Odd	4	5

*Data from the General Electric Chart of Nuclides.

stable isotones. For instance, element number 50, tin, has ten stable isotopes, and for neutron number $N = 82$, there are seven stable isotones. Compared with the number of stable isotopes and isotones for other values of Z and N, these numbers are unusually large. These "magic numbers," as they are called, play a role in nuclear physics similar to that played by the element numbers for the noble gases in atomic physics. A theory of nuclear structure incorporating these facts is given in Chapter 6.

PROBLEMS

4–1. Calculate the overall magnification of Nier's spectrometer (from S_1 to S_4).

4–2. Calculate the distance in centimeters between the images for the $C_{12}H_{16}$ ions and the Gd^{160} ions (p. 96) as measured at position S_4 of Nier's spectrometer.

4–3. Derive a formula for the resolving power of the mass synchrometer in the following way: Assume that the slit S_1 is infinitesimally small. Calculate the displacement of the beam on slit S_7 when the condition $f_0 = nf_c$ is not quite fulfilled, and compare the result with the size of S_7. Assume that $\Delta_1 = \Delta_2 = \Delta_3$ and ΔD_m (Fig. 4–5) are given.

4–4. The Q-value for the $C^{12}(d, \alpha)B^{10}$ reaction is -1.342 MeV. What is the mass of B^{10} in mass units u? (Use Table 1–3.)

4–5. In a mass spectrograph utilizing 180° magnetic focusing (Section 10–2), the ions $(C^{12})^+$ and $(B^{11}H)^+$ are recorded simultaneously. (a) Which has the larger orbit diameter? (b) The separation between the lines recorded on the photographic plate is 0.0143 cm and the orbit diameter for the $(C^{12})^+$ ions is 20 cm. What is the atomic mass of B^{11}?

4–6. Assume that the levels in Fig. 4–7 are equidistant with energy separation Δ. Starting with $N = Z$, change one proton pair at a time into neutrons and show that the energy needed to lift the nucleons into the nearest available levels is

$$E = 2\Delta[1 + 3 + 5 + \cdots + (2n - 1)] = \frac{\Delta}{2}(A - 2Z)^2.$$

5 Nuclear Moments

5-1 *Hyperfine Structure of Atomic Spectra*

Optical spectroscopy was developed to an extremely exact science in the latter part of the last century. Very high resolving powers were obtained with interferometers, and with such an instrument Michelson in 1891 discovered a new effect, a fine structure which could be seen only with the ultimate of resolutions. When it was discovered later that the elements may have nuclei of different masses, the ultrafine splitting of the lines was thought to be related to this fact, an interpretation that appears to be correct in some cases. However, it was soon revealed that some of the elements displaying this ultrafine structure are monoisotopic, and a different explanation had to be sought. In 1924 Pauli correctly contended that the nucleus might possess an angular momentum and an associated magnetic dipole moment, which, through a coupling with the magnetic field produced by the electrons, gives rise to a very fine splitting of the levels. It has been found that part of the effect is sometimes caused by an electric quadrupole moment of the nucleus interacting with an electric field gradient.

The splitting of the atomic levels resulting from the fact that the various isotopes have different masses is now called the *isotope effect,* and the splitting caused by the magnetic moment and quadrupole moment of the nucleus is called *hyperfine structure.* Figure 5–1 shows two exposures taken with an interferometer called the Fabry-Perot etalon. Figure 5–1(a) shows the splitting of a line in the element tungsten which has five stable isotopes, the three at mass numbers 182, 184, and 186 being more abundant than the others. The three lines in Fig. 5–1(a) are believed to be caused by atoms having these three isotopes as nuclei. The shifts in energy are caused not only by the differences in mass of the nuclei, but also by differences in nuclear size and charge distribution which produce minute changes in the electron wave functions at the position of the nucleus. The repetition of the pattern of the three lines in Fig. 5–1(a) results from higher-order reflections in the interferometer.

The photograph in Fig. 5–1(b) shows the hyperfine splitting of a certain line in the tantalum spectrum into eight components. Tantalum is virtually mono-

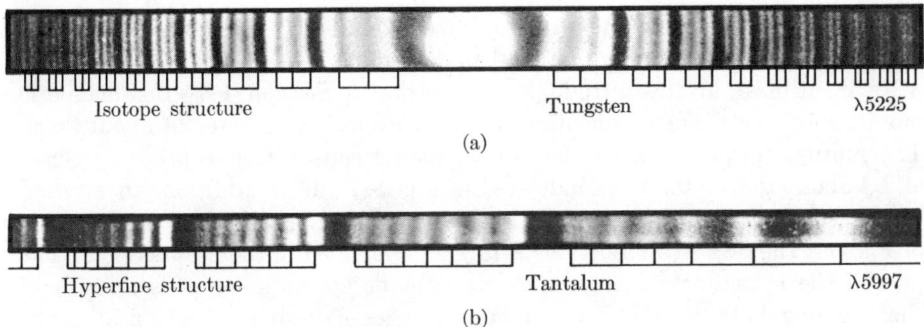

Fig. 5–1. High-resolution optical spectra taken with a Fabry-Perot etalon: (a) isotope effect in tungsten, (b) hyperfine structure of a tantalum line. (Adapted from H. E. White, *Introduction to Atomic Spectra*, New York: McGraw-Hill Book Company, 1934. Reproduced by permission.)

isotopic, and the splitting is caused by a coupling between the magnetic moment of the tantalum nucleus and the magnetic field produced at the nucleus by the electrons.

Angular momenta of electrons in atoms and angular momenta of nuclei are of the same order of magnitude (approximately $\hbar$). The total angular momentum for the atom results from a vector addition of the nuclear angular momentum* **I** with numerical value $\sqrt{I(I+1)}\hbar$ and the electronic angular momentum **J** with numerical value $\sqrt{J(J+1)}\hbar$. The same rules apply for this coupling as for the coupling between **L** and **S** to **J**; indeed, they apply for the coupling of any two quantum-mechanical angular momenta. Figure 5–2 illustrates this vectorial coupling of **I** and **J** to a grand total angular momentum **F** with quantum number F and numerical value $\sqrt{F(F+1)}\hbar$. If I and J are both integral or both half-integral, F can take on any integral value between $|J-I|$ and $J+I$. If one of the two numbers is half-integral, then F takes on half-integral values only, but the same rules for maximum and minimum apply. When J and I are given, the number of different

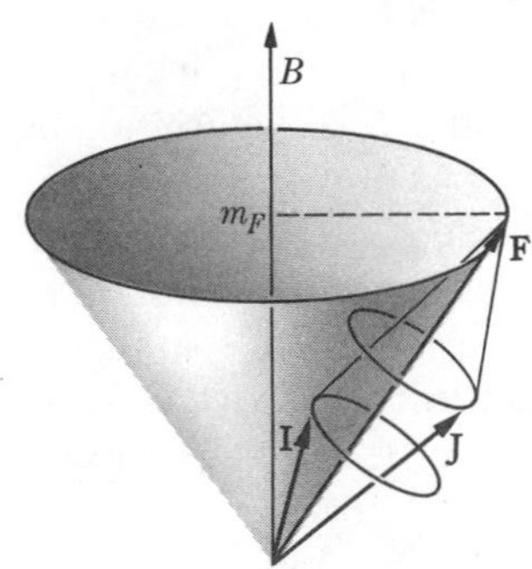

Fig. 5–2. Vector diagram illustrating the coupling of the nuclear angular momentum **I** and the electronic angular momentum **J** to a total angular momentum **F** with quantized z-component m_F.

* Throughout this chapter we shall use the symbol I for nuclear angular momentum and J for electronic or rotational angular momentum.

values of F, that is, the number of hyperfine levels, is $2I + 1$ or $2J + 1$, whichever is smaller. This fact can be used to determine I when $I < J$.

As mentioned in the introductory remarks in Section 1–7, the magnetic moments of nuclei are smaller than those of atoms by a factor of about 2000. The mutual torque between the two moments causes a slow precession of **I** and **J** about the vector **F**, as indicated in Fig. 5–2. If, in addition, an external torque is provided, for instance by a magnetic field in the z-direction, a precession of **F** about the z-axis results. This is further explained in the next section. The part of the hyperfine structure that concerns us at the moment is a result of the coupling between the two magnetic dipoles $\boldsymbol{\mu}_I$ and $\boldsymbol{\mu}_J$. Classically, the energy of the coupling is given by

$$E_{\mathrm{H}} = \frac{\mu_0}{4\pi}\left[\frac{\boldsymbol{\mu}_I \cdot \boldsymbol{\mu}_J}{r^3} - 3\,\frac{(\boldsymbol{\mu}_I \cdot \mathbf{r})(\boldsymbol{\mu}_J \cdot \mathbf{r})}{r^5}\right], \tag{5–1}$$

where $\mu_0 = 4\pi \times 10^{-7}$ is the permeability of free space and $\mathbf{r}$ is the separation between the dipoles measured in meters. The quantum-mechanical calculation of the hyperfine splitting is quite complex, and the reader is referred to other texts.* For a hydrogenlike (single-electron) atom of nuclear charge Z, the coupling energy is

$$E_{\mathrm{H}} = \frac{\mu_0}{4\pi}\,\mu_I\mu_{\mathrm{B}}\,\frac{Z^3}{n^3a_0^3}\,\frac{F(F+1) - I(I+1) - J(J+1)}{IJ(J+1)(L+\frac{1}{2})}, \tag{5–2}$$

where μ_I is the magnetic moment of the nucleus in MKS-units, μ_{B} is the Bohr magneton, n is the principal quantum number of the atom, a_0 is the first Bohr radius, and L is the orbital angular momentum of the electron.

As an example, consider the electronic ground state of the hydrogen atom, for which $I = \frac{1}{2}$, $J = \frac{1}{2}$, and $F = 0$ or 1. In the lowest state, the magnetic moments are antiparallel, and, since the magnetic moment is antiparallel with J for the electron and parallel with I for the proton, it follows that I and J are parallel in the lowest state, which therefore is the $F = 1$ state. The $F = 0$ state, then, is actually an excited state removed in energy from the ground state only by a hyperfine splitting. We calculate the difference in energy by using Eq. (5–2) and find

$$\Delta E_{\mathrm{H}} = 5.88 \times 10^{-6}\ \mathrm{eV}.$$

This is much less than the energy per degree of freedom caused from heat motion of the hydrogen atoms at normal and particularly at arc or spark temperatures, so that the two states will be almost equally populated. The frequency of the photon emitted in a transition from the $F = 0$ to the $F = 1$ state is $\nu = \Delta E_{\mathrm{H}}/h = 1420$ Mc/sec ($\lambda = 21$ cm). This spectral line, which is in the

* For example, J. C. Slater, *Quantum Theory of Atomic Structure,* New York: McGraw-Hill, 1960, Vol. II, p. 266.

radiofrequency part of the spectrum, has not been observed in laboratory-produced transitions. It has, however, been detected in radiation received from outer space.

Another contribution affecting the magnitude of the hyperfine-structure splitting arises from the coupling between the quadrupole moment of the nucleus and the gradient of the electric field produced by the electrons. To estimate the order of magnitude of the effect of the nuclear quadrupole moment on the hyperfine structure, we use a simple model consisting of a nucleus with quadrupole moment $Q = 1$ barn separated from a unit charge by 1 angstrom unit. This unit charge is taken to represent the charge asymmetry surrounding the nucleus in the atom (or molecule), and it will produce a field gradient $\partial^2 U/\partial z^2$, which enters into Eq. (1–13) for the energy shift. With the unit charge on the z-axis, we find

$$\frac{\partial^2 U}{\partial z^2} = \frac{\partial^2}{\partial z^2}\left(\frac{e}{4\pi\epsilon_0 z}\right) = \frac{e}{2\pi\epsilon_0 z^3} = 2.88 \times 10^{21}\ \text{V/m}^2,$$

which, with $Q = 10^{-28}\ \text{m}^2$, yields (Eq. 1–13 with energy unit eV)

$$E_2 = \frac{Q}{4}\frac{\partial^2 U}{\partial z^2} = 7.2 \times 10^{-8}\ \text{eV}.$$

In atoms, the effect of the electric quadrupole moment on the hyperfine structure is usually smaller than the effect of the magnetic dipole moment. In molecules, where a magnetic field from the electrons is frequently absent and the field produced by rotation of the molecule may be very weak, the situation is often reversed (e.g., for D_2, Section 5–6).

Because of the relatively minute spacings of the hyperfine levels and difficulties, such as Doppler broadening, caused by heat motion of the emitter, the task of determining I and Q from studies of hyperfine splitting of spectral lines is a formidable one. Several other ingenious and more accurate methods have been developed, notably some in which the very small quantum jumps between neighboring hyperfine magnetic substates are measured with radiofrequency equipment. In the following sections, some of the better known of these methods are described, and a few examples of experimental results are included. But first we shall discuss in general the action of a magnetic field on an atom for which both I and J are different from zero.

5–2 *Effect of an External Magnetic Field on the Hyperfine Structure*

The effect of a magnetic field B on an object possessing a magnetic dipole moment μ_1 is to produce a torque

$$\boldsymbol{\tau} = \boldsymbol{\mu}_1 \times \mathbf{B},$$

which, according to Newton's Second Law, equals the time rate of change of angular momentum $d\mathbf{p}_I/dt$. Figure 5–3 shows the angular momentum vector $\mathbf{p}_I$, the associated magnetic dipole moment $\boldsymbol{\mu}_1$, and the torque $\boldsymbol{\tau}$ resulting from the interaction with the B-field. Since the change of the angular momentum is always perpendicular to $\mathbf{p}_I$, the result is *Larmor precession* with angular frequency

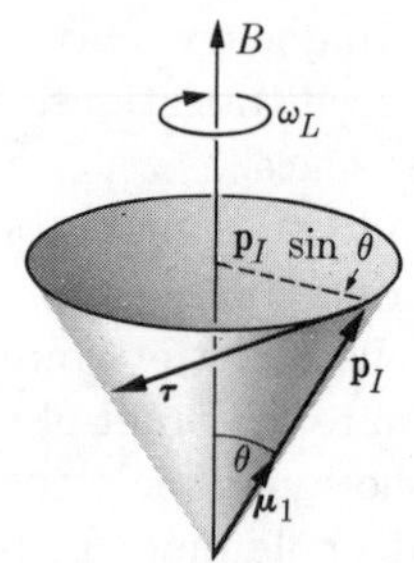

Fig. 5–3. Illustration of Larmor precession.

$$\omega_{\mathrm{L}} = \frac{1}{p_I \sin\theta}\,\frac{dp_I}{dt} = \frac{\mu_1 B \sin\theta}{p_I \sin\theta} = \frac{\mu_1 B}{p_I}.$$

The magnetic dipole moment μ quoted for nuclei is the maximum z-component of μ_1. The relationship is (see Section 1–7) $\mu_1/p_I = \mu/\hbar I$, and this yields

$$\omega_{\mathrm{L}} = \frac{\mu B}{\hbar I}. \tag{5–3}$$

For $\mu = 1$ nm, $I = 1$, and $B = 1\ \mathrm{Wb/m^2}$, we obtain

$$f_{\mathrm{L}} = \omega_{\mathrm{L}}/2\pi = 7.62\ \mathrm{Mc/sec}.$$

Electromagnetic radiation having the same frequency as this mechanical precession is in the radiofrequency part of the spectrum, a fact that is utilized in several experimental setups described in following sections.

A given hyperfine level, as defined by a quantum-mechanical state with angular-momentum parameters I, J, and F, has a degeneracy $2F + 1$, which is the number of possible orientations of the **F**-vector relative to a given direction in space. When the direction is defined by a magnetic field, the interaction between this field and the magnetic dipole moment associated with the **F**-vector will remove the degeneracy, and $2F + 1$ levels emerge from each hyperfine level. When the field is very weak, the **F**-vector will precess about an axis in the field direction and the **I**- and **J**-vectors, because of their mutual interaction, will precess about **F** (Fig. 5–2). When the external field is increased beyond typically 100 gauss, a decoupling of the **I**- and **J**-vectors takes place, **F** loses its identity, and the two vectors **I** and **J** will precess independently about the field direction (Fig. 5–4).

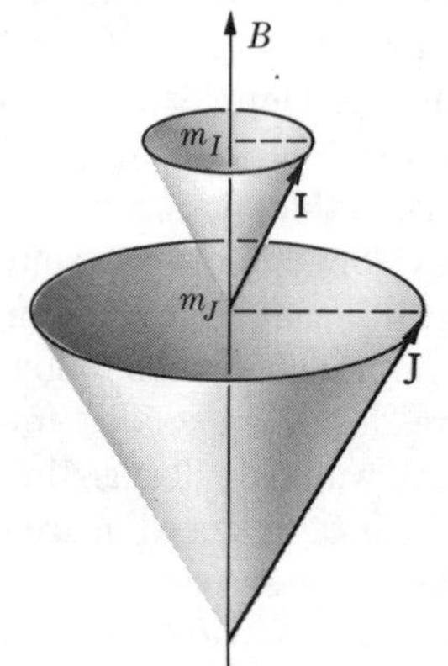

Fig. 5–4. Breakup of the coupling between **I** and **J** (μ_I and μ_J) by a stronger external field (compare with Fig. 5–2).

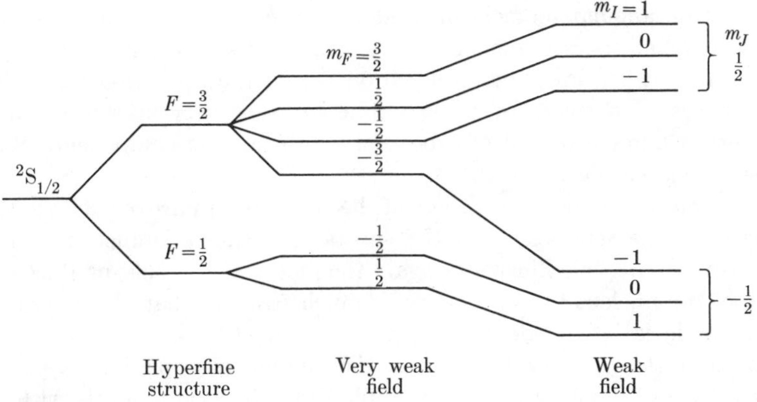

Fig. 5-5. Schematic drawing of the splitting of a $^2S_{1/2}$ state ($L = 0, S = \frac{1}{2}, J = \frac{1}{2}$) with nuclear angular momentum $I = 1$ caused by internal fields (hyperfine structure) and a weak external field.

Consider as an example one of the alkali atoms, Li, Na, K, Rb, or Cs, in its atomic ground state, a $^2S_{1/2}$ state. The magnetic induction produced at the position of the nucleus by the magnetic moment of the electron will fluctuate wildly in magnitude and direction, depending on the position of the electron and the orientation of its spin vector. The average value of this induction can be computed, and the result is (compare Eq. 5-1):

$$B \approx \frac{\mu_0}{2} \frac{\mu_B}{a_0^3} \approx 15 \text{ Wb/m}^2 = 150{,}000 \text{ gauss.}$$

On the other hand, the field from the nucleus at the position of the electron is about a factor of 1000 smaller than this because the magnetic moments of these nuclei are only of the order of magnitude of 10^{-3} μ_B (0.5 to 3 nm). When the external field at the position of the electron is larger than the average field produced by the nucleus, the electron will start precessing about an axis parallel to the external field. This in turn will align the average field produced by the electron at the position of the nucleus in the same direction, and therefore the nucleus will also precess about the external field axis. The action of the external field on the nucleus is mostly an indirect one in that it aligns the usually much stronger field produced by the electron.

Figure 5-5 illustrates on an energy scale the hyperfine splitting of a $^2S_{1/2}$ state ($L = 0$, $S = \frac{1}{2}$, $J = \frac{1}{2}$) with nuclear angular momentum $I = 1$ and the further splitting of the magnetic substates in an external field. At very weak fields, i.e., below 100 gauss, the appropriate designation of the states and substates is given in terms of the quantum numbers F and m_F. At weak fields, i.e., a few hundred gauss, the appropriate designation of the states is in terms of the electron angular momentum J and its z-component m_J and the nuclear momentum I and its z-component m_I. From an atomic S-state, which is what we are dealing with now, this designation is still the appropriate one at high field strengths. However, for other atomic states at very high field strengths, the quantum number J will also be broken up into its components S and L (Paschen-Back effect).

In the weak-field region, the orders of the substates m_I are opposite in the two branches and the separations of the substates within a branch are virtually independent of B. This illustrates again the fact that the field produced at the position of the nucleus by the electron is much stronger than the external field, the magnitude is independent of B, and the direction is determined by m_J. Another interesting observation is that the number of hyperfine levels in each branch is $2I + 1$. This fact, which applies also to atomic levels with higher J-values, can be used for determining I.

5–3 Molecular Excitations and Determination of I from Molecular Band Spectra

For readers who have not previously studied the quantum physics of molecules, the latter part of this section (in fine print) may be difficult. However, it is important to read the first part, which explains molecular rotational motion, before one reaches Section 6–9, which treats nuclear rotational motion.

Optical measurements of band spectra from diatomic molecules with two identical nuclei can sometimes be used to determine the nuclear angular momentum I. The effects detected do not come about because of the minute interactions between the nuclear magnetic moment or quadrupole moment with the magnetic or electric field in the molecule. Rather, they are caused by the fact that the nuclear angular momentum I in these cases influences the intensity ratios of alternate lines in the band spectrum. Before we discuss the details of this effect, it may be wise to review some of the main features of molecular excitations and transitions.

In the molecular spectra, evidence is usually found for three kinds of excitations. The first type, which ordinarily involves the largest change in energy, is electronic excitation, in which the orbital state of one electron is different from the ground state, just as in atomic excitations. The second type is "vibrational" excitation, in which the atoms of the molecule execute harmonic or near-harmonic oscillations with respect to the center of mass. Governing these vibrations are the binding forces between the atoms, which are zero in the equilibrium positions of the individual atoms and increase approximately linearly with the displacement of an atom, exactly as does a classical spring force. The third type of excitation consists of a rotation of the entire molecule about its center of mass. In the analysis of these types of excitations, it is possible in the first approximation to keep them separate because the frequencies of the various excitations are so different. For instance, the electronic frequencies are so high compared with the rotational frequencies that a rotation of the molecule has very little influence on the energies of the electron states.

Theoretically, the electronic-excitation part is most difficult to handle, since it involves solving Schrödinger's equation for electrons subject to mutual repulsions and moving in the field of two or more nuclei. The vibrational part of the motion is to a reasonable degree of accuracy described by harmonic-oscillator wave functions with the normal mode displacements as variables. We shall discuss the rotational part in greater detail.

Figure 5-6 shows a diatomic molecule free to rotate about its center of mass. The molecular axis is a symmetry axis, which implies that there are no marks on the molecule that can define a time-varying coordinate describing a rotational motion about this axis. Therefore the rotational motion observed will be a motion about an axis perpendicular to the symmetry axis. Since the molecule is not spherically symmetric, the forces acting on the electrons are not central forces and hence the total electronic angular momentum is not, in general, conserved, but its component K along the symmetry axis is conserved. The transverse component is subject to a continuous interchange with rotational motion of the molecule, which is also in the lowest possible energy state ("zero-point" rotation). Assuming a given electronic state, we find that the lowest state of rotation is the one for which $J = K$. This does not mean that the transverse component R is zero, since the length of the **J**-vector, as usual, is given by $|\mathbf{J}| = \sqrt{J(J+1)}$. Higher rotational states can be excited by increasing J by one unit but keeping K constant. Since the rotation is free with no external torques acting that can change the total angular momentum J, neither in magnitude nor in direction, the rotation has to be in the form of a nutation about the **J**-vector. The quantum-mechanical calculation of the rotational energy leads to exactly the same formula as can be calculated semiclassically in the following way:

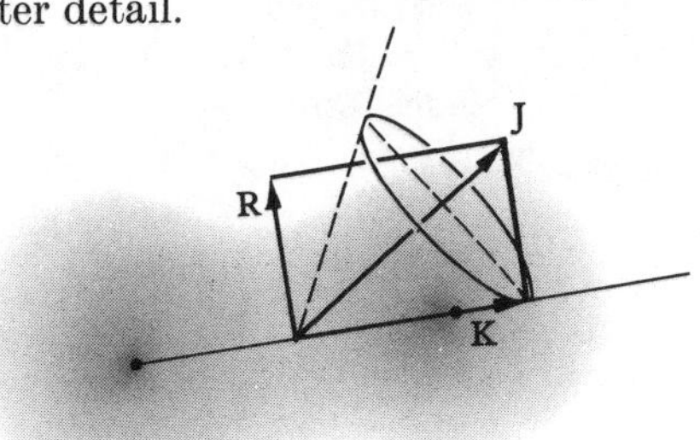

Fig. 5-6. Rotation (nutation) of a diatomic molecule about the J-axis. When $K \neq 0$, the rotational angular momentum vector **R** continuously changes direction since the total angular momentum **J** is conserved.

$$E = \frac{(R\hbar)^2}{2\mathcal{I}} = \frac{\hbar^2}{2\mathcal{I}}\,[J(J+1) - K^2]. \tag{5-4}$$

Here $\mathcal{I}$ is the moment of inertia of the molecule about an axis perpendicular to the symmetry axis and passing through the center of mass. In the ground state of a diatomic homonuclear molecule, $K = 0$.

The symmetry of the wave functions, as well as the selection rules, is important in the following discussion. We consider only diatomic molecules with two identical nuclei (N_2^{14}, O_2^{16}, etc.). The part of the total wave function that depends on the nuclear coordinates can be written as

$$\psi = \psi_e \psi_v \psi_r \chi. \tag{5-5}$$

In this expression

- ψ_e is the part of the ordinary molecular electronic wave function that contains the position coordinates of the nuclei,
- ψ_v is a harmonic oscillator wave function describing vibrational motion of the two nuclei with respect to each other,
- ψ_r describes the rotation of the molecule, and
- χ is the nuclear spin wave function having as variables the angular momenta $\mathbf{I}_1$ and $\mathbf{I}_2$ (numerically, $I_1 = I_2 = I$).

Let us consider first the symmetry of the function, Eq. (5-5). If the quantum number I is half-integral, the total wave function ψ must be antisymmetric in the exchange of the two nuclei (Fermi particles). If I is integral, the total wave function ψ must be symmetric in the exchange of the two nuclei (Bose-Einstein particles). The function ψ_e can be either symmetric or antisymmetric in the exchange of the two nuclei, but it is always symmetric in the electronic ground state of the molecule. The function ψ_v, describing the two atomic centers in the same state of vibration, can be symmetric only.

The wave function ψ_r is characterized by the rotational angular-momentum quantum number which takes on integral values $J = K, K + 1, \ldots$ For $K = 0$, we get $J = 0, 1, 2, 3, 4, \ldots$ For this case the motion is a pure rotation about an axis perpendicular to the symmetry axis, and the wave function ψ_r is simply a spherical harmonic $Y_{J,m}(\theta, \phi)$. The exchange of the two particles then corresponds to a rotation of the molecular axis by 180°; in other words, it corresponds to a parity check. Consequently, the wave functions with even J are symmetric; the wave functions with odd J are antisymmetric.

Finally, the spin function χ can be either symmetric or antisymmetric. In the former case the molecule is called an *ortho*molecule; in the latter it is called a *para*molecule. More about these states later.

Now, a look at selection rules: First we observe that the coupling between the nuclear angular momenta I and the electrons or the rotational motion is so extremely weak that the total nuclear angular momentum $\mathbf{I}_1 + \mathbf{I}_2$ can be regarded as a constant of the motion. In other words, a paramolecule stays a paramolecule and an orthomolecule stays ortho through thousands of excitations and de-excitations.

Since total symmetry is conserved and the symmetry of χ does not change, it follows that the symmetry of the product $\psi_e\psi_v\psi_r$ does not change in any transition of absorption or emission. In pure rotational or vibration-rotation transitions, for which ψ_e does not change, the selection rule is

$$\Delta J = \pm 1$$

for electric dipole radiation. Since this change, according to the discussion above, involves a change of symmetry, it follows that pure rotational or vibration-rotation transitions do not take place in homonuclear diatomic molecules. If, however, ψ_e

is allowed to change as well, an opposite symmetry change may be supplied, and electric dipole transitions are allowed. In a band spectrum resulting from such transitions, alternate lines start from alternately even and odd values of J; $J = 8 \rightarrow 7$, $J = 7 \rightarrow 6$, etc. Therefore, *alternate lines involve ortho- and paramolecules.* The intensity of the lines throughout a band spectrum is, in general, a slowly varying function of J, depending largely on the temperature of the gas. For the diatomic homonuclear molecules, we see, in addition, an alternation of intensities between neighboring lines given by

$$\text{Intensity ratio} = \frac{\text{Number of orthomolecules in gas}}{\text{Number of paramolecules in gas}}.$$

According to the principle of equipartition, this ratio equals the ratio of statistical weights of the two kinds of molecules. In order to calculate this quantity, we need to look into the form of the function χ.

An antisymmetric spin function (parafunction) can be written in the following way:

$$\chi_{\text{para}} = 2^{-1/2}[\chi_i(1)\chi_j(2) - \chi_j(1)\chi_i(2)]. \tag{5–6}$$

Each of the functions $\chi_i(1)$ is a spin wave function describing a state with total angular momentum $\sqrt{I(I+1)}\hbar$ and z-component $m_I\hbar$. There are therefore a total of $2I + 1$ such states. Each of the $2I + 1$ states for particle (1) can be combined with any one of the other $2I$ states for particle (2). The $2I(2I + 1)$ states thus formed are pairwise identical, except for the sign; that is, we have taken all the combinations twice. We therefore divide by a factor of 2 and obtain the total number of different parastates χ_{para} that can be formed by two identical nuclei with angular momenta I:

$$N_{\text{para}} = I(2I + 1).$$

We can form a set of symmetric states in exactly the same manner by simply changing the minus to a plus sign in Eq. (5–6). In addition, we do have symmetric states of the type

$$\chi_i(1)\chi_i(2),$$

in which both particles are in identical spin states. The total number of combinations of symmetric, or ortho, states is therefore

$$N_{\text{ortho}} = N_{\text{para}} + 2I + 1 = (I + 1)(2I + 1).$$

The ratio of the number of orthostates to parastates is then

$$\frac{N_{\text{ortho}}}{N_{\text{para}}} = \frac{I + 1}{I}. \tag{5–7}$$

Since, as explained above, in a given band spectrum alternate lines are emitted by para- and orthomolecules, the intensity of these lines will alternate as $I + 1$ to I.

Figure 5–7 shows, as an example, a section of the molecular band spectrum of He^3—He^3. The curve is a densitometer tracing of the blackening of a photographic plate used in the optical spectrograph. Since the blackening of the

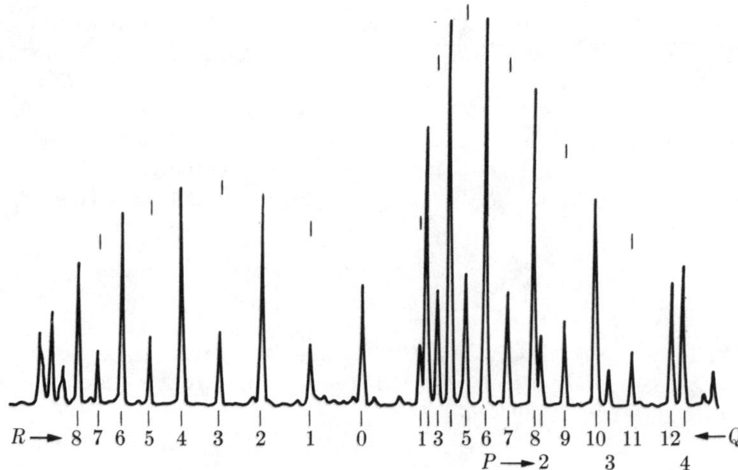

Fig. 5–7. Band spectrum of He_2^3 near $\lambda = 4650$ angstroms. The letters P, Q, and R refer to different branches of the optical transitions. [From G. H. Dieke and E. S. Robinson, *Phys. Rev.* **80**, 4 (1950).]

photographic emulsion is not a linear function of the intensity, a calibration exposure was made, and to the accuracy of this calibration, the experimental ratio $(I + 1)/I = 2.8$. For $I = \frac{1}{2}$, Eq. (5–7) gives 3, and for $I = \frac{3}{2}$, it gives an expected ratio of 1.67. There is, therefore, little doubt that the angular momentum of He^3 is $I = \frac{1}{2}$.

5–4 Nuclear Parameters as Determined by Microwave Spectroscopy Methods

Electromagnetic radiation of wavelengths 0.05 to 10 cm can be produced and detected by techniques developed during World War II for use in radar equipment. The frequencies can be measured with extreme accuracy through comparison with harmonics of ordinary radiofrequencies, the standards for which are readily available from certain broadcasting stations. Two areas of application of microwave spectroscopy will be discussed below.

(*a*) *Gaseous absorption spectra.* The rotational absorption spectra of gases of heavy and medium-heavy molecules are in the right range for microwave techniques. For instance, the ICl molecule has a rotational transition $J = 3 \rightarrow 4$ at a frequency of 27,200 Mc/sec, corresponding to a wavelength of about 1.1 cm. The rotational motion produces a weak magnetic field which, coupled with the magnetic moments of the nuclei, gives rise to a small effect. The magnitude of the level separation is much enhanced by the interaction between the internal electric field at the positions of the nuclei and the nuclear quadrupole moments. The energy shifts caused by this interaction are of the order of magnitude

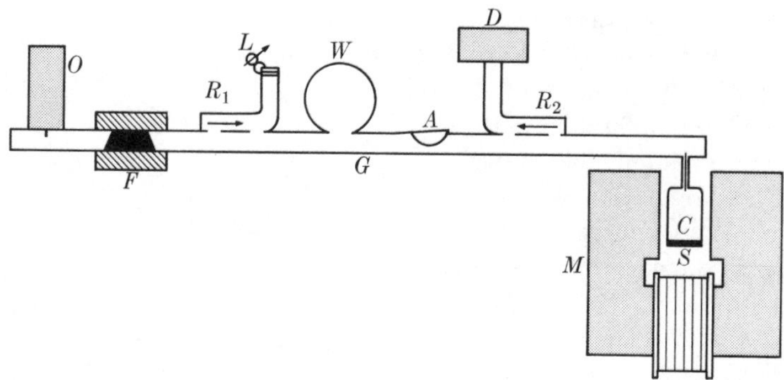

Fig. 5–8. Schematic diagram of a paramagnetic resonance absorption apparatus. O = oscillator, G = waveguide, W = wavemeter, A = attenuator, D = detector, R = directional coupler, C = resonance cavity, S = sample, M = magnet. [Adapted from J. S. Van Wieringen, *Philips Tech. Rev.* **19,** 301 (1958).]

estimated in Section 5–1; that is, extremely small. The crucial point is, however, that the energy of the rotational transition itself is small so that the relative resolving power does not need to be excessively high.

For the purpose of simplifying the discussion, assume that only one of the nuclei in a given molecule has angular momentum different from zero. For rotational states with $J > I$, the number of hyperfine levels is $2I + 1$, and the spacing between the lines is determined mainly by the quadrupole effect (Eq. 1–13). In other words, a study of the hyperfine structure of molecular rotational transitions results in determinations of I and Q. The accuracy of the latter depends on the accuracy with which one can determine the factor $\partial^2 U/\partial z^2$ in Eq. (1–13) from the molecular wave functions.

(*b*) *Paramagnetic resonances.* Paramagnetic crystals usually contain one unpaired electron per atom, and the crystal wave functions are such that these electrons behave like S-electrons. In an external magnetic field, they tend to align with the field in the lowest state, but the energy of alignment is so small that heat motion practically washes out the effect at normal temperatures. The net magnetic polarization is therefore very small; however, there exists a distinct energy gap between the two states of opposite orientation of any given electron.

Let us assume that the effective magnetic moment is one Bohr magneton and that the crystal is immersed in a field of magnitude $B = 1\ \mathrm{Wb/m^2}$. The frequency of transition in a jump from a state in which the spin is parallel with the magnetic field to a state in which it is antiparallel is therefore

$$\nu = \frac{\Delta E}{h} = \frac{2\mu_B B}{h} = 2.80 \times 10^{10}\ \text{cycles/sec},$$

corresponding to a wavelength $\lambda = 1.07$ cm. Immersed in an electromagnetic field of this frequency, the crystal will both absorb photons and emit photons (by stimulated emission). Since, however, the population of the lower state will be slightly larger than that of the higher state, absorption will predominate.

Figure 5–8 shows the apparatus used by Van Wieringen* to study paramagnetic resonances. The crystal is mounted in a resonant cavity which is situated between the pole pieces of an electromagnet. The cavity C with the sample S is being fed by electromagnetic radiation from the oscillator O through the waveguide G and attenuator A. Reflected waves are detected by the detector D which, by a directional coupler R, is made relatively insensitive to the radiation which is coming directly from the oscillator.

A splitting of the observed absorption line results from a coupling between the magnetic field produced by the electron and the magnetic moment of the nucleus, as described in Section 5–2. Figure 5–9(a) shows schematically how the paramagnetic levels of a crystal containing $I = \frac{3}{2}$ nuclei split in a magnetic field and where absorption resonances are expected to fall for varying field strength, assuming a constant frequency of the microwave field. Note that the coupling with the magnetic moment of the nucleus is so weak that $\Delta m_I = 0$ in a paramagnetic transition. The number of resonances observed is therefore simply $2I + 1$. Figure 5–9(b) shows a typical paramagnetic absorption spectrum taken from a work of Bleaney and Stevens.†

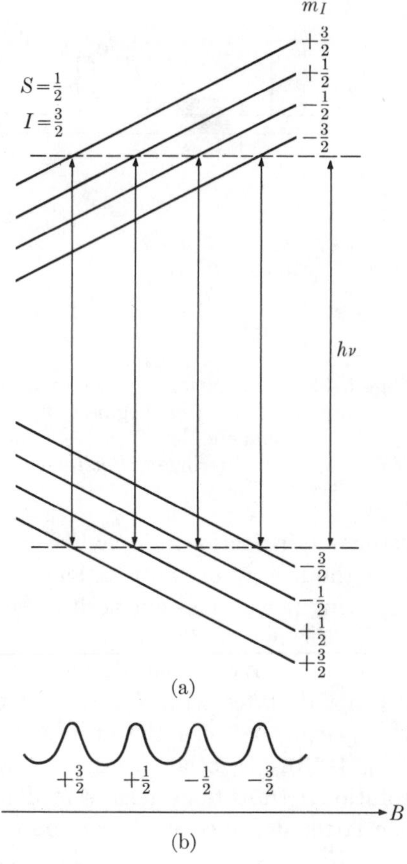

Fig. 5–9. (a) Splitting in a magnetic field of a microwave absorption line in a paramagnetic crystal containing $I = \frac{3}{2}$ nuclei; (b) observed absorption spectrum at constant frequency and varying B. [From B. Bleaney and K. W. H. Stevens, *Rept. Progr. Phys.* **16,** 108 (1953).]

---

* J. S. Van Wieringen, *Philips Tech. Rev.* **19,** 301 (1958).

† B. Bleaney and K. W. H. Stevens, *Rept. Progr. Phys.* **16,** 108 (1953).

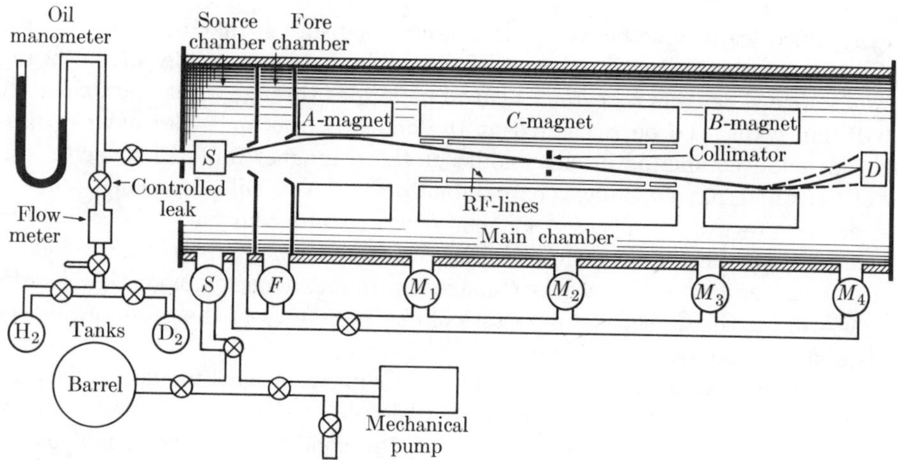

Fig. 5–10. Modern molecular-beam apparatus. The symbols S, F, M, etc., represent locations of diffusion pumps. (From N. F. Ramsey in *Experimental Nuclear Physics*, Vol. I, ed. by E. Segrè. New York: John Wiley and Sons, 1953, p. 395. Reproduced by permission.)

5–5 Molecular-Beam Resonance Methods

The beautiful demonstration of the existence of magnetic moments of atoms and of space quantization by Stern and Gerlach in 1922 has been adequately described in textbooks on atomic physics. Very briefly, Stern and Gerlach directed a well-defined beam of neutral silver atoms into the region of an inhomogeneous magnetic field. The beam split into two components, one of which was deflected in the direction of the field and the other in the opposite direction, exactly as expected from quantum physics for an atom with a $^2S_{1/2}$ ground state. The deflecting forces arise from an interaction between the magnetic moment of the atom (unpaired electron) with the inhomogeneous magnetic field.

A very powerful extension of the Stern-Gerlach technique was introduced by Rabi and coworkers in 1939.* Figure 5–10 shows a modern molecular-beam apparatus† operating on the same principles as Rabi's original apparatus. The A-magnet and the B-magnet are both inhomogeneous magnets with the same direction of the field B, but with opposite field gradient dB/dz. The C-magnet is a homogeneous-field magnet. In Rabi's original apparatus, a single "hairpin" loop inside the gap of the C-magnet was connected to a radiofrequency (RF) generator producing an oscillating magnetic field with B-vector perpendicular to the main field. As explained in more detail below, this radiofrequency field

---

* I. I. Rabi, J. Millman, P. Kusch, and J. R. Zacharias, *Phys. Rev.* **55,** 526 (1939).
† N. F. Ramsey in *Experimental Nuclear Physics*, ed. by E. Segrè. New York: John Wiley and Sons, 1953, Vol. 1, p. 395.

can induce transitions between the magnetic substates; that is, it can flip the direction of the magnetic moment of the nuclei in the molecules of the beam. The source S delivers a beam of neutral molecules through a slit approximately 0.01 mm wide. To be registered at the detector, the molecules have to pass through the collimator in the middle of the C-magnet and the detector slit, both of which have openings comparable to the source slit. Molecules that are deflected downward in the A-magnet must, in order to pass the collimator, emerge from the source with an initial direction slightly upward, as indicated on the figure. If they do pass the C-magnet without change of magnetic substate, they will hit the detector slit because of the symmetry of the orbits inside the A- and B-magnets.

The apparatus is used for molecules with no resulting atomic angular momentum, so that the force acting on a molecule in the inhomogeneous field is $\mu_z \partial B/\partial z$, where μ_z is the z-component of the combined magnetic moment of the nuclei in the molecule. For a resulting magnetic moment of, typically, 1 nm, the excursion of the beam from the center line, shown greatly exaggerated in the figure, is only of the order of magnitude of 0.05 mm.

While the main field in the C-magnet causes the nuclear angular-momentum vectors to precess about a vertical axis maintaining constant z-components, the radiofrequency B-field tries to make these **I**-vectors precess about a horizontal axis and thus force them to change magnetic substate. It is well known that a field varying sinusoidally with time can be thought of as two fields rotating in opposite directions, both having magnitudes that are half of the amplitude of the sinusoidal field. If one of these rotating fields is in resonance with a precessing **I**-vector, a constant torque will be exerted which will tend to decrease or increase the z-component of **I**. This is roughly the situation in the middle of the C-magnet expressed classically; quantum mechanically, of course, the torque exerted by the radiofrequency field in resonance will build up probability density for finding the nuclear angular momentum in another magnetic substate.

The resonance condition for a transition to take place is fulfilled when the radiofrequency field oscillates with the Larmor precession frequency (Eq. 5–3) for the nucleus in question in the main field of the C-magnet.

Another way of looking at these transitions is the following. The radiofrequency coil will fill the gap of the C-magnet with photons of energy $h\nu$, where ν is the frequency of the radiofrequency signal. These photons can induce transitions through absorption or stimulated emission by the molecule in the dc field, provided the energy is right for such a transition. The interaction energy between the field B and the magnetic moment μ in substate m_I is

$$E = \mu B(m_I/I).$$

The selection rule for a transition is $\Delta m_I = \pm 1$. We therefore get $\Delta E = h\nu = \mu B/I$, corresponding to an angular frequency $\omega = \mu B/\hbar I$. This result is identical with Eq. (5–3) for the Larmor precession frequency.

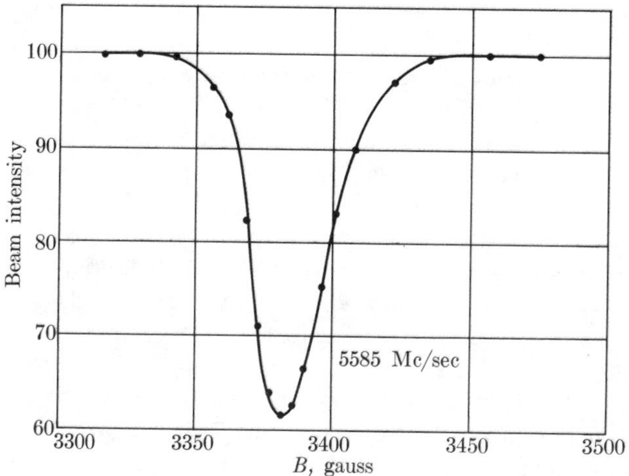

Fig. 5–11. Molecular-beam resonance for Li^7. [From Rabi *et al.*, *Phys. Rev.* **55**, 526 (1939).]

Since the forces acting on the molecule in the A- and B-magnets are proportional to the z-component of the magnetic moment, the molecules that have changed magnetic substates inside the C-magnet will break away from the symmetric orbit and miss the detector slit, as indicated by dashed lines in Fig. 5–10. The resonance condition is usually found by keeping the frequency of the RF-signal constant and varying the main field of the C-magnet.

Figure 5–11 shows a typical resonance curve obtained with Rabi's apparatus* using a beam of lithium chloride molecules. The source in this case is an oven containing a sample of lithium chloride heated to a temperature at which a sufficient stream of molecules evaporates and escapes through the source slit. The detector is a tungsten wire which, on being hit by a LiCl molecule, liberates an electron. The reduction in current to the wire is therefore an indication that the resonance condition is met. Since the experiment is carried out with LiCl molecules, resonances resulting from the interaction between the magnetic moments of Cl^{35} and Cl^{37} with the external field are also expected. These resonances occur for other values of the field strength, and that the present one really can be assigned to Li^7 is best tested by using other compounds containing lithium.

The value of the magnetic moment for Li^7 that can be derived from the results depicted in Fig. 5–11 is (Eq. 5–3):

$$\mu = 2\pi f\hbar I/B = 1.635 \times 10^{-26}\ \text{J-m}^2/\text{Wb} = 3.24\ \text{nm}.$$

---

* Rabi *et al.*, *loc. cit.*

The best modern value, obtained with the technique described in Section 5–8, is 3.2560 nm.

At the lithium resonance of Fig. 5–11, one might expect to see a fine structure resulting from the coupling between the Li^7 and Cl^{35} (or Cl^{37}) magnetic moments and possibly also from the coupling with a weak magnetic field produced by the rotation of the molecule. In Fig. 5–11 this fine structure is not resolved. It was resolved, however, in experiments carried out on H_2 and D_2, which are described in the next section.

A significant improvement in the accuracy of a molecular-beam apparatus was attained by Ramsey and coworkers through the introduction of *two* RF hairpin loops in the *C*-magnet, one at each end. The two loops are fed by the same RF-oscillator, and for a nucleus to receive a maximum angular impulse about a horizontal axis, it has to hit both regions of the RF fields with its precessional motion in phase with the field. One necessary condition is that the *average* main field traversed between the loops must satisfy the Larmor expression (Eq. 5–3).

5–6 Molecular-Beam Experiments on Hydrogen

The existence of a quadrupole moment in the deuteron was discovered in a molecular-beam experiment carried out with D_2 gas by Kellogg, Rabi, Ramsey, and Zacharias.* This discovery had a profound effect on the direction of research on nuclear forces, since it made it clear that these forces are not central (see Chapter 2). We shall discuss the D_2 experiment, after presenting the result of an experiment on H_2 reported in the same paper. At the time the H_2 experiment gave a relatively precise measurement of the magnetic moment of the proton. More accurate determinations of this quantity have later been made (Section 5–8), and the molecular-beam experiment on H_2 gas is discussed here mainly as an introduction to the D_2 experiment. The source in the molecular-beam apparatus for these experiments was connected to a supply of hydrogen gas through an adjustable leak. The detector chamber was equipped with a vacuum gauge measuring the buildup of gas pressure from the hydrogen beam.

(*a*) *The* H_2 *experiment.* Since the proton has spin $s = \frac{1}{2}$, the only antisymmetric (para) state of the H_2 molecule is the $S = 0$ state. The electronic ground state is symmetric, with $K = 0$, and therefore the paramolecules have even angular momenta: $J = 0, 2, 4, 6, \ldots$ Of course, in the lowest state, $J = 0$, parahydrogen has zero total magnetic moment. A spin flip of one proton is not allowed, since the state then formed would have the wrong symmetry (even). In orthohydrogen the two proton spins combine to a total $S = 1$, and the corresponding rotational angular-momentum quantum numbers

---

* J. M. B. Kellogg, I. I. Rabi, N. F. Ramsey, and J. R. Zacharias, *Phys. Rev.* **55**, 318 (1939).

are $J = 1, 3, 5, \ldots$ The following discussion concerns only orthohydrogen in the state with $J = 1$ and $m_J = -1, 0$, or $+1$. The rotational motion of the H_2 molecule in these states produces a magnetic moment which, by coupling with the external field, causes energy splitting. The total spin $S = 1$ has components $m_S = -1, 0$, or $+1$ in the field direction, and the magnetic moment of the proton coupled with the external field will again cause energy splitting. Mutual magnetic interaction between the rotational magnetic moment and the proton magnetic moment results in perturbations, which are a major object of this study. The field strengths used in these experiments are sufficiently high so as to decouple J and S; it is therefore appropriate to use the quantum numbers m_J and m_S. It is not appropriate to treat the two proton spins individually (quantum numbers m_{s1} and m_{s2}), since only the combination spin wave functions with $S = 1$ have the appropriate symmetry. A spin flip of a single proton does, however, change the total m_S value by one unit (compare Fig. 3–9).

The frequency of the RF-field in the C-magnet for the H_2 experiment was 6.987 Mc/sec. This is the Larmor precession frequency (Eq. 5–3) for a proton (or the combined S-vector) in a magnetic field of about $B = 1650$ gauss. At about this field strength, then, we expect proton spin flips to take place in the C-magnet of the molecular-beam apparatus, causing changes in the magnetic substates m_S. Because of the relatively weak perturbations of the magnetic field produced by the rotational motion of the molecule and by the other proton, the exact field at the positions of the protons is not equal to B but does depend on m_J and m_S. As a result of this, not one line, but six lines are seen in the RF-spectrum of H_2 in this region (Fig. 5–12). Kellogg *et al.* calculated the expected position of the lines, using as adjustable parameters essentially the magnetic moment of the proton μ_p and the field B_J produced at the positions of the protons by the rotational motion. Interpreting the six observed lines in accordance with the scheme shown in Table 5–1, they obtained perfect agree-

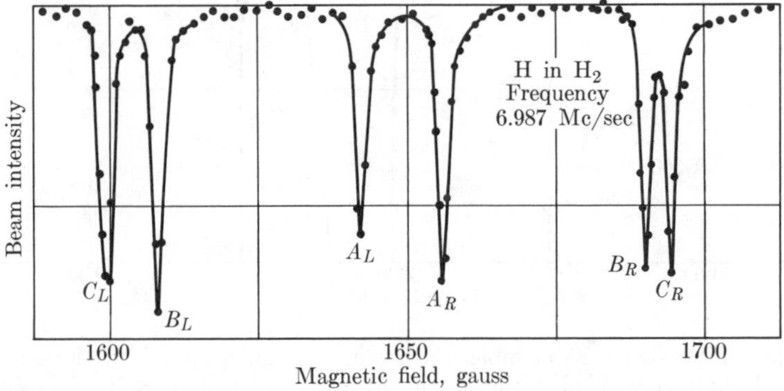

Fig. 5–12. Fine structure in molecular-beam resonance for H_2 in the state $J = 1$ (rotational) and $S = 1$. [From Kellogg *et al.*, *Phys. Rev.* **55**, 318 (1939).]

Table 5–1. RF-spectral lines in H_2

m_J	m_S	Line
-1	$0 \rightleftharpoons +1$	A_L
-1	$-1 \rightleftharpoons 0$	C_L
0	$0 \rightleftharpoons +1$	B_L
0	$-1 \rightleftharpoons 0$	B_R
$+1$	$0 \rightleftharpoons +1$	C_R
$+1$	$-1 \rightleftharpoons 0$	A_R

ment between theory and experiment using $\mu_p = 2.785$ nm and $B_J = 27.2$ gauss.

(*b*) *The* D_2 *experiment.* When the hydrogen gas was replaced by D_2, the spectrum shown in Fig. 5–13 was found. In addition to the six lines with interpretation identical to the one given for H_2 ($J = 1$, $S = 1$), there is a strong seventh line in the center of the spectrum. This arises from deuteron spin-flip transitions $\Delta m_S = 1$ for the state $J = 0$, $S = 2$. The position of this central resonance provides a measurement of μ_D. With this information and the previous results from the H_2 molecule, it is possible to compute the expected positions corresponding to the six resonances observed in the H_2 case. These predicted positions, indicated by dashed lines at the top of Fig. 5–13, are clearly in sharp

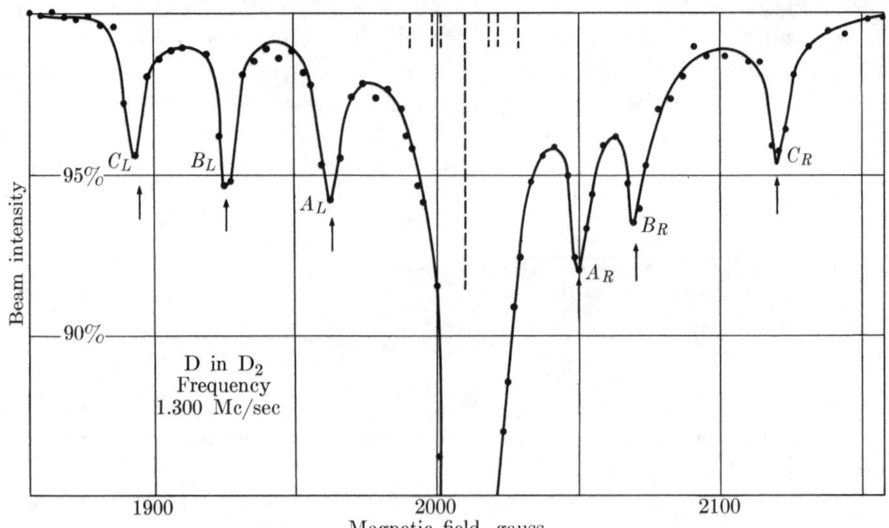

Fig. 5–13. Fine structure in molecular-beam resonance for D_2 in the state $J = 1$ (rotational) and $S = 1$ plus the single strong line from $J = 0$, $S = 2$. (From Kellogg *et al.*)

disagreement with the observed spectrum. The discrepancy was resolved by Kellogg *et al.* by assigning to the deuteron a quadrupole moment $Q = 0.00273$ barn which, combined with the known electric field gradient $\partial^2 U/\partial z^2$ in the hydrogen molecule, shifted the calculated resonance fields to the positions indicated by the arrows in Fig. 5–13. The experiment described gave the first indication of the existence of a quadrupole moment for the deuteron. Since then, the experiment has been repeated with better resolving power; in addition, we have now more accurate knowledge regarding the magnitude of the field gradient at the sites of the deuterons in the D_2 molecule. By combining this new information, one obtains the accepted value of the quadrupole moment of the deuteron, $Q = 0.00282$ nm, as quoted in Section 2–2.

5–7 Nuclear Magnetic Resonances in Liquids and Solids

It was pointed out by Gorter* in 1936 that it should be possible to measure the Larmor precession frequency of nuclei in a magnetic field by detecting the induced electromagnetic fields produced when the magnetic moments of a large number of nuclei simultaneously are forced to change direction. Ten years later, Purcell† and coworkers and, independently, Bloch‡ and coworkers succeeded in building sufficiently sensitive electronic equipment to accomplish this feat. These methods have since been used to determine with extremely high accuracy the magnetic moments of many nuclei. In accordance with both methods, a small sample, usually a fraction of a gram, of a material containing the nuclei to be studied is placed in a homogeneous magnetic field. The *average* field strength at the position of a nucleus will, except in ferromagnetic materials, be almost exactly equal to the external field. Internal molecular fields might be present because of the influence of unpaired electrons; however, these internal fields fluctuate very rapidly because of heat motion, and, since, in general, the precession frequency for a nucleus is small compared with the electron collision frequency, the effect is averaged out. The field governing the precession is therefore taken to be the external field times a permeability coefficient, which may be slightly smaller than unity because of diamagnetism.

In one important respect the principle utilized in both Purcell's and Bloch's methods is identical with that used in the molecular-beam resonance apparatus; an RF-signal produced by a driver coil and having its magnetic field perpendicular to the direction of the external field is tuned to resonance with the Larmor precession frequency of the nucleus. In the same manner as described earlier, the angular momentum of the nucleus may flip over from one magnetic sub-

---

* C. J. Gorter, *Physica* **3,** 503 and 995 (1936).

† E. M. Purcell, H. C. Torrey, and R. V. Pound, *Phys. Rev.* **69,** 37 (1946).

‡ F. Bloch, W. W. Hansen, and M. Packard, *Phys. Rev.* **69,** 127 (1946); and **70,** 474 (1946).

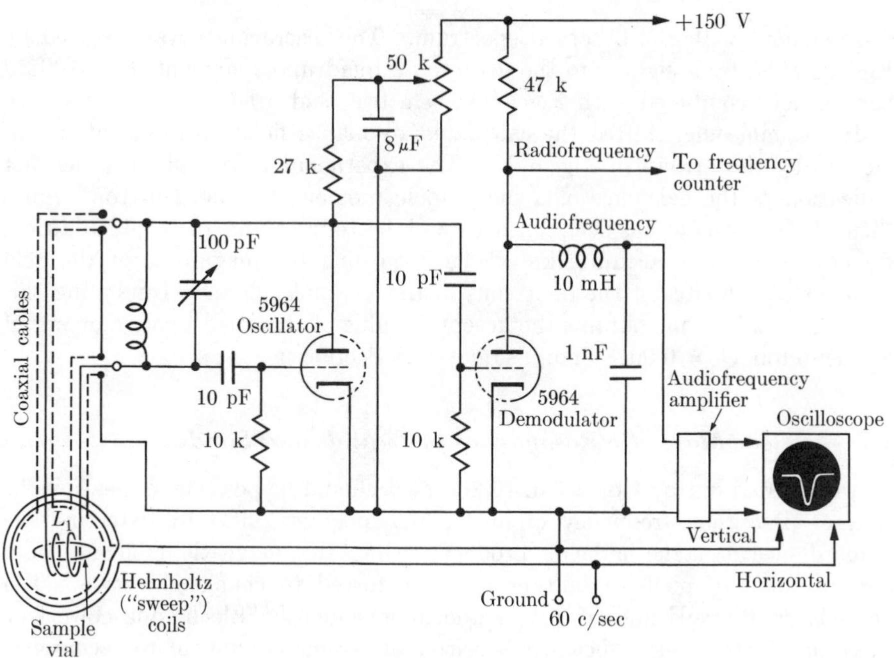

Fig. 5–14. Simple circuit for detecting nuclear-resonance absorption.

state to another. The two methods differ slightly in the way of detecting these changes in substates. In Bloch's apparatus, an RF-pickup coil at right angles to the driver coil is used to detect a very weak RF-signal induced when millions of nuclei simultaneously change the directions of their magnetic moment. By Purcell's method, this same signal is detected, in the driver coil itself, as a minute power loss when the resonance condition is fulfilled.

Figure 5–14 is a diagram of a very simple circuit basically utilizing Purcell's method for detecting nuclear-resonance absorption. The coil L_1 surrounding the sample is part of the tank circuit of an RF-oscillator. The regenerative coupling in this oscillator (over internal tube capacitances) is very weak, so that the oscillations are just barely sustained. A small change in the power loss to the coil L_1 will therefore have the effect of substantially reducing the amplitude of oscillations.

As an example, consider that the sample is of a hydrogenous material, such as mineral oil, and that the oscillator initially is *not* tuned to resonance with the Larmor frequency for protons. The protons will, however, interact with the randomly oriented and continuously changing internal molecular fields which will force them to change magnetic substates, some of them while absorbing the energy $\Delta E = 2\mu_p B$ ($\Delta m_s = -1$) and others, while giving off the same amount ($\Delta m_s = +1$). The equilibrium population of the two states is governed by

Boltzmann's law:

$$N_{-1/2}/N_{+1/2} = e^{-\Delta E/kT} = e^{-2\mu_p B/kT} \approx 1 - 2\mu_p B/kT.$$

For $B = 10{,}000$ gauss and $T = 300°$K, the second term in the expansion above, i.e., the fractional difference in population, is 6.8×10^{-6}. This difference, however minute, is crucial for the operation of the magnetic resonance-absorption apparatus.

Let us assume now that the magnetic field or the oscillator frequency is varied so that it sweeps through the Larmor resonance. At resonance, the RF-field will force protons to change substate, again in both directions, but, because of the population difference, slightly more protons will absorb energy from the field than give up energy. The net effect is a power loss from the electronic circuit, which, as explained above, manifests itself as a modulation of the RF-amplitude. This modulation dip in amplitude can be detected by standard methods of radio circuitry.

In the circuit of Fig. 5–14 the sample is swept through the resonance 120 times per second by a sinusoidal field superimposed on the main field by an alternating current through two small "Helmholtz" coils. The demodulated signal from the RF-oscillator is displayed on a cathode-ray oscilloscope, whose horizontal sweep is in synchronism with the current in the Helmholtz coils. This simple circuit is not ordinarily used for magnetic-moment determinations, but rather as an accurate fluxmeter for homogeneous-field magnets. The frequency for magnetic-resonance absorption by protons is observed, and the induction is then given by Eq. (5–3) as

$$B = h\nu I/\mu_p = \nu/42.577 \text{ Wb/m}^2, \text{ with } \nu \text{ in Mc/sec.}$$

For very accurate measurements of nuclear magnetic dipole moments, more elaborate circuits are used.* An oscilloscope trace of the magnetic resonance from protons in water, taken by Bloembergen *et al.*, is shown in Fig. 5–15. A paramagnetic salt, ferric nitrate, was dissolved in the water to provide sufficient coupling between the proton spins and the carriers of heat motion. This was necessary to avoid saturating the sample by equalizing the substate population through the action of the RF-field.

The magnetic dipole moments of a large number of nuclei have been determined by resonance absorption or induction, by comparing the ratio of their Larmor frequency to that of protons in the same field. One example is the very accurate measurement of the ratio between the deuteron and proton frequencies mentioned in Section 2–2.

---

* See, for instance, N. Bloembergen, E. M. Purcell, and R. V. Pound, *Phys. Rev.* **73**, 679 (1948).

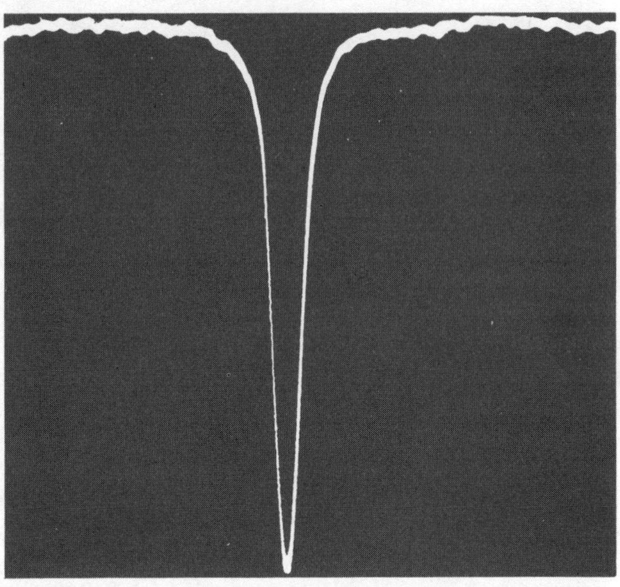

Fig. 5–15. Oscilloscope trace of nuclear magnetic resonance for protons in water. [From Bloembergen *et al.*, *Phys. Rev.* **73,** 679 (1948).]

Since the proton moment is used as a substandard for magnetic dipole moments, it is pertinent to discuss the most accurate determinations of this important quantity. Two experiments yielding results in substantial agreement with each other should be mentioned. In one experiment,* the proton Larmor frequency was compared with the cyclotron frequency for electrons in the same magnetic field. In the other† it was compared with the cyclotron frequency for protons. The cyclotron frequency, that is, the number of revolutions per second of a charged particle in a magnetic field B, is (from Appendix 1, Eq. A1–8):

$$\nu_C = \frac{v}{2\pi\rho} = \frac{eB}{2\pi m} \cdot$$

The ratio of the proton Larmor frequency (5–3) to the cyclotron frequency of either the electron or the proton is therefore

$$\frac{\nu_L}{\nu_C} = \frac{\mu_{\text{p}} m}{\hbar I e} = \frac{\mu_{\text{p}}}{e\hbar/2m}, \tag{5–8}$$

where the mass is the electron mass in one case and the proton mass in the other.

---

* J. H. Gardner, *Phys. Rev.* **83,** 996 (1951).

† J. A. Hipple, H. Sommer, and H. A. Thomas, *Phys. Rev.* **80,** 487 (1950).

Equation (5–8) shows that the frequency ratio measured in one experiment is the proton magnetic dipole moment in Bohr magnetons; in the other experiment, it is obtained in nuclear magnetons. The results of the two experiments mentioned are:

$$\mu_p = 2.79274 \pm 0.00006 \qquad \text{nuclear magnetons,}$$

and

$$\mu_p = (1.52101 \pm 0.00002) \times 10^{-3} \qquad \text{Bohr magneton.}$$

The ratio between these two numbers yields a value for the proton-electron mass ratio $m_p/m_e = 1836.07$, consistent with other measurements.

5–8 Measurement of the Magnetic Moment of the Neutron

In principle, one should be able to use a molecular-beam apparatus for determining the magnetic moment of the neutron. However, in practice, it is impossible to confine a sufficiently high-intensity neutron beam to a cross section small enough to permit observation of the very small deflections in the A- and B-magnets. The solution is to replace these magnets with other means of discriminating between directions of polarization of the neutrons. One possibility is to use the fact that the scattering cross section for slow neutrons in a target of highly saturated ferromagnetic material is larger for neutrons with spin aligned with the magnetic field than for those aligned in the opposite direction.

Figure 5–16 is a sketch of an apparatus used by Bloch *et al.** for determining the magnetic dipole moment of the neutron. Neutrons produced in a beryllium target by cyclotron-accelerated deuterons are thermalized (slowed down) in a block of paraffin, then emerge through a hole in a 9-in. shielding wall and move as a collimated beam through a sequence of three magnets, all with their B-fields directed upward. After passing through a highly saturated piece of iron in the gap of the first magnet, the neutrons in the beam are partly polarized (down) because more spin-up than spin-down neutrons have been scattered out of the beam.

Let us assume first that nothing happens to the neutrons in the second magnet that can change their magnetic substates. In passing through the saturated piece of iron in the gap of the third magnet, some of the neutrons in the beam will be scattered out of it, and clearly the amount of reduction of the beam intensity depends on the magnitude of the polarization previously attained. The relative scattering loss in the third magnet is less than in the first, since more than half of the neutrons in the beam hitting the scatterer have spin down.

In the gap of the second magnet an RF-field is produced with field direction perpendicular to the main field, exactly as in the molecular-beam apparatus.

* F. Bloch, D. Nicodemus, and H. H. Staub, *Phys. Rev.* **74,** 1025 (1948).

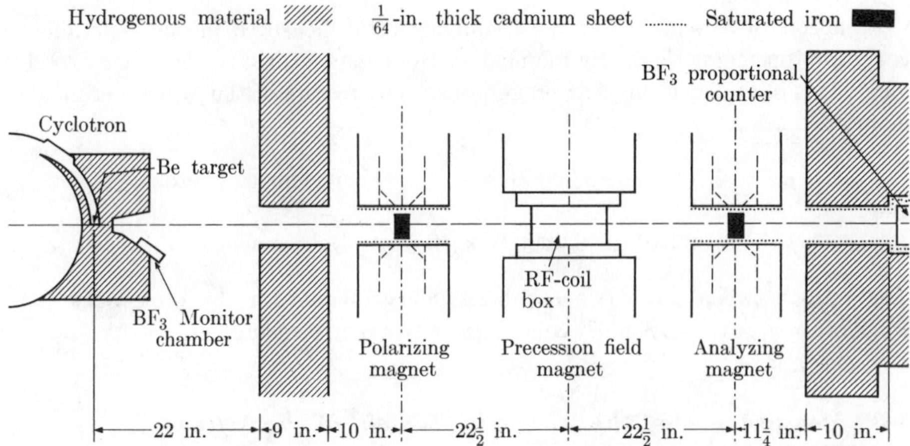

Fig. 5–16. Apparatus used by Bloch *et al.* to observe nuclear magnetic resonance of neutrons. [From Bloch *et al.*, *Phys. Rev.* **74**, 1025 (1948).]

When the RF-field equals the Larmor frequency of the neutrons in this magnet such that the neutron spins can be flipped, the effect is to destroy, partly or fully, the polarization of the beam. The average scattering cross section in the iron scatterer of the third magnet will then be larger, and the result is a reduction in the intensity observed at the counter.

The slow-neutron detector in Fig. 5–16 is a BF_3 gas counter, which is described in Section 7–9. For a constant field in the precession magnet, the frequency ν_n of the RF-field was varied and the following quantity was measured:

$$E_T = \frac{I_{on} - I_{off}}{I_{off} - I_{Cd}}.$$

Here, I_{on} and I_{off} are the counting rates with the RF-field turned on and off, respectively, and I_{Cd} is the background counting rate observed by intercepting the neutron beam with a sheet of cadmium, which is a very effective absorber for slow neutrons. Figure 5–17 shows a typical neutron resonance observed by Bloch *et al.* The reduction in counting rate, E_T (in percent) is plotted vs. the frequency of the RF-field, or rather increment $\Delta\nu_n'$ in the RF-field, as further explained below.

Instead of attempting to measure directly the induction B in the precession magnet and determining μ_n from Eq. (5–3), Bloch *et al.* measured the ratio $|\mu_n|/\mu_p = \nu_n/\nu_p$, where ν_n and ν_p are the Larmor frequencies for the neutron and the proton in the same field. The Larmor frequency for the proton was determined by the induction method, which is essentially the technique discussed in Section 5–7. Furthermore, Bloch *et al.* made use of the fact that the ratio

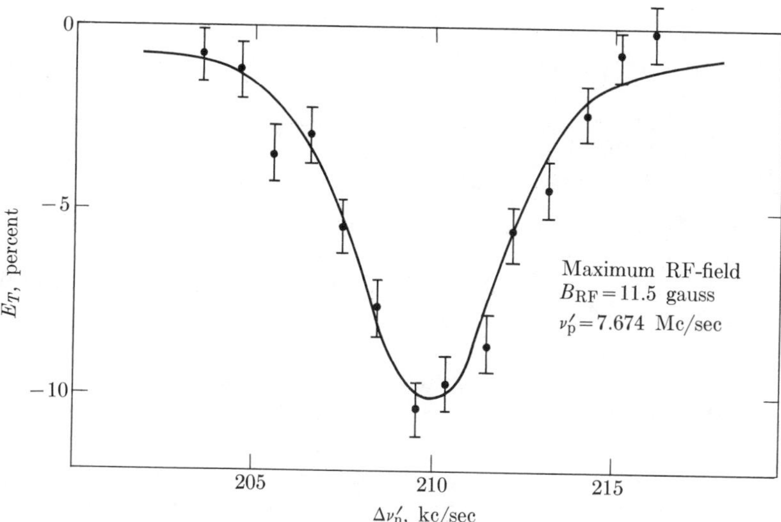

Fig. 5–17. Typical neutron resonance observed by Bloch *et al.* with the apparatus shown in Fig. 5–16. (From Bloch *et al.*, *op. cit.*)

ν_n/ν_p is close to the simple fraction $\frac{2}{3}$. The signal used in the proton resonance apparatus was the sixth harmonic of a master oscillator of frequency $\nu'_p = \nu_p/6$. Similarly, the frequency of another master oscillator was $\nu'_n = \nu_n/4$. The difference $\Delta\nu'_n = \nu'_n - \nu'_p$ between the two master oscillators was measured very accurately, and this difference is the variable used in Fig. 5–17. With ν'_n and ν'_p being the frequency values at resonance, we have

$$\frac{|\mu_n|}{\mu_p} = \frac{\nu_n}{\nu_p} = \frac{4\nu'_n}{6\nu'_p} = \frac{2}{3}\left(1 + \frac{\Delta\nu'_n}{\nu'_p}\right).$$

For the resonance curve in Fig. 5–17, we have $\nu'_p = 7.674$ Mc/sec and $\Delta\nu'_n = 210.5$ kc/sec at resonance. From this we get

$$\frac{|\mu_n|}{\mu_p} = \frac{2}{3}\left(1 + \frac{0.2105}{7.674}\right) = 0.6850.$$

The ratio quoted by Bloch *et al.* as the average of a number of determinations is

$$\frac{|\mu_n|}{\mu_p} = 0.685001 \pm 0.000030.$$

Combined with the results quoted at the end of Section 5–7, this yields

$$|\mu_n| = 1.91303 \text{ nm}.$$

5–9 Results of Measurements of Nuclear Moments

All experimental methods discussed in this chapter deal with the measurement of one or more of the quantities I, μ, and Q for the ground state of stable or long-lived nuclei. Other experimental methods exist for measuring these quantities in excited states or in ground states of short-lived nuclei. In particular, the determination of angular momentum (and also parity) of short-lived states is made by use of selection rules in disintegration processes (Chapters 9 through 11) and nuclear reactions (Chapter 13). The magnetic moment has also been measured for a few excited states by use of nuclear-reaction techniques, but these measurements are quite intricate and will not be discussed further in this book.

Excellent compilations of published results of nuclear-moment measurements have appeared from time to time in the literature,* and also in *Nuclear Data Sheets*.† These compilations are the most important sources of data for the theoretical physicist who wants to test his ideas about nuclear structure. For instance, as will be shown in Chapter 6, the compilation of I-values for the ground states of odd-A nuclei represents the most convincing test for the nuclear shell model to be discussed in that chapter. These angular momenta, when plotted vs. Z, N, or A, do not show any simple obvious trend but they do fit extremely well into the picture presented by the nuclear shell model. Incidentally, the observation made in Section 1–5 that odd-A nuclei have half-integral I, and even-A nuclei have integral I is substantiated by experiment. It is also observed that even-Z–even-N nuclei have $I = 0$ in the ground state, a fact that will be further commented on in Chapter 6. In Section 6–6, we also discuss the predictions for the magnetic moments of nuclear ground states based on the shell model. The agreement is no longer very good, and the observed values of the magnetic moments are used to test more refined nuclear models.

The quadrupole moments of nuclear ground states do exhibit a definite trend when plotted against A, Z, or N. Figure 5–18 shows Q/ZR^2 for odd-A nuclei, plotted against Z or N, whichever is the odd number. Here Q is the observed quadrupole moment referred to a space-fixed axis, and is, according to the discussion in Section 1–8, smaller than the intrinsic quadrupole moment referred to the nuclear symmetry axis. Neglecting this difference for the moment, we see from Eq. (1–16) that what is plotted in Fig. 5–18 is essentially $\Delta R/R$.

The quadrupole moment falls sharply through zero for certain values of the nucleon number. These are the "magic" numbers encountered at the end of Section 4–7 and further discussed in Chapter 6.

---

* For example, D. Stromiger, J. M. Hollander, and G. T. Seaborg, *Rev. Mod. Phys.* **30**, 585 (1958).

† National Research Council–National Academy of Sciences, *Nuclear Data Sheets*, Oak Ridge National Laboratory, Oak Ridge, Tennessee.

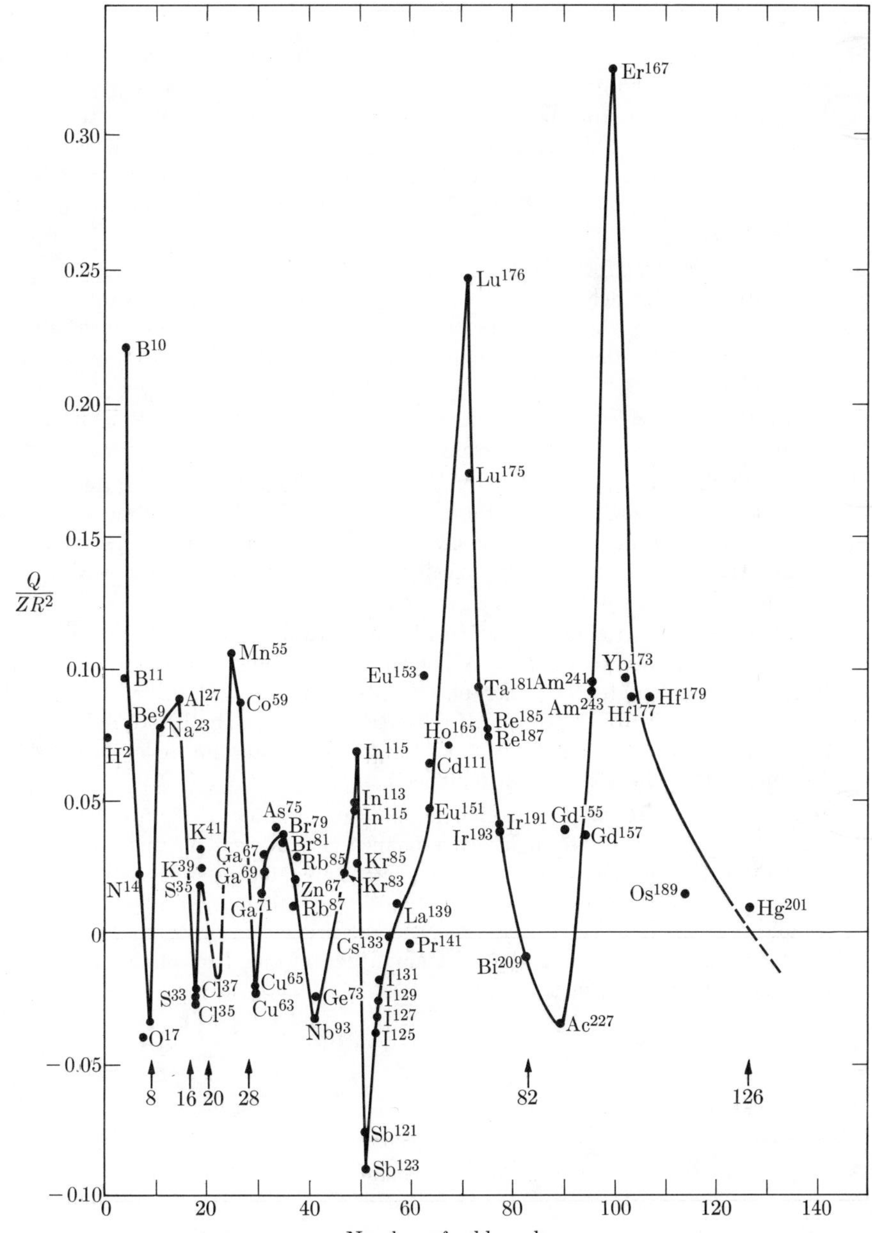

Fig. 5–18. Quadrupole distortion Q/ZR^2 ($\approx \Delta R/R$) for odd-A nuclei plotted vs. the odd nucleon number Z or N. (From E. Segrè, *Nuclei and Particles*, New York: W. A. Benjamin, Inc., 1964. Reproduced by permission.)

PROBLEMS

5–1. Calculate the wavelength for the hyperfine transition in atomic deuterium in its electronic ground state.

5–2. A quadrupole consisting of two plus charges (+e) at positions $z_1 = 5$ F and $z_2 = -5$ F interacts electrostatically with another unit charge which is situated at $z = 1$ angstrom. Calculate the change in electrostatic energy (eV) when the quadrupole is rotated by 90° about the x-axis (a) by using basic principles; (b) by using Eqs. (1–13) and (1–14).

5–3. Using the classical formula for rotational energy $E = p_\phi^2/2m$ (p_ϕ = angular momentum), write Schrödinger's equation for a rigid body free to rotate about its center of mass. Show that the eigenvalues for energy are given by Eq. (5–7) with $K = 0$ and that the eigenfunctions are spherical harmonic functions (Appendix 1).

5–4. Given that the $I^{127}Cl^{35}$ molecule has a rotational transition $J = 3 \rightarrow 4$ at 27,200 Mc/sec, calculate the internuclear distance in this molecule.

5–5. Calculate the angular deflection of a hydrogen molecule in the state $m_S = 1$ and $m_J = 0$, passing through the A-magnet of a molecular-beam apparatus. Assume that the field gradient is $dB/dz = 100$ Wb/m^3, that the length of the magnet is $L = 1$ m, and that the velocity of the molecule is given by $\frac{1}{2}mv^2 = \frac{3}{2}kT$ (thermal) with $T = 300$°K.

5–6. The order of magnitude of the effect of the quadrupole interaction in Fig. 5–13 is given by $\Delta E/h\nu = \Delta B/B \approx 5$ percent with $\nu = 1.3$ Mc/sec. From this information, calculate the order of magnitude of ΔE and, using Eq. (1–13), calculate the order of magnitude of $\partial^2 U/\partial z^2$. Is the value of $\partial^2 U/\partial z^2$ obtained reasonable when the average value of r^{-3} for the deuterium molecule is 2.44×10^{30} m^{-3}? (r is the internuclear distance.)

5–7. One cubic millimeter of mineral oil contains approximately 10^{20} protons. Assume that in a single sweep through the resonance of a nuclear magnetic absorption apparatus, the populations of the magnetic substates $m_s = 1$ and $m_s = -1$ are equalized (see Section 5–7). Calculate the total energy absorbed by the sample at 40 Mc/sec and compare this with the circulating energy in the electronic resonance circuit, assuming that the amplitude of the RF-voltage is 2 V and that the tuning capacitor is 50 $\mu\mu$f.

6 Nuclear Models

6–1 Review of the Atomic Shell Model and Predicted Ground-State Angular Momenta

Schrödinger's equation can be solved exactly for the atomic two-body problem in which the interaction is given by the electrostatic potential between two point charges. The hydrogen atom is such a two-body system and so is any hydrogenlike atom, that is, an ion with nuclear charge Ze but with only one electron. Figure 6–1(a) gives the energy-level diagram for a hydrogenlike atom, without the perturbations caused by the electron spin. The energy levels are degenerate, which means that in the simple theory, the S-, P-, and D-states have the same energy so long as the principal quantum number n is the same. With the inclusion of the electron spin, the relativistic effects, etc., this is no longer true. In particular, we get the so-called fine-structure splitting of the

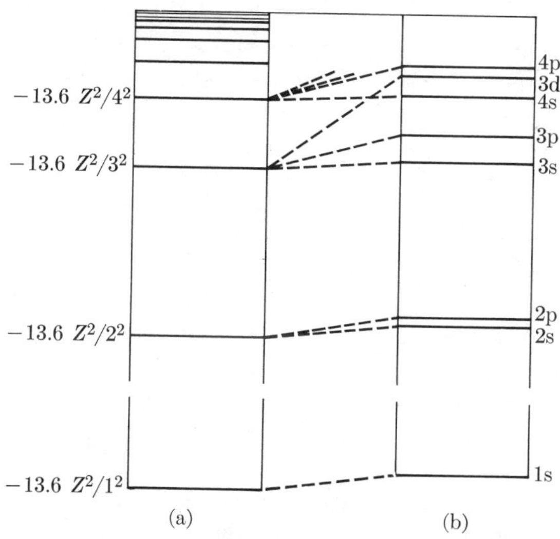

Fig. 6–1. Atomic levels in (a) hydrogenlike atom and (b) many-electron atom.

states because of the magnetic coupling between the spins and the orbital angular momenta.

In a many-electron atom, each individual electron is no longer moving in the field from the nucleus alone, and, for this reason, the mathematics of the wave-mechanical theory becomes extremely complex. The method that is usually employed in computing the energy-level diagram for complex atoms is Hartree's method of the self-consistent field. A given electron moves in the field of the nucleus, which is practically stationary, and in the rapidly changing field of the other electrons. The latter can be approximated with an average spherically symmetric field distribution, the shape of which can be guessed, and Schrödinger's equation can then be solved numerically for each individual electron. The time average of the charge density can be computed from these one-electron wave functions. From the charge distribution, one can compute the potential, and, if the potential does not agree with the potential originally assumed, one starts over again until a self-consistent result evolves. Figure 6–2 shows a typical charge density (probability density) plot for a medium-weight

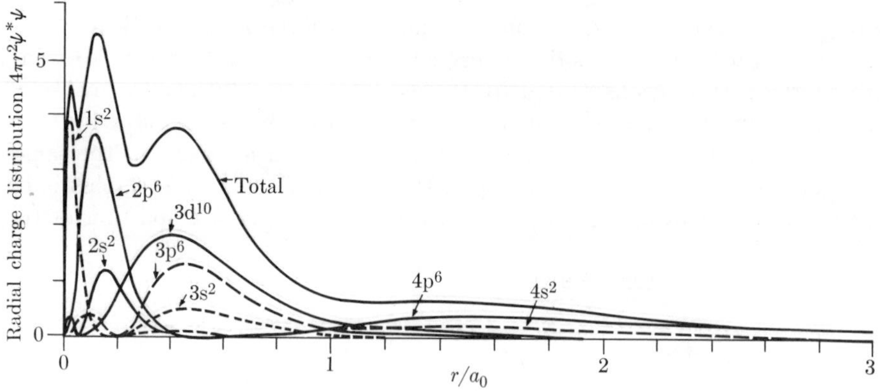

Fig. 6–2. Radial charge distribution of other electrons seen by the last electron in Rb. The unit for r is $a_0 = 0.529$ angstrom. (From R. B. Leighton, *Principles of Modern Physics*, New York: McGraw-Hill Book Co., 1959. Reproduced by permission.)

Calculations of the kind discussed above, as well as experiments, indicate that the levels, which are degenerate in the hydrogenlike atoms, in the many-electron atom split in the fashion shown in Fig. 6–1(b). In general, the higher orbital angular-momentum states will be lifted highest because the electron in such a state spends most of its time far away from the nucleus. The "screening" of the nuclear charge caused by the other electrons is then most pronounced. The exact location and, to some extent, the relative position of the various levels in the energy-level diagram change with the number of electrons. For the most part, however, the level sequence is as follows:

$(1s)^2$		$(2s)^2(2p)^6$		$(3s)^2(3p)^6$		$(4s)^2(3d)^{10}(4p)^6$		$(5s)^2 \ldots$
	He		Ne		Ar		Kr	
K-shell		L-shell		M-shell		N-shell		

The inertness of the noble-gas atoms can be explained from the following two observations: (1) the binding energy of the last electron is large, therefore the atom does not easily give up one electron; and (2) other atoms will readily accept an extra electron to form a relatively tightly bound negative ion, but because of the large level spacing between shells, the negative noble-gas ions are very weakly bound, if bound at all. These two facts imply that noble-gas atoms very reluctantly share electrons with other atoms to form neutral molecules. Figure 6–3 shows the binding energy of the last electron (the ionization potential) as a function of atomic number Z. The fluctuations in the ionization potential reflect the fluctuations in the level separations of Fig. 6–1(b). It should be remembered, however, that the nuclear charge increases with the element number and that the vertical scale of the energy-level diagram, Fig. 6–1(b), changes drastically with increasing Z.

An atom in its ground state will always have all its electrons in the lowest possible shell. In any subshell (for example, 2p), the orbital angular momenta and spins of all electrons will cancel. The total angular momentum for the

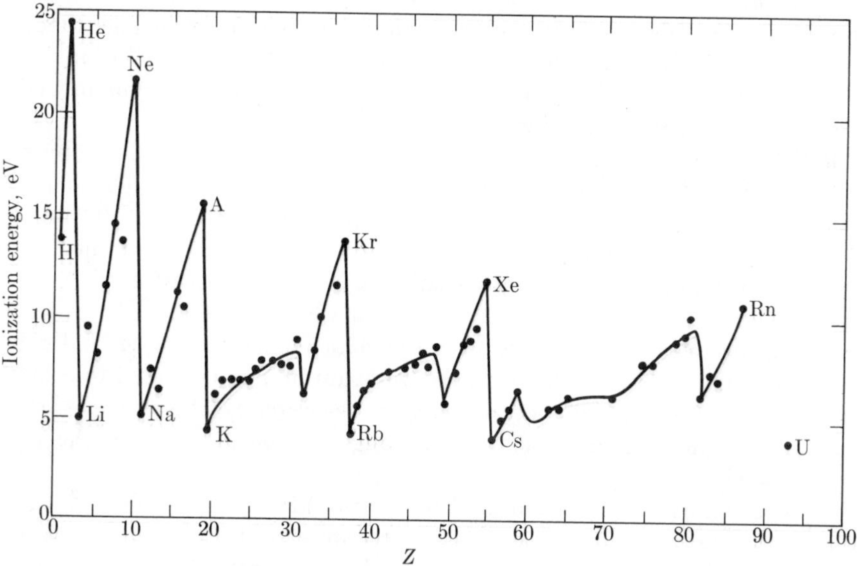

Fig. 6–3. Ionization energies. (From R. M. Eisberg, *Fundamentals of Modern Physics*, New York: John Wiley and Sons, 1961, p. 413. Reproduced by permission.)

ground state of an atom in which a subshell is completely filled is therefore equal to zero. If the last subshell is only partly filled, then there are certain rules that describe how these last electrons combine their spins and orbital angular momenta in the lowest state, the *ground state*. These rules, which are empirical but theoretically understood, are given below.

In the light elements, the coupling (or indirect interaction) between the spins of all the electrons in the last subshell is stronger than the coupling between the spin and orbital angular momentum of each individual electron. The result is that the spins combine to a total spin quantum number S, and the orbital angular momenta combine to a total orbital angular-momentum quantum number L, and, finally, the quantum numbers L and S combine to a total angular momentum J. This is known as L-S coupling. The Pauli principle excludes certain combinations of L and S. Subject to this restriction, we find the following rules for the total angular momentum of the ground state of an atom with a partly filled last subshell.

(1) Hund's rule, which predicts that the lowest level (i.e., the ground state) will have the maximum possible value of S that can be obtained by combining the spins of all electrons in the partly filled subshell. The reason for this is that the maximum value of S will give a maximum symmetry of the spin function and therefore a maximum antisymmetry in the space part of the wave function. This gives a minimum effect from the repulsive (positive) potential acting between the electrons because, on the average, they stay farther apart.

(2) If there are several possible values of L that can be combined with the same maximum value of S without violating the exclusion principle, then the ground state will have the highest of these values of L. The reason for this is, again, that the "residual" electrostatic interaction will be a minimum in this case (minimum overlap of the wave functions).

(3) With L and S given and both different from zero, one still can make a number of combinations for the final angular momentum J. The magnetic coupling between L and S (fine-structure splitting) results in a total angular momentum J for the ground state equal to $J = |L - S|$ if the subshell is less than half filled and $J = L + S$ if the subshell is more than half filled.

For heavier elements, the situation is somewhat reversed. The magnetic interaction between the spin and orbital angular momentum of the individual electron is sufficiently strong that these two quantum numbers tend to combine to a total angular momentum for the individual electron, j. The j's of an electron in a subshell will then combine to a total angular momentum J for the atom. This is known as j-j coupling.

In L-S coupling, the notation used to describe the energy levels is ${}^{(2S+1)}L_J$; for example, ${}^3\mathrm{D}_3$, ${}^1\mathrm{S}_0$, ${}^4\mathrm{P}_{3/2}$, etc. The superscript gives the S-value (or $2S + 1$, actually), the body gives the L-value, and these two can combine to as many J-values as the superscript denotes, except when $S > L$, in which case the number of states is $2L + 1$. For instance, the quadruplet D-state has four members, ${}^4\mathrm{D}_{1/2}$, ${}^4\mathrm{D}_{3/2}$, ${}^4\mathrm{D}_{5/2}$, and ${}^4\mathrm{D}_{7/2}$, but the "quadruplet" P-state really has only three members: ${}^4P_{1/2}$, ${}^4P_{3/2}$, and ${}^4P_{5/2}$. Note that atoms with even numbers of electrons have integral values of S and therefore form only singlets and triplets, etc., whereas atoms with odd numbers of electrons have half-integral values of S and therefore form doublets, quadruplets, etc.

6–2 *Single-Particle Model of the Nucleus*

The shell model of the atom, as described in the previous section, essentially pictures the electrons as moving in practically independent orbits in an average field of the nucleus and the other electrons. The gross level scheme computed on the basis of this picture is modified by the perturbations caused by the electron spin and accompanying magnetic moment. Since the early days of nuclear physics several workers have tried the same approach in attempting to find a model for the nucleus. However, these attempts were not very successful before 1949 when, independently, M. G. Mayer* and Haxel, Jensen, and Suess† postulated a strong coupling between the spin and orbital angular momentum of each nucleon. This produced qualitative agreement between theory and certain experimental observations, discussed in Section 6–3.

The question of whether a nucleon in the nucleus has a sufficiently long mean free path so that one is justified in assuming a fairly independent motion, will be postponed. Here, we will assume that this is the case and that the interaction between the nucleon that is being studied and all the other nucleons can be represented by a spherically symmetric potential, for simplicity, a square well. We will, here, first treat the manageable problem of calculating the position of the various energy levels in an infinitely deep square well of radius r_0, realizing, of course, that the nuclear well actually has a finite depth. For simplicity, assume that the potential is zero inside the well and infinite outside. The solution of the one-particle Schrödinger equation in a spherically symmetric potential is, in general,

$$\psi = R_l(r) Y_{l,m}(\theta, \phi), \tag{6–1}$$

where the radial wave function‡ $R_l(r)$ is a solution of

$$\frac{1}{r^2}\frac{d}{dr}\left(r^2\frac{dR_l}{dr}\right) + \frac{2m}{\hbar^2}\left[E - \frac{l(l+1)\hbar^2}{2mr^2}\right] R_l = 0. \tag{6–2}$$

Here, E is the part of the total energy which is due to the motion of the nucleon studied and m is the reduced mass, which, in a heavy nucleus, is practically equal to the nucleon mass. We require that the wave function be finite for all

* M. G. Mayer, *Phys. Rev.* **75,** 1969 (1949).
† O. Haxel, J. H. Jensen, and H. E. Suess, *Phys. Rev.* **75,** 1766 (1949).
‡ In Chapters 1 and 2, we wrote $R_l(r) = u_l/r$. Here it is more convenient to use $R_l(r)$ rather than $u_l(r)$.

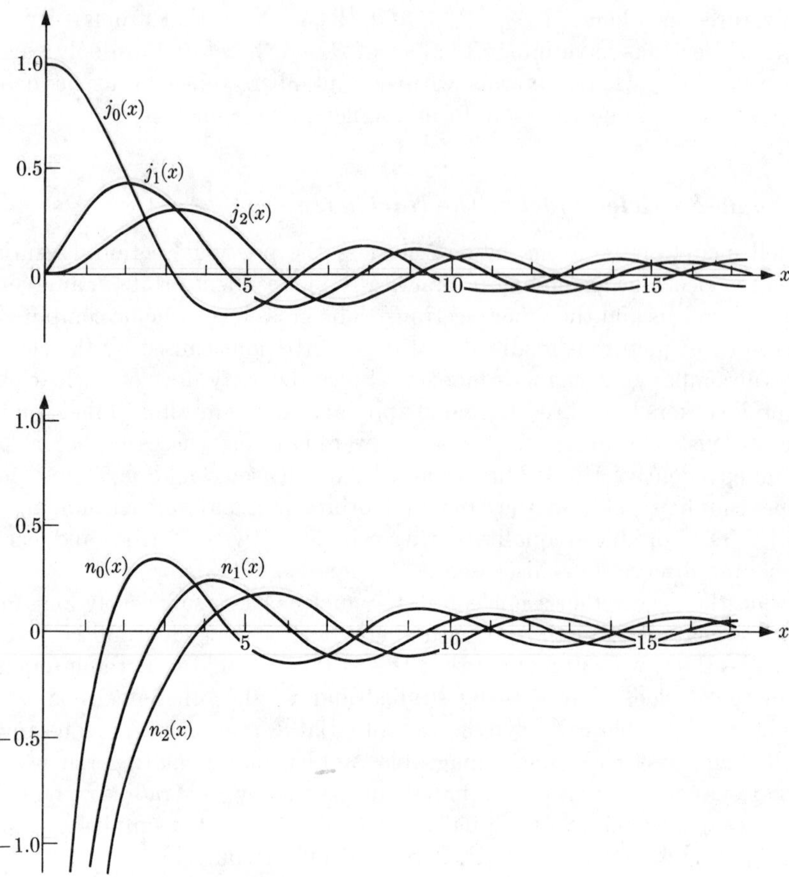

Fig. 6–4. Spherical Bessel and Neumann functions for $l = 0, 1, 2$. (From R. H. Dicke and J. P. Wittke, *Introduction to Quantum Mechanics*, Reading, Mass.: Addison-Wesley, 1960.)

values of r. The solutions of Eq. (6–2) that satisfy this requirement are the spherical Bessel functions

$$R_l(r) = j_l(kr) = \left(-\frac{r}{k}\right)^l \left(\frac{1}{r}\frac{d}{dr}\right)^l \left(\frac{\sin kr}{kr}\right), \tag{6–3}$$

where

$$k = \frac{1}{\hbar}\sqrt{2mE}. \tag{6–4}$$

The three lowest-order spherical Bessel functions ($l = 0$ to 2) are plotted in Fig. 6–4. Also shown are spherical Neumann functions $n_l(kr)$ which have the same mathematical form as $j_l(kr)$ except that $-\cos kr$ is substituted for $\sin kr$ in Eq. (6–3). The Neumann functions satisfy Eq. (6–2) but are irregular at $r = 0$.

For our particular problem there is an additional boundary condition, namely, that the wave function (6–1) should be zero for all values of θ and ϕ at $r = r_0$. We call any value of the argument kr that makes a spherical Bessel function equal to zero a "zero" for the function and denote it by η. Each l-value has a set of zeros, and to each of them corresponds, for our particular problem, a value of k, given by $kr_0 = \eta$. From Eq. (6–4), we then get for the energy of a given level, described by a radial wave function terminating at the zero η,

$$E = \frac{\hbar^2 k^2}{2m} = \frac{\hbar^2 \eta^2}{2mr_0^2}. \tag{6–5}$$

The zeros η can be taken from Fig. 6–4 or they can be found in a table of functions. Table 6–1 gives the squares of the zeros or, according to Eq. (6–5), the energy levels of the infinite square well in units of $\hbar^2/2mr_0^2$.

Table 6–1. Energy levels in infinite square well

State	1s	1p	1d	2s	1f	2p	1g	2d
η^2	9.87	20.14	33.21	39.48	48.83	59.68	66.96	82.72
State	1h	3s	2f	1i	3p	1j	2g	
η^2	87.53	88.83	108.51	110.52	118.90	135.86	137.01	

The notation for nuclear levels is the same as for atomic levels, except for the principal quantum number. To discern between, for instance, the d-states, we label them 1d, 2d, 3d, etc., and 1d simply means the first d-level. The letters s, p, d, f, g, and so forth, stand for levels with orbital angular-momentum quantum number $l = 0, 1, 2, 3$, and 4, respectively, just as in atomic physics. Each shell-model level, for instance 2d, actually consists of $2l + 1$ substates, each with a different angular wave function $Y_{l,m}(\theta, \phi)$. Because of the two different possible orientations of the nucleon spin, a level can accommodate $2(2l + 1)$ protons. In addition, it can accommodate $2(2l + 1)$ neutrons, since the two particles are different and they do not therefore mutually exclude each other.

Figure 6–5 shows in the second column the relative positions of the energy levels of the infinite square well. The first column shows the levels of a harmonic-oscillator well adjusted to match the 1s- and 4s-levels with those of the square well. The drawing is only schematic.

The infinite square-well potential as a model for the nucleus is, of course, unrealistic, and a much more realistic potential is a well with finite depth V_0. The depth and also the radius r_0 can be determined for a given nucleus by imposing the requirement that the well produce a theoretical nucleus which has the observed radius and total binding energy. The calculation proceeds as above, except that the wave function does not go to zero at r_0 but penetrates into the region with negative kinetic energy. In this region, that is, for $r > r_0$,

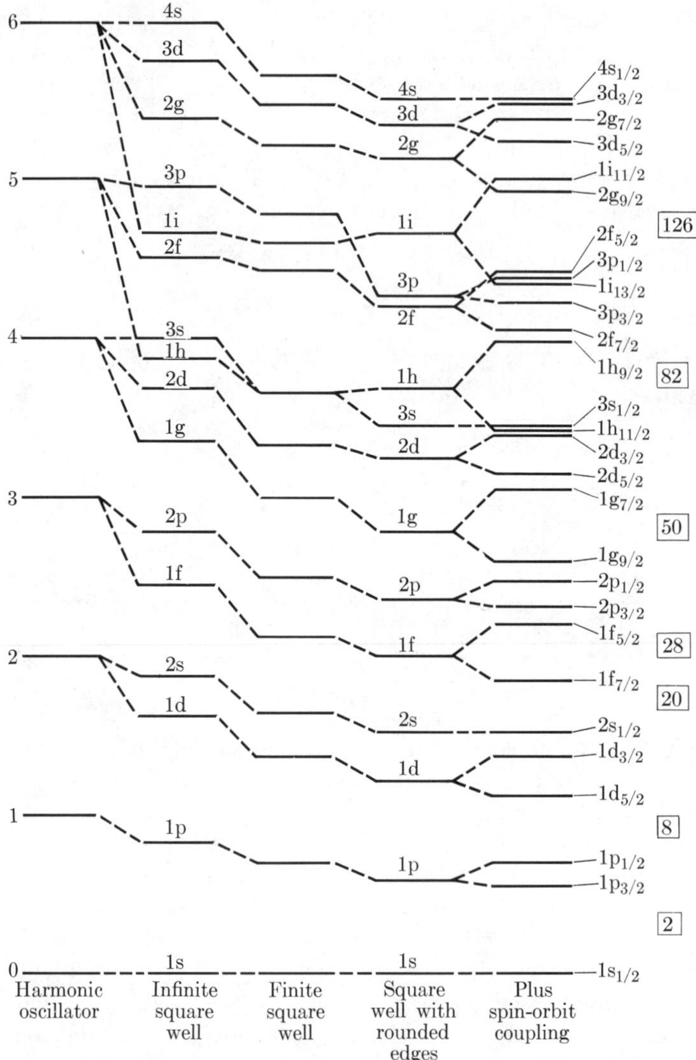

Fig. 6–5. Order of energy levels according to the independent-particle model with various assumptions for the shape of the nuclear potential. [From B. T. Feld, *Ann. Rev. Nucl. Sci.* **2,** 249 (1953). Reproduced by permission.]

the radial wave function is a solution of Eq. (6–2) with negative energy E. The solutions that satisfy boundary conditions at $r \to \infty$ are spherical Hankel functions

$$h_l(kr) = j_l(kr) + in_0(kr),$$

with complex argument

$$k = i\kappa = (2mE)^{1/2}/\hbar; \qquad \text{that is,} \qquad \kappa = (-2mE)^{1/2}/\hbar.$$

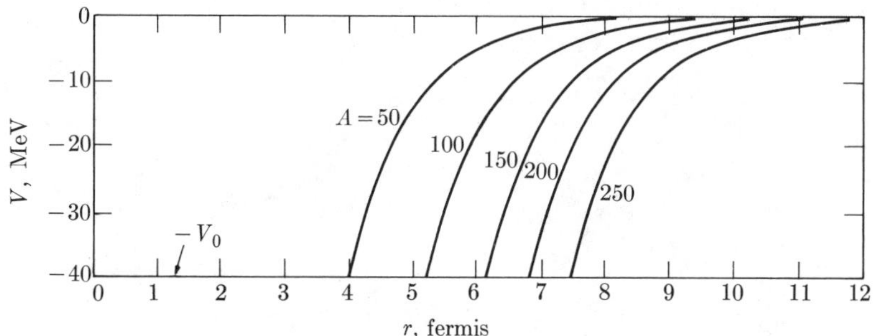

Fig. 6–6. Potentials used by Green in calculations of single-particle states in nuclei. [From A. E. S. Green, *Phys. Rev.* **102,** 1325 (1956).]

The first few of these functions are:

$$h_0(i\kappa r) = -\frac{1}{\kappa r}\, e^{-\kappa r}, \qquad \text{for } l = 0;$$

$$h_1(i\kappa r) = i\left(\frac{1}{\kappa r} + \frac{1}{(\kappa r)^2}\right) e^{-\kappa r}, \qquad \text{for } l = 1;$$

$$h_2(i\kappa r) = \left(\frac{1}{\kappa r} + \frac{3}{(\kappa r)^2} + \frac{3}{(\kappa r)^3}\right) e^{-\kappa r}, \qquad \text{for } l = 2;$$

$$h_3(i\kappa r) = -i\left(\frac{1}{\kappa r} + \frac{1}{(\kappa r)^2} + \frac{15}{(\kappa r)^3} + \frac{15}{(\kappa r)^4}\right) e^{-\kappa r}, \qquad \text{for } l = 3;$$

$$h_4(i\kappa r) = -\left(\frac{1}{\kappa r} + \frac{10}{(\kappa r)^2} + \frac{45}{(\kappa r)^3} + \frac{105}{(\kappa r)^4} + \frac{105}{(\kappa r)^5}\right) e^{-\kappa r}, \qquad \text{for } l = 4. \tag{6–6}$$

The solutions outside and inside the well have to be matched at the boundary $r = r_0$. If V_0 and r_0 are given, the matching equation can be used to determine the energy E. The results of these calculations are that the levels are depressed slightly as compared with the levels for the infinite square well. This is shown, again only schematically, in Fig. 6–5 (finite square well).

Finally, the square well does not give a self-consistent image of the nucleus. The particle density in the nucleus, as computed from the wave functions discussed above, will be approximately constant in the central region but will taper off toward and through the boundary. This has also been experimentally observed (Fig. 1–3). Clearly, since the potential is produced by the interaction between the particles, the potential must also taper off in similar fashion. Calculations on tapered wells have been performed by A. E. S. Green,* among others. Figure 6–6 shows the potential used in Green's calculations. The well has a constant attractive potential $V_0 = 40$ MeV out to a radius of

$$a = 1.32A^{1/3} - 0.8 \text{ F}. \tag{6–7}$$

For larger radii, it tapers off exponentially.

* A. E. S. Green, *Phys. Rev.* **102,** 1325 (1956).

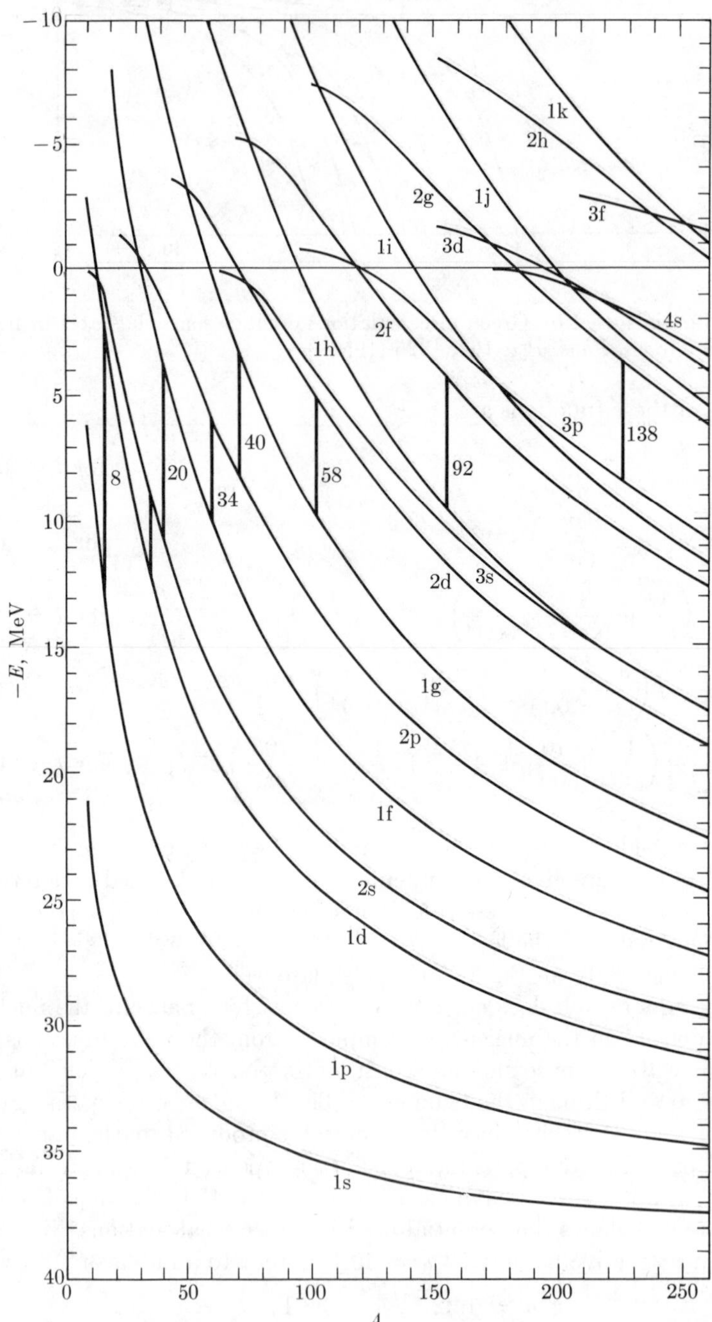

Fig. 6–7. Neutron energy eigenvalues vs. nuclear number A. (From Green, *op. cit.*)

The results of Green's calculations are shown in Fig. 6-7. Since the energy of a given state decreases rapidly with the radius of the well (compare Eq. 6-5), it decreases with A, and therefore more and more states become bound states. Figure 6-7 applies to neutrons. A similar diagram can be plotted for protons; the only difference is that the Coulomb repulsion has to be taken into account. This gives rise to some raising of the levels, especially for large values of A. Qualitatively, however, the picture is the same as for neutrons.

Each level in Fig. 6-7 can accommodate $2(2l + 1)$ neutrons. In general, therefore, as a given state fills with neutrons, the binding energy of the last neutron will increase as we follow the curve down for increasing A. When the state is filled and the next neutron has to go into the next higher state, there will be a jump in binding energy. According to the diagram, we might expect particularly large jumps after the filling of the 1s-, 1p-, 2s-, 1f-, 2p-, 1g-, 1h-, and the 3p-levels. The numbers of neutrons that can be accommodated up to and including these states are 2, 8, 20, 34, 40, 58, 92, and 138. According to our model, these numbers of neutrons or protons should play essentially the same role in nuclear physics as the element numbers for the noble gases in atomic physics. As we shall see in the next section, this prediction does not quite agree with experiments, but with some modification (i.e., the introduction of an *ad hoc* spin-orbit coupling), it can be made to agree.

6-3 Magic Numbers; Spin-Orbit Coupling

To test whether the predictions of Fig. 6-7 are borne out in practice, we could plot the separation energy (binding energy) of the last neutron as a function of neutron number N. Such a plot should then show characteristic jumps similar to the jumps at the positions of the noble gases in Fig. 6-3. In nuclear physics, however, the situation is complicated by the fact that we also have another variable, the proton number Z, and a closed-shell effect should show up both for certain values of the neutron number N, as well as for the proton number Z. In Fig. 6-8, taken from a paper by Yamada and Matumoto,* the neutron-separation energy is plotted as a function of A (even) and N. Relatively large jumps are seen to occur at $N = 28$, 50, 82, and 126. Similar jumps are present in a graph of the proton separation energies at $Z = 28$, 50, and 82. Less evident on these graphs, but still significant, is the tight binding of nuclei with Z or $N = 2$, 8, or 20, and in particular nuclei with Z and N both equal to 2, 8, or 20. Closed-shell effects, similar to but not so pronounced as for the noble gases in atomic physics, therefore, occur at nucleon numbers Z or $N = 2$, 8, 20, 28, 50, 82, and 126. The first three of these numbers agree with those given in the previous section, but the rest of the numbers do not. For some time in the late 1940's after the experimental facts had been established, this disagreement presented an unsolved puzzle, and the numbers were called "magic numbers."

* M. Yamada and Z. Matumoto, *J. Phys. Soc. Japan* **16,** 1497 (1961).

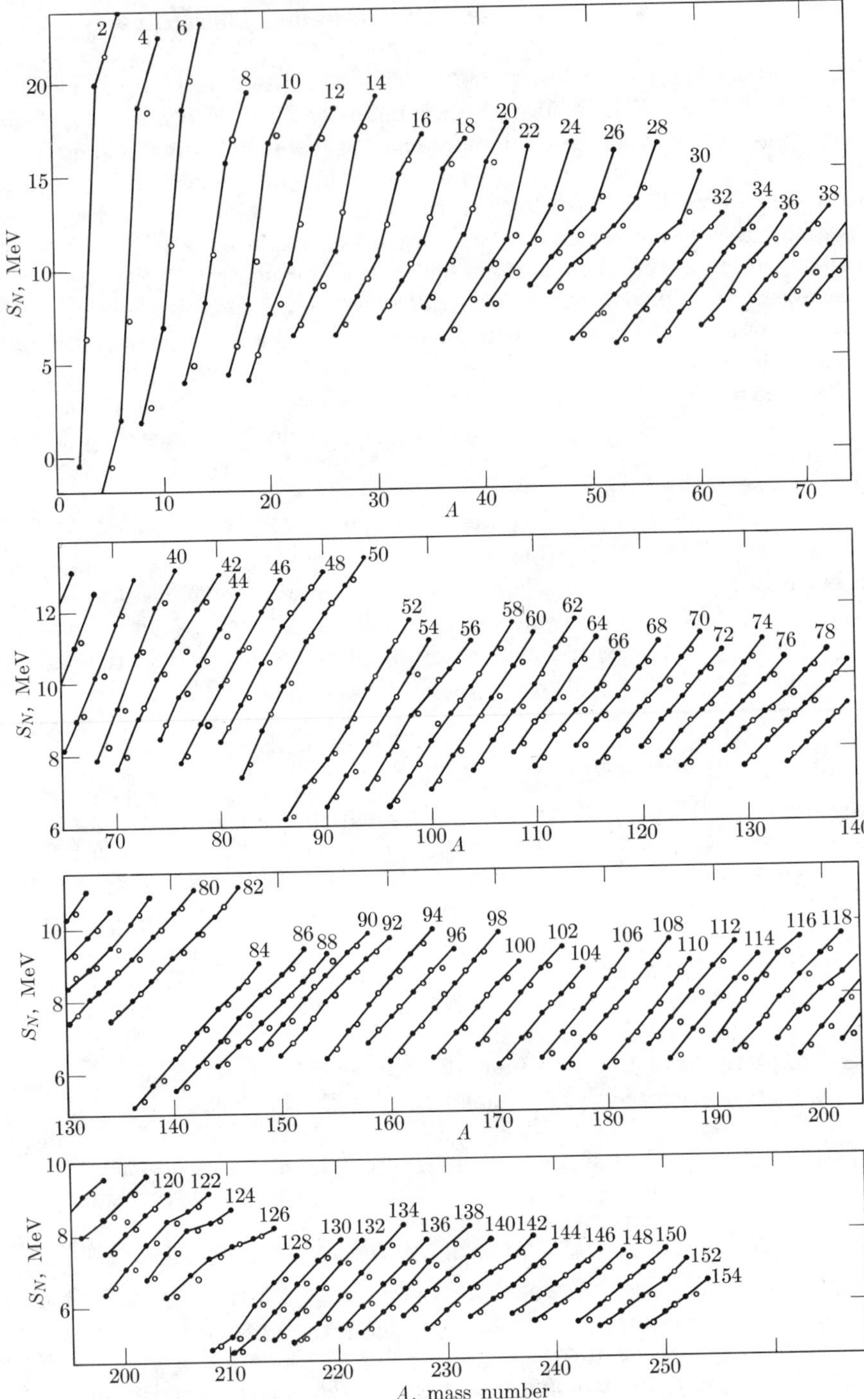

Figure 6–8

Other experimental evidence directly related to the large binding energy of magic-number nuclei was mentioned in Section 4–7. This evidence was the fact that elements with magic Z have unusually large numbers of stable isotopes, and that unusually large numbers of stable isotones are found when N is magic. In Section 5–9 it was pointed out that measured quadrupole moments for odd nuclei are small when the number of odd nucleons is near magic. This indicates that nuclei with magic N and/or magic Z are spherical or nearly spherical.

The experimental evidence thus indicates that the energy-level diagram of Fig. 6–7 is not correct. As mentioned earlier, a phenomenological explanation for the observed discrepancy was found independently by M. G. Mayer and O. Haxel *et al.*

These authors assumed that, for some hitherto unexplained reason, there is a strong coupling between the spin and orbital angular momentum of each individual nucleon. This interaction is assumed to have the form

$$V_{SL} = f(r)(\mathbf{s} \cdot \mathbf{l}), \tag{6–8}$$

where $\mathbf{s}$ and $\mathbf{l}$ denote the spin and orbital angular-momentum vectors, respectively, and $f(r)$ is a potential function (for instance, a square well). The squares of the numerical values of $\mathbf{s}$ and $\mathbf{l}$ are $s(s+1)$ and $l(l+1)$. Because of the strong coupling, the two vectors combine to a total angular momentum $\mathbf{j}$ for the particle. The cosine rule applies to the triangle formed by the vectors $\mathbf{s}$, $\mathbf{l}$, and $\mathbf{j}$, as follows:

$$j(j+1) = l(l+1) + s(s+1) + 2\mathbf{s} \cdot \mathbf{l}.$$

From this, we can find the product $\mathbf{s} \cdot \mathbf{l}$. Since $s = \frac{1}{2}$, there are only two possible ways of combining s and l, resulting in the "stretch" case $j = l + s$ and the "jackknife" case $j = l - s$. By inserting these values for j and $s = \frac{1}{2}$, we get

$$(\mathbf{s} \cdot \mathbf{l})_{\text{str}} = \tfrac{1}{2}[(l + \tfrac{3}{2})(l + \tfrac{1}{2}) - l(l+1) - \tfrac{3}{4}] = \tfrac{1}{2}l,$$

$$(\mathbf{s} \cdot \mathbf{l})_{\text{jkn}} = \tfrac{1}{2}[(l + \tfrac{1}{2})(l - \tfrac{1}{2}) - l(l+1) - \tfrac{3}{4}] = -\tfrac{1}{2}(l+1) \quad (\text{not for } l = 0).$$

These expressions can be inserted into Eq. (6–8). We are primarily interested in the difference between the potential energy for the stretch case and that for the jackknife case. This difference is

$$\Delta V_{SL} = \tfrac{1}{2}f(r)(2l+1). \tag{6–9}$$

Fig. 6–8. Neutron separation energies $S_N(A)$ for even N-values. The filled circles represent nuclei with even Z and the open circles represent nuclei with odd Z. The number beside each line is the N-value. [From Yamada and Matumoto, *J. Phys. Soc. Japan* **16,** 1497 (1961).]

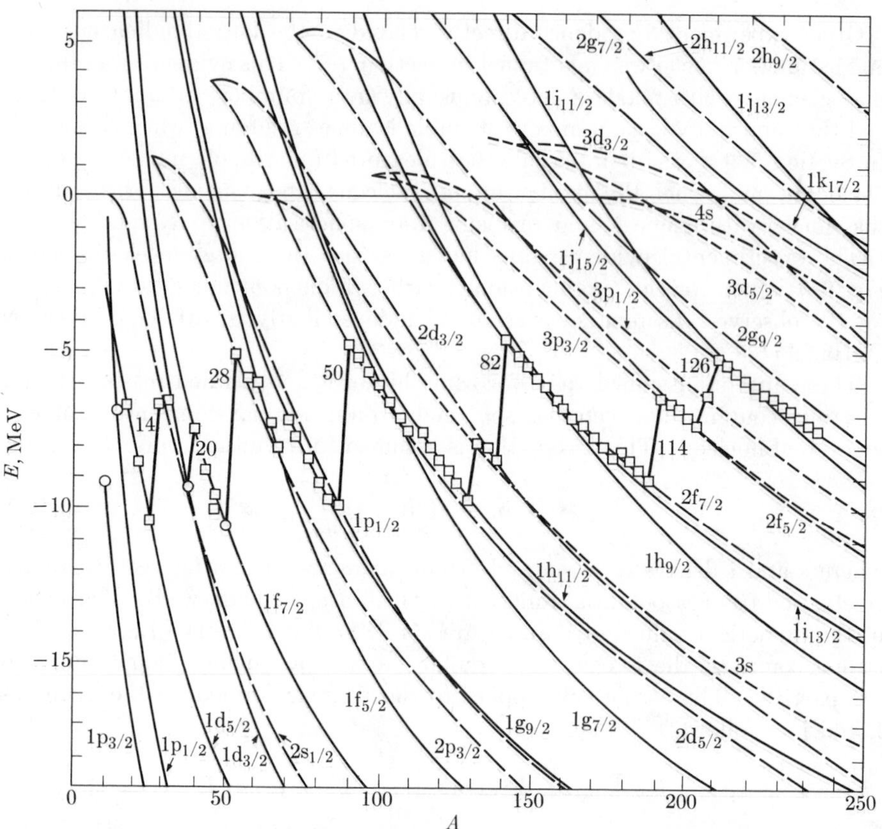

Fig. 6–9. Nuclear energy levels as calculated from the shell model. The predicted energies of the last neutron in beta-stable odd nuclei are indicated. [From A. E. S. Green, *Phys. Rev.* **104,** 1617 (1956).]

The effect of such a spin-orbit coupling is analogous to the effect of the magnetic coupling that causes the fine-structure splitting in atomic physics. However, in nuclear physics, to generate the magic numbers, the spin-orbit coupling has to have a sign opposite to the one it has in atomic physics, and it has to be much stronger. Relativistic theories predict a nuclear spin-orbit term of the correct sign but about 45 times weaker than is necessary to account for the observed effect.

It remains to be shown that the inclusion of the spin-orbit potential, Eq. (6–9), will produce the observed magic numbers. As an example, we give again some results of calculations performed by A. E. S. Green.* Green used a spin-orbit interaction given by

$$V_{SL} = -a_{SO}^2 \frac{1}{r} \frac{\partial V}{\partial r} \mathbf{l} \cdot \mathbf{s}, \tag{6–10}$$

* A. E. S. Green, *Phys. Rev.* **104,** 1617 (1956).

where V is the central potential given in Fig. 6–6. The form of Eq. (6–10) is the one predicted by relativistic theory, but in Green's work the strength, i.e., the factor a_{SO}, is adjusted to produce approximately the jumps in separation energy observed at the magic numbers. The best agreement between experiment and theory was found with $a_{SO} \approx 1$ F.

The final results of Green's calculations are given in Fig. 6–9, which should be compared with Fig. 6–7. As mentioned earlier, all states in Fig. 6–7 contain $2(2l + 1)$ substates. Except for S-states, these substates, in the presence of spin-orbit coupling, can be ordered into $2j_{\text{str}} + 1$ stretch states and $2j_{\text{jkn}} + 1$ jackknife states. Figure 6–9 shows how the inclusion of the spin-orbit interaction separates the two kinds of states, always lowering the energy of the stretch states relative to the others. Figure 6–9 indicates again how the various states fill in with up to $2j + 1$ neutrons in each state. We see that large energy jumps occur at neutron numbers $N = 2, 8, 14, 20, 28, 50, 82$, and 114. These calculations do not produce a clear energy jump at $N = 126$, and they produce jumps at $N = 14$ and 114 which are not present in the experimental separation-energy data. Most important, however, is the fact that the spin-orbit calculations have produced a level sequence such that the neutron (or proton) numbers 28, 50, 82, and 126 (as well as 2, 8, and 20) occur at completely filled states (subshells). It is very probable that a small change in the shape of the potential will pull down the 3p-level somewhat so as to reduce the gap at 114 neutrons and produce a larger gap at 126 neutrons. For the protons the Coulomb energy changes the position of the curves in Fig. 6–9. However, qualitatively the result is the same as for the neutrons. Pronounced energy jumps occur at the magic numbers.

Additional, and perhaps more convincing, evidence for the reasonableness of the shell model is given in the next section.

6–4 *Predicted Angular Momenta of Nuclear Ground States*

In shell-model terminology, each level, characterized by a principal quantum number, an l-value, and a j-value ($l \pm \frac{1}{2}$), is referred to as a single-particle state or a shell-model state. (Examples: $1f_{5/2}$, $2p_{3/2}$, etc.) The lowest shell-model states are filled first, up to the maximum number of $(2j + 1)$ like particles in a given state. This is essentially what Fig. 6–9 predicts, except that in some cases the levels are very close, or actually cross over, so that competition between them might be expected.

So far we have considered the overall effect of the attraction between a given nucleon and all other nucleons and also the spin-orbit interaction for each individual nucleon. These factors represent the most important parts of the total interaction energy. As in atomic physics, there is a so-called *residual interaction* between particles in each state (subshell), observable in the last subshell if it is only partly filled. Since all completely filled levels contribute zero angular momentum and positive parity to the nucleus, the angular momentum and parity of the ground state are determined only by residual interaction.

As mentioned in Section 4–6, from a study of atomic masses we find that the separation energy for a pair of neutrons is larger than twice the separation energy of a single *odd* neutron; the same applies for protons. The difference, the pairing energy, amounts to about 1 to 2 MeV and is the most important part of the residual interaction. Apparently, the pairing energy arises from the fact that, when two like particles in a subshell have opposite m_j-values, their wave functions overlap as much as possible. Since the interaction potential between them is attractive, this gives rise to a more strongly bound nucleus.

Because of the pairing energy, an even number of like nucleons in the partly closed subshell forms pairs so that their contribution to the ground-state angular momentum is 0^+. If the total number of neutrons (protons) in the subshell is odd, one will, of course, remain unpaired. These considerations lead to the following rules for the angular momenta and parities of nuclear ground states:

(1) Even-even nuclei, that is, nuclei with even Z and even N, have total ground-state angular momentum $J = 0^+$. There is no known exception to this rule.

(2) An odd nucleus, that is, a nucleus with odd Z or odd N, will have a total ground-state angular momentum and parity equal to the half-integral angular momentum j and the parity $(-1)^l$ of the unpaired particle. There are some exceptions to this rule, and they will be discussed below.

(3) An odd-odd nucleus will have a total angular momentum which is the vector sum of the odd-neutron and odd-proton j-values

$$\mathbf{J} = \mathbf{j}_{\mathrm{n}} + \mathbf{j}_{\mathrm{p}}.$$

The quantum number J is therefore an integer between the limits

$$|j_{\mathrm{n}} - j_{\mathrm{p}}| \leqq J \leqq j_{\mathrm{n}} + j_{\mathrm{p}}.$$

The parity will be the product of the proton and the neutron parity, that is, $\pi = (-1)^{l_{\mathrm{n}}+l_{\mathrm{p}}}$.

Observed angular momenta of nuclear ground states provide a more stringent test for the shell model than do the magic numbers.* These experimental data indicate that the sequences of energy levels are as shown below (compare Fig. 6–5).

(*a*) *Odd-proton nuclei:*

$(1s_{1/2})^2$ 2 $(1p_{3/2})^4$ $(1p_{1/2})^2$ 8 $(1d_{5/2})^6$ $(2s_{1/2})^2$ $(1d_{3/2})^4$ 20 $(1f_{7/2})^8$ 28 $(2p_{3/2})^4$

$(1f_{5/2})^6$ $(2p_{1/2})^2$ $(1g_{9/2})^{10}$ 50 $(1g_{7/2})^8$ $(2d_{5/2})^6$ $(1h_{11/2})^{12}$ $(2d_{3/2})^4$

$(3s_{1/2})^2$ 82 $(1h_{9/2})^{10}$ $(2f_{7/2})^4$ $(3p_{3/2})^4$

---

* P. F. A. Klinkenberg, *Rev. Mod. Phys.* **24,** 63 (1952).

(*b*) *Odd-neutron nuclei:*

$(1s_{1/2})^2 \; (1p_{3/2})^4 \; (1p_{1/2})^2 \; (1d_{5/2})^6 \; (2s_{1/2})^2 \; (1d_{3/2})^4 \; (1f_{7/2})^8 \; (2p_{3/2})^4$
2 8 20 28

$(1f_{5/2})^6 \; (2p_{1/2})^2 \; (1g_{9/2})^{10} \; (2d_{5/2})^6 \; (1g_{7/2})^8 \; (3s_{1/2})^2 \; (2d_{3/2})^4$
50

$(1h_{11/2})^{12} \; (2f_{7/2})^8 \; (1h_{9/2})^{10} \; (3p_{3/2})^4 \; (2f_{5/2})^6 \; (3p_{1/2})^2 \; (1i_{13/2})^{14} \; (2g_{9/2})^{10}$
82 126

$(3d_{5/2})^6 \; (1i_{11/2})^{12} \; (2g_{7/2})^8$

The number of particles that can be accommodated in each term is indicated by the superscript. The positions of the major shells, 2, 8, 20, etc., are also indicated. These level sequences are in good agreement with the calculated level schemes (e.g., Fig. 6–9). However, some of the levels inside a major closed shell are quite close in energy, so that the sequences given are not always strictly followed. In particular, there is a tendency for *pairs* of particles to go into higher orbital angular-momentum states rather than into s- or p-states, for instance, when the competing states are close. This is because the pairing energy that was discussed earlier increases with increasing l. Such competition, of course, only takes place between levels inside the same major shell. Some examples of predicted shell-model configurations and observed ground-state angular momenta for odd-A nuclei are given in Table 6–2.

Table 6–2. Shell-model terms and observed ground-state angular momenta

Nuclide	Z	N	Shell-model terms	Observed J^π
O^{17}	8		$(1s_{1/2})^2 \; (1p_{3/2})^4 \; (1p_{1/2})^2$	$5/2^+$
		9	$(1s_{1/2})(1p_{3/2})^4 \; (1p_{1/2})^2 \; (1d_{5/2})^1$	
Al^{27}	13		$(1s_{1/2})^2 \; (1p_{3/2})^4 \; (1p_{1/2})^2 \; (1d_{5/2})^5$	$5/2^+$
		14	$(1s_{1/2})^2 \; (1p_{3/2})^4 \; (1p_{1/2})^2 \; (1d_{5/2})^6$	
K^{39}	19		$(1s_{1/2})^2 \; (1p_{3/2})^4 \; (1p_{1/2})^2 \; (1d_{5/2})^6 \; (2s_{1/2})^2 \; (1d_{3/2})^3$	$3/2^+$
		20	$(1s_{1/2})^2 \; (1p_{3/2})^4 \; (1p_{1/2})^2 \; (1d_{5/2})^6 \; (2s_{1/2})^2 \; (1d_{3/2})^4$	
Zn^{67}	30		(28 protons) $(2p_{3/2})^2$	$5/2^-$
		37	(28 neutrons) $(2p_{3/2})^4 \; (1f_{5/2})^5$	
Mo^{95}	42		(28 protons) $(2p_{3/2})^4 \; (1f_{5/2})^6 \; (2p_{1/2})^2 \; (1g_{9/2})^2$	$5/2^+$
		53	(50 neutrons) $(2d_{5/2})^3$	

The shell-model theory is based on a spherically symmetric potential, and the conclusions that can be drawn from it are, strictly speaking, only valid for spherical or near-spherical nuclei. In regions of the chart of nuclides where large quadrupole moments are found, the ground-state angular momenta do not, in general, follow the predictions above. Among light nuclei this applies to F^{19}, Ne^{19}, and Na^{23}, which have ground-state J-values $1/2^+$, $1/2^+$, and $3/2^+$, whereas the shell model predicts $5/2^+$. This problem is discussed further in Section 6–8.

6–5 *Excited States and the Shell Model*

In atomic physics, the shell model not only gives a good description of the atomic ground state, but it can also be used in predicting the sequence and relative positions of excited states. We may attempt to predict the positions, angular momenta, and parity of nuclear energy levels by using the nuclear shell-model sequence. As an example, let us consider the nucleus Ca^{41}. According to the shell model, this nucleus is formed by adding one neutron to the doubly magic nucleus ${}_{20}Ca^{40}$. The ground state of Ca^{41} should therefore be an $f_{7/2}$-state, and there should be excited states of configurations $p_{3/2}$, $f_{5/2}$, $p_{1/2}$, and so forth. In addition, of course, there should be other excited states that can be formed by promoting one or more of the inner nucleons, core nucleons, to higher orbits. For increasing energy, there will be an increasing number of possibilities of reorientations, so we expect, in general, that the density of energy levels will increase rapidly with increasing excitation energy.

An energy-level diagram of Ca^{41} is shown in Fig. 6–10. To the left of the diagram is a scale of excitation energies in MeV; to the right are indicated the J-values, when known, and also the orbital angular momentum of the odd neutron as measured by a "stripping" reaction (Section 13–12). The ground state is an $f_{7/2}$ level, as expected, but *two* levels, at 1.947 and 2.469 MeV, appear to have $p_{3/2}$ character, and no fewer than five levels at about 4 MeV are identified as $p_{1/2}$ levels. This multiplicity of the p-states is not easy to explain on the basis of a pure closed-shell Ca^{40} core with one outer neutron added. The $f_{5/2}$ state is also fragmented; at least three levels between 4.8 and 5.8 MeV are formed by adding an $l_n = 3$ neutron to the Ca^{40} target nucleus. Presumably, the other levels in Fig. 6–10 are formed by promotion of "core" nucleons into higher states. No simple shell-model scheme involving only one or two particles can explain the character and position of these core excitations any more than it can explain the fragmentation of the single-particle states mentioned above. A certain measure of success can be obtained, however, by assuming that the Ca^{40} core in Ca^{41} has a wave function that is a mixture of shell-model terms in much the same fashion as for the deuteron (Section 2–6), although it is more complex. The Ca^{41} example illustrates the limited success and the shortcomings of the shell model in describing the excited states of nuclei.

In atomic physics, as mentioned earlier, the electrons in the last unfilled shell have a residual interaction in addition to the Hartree central potential. This interaction is quite small and is due to forces that are well understood; i.e., Coulomb repulsion influenced by the operation of the exclusion principle. In nuclear physics, however, the corresponding residual interaction is much larger. It is of the same order of magnitude as the separation between subshells; sometimes even of the same order of magnitude as the separation between major shells. This is one of the reasons why it is difficult to predict the position of nuclear energy levels from the shell model. Another important consideration is that the shell model in the form described above is based on calculations giving the positions of energy levels in a spherically symmetric potential, whereas we know that most nuclei are not spherically symmetric. The calculations, therefore, must be expected to be inaccurate, particularly for nuclei with large quadrupole moments. With a more refined shell model, based on a nonspherical nucleus, more insight is being gained into the level structure of nuclei.

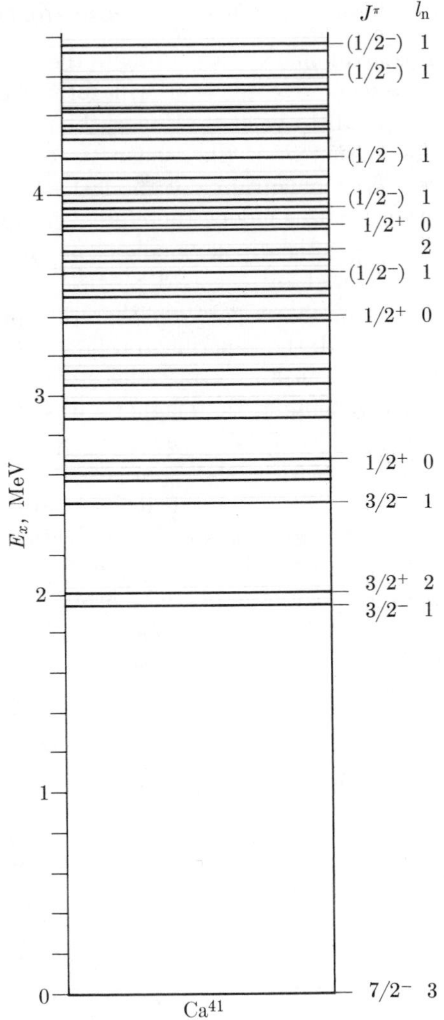

Fig. 6-10. Energy-level diagram of Ca^{41} showing excitation energies, total angular momenta J, parities, and orbital angular momenta l_n of unpaired neutrons. Values in parentheses are uncertain. (From T. A. Belote *et al.*, *Phys. Rev.* **139,** B80 (1965).

For nuclei with particularly large quadrupole moments, another quite different but successful approach has been taken, involving collective motions of a large number of nucleons (Section 6-9). Surprisingly good agreement between theory and experiment has been obtained with this "collective" model in specific cases; surprising because we must remember that no simple "model" can ever give exact results. The models used in nuclear physics, as well as in atomic physics, are invented because we do not know how to tackle mathematically the many-body Schrödinger equation, either with Coulomb forces or with nuclear forces.

6–6 *Magnetic Moments and the Shell Model; Schmidt Lines*

In an odd nucleus, according to the shell model, all except one nucleon will form pairs with antiparallel j-vectors. Hence, the total angular momentum J of the nucleus is equal to the angular momentum j of the last unpaired nucleon. In this model, therefore, we expect that the magnetic dipole moment of the nucleus is produced by the odd particle alone. We shall now investigate whether this prediction agrees with the experimental facts. If the last nucleon is in an S-state, the situation is particularly simple; the magnetic dipole moment will be equal to the magnetic dipole moment associated with the spin of the unpaired nucleon, 2.79275 nm if it is a proton, and −1.9135 nm if it is a neutron (Section 1–7).

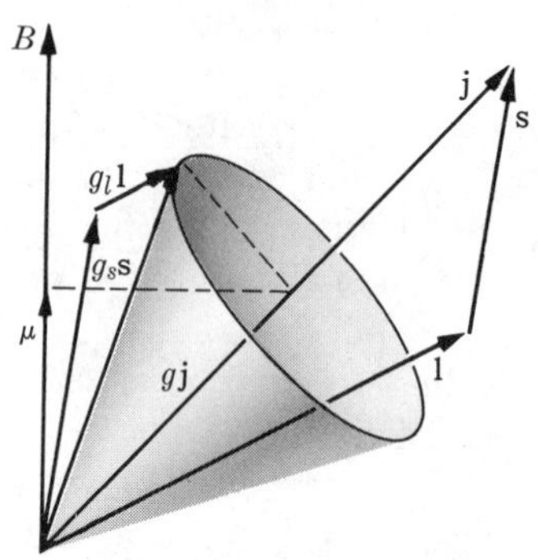

Fig. 6–11. Vector diagram for calculation of nuclear magnetic moments.

When the orbital angular momentum differs from zero, the situation is as depicted in Fig. 6–11. The orbital angular momentum $\mathbf{l}$ with numerical value $[l(l+1)]^{1/2}$ and the spin $\mathbf{s}$ with numerical value $[s(s+1)]^{1/2}$ couple to a total angular momentum $\mathbf{j}$ with numerical value $[j(j+1)]^{1/2}$, all in units of $\hbar$. With the spin angular momentum there is associated a magnetic moment

$$\boldsymbol{\mu}_s = g_s \mathbf{s}, \tag{6–11}$$

where the "g-factor" is

$$g_{s\text{p}} = \quad 5.5855 \quad \text{for the proton,}$$

and

$$g_{s\text{n}} = -3.8270 \quad \text{for the neutron.}$$

Similarly, for the orbital motion, we can write

$$\boldsymbol{\mu}_l = g_l \mathbf{l}, \tag{6–12}$$

where

$$g_{l\text{p}} = 1 \quad \text{for the proton,}$$

and

$$g_{l\text{n}} = 0 \quad \text{for the neutron.}$$

The magnetic moment is observable when the nucleus is placed in an external magnetic field, as indicated in Fig. 6–11. However, the vectors $\mathbf{s}$ and $\mathbf{l}$ do not have sharp components in the z-direction (field direction). Only the total $\mathbf{j}$-vector has. We must therefore compute the sum of the components of the vectors $g_l\mathbf{l}$ and $g_s\mathbf{s}$ along the $\mathbf{j}$-vector. This component sum is labeled $g\mathbf{j}$ in Fig. 6–11. It is sharp, and its z-component gives the observable interaction with the magnetic field.

From Fig. 6–11, we see that the components of the magnetic moment in the direction of the **j**-vector are

$$g\sqrt{j(j+1)} = g_l\sqrt{l(l+1)}\cos(lj) + g_s\sqrt{s(s+1)}\cos(sj). \tag{6–13}$$

By applying the cosine rule to the triangle formed by the vectors **l**, **s**, and **j**, we find for the cosines in the expression above

$$\cos(lj) = \frac{j(j+1) + l(l+1) - s(s+1)}{2\sqrt{l(l+1)j(j+1)}},$$

$$\cos(sj) = \frac{j(j+1) + s(s+1) - l(l+1)}{2\sqrt{s(s+1)j(j+1)}}.$$

Inserting this into Eq. (6–13), we get for the g-factor,

$$g = \frac{[j(j+1) + l(l+1) - s(s+1)]g_l}{2j(j+1)} + \frac{[j(j+1) + s(s+1) - l(l+1)]g_s}{2j(j+1)}. \tag{6–14}$$

Since, for a single particle, the spin is $s = \frac{1}{2}$, there are, for a given value of j, only two possibilities for l; namely, $l = j - \frac{1}{2}$ (stretch case), and $l = j + \frac{1}{2}$ (jackknife case). Using the single-particle model, we replace j with J and calculate the g-factors as functions of J for the stretch and jackknife cases.

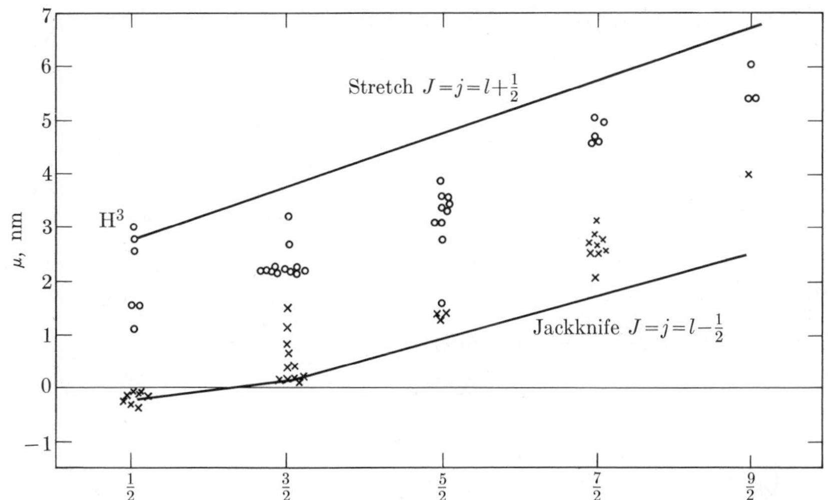

Fig. 6–12. Experimental magnetic dipole moments and Schmidt lines for nuclei of odd Z.

Simultaneously we multiply the result by $[J(J+1)]^{1/2}$ to get the magnetic moment along the J-vector and by the maximum value of the cosine of the angle between the field direction and $\mathbf{J}$, thus obtaining the maximum observable component of the magnetic moment. By convention, this is what experimentalists quote as *the* magnetic moment (Section 1–7). We obtain

$$\mu = g\sqrt{J(J+1)}\left(\frac{J}{\sqrt{J(J+1)}}\right) = gJ.$$

From Eq. (6–14), we then get for the stretch and jackknife cases:

$$\mu = \tfrac{1}{2}g_s + (J - \tfrac{1}{2}g_l), \qquad \text{stretch case;} \tag{6–15}$$

$$\mu = \frac{1}{J+1}\left[-\tfrac{1}{2}g_s + (J + \tfrac{3}{2})g_l\right], \qquad \text{jackknife case.} \tag{6–16}$$

Equations (6–15) and (6–16) are plotted in Fig. 6–12 for odd-proton nuclei and in Fig. 6–13 for odd-neutron nuclei. The resulting lines represent the magnetic moments predicted by the simple shell model. Experimentally observed magnetic moments are also shown in the figures, with crosses indicating jackknife cases and circles indicating stretch cases. The agreement between the simple theory and experiment is quite poor; however, it is a consolation that practically all the points fall between the two lines and that each point is, in general, closer to the line on which the theory predicts that it should fall than to the other line.

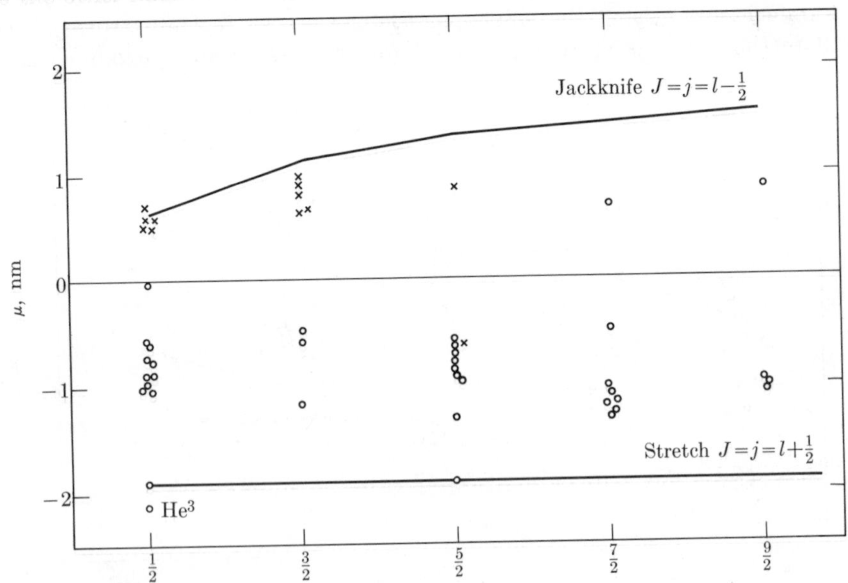

Fig. 6–13. Experimental magnetic dipole moments and Schmidt lines for nuclei of odd N.

There may be several reasons for the discrepancy between our simple theory and the experimental data. Perhaps the most important one is that our shell model is based on a spherically symmetric potential, whereas in reality nuclei are ellipsoidal. Except in the immediate neighborhood of closed major shells where the quadrupole moments are small, a single shell-model wave function does not give a true representation of a nuclear state. Rather, the energy eigenfunctions can be written as a linear combination of shell-model terms. Some of these terms correspond to stretch and some to jackknife cases. Consequently, the resulting magnetic dipole moment is expected to fall somewhere between the two Schmidt lines.

Another possible reason for the discrepancy is that it is not at all certain that the magnetic dipole moments of the nucleons in nuclear matter are the same as in the free states. It is reasonable to assume that the meson "clouds" around the nucleons are changed appreciably by the presence of other nucleons nearby.

6–7 *Symmetry; Isospin*

In atomic physics a complete wave function for a single electron contains a description of the spin direction. Let us use the symbol α to indicate spin "up" (spin projection $m_s = \frac{1}{2}$) and β to indicate spin "down" (projection $m_s = -\frac{1}{2}$). These symbols represent spin wave functions with eigenvalue $s(s+1) = \frac{3}{4}$ for the square of the spin angular momentum and $+\frac{1}{2}$ and $-\frac{1}{2}$, respectively, for the z-component of angular momentum measured in units of $\hbar$. Beyond this, the form of the functions and of the spin operators does not need to concern us.* The total wave function for a single electron can be written as a product of a spin function and a space wave function, for instance ψ_n for space state n and α for spin up:

$$\psi = \psi_n(\mathbf{r})\alpha.$$

For two particles, one in space state n and the other in space state k, we write in the L-S representation

$$\text{Singlet state, } S = 0: \quad \psi = \tfrac{1}{2}(\psi_{nk} + \psi_{kn})(\alpha\beta - \beta\alpha), \qquad m_S = 0; \tag{6–17}$$

$$\text{Triplet states, } S = 1: \quad \psi = \begin{cases} \dfrac{1}{\sqrt{2}}(\psi_{nk} - \psi_{kn})\alpha\alpha, & m_S = 1, \\ \tfrac{1}{2}(\psi_{nk} - \psi_{kn})(\alpha\beta + \beta\alpha), & m_S = 0, \\ \dfrac{1}{\sqrt{2}}(\psi_{nk} - \psi_{kn})\beta\beta, & m_S = -1. \end{cases} \tag{6–18}$$

---

* Pauli's spin matrices, which represent the simplest mathematical description of the spin wave functions and operators, are discussed, for instance, in M. A. Preston, *Physics of the Nucleus*, Reading, Mass.: Addison-Wesley Publishing Co., 1962, p. 602.

The shorthand symbols used mean

$$\psi_{nk} \equiv \psi_n(\mathbf{r}_1)\psi_k(\mathbf{r}_2),$$
$$\alpha\beta \equiv \alpha(1)\beta(2),$$

where 1 and 2 are labels on the two particles.

The only spin eigenfunctions that can be constructed for two $s = \frac{1}{2}$ particles are those shown in Eqs. (6–17) and (6–18) with quantum numbers S and m_S as indicated. As required by the Pauli's exclusion principle, all total wave functions in Eqs. (6–17) and (6–18) are antisymmetric. This means that the functions change sign under exchange of the coordinates of the two particles; that is, interchange of the labels 1 and 2. In the singlet state, the space part of the wave function is symmetric, and the spin part is antisymmetric. In the triplet state, the situation is reversed.

It can be shown in general that symmetry of a two- or many-body wave function is conserved when the particles are acted on by the same potential. In other words, an antisymmetric wave function stays antisymmetric, and a symmetric wave function stays symmetric. Pauli's exclusion principle expresses the experimental fact that the wave function for identical fermions, that is, particles with $s = \frac{1}{2}$, is antisymmetric under exchange of any pair of particles.

Proceeding now to a discussion of the nucleus, which consists of two different kinds of fermions, we see immediately that any complete nuclear wave function must be antisymmetric in the exchange of the positions of any two protons or any two neutrons. But, how about the exchange of the positions of a neutron and a proton? The exclusion principle does not require that the total wave function be antisymmetric under such exchanges, since the particles are not identical. Indeed, the wave function does not even possess a definite symmetry, since the potential energy at a given point inside the nucleus is not the same for a proton and for a neutron. However, all information obtained so far on nuclear forces indicates that the Coulomb force acting only between the protons is the only force of significance that does not remain the same when a proton is exchanged for a neutron or vice versa. For light nuclei, the Coulomb force is relatively unimportant, and nuclear wave functions are therefore nearly symmetric or nearly antisymmetric in exchange of neutrons and protons. These symmetry properties of the total wave function can be labeled by the use of a new quantum number, the *isospin*.

Let us first look at one single nucleon that can be either a proton or a neutron. We introduce a quantum number t_3 which we call the *isospin projection*. By definition it is given the value $t_3 = \frac{1}{2}$ for a proton and $t_3 = -\frac{1}{2}$ for a neutron. The term "projection" implies, of course, that there is a total isospin and also that an axis exists along which we can measure its projection. As for the total isospin, it is defined below; as for the axis, it is, in classical terms, entirely fictitious. If we combine the isospin-projection quantum numbers for all nucleons in a system to a total isospin projection, we get

$$T_3 = \tfrac{1}{2}(Z - N). \tag{6–19}$$

In this formalism we are considering the proton and the neutron as different quantum states of the same particle, the nucleon. In any system with more than one nucleon, the isospin projection T_3 measures, according to Eq. (6–19), the proton excess of the system. By introducing $N = A - Z$, we see that, in general, for A nucleons, the total charge of the system is given by

$$Z = T_3 + A/2 \tag{6–20}$$

unit charges. In a nuclear reaction, since the total charge is conserved and the total nucleon number is conserved, obviously the total isospin projection is also conserved. In beta-decay processes, T_3 for the nucleus changes by one unit while at the same time an electron or a positron is created, so that total charge is conserved.

There is no fundamental importance attached to the isospin projection number T_3 beyond what we have already discussed. It sometimes offers a slightly more convenient way of writing total wave functions. For a single nucleon, the two possible values of t_3 remind us of the two possible values of the ordinary spin projection m_s for a single fermion. In the spin formalism, however, we are also dealing with a total spin quantum number $s = \frac{1}{2}$ for a single particle, $S = 0$ or 1 for two particles, etc. It seems logical to ask: "Does it make sense to talk about a total isospin quantum number T, and what would be the meaning of such a quantum number?" It turns out that it is possible and convenient to use such a formalism to express the symmetry of a total wave function. Let us consider first the ordinary spin states of two nucleons. The total spin quantum number is either $S = 0$ or $S = 1$. In the former case, the spin projection is $m_S = 0$; in the latter case, $m_S = 0, \pm 1$. The total spin quantum number S is associated with the mechanical angular momentum through the equation

$$p_S^2 = S(S + 1)\hbar^2. \tag{6–21}$$

There is, therefore, a concrete physical quantity associated with S. In contrast, we now introduce an apparently completely abstract quantum number t, which is equal to $\frac{1}{2}$ for a single nucleon, and a total isospin quantum number T, which is equal to 0 or 1 for two nucleons, etc., in complete formal analogy with ordinary spin. What is the meaning of this new quantum number?

Consider again two nucleons. The isospin quantum number is then $T = 0$ or 1; in the former case, we have an isospin singlet, and the projection T_3 must be equal to 0 by analogy with ordinary spin formalism. According to Eq. (6–19), this means that $Z = N$; that is, the system consists of a proton and a neutron.

When $T = 1$, we have an isospin triplet, and the projection can be either -1, 0, or 1, representing two neutrons, a neutron and a proton, or two protons, respectively (Eq. 6–19). Figure 6–14 shows an energy diagram of the three possible two-body systems, the dineutron, the deuteron, and the diproton (He^2). Only the $J = 1^+$ state of the deuteron is a bound state; the others are virtual states, but this does not concern us for the present. In the deuteron ground state, both particles are in the same space-spin state. This state is therefore symmetric, which is possible because the two particles are not identical. However, two protons or two neutrons cannot occupy this state. Therefore, T_3 can only be zero, and we have $T = 0$, an isospin singlet. Two neutrons or two protons can combine to an antisymmetric state, for instance a $^1S_0$-state, where they are in the same space state ($l = 0$) but opposite spin states. A neutron and a proton can also form the same state. This then is an isospin triplet (Fig. 6–14). If the forces are independent of isospin projection (charge), the isospin triplet is energy degenerate. In practice, of course, this degeneracy is removed by the action of the Coulomb force. The diproton state, in other words, should be somewhat higher than the other $T = 1$ states in Fig. 6–14.

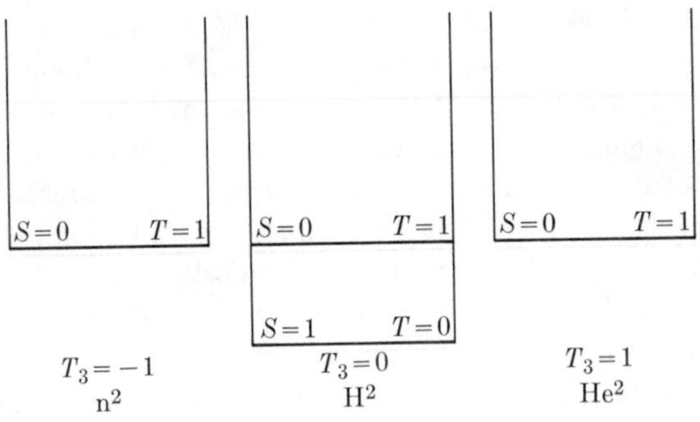

Fig. 6–14. The lowest states of the three possible two-nucleon systems. None of the $S = 0$, $T = 1$ states are stable.

As we have seen in the example discussed above, the isospin formalism can be used to express the fact that several nuclear isobars can have similar states, the only difference between the members of an isospin multiplet being the charge of the nucleons. Table 6–3 summarizes the results for two nucleons, that is, only two nucleons as in Fig. 6–14, or two nucleons outside a shell closed for both neutrons and protons.

In the isospin formalism, the total wave function is written as a product of a space part, a spin part, and an isospin part. The form of the isospin part is identical to the form of the spin part (Pauli's spin matrices). In analogy with the spin wave functions α and β discussed previously, let us use δ to indicate isospin "up" (proton) and γ to indicate isospin "down" (neutron). The total wave functions for the isospin singlet of the first entry in Table 6–3 (deuteron)

Table 6–3. Symmetries of two-nucleon systems

	T	T_3	Particles	Symmetry		
				Isospin	Space spin	Total
Isospin singlet	0	0	n p	Antisymmetric	Symmetric	Antisymmetric
Isospin triplet	1	1 0 −1	p p n p n n	Symmetric	Antisymmetric	Antisymmetric

are then, depending on spin direction:

$$\psi = \begin{cases} \dfrac{1}{\sqrt{2}}\,\psi_{nn}\alpha\alpha(\delta\gamma - \gamma\delta), & S = 1, \quad m_S = 1, \quad T_3 = 0; \\ \tfrac{1}{2}\,\psi_{nn}(\alpha\beta + \beta\alpha)(\delta\gamma - \gamma\delta), & S = 1, \quad m_S = 0, \quad T_3 = 0; \\ \dfrac{1}{\sqrt{2}}\,\psi_{nn}\beta\beta(\delta\gamma - \gamma\delta), & S = 1, \quad m_S = -1, \quad T_3 = 0. \end{cases}$$

For the isospin triplet of Table 6–3, we get

$$\psi = \begin{cases} \dfrac{1}{\sqrt{2}}\,\psi_{nn}(\alpha\beta - \beta\alpha)\delta\delta, & S = 0, \quad m_S = 0, \quad T = 1, \quad T_3 = 1; \\ \tfrac{1}{2}\,\psi_{nn}(\alpha\beta - \beta\alpha)(\delta\gamma + \gamma\delta), & S = 0, \quad m_S = 0, \quad T = 1, \quad T_3 = 0; \\ \dfrac{1}{\sqrt{2}}\,\psi_{nn}(\alpha\beta - \beta\alpha)\gamma\gamma, & S = 0, \quad m_S = 0, \quad T = 1, \quad T_3 = -1. \end{cases}$$

As written above with inclusion of the isospin wave functions, all *total wave functions are antisymmetric.* Pauli's exclusion principle does permit a neutron and a proton to be in the same space-spin state, so that this part of the wave function may be symmetric. In this case, however, the isospin function is antisymmetric. Conversely, when space spin is antisymmetric, isospin is symmetric. Isospin can therefore be regarded as a label identifying the symmetry of the space-spin wave function, or for more than two particles, the degree of symmetry of the wave function.

Since symmetry of a two- or many-body wave function is conserved when the forces are symmetric, isospin is conserved. In particular, for light nuclei where the Coulomb forces do not play such an important role, one expects isospin to be a "good quantum number." Nuclear reactions between states of different total isospin are then expected to be inhibited.

6–8 Single-Particle Orbits in a Distorted Well

We saw in preceding sections that the shell model is very successsful in predicting ground-state angular momenta, but is not so successful in describing excited states and magnetic moments. It is therefore clear that the shell model gives an oversimplified picture of the actual situation inside a nucleus. One assumption that we have made is obviously wrong in most cases: this is the assumption of a spherically symmetric potential. We discussed in Section 1–8 and further in Chapter 5 the fact that nuclear states possess a sometimes appreciable quadrupole moment, indicating that the self-consistent nuclear potential is quite far from spherically symmetric. This is particularly true for nuclides in the regions between major closed shells. It should be quite clear to us that unless the occupied subshells are filled, a spherically symmetric potential is not self-consistent, since the probability densities of the calculated shell-model states (except S-states) are not spherically symmetric. As will be further discussed in Section 14–1, the Coulomb force has a tendency to enhance the eccentricity originally formed by nonspherical states for some of the nucleons. In general, therefore, the true self-consistent potential for the independent-particle model is not spherically symmetric.

In this section, we shall not go so far as to determine a self-consistent potential, but we shall treat a part of this problem, namely, the study of single-particle states in an assumed spheroidal potential. Most of the pioneering work on deformed nuclei was done in the Copenhagen school, and the particular calculations described here were made by S. G. Nilsson.*

Figure 6–15 shows the outline of a spheroidal nucleus with a symmetry axis z'. Consider first the classical case of a single particle bouncing back and forth inside a spheroidal shell with frictionless walls. Clearly, if the shell were spherical, the particle could not impart an angular impulse to the shell. Classically, the angular momentum of the particle is then conserved; quantum mechanically, it has a sharp value. A single particle bouncing back and forth inside a frictionless spheroidal shell, as in Fig. 6–15, can, however, impart an angular impulse to the shell, and if the shell is free to rotate about the center of mass, there will be a continuous exchange of angular momentum between the particle and the shell. Because of the rotational symmetry of the shell, the component of angular momentum in the direction of the symmetry axis cannot be exchanged. Quantum mechanically, therefore, this component of the particle's angular momentum (Ω in Fig. 6–15) is sharp. The total angular momentum $\mathbf{J}$, as well as its component M along a space-fixed axis z, is of course conserved. In Fig. 6–15, $\mathbf{j}$ indicates the particle's instantaneous total angular momentum and $\mathbf{R}$ indicates the total angular momentum for the rest of the nucleus with possible contributions from rotation, vibration (Section 6–10), and from other unpaired particles. The quantities $\mathbf{R}$ and $\mathbf{j}$ are not sharp but are subject to

* S. G. Nilsson, *Mat. Fys. Medd. Dan. Vid. Selsk.* **29**, No. 16, 1955 (2nd ed., 1960).

rapid exchanges, as described above. The component Ω of the particle's angular momentum and the component K of the total angular momentum are sharp. For an odd nucleus with the even-even core in the lowest state, R is perpendicular to z', so that $K = \Omega$.

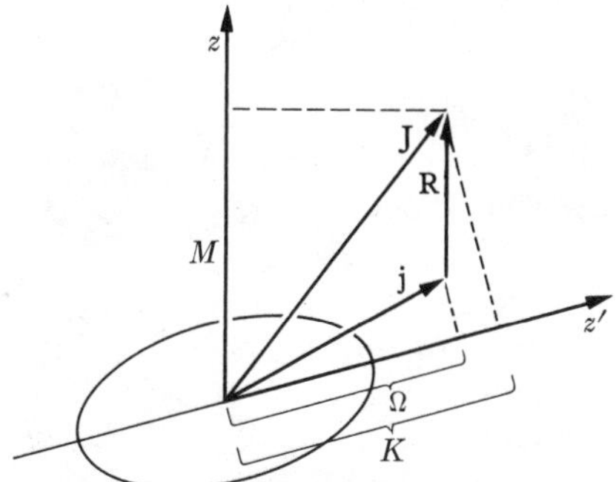

Fig. 6-15. Coupling scheme for angular momenta of a single particle interacting with a spheroidal shell or nuclear surface.

The rapidly changing state of rotation of the nucleus does not correspond closely to a rigid-body rotation, but rather to a rotation of the surface caused by a collective motion of particles that resemble a surface wave. What we are concerned with in this section is the lowest ("zero point") state of rotation caused by the interaction with the particle studied. In Section 6-9, we discuss rotational excited states, in which this rotational energy is increased.

Since the spherical harmonic functions form a complete orthonormal set, it must be possible to describe the wave function for a particle in a distorted well in terms of the wave functions calculated for the spherically symmetric shell model. This is essentially what Nilsson does in his calculations, but instead of attempting to use the full range of the complete set, he limits the number of terms to the states derived from the same harmonic-oscillator level; that is, essentially to states within the same major closed shell (Fig. 6-5).

We shall here give a short outline of Nilsson's calculations. His starting point is a series of harmonic-oscillator wave functions, that is, the eigenfunctions of the Hamiltonian operator:

$$H_0 = -\frac{\hbar^2}{2m}\nabla^2 + \tfrac{1}{2}m\omega_0^2 r^2. \tag{6-22}$$

The symmetry axis of the nucleus (z') is chosen as the quantization axis for these wave functions. The eigenvalues for the Hamiltonian operator H_0 are:

$$E_0 = (N + \tfrac{3}{2})\hbar\omega_0, \tag{6-23}$$

where N is the principal quantum number. What we are seeking are the eigenfunctions and eigenvalues for the Hamiltonian operator:

$$H = H_0 + H_\delta + C\mathbf{l}\cdot\mathbf{s} + D\mathbf{l}^2. \tag{6-24}$$

This operator contains as a principal element the Hamiltonian H_0 (Eq. 6-22) and three additional terms. The first of these terms describes the deviation from spherical symmetry. This can be expressed in the following form:

$$H_\delta = -\tfrac{4}{3}\sqrt{\pi/5}\,\delta m\omega_0^2 r^2 Y_{20}, \tag{6–25}$$

where δ is the deformation parameter, approximately equal to

$$\delta \approx \Delta R/R,$$

and the angular dependence is expressed by the function $Y_{20}(\theta, \phi)$. The two other terms in Eq. (6–24) are, respectively, $C\mathbf{l}\cdot\mathbf{s}$, the familiar spin-orbit term, and $D\mathbf{l}^2$, a term that has the effect of distorting the harmonic-oscillator potential to a more flat-bottomed potential, closer in shape to the actual nuclear potential.

A total wave function for a given set of the principal quantum number N and the angular momentum projection Ω in the distorted potential is written as:

$$\psi = \sum_k C_k \psi_k^0, \tag{6–26}$$

where the ψ_k^0's are a set of harmonic-oscillator wave functions with given N and Ω, and k is merely a running index (no quantum number). The objective of the calculations is to find the coefficients C_k and the energy eigenvalue for each of the final wave functions. The techniques involved in solving this problem include a diagonalization of the matrix whose elements are:

$$H_{nm}^0 = \int \psi_n^{0*} H \psi_m^0 \, d\tau. \tag{6–27}$$

This technique is described in Appendix 5.

Let us look at some examples of Nilsson wave functions of the form Eq. (6–26). The notation used is the following: A harmonic-oscillator wave function ψ_k^0 quantized along the axis z' can be completely specified by giving the principal quantum number N, the orbital angular momentum quantum number l, the projection of the orbital angular momentum along the z'-axis Λ, and the projection of the particle's spin along the z'-axis. These numbers are arranged in the following way: $|Nl\Lambda\Sigma\rangle$, symbolizing the wave function. The spin projection Σ is of course either $+\frac{1}{2}$ or $-\frac{1}{2}$; so, for short, one simply writes the sign and leaves out the value $\frac{1}{2}$. This sign must not be misunderstood as indicating parity; for the harmonic oscillator, parity is given by $(-1)^N$ and also by $(-1)^l$.

Table 6–4 lists all harmonic-oscillator wave functions with $N = 2$. All these functions are doubly degenerate; that is, they can contain two neutrons or two protons with opposite Λ and Σ. In all, Table 6–4 gives six different wave functions; hence, the $N = 2$ shell can accommodate twelve protons and twelve neutrons. The dis-

Table 6–4. Harmonic-oscillator wave functions in the $N = 2$ shell

l \ Ω	1/2	3/2	5/2
0	$\|200+\rangle$		
2	$\|220+\rangle$	$\|221+\rangle$	$\|222+\rangle$
2	$\|221-\rangle$	$\|222-\rangle$	

tortion, as expressed by the three last terms in Eq. (6–24), mixes the states as expressed by Eq. (6–26), but it does not change the total number of particles that can be accommodated. With only the two last terms in Eq. (6–24) included, the result is shell-model wave functions that are, at the most, a sum of two of the wave functions of Table 6–4, since both Ω and l are conserved.* When the deformation parameter δ is different from zero, neither the orbital angular momentum l nor the total angular momentum j for the particle is conserved, as discussed earlier; however, Ω is conserved. The new wave functions in this case must then be written in terms of all the harmonic-oscillator wave functions in a given column of Table 6–4. For instance, the three new wave functions with $\Omega = \frac{1}{2}$ are for the case of $\delta = 0.16$:

$$\mathrm{d}_{5/2} \rightarrow 0.396\,|200+\rangle + 0.787\,|220+\rangle + 0.472\,|221-\rangle,$$

$$\mathrm{s}_{1/2} \rightarrow 0.806\,|200+\rangle - 0.051\,|220+\rangle - 0.590\,|221-\rangle,$$

$$\mathrm{d}_{3/2} \rightarrow 0.440\,|200+\rangle + 0.614\,|220+\rangle + 0.653\,|221-\rangle.$$

These correspond to distorted states emanating from the three $N = 2$ shell-model states, as indicated.

In Fig. 6–16, the energy of some of the lowest single-particle levels in a distorted potential is plotted vs. the distortion parameter δ. The various levels are identified by a half-integral numeral indicating Ω, a sign indicating the parity, and three other numerals in parentheses. These are the so-called "asymptotic quantum numbers" (N, n_z, Λ), which are appropriate quantum numbers for an infinitely distorted, axially symmetric, harmonic-oscillator potential. They are:

$$\begin{aligned} N &= \text{principal quantum number} \\ &= \text{total number of nodes in the wave function (as above)}, \\ n_z &= \text{number of nodal planes in axial direction (new)}, \\ \Lambda &= \text{component of } l \text{ along } z' \text{ (as above).} \end{aligned}$$

The numbers n_z and Λ are "good" quantum numbers only for infinite distortion. As can be seen from Fig. 6–16, the lowest of the $2j + 1$ states emanating from a given shell-model state is always the $\Omega = \frac{1}{2}$ state when $\delta > 0$. In the limit of very large deformation, this state resembles a plane wave bouncing back and forth in the axial direction and thereby creating a standing wave with the number of nodes $n_z = N$.

Figure 6–16 should not, in general, be interpreted as giving, directly, the total energy of the nucleus. We have mentioned earlier that the rest of the nucleus exchanges angular momentum and rotational energy with the particle. Clearly, the total angular momentum J and the total energy depend also on the state of the rest of the nucleus. When the equilibrium deformation is reasonably small,

* Since there is no nuclear symmetry axis when $\delta = 0$, Ω for the pure shell-model states could be thought of as the projection of the angular momentum along a space-fixed axis.

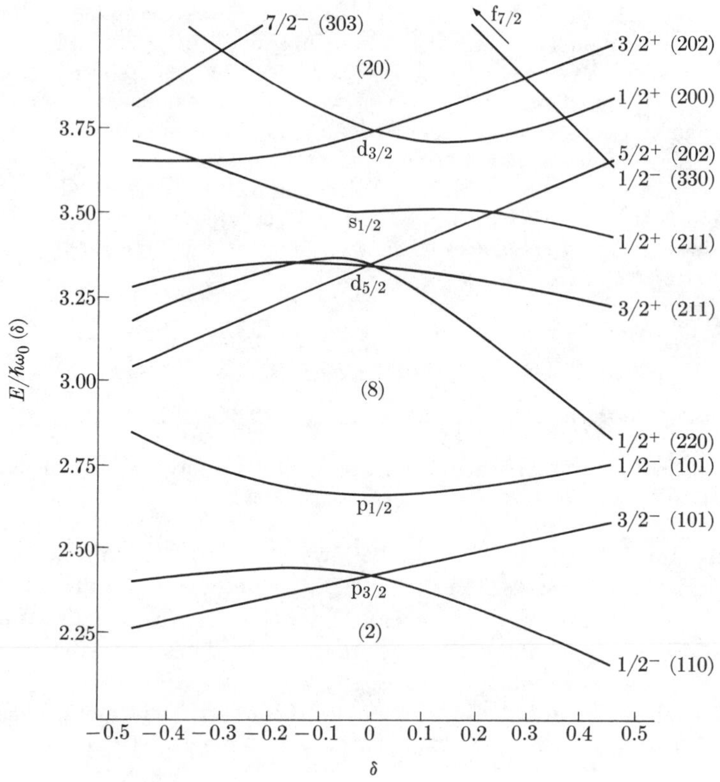

Fig. 6–16. Energy of some low single-particle levels plotted vs. distortion parameter δ. [Adapted from B. R. Mottelson and S. G. Nilsson, *Mat. Fys. Skr. Dan. Vid. Selsk.* **1**, No. 8 (1959).]

the total angular momentum for the nucleus remains the value predicted by the shell model. When the deformation is large, however, an odd nucleus has in the ground state $J = \Omega_{\text{odd}}$, where Ω_{odd} for the last particle is found by filling Nilsson orbits in exactly the same way as we have done before for shell-model orbits. In the region of light elements, the three nuclei F^{19}, Ne^{19}, and Na^{23} have considerable distortion. Their ground-state J-values are $1/2^+$, $1/2^+$, and $3/2^+$, in agreement with Fig. 6–16 and in disagreement with the simple shell-model prediction, which is $5/2^+$ for all three.

6–9 *Collective Motion; Rotational States*

In molecular spectra, as discussed briefly in Section 5–3, one finds evidence for three kinds of excitation: electronic, vibrational, and rotational. In nuclei, one has been able to identify essentially the same types of excitation. First, of course, the change of an electronic state in the molecule corresponds to the change of the state of an individual nucleon, whether this nucleon is considered as occupying a shell-model orbit or a Nilsson orbit. The vibrational states of nuclei are formed by flexings of the nuclear surface and are therefore of a somewhat more complex nature than the simple picture outlined in Section 5–3 for molecular vibrations. Nuclear rotational motion is also, as we shall see, somewhat more complex in that it is not a rigid-body rotation but a rotation of the shape of the deformed surface enclosing A free particles. Both nuclear vibrational motion and rotational motion involve orderly displacements of many nucleons, and both types are therefore classified as nuclear collective motion. In this section we discuss the rotational type of excitation, which is the type responsible for the low-lying excited states of nuclei with large quadrupole deformations. The frequency of such rotation is low, so that to a good approximation the internal motion of the nucleons and the rotational motion can be treated separately. As mentioned earlier, the rotation should not be thought of as a rigid-body rotation; the spheroidal surface of the nucleus will rotate, but it does not necessarily follow that the orbital planes of all the nucleons, if such could be defined, will rotate.

Scores of nuclear energy levels have been identified as rotational levels, because they display spectra of the type predicted by Eq. (5–4). In every instance it has been found that the moment of inertia $\mathcal{I}$, which has to be used to fit the data, is smaller than the rigid-body moment of inertia by a factor of 2 to 4. This might be taken as a measure of the extent to which the nucleons are dragged with the surface in the rotational motion. It has been found experimentally, and it might be expected that the ratio $\mathcal{I}/\mathcal{I}_{\text{rigid}}$ increases with increasing deformation parameter δ. For nuclei with small deformation parameter β, no rotational spectrum is found at all.

For nuclear rotational motion, in analogy with the molecular case discussed in Section 5–3, an interesting case arises when $K = 0$ for an even-even nucleus with ground-state $J = 0^+$. The same arguments of exchange symmetry apply here as for the molecular case. The appropriate statistics is Bose-Einstein, because there is an even number of nucleons in each half of the nucleus, and therefore the resulting angular momentum in each half is integral. When, in a 180° rotation, one half is exchanged with the other, the wave function ψ_r should be symmetric. We therefore expect a rotational energy-level diagram with angular momentum values $J = 0^+, 2^+, 4^+$, etc., for a deformed even-even nucleus.

As an example, Fig. 6–17 shows the energy-level diagram of $_{72}\text{Hf}^{180}$. The excitation energies, measured with great precision with a bent-crystal spectrometer (Chapter 9), are listed to the immediate right of each level in the diagram. Next to the experimental excitation energies are shown the energies predicted by Eq. (5–4), with $\mathcal{I}$ adjusted so as to give exactly the right energy for the 2^+ level. The agreement is quite good, but there is a systematic difference which increases with increasing excitation energy. This difference may be explained as resulting from an increase in the moment of inertia with increasing

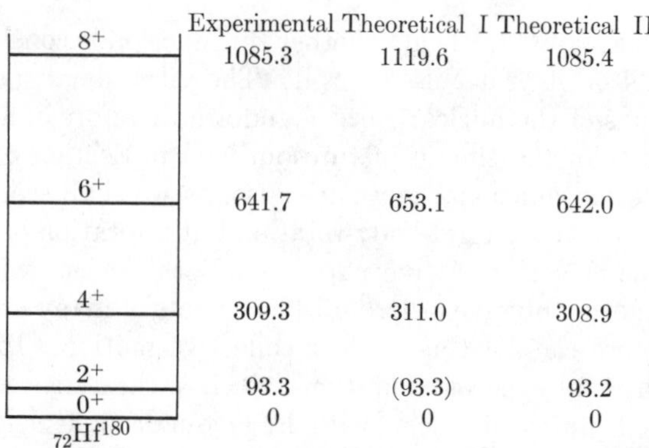

Fig. 6–17. Energy-level diagram of Hf^{180} with experimental and calculated excitation energies. [From A. Bohr, "Rotational States of Atomic Nuclei," *Mat. Fys. Skr. Dan. Vid. Selsk.* **1**, No. 8 (1959).]

angular momentum of rotation because of the action of the centrifugal force. When a correction for this effect is included, one obtains a formula for the energies of the rotational states of an even-even nucleus:

$$E = \frac{\hbar^2 J(J+1)}{2\mathcal{J}} - BJ^2(J+1)^2, \qquad \text{with } J = 0, 2, 4, 6, \text{etc.} \tag{6–28}$$

This equation has two adjustable parameters ($\mathcal{J}$ and B). Using a least-square fit to the experimental values of Fig. 6–17, one obtains the theoretical values in the third column of Fig. 6–17. The agreement with experimental values is now, as one can see, extremely good.

An example of a rotational energy-level scheme for an odd nucleus is given in Section 10–7.

6–10 *Vibrational States*

To introduce the subject of vibrational states in nuclei, we turn again for a moment to molecular levels. Figure 6–18 pictures a triatomic linear molecule, for instance, CO_2. This molecule can execute vibrational oscillations by bending. There will then, of course, be a restoring force which, to a first approximation, is proportional to the displacement. The result is, therefore, harmonic motion. If two such harmonic oscillations occur simultaneously and 90° out of phase with each other, the result is a rotation, as indicated in the figure. Note carefully the difference between this rotation and the kind of rotation which gives rise to the molecular-rotation spectrum. Such a spectrum is produced when the molecule rotates without appreciably changing the shape it has in its lowest state. The motion of the CO_2 molecule of Fig. 6–18 can also be thought of as a rotation where the spring force balances the centrifugal force. This is, as explained above, really harmonic oscillation, and the resulting energy spectrum

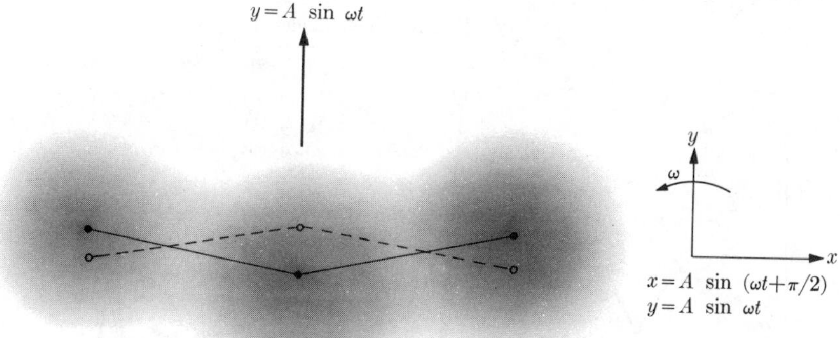

Fig. 6–18. Triatomic linear molecule (e.g., CO_2). Two vibrational motions superimposed give rotation where restoring force is balanced by centrifugal force.

is therefore the spectrum of a harmonic oscillator; that is, the levels are equally spaced with separation $\Delta E = \hbar\omega$. The angular frequency is given by the familiar formula $\omega = \sqrt{k/m}$, where m is the reduced mass and k the "spring" constant, or restoring force, per unit displacement.

As mentioned in the previous section, a spherical or nearly spherical nucleus does not display rotational energy levels; however, it can display vibrational energy levels of a type somewhat similar to those discussed above for the CO_2 molecule. The motion is that of a surface wave going around the nucleus carrying

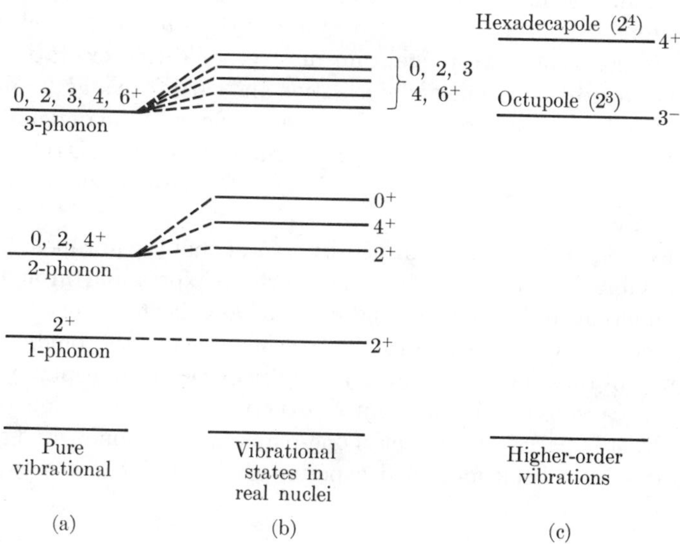

Fig. 6–19. Schematic vibrational energy-level diagrams of medium-mass even-even nuclei. [From E. Eichler, *Rev. Mod. Phys.* **36,** 809 (1964).]

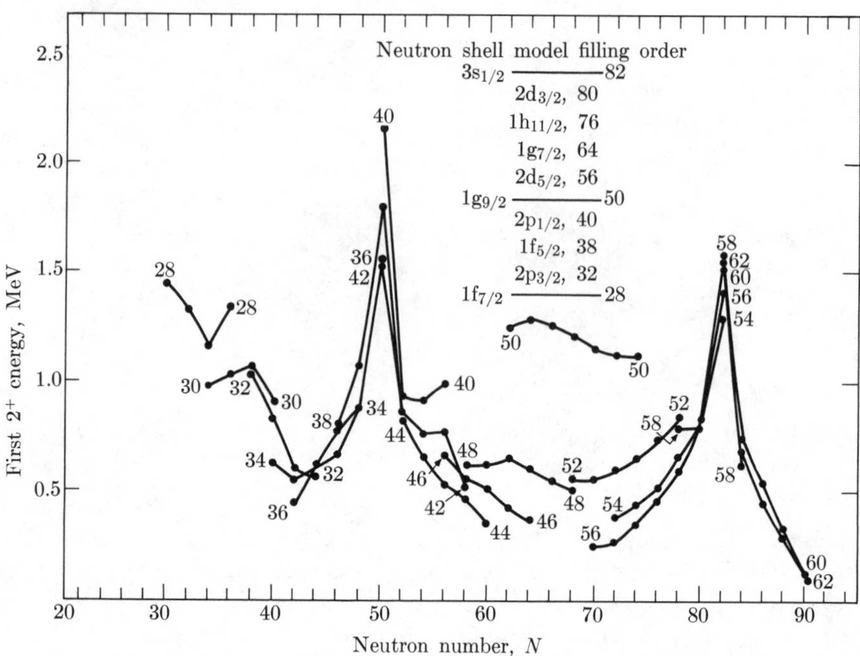

Fig. 6–20. Plot of the energies of the first 2^+ states of even-even nuclei vs. neutron number. Lines join isotopic chains and are marked with proton numbers Z. (Adapted from Eichler *op. cit.*)

a certain amount of mass that produces a pressure on the bulge because of the centrifugal force. This is counteracted by the surface tension, which represents the spring force. The lowest quantum of such collective excitation, called a *phonon*, has a quadrupole type of deformation and carries an angular momentum of two units and positive parity. In even-even nuclei with small deformations δ, one therefore expects to find a $J = 2^+$ first excited state which is the one-phonon vibrational state, whereas in nuclei with large deformations one finds a $J = 2^+$ rotational state.

Higher excited states can be formed by two or more quadrupole phonons or by octupole vibrations, the latter having distortions expressible through spherical harmonic functions of third order and carrying angular momenta of three uuits with negative parity. Figure 6–19 shows schematically the predicted energy-level diagram of those even-even nuclei that are expected to display vibrational-type spectra. A considerable amount of experimental information verifies this scheme, at least in part.* A number of one-phonon, two-phonon, and even three-phonon states have been identified experimentally, and many octupole states have also been seen.

* See the review paper by E. Eichler, *Rev. Mod. Phys.* **36,** 809 (1964).

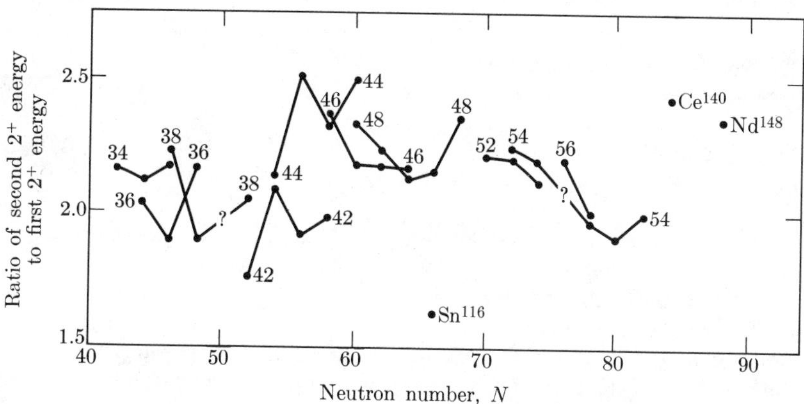

Fig. 6–21. Ratio of the energies of the second 2^+ state to that of the first 2^+ state in even-even nuclei. Lines join isotopic chains. (From Eichler *op. cit.*)

With very few exceptions, the first excited states in even-even nuclei have $J = 2^+$. Figure 6–20 shows a plot of the energy of these 2^+ states vs. neutron number N. Since both the vibrational spectrum and the rotational spectrum, as well as certain shell-model considerations, at least in some cases, predict a 2^+ first excited state, these observations do not prove the validity of the vibrational scheme. Assuming, however, that most of the states plotted in Fig. 6–20 can be characterized as one-phonon states, we see the effect of a stiffening of the nucleus when a magic N or Z is approached, and we see a drastic lowering of the energy of the first excited state when the rotational region beyond $N = 90$ is approached.

Some experimental information has been collected for the two-phonon triplet, and in particular a number of second 2^+ states have been observed. Figure 6–21 is a plot of the ratio of the energy of the second 2^+ state to that of the first. The observed ratio fluctuates around the value 2 predicted for the vibrational model (Fig. 6–19). This is all the more remarkable when the wide range of energies of the first excited states is considered.

In some nuclei all three two-phonon states have been identified. Some three-phonon states have been found, and the existence of the octupole vibrational state has also been definitely demonstrated. The existence of collective vibrational motion, as well as rotational motion, in nuclei has therefore been firmly established. For odd nuclei a certain amount of insight can be gained by considering the odd nucleon coupled to the collective motion in the vibrational state.

It is important to emphasize again that the collective motions of nucleons in rotational and vibrational states are motions with velocities much lower than the individual nucleon velocities. The mass transported in the crest of a collective wave is therefore continuously and rapidly exchanged.

PROBLEMS

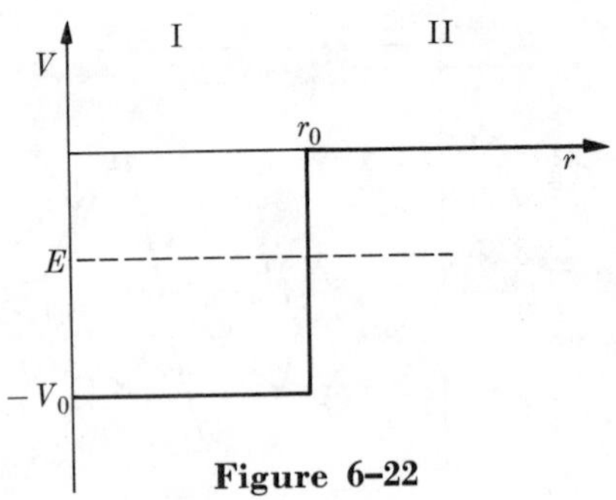

Figure 6–22

6–1. A neutron is bound in the lowest possible state ($l = 0$) to a heavy nucleus. The binding energy is $E_B = 16$ MeV ($E = -16$ MeV). The shape of the potential acting on the neutron is as shown in Fig. 6–22, with $V_0 = 32$ MeV and r_0 unknown. (a) Solve the radial wave equation for $l = 0$ in regions I and II, and sketch the wave function u. (b) Apply boundary conditions at $r = 0$ and $r = r_0$ to obtain an equation between pertinent wave numbers and r_0. (c) Find the numerical values of the wave numbers and solve the equation mentioned under (b) for r_0. For the reduced mass, use $m = 1$ u.

6–2. Prove that Eq. (6–3) is a solution of Eq. (6–2). [Note that

$$\left(\frac{1}{r}\frac{d}{dr}\right)^l \equiv \left(\frac{1}{r}\frac{d}{dr}\right)\left(\frac{1}{r}\frac{d}{dr}\right)\cdots\cdots\left(\frac{1}{r}\frac{d}{dr}\right) \qquad (l \text{ times})$$

so that $(1/r)^l$ cannot be multiplied out of the parentheses.]

6–3. (a) Write the radial wave functions for $l = 0$ and $l = 1$ as given by Eq. (6–3). (b) Find the values of kr which give the first zeros of the two functions. (c) Use the results of (a) and (b) to calculate the distance in MeV between the lowest s-state and the lowest p-state in an infinitely deep well of radius 5 F.

6–4. Show that the spherical Hankel function for $l = 1$ (p. 147) is a solution of Eq. (6–2).

6–5. A general expression for the spherical harmonic function is

$$Y_{lm}(\theta, \phi) = \frac{(-1)^{l+m}}{(2l)!!}\left[\frac{(2l+1)(l-m)!}{4\pi(l+m)!}\right]^{1/2} (\sin\theta)^m \times \frac{d^{l+m}}{(d\cos\theta)^{l+m}}[(\sin\theta)^{2l}]\exp(im\phi).$$

Compute $Y_{22}(\theta, \phi)$, and check the parity. ($X!! \equiv 1{\cdot}3{\cdot}5\cdots X$ for odd X and $X!! \equiv 2{\cdot}4{\cdot}6\cdots X$ for even X.)

6–6. What angular momenta and parities are predicted by the shell model for the ground states of C^{12}, B^{11}, O^{17}, Ne^{20}, Al^{27}, Ca^{41}, and Ga^{69}?

6–7. What are the parities and what are the upper and lower limits for the angular momenta predicted for the ground states of Li^6, N^{14}, Al^{28}, K^{40}, and Co^{60}?

*6–8. Find the matching equation for the wave function at the boundary of a finite square well with radius r_0 and depth V_0 (general case, l not necessarily equal to zero). Use general Bessel-function relations to get the expression in a form convenient for calculations. Find the energy difference between the 1s-state and the 1p-state when $V_0 = 30, 35, 40, 45, 50$ MeV and $r_0 = 4, 4.5, 5, 5.5, 6$ F. (Choose one set.)

*6–9. Use perturbation theory to calculate the spin-orbit splitting of the 1p, 1d, 1f shell-model states for a nucleus with $A = 10, 20, 30, 40, 50$. (Choose one.) The spin-orbit potential is given by Eq. (6–10) with $a_{SO} = 1$ F. Use a square well with

$$V_0 = 40 \text{ MeV} \qquad \text{and} \qquad r_0 = 1.4\, A^{1/3} \text{ F}.$$

In the perturbation calculations you can assume that the slope of the well at $r = r_0$ is finite; that is, $V = -V_0$ at $r = r_0$ and $V = 0$ for $r = r_0 + \Delta$.

PART 4

Nuclear-Disintegration Studies

7

Stopping and Detecting Nuclear Radiations

7–1 Stopping Power and Range for Charged Nuclear Particles

When a proton, an alpha particle, or another charged nuclear particle moves through matter, it ionizes, or excites, the atoms to which it comes sufficiently close. These changes of state are caused by the Coulomb force, which can give a sharp impulse to an electron as the particle moves swiftly by. The energy transferred to the electrons represents a loss of kinetic energy of the moving particle, which therefore will slow down and eventually stop. The energy transfer to the positive heavy ions released in ionization is, in general, negligible. A close enough encounter between the particle and a nucleus to initiate a nuclear reaction or scattering process is, relatively speaking, so rare as to be completely negligible in a discussion of the stopping process. The slowing-down or stopping process is therefore an atomic process, and the reason why we discuss it in a text on nuclear physics is that it is of great importance, first, for understanding all types of nuclear detectors and, second, for choosing the thickness of targets, shielding materials, etc.

Because the topic is only of peripheral interest for nuclear physics, we shall not go into the details of the quantum-mechanical theory of the slowing-down process. However, some simple classical considerations are in order, since they help in the understanding of the physics of the process. Consider a particle of mass m and velocity v colliding head on with an electron of mass m_0. The maximum velocity that can be imparted to the electron is $2v$, so that the electron gets a maximum kinetic energy

$$T_1 = \tfrac{1}{2}m_0(2v)^2 = 4\frac{m_0}{m}(\tfrac{1}{2}mv^2) = 4\frac{m_0}{m}T. \tag{7–1}$$

For example, a 5-MeV proton can impart a maximum of approximately 10 keV to an electron.

Let us assume that the collision is not head on, but that there is a small impact parameter a between the electron in question and the straight-line orbit of a moving particle (Fig. 7–1). The particle moves by the atom with a velocity v, which we assume is so great that in most cases (when a is sufficiently

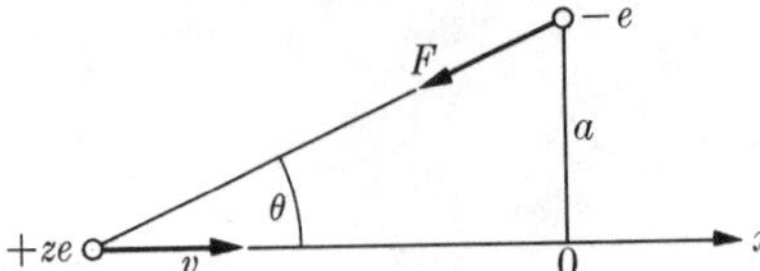

Fig. 7–1. Diagram used to calculate the impulse imparted to an electron by the Coulomb force from another charged particle moving swiftly by.

large) the electron has not appreciably changed its position before the particle has passed by. However, it does get a net impulse given by

$$p = \int_{-\infty}^{\infty} F \sin\theta \, dt. \tag{7–2}$$

The force F is the Coulomb force $ze^2/4\pi\epsilon_0 r^2$, where ze is the charge of the particle, and the distance r can be expressed as $r = a/\sin\theta$. The relationship between the time t and x is $dt = dx/v = a\,d\theta/v\sin^2\theta$, where we have used the relationship $x = -a\cot\theta$. By inserting these relationships into Eq. (7–2), we find the momentum of the electron after the particle has passed:

$$p = \int_0^{\pi} \frac{ze^2 \sin\theta \, d\theta}{4\pi\epsilon_0 av} = \frac{ze^2}{2\pi\epsilon_0 av}.$$

Assuming that the velocity of the electron is sufficiently low so that we can use classical formulas, we find for the kinetic energy of the electron, as a function of impact parameter a:

$$T_e = \frac{p^2}{2m_0} = \frac{z^2e^4}{8\pi^2\epsilon_0^2a^2m_0v^2}. \tag{7–3}$$

We now introduce a concept called the *stopping cross section.* It has a dimension of area times energy and is defined as

$$\sigma_e = \int \Delta T \, dA, \tag{7–4}$$

where ΔT is the loss of kinetic energy sustained by the particle when moving through the area dA. Ordinarily, a cross section is a measure of the probability of removing a particle from the primary beam. In the process we are discussing now, the particle is not completely removed, it is only slowed down. If the dimension of the cross section of Eq. (7–4) is cm^2-eV, for instance, it can be regarded as a measure for the probability of removing 1 eV from the particle. We equate the kinetic energy lost by the particle to the kinetic energy gained by the electron (Eq. 7–3) and find the stopping cross section per electron

$$\sigma_e \approx \int_{a_1}^{a_2} T_e 2\pi a \, da = \frac{z^2e^4}{4\pi\epsilon_0^2 m_0 v^2} \ln\frac{a_2}{a_1}.$$

Instead of performing the integration from zero to infinity, we have put two limits on the impact parameter, a_1 and a_2. The lower limit a_1 is determined by the uncertainty principle as $a_1 \approx h/2m_0v$; this is approximately the size of the electron as seen by the moving particle (see also Problem 7–1). The upper integration limit is set as $a_2 = v/\nu$, where ν is an average of the frequencies of oscillations of the electrons in the atom. The argument is that the perturbing field from the charged particle will not change the state of an electron unless the duration ($\approx a/v$) is small compared with the period of oscillation.

With the values of the integration limits inserted, we get for the stopping cross section

$$\sigma_e = \frac{z^2e^4}{4\pi\epsilon_0^2 m_0 v^2} \ln \frac{2m_0v^2}{h\nu}.$$

The energy $h\nu$ is an average excitation energy or binding energy I for the electrons in the atoms of the stopping medium.

This crude derivation of the stopping cross section of one single electron gives a formula which is identical to the formula derived by use of quantum mechanics for $v \ll c$. With relativistic correction terms, the quantum-mechanical formula per atom (Z electrons) is

$$\sigma = \frac{z^2Ze^4}{4\pi\epsilon_0^2 m_0 v^2}\left[\ln \frac{2m_0v^2}{I} - \ln\left(1 - \frac{v^2}{c^2}\right) - \frac{v^2}{c^2}\right]. \tag{7–5}$$

The "average" excitation potential I is very vaguely defined and is difficult to calculate theoretically. In practice, therefore, I is treated as a parameter that can be adjusted to fit experimental data. It varies from material to material, but for low-Z material it is independent of the particle's energy, provided that $T \gg I$. For high-Z materials, it varies slightly with energy because only high-energy particles can excite the inner electrons. Table 7–1 gives the ionization potential I for some gases and solids for low-energy nuclear particles ($T < 100$ MeV). In the third column is also given a quantity I/Z which is seen to be remarkably constant for element numbers greater than $Z = 13$. This fact can be used for determining I by interpolation in materials for which it has not been measured.

It is worth noting that the stopping cross section (Eq. 7–5) does not depend on the mass of the particle, but is only a function of its velocity and charge. Therefore, if one measures the stopping cross section in a given material for protons for instance, then according to Eq. (7–5) the stopping cross section for any other nuclear particle at the same velocity can be calculated as z^2 times the proton cross section. However, two reservations should be made. First, Eq. (7–5) clearly breaks down for velocities smaller than $v = (I/2m_0)^{1/2}$, for which it gives a negative cross section. Second, at low velocities there is a considerable amount of charge exchange between the atoms and the particle, in particular for multiply charged particles. For instance, an alpha particle with

Table 7-1. Mean excitation potential I*

Substance	Z	I, eV	I/Z
H_2	1	19	19
He	2	44	22
Be	4	64	16
Air	7.2	94	13.1
Al	13	166	12.7
Ar	18	230	12.8
Cu	29	371	12.8
Ag	47	586	12.5
Xe	54	660	12.2
Au	79	1017	12.8
Pb	82	1070	13.1

* For references to original measurements, see R. M. Sternheimer, *Methods of Experimental Physics*, ed. L. Marton, Vol. 5, part A. New York: Academic Press, 1961. (Reproduced by permission).

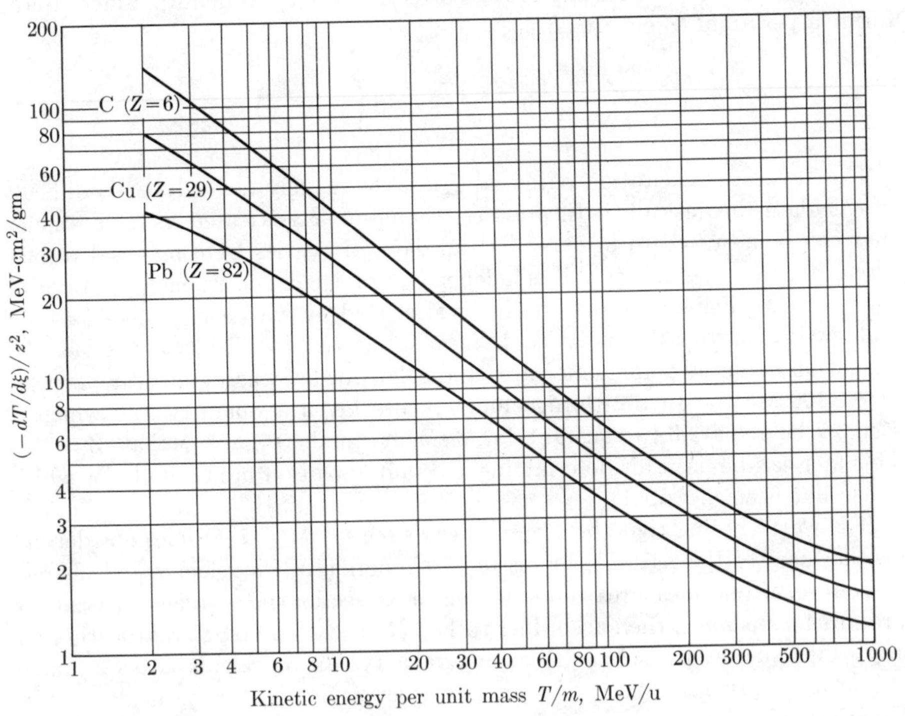

Fig. 7-2. Stopping power for protons in carbon, copper, and lead. The scales are given in such units that the graph can also be used for particles other than protons, provided charge exchange between the particle and absorber can be neglected (see text). Particle charge = ze, particle mass = m, mass units u.

a kinetic energy of less than 5 MeV frequently picks up an electron from the material it is moving through and loses it again, perhaps a thousand times before it comes to rest. The effective charge z of the particle in this velocity range is therefore less than 2 units.

A new concept, the *stopping power*, can now be defined and calculated in the following way. Stopping power is the amount of energy lost by a particle per unit length of path through the stopping material. If the density of atoms in the material is n per unit volume, the stopping power is

$$-\frac{dT}{dx} = \frac{n\sigma\,dx}{dx} = n\sigma = \frac{z^2Zne^4}{4\pi\epsilon_0^2 m_0 v^2}\left[\ln\frac{2m_0v^2}{I} - \ln\left(1 - \frac{v^2}{c^2}\right) - \frac{v^2}{c^2}\right]. \tag{7–6}$$

From an experimenter's point of view, it is convenient to measure the thickness of a given absorber in grams per square centimeter rather than in meters or centimeters. The relationship between mass per unit area and thickness x is of course $\xi = \rho x$, where ρ is the density of the material. Figure 7–2 gives several curves of stopping powers $-dT/d\xi$ for protons as a function of element number Z and proton energy. The curves have been calculated by use of Eq. (7–6) with the empirical values for the adjustable parameter I given in Table 7–1.

The total range of a particle in a given material, that is, the length of the flight path before the particle comes to a complete stop, can, in principle, be calculated by an integration of the inverse of Eqs. (7–5) or (7–6):

$$R = \int_T^0 dx = \int_T^0 -\frac{dT}{\sigma n} = \int_T^0 \frac{-dT}{\rho(-dT/d\xi)}.$$

In practice, of course, this integration cannot be performed all the way down to zero energy because of the breakdown of Eq. (7–5) for low energies. If, however, a range R_1 is measured for an energy T_1, then the range for higher-energy particles can be calculated as

$$R_2 = R_1 + \int_{T_2}^{T_1} \frac{-dT}{n\sigma(T)}, \tag{7–7}$$

provided that T_1 is higher than the energy for which Eq. (7–5) breaks down. Figure 7–3 shows the ranges for protons in carbon, copper, and lead. The graph can also be used for other particles (of mass m and charge z) with scale changes as indicated (Problem 7–3).

In the preceding discussion, we have only touched on the *primary* process of ionization, in which the nuclear particle tears loose electrons from the atoms along its path. As discussed above, these electrons can have energies up to several keV, and therefore they are themselves very potent ionizing agents. Thus many of them will knock out *secondary* electrons, and the result is a multiplication of the number of ion pairs by a factor of 10 or more. In addition

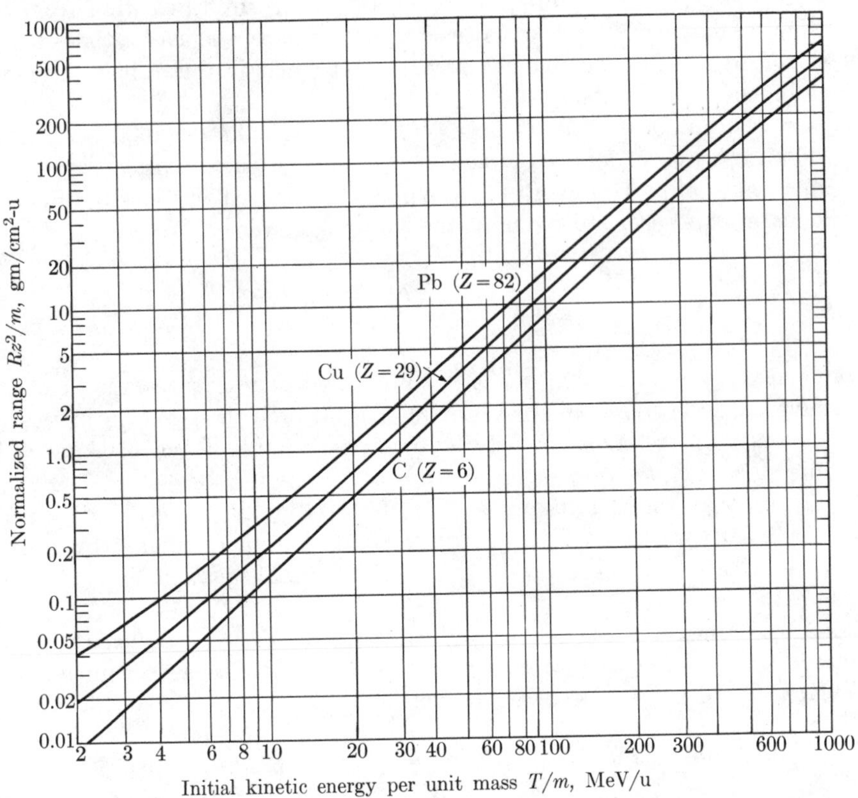

Fig. 7-3. Ranges for protons in carbon, copper, and lead, measured in gm/cm^2. The scales are given in such units that the graph can be used for particles other than protons, provided exchange between the particle and the absorber can be neglected (see text). Particle charge = ze, particle mass = m, mass units u.

to these primary and secondary processes of complete ionization, many events of atomic excitation take place, and a large number of photons are released in the following de-excitations. Of very great importance for several energy-measuring apparatuses is the fact that the total number of primary and secondary ion pairs produced in a given material is approximately proportional to the energy loss of the particle. In air, for instance, the total energy loss is about 34 eV per ion pair produced, practically independent of the particle's energy, charge, and mass. If all ions produced by a particle coming to stop in a volume of air can be collected, the total charge (of either sign) is therefore a measure of the particle's energy. The ion-chamber spectrometer operates on this principle. It is not a very exact instrument, partly because the total number of ion pairs produced is subject to statistical fluctuations, and accuracies much better than one percent cannot be expected. However, it is simple and reliable and has therefore enjoyed a certain degree of popularity.

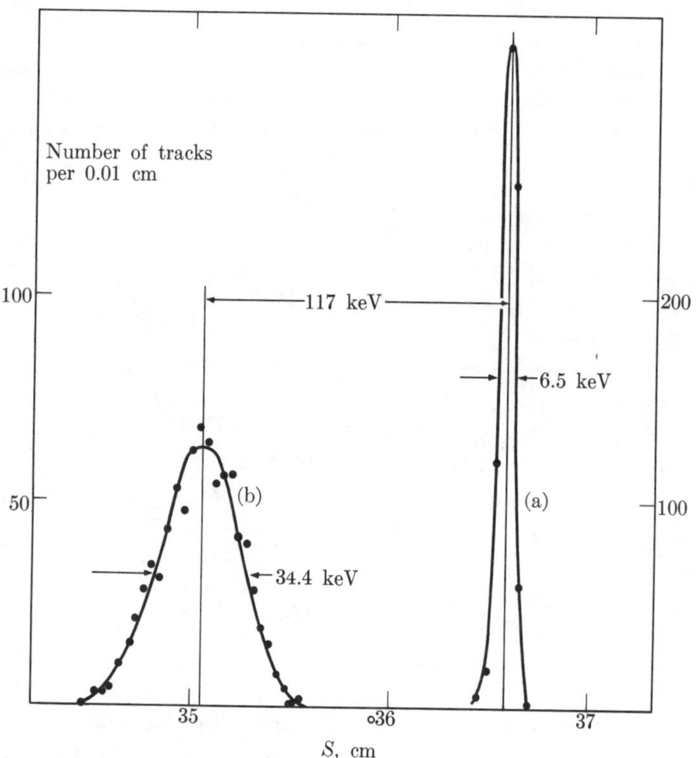

Fig. 7-4. Energy spectrum of 3-MeV protons before (a) and after (b) passage through 3.3-mg/cm^2 gold foil. [From Lis P. Nielsen, *Dan. Mat. Fys. Medd.* **33,** No. 6 (1961).]

The statistical nature of the slowing-down process is also responsible for another phenomenon called *straggling,* which is a manifestation of the fact that identical particles of identical energies do not suffer the same energy loss in passing through a target of given thickness. Figure 7-4 illustrates an example of straggling for protons which have passed through a 3.3-mg/cm^2 gold foil. The energies of the protons were measured by a charged-particle magnetic spectrograph (Sections 10-2 and 13-3) after scattering by another, very thin, gold foil, which served only the purpose of reducing the intensity of the proton beam to one that could be handled by the spectrograph. The narrow peak (a) represents the energy distribution of protons from the direct beam scattered from the very thin target; the wide peak (b) gives the energy distribution of protons scattered by the thin target, but after they have passed through the relatively thick 3.3-mg/cm^2 gold foil. The average energy loss of protons in passing through the gold foil is 117 keV, and the widening of the peak from 6.5 keV to 34.4 keV, full width at half-maximum (also called half-width), is a result of straggling. This simply means that some of the protons in passing through the gold foil have more energetic encounters with electrons than the others. The energy distribution of protons is approximately gaussian; that is, we can write:

$$N = N_0 e^{-(\Delta T)^2/2\Omega^2}, \tag{7-8}$$

where the standard deviation Ω, according to a theory of straggling by Bohr,* is given by

$$\Omega = \sqrt{z^2 e^4 Z N_A \,\Delta\xi/4\pi\epsilon_0^2 A} = 8.85 z\sqrt{2Z/A}\,\sqrt{\Delta\xi}\ \text{keV}, \tag{7-9}$$

with $\Delta\xi$ in mg/cm^2 and N_A = Avogadro's number. This formula is valid when the velocity of the particle is sufficiently high so that the logarithmic term in Eq. (7–5) is greater than 1.

When the average energy loss is smaller than the energy that can be imparted to a single electron (Eq. 7–1), the distribution is no longer gaussian, as in Fig. 7–4, but has a tail on the low-energy (higher loss) side. This effect, which is treated theoretically by Landau and by Symon,† has been demonstrated experimentally by Igo *et al.*‡ for 31.5-MeV protons passing through a gas counter acting as an absorber.

7–2 *Stopping Power and Range for Electrons*

Electrons lose energy by ionization in gases, liquids, and solids in essentially the same way as charged nuclear particles do. There are two important differences, however. One is that, because of the small mass of the electron, it can sustain deflections through much larger angles than the heavier particles can. While the slowdown of a heavier particle takes place along virtually a straight line, this is not so for electrons. The second difference arises from the fact that the scatterer and the scatteree are identical particles. Exchange phenomena therefore have to be considered when the theory is worked out. The following formula§ is given for the stopping power for electrons produced by ionization and atomic excitations in the stopping material:

$$\left(-\frac{dT}{dx}\right)_i = \frac{e^4 NZ}{8\pi\epsilon_0^2 m_0 v^2}\left[\ln\frac{m_0 v^2 T}{2I^2(1-\beta^2)} - \left(2\sqrt{1-\beta^2} - 1 + \beta^2\right)\ln 2 + 1 - \beta^2 + \tfrac{1}{8}\left(1-\sqrt{1-\beta^2}\right)^2\right]. \tag{7-10}$$

This equation is quite similar to Eq. (7–5), and a comparison again brings out the fact that the stopping power for nonrelativistic particles mainly depends

---

* N. Bohr, *Mat. Fys. Medd. Dan. Vid. Selsk.* **18,** No. 8 (1948).

† L. Landau, *J. Phys.* (*USSR*) **8,** 201 (1944); K. R. Symon, unpublished Ph.D. thesis, Harvard University (1948).

‡ G. J. Igo, D. D. Clark, and R. M. Eisberg, *Phys. Rev.* **89,** 879 (1953).

§ H. A. Bethe, *Handbuch der Physik*, Vol. 24. Berlin: Julius Springer, 1933, p. 273.

Table 7–2. Radiation lengths X_0 and critical energy T_c for various substances*

Absorber	Z	M_A	X_0, gm/cm^2	T_c, MeV
Hydrogen	1	1	58	340
Helium	2	4	85	220
Carbon	6	12	42.5	103
Nitrogen	7	14	38	87
Oxygen	8	16	34.2	77
Aluminum	13	27	23.9	47
Argon	18	39.9	19.4	34.5
Iron	26	55.8	13.8	24
Copper	29	63.6	12.8	21.5
Lead	82	207.2	5.8	6.9
Air			36.5	83
Water			35.9	93

* H. A. Bethe and J. Ashkin, *Experimental Nuclear Physics*, ed. E. Segrè, Vol. I. New York: John Wiley and Sons, Inc., 1953. (Reprinted by permission.)

on the velocity and the charge of the particle. Electrons of the same energy as a heavy particle have a much longer range or a smaller stopping power in a given material, simply because the velocity of the electron is higher than that of the heavier particle.

At relativistic velocities, a process other than ionization plays an important role in the slowing down of charged particles. This is the energy loss by *bremsstrahlung*, or radiation loss, suffered by the particle when it is subjected to acceleration in the field of the nucleus or of the electrons. At energies employed in nuclear-structure physics, the radiation loss suffered by charged nuclear particles is insignificant, and we can safely ignore it. For electrons and positrons, Bethe and Heitler* give the following formula applicable for kinetic energies $T \gg m_0c^2$:

$$\left(-\frac{dT}{dx}\right)_r \approx \frac{4Ze^6nT(Z+1.3)[\ln(183Z^{-1/3})+\frac{1}{8}]}{(4\pi\epsilon_0)^3\hbar m_0^2c^5}. \tag{7–11}$$

An interesting fact is that the loss is proportional to the kinetic energy T. A consequence of this is that, when the radiation loss predominates, the electron will suffer an exponential loss of energy as it moves through matter. This can be seen in the following simple analysis. We rewrite Eq. (7–11) as

$$-\frac{dT}{d\xi} = \frac{T}{X_0}, \tag{7–12}$$

* H. A. Bethe and W. Heitler, *Proc. Roy. Soc.* (*London*) **A146,** 83 (1934).

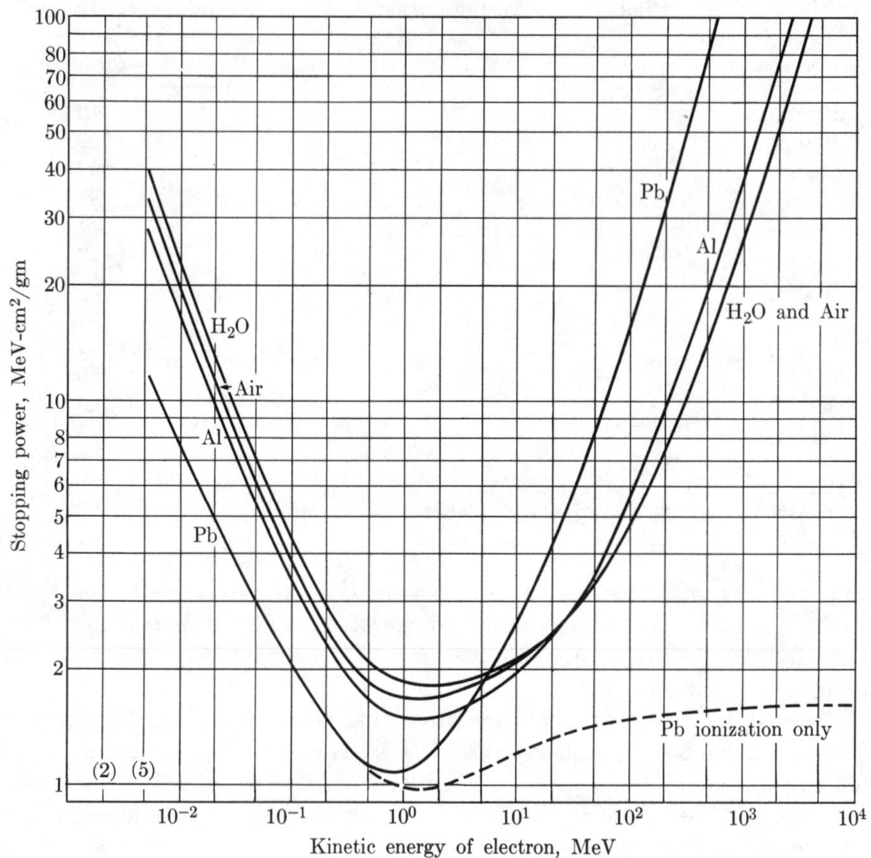

Fig. 7–5. Total stopping power for electrons in air, water, aluminum, and lead. For lead, the contribution from ionization (collision) alone is also shown. (Adapted from W. Heitler, *The Quantum Theory of Radiation*, London: Oxford University Press, 1954.)

where ξ is the distance traveled measured in gm/cm^2, and X_0 is a constant which can be found from Eq. (7–11) with $n = N_A\rho/M_A$ (M_A = atomic weight $\approx A$). We find that

$$X_0 = \frac{(4\pi\epsilon_0)^3\hbar m_0^2c^5M_A}{4e^6N_AZ(Z+1.3)[\ln(183Z^{-1/3})+\frac{1}{8}]}$$

$$= \frac{716M_A}{Z(Z+1.3)[\ln(183Z^{-1/3}+\frac{1}{8}]}\ \text{gm/cm}^2. \qquad (7\text{–}13)$$

The solution of Eq. (7–12) is

$$T = T_0e^{-\xi/X_0}. \qquad (7\text{–}14)$$

The constant X_0, which is called the *radiation length*, is the absorber thickness needed to reduce the electron energy by radiation loss to $1/e = 0.367$ of its original value. Table 7-2 gives the radiation length X_0 for various types of absorbers and also the *critical energy* T_c at which the radiation loss equals the collision loss in the various substances.

Figure 7-5 shows the combined ionization and radiation loss $-dT/d\xi = (-dT/d\xi)_i + (-dT/d\xi)_r$ suffered by electrons in various materials as functions of the kinetic energy of the electrons.

7-3 Absorption of Gamma Rays

As explained in the previous sections, charged nuclear particles and electrons are gradually slowed down when traveling through matter. The heavier nuclear particles travel along practically a straight line, but the electrons or positrons, being lighter, will be more scattered, so that an originally well-collimated beam of electrons will fan out in such a manner that the beam resembles an exponential horn. For gamma rays or neutrons, the processes by which they interact with matter are such that a single event will remove the neutron or gamma ray from the beam. For such processes, then, we can use the concept of a total cross section, which is an area, as defined in Section 3-2, rather than the stopping cross section for which the unit is area times energy (Section 7-1). It follows that the intensity of the beam—if we are dealing with a collimated beam—will decrease exponentially, as discussed in Section 3-2:

$$N = N_0 e^{-n\sigma x} = N_0 e^{-\mu x}.$$

The constant μ is called the absorption coefficient and has dimension $(\text{length})^{-1}$. Again we prefer to measure absorber thicknesses in gm/cm^2 and therefore write

$$N = N_0 e^{-\mu_m \xi},$$

where the *mass absorption coefficient* μ_m is given by

$$\mu_m = \frac{\mu}{\rho} = \frac{n\sigma}{\rho} = \frac{N_A \sigma}{M_A},$$

where N_A is Avogadro's number and M_A is the atomic weight of the element in the absorber. If several elements are present, we get

$$\mu_m = N_A \sum_i \frac{\alpha_i \sigma_i}{M_{Ai}},$$

where α_i is the abundance ratio of the ith element.

There are three major processes responsible for absorption of gamma rays in matter. They are the photoelectric effect, the Compton effect, and pair production. The total absorption cross section per atom for removing a photon is the sum of the cross section for each of these three processes. In the following paragraphs, we shall discuss briefly the various processes and their relative importance under various circumstances.

(*a*) *The photoelectric effect.* Einstein's treatment of the photoelectric effect is discussed in all textbooks of atomic physics or of modern physics. The process is one in which a photon interacts with an atom in such a way that its total energy is absorbed and concentrated on one electron which is thereby expelled. The kinetic energy of the emitted electron equals the photon energy minus the binding energy. Whenever the energy of the photon is high enough, the probability of expelling a K-electron is higher than it is for any of the other electrons. At a photon energy equal to the K-electron binding energy, there is a sharp step in the cross section for photoelectric emission. For energies above this K-*absorption edge*, Hall* gives the following cross-section formula for the emission of a K-electron:

$$\sigma_{\text{ph K}} = \frac{32\pi\sqrt{2}Z^5}{3(137)^4}\left(\frac{m_0c^2}{h\nu}\right)^{7/2}. \tag{7-15}$$

This formula applies when the photon energy is much smaller than the rest energy of an electron, $h\nu \ll m_0c^2$; at higher energies, the dependence on $h\nu$ is not so drastic. For increasing energy, the exponent, which is $\frac{7}{2}$ in Eq. (7–15), decreases until it reaches unity at very high energies. The dependence on Z to the fifth power is retained, however, throughout the energy range.

Figure 7–6 shows the mass-absorption coefficient of lead ($Z = 82$) as a function of photon energy and the various contributions to it from photoelectric effect, Compton effect, and pair production. For a lighter element, the contribution from the photoeffect, in particular, is much reduced because of the Z^5 term.

(*b*) *The Compton effect.* This effect, which is also discussed in all textbooks on modern physics, is due to a scattering process between the photon and an atomic electron, which for this purpose can be regarded as free. The gamma ray is then not completely absorbed but merely scattered out of the beam. It may still be moving in a forward direction but, of course, with reduced energy. The Compton scattering cross section per electron was calculated by Klein and Nishina† shortly after Dirac introduced relativistic quantum mechanics. It is

$$\sigma_c = \pi\left(\frac{e^2}{4\pi\epsilon_0 m_0c^2}\right)^2\left\{\left[1 - \frac{2(\gamma+1)}{\gamma^2}\right]\ln(2\gamma+1) + \frac{1}{2} + \frac{4}{\gamma} - \frac{1}{2(2\gamma+1)^2}\right\}, \tag{7-16}$$

* H. Hall, *Rev. Mod. Phys.* **8,** 358 (1936).
† O. Klein and Y. Nishina, *Z. Physik* **52,** 853 (1929).

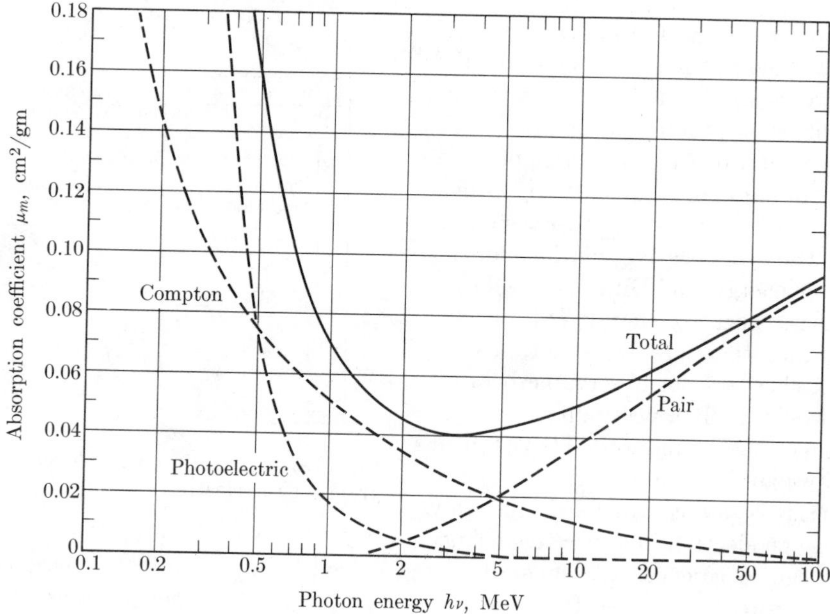

Fig. 7-6. Total mass-absorption coefficients for gamma rays in lead and the contributions from the photoelectric effect, the Compton effect, and pair production.

where $\gamma = h\nu/m_0c^2$. The total cross section for an atom is found simply by multiplying by Z. The contribution to the total gamma-ray absorption coefficient from the Compton effect, as calculated from Eq. (7-16), is given in Fig. 7-6 for lead.

For various problems, for instance in calculating the shielding thickness required for background reduction or personnel protection, one cannot neglect the forward-scattered gamma rays. The cross section can then be redefined in various ways, depending on whether one is interested in the number of photons no longer moving in the forward direction, the total amount of energy converted into electron kinetic energy, etc. This point is taken up again at the end of this section.

(c) *Pair production.* The last of the three important processes for gamma-ray absorption is the pair-production process, in which a positron and an electron are created with a total energy equal to the energy of the photon. This can clearly take place only when the photon energy exceeds $2m_0c^2 = 1.02$ MeV, which is the sum of the rest energies of the two particles created. A proper theory for pair production is a field theory, which we cannot go into in this text. We shall therefore give a qualitative discussion of pair production in terms of Dirac's electron-hole image. Figure 7-7 shows an energy-level diagram for the electron, as derived from Dirac's relativistic theory. The rest energy of the electron is m_0c^2 and, for energies above this threshold, there is in infinite space a continuum of electron states or, in a space of limited volume, a very high density of energy levels. Dirac's equations also give negative solutions for the electron energy, and Dirac assumed that all these negative-energy states were filled and therefore were not observable. They are not observable because this would imply a possibility of changing their state of motion. That is ruled out by Pauli's exclusion principle; since all negative states are filled, the only change an electron in a negative-energy state can experience is to cross the band of width $2m_0c^2$ so that it becomes a free positive-energy electron in one of the empty positive-energy states. The hole produced in the negative state left by the electron is observable as a positron. In the pair-production process, the energy needed by the electron for crossing the empty band is supplied by the photon, as indicated in Fig. 7-7. The same figure also indicates a bremsstrahlung process, in which one electron falls down to a lower energy level by emission of a photon. The pair-production process and the bremsstrahlung process are very similar, except that one is an absorption process, and the other is an emission process. For an intermediate-energy region, defined by $2m_0c^2 \ll h\nu \ll 137m_0c^2Z^{-1/3}$, the cross section for pair production in the field of the nucleus is

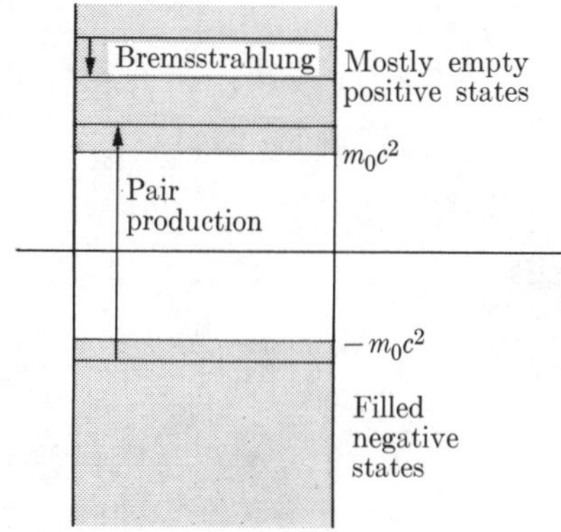

Fig. 7-7. Dirac's energy-level diagram for the electron.

$$\sigma_{\text{pair}} = \frac{Z^2}{137}\left(\frac{e^2}{4\pi\epsilon_0 m_0c^2}\right)^2\left(\frac{28}{9}\ln\frac{2h\nu}{m_0c^2} - \frac{218}{27}\right). \tag{7-17}$$

Pair production takes place in the field of a nucleus; however, no change of the state of the nucleus or its atomic electrons is involved, except that the nucleus absorbs some of the momentum of the photon. Pair production cannot take place in free space because conservation of energy and conservation of momentum cannot then be simultaneously observed. An assembly of relativistic particles has maximum total momentum at a given total energy when all particles are moving in the same direction and with the same velocity. If the energy is E, the momentum then is

$$p = \sqrt{(E/c)^2 - (\sum m_0c)^2} < E/c.$$

The gamma ray has momentum $p = E/c$, which is larger than the amount an assembly of particles with the same total energy can absorb.

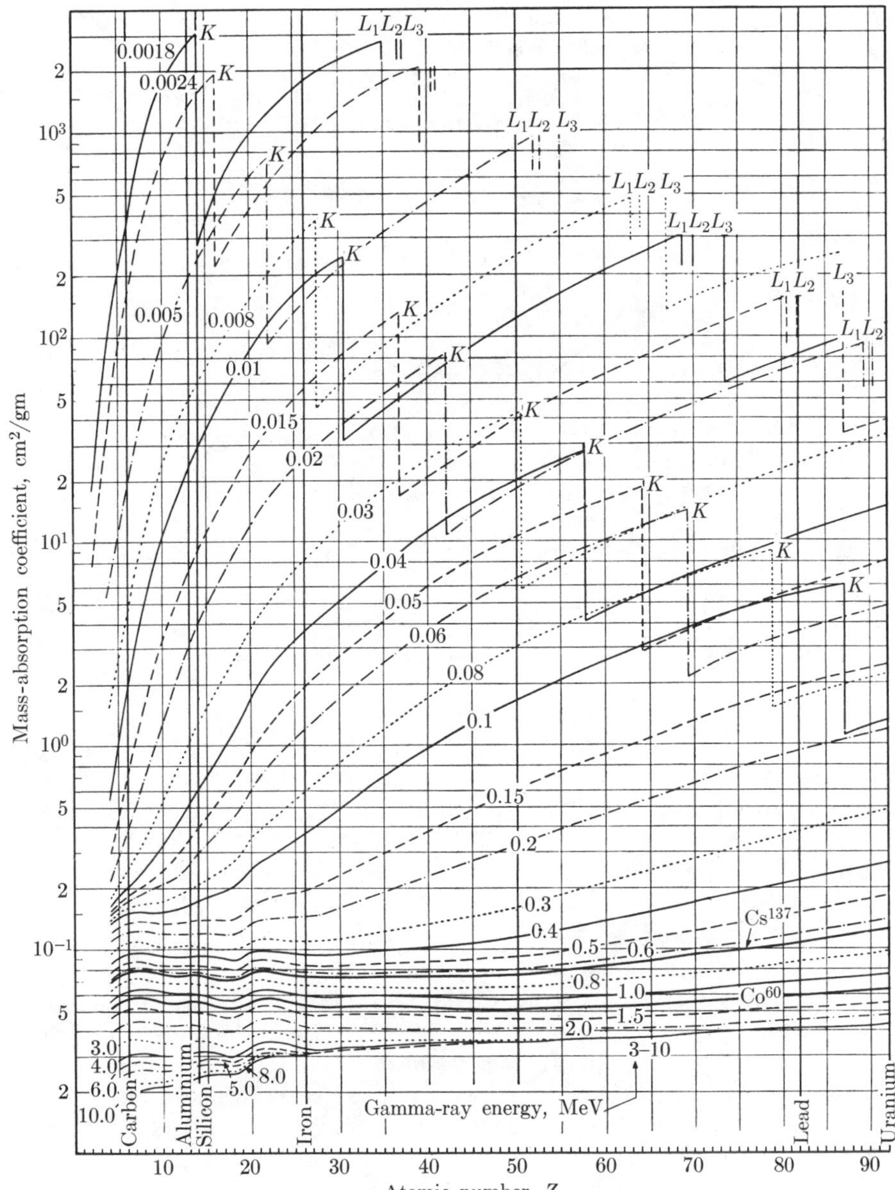

Fig. 7-8. Total mass-absorption coefficients for gamma rays in all elements from Be to U. Energy range 1.8 keV to 10 MeV. [From *Nucleonics* **19,** 62 (1961). (Reproduced by permission of the McGraw-Hill Publishing Company, Inc.)]

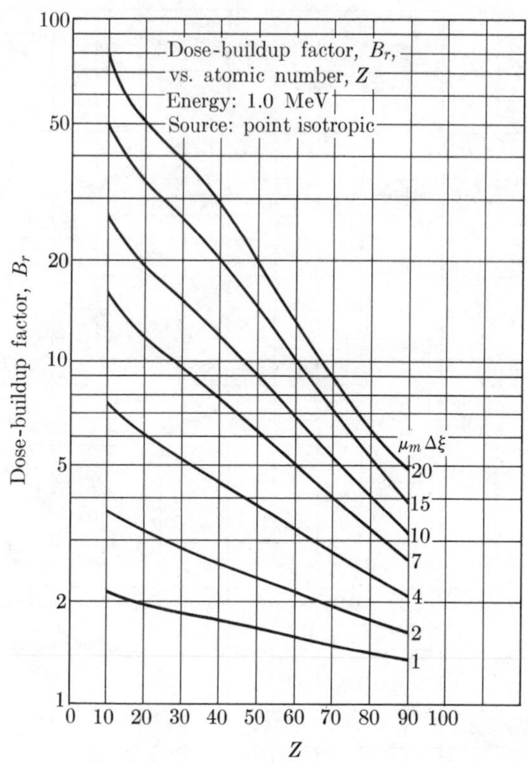

Fig. 7–9. Dose-buildup factor for 1.0-MeV gamma rays emitted from a source at the center of a spherical shell of shielding material. (From H. Goldstein and J. E. Wilkins, Jr., *Calculations of the Penetration of Gamma Rays*, NYO-3075, June 30, 1954.)

The contribution to the total gamma-ray absorption coefficient from the pair-production process is shown in Fig. 7–6 for lead. Figure 7–8 shows the total absorption coefficient for gamma rays of energies up to 10 MeV for all elements. At the lower energies, almost all of the absorption is caused by the photoelectric effect, and it is interesting to note in Fig. 7–8 that the drop in absorption coefficient in passing the K-edge is almost one order of magnitude.

As mentioned earlier, in the discussion of the Compton effect, the forward-scattered Compton gamma rays somewhat complicate the calculations of the gamma-ray intensity behind an absorber. Consider a point source of monoenergetic gamma rays at the center of a spherical-shell absorber with a total mass-absorption coefficient μ_m as given in Fig. 7–8. The intensity of *full-energy* gamma rays at a point outside the absorber is then given by

$$I_f = I_0 e^{-\mu_m \Delta\xi}, \tag{7–18}$$

where $\Delta\xi$ is the absorber thickness and I_0 is the intensity at the observation point in the absence of an absorber. The intensity can be measured in number of photons per unit area and unit time. If we are now interested not only in the number of full-energy photons but also in the total effect of all photons measured, for instance, as a *radiation dosage* in roentgen units (R) (Section 8-7), we must, in addition, consider the lower energy Compton-scattered photons. We then rewrite Eq. (7-18) as

$$I_D = I_{0D} B_r e^{-\mu_m \Delta\xi}, \tag{7-19}$$

where I_D and I_{0D} are dosages measured with and without absorber and the factor B_r is the *dose-buildup factor*. This factor can, of course, be calculated for various energies and element numbers. Figure 7-9 is a graph of the dose-buildup factor for various materials for a 1-MeV gamma-ray source. For lower-energy gamma rays, the buildup factor is somewhat higher, and for higher-energy gamma rays, it is lower.

7-4 Stopping of Neutrons

In the discussion of the stopping of charged nuclear particles (Section 7-1), we considered only the interaction between the particles and the atomic electrons, neglecting completely the nuclear events because of their relatively low rate of occurrence. For neutrons the situation is reversed. Because the neutron has a magnetic moment, the electromagnetic interaction between a neutron and the atomic electrons is not entirely absent. It can, however, be completely neglected in a discussion of the stopping process for neutrons in matter. Neutrons of all energies above thermal are slowed down as a result of scattering with nuclei and are absorbed by the nuclei in neutron-capture reactions either in an early close encounter with the nucleus or after having been slowed down to thermal energies by elastic-scattering events. Whether or not they stand a fair chance to reach thermal energy before absorption depends on the material of the absorber. The following discussion is divided into two parts: the first deals with fast neutrons, a term which, loosely defined, means neutrons in the MeV range; the second deals with slow neutrons, which, again loosely defined, means neutrons in the eV range. When neutrons are slowed down to thermal velocities, that is, to the equilibrium velocity in matter of temperature of about 300°K, their energies have a Maxwellian distribution with an average of $3kT/2 = 0.025$ eV.

(*a*) *Fast neutrons.* A discussion of neutron-proton scattering is given in Section 3-3, and Fig. 3-3 shows the general setup used in measuring total neutron cross sections, that is, the cross section for removal of the neutrons from the incident beam, whether such removal is caused by scattering or by absorption. For neutron-proton collisions, as discussed in Chapter 3, the absorption cross section is negligible compared with the scattering cross section. In Section 13-10 and in Fig. 13-24 we discuss experimental results of neutron scattering and absorption by other nuclei. As a very rough guideline, one can say that the total cross section for fast neutrons in any element is of the order of magnitude 3 to $4\pi R^2$, where R is the nuclear radius. This is 3 to 4 times the geometrical cross section, with part of it representing scattering and the other part, absorption.

Eventually, the neutron is absorbed by a nucleus, and in most cases the binding energy (about 6 to 8 MeV) is then given off in the form of one or several gamma rays. In some cases an (n, α) reaction might take place, and for certain heavy nuclei the absorption of slow neutrons may lead to fission (Section 14–1). After an (n, α), as well as an (n, γ), process, the ground state of the residual nucleus may be beta unstable. In any event, the stopping of a neutron results in emission of other ionizing radiation which produces motion of electrons and emission of lower-energy photons (light). In a sufficiently thick absorber, all the kinetic energy of the neutron and all the energy released in capture will end up as heat energy and, in cases where molecules are fragmented, partly as stored-up chemical energy.

For neutrons with energy less than 10 MeV, the scattering cross section of hydrogen is relatively large (Fig. 3–12), and, also, the neutron mass and the proton mass are practically identical. These two facts combined are utilized in certain types of neutron detectors and in neutron shielding. In a head-on

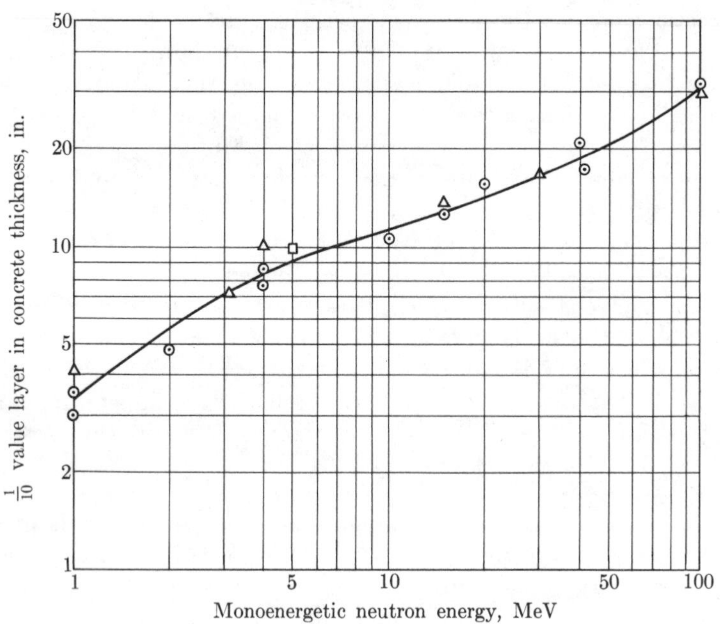

Fig. 7–10. Thickness of concrete of density 2.3 gm/cm^3 needed to reduce the neutron flux by a factor of 10 vs. neutron energy. (Adapted by permission from E. A. Burrill, Jr., *Neutron Production and Protection*, Burlington, Mass.: High Voltage Engineering Corporation. For references to original measurements, see this publication.)

collision with a proton, the neutron transfers practically all of its energy to the proton, and in a more grazing collision, a larger fraction of the energy is transferred than in a collision with any other nucleus. A good absorber for fast neutrons in this range is paraffin, with a small amount of boron added. The neutrons slow down rapidly as a result of collisions with protons, and then are absorbed by B^{10} when the energy is in the thermal region where B^{10} has a huge (n, α) cross section. Steel is also a good shield for fast neutrons, and so is concrete. Figure 7–10 gives the thickness of concrete needed to reduce the neutron intensity by a factor of 10, plotted as a function of the neutron energy between 1 and 100 MeV.

(*b*) *Slow neutrons.* In the theory of low-energy neutron-proton scattering (Section 3–4 and Eq. 3–16), we showed that if the phase shift δ is close to 90°, the scattering cross section can be very large, particularly if this occurs at a low energy (k^2 small). This theory applies to low-energy neutron-nucleus encounters as well, and the incident energy (k^2) occurs in the denominator for absorption cross sections, as well as for scattering cross sections (Section 13–8).

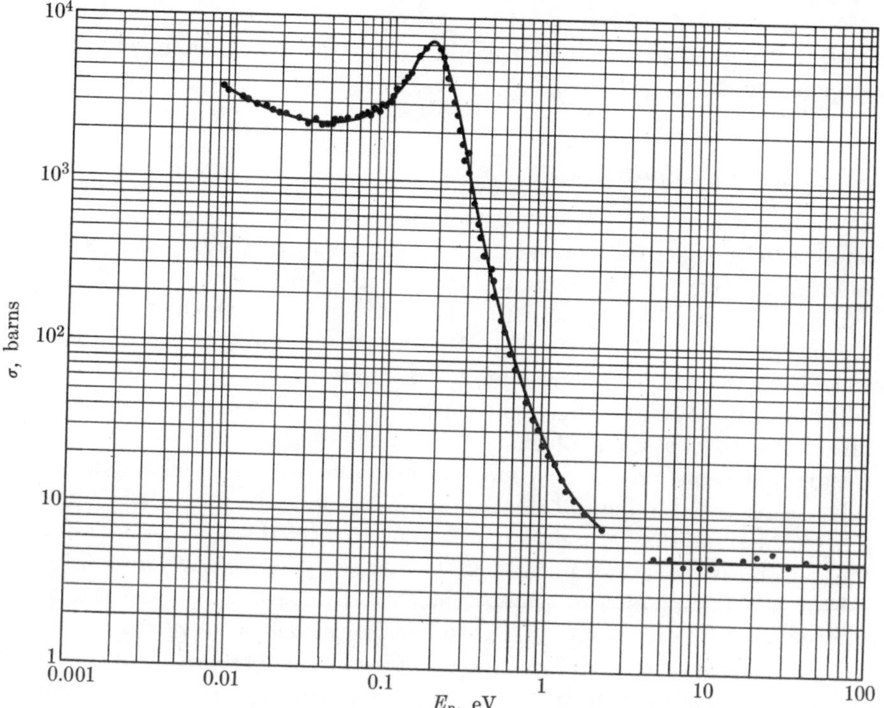

Fig. 7–11. Average cross section of natural cadmium for neutrons in the electron-volt range. Practically all the cross section is due to Cd^{113}, which has a 12.3% abundance. [From H. H. Goldsmith, H. W. Ibser, and B. T. Feld, *Rev. Mod. Phys.* **19**, 261 (1947).]

If a resonance occurs, i.e., $\sin \delta \approx 1$, at very low energies, both the absorption and the scattering cross sections may, in a limited energy range, be several thousand times the geometrical cross section of the nucleus. An example is shown in Fig. 7–11, which gives the total cross section of cadmium for neutrons. The resonance is due to Cd^{113} (relative abundance, 12.3%). If the experiment had been performed on isotopic Cd^{113}, the total cross section measured therefore would have been approximately 57,000 barns at the maximum. Let us calculate the thickness of a layer of cadmium needed to reduce the intensity of thermal neutrons by a factor of 10. The atomic weight for cadmium is 112.4, and from Fig. 7–11, we find that the average cross section per atom for 0.025-eV neutrons is 2700 barns. The mass-absorption coefficient is therefore

$$\mu_m = \frac{6.025 \times 10^{23} \times 2700 \times 10^{-24}}{112.4} = 14.48 \text{ cm}^2/\text{gm}.$$

The total thickness, $\Delta\xi$, needed is given by $0.1 = e^{-\mu_m \Delta\xi}$, which gives $\Delta\xi = \ln 10/14.48 = 0.159 \text{ gm/cm}^2$, or approximately 0.018 cm.

We see that with the proper selection of material, slow neutrons are as easy to stop as charged nuclear particles. However, it should be noted that the absorption of neutrons in Cd^{113} leads to the emission of gamma rays with associated shielding problems.

7–5 *Gas-Filled Counters*

One of the oldest and simplest detectors for nuclear radiation is a gas-filled container with a central electrode, which may be a thin wire, kept at a positive potential relative to the conducting wall of the container. Figure 7–12(a) is a sketch of such a counter and the electrical circuit to which it is connected. Ionizing radiation passing through the counter will produce positive ions and electrons in the gas, which may be, for instance, argon. The electrons will be pulled toward the center wire, and the positive ions will move toward the outside walls. The total amount of charge that passes through the counter and the resistor R depends on the dc voltage V between the central electrode and the walls, as described in detail below.

Let us assume that the electronic circuit connected to the resistor R is designed to measure the magnitude of the voltage pulses v developed across the resistor R. Figure 7–12(b) shows schematically $\log v$ vs. V for two different types of events in the counter. One event is the passage of a low-ionizing electron through the gas, and the other is the passage of a highly ionizing alpha particle. In region A, the dc voltage V is so low that recombination of positive and negative ions takes place, so that not all the ion pairs formed are detected by the electronic circuit. In region B, the voltage V is sufficiently high so that only a negligible amount of recombination takes place. This is called the *ion-chamber region*. In region C the voltage is sufficiently high so that electrons approaching

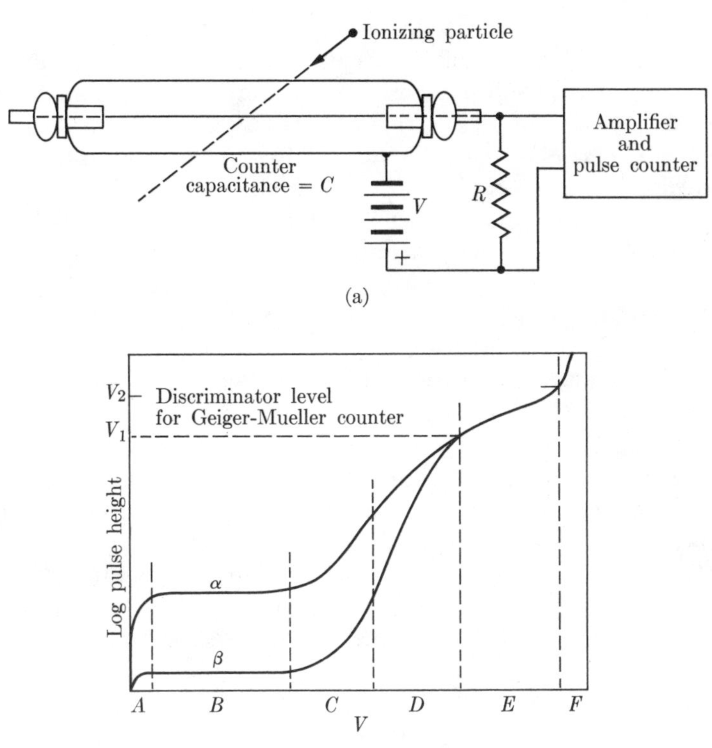

Fig. 7-12. (a) Gas-filled counter with associated circuit. (b) Voltage pulses produced across the resistor R vs. voltage V for two events with greatly different numbers of primary ion pairs produced.

the center wire, where the field gradient is high, attain sufficient energy between collisions with gas molecules to produce new ion pairs. A limited cascade takes place, and the total amount of charge passing through R may be up to a thousand times the charge produced by the primary radiation. This region is called the *proportionality region*. For still higher values of V, in region D, the proportionality feature is lost, and in region E even a minimum-ionizing particle will produce a very large pulse. This is called the *Geiger-Mueller region.*

In the Geiger-Mueller region, the ionization process spreads along the total length of the center wire, partly involving photons as intermediaries. The initial ionization actually triggers a complete gas breakdown which must be stopped to prepare the counter for a new event. This "quenching," as it is called, may be accomplished by electronically lowering the voltage V after each count. It is, however, usually done more elegantly in the gas itself, as described below. For the discharge to maintain itself, either one or more of the huge number of positive ions formed in an avalanche or a photon must release a new electron in the gas or at the cathode to start the process over again. When a positive argon ion, for instance, is neutralized on a metallic surface, a considerable amount of energy is released that may be used to expel an electron from the surface. Certain other gases do not behave this way, however. If the gas is argon with about 10% ethyl alcohol, then because of charge exchanges on the way, the positive ions reaching the cathode are alcohol ions, and they do not, in general, release electrons from the surface; the energy is used instead to break up the gas molecule. The alcohol is also an effective absorber for photons, and the absorption usually takes place without ionization.

When the voltage V is increased beyond region E, spurious untriggered breakdowns start to occur, and for a further increase in voltage a continuous unquenchable discharge results. Some further details of gas counters operating in regions B, C, or E are given below.

(*a*) *The ionization chamber.* The ionization chamber can be used as a charged-particle spectrometer with a resolving power of the order of one percent or better. A 10-MeV charged particle will produce approximately 300,000 ion pairs in the gas if it is completely stopped inside the counter. If the total capacitance of the chamber is, for instance, $C = 50$ pF, the total voltage burst applied to the electronic circuit is then of the order of magnitude

$$v \approx \frac{3 \times 10^5 \times 1.6 \times 10^{-19}}{50 \times 10^{-12}} \approx 10^{-3}\ \text{V},$$

or about 0.1 mV/MeV. In order to record the complete energy spectrum of a given radiation simultaneously, the counter output is, after amplification, fed into a "kicksorter" or pulse-height analyzer, which sorts out the various events according to the voltage amplitudes of the pulses.

One difficulty with the simple two-electrode ionization chamber is that the drift time for the positive ions to the cathode is much longer than the time it takes for the electrons to reach the anode. This results in a voltage-time characteristic shown in Fig. 7–13. The time constant RC may be assumed to be large compared with the drift time of the positive ions as well as the drift time of the electrons. We can therefore initially regard the counter with capacitance C charged to a voltage V and isolated. The positive and negative charges $\pm q$ produced in the gas have no effect on the voltage before they are separated, but then the effect is one of polarization, similar to the effects in a dielectric material. Over the capacitor a voltage drop is produced proportional to the separation and reaching the maximum value $\Delta V = -q/C$ when all the charges have reached their respective electrodes. Since the electrons move faster, a fast rise is seen in Fig. 7–13, followed by a slower rise caused by the motion of the positive ions. The exponential fall-off results from the recharging of the capacitor over the resistor R. The relative amplitudes of the fast rise and the

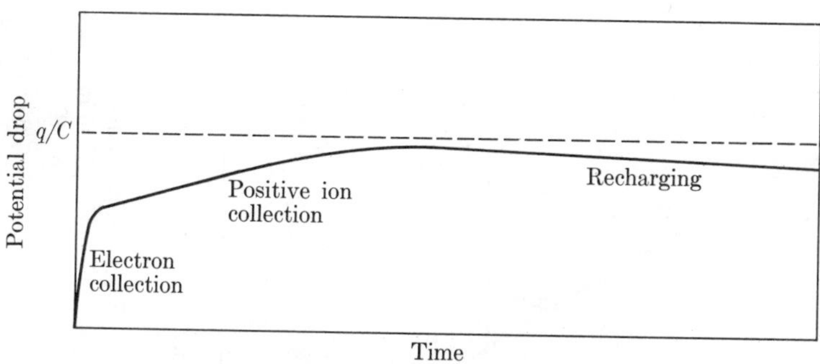

Fig. 7-13. Voltage across the resistor R in Fig. 7-12(a) vs. time after the passage of one ionizing particle. The supply voltage V is in region B (Fig. 7-12b).

slow rise depend upon in which part of the ion chamber the primary particle produced the charges. This causes difficulties for the design of a reasonably fast electronic circuit for accurately measuring the pulse height. This difficulty can be avoided by surrounding the central anode with a shielding grid, with a potential intermediate between the potential of the anode and that of the cathode. The ionizing particles are collimated so that they produce the ionization outside the grid. Only the electrons pass through the space between the grid and the anode, and the drop in the potential between these two electrodes has only a fast component, proportional to the total number of ion pairs produced. An example of a spectrum measured with a gridded ionization chamber is shown in Fig. 7-14.

The ionization chamber has also found use as an instrument for measuring radiation intensity without regard to the energies of the individual events. In particular, for gamma rays for which the unit radiation dose is defined in terms of the number of ion pairs produced per unit volume in a gas, the ionization chamber is the natural instrument. A gamma-ray *dose* of 1 *roentgen* unit (R) produces $\frac{1}{3} \times 10^{-9}$ coul charge of both signs in 1 cm^3 of air at standard temperature and pressure (see also Section 8-4). A *dosage rate* of 1 R/hr will therefore produce in an ion chamber of volume 1 liter = 1000 cm^3 a current of

$$\tfrac{1}{3} \times 10^{-9} \times 10^3/3600 = 0.927 \times 10^{-10} \text{ A/liter}.$$

Since one would like to be able to use such an instrument to detect radiation dosage rates as low as 1 mR/hr, an electroscope or a very sensitive vacuum-tube-voltmeter circuit combined with a large resistor must be used for measuring the current.

(*b*) *Proportional counter.* Gas counters operating in the region of proportionality (C in Fig. 7-12) are used for a variety of purposes, for instance as a dE/dx detector, in which a particle passes through a shallow counter and leaves

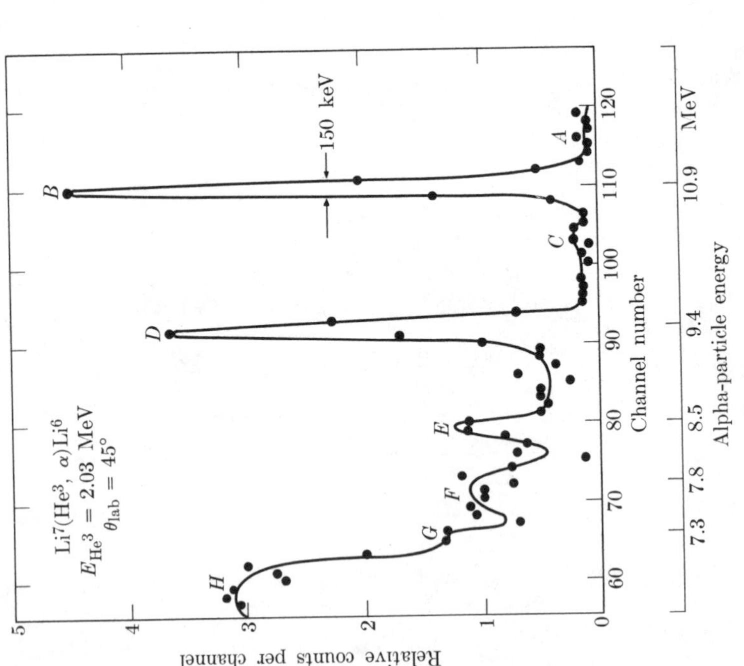

Fig. 7-14. Pulse-height spectrum from alpha particles stopped in a gridded ionization chamber. The resolving power is $E/\Delta E \approx 10.9/0.15 = 73$ (the inverse is about 1.4%). (Courtesy D. A. Bromley.)

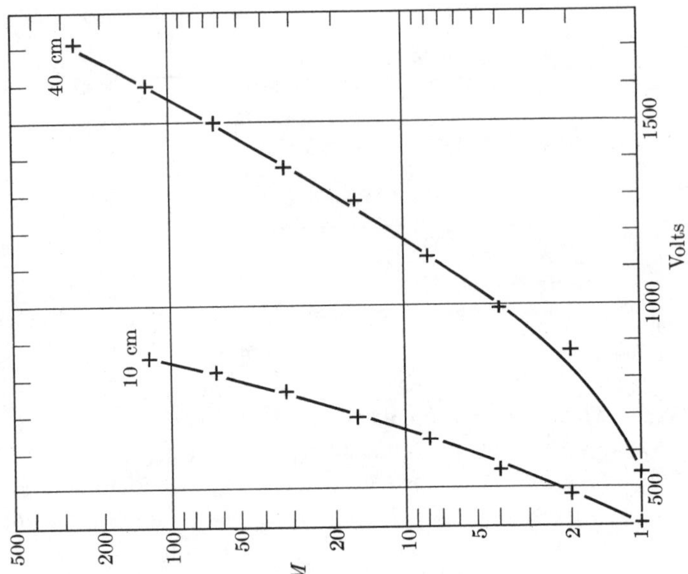

Fig. 7-15. Multiplication factor for a proportional argon counter with concentric electrodes of radii 0.005 in. and 0.435 in. Argon pressures $p = 10$ cm Hg and 40 cm Hg. (From H. H. Staub in *Experimental Nuclear Physics*, ed. E. Segrè, Vol. I. New York: John Wiley and Sons, Inc., p. 33. Reproduced by permission.)

a trail of ions with a total charge proportional to dE/dx. If the particle thereafter enters a second counter, in which it gives up all its energy, the arrangement can be used not only to measure the total energy of the particle, but also to identify the particle. The first counter essentially measures the particle velocity (compare Eq. 7–6), and the sum of the pulses from the first and second counter is a measure of the total energy. Figure 7–15 is a chart giving the multiplication factor for an argon counter with an outer diameter of 0.435 in. and a center-wire anode of diameter 0.005 in. The two curves are for argon pressures of 10 cm Hg and 40 cm Hg.

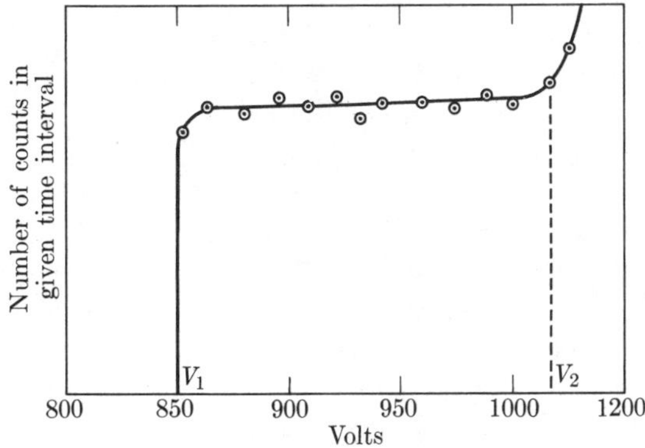

Fig. 7–16. Typical plot of number of counts vs. voltage across a gas counter operating in the Geiger-Mueller region (region E, Fig. 7–12b). The electronic circuit is set to record all pulses above a minimum peak voltage.

(c) *Geiger-Mueller counter.* Figure 7–12 shows that the pulse height produced in the Geiger-Mueller region is independent of the number of primary ion pairs produced, but that it increases rapidly with applied voltage. Normally the Geiger-Mueller counter is connected to an electronic circuit in which all pulses exceeding a certain lower limit (discriminator level, Fig. 7–12) are recorded. A Geiger-Mueller counter will therefore ideally register all events that produce at least one ion pair in the gas independently of the voltage V between V_1 corresponding to the discriminator level, and V_2, corresponding to the onset of spurious counts. The independence, or near-independence, of the counting rate of V is illustrated in Fig. 7–16, which gives the number of counts registered in a given radiation field as a function of applied voltage. The plateau in the counting-rate curve between V_1 and V_2 is called the Geiger-Mueller plateau.

In spite of the many other significant advances in the area of more sophisticated nuclear-detecting methods, some of which are discussed below, the Geiger-Mueller counter remains an inexpensive but reliable tool for nuclear-physics research, as well as for applied-radiation fields.

7–6 The Solid-State Counter

An ionization chamber does not necessarily need to have gas filling. In principle, it would work just as well with a solid-state insulator between the electrodes. Positive and negative charges are produced by the ionizing radiation, and these charges are pulled toward the electrode of opposite sign. An insulator is an insulator because it normally does not contain charge carriers and not because charge carriers, once produced, cannot move in the insulator. To understand this and the principle of operation of the solid-state counter, one must be familiar with the rudiments of the band theory of solids. We shall therefore discuss this theory very briefly.

In a solid the atomic energy levels of the outer electrons, by the operation of exchange effects between the individual atoms, split into a large number of levels forming a band which occupies a certain width ΔE in the energy-level diagram (Fig. 7–17). An electron in a given state is shared by all atoms, and the solid is an insulator or a conductor, depending on whether or not the last band occupied by electrons is filled. If it is filled, the number of electrons moving in two opposite directions is the same, so that the net current is zero. If it is not filled, in the absence of an electric field, the configuration of lowest energy also has an equal number of electrons moving in two opposite directions, so that again there is no net current. By the application of an electric field, however, one can make this distribution lopsided and produce a net current. This, then, is the situation in a conductor.

In an *intrinsic semiconductor* the gap between the last filled band, the *valence band,* and the next band, the so-called *conduction band,* is sufficiently small so that by thermal excitation some electrons are lifted to the conduction band and thereby give the material a certain conductivity. Another type of semiconductor has a relatively large gap between the two bands, but it contains impurities with energy levels close to the conduction band so that it is easier by thermal excitation to promote electrons up to the conduction band. In this N-*type* semiconductor, the current is transported by negative carriers produced by the *donor* impurity. Another possibility is that an *acceptor* impurity, that is, atoms with strong affinity for electrons because of vacancies, removes electrons from a lower filled band. The holes produced in the lower band represent positive-charge carriers, and the material is called a P-*type* semiconductor.

The first solid-state counters were made of insulating crystals with two metallic electrodes in good contact for providing an electric field inside the crystal to collect the ions produced. These *crystal* counters functioned satisfactorily as counters but not as spectrometers, that is, the pulse height that they gave out was not a reliable measure of the total energy deposited by the particle in the counter. Part of the difficulty was that impurities trapped varying amounts of the electrons released, so that sharp uniform pulses were not obtained. These difficulties have been overcome by use of semiconductor diodes instead of insulating materials in the counter.

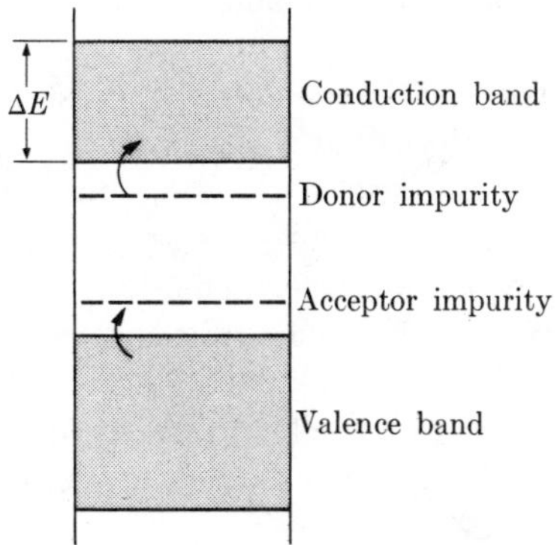

Fig. 7-17. Energy-level diagram for a semiconductor with impurities that can, by thermal excitation, donate "free" electrons to the conduction band or capture electrons from the filled valence band leaving mobile holes there.

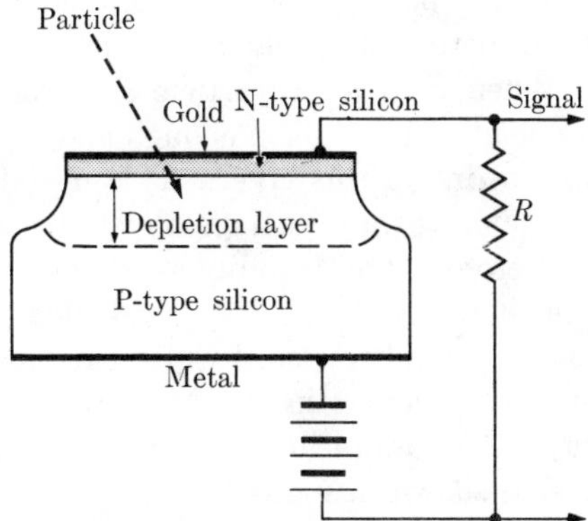

Fig. 7-18. A PN-junction detector. The operation is similar to the gas counter working in the ionization-chamber region (region B, Fig. 7-12b).

In a semiconductor diode, a junction has been produced between an N-type and a P-type semiconductor. A schematic drawing of such a PN-junction used as a particle detector is shown in Fig. 7-18. The basic material of the conductor is P-type silicon; that is, silicon with an acceptor-type impurity which produces positive charge carriers. From the surface of the P-type silicon, an N-type (donor type) impurity is diffused into the material, producing N-type silicon in a thin layer at the surface. Contact is made with this layer by a thin evaporated film of gold, through which the particles to be detected can pass. A positive (reverse) bias applied to the gold film will push all the positive-charge carriers away from the junction and produce a *depletion layer*, indicated in the figure. The negative space charge of the depletion layer produces an electric field and an accompanying potential drop corresponding to the bias voltage. The higher the bias voltage, the deeper the depletion layer will be, and the limit is set by electrical breakdown in the semiconductor. An ionizing particle passing through the gold foil and into the depletion layer will produce both negative and positive charge carriers that are swept away by the applied field and registered as a voltage pulse over the resistor R.

The number of charge-carrier pairs produced in a semiconductor material is approximately 10 times as large as the number of ion pairs produced in a gas ion chamber, i.e., the energy expended per pair is about 3 eV instead of 30. The voltage pulse will therefore be about 10 times larger, assuming that the circuits have approximately the same capacitances. The greatest significance of this factor 10 in the number of pairs N lies in the fact that the relative statistical fluctuations in the voltage pulses produced is $\sqrt{N}/N$ and therefore down by about a factor of $\sqrt{10}$ for the solid-state counter. Hence the inherent resolving power of a solid-state counter used as a spectrometer is about three times better than that for an ion chamber.

When used as a particle spectrometer, the solid-state detector must have a depletion layer deep enough and/or wide enough so that the particle can come to rest inside this layer. This initially limited the use of the solid-state spectrometer to applications involving alpha particles or low-energy protons or deuterons. The techniques for producing larger and larger depletion volumes are, however, being improved at a rapid rate. The solid-state spectrometer has already been used quite extensively for longer range particles as, for instance, electrons in the MeV range and, as described below, also for gamma rays. An example of a spectrum of protons obtained with a solid-state spectrometer is shown in Fig. 13–6.

In solid-state detectors for charged particles, silicon has been used most because of its low intrinsic conductivity. This means that the detector can be operated at room temperature without excessive leakage current. The silicon detector has not been found to be very suitable as a gamma-ray detector, since its relatively small volume and low Z give a very low counting efficiency. Germanium is much better in this respect because of its higher element number; on the other hand, germanium has a smaller gap between the valence band and the conduction band, and therefore its intrinsic conductivity is higher. This prevents the establishment of a thick depletion layer if the detector is kept at

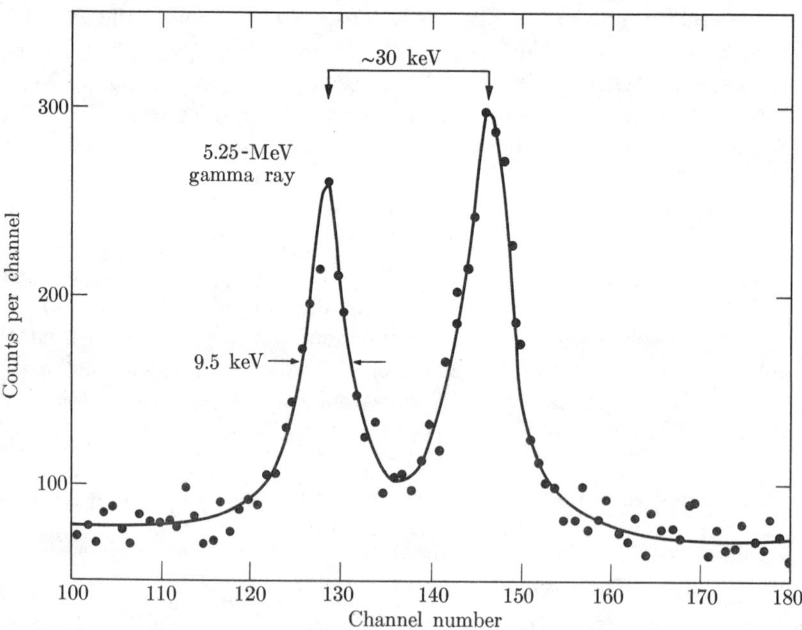

Fig. 7–19. Part of a gamma-ray spectrum obtained with a germanium counter. (Courtesy of A. E. Litherland.)

room temperature. However, by cooling the germanium to liquid-nitrogen temperatures, this problem can be alleviated. Methods have also been developed to reduce the conductivity produced by impurities, thus making feasible depletion layers of 1 cm thickness.

Figure 7–19 shows, as an example, part of the gamma-ray spectrum obtained with a germanium counter from a nitrogen target bombarded with deuterons. The left-hand peak results from the decay of the first excited state of N^{15} produced in the $N^{14}(d, p)N^{15}$ reaction. The event in the detector material is pair production of a 5.25-MeV gamma ray depositing 4.23 MeV in the material from the stopping of the electron and the positron. The positron is annihilated in the detector but the annihilation radiation, two 0.51-MeV gamma rays, escapes. Events in which one or both of the annihilation quanta are absorbed give rise to other (smaller) peaks in the pulse-height spectrum, corresponding to deposited energies of 4.74 and 5.25 MeV. The right-hand peak corresponds in similar fashion to the decay of the second excited state of O^{15} produced in the $N^{14}(d, n)O^{15}$ reaction. In many of the events, of course, the electron and/or positron may not come to complete rest inside the material. This gives rise to a reduced voltage pulse, contributing to the more or less continuous background shown in Fig. 7–19.

7–7 *The Scintillation Counter*

The famous measurements by Rutherford and his associates of alpha particles scattered from thin metal foils were performed by viewing the scintillations caused by the alpha particles impinging on a zinc sulfide screen. The photons in the visible range produced by the slowing-down process of the alpha particles were directly viewed by the eye through a low-power microscope. A modern scintillation counter operates on exactly the same principle, except that the human eye is replaced by an electronic device called *a photomultiplier tube.* Figure 7–20 shows schematically the arrangement. Photons produced in the scintillation crystal cemented to the surface of the photomultiplier tube liberate electrons from the photocathode. These electrons are accelerated over approximately 100 to 150 V and are electrostatically focused so that they impinge on the first dynode. By the impact, a number of secondary electrons are released, usually of the order of 2 to 5 per primary electron. The secondary electrons are accelerated again across the gap to the second dynode, where the number is further multiplied. A photomultiplier tube usually contains 10 to 18 dynodes, each with a multiplication factor of 2 to 5, depending on the voltage between the dynodes. Photons striking the photocathode therefore cause an avalanche of electrons which eventually hits the anode and produces a voltage pulse over the resistor R. This voltage pulse is proportional to the energy deposited by the primary radiation in the crystal, or approximately so. The scintillation counter therefore can be used as a spectrometer in conjunction with an electronic pulse-height analyzer.

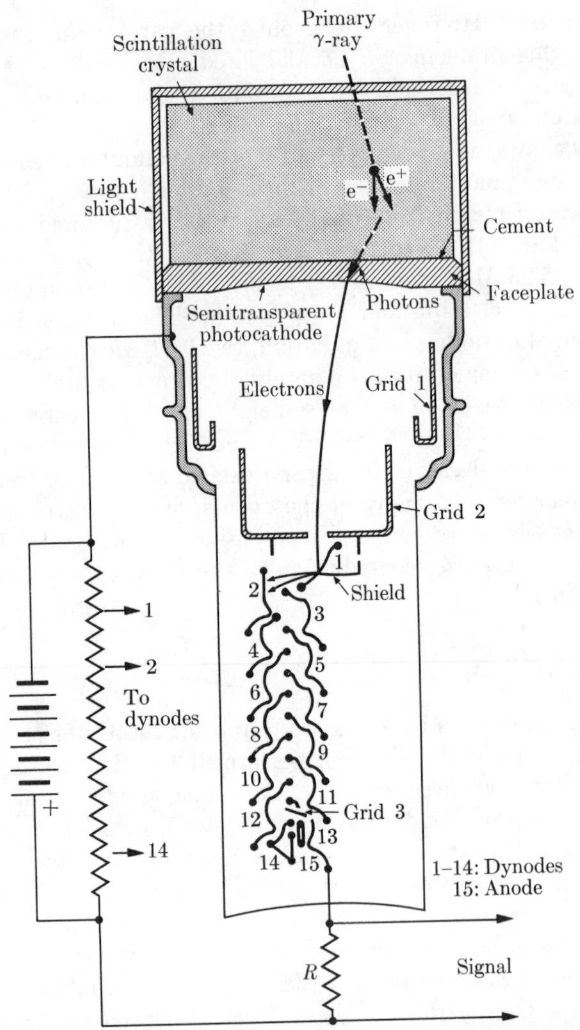

Fig. 7–20. Large scintillation crystal (for gamma rays) and photomultiplier tube (RCA 7046).

Table 7–3 lists the properties of several of the common phosphors used in scintillation counters or spectrometers. Column 5 of the table lists the decay constant; that is, the time it takes for the phosphor to release its stored-up energy in the form of photons. The slowest of the crystals, the cesium iodide crystal, is still much faster than a Geiger-Mueller tube, which has a dead time of about 10^{-4} sec. The importance of fast response in nuclear detectors is discussed in Section 8–6.

Table 7-3. Properties of some common phosphors used as scintillation detectors*

Phosphor	Density, gm/cm^2	Index of refraction	Relative response	Decay constant ($\times 10^{-9}$ sec)	Approximate range of a 10-MeV proton,[a] mg/cm^2	Remarks
Anthracene	1.25	1.59	1.00	30	107	Response standard with RCA 5819 or equivalent phototube
trans stilbene	1.16		0.60	6.4	105	
p-terphenyl in toluene	0.86	1.50[b]	0.35	2.2	99	Typical liquid scintillator at 5 gm/liter concentration of terphenyl
p-terphenyl in polystyrene	1.06	1.59[c]	0.39	4.0	101	Typical plastic scintillator 36 gm/liter of monomer 0.2 gm/liter of 1,1,4,4, tetraphenyl-1,3-butadiene
NaI(Tl)	3.67	1.77	2.10	250	250	
CsI(Tl)	4.51	1.79	0.5	1100	260	
ZnS(Ag)	4.09	2.4	1 4[d]	10^4	190	Not available except as powder, partially opaque to own radiation

* From N. S. Wall, *Nuclear Spectroscopy*, ed. Fay Ajzenberg-Selove, Part A. New York: Academic Press, 1960, p. 39. (Reprinted by permission.)
[a] Computed from range-energy curves of Aron *et al.*, AECU 663 revised
[b] For pure solvent
[c] For pure polymer
[d] ZnS has a large light output when the signal is integrated over long times.

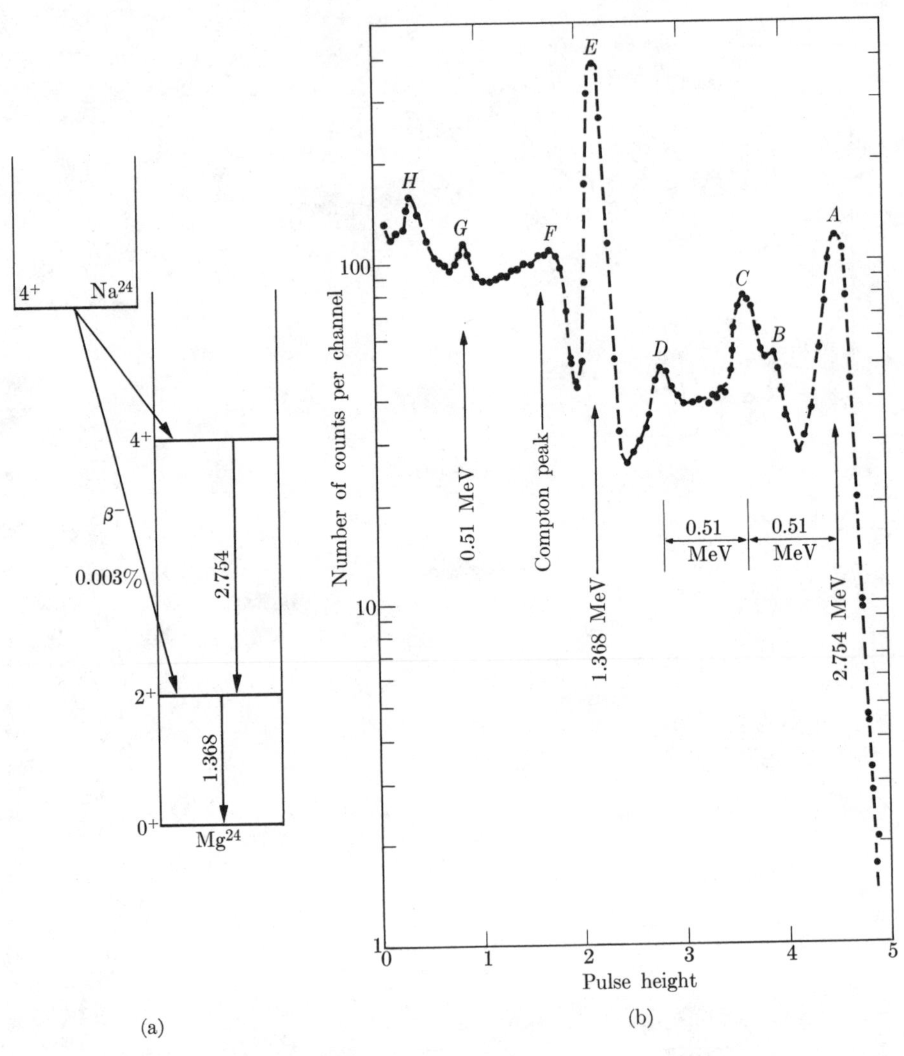

Fig. 7–21. (a) Decay scheme for Na^{24} and (b) pulse-height spectrum for the gamma rays emitted in the decay obtained with a 3-in. × 3-in. NaI scintillation crystal. (Data from P. R. Bell in *Beta- and Gamma-Ray Spectroscopy*, ed. by K. Siegbahn. Amsterdam: North-Holland Publishing Company, 1955.)

The scintillation spectrometer has found many applications in low-energy, as well as in high-energy, nuclear physics. It has been particularly popular in the area of gamma-ray spectroscopy, for which usually a large (e.g., 3-in. diameter, 3-in. thick) NaI crystal is used. Unfortunately, even monoenergetic gamma rays produce a complex pulse-height spectrum, reflecting the fact that varying amounts of the gamma-ray energy may be deposited in the crystal.

This subject was touched upon in the discussion of the germanium detector above, but it is more serious for the scintillation spectrometer that does not have nearly the resolving power of the germanium detector.

Figure 7–21 shows as an example the pulse-height spectrum produced by gamma rays from the lower excited states of Mg^{24}. This isotope is produced in low-lying states by beta emission of Na^{24}, as shown in the decay scheme (Fig. 7–21a). Two gamma rays of differing energy are emitted, one at 2.754 MeV and one at 1.368 MeV. The peak, A, to the far right in the pulse-height spectrum arises from events in which the full energy of the 2.754-MeV gamma ray is deposited in the crystal, i.e., pair production with no escape or photoelectric events. The next lower peak, B, results from electrons produced in Compton events, where the scattered gamma ray has escaped from the crystal. This then gives rise to a fairly broad spectrum, because the energy of the electrons depends on the scattering angle. The third peak, C, is caused by pair-production processes in which one of the two annihilation photons has escaped, and peak D arises from processes in which both of the annihilation photons have escaped. The sharp peak, E, in the middle of the spectrum is ascribed to photoelectric events, or pair-production events caused by the 1.368-MeV gamma rays. The corresponding Compton peak, F, is also seen, but the 1-quantum and 2-quanta escape peaks are not distinguishable. This is presumably because at 1.368 MeV, pair production is relatively unimportant, so that the photoelectric effect is responsible for most of the amplitude of the 1.368-MeV peak. Finally, peak G arises from 0.51-MeV annihilation photons produced outside the crystal but absorbed in it, and peak H results from back-scattered photons from Compton events.

7–8 Nuclear Emulsions

A nuclear emulsion is a modified photographic emulsion; that is, it consists of AgBr, silver bromide, in a matrix of a gelatin. An ionizing particle passing through or stopping in the emulsion will reduce some of the AgBr molecules in exactly the same way as photons do in the normal photographic process. After development, the nuclear emulsion can be studied under a microscope, and the path of the ionizing particle can be directly examined. Nuclear emulsions are most often supported on glass plates, although for some high-energy work stacks of self-supporting emulsions have been used. Table 7–4 shows the composition of commercially available emulsions. All the companies mentioned in this table have selections of emulsions with different sensitivities. Some are sensitive only to very highly ionizing particles, as, for instance, fission products and low-energy alpha particles, and others are sensitive also to minimum ionizing particles (fast electrons or other singly ionized particles with $v \approx c$).

In nuclear-structure physics, nuclear emulsions are being used extensively as detectors of charged particles in magnetic spectrographs (Sections 10–2 and 13–3). In these situations, the particles are momentum analyzed by the mag-

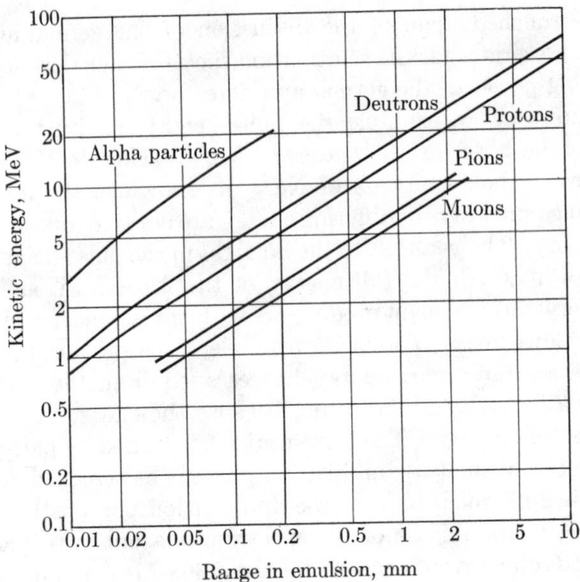

Fig. 7–22. Ranges of various particles in nuclear emulsions. [From A. Beiser, *Rev. Mod. Phys.* **24,** 273 (1952).]

netic spectrograph, and the track length in the emulsion is used to discriminate between different types of particles. Also, the wanted tracks are all oriented in the same direction, so that background radiation can be discounted on the basis of lengths and directions of the tracks. Figure 7–22 gives the range of protons, deuterons, alpha particles, pions, and muons in Eastman Kodak NTA emulsions as a function of particle energy.

Nuclear emulsions can also be used for neutron spectroscopy, because the gelatin of the emulsion contains a considerable amount of hydrogen, so that

Table 7–4. The compositions in gm/cm^3 of dry nuclear emulsions produced by Ilford, Kodak Ltd., and Eastman Kodak*

Element	Ilford	Kodak Ltd.	Eastman Kodak
Silver	2.025	1.97	1.70
Bromine	1.465	1.44	1.22
Iodine	0.057	0.036	0.054
Carbon	0.30	0.27	0.34
Hydrogen	0.049	0.038	0.043
Oxygen	0.20	0.16	0.17
Sulfur	0.011	–	–
Nitrogen	0.073	0.080	0.11

* From A. Beiser, *Rev. Mod. Phys.* **24,** 273 (1952).

a neutron in passing through the emulsion may collide with a proton and give up most of its energy. If the neutron's direction is known and the proton's direction and track length are measured under the microscope, the neutron energy can be calculated. This application is further discussed in Section 13–4.

7–9 Neutron Detection

All the processes that are involved in stopping neutrons in matter can be used for detecting neutrons, because in all processes charged particles are set into motion, in some cases as a secondary effect after the emission of a gamma ray. The processes utilized in neutron detection are:

(1) neutron-induced nuclear reactions yielding charged-particle reaction products (protons, alpha particles, etc.),

(2) induced fission in certain heavy elements,

(3) elastic collisions between neutrons and nuclei, notably hydrogen nuclei, which are thereby set into motion,

(4) capture of neutrons by certain stable isotopes, which are thereby converted into radioisotopes emitting β- and γ-rays (activation method).

The following are short examples of the applications of the above-mentioned principles for neutron detectors.

(*a*) *Reaction-product detectors.* The classical example is the boron counter for slow neutrons. This is a gas counter in which the inside wall is lined with boron or the counter is filled with BF_3 gas, preferably enriched in B^{10}. The responsible reaction is $B^{10}(n, \alpha)Li^7$, for which an energy-level diagram is shown in Fig. 7–23. The cross section for this reaction at a neutron energy of 0.025 eV is 3840 barns, and at lower energies it varies as the inverse of the neutron velocity. The alpha particle and the Li^7 recoil nucleus both have short ranges, so that in most of the events they come to rest in the gas with all the released energy converted into ionization and atomic excitations. The counter is operated in the proportionality region, and it is then reasonably easy to discriminate between the neutron-induced events and gamma-ray or cosmic-ray background. Other examples of reactions that have been used for slow-neutron detectors are $Li^6(n, t)He^4$, $N^{14}(n, p)C^{14}$, and $Cd^{113}(n, \gamma)Cd^{114}$.

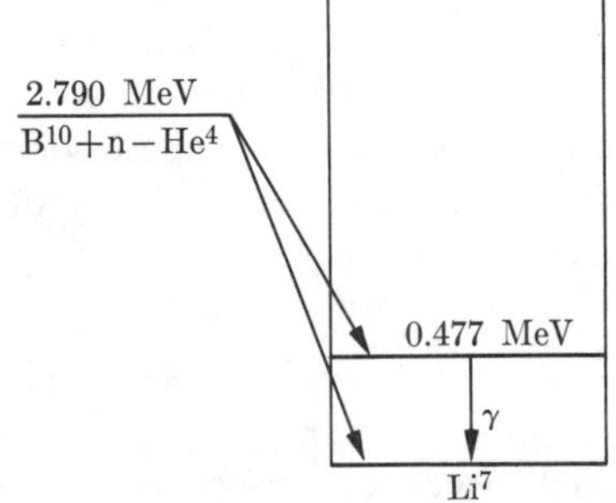

Fig. 7–23. Energy-level diagram showing the reaction $B^{10}(n, \alpha)Li^7$.

Nuclear reactions have been utilized also in fast-neutron detectors; however, the efficiency is not so high as in the boron counters for slow neutrons, since no fast-neutron cross section comes anywhere close to the magnitude of the B^{10}

cross section for slow neutrons. Since the BF_3 counter is such an efficient and simple counter for slow neutrons, one natural way of making a detector for fast neutrons is to surround a BF_3 counter with paraffin in which the fast neutrons slow down by elastic collisions so that they can diffuse into the counter as thermal neutrons. The complete fast-neutron counter can be made insensitive to slow neutrons by cadmium shielding.

(*b*) *Fission detectors.* In the fission process (Section 14–1), a very large amount ($\approx$200 MeV) of energy is released as kinetic energy of heavy, short-range particles. This process can therefore be used, for instance, in conjunction with any charged-particle counter as a detector for neutrons. The isotope U^{235} has a very large fission cross section for slow neutrons, whereas U^{238} has a large cross section for fast neutrons. A gas counter lined with uranium, where U^{235} and U^{238} occur in the natural mixture, is therefore an efficient counter for both slow and fast neutrons. The slow-neutron component can again be cut out, if desired, by shielding the counter either with cadmium or boron.

(*c*) *Proton-recoil detectors.* A counter filled with gas containing hydrogen and operating in the proportionality region is an efficient fast-neutron detector. At not-too-low neutron energies, the proton recoils give considerably stronger pulses than most background pulses caused by gamma rays or cosmic rays. Other variations of the neutron-proton recoil detector include the nuclear emulsion mentioned in Section 7–8 and plastic scintillators that are used, for instance, in time-of-flight spectrometers (see Section 13–4). A large neutron detector described by E. J. Winhold *et al.** is a 20-in. diameter can filled with toluene and terphenyl in a mixture that produces an efficient liquid scintillator. This is viewed by five multiplier tubes, any one of which can trigger an electronic circuit that signals that an n-p scattering event has taken place in the scintillator. For 10-MeV neutrons striking the counter in the axial direction, the efficiency is of the order of 20%. For the particular application that this counter is designed for, time resolution is very important. The arrival time of a neutron, as measured by the pulse front, can be determined to less than 10^{-8} sec uncertainty.

(*d*) *Activation experiments.* The flux of slow neutrons, for instance in the middle of a nuclear reactor, can be measured by means of the radioactivity induced in certain absorbers placed in the neutron flux for a specified time. Several nuclides have very large resonance peaks in the cross section for slow neutrons. Figure 7–24 shows as an example the total cross section for indium in the neutron energy range 0.01 eV to 100 eV. At 1.44 eV, the cross section for

---

* E. J. Winhold, R. H. Augustson, N. N. Kaushal, H. A. Medicus, M. R. Moyer, and P. F. Yergin, *Bull. Am. Phys. Soc.* **9**, 432 (1964).

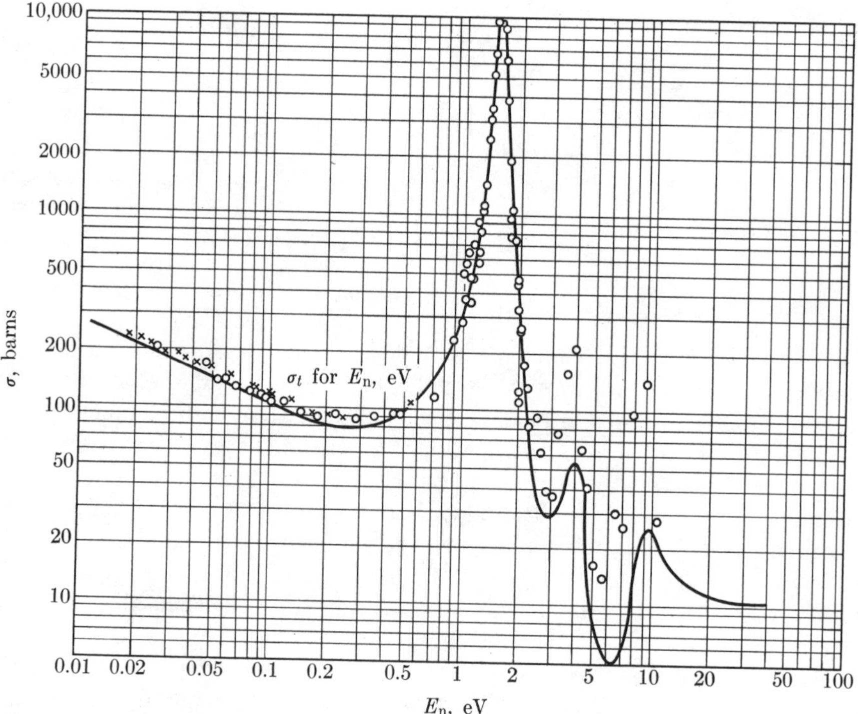

Fig. 7-24. Total cross section for slow neutrons in indium; $\sigma_{max} = 26{,}400$ barns at $E_n = 1.44$ eV. [From H. H. Goldsmith, H. W. Ibser, and B. T. Feld, *Rev. Mod. Phys.* **19**, 261 (1947).]

the process $In^{115}(n, \gamma)In^{116}$ is enormously large, and since the residual nucleus is radioactive, the amount of In^{116} produced can be determined by the use of a beta or gamma counter after the neutron exposure. Indium is therefore a very efficient detector for slow neutrons at that energy. Other materials that have been found to have large capture cross sections for slow neutrons and that leave a residual nucleus which is radioactive are gold, manganese, and dysprosium.

7-10 Special Detectors for High-Energy Radiation

There is of course no fundamental difference between low-energy radiation and high-energy radiation with respect to detection problems. Most of the techniques described above are applied also at high energies, that is, in elementary-particle research and in cosmic-ray research. However, there are also a few detection techniques that have been developed specifically for high-energy research, and since we want to refer to these techniques in the chapter on elementary particles, we discuss them briefly here.

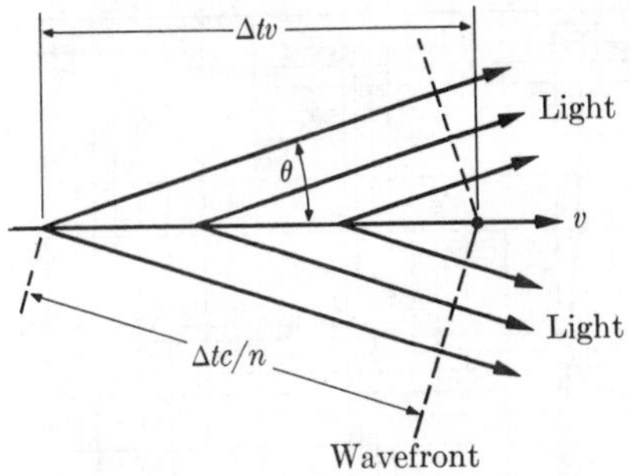

Fig. 7–25. Emission of Cerenkov radiation from polarized atoms along the track of a particle moving with velocity v. Construction of wavefronts by use of Huygen's principle.

(*a*) *Cerenkov counter.* The velocity of light in a transparent solid or liquid is given by $v = c/n$, where n is the index of refraction. If a charged particle moving through this medium has a velocity greater than v, that is, greater than the velocity of light in the medium, light is emitted from the atoms that are momentarily electrically polarized by the charged particle moving nearby. The process is one in which the perturbation on the electric field of the atom produces a transient dipole moment which then causes emission of electromagnetic waves. The reason why such light is emitted only when the velocity exceeds $v = c/n$ is that only in this case can light from all atoms along the track be coherent. Figure 7–25 shows how a wavefront can be constructed, by use of Huygen's principle, from elementary waves emitted from various points along the path of the particle. For a given velocity v, the light is emitted in a cone, with the angle θ given by $\cos\theta = c/nv$. A sizable fraction of the Cerenkov radiation is given off in the visible part of the spectrum, which also corresponds approximately to the region of highest sensitivity of photomultiplier tubes. Various types of Cerenkov detectors have been built, in which only the light emitted in a particular direction is recorded. The detector then is a velocity-sensitive device. Obviously, it can be used only for particles with $v/c > 1/n$.

(*b*) *Bubble chamber and cloud chamber.* One of the most efficient means for collecting high-quality data in elementary-particle research with high-energy accelerators is afforded by the bubble chamber. The bubble chamber is a relatively new invention, but its predecessor, the cloud chamber, was invented by C. T. R. Wilson in 1912. The cloud chamber works on the following simple principle: A gas mixed with a saturated vapor of, for instance, alcohol or ether, is contained in a shallow cylinder (Fig. 7–26). The gas can be expanded rapidly by a fast but relatively short motion of a piston. Because of the sharp drop in temperature during the adiabatic expansion, the vapor becomes supersaturated, and will condense in droplets on dust particles in the gas or on other disturbances acting as nuclei of condensation. If a charged particle moves through the gas immediately before or during the period of supersaturation, the ions left along the trail of the particle will act as condensation nuclei for the vapor. In proper illumination, this vapor trail can be seen and photographed.

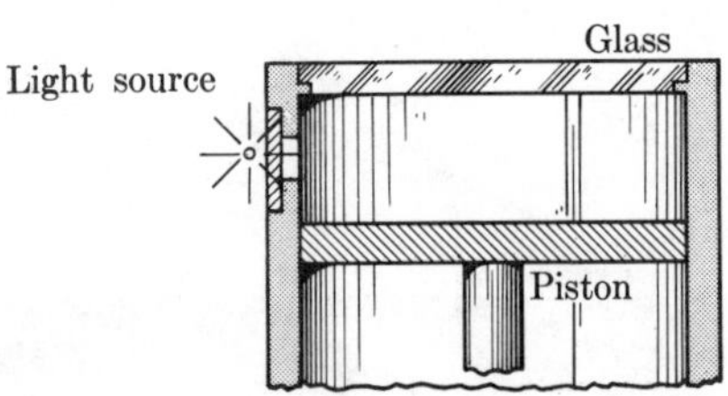

Fig. 7–26. Schematic diagram of a Wilson cloud chamber. The volume enclosed by the piston is filled with a gas mixed with a saturated vapor.

For high-energy particles, one disadvantage of the cloud chamber is that the density of the gas is not high enough to cause an appreciable amount of interactions to take place within the chamber. More important perhaps is that it has a very long recovery time after each expansion. In elementary-particle research, therefore, the cloud chamber has been all but replaced by the bubble chamber, which is, one might say, an inverse cloud chamber, and also by the spark chamber. In the hydrogen bubble chamber, superheated liquid hydrogen is the medium through which the particles move. The trail of ions left in the path of a charged particle becomes evaporation nuclei for the liquid hydrogen, and this trail can be seen and photographed as a chain of bubbles. When particles that interact strongly with protons pass through the bubble chamber, reactions take place, and the trails of the incoming particle, as well as the reaction products, can be studied. If the bubble chamber is immersed in a magnetic field, the charge and the momentum of the various particles can be measured. Figure 7–27 is an example of a reasonably simple bubble-chamber picture showing pair-production events produced by a gamma-ray beam passing through the chamber from left to right. The chamber is 12 in. in diameter and has liquid hydrogen filling. A magnetic field perpendicular to the plane of the picture deflects electrons to the right and positrons to the left. Most of the events take place in the field of the nucleus (proton), and the nuclear recoil is not energetic enough to leave a visible track. Note, however, the event near the center of the picture that shows a positron track and two electron tracks emerging from the same point. This, presumably, is a pair-production event taking place in the field of an electron. Note also the single electron track near the center of the picture. This is the recoil electron from a Compton event.

(*c*) *Spark chamber.* One of the newest inventions in the area of high-energy detectors is the spark chamber, which consists of a number of metallic plates insulated from each other and with a uniform neon-filled gap of the order of a few millimeters between them. Every other plate is grounded, and the interleafing plates can be given a short voltage pulse (0.5 μsec) of such a magnitude that sparks will occur at places where the gas is ionized. The trail of ions left by a penetrating particle will trigger such sparks and a photograph of the

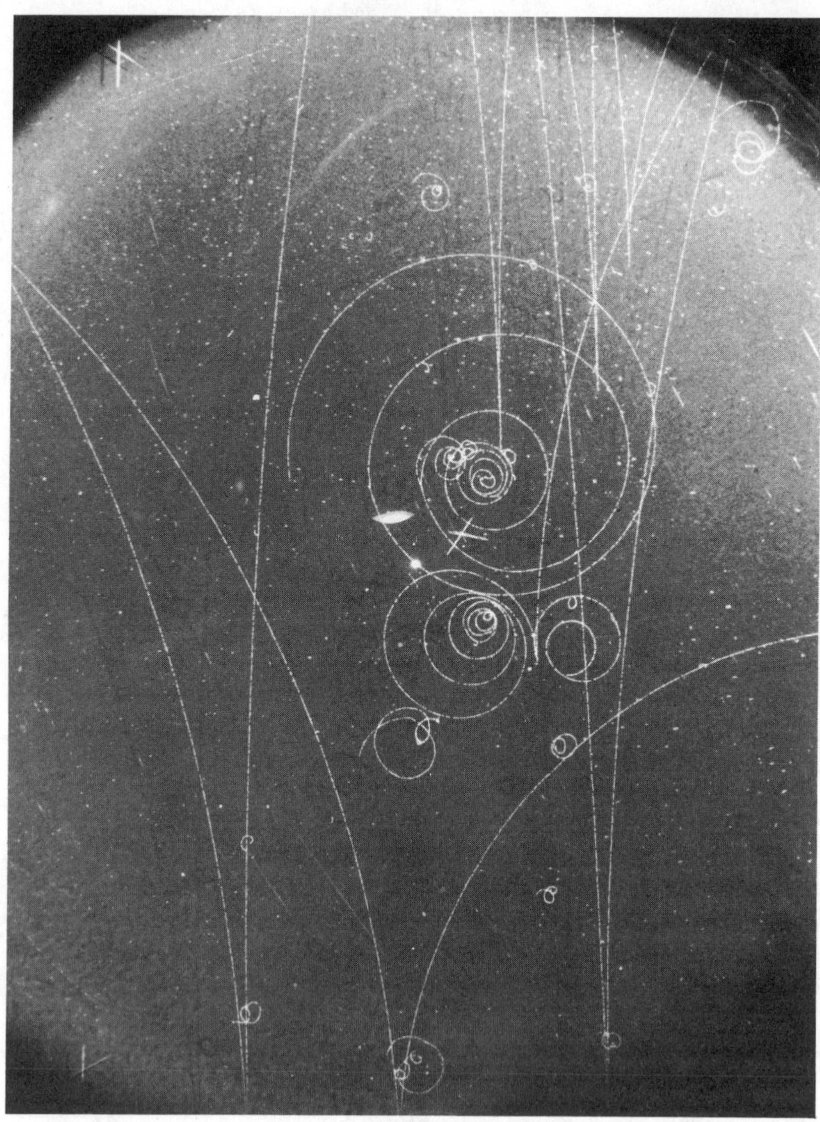

Fig. 7–27. Picture of a liquid hydrogen bubble chamber showing tracks of electrons and positrons produced by high-energy gamma rays entering from the left. (Courtesy of L. Rosenson.)

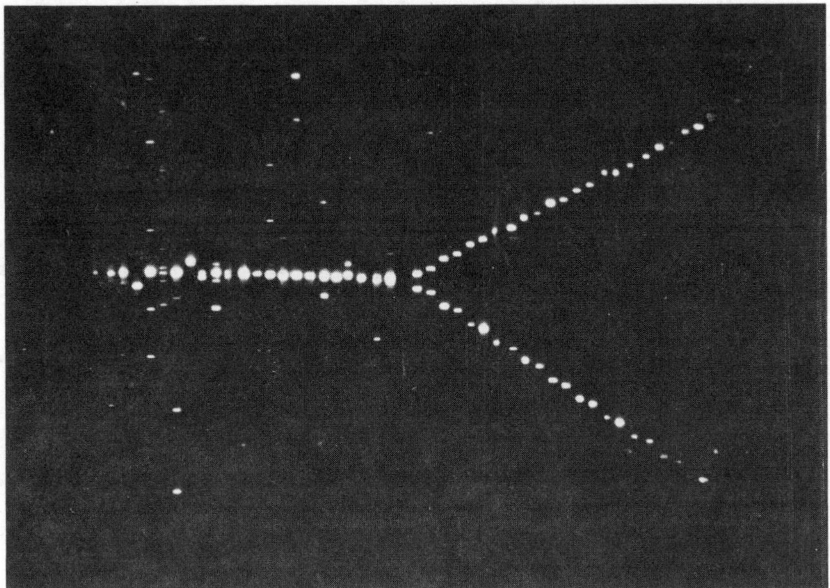

Fig. 7–28. Spark-chamber picture of an event initiated by a 1.5-BeV π^- meson entering from the left. (Courtesy of L. Rosenson.)

sparks between all the plates therefore gives an outline of the path of the particle. Figure 7–28 shows as an example a picture taken of a spark chamber consisting of 2-mm steel plates with 3-mm separation. The gas is neon with helium contamination at atmospheric pressure, and the triggering voltage between plates is 10 kV. The event shown is a 1.5-BeV π^- meson entering from the left and producing two unidentified charged particles in one of the steel plates.

PROBLEMS

7–1. Show that the lower limit $a_1 = h/2m_0v$ used in the classical derivation of the stopping-power formula (Section 7–1) gives electron energies that are smaller than the maximum predicted by Eq. (7–1) for reasonable values of v (particles in the MeV region).

7–2. Calculate the percentage error which arises from neglecting the relativistic correction terms in Eq. (7–5) for protons with $T = 20$ MeV in an aluminum absorber.

7–3. Prove that the scale factors used in Fig. 7–2 ($1/m$ and $1/z^2$) and Fig. 7–3 ($1/m$ and z^2/m) are correct, assuming that Eq. (7–6) holds.

7–4. Attempt a classical derivation of the bremsstrahlung loss for an electron moving through the Coulomb field of a nucleus. Start by calculating the radiated energy given off by the electron being accelerated and decelerated as it moves past the nucleus along an approximately straight line (as the particle passes the electron in Fig. 7–1). The radiated power is $e^2F^2/6\pi\epsilon_0 m_0^2 c^3$, where F is the accelerating (Coulomb) force. Find the stopping cross section by an integration similar to the one carried out in Section 7–1. The integration limits are taken as $a_1 = \hbar/p$ and $a_2 = \infty$. The derivation is not a good one in any velocity range, but the result can be compared, at least dimensionally, with Eq. (7–11) in the relativistic range by putting $p/v = m \approx T/c^2$.

7–5. A 1-MeV gamma-ray source delivers a dosage rate of 300 R/hr at a distance of 2 m. Calculate the thickness of a spherical lead shield needed to cut down this dosage rate to 0.3 R/week at a distance of 1m.

7–6. Consider a proportional counter with an 0.2-mm diameter center wire and filled with argon at 10 cm Hg. Estimate the average energy gained by an electron between collisions with argon atoms near the center wire when the voltage on the wire is 1000 V and the collision cross section is approximately 5×10^{-16} cm^2. Is this energy sufficient for ionizing argon?

7–7. The space charge density of negative ions left when the charge carriers (holes) have been removed in the depletion region of the silicon counter (Fig. 7–18) is constant. Show that a result of this is that the depletion thickness is proportional to the square root of the applied voltage.

7–8. A silicon semiconductor detector has a depletion thickness of 1 mm when 400 V are applied to it. Calculate the number of ions per cm^3 in the depletion region and compare this with the total number of atoms per cm^3. What energy protons and alpha particles will be stopped in the depletion layer when striking the counter normal to the surface?

7–9. One gram of indium is exposed for one hour to a beam of neutrons that has an energy distribution proportional to e^{-E_n/E_0}, where $E_0 = 1$ eV. The total flux of neutrons is $S = 10^8$ neutrons /cm^2–sec. Set up an exact integral expression for the number of radioactive nuclei produced in the $In^{115}(n, \gamma)In^{116}$ process, assuming that the cross section $\sigma(E_n)$ is known. Estimate the order of magnitude of the integral by using for $\sigma(E_n)$ the cross-section curve in Fig. 7–24 (neglecting the fact that part of this total cross section arises from scattering).

*7–10. Design an experiment to measure selectively the intensities and energies of beta rays, gamma rays, and neutrons from a sample containing fission products. (The processes that result in emission of delayed neutrons are described in Section 14–2.)

8 *Radioactivity*

8–1 *Natural Radioactivity*

Natural radioactivity was discovered quite accidentally by Henri Becquerel in 1896. Becquerel had left a substance containing uranium on a photographic plate which was wrapped in black paper. After it was developed, the plate showed images of the crystals of uranium compounds. Intensive research by Becquerel, Madame Curie, Rutherford, and others led to the discovery of several other radionuclides (radioactive elements). Three different kinds of radiations were found, alpha, beta, and gamma, and subsequently it was shown that the alpha particle is identical to the helium nucleus, that beta radiation consists of electrons, and that gamma radiation is electromagnetic waves, as are also, for instance, x-rays. The three kinds of radiation, the theories of their emission, and the experimental methods of study are discussed in Chapters 9, 10, and 11. In particular, it is shown in Chapter 10 why an alpha particle, which consists of two neutrons and two protons, is emitted rather than a neutron or a proton. In Chapter 11, it is shown that of two neighbor isobars, the one with the greater atomic mass is always unstable, and will decay by a beta process into the other. In natural radionuclides, alpha processes and beta processes very often compete; that is, they may both be energetically possible. Whether or not a given nuclide is observed to be simultaneously an alpha emitter and a beta emitter depends on whether the probabilities of occurrence of the two processes are sufficiently close in order of magnitude.

In alpha emission the nucleon number A changes by four units; in beta emission the nucleon number A does not change, but Z and N change by one unit in opposite directions. In gamma emission neither Z nor N changes. There is, then, what we may call beta-decay correspondence between all members of a chain of nuclides with the same nucleon number A, and alpha-decay correspondence between this chain and the chain in which the nucleon number is $A - 4$. There are thus four families of natural radioactive nuclides, one with $A = 4n$, where n is an integer, and others with $A = 4n + 1$, $4n + 2$, and

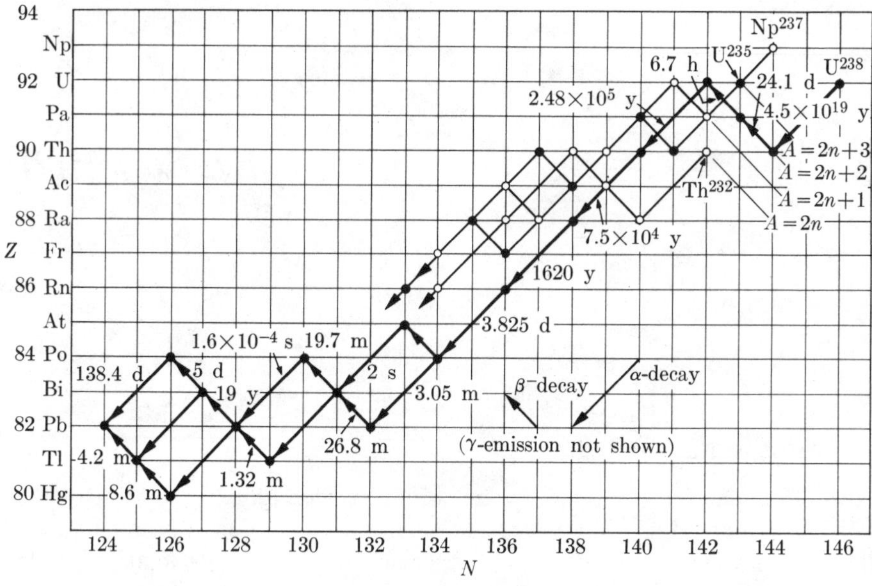

Fig. 8–1. The $A = 4n + 2$ radioactive series and the first few links of the other three series. Where branching occurs, the half-life is written beside the main branch.

$4n + 3$. Figure 8–1 shows as an example the uranium-radium $4n + 2$ series marked out on a part of the chart of the nuclides, with arrows indicating directions of decays. Figure 8–1 shows only the branches of the chain that have been observed in natural radioactivity. Many radioactive isotopes with $A = 4n + 2$ have been artificially produced on both sides of this chain, and they are found to be linked to it as side branches.

Table 8–1 is a list of the members of the uranium-radium series, their types of disintegration, and half-lives. The parent nuclide (origin) of this series is U^{238}, with a half-life of 4.5×10^9 y. Since the elements in our solar system are presumed to have been formed about 3×10^9 years ago, U^{238} is sufficiently long-lived so that a large fraction of what was originally formed has survived up to the present. The end product of the uranium-radium series is Pb^{206}, which is stable. The nuclide Pa^{234} is listed twice in Table 8–1; one faction, UX_2, is an excited state of Pa^{234}, an isomeric state (Section 1–2) with a half-life of 1.18 m. Both factions are formed by beta decay of Th^{234}. An excited state will, in general, decay by gamma emission to the ground state much faster than it can decay by beta or alpha emission; however, in the case of UX_2, the difference in angular momentum between the excited state and the ground state is so large that the gamma lifetime, relatively speaking, is very large (see Chapter 9). A large fraction of the Pa^{234} nuclei formed in the isomeric state, therefore, decays by beta emission to U^{234}.

Table 8–1. The uranium-radium ($4n + 2$) series, with type of disintegration and half-life

Old name	Old symbol	Atomic number	New symbol	Half-life	Main type of decay	Alternate branch Decay	Alternate branch Fraction
Uranium I	UI	92	U^{238}	4.50×10^9 y	α		
Uranium X_1	UX_1	90	Th^{234}	24.1 d	β^-		
Uranium X_2	UX_2	91	Pa^{234m}	1.18 m	β^-	γ	0.005
Uranium Z	UZ	91	Pa^{234}	6.7 h	β^-		
Uranium II	UII	92	U^{234}	2.48×10^5 y	α		
Ionium	Io	90	Th^{230}	7.5×10^4 y	α		
Radium	Ra	88	Ra^{226}	1620 y	α		
Radon	Rn	86	Rn^{222}	3.825 d	α		
Radium A	RaA	84	Po^{218}	3.05 m	α	β^-	2×10^{-4}
		85	At^{218}	2 s (1.3)	α		
Radium B	RaB	82	Pb^{214}	26.8 m	β^-		
Radium C	RaC	83	Bi^{214}	19.7 m	β^-	α	4×10^{-4}
Radium C′	RaC′	84	Po^{214}	1.6×10^{-4} s	α		
Radium C″	RaC″	81	Tl^{210}	1.32 m	β^-		
Radium D	RaD	82	Pb^{210}	19 y	β^-	α	1.8×10^{-8}
Radium E	RaE	83	Bi^{210m}	5.0 d	β^-	α	5×10^{-7}
Polonium	Po	84	Po^{210}	138.4 d	α		
		80	Hg^{206}	8.6 m	β^-		
	RaE″	81	Tl^{206}	4.2 m	β^-		
Radium G	RaG	82	Pb^{206}		Stable		

8–2 *The Radioactive Decay Law*

Let us consider a sample containing a very large number of radionuclides, all of the same kind and assume that all of these nuclides decay by the same process, whether by the emission of an alpha particle, a beta particle, or a gamma quantum. The process is a statistical one-shot process, meaning that when one particular nucleus has decayed, it cannot repeat the process again. As long as the nucleus has not decayed, the probability for its so doing during the next second remains a constant. In other words, the nucleus does not age as does a biological system. The probability for it to decay between now and a second from now may be, for instance, one percent; and, if it happens to survive for an hour, the probability for it to decay during a given second is still one percent. Assume that in a given sample at time t there are N nuclei that have not decayed. The number that decays during the time interval from t to $t + dt$ must be proportional to N and also proportional to dt. This can be written as

$$-dN = \lambda N \, dt, \tag{8–1}$$

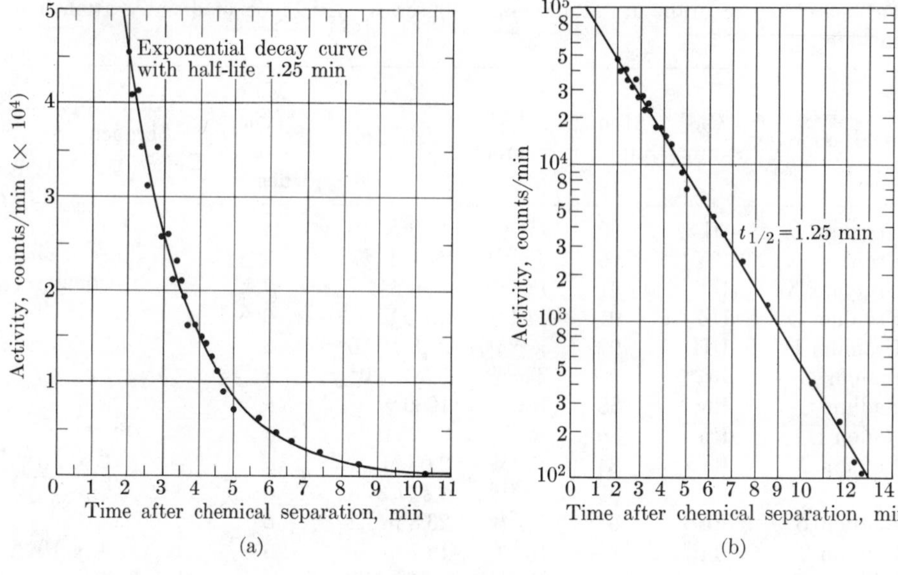

Fig. 8–2. Counting-rate data showing the positron decay of metastable (isomeric) Rb^{82}, (a) plotted on a linear scale and (b) plotted on a logarithmic scale. The experimental points are taken from L. M. Litz, S. A. Ring, and W. R. Balkwell, *Phys. Rev.* **92,** 288 (1953).

where the proportionality coefficient λ is called the decay constant. We rewrite Eq. (8–1) as

$$\lambda = -\frac{1}{N}\frac{dN}{dt},$$

and see that the decay constant is equal to the fraction of nuclei in a given sample that decays per unit time, or, for a single nucleus, it is the probability for decay per unit time. We integrate Eq. (8–1) and find that

$$N = N_0 e^{-\lambda t}, \tag{8–2}$$

where N_0 is the total number of radioactive nuclei at time $t = 0$. The exponential decay of the number N of nuclei left, as expressed by Eq. (8–2), is usually observed by measuring the *counting rate*, $-dN/dt$, as a function of the time. By taking the derivative of Eq. (8–2), we find

$$-\frac{dN}{dt} = \lambda N = \lambda N_0 e^{-\lambda t} = \left(-\frac{dN}{dt}\right)_0 e^{-\lambda t}. \tag{8–3}$$

As expressed by Eq. (8–3), the counting rate shows the same exponential behavior as the number of undecayed nuclei. Taking the logarithm of base 10 of Eq. (8–3), we find

$$\log_{10}\left(-\frac{dN}{dt}\right) = \log_{10}\left(-\frac{dN}{dt}\right)_0 - \lambda t \log_{10} e.$$

This shows that, when the counting rate is plotted on a semilogarithmic paper, as a function of time, the resulting plot should be a straight line with slope $-\lambda \log e$. Figure 8–2(a) shows an example of counting-rate data plotted on a linear scale, and Fig. 8–2(b) gives the same data on a semilogarithmic scale.

The half-life of a radioactive nucleus is defined as the time $t_{1/2}$ during which the number of nuclei reduces to one-half the original value. Using Eq. (8–2), we get $\frac{1}{2} = e^{-\lambda t_{1/2}}$, which gives

$$t_{1/2} = \ln 2/\lambda = 0.693/\lambda. \tag{8–4}$$

The mean life, or average life, of the radioactive nuclei is given by

$$\tau = \frac{1}{N_0}\int_0^\infty t(-dN) = \int_0^\infty t\lambda e^{-\lambda t}\, dt = \frac{1}{\lambda}, \tag{8–5}$$

where we have used Eq. (8–3). From Eqs. (8–4) and (8–5) we see that the mean life and half-life differ by a factor ln 2 = 0.693.

The decay constant λ, together with the type of decay and the energy of decay, characterizes a given radioactive nucleus and can be regarded as its signature.

8–3 Artificially Produced Radionuclides

As revealed by the Chart of the Nuclides, about 330 nuclear species are found in nature. About 25 of these have proved to be unstable, but with sufficiently long half-lives to survive from the time of formation of the earth to the present. Another approximately 35 heavy nuclides have much shorter half-lives, but are being continuously produced as decay products of the parent nuclides in the radioactive chains to which they belong. The Chart of the Nuclides also shows that so far approximately 1000 artificially produced nuclides have been discovered and identified. A few of the entries in the Chart of Nuclides have extremely short half-lives and break up by heavy-particle emission in a lifetime of the order of magnitude of 10^{-20} sec. Examples are Li^5, which breaks up into an alpha particle and a proton, and B^9, which breaks up into two alpha particles and a proton. Excluding these two and a few other entries, the chart of nuclides contains only examples of nuclear species that are dynamically stable against neutron or proton emission.

In the region of light or intermediate masses, all the unstable systems decay toward stable isobars by a beta process. In the region of heavier masses, alpha decay very often competes with the beta process. When a nuclide is unstable against both alpha and beta decay, the total decay constant is the sum of the probability for alpha decay and the probability for beta decay. Very often only one of the processes is observed, because the corresponding decay constant λ is much larger than the other.

The great majority of the artificially produced radioactive nuclides decay by beta processes (Chapter 11) and have half-lives ranging from a fraction of a second to millions of years. Both in alpha decay and in beta decay, the residual nucleus may be left in an excited state that most often decays to the ground state by a gamma transition (Chapter 9).

The artificial radionuclides are produced in nuclear reactions or by induced fission, that is, by neutron or charged-particle bombardment of stable nuclei. As an example, we shall here describe briefly an experiment by G. E. Boyd *et al.** in which isotopes of the element technetium were produced. Element number 43, technetium, which does not exist in detectable quantities in nature, was first produced in 1937 by C. Perrier and E. Segrè† by deuteron bombardment of molybdenum. The objective of the experiment by Boyd *et al.* was partly to establish the existence of three long-lived isotopes of the element.

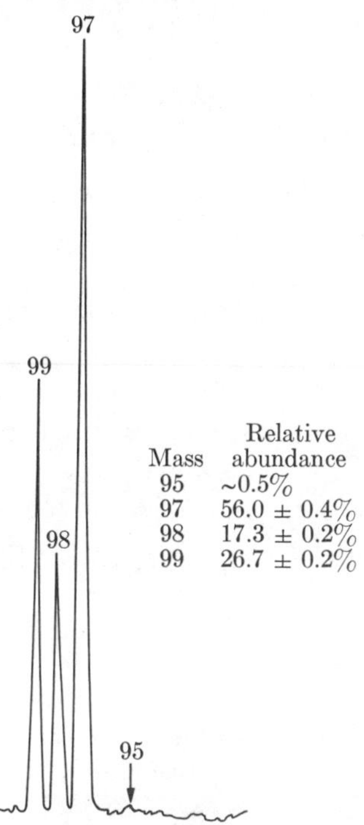

Fig. 8–3. Mass spectrum of technetium produced by the irradiation of molybdenum metal with 22-MeV protons. [From G. E. Boyd, J. R. Sykes, Q. V. Larson, and C. R. Baldock, *Phys. Rev.* **99,** 1030 (1955).]

Molybdenum has stable isotopes at mass numbers 92, 94, 95, 96, 97, 98, and 100. From Mo^{100}, for instance, the isotopes of technetium with mass numbers 99, 100, and 101 can be formed by proton bombardment through the $Mo^{100}(p, \gamma)Tc^{101}$, $Mo^{100}(p, n)Tc^{100}$, and $Mo^{100}(p, nn)Tc^{99}$ reactions. From the whole series of molybdenum isotopes, therefore, technetium isotopes from mass numbers 91 to 101 can be formed. A piece of molybdenum metal was bombarded with 22-MeV protons from a cyclotron for a time sufficiently long to produce several micrograms of technetium. To allow for practically complete decay of the shorter-lived technetium isotopes, the sample was "cooled" for 270 days. The target was then processed chemically and the technetium fraction was separated and purified. Approximately 1 μgm of technetium was electroplated onto an iridium strip which was employed as a filament ion source

* G. E. Boyd, J. R. Sykes, Q. V. Larson, and C. R. Baldock, *Phys. Rev.* **99,** 1030 (1955).
† C. Perrier and E. Segrè, *J. Chem. Phys.* **5,** 713 (1937).

Table 8–2. The transuranic elements, with symbol and half-life of longest-lived isotope known in each case

Name	Longest-lived isotope	Half-life	Name	Longest-lived isotope	Half-life
Neptunium	$_{93}Np^{237}$	2.14×10^6 y	Einsteinium	$_{99}Es^{254}$	480 d
Plutonium	$_{94}Pu^{244}$	7.6×10^7 y	Fermium	$_{100}Fm^{253}$	4.5 d
Americium	$_{95}Am^{243}$	7650 y	Mendelevium	$_{101}Md^{256}$	1.5 h
Curium	$_{96}Cm^{247}$	1.7×10^7 y	Nobelium	$_{102}No^{255}$	15 s
Berkelium	$_{97}Bk^{247}$	10^4 y	Lawrencium?	$_{103}Lw^{256}$	8 s
Californium	$_{98}Cf^{251}$	800 y			

in a mass spectrometer. The mass spectrogram produced (Fig. 8–3) demonstrates clearly that technetium has three long-lived isotopes, with mass number 97, 98, and 99. The relative intensities of the peaks and the relative-abundance figures given are not very significant because they depend on the details of the production process. The small amount of mass number 95 indicated in Fig. 8–3 arises from an isomer of Tc^{95} with a 60-day half-life. In other experiments, the half-lives of Tc^{97}, Tc^{98}, and Tc^{99} have been found to be 2.6×10^6 y, 1.5×10^6 y, and 2.1×10^5 y, respectively. The other intermediate-weight element that does not occur in nature, promethium, has no isotope with half-life longer than 18 years (Pm^{145}).

Artificially produced elements with element numbers higher than that of uranium (92) comprise another fascinating area of research. Neptunium, element number 93, and plutonium, element number 94, were produced in 1940 by MacMillan and coworkers through deuteron bombardment of uranium. Most of the other transuranic elements have been produced by successive bombardments by neutrons and by alpha particles. Neutron absorption, of course, produces only a heavier isotope of the same element; however, in the extremely high-intensity fluxes of neutrons present in the core of nuclear reactors, one can build up neutron-rich isotopes that decay by one or more β^- transitions to isobars with higher element numbers. Table 8–2 lists the names of the transuranic elements, and the lifetime of the most long-lived isotope in each case. Beyond element number 100 the information at present is very scarce, and it is likely that isotopes with longer lifetimes than those listed will be found.

8–4 Units of Radiation

In Section 8–2 we introduced the decay constant λ, showed how it is related to the half-life, and mentioned that λ is part of the signature that characterizes a given radionuclide. For the nuclear-structure physicists, λ or $t_{1/2}$ is therefore of fundamental importance, and the total number of disintegrations per second is only of secondary interest. In practical applications, as for instance in radiography, radiation sterilization, radioactive tracer work, etc., it is often the other way around. A unit commonly used to measure number of disintegrations per second is the curie, which is defined as the amount of radioactive material of a given kind that produces 3.7×10^{10} disintegrations per second.

Originally, the curie was defined as the amount of radioactive material that gives as many disintegrations per second as 1 gm of radium. Since Ra^{226} has a half-life of 1620 y, the decay constant λ is therefore

$$\lambda = \frac{\ln 2}{1620 \times 365 \times 24 \times 3600} = 1.36 \times 10^{-11}.$$

The total number of disintegrations per second from 1 gm is

$$-\frac{dN}{dt} = \frac{6.025 \times 10^{23}}{226} \times 1.36 \times 10^{-11} = 3.65 \times 10^{10}.$$

The curie defines strictly the number of disintegrations per second of the parent product, and the decay scheme may or may not be a complex one. For instance, in the case of Co^{60}, one disintegration entails the emission first of one beta ray, leaving the daughter nucleus, Ni^{60}, in its second excited state. This subsequently decays to the ground state via the first excited state by emission of two gamma rays. In the case of Ra^{226}, an alpha particle is emitted, leaving the daughter nucleus, Ra^{222}, either in its ground state or in an excited state. This daughter nucleus is radioactive also in the ground state and so are the nearest further descendants. A whole string of alpha rays, beta rays, and gamma rays, therefore, results from each disintegration of a parent Ra^{226}. Most of these descendants are very short-lived, so that at least if the sample of radium is more than a few days old, and all the daughter products are trapped in it, 1 curie of Ra^{226} represents more total radiation given off than, for instance, 1 curie of cobalt.

In work with x-rays and gamma rays, one uses the ionizing power of the radiation as a basis for a dosage unit. This unit, the roentgen, which was mentioned in Section 7–5, is used in radiography and as a standard for personnel safety when the radiation is x-rays or gamma rays. One roentgen unit, R, is defined as *the amount of radiation which releases in 0.001293 gm of dry air one electrostatic unit of charge of either polarity.* The sample, 0.001293 gm, which represents 1 cm^3 at standard temperature and pressure, is supposed to be surrounded by air so that the production and absorption of electrons are in equilibrium at the point where the measurement is taken. In practice, one encloses the measuring volume in an ionization chamber, the walls of which are made of materials with element number close to the average element number of air. In Section 7–5, we calculated that an ionization chamber with a volume of 1 liter yields a current of 0.925×10^{-10} A when immersed in a radiation field in which the dosage rate is 1 R/hr.

A short-time full-body exposure of approximately 300 R is fatal in about 50% of the cases. Smaller nonfatal doses are believed to have cumulative effects in producing certain diseases or in breaking down the body's resistance to them. The ill effects of mutations in man are very difficult to evaluate, but loom as a danger not to be taken lightly. For these reasons the allowed dose for radiation workers (currently an average of 0.1 R/week) is set much lower than the figure one would arrive at by considering only immediately detectable biological effects.

Because of their short range, alpha particles from radioactive sources do not constitute a health hazard unless the material is taken internally. Beta particles have more penetrating power, but they are relatively easy to stop. Neutrons, however, have very high penetrating power and require very thick shielding walls to reduce their intensity. In order to set a standard for amount of neutron radiation, in particular with an eye to personnel safety, other units of radiation have been introduced; for instance, a unit called REM, roentgen equivalent man, which is defined as the amount of radiation that produces the same effect in man as 1 R of x-radiation or gamma rays.

From the above discussion, it ought to be clear that there is no unique relation between the two units, curie and roentgen. Knowing the disintegration scheme for a given radionuclide, we can, however, calculate the amount of gamma-ray dosage in roentgens received over a given time interval at a given distance from a 1-curie source. Consider as an example a hypothetical nucleus that emits a beta ray and a 1-MeV gamma quantum. Assume also that there is no appreciable competition from internal conversion; in other words, for each β-disintegration, one gamma ray is emitted. At a distance of 1 m from the source, this gives a flux of photons equal to

$$\frac{3.7 \times 10^{10}}{4\pi \times 10^4} = 2.94 \times 10^5 \text{ photons-cm}^{-2}\text{-sec}^{-1}.$$

The energy absorption coefficient for 1-MeV photons in air is 0.0275 cm^2/gm.* This is the coefficient for total absorption of energy and not the total attenuation as given in Fig. 7-8. In computing the total attenuation coefficient, we have considered Compton-scattered gamma rays as removed from the beam. However, not all the *energy* is absorbed; therefore, the total attenuation coefficient is larger than the total absorption coefficient.

The total energy absorbed per cm^3 is

$$2.94 \times 10^5 \times 0.0275 \times 0.001293 = 1.044 \times 10^7 \text{ eV-cm}^{-3}\text{-sec}^{-1}.$$

The energy absorbed per ion pair produced in air is 32.4 eV, so that the total

---

* See R. D. Evans, *The Atomic Nucleus*, New York: McGraw-Hill Company, 1955, p. 713.

number of ion pairs produced per cm^3 in the example is

$$\frac{1.044 \times 10^7}{32.4} = 3.23 \times 10^5 \text{ ion pairs-cm}^{-3}\text{-sec}^{-1}.$$

This, multiplied by the amount of charge in esu per ion, gives for the radiation dosage rate

$$3.23 \times 10^5 \times 4.8 \times 10^{-10} = 1.55 \times 10^{-4} \text{ R/sec} = 0.558 \text{ R/hr}.$$

This calculation was carried out for a gamma-ray energy of 1 MeV. Clearly, the dosage rate is proportional to the gamma-ray energy and also to the energy-absorption coefficient in air. The latter varies between 0.014 and 0.030 cm^2/gm between 0.1 MeV and 100 MeV. Using this information, we can write the following general expression for the dosage rate from a gamma emitter:

$$D = (0.60 \text{ to } 0.28) \times \sum h\nu \text{ (R/hr)/curie at 1 m}, \tag{8–6}$$

where the sum applies to all gamma quanta emitted in the disintegration and the unit for $h\nu$ is MeV. When competition from internal conversion is important, the total amount of photon energy emitted per disintegration is, of course, reduced (see Section 9–8). The constant factor in parentheses above has its maximum, 0.60, at 5 MeV and the minimum, 0.28, at approximately 25 MeV.

8–5 *Statistics of Counting*

Radioactive decay is a statistical process, and the total number of counts registered by a particle detector is subject to a statistical uncertainty. In this section we shall discuss the magnitude of this statistical uncertainty, and in the next section we shall treat the systematical counting errors associated with counter dead time. The problem of the statistical uncertainty is dealt with in the following discussion of three statistical distribution laws.

(*a*) *The binomial distribution.* Consider z dice, which are not necessarily cubical, painted partly black and partly white. All dice are identical, and the probability for a die to show black is p, where $0 < p < 1$. The probability of showing white is therefore $q = 1 - p$. We throw all z dice and record the number n which show black. The probability of finding $n = z$ is clearly $P_z = p^z$, and the probability of finding none that show black is $P_0 = q^z$. The probability of finding $z - 1$ dice with black up is $P_{z-1} = zp^{z-1}q$. The factor z arises from the fact that there are z different combinations of one black down and the rest up. In general, P_n is given by the nth term in the binomial expansion of $(q + p)^z$

$$P_0 + P_1 + \cdots + P_z = q^z + (z/1!)q^{z-1}p + \cdots + p^z,$$

Table 8–3. Probability for $z = 4$ dice showing $n = 0, 1, 2, 3$, or 4 black when the probability for black on each individual die is $p = \frac{1}{3}, \frac{1}{2}$, or $\frac{2}{3}$

p	$n = 0$	1	2	3	4	$\bar{n} = n_{av} = pz$
$\frac{1}{3}$	$\frac{16}{81}$	$\frac{32}{81}$	$\frac{24}{81}$	$\frac{8}{81}$	$\frac{1}{81}$	$\frac{4}{3}$
$\frac{1}{2}$	$\frac{1}{16}$	$\frac{4}{16}$	$\frac{6}{16}$	$\frac{4}{16}$	$\frac{1}{16}$	2
$\frac{2}{3}$	$\frac{1}{81}$	$\frac{8}{81}$	$\frac{24}{81}$	$\frac{32}{81}$	$\frac{16}{81}$	$\frac{8}{3}$

where each term on the left-hand side equals the corresponding term on the right-hand side. The general expression for P_n is

$$P_n = \frac{z!}{n!(z-n)!} p^n q^{z-n}. \tag{8–7}$$

Table 8–3 gives three examples of binomial distributions for four dice that are painted in such a manner that $p = \frac{1}{3}, \frac{1}{2}$, or $\frac{2}{3}$. If the experiment is repeated very many times, the average number of dice showing black is $\bar{n} = pz$, which is given in the last column of Table 8–3 for the three cases. Figure 8–4 shows the distribution curves P_n for the three examples and the values of $\bar{n}$.

(*b*) *The Poisson distribution.* We shall now apply the binomial distribution to the following problem. We have a supply of identical radioactive nuclei with a half-life that is so long that the average counting rate r over our observa-

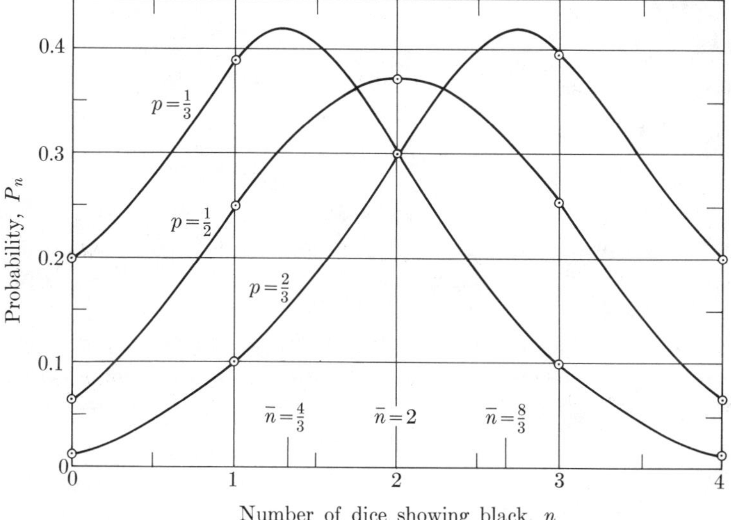

Fig. 8–4. Probability for $z = 4$ dice showing $n = 0, 1, 2, 3$, or 4 black when the probability for black on each individual die is $p = \frac{1}{3}, \frac{1}{2}$, or $\frac{2}{3}$.

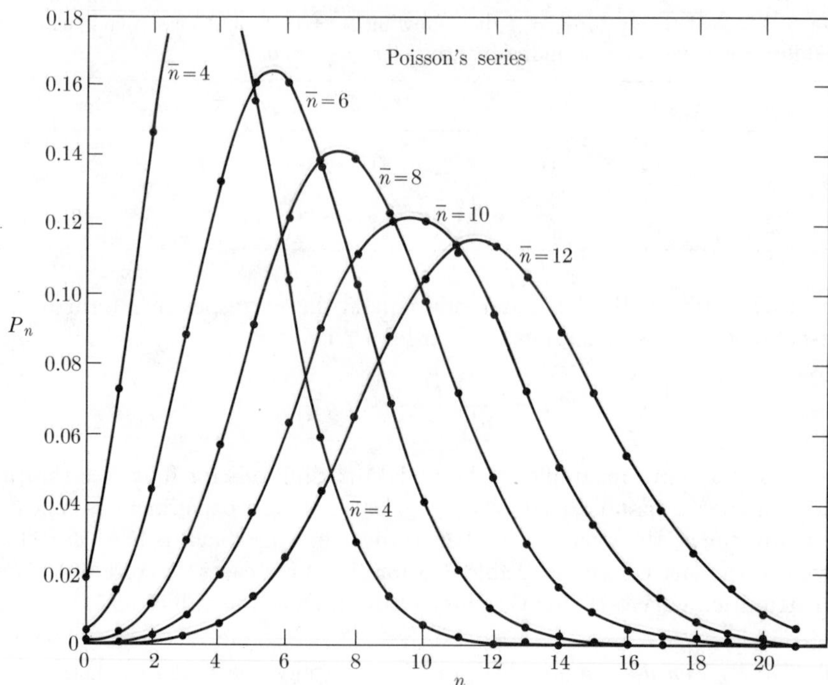

Fig. 8–5. Poisson distribution for various values of $\bar{n}$. This is the binomial distribution of Fig. 8–4 with $z \to \infty$ and $p \to 0$, such that $pz = \bar{n}$ stays finite. (From E. Segrè, *Experimental Nuclear Physics*, Vol. III, New York: John Wiley and Sons, Inc., 1959, p. 26. (Reprinted by permission.)

tion time t remains virtually constant. We want to calculate the probability of observing in a given experiment n counts in the time t which is of such a length that the average of n in a large number of experiments would be $\bar{n} = rt$. This is similar to the die-throwing experiment that we have analyzed above. We divide the time t in z small intervals of length $\Delta t = t/z$ and introduce the probability p for observing a count in the interval Δt as $p = \Delta tr$. Equation (8–7) can then be used directly to calculate the desired probability. However, we must be careful with regard to one point: One die can give only one count of black, but *unless we make* Δt *approach zero*, there is always a finite possibility of observing more than one count in any one interval. Consequently, we seek the limit of Eq. (8–7) when $\Delta t \to 0$ so that $p = \Delta tr \to 0$ and $z = t/\Delta t \to \infty$ while n and $\bar{n} = rt = pz$ remain finite. We write

$$\frac{z!}{(z-n)!} \to z^n$$

when $z \gg n$ and

$$(1-p)^z \to e^{-pz} = e^{-\bar{n}}.$$

Equation (8–7) then becomes

$$P_n \approx \frac{z^n p^n}{n!} (1 - p)^z = \frac{\bar{n}^n}{n!} e^{-\bar{n}}. \tag{8–8}$$

This formula expresses the probability of observing a given number of counts n in the time interval t when the average counting rate r, observed over a long time or in repeated experiments, is $r = \bar{n}/t$. Figure 8–5 shows plots of the Poisson formula for various integral values of $\bar{n}$.

Consider, for example, that in a given counting experiment repeated over and over again the average number of counts in the time t is found to be 12. As seen from Fig. 8–5, the probability for obtaining just 12 in any given experiment is $P_{12} = 0.115$; the probability for finding $n = 11$ is exactly the same (Problem 8–6). Even the probability of obtaining no counts is $P_0 = 6.2 \times 10^{-6}$, which is not entirely negligible.

(*c*) *The standard deviation.* When in a given counting experiment we observe n counts, this is not, in general, equal to $\bar{n}$, which we might regard as the true value, that is, the average value obtained in a very large number of experiments. *Our best guess for the true value, however, is that* $\bar{n} = n$. We need a measure for the uncertainty of this result, that is, we need a measure for the width of the Poisson distribution curve. A convenient measure is the standard deviation, σ, defined as the root-mean-square deviation from the average,

$$\sigma^2 = \frac{\sum_{n=0}^{\infty} (\bar{n} - n)^2 P_n}{\sum_{n=0}^{\infty} P_n}. \tag{8–9}$$

The denominator is simply the sum of the probabilities of all possible results and is obviously equal to 1. It is easy to show, by multiplying out the parentheses and inserting Eq. (8–8), that $\sigma^2 = \bar{n}$ (Problem 8–7). Since, in a given counting experiment, our best guess for the average value is $\bar{n} = n$, we also write

$$\sigma = \sqrt{n}. \tag{8–10}$$

The result of the experiment is usually quoted as $n \pm \sigma$, and the values $n + \sigma$ and $n - \sigma$ are called *error brackets.* Clearly, the true result $\bar{n}$ does not need to lie between these error brackets; indeed, only approximately two times out of three will it lie there. For instance, consider again the example with $\bar{n} = 12$. According to Fig. 8–5, the probability of obtaining $n = 9$ in the only experiment we carry out is quite large. We calculate $\sigma = \sqrt{9} = 3$, and quote as our result 9 ± 3. In this case, the upper bracket happens to be 12, which is $\bar{n}$, or the true result. If the experiment had yielded 16, the lower bracket would have been equal to $\bar{n}$. If the counting experiment had yielded $n < 9$ or $n > 16$, our error brackets would not have included $\bar{n}$.

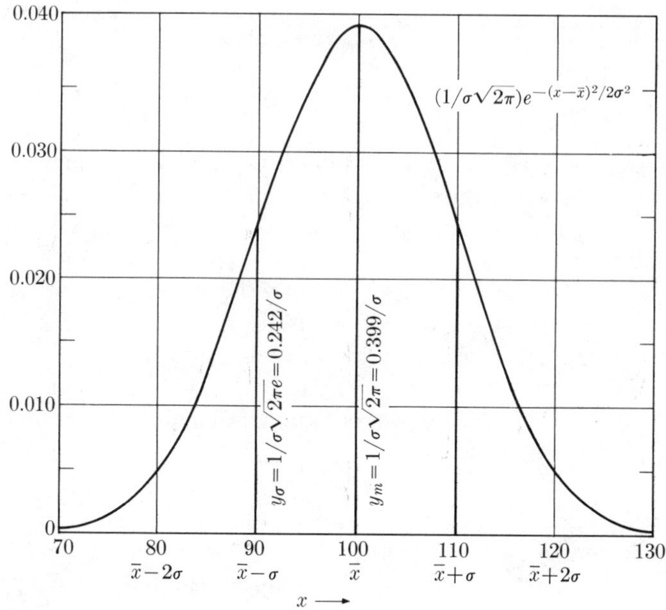

Fig. 8–6. The normal distribution or gaussian error curve. It is derived from the Poisson distribution by letting $\bar{n} \to \infty$, but it also has a wider application. In the case shown, $\bar{x} = 100$ and $\sigma = 10$.

(*d*) *The normal distribution.* When $\bar{n}$ in Eq. (8–8) is very large, one can use Stirling's formula for the factorial and show that the Poisson distribution goes over into the *normal distribution*, also called the gaussian error curve,*

$$P_n = \frac{e^{-(n-\bar{n})^2/2\bar{n}}}{(2\pi\bar{n})^{1/2}} = \frac{e^{-(n-\bar{n})^2/2\sigma^2}}{(2\pi)^{1/2}\sigma}. \tag{8–11}$$

This distribution function applies not only to integral variables, but also to continuous functions (distance, velocity, temperature, weight, or other physical variables). We call the variable x and the average result of a large number of experiments $\bar{x}$. The probability of observing in a given experiment the value between x and $x + dx$ is then

$$P_x\,dx = \frac{e^{-(x-\bar{x})^2/2\sigma^2}}{(2\pi)^{1/2}\sigma}\,dx. \tag{8–12}$$

The normal distribution function is shown in Fig. 8–6. The amplitude of the function at the values $x = \bar{x} \pm \sigma$ is $P_x = e^{-1/2}\,P_{\bar{x}} = 0.607\,P_{\bar{x}}$. The total area under the normal distribution curve is 1, and the portion of the area that

---

* See, for instance, E. Segrè, *Experimental Nuclear Physics*, Vol. III. New York: John Wiley and Sons, 1959, p. 26.

is between the values $x + \sigma$ and $x - \sigma$ is 0.6827. This then expresses the probability that the true value is between the error brackets assigned to the measured value. In other words, in approximately one time out of three, the true value is outside the error brackets.

8–6 Effects of Limited Time Resolution of Counting Equipment

(*a*) *Counting losses.* A particle detector and its associated electronic equipment always has a certain paralysis time or dead time after one event has triggered the counter. For a Geiger-Mueller counter, this dead time is of the order of 10^{-4} sec, whereas fast scintillators and associated equipment may have dead times shorter than 10^{-8} sec. When the counting rate is very high, a certain number of counts are lost because of this dead time, but a correction can be made for this loss in the following way. If the observed number of counts/sec is n' and the counter dead time is τ sec, then the fraction of the second in which the counter is paralyzed is $n'\tau$. Of the true number n of particles that should have been recorded by the counter, only the fraction $1 - n'\tau$ is really registered. We therefore get $(1 - n'\tau)n = n'$, which gives

$$n = \frac{n'}{1 - n'\tau}. \tag{8–13}$$

(*b*) *Random coincidences.* In a coincidence experiment the objective is to establish how often two events triggering two different counters occur simultaneously. For instance, two gamma rays may be emitted in cascade; that is, a gamma transition may take place from an excited state to a lower lying level which subsequently decays to the ground state. The lifetime of the intermediate state is very often much shorter than the resolving time of any counter, so that the two events when triggering two different counters are judged by the appropriate electronic circuit to be simultaneous. Let us assume that the counting rate in detector 1 is n_1 counts/sec and in counter 2, n_2 counts/sec. Let us assume further that the circuit has a coincidence resolving time τ, meaning that a count in the second channel must occur within $\pm\tau$ sec of an event in the first channel for the circuit to rule them to be coincident. If there is no correlation whatever between the events occurring in the two counters, there still will be a certain number of accidental coincidences recorded. In any coincidence experiment, this random rate can be calculated and subtracted from the observed rate to give the number of true coincidences per second. The random rate can be found as follows: Assume that counter 1 triggers a gate that opens for counts from counter 2. Then if such counts pass the gate, they are recorded as coincidences. The gate is open for a time $2n_1\tau$ every second. This is therefore the fraction of the counting rate n_2 that will go through the gate every second if the events are completely random. The random coincidence rate is therefore

$$n_r = 2n_1n_2\tau. \tag{8–14}$$

The corrections for counting losses (Eq. 8–13) and for random coincidences (Eq. 8–14) do, of course, add to the uncertainties of an experiment. The only way to keep these uncertainties to a minimum when the counting rate is high is to design circuits and counters with very short dead times and resolving times. Good time resolution is even more important in time-of-flight experiments, where the energy of neutrons, for instance, is determined by measuring their flight time over a given length of path.

PROBLEMS

8–1. Draw diagrams like Fig. 8–1 for the three other radioactive series, obtaining your information from Appendix 6 and/or the Chart of the Nuclides.

8–2. Assume that a given radioactive nuclide has a decay constant λ_1 and that at time $t = 0$ there are N_{10} parent nuclei and $N_{20} = 0$ daughter nuclei. Assume further that the daughter nucleus is radioactive with decay constant λ_2. Show that the number of daughter nuclei N_2 at time $t > 0$ is

$$N_2 = N_{10}(e^{-\lambda_1 t} - e^{-\lambda_2 t})\,\lambda_1/(\lambda_2 - \lambda_1).$$

8–3. Show that if the parent of a radioactive series is very long-lived, that is, $\lambda_1 \ll \lambda_n$, where λ_n is the decay constant for any other nuclide in the series, an equilibrium in production and decay of all daughter products will be reached such that

$$\lambda_1 N_1 = \lambda_2 N_2 = \lambda_3 N_3 = \cdots$$

8–4. A radioactive nuclide with decay constant λ is produced in a reactor at a rate R (nuclides per second) during the time interval $t = 0$ to $t = t_1$. At time t_1 the sample is removed from the reactor. Find the formulas for the number of nuclei, N, that have been produced but not decayed (a) for $0 < t < t_1$, and (b) for $t > t_1$.

8–5. A radioactive source, consisting of 1 gm of concentrated Ra^{226}, is enclosed in a thin metallic shell hanging in a quartz fiber. Is this source likely to have a much higher temperature than its surroundings?

8–6. For the Poisson distribution, show that $P_{\bar{n}-1} = P_{\bar{n}}$.

8–7. Prove that Eq. (8–9) gives $\sigma^2 = \bar{n}$.

8–8. The principal contribution to the peak width in the pulse-height spectrum from a NaI spectrometer comes from statistical fluctuations of the number of electrons released from the photocathode. Assume a Poisson distribution for this number, and estimate $\bar{n}$ for peak A in Fig. 7–21.

*8–9. Design a coincidence experiment to study the energies of gamma rays given off in the decay of selected excited states populated by alpha decay. Assume that the lifetimes of these states are much shorter than the time resolution of the equipment. Pay attention to source thickness (affecting the resolving power), source strength (range of half-lives feasible for a desired counting rate), coincidence resolving time, and so on.

9 Gamma Transitions

9–1 Introduction

The existence of excited states of nuclei was discussed briefly in Section 1–12 and in Chapter 6. Nuclear physics is concerned, in large part, with the study of these excited states, and there is a tremendous amount of experimental data being accumulated for the purpose of obtaining descriptions of the individual states. For some nuclei, notably in the vicinity of closed shells, the shell model seems to be capable of giving a fair description of excited levels. In such cases, we should like, whenever possible, to determine experimentally which shell-model states are occupied and how the individual j-values are coupled. In other areas, where other models are more applicable, there are other parameters to be determined. Most of the measurable parameters can, however, be defined without resort to a particular model. These parameters are the energy of the excited state, the transition probability (lifetime), the angular momentum, the parity, and, whenever applicable, the isotopic spin quantum number T (Section 6–7). Two other parameters that are measurable for the nuclear ground state are sometimes also measurable for excited states. These are the magnetic dipole moment and the electric quadrupole moment.

In this chapter we study the electromagnetic de-excitation of nuclear levels. This, for the present, means gamma-ray emission and internal conversion, the latter being transfer of the excitation energy to one of the electrons in the atomic K-, L-, or M-shell, etc. There are other more rare processes that normally do not compete with the two mentioned. The purpose of this study is to:

(1) compare experiment and theory of the *de-excitation* process, because this will throw some light on nuclear structure, and

(2) learn how characteristic energy-level parameters, as for instance angular momentum and parity, can be extracted from the experimental data.

To study a given state, the nucleus can be excited to this state by an electromagnetic interaction (e.g., absorption of a gamma quantum) that brings about a transition from the ground state. More often, the nucleus is produced directly in the excited state through a nuclear reaction or through a disintegration process (alpha, beta, fission).

Nuclei in highly excited states most often de-excite themselves by the emission of a heavy particle, whenever this is energetically possible. Below the dissociation energy, i.e., the binding energy of the last neutron, proton, or alpha particle, whichever is smallest, the de-excitation can only take place by electromagnetic interaction (and sometimes by beta decay, which ordinarily is a slower process). In the electromagnetic de-excitation process the nucleus drops to a lower excited state or to the ground state, in exact analogy with the emission of light from excited atoms. However, the energies of the electromagnetic quanta emitted by nuclei are mostly in the range 10^4 to 10^6 times the energy of a photon in the visible spectrum. The wavelength is therefore smaller than the optical wavelength by the same factor. The relationship between the energy and the wavelength of an electromagnetic quantum is, in general:

$$E_\gamma = h\nu = hc/\lambda = 1239.8/\lambda \text{ MeV}, \tag{9–1}$$

with λ in fermis. This formula shows that a 1-MeV gamma ray has a wavelength which is of the order of magnitude of 100 nuclear diameters.

9–2 Measurements of Gamma-Ray Energies

In atomic physics (optics and x-rays) photon energies are determined almost exclusively by means of wavelength measurements. Since the energy ranges of gamma rays and of characteristic x-rays overlap, it is possible to some extent to employ the same techniques for wavelength measurements in the two areas of physics. The physical process utilized is, of course, the coherent scattering of the electromagnetic radiation by a crystal lattice. A quartz-crystal spectrometer designed specifically for gamma-ray studies is described below. In other types of instruments, which are also called gamma-ray spectrometers, the gamma-ray energy is converted into electron energy by one of the three processes discussed in Section 7–3; that is, the photoelectric process, Compton scattering, or pair production. Brief descriptions of the most important gamma-ray spectrometers follow.

(*a*) *The bent-crystal spectrometer*. One version of the bent-crystal spectrometer was discussed in Section 2–2 (see Fig. 2–1). In a different and earlier version of the bent-crystal spectrometer developed by J. W. M. DuMond,* the direction of the photons is reversed (Fig. 9–1). In this setup, the source rather than the recorder is placed on the focusing circle (point R). The detector, a gamma-ray counter G, is placed on the other side of the quartz crystal C behind a lead collimator A. The counting rate is measured as a function of the angle θ, i.e., as a function of the source position. For a given gamma-ray energy, a maximum is observed in the counting rate for the Bragg angle θ, given by Eq. (2–1).

---

* J. W. M. DuMond, *Rev. Sci. Instr.* **18**, 626 (1947).

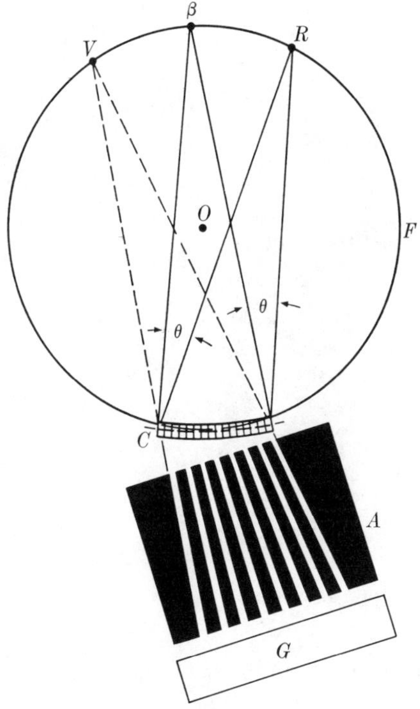

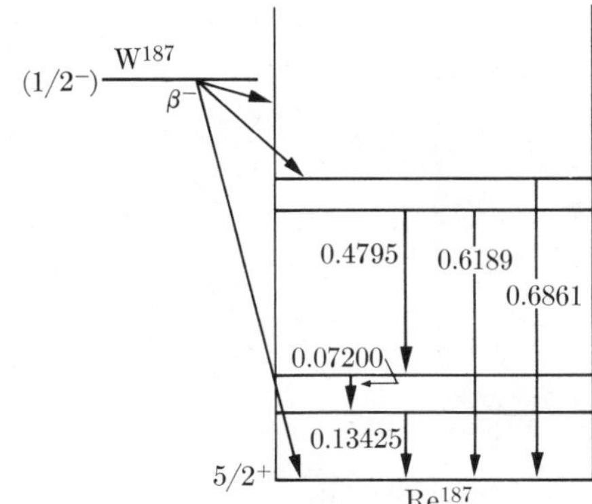

Fig. 9–2. Decay scheme for W^{187} with gamma transitions in Re^{187} measured with the bent-crystal spectrometer.

Fig. 9–1. Bent-crystal spectrometer after J. W. M. DuMond. The source is at position R; C is the crystal; A is a lead shield, and G is the gamma-ray detector.

Figure 9–2 shows an example of four very accurately determined gamma-ray energies arising from the decay of excited states in Re^{187}. The 72-keV line is determined with an accuracy of ± 1 part in 10,000, and the 686-keV line is determined with an accuracy of ± 1 part in 1800. At still higher energy, the accuracy rapidly decreases. However, below 1 MeV, this method is definitely more accurate than any other presently used for determining gamma-ray energies. One drawback of the method is that one needs very concentrated and extremely potent gamma-ray sources.

(*b*) *The pair spectrometer.* This instrument, illustrated in Fig. 9–3, operates on the principle of simultaneously detecting the electron and the positron created in a pair-production process. The conversion process takes place in a thin metal foil, the radiator, which is struck by the incident gamma rays at an angle of approximately 90°. The radiator is inside a vacuum enclosure and between the pole pieces of an electromagnet. In the pair-production process, both particles tend to be emitted in the forward direction. They therefore leave the radiator approximately along the normal to its surface, and thereafter they are deflected in the magnetic field, one to the left and one to the right because of their dif-

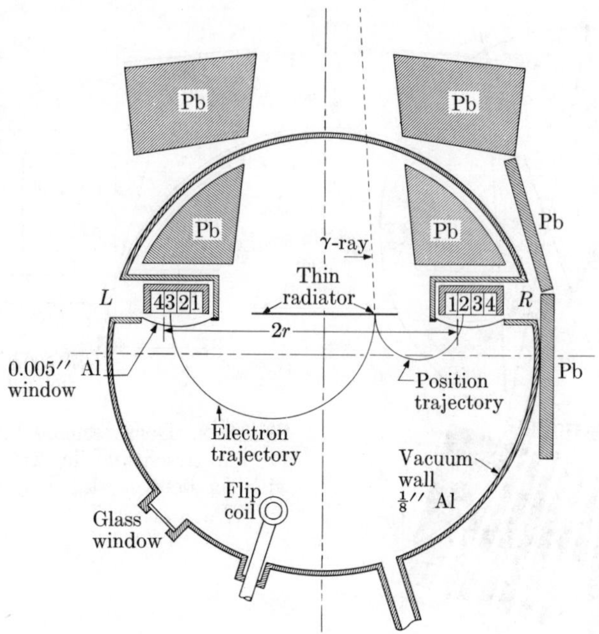

Fig. 9–3. Schematic diagram of a pair spectrometer. [From R. L. Walker and B. D. McDaniel, *Phys. Rev.* **74,** 315 (1948).]

ferent charge. The electron, if it has the appropriate momentum, will hit an electron detector, and the positron, if it has the appropriate momentum, will hit a positron detector. The two detectors are connected to a coincidence circuit, which will register a count when they are simultaneously triggered. In this case, the sum of the electron and positron orbital diameters is equal to the distance $2r$ between the counters.

Since in the pair-production process, the total energy of the gamma ray is converted into rest energy and kinetic energy of the two particles, we have

$$E_\gamma = m_1c^2 + m_2c^2. \tag{9–2}$$

The instrument actually measures the sum of the momenta of the two particles,

$$p_1 + p_2 = eB(\rho_1 + \rho_2) = eBr. \tag{9–3}$$

We can rewrite Eq. (9–2) in the following way (with $\beta = v/c$):

$$E_\gamma = c\left(\frac{m_1v_1}{\beta_1} + \frac{m_2v_2}{\beta_2}\right) = \frac{c}{\beta_1}\left(m_1v_1 + \frac{\beta_1}{\beta_2}\,m_2v_2\right) \approx \frac{c}{\beta_1}\,(p_1 + p_2) = \frac{ceBr}{\beta_1}\cdot \tag{9–4}$$

Here we have put $\beta_1 \approx \beta_2$. For high energies, β is close to 1, so that the approximation is a good one. For instance, for $E_\gamma = 5$ MeV, the average energy of the two particles is 2.5 MeV corresponding to $\beta = 0.98$.

The pair spectrometer at the Chalk River Laboratories in Canada* has been extensively used to determine the energies of gamma rays emitted after the capture of slow neutrons in a variety of target materials.†

The binding energy of the last neutron in most nuclei is approximately 7 to 8 MeV. This means that after slow neutron capture, the nucleus is in a state of excitation energy $E \approx 7$ to 8 MeV. From this state, it decays to the ground state, directly or via one or more intermediate levels. The gamma-ray spectrum produced does not unambiguously determine the position of the levels. For instance, if the binding energy is 7 MeV, and gamma rays of 3 and 4 MeV are observed, they are likely to be the result of a cascade over an intermediate level. The question is: Is the level at 3 or 4 MeV? Usually, other data, for instance the results of charged-particle reactions, are available for piecing together the full picture.

(*c*) *Other magnetic spectrometers.* As mentioned above, gamma-ray energy can be converted into electron energy, which is more easily measured, through three processes: pair production, Compton scattering, and photoemission. The relative importance of these three processes depends on the gamma-ray energy and the atomic number of the radiator in which the conversion process takes place. Among the three processes, the part of the gamma-ray energy that is converted into *kinetic* electron energy differs. Therefore, to determine the former from a measurement of the latter, it is necessary that we identify the process. In the spectrometer described above, a recorded event is identified as arising from the pair-production process, because of the simultaneous detection of the positron and the electron. Correspondingly, it is, in principle, possible to distinguish a Compton process from the other two by simultaneously detecting the electron and the scattered gamma ray. This technique has been utilized in Compton spectrometers in which the energy of an electron emitted in a forward direction is measured through the deflection in a magnetic field, and the process is identified as a Compton process by the simultaneous observation of the gamma ray scattered in the backward direction. The relationship between the energy E_γ of the incident gamma ray and the kinetic energy T of the Compton electrons is (Problem 9–5)

$$T = \frac{E_\gamma}{1 + m_0c^2/E_\gamma(1 - \cos\phi)}, \tag{9–5}$$

where ϕ is the angle between the incident and scattered gamma rays. The energy of this gamma ray, of course, does not have to be measured.

---

* B. B. Kinsey and G. A. Bartholomew, *Can. J. Phys.* **31,** 537 (1953).

† G. A. Bartholomew and L. A. Higgs, *Compilation of Thermal Neutron Capture Gamma Rays*, Atomic Energy of Canada, Limited, Report No. 669 (1958).

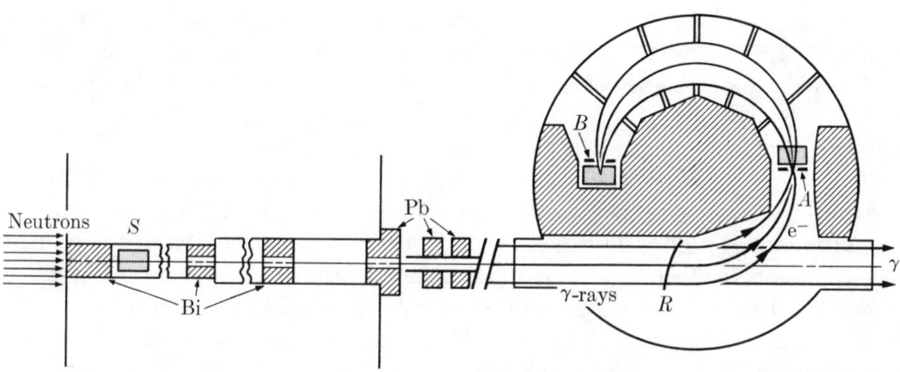

Fig. 9–4. Compton spectrometer used by Groshev *et al.* to measure the energy of gamma rays emitted from various materials (sample S) after slow neutron capture; R is a polystyrene radiator, A and B are slits and counters.

In another type of Compton spectrometer, a different approach has been taken. In the energy range 0.5 to 10 MeV, the Compton process is dominant, particularly in low Z materials. In this energy range, therefore, only an extremely small fraction of the electrons arises from either pair production or photoemission if, for instance, beryllium or carbon is used as converter. Figure 9–4 shows the principle of operation of a Compton spectrometer utilized by Groshev *et al.** for measuring the energies of gamma rays emitted from various materials after slow neutron capture. A well-collimated gamma-ray beam emitted from the sample S falls on the radiator R which is a polystyrene sheet about 100 microns thick. The radiator is inside the field of a large electromagnet, and the electrons of the proper momentum that are emitted in the forward direction within about 1° of the direction of the gamma rays will, after deflection and focusing in the magnetic field, pass through a slit A. Behind A, they pass through a thin-window Geiger-Mueller counter, are thereafter deflected 180°, and finally arrive at the slit and counter B. Only events that trigger both counters are recorded. This is necessary to cut down the "background" counts from counter B alone.

The energy of the electrons that gives rise to coincidence counts between counters A and B is varied by varying the magnetic field of the instrument. Figure 9–5 shows the spectrum of Compton electrons resulting from gamma rays following slow neutron capture in chlorine; that is, resulting from de-excitation of Cl^{36} and Cl^{38} formed in excited states. The bottom horizontal scale gives the magnetic rigidity $B\rho$ of the recorded electrons, and the top horizontal scale gives the corresponding energy in MeV of the gamma rays. The resolving power of the instrument, defined as $E_\gamma/\Delta E_\gamma$, is about 40. Here, ΔE_γ is taken as the

* L. V. Groshev, B. P. Adyasevich, and A. M. Demidov, *Proc. Intern. Conf. Peaceful Uses At. Energy*, Geneva, **2,** 39 (1955) and United Nations, New York (1956).

full width of a peak in the spectrum, measured at half amplitude (see Fig. 9–5). This resolving power is somewhat inferior to that of the pair spectrometer described above.

(*d*) *Photoelectric conversion.* At low gamma-ray energies (100-keV range), the photoelectric process is dominant, in particular for radiator materials with high Z. In this range, photoelectric conversion has been used very successfully for determining gamma-ray energies. Beta spectrometers (Section 11–2) are used for measuring the energies of electrons from a thin high Z radiator foil covering the γ-ray source. This is called external conversion, as contrasted to internal conversion in which an electron is emitted directly from the excited atom without the intermediary of a gamma ray (Section 9–9).

(*e*) *The lithium-drifted germanium spectrometer.* The solid-state counter or spectrometer was described in Section 7–6, and Fig. 7–19 shows part of a pulse-height spectrum obtained with a lithium-drifted germanium spectrometer.

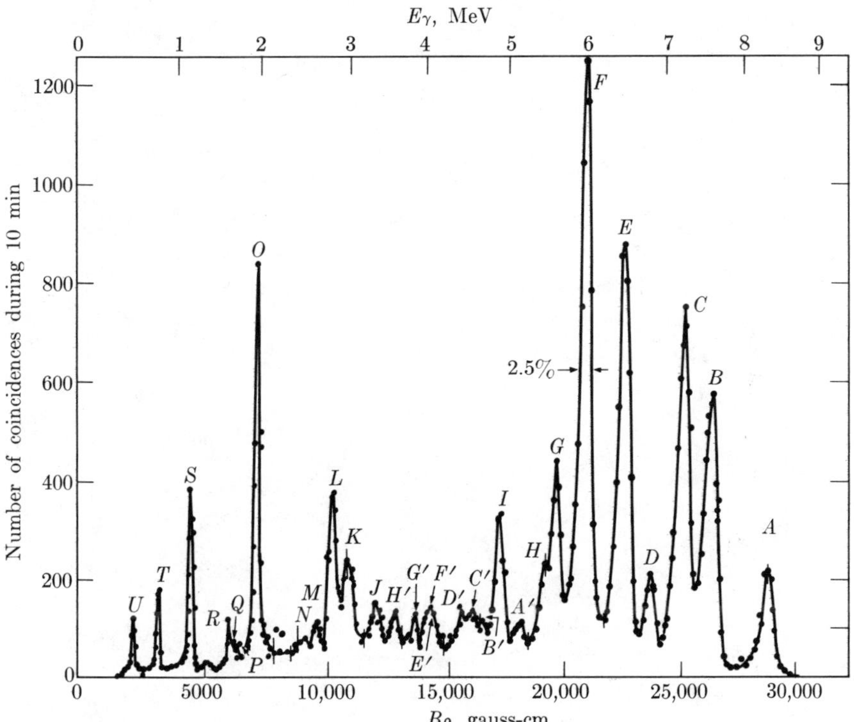

Fig. 9–5. Coincidence gamma-ray spectrum from chlorine obtained with the instrument in Fig. 9–4. [From L. V. Groshev *et al.*, *Proc. Intern. Conf. Peaceful Uses At. Energy*, Geneva, **2,** 39 (1955) and United Nations, New York (1956).]

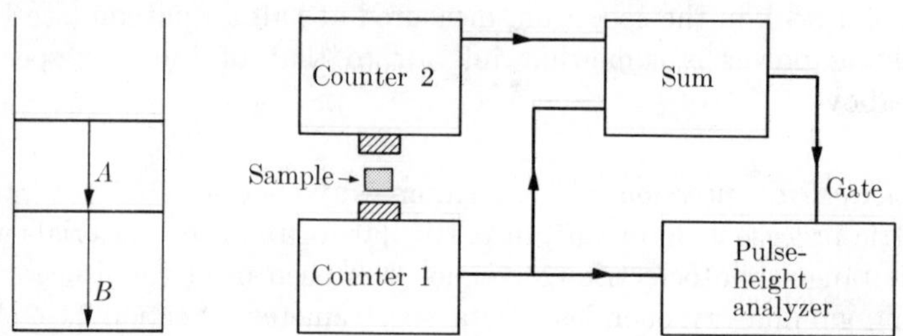

Fig. 9–6. Hoogenboom's coincidence circuit and a typical decay scheme of cascading gamma rays.

(*f*) *The scintillation cascade spectrometer.* The scintillation counter, or spectrometer, was described in Section 7–7, and a typical pulse-height spectrum from two gamma rays incident on a sodium-iodide crystal was shown in Fig. 7–21. In spite of the complexity of the pulse-height spectra, the scintillation spectrometer is extensively used because of its simplicity and also because of its large solid angle of acceptance of gamma rays from a given source.

An interesting technique for studying cascade gamma rays with the aid of two scintillation spectrometers was devised by Hoogenboom.* The objective

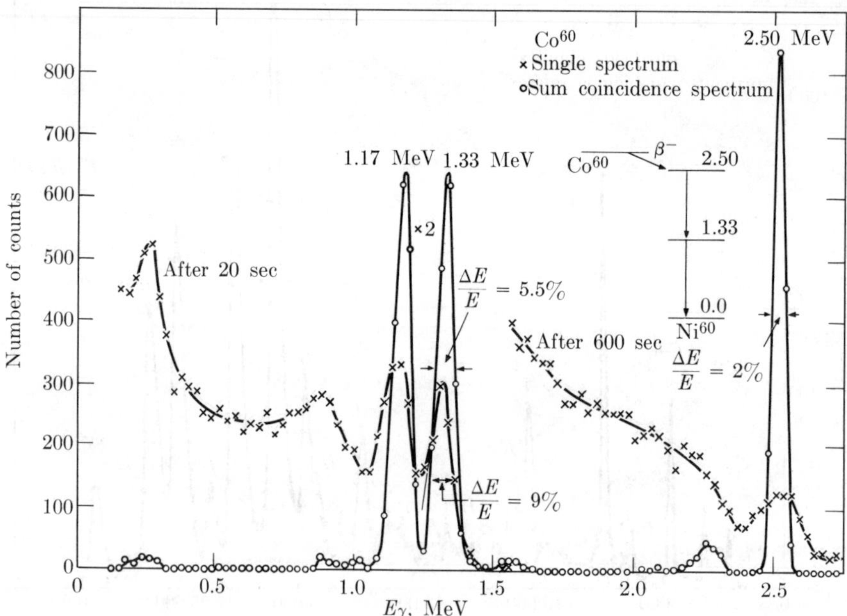

Fig. 9–7. Single and sum-coincidence spectrum of Co^{60} as measured by the apparatus of Fig. 9–6. The sum-channel setting is 2.50 MeV. [From A. M. Hoogenboom, *Nucl. Instr. Methods* **3**, 57 (1958).]

* A. M. Hoogenboom, *Nucl. Instr. Methods* **3**, 57 (1958).

is to determine over which intermediate states the de-excitation of a given level of known excitation energy passes. Figure 9–6 illustrates the principle of operation of Hoogenboom's apparatus. The pulse-height spectrum from counter 1 is analyzed, but only for events for which the sum of the pulse heights from the two counters corresponds to the full energy $A + B$ (Fig. 9–6). All Compton and pair-production events for which the full energy is not delivered to the counters are hereby eliminated. Figure 9–7 gives as an example the gamma-ray cascade spectrum from Co^{60} measured with Hoogenboom's apparatus. The normal single-counter spectrum with Compton peaks, etc. is shown for comparison.

9–3 Measurements of Lifetimes of Excited States

When the excitation energy of a nucleus is higher than the dissociation energy for a neutron or a proton, it almost always decays by particle emission. This decay is extremely rapid, usually the mean life is shorter than 10^{-20} sec. Below the dissociation energy, however, when the de-excitation usually goes by electromagnetic interaction to the ground state, the lifetimes are much longer; that is, from about 10^{-17} sec to a few years. In this section, we discuss various methods for directly or indirectly measuring these lifetimes.

Quantum-mechanical states that are not completely stable do not have truly sharp values for the energy. The uncertainty principle tells us that the relationship between the uncertainty in energy and uncertainty in time is given by

$$\Delta E \, \Delta t \geq \hbar. \tag{9–6}$$

In Section 9–5 we show in a semiclassical discussion that the energy distribution of photons emitted from a source of mean life τ(sec) has the character of a resonance curve with width (at half amplitude) given by

$$\Gamma = \frac{\hbar}{\tau} = \frac{6.58 \times 10^{-16}}{\tau} \text{ eV}. \tag{9–7}$$

This is in accordance with Eq. (9–6). In order to determine the mean life, therefore, we can measure either Γ or τ.

(*a*) *Direct measurement of the mean life* τ. Reasonably long lifetimes of nuclear states can, of course, be measured by directly observing the decrease in the counting rate from a given source as a function of time. With fast electronic circuitry, this method can be used for measuring mean lives down to approximately 10^{-6} sec.

By more exotic schemes, considerably shorter mean lives can be measured. One of these is the method of delayed coincidence. The time of formation of the excited state is precisely recorded, for instance by observation of a beta ray that leaves the daughter nucleus in the state to be studied. This "formation" pulse is compared on a time scale with the "de-excitation" pulse from a gamma-ray counter. The method involves electronic delay of the formation pulse and observation of coincidences between it and the de-excitation pulse. When an event is recorded, the delay time, of course, represents exactly the gamma lifetime of the state in the particular nucleus giving rise to the event. A study of the distribution of the number of events vs. delay time yields the mean life τ. This method can be used for measuring mean lives down to about 10^{-11} sec.

(*b*) *Measurement of the natural width* Γ. According to Eq. (9–7), the extremely short mean life of 10^{-17} sec corresponds to the "large" natural width $\Gamma =$ 65.8 eV. Only certain transitions with comparatively high gamma-ray energy (e.g., 6 MeV) have such large natural widths. Therefore, to observe directly the natural widths, one needs resolving powers for the gamma-ray spectrometers of the order of 10^5 or more. No existing gamma-ray spectrometer has such a good resolving power; however, the natural width can be indirectly measured by various methods.

One of these methods consists of measuring the probability or cross section for *absorption* of a gamma ray by a nucleus in its ground state. When the incident gamma rays have a uniform energy distribution covering the width of the state to which the nucleus is elevated, the absorption cross section is proportional to this width. Several different methods have been devised to study the absorption cross section for gamma rays with an energy range covering the excitation energy of the state studied. For example, a continuous gamma-ray spectrum, the bremsstrahlung spectrum, can be obtained by letting an electron beam of sufficient energy impinge on a high Z target. The nuclei to be studied are exposed to these bremsstrahlung gamma rays, which may be absorbed, thereby exciting the nuclei to a higher level. The gamma rays subsequently de-exciting the nuclei, the nuclear-resonance fluorescence radiation, can be measured by a scintillation spectrometer that is shielded from the radiation of the primary source. This method has been

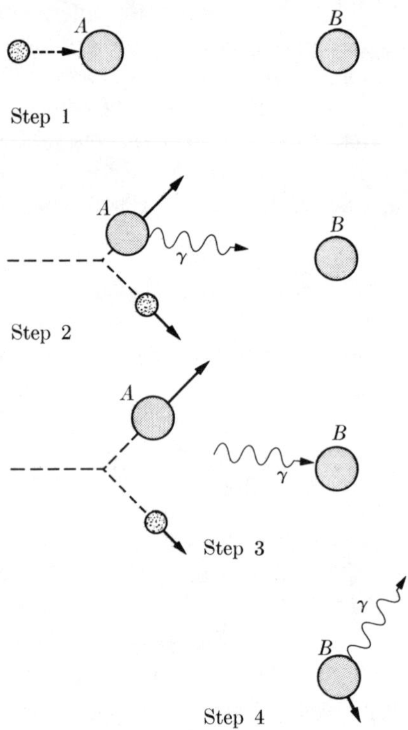

Fig. 9–8. Self-absorption of gamma rays by nucleus B. The gamma ray is emitted by nucleus A while in motion following a nuclear reaction.

used, for instance, by Booth *et al.** to measure excited-state lifetimes in the range 10^{-13} to 10^{-15} sec.

Another method consists of measuring the "self-absorption" of one nucleus of a gamma ray emitted from another nucleus of the same kind. A difficulty is that part of the energy of the excited state of the radiating nucleus is used to give this nucleus a recoil energy (Doppler shift), so that the energy of the emitted gamma ray is usually not sufficient to excite another nucleus. This difficulty can be overcome if the emitting nucleus is in motion during the emission. Figure 9–8 illustrates the technique used by Swann and Metzger† to overcome the Doppler effect. Nucleus A is formed in an excited state by a nuclear reaction (step 1) and is moving towards nucleus B when it emits a gamma ray in a transition to the ground state (step 2). This gamma ray has an energy slightly higher than the excitation energy of the state in question and can therefore, in being absorbed by nucleus B (step 3), supply both this excitation energy plus the recoil energy of B. In step 4 the nucleus B is de-excited again with emission of a gamma ray or gamma rays. The resonance radiation emitted in step 4 can be detected by counters shielded for the radiation of step 2.

Another ingenious method of overcoming the difficulties connected with the recoil energy has been devised by Mössbauer.‡ The nuclei, both the emitter and the absorber, are "clamped" in crystals, in which they can be brought by impact into vibrational motion, but only if the impact is large enough to excite the first vibrational state in the crystal. Unless the gamma-ray momentum is sufficiently large to accomplish this, the whole massive crystal has to recoil, and the recoil energies of both emitter and absorber are then negligibly small.

Figure 9–9 is an illustration of Mössbauer's apparatus. The source in the original experiment was 16-day Os^{191} which decays by β^- to an excited state

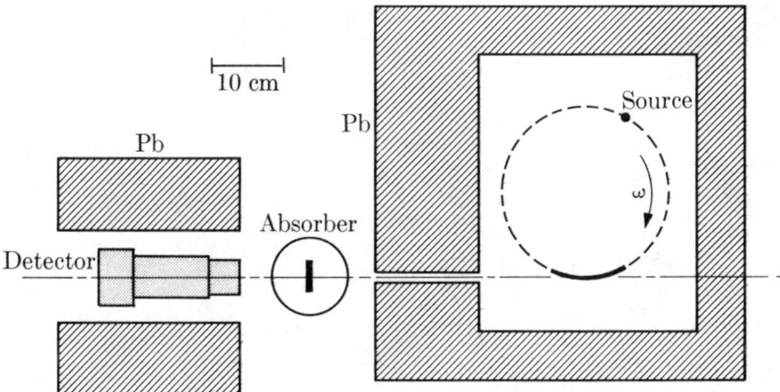

Fig. 9–9. Mössbauer's original apparatus. The source is mounted in a rotating cryostat and is seen by the absorber only while moving along the outlined circle segment.

---

* E. C. Booth, B. Chasen, and K. A. Wright, *Nucl. Phys.* **57,** 403 (1964).

† C. P. Swann and F. R. Metzger, *Phys. Rev.* **108,** 982 (1957).

‡ R. Mössbauer, *Z. Physik* **151,** 125 (1959).

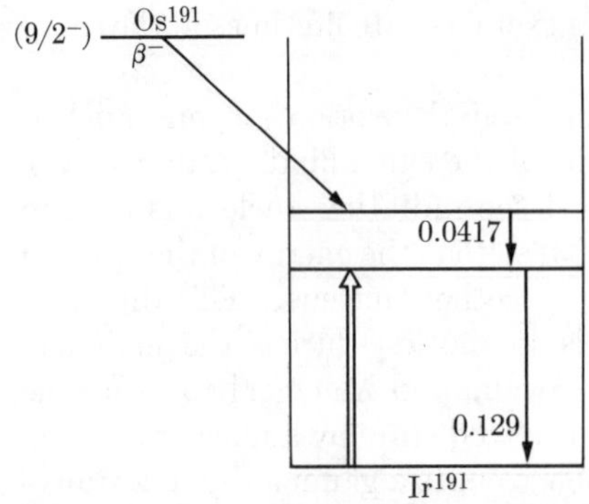

Fig. 9–10. Decay scheme for Os^{191} showing the absorption line (double arrow) to the 129-keV level and the emission line back to the ground state.

at 171 keV in Ir^{191}. This cascades over a level at 129 keV to the ground state (Fig. 9–10). The source was cooled in a cryostat to minimize lattice vibrations, and the cryostat could be rotated to give it a small velocity relative to the Ir^{191} absorber, which was also cooled. At small velocities centered around zero, considerable self-absorption of the 129-keV gamma ray takes place in the Ir^{191} absorber (double arrow in Fig. 9–10). The counting-rate data, as a function of source velocity, are shown in Fig. 9–11. From the Doppler equation, we find that the relationship between energy shift and source velocity is

$$\Delta E_\gamma / E_\gamma = \Delta\nu/\nu = v/c. \tag{9–8}$$

This equation has been used to calculate the energy scale in Fig. 9–11. Although the curve in Fig. 9–11 actually reflects the amount of overlap between the emission and the absorption lines, it is an almost direct measure of the width of a gamma-ray line in the microvolt range. These measurements of line widths by

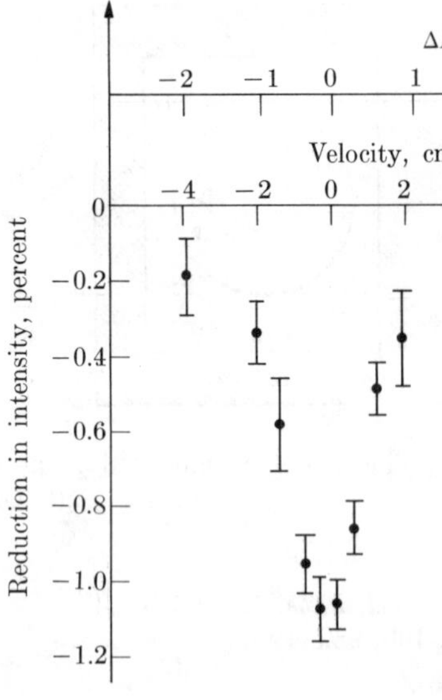

Fig. 9–11. Counting-rate data showing a 1% reduction in gamma-ray intensity as the relative velocity of source and absorber approaches zero. This is caused by self-absorption of the 129-keV line in the Ir^{191} absorber. [From R. Mössbauer, *Z. Physik* **151,** 125 (1959).]

Mössbauer's method are subject to considerable errors, and the technique has found more exciting applications in other areas of physics.

(c) *Coulomb excitation.* It is possible to excite a nucleus through the intermediary of electromagnetic forces by bombarding it with charged particles. If the particle energy is sufficiently low, the Coulomb barrier will prevent close contact, so that nuclear forces do not come into play. The cross section for Coulomb excitation is again proportional to the width of the excited state. This process is treated in some detail in Section 13–13.

9–4 Multipole Moments

As a preliminary to the theoretical determination of decay constants λ (or mean lives $1/\lambda$), in this and the next section we shall outline classical calculations of the radiated power from an oscillating charge assembly. We follow the treatment of Blatt and Weisskopf;* the reader is referred to their book for details. First, we discuss briefly a generalized formula for an electric multipole moment. We define an element of an electric multipole moment as

$$Q_{lm} = \int r^l Y^*_{lm}(\theta, \phi)\rho \, d\tau, \tag{9–9}$$

where $Y^*_{lm}(\theta, \phi)$ is the complex conjugate of the spherical harmonic function of orders l and m, ρ is the charge density, and $d\tau$ is the volume element. The integral is taken over the region of space occupied by the charge, in the present case, the whole nucleus.

With the definition given above, we get, for instance, for the electric dipole moment ($l = 1$) three components, corresponding to the three spherical harmonic functions with $l = 1$ and $m = -1$, 0, and 1. These components are

$$\begin{aligned}
Q_{11} &= \sqrt{3/8\pi}\int r \sin\theta(\cos\phi - i \sin\phi)\rho \, d\tau = \sqrt{3/8\pi}\int (x - iy)\rho \, d\tau, \\
Q_{10} &= \sqrt{3/4\pi}\int r\rho \cos\theta \, d\tau = \sqrt{3/4\pi}\int z\rho \, d\tau, \\
Q_{1-1} &= \sqrt{3/8\pi}\int r \sin\theta(\cos\phi + i \sin\phi)\rho \, d\tau = \sqrt{3/8\pi}\int (x + iy)\rho \, d\tau.
\end{aligned} \tag{9–10}$$

In Section 1–8 and in most textbooks on electricity and magnetism, the dipole moment is defined as a vector with x-component

$$P_{\mathrm{Ex}} = \int x\rho \, d\tau, \text{ etc.} \tag{9–11}$$

---

* J. M. Blatt and V. F. Weisskopf, *Theoretical Nuclear Physics*, New York: John Wiley and Sons, 1952, p. 583.

We see that our present definition yields three components for the dipole moment that can be derived from the components of type (9–11) by linear combination.

If we insert in Eq. (9–9) the spherical harmonic functions of order $l = 2$, we get five linearly independent components of the *quadrupole* moment. One of these components is

$$\begin{aligned} Q_{20} &= \sqrt{5/16\pi}\int r^2(3\cos^2\theta - 1)\rho\, d\tau \\ &= \sqrt{5/16\pi}\int (3z^2 - r^2)\rho\, d\tau. \end{aligned} \tag{9–12}$$

Aside from the constant factor $\sqrt{5/16\pi}$, this expression is the same as that given by Eq. (1–14). If the nuclear charge density has the symmetry of an ellipsoid of rotation with the z-axis as the symmetry axis, the other components of the quadrupole moment will be equal to zero.

An element of a magnetic multipole moment can be defined in a similar fashion as for the electric multipole moment. The definition is

$$M_{lm} = -\int r^l Y^*_{lm}(\theta, \phi)\, \frac{\text{div}\,(\mathbf{r} \times \mathbf{j})}{(l+1)}\, d\tau. \tag{9–13}$$

In this expression, $\mathbf{j}$ is the current density inside the charge assembly.

It can be shown, in general, that a multipole moment of order l has zero expectation value for any nucleus for which the angular momentum J is smaller than $l/2$. It can also be proved, in general, that the electric dipole moment of any nucleus is equal to zero (Section 1–8). These considerations will not detain us from proceeding to compute the radiated power from an oscillating multipole, whether it be a dipole, quadrupole, or higher-order multipole. The final quantum-mechanical formulas do not contain the electric or magnetic multipole moments, as defined above, but they do contain *matrix* elements, the definitions of which are very similar to Eqs. (9–9) and (9–13) (see below). Nuclei, as well as atoms, do indeed emit electric dipole radiation, in spite of the fact that they do not possess electric dipole moments. This is predicted by the quantum theory of radiation and cannot be explained in classical terms.

9–5 *Theoretical Predictions of Decay Constants*

The classical calculation of the power radiated from an oscillating charge assembly involves the solutions of Maxwell's equations outside and inside the charged region (the nucleus), and an integration of Poynting's vector over an area surrounding the nucleus. The result of these calculations, taken from Blatt and Weisskopf, shows that the radiated power can be expressed in terms of the magnitude of the oscillating multipole moment, the order number l, and the oscillation frequency. Specifically, an electric multipole moment Q_{lm} oscillating with an angular frequency ω gives a total radiated power

$$P_E(lm) = \frac{2(l+1)c}{\epsilon_0 l[(2l+1)!!]^2}\left(\frac{\omega}{c}\right)^{2l+2} |Q_{lm}|^2 \text{ watts,} \tag{9–14}$$

where the double factorial means, for example, $7!! = 1\cdot 3\cdot 5\cdot 7$, $8!! = 2\cdot 4\cdot 6\cdot 8$, etc. An oscillating magnetic multipole moment M_{lm} gives a total radiated power

$$P_M(lm) = \frac{2(l+1)c\mu_0}{l[(2l+1)!!]^2}\left(\frac{\omega}{c}\right)^{2l+2} |M_{lm}|^2 \text{ watts.} \tag{9–15}$$

Let us study in some more detail the case of classical electric dipole radiation. For a single proton moving in a circular orbit of radius r, the numerical value of the dipole moment, as defined in Eq. (9–10) is $\sqrt{3/8\pi}er$. If the angular frequency is ω_0, the radiated power is, according to Eq. (9–14):

$$P_E(11) = \frac{\omega_0^4 e^2 r^2}{6\pi\epsilon_0 c^3} = \frac{e^2 a^2}{6\pi\epsilon_0 c^3} \text{ watts,} \tag{9–16}$$

where $a = \omega_0^2 r$ is the acceleration of the proton. This is in agreement with expressions given in texts on electricity and magnetism. The radiated power deprives the proton of mechanical energy so that, according to classical notions, the radius continuously decreases. We assume that the proton moves in a harmonic potential so that the frequency stays constant. The total mechanical energy is then $E = m\omega_0^2 r^2$, so that we can write

$$\frac{dE}{dt} = -P_E(11) = -\frac{\omega_0^2 e^2}{6\pi\epsilon_0 mc^3} E.$$

Integrating this equation we get

$$E = E_0 e^{-\lambda t} \tag{9–17}$$

with

$$\lambda = \frac{\omega_0^2 e^2}{6\pi\epsilon_0 mc^3} = \frac{P_E(11)}{E}\cdot \tag{9–18}$$

We have shown here that, classically, the energy of the circulating proton decays exponentially with a decay constant given by Eq. (9–18). It is also worth noting that the angular momentum $L = m\omega_0 r^2 = E_0/\omega_0$ is carried away by the radiation field as the energy decays to zero.

Before we make the transition from classical theory to wave-mechanical theory, we will discuss another important aspect of atomic radiation. This concerns the width of spectral lines. At a given point in the radiation field, the electric field strength from the circulating proton is, in accordance with Eq. (9–17)

$$\mathcal{E} = \mathcal{E}_0 e^{-\lambda t/2} \sin \omega_0 t. \tag{9–19}$$

Let us assume that the radiation is turned on at time $t = 0$ and then allowed to decay by the loss of mechanical energy as described above. By performing a Fourier analysis on Eq. (9–19) to find the frequency spectrum of the electromagnetic field, we get

$$A(\omega) = \mathcal{E}_0 \int_{-\infty}^{\infty} e^{i\omega t} e^{-\lambda t/2} \sin \omega_0 t \, dt$$

$$= \frac{\mathcal{E}_0}{2i} \int_0^{\infty} \left(e^{(-\lambda/2 + i\omega + i\omega_0)t} - e^{(-\lambda/2 + i\omega - i\omega_0)t}\right) dt.$$

The first term in the integrand gives a resonance for $\omega = -\omega_0$, and the second term gives a resonance for $\omega = \omega_0$. Since a change of sign of ω only amounts to a phase shift, we only look at the second term, as the first term yields essentially the same result. (See also Problem 9–7.) We find that

$$A(\omega) \sim \frac{\mathcal{E}_0}{2i(-\lambda/2 + i\omega - i\omega_0)}.$$

The frequency spectrum for emitted energy is therefore

$$|A(\omega)|^2 = \frac{\text{const}}{(\omega - \omega_0)^2 + (\lambda/2)^2}. \tag{9–20}$$

The *natural width* of a spectral line, defined as the full width at half maximum of the resonance-type spectrum produced by Eq. (9–20) is clearly

$$\Delta\omega_{1/2} = \lambda. \tag{9–21}$$

A slow decay (λ small) gives a sharp line, and a fast decay corresponds to a larger line width.

We now make the transition to wave mechanics. Briefly outlined, the problem is solved by time-dependent perturbation theory (Appendix 4) in which the perturbation is the electromagnetic interaction between a system of charges and the quantized field in a reflective spherical enclosure. The results of these calculations are in agreement with the classical calculations, with only the following two modifications.

(1) The energy radiated is quantized as $E = \hbar\omega$. The decay constant λ, which is the probability for emission of a quantum per unit time, is calculated as the *number* of quanta emitted per unit time when the rate of energy emitted is given by the classical expressions. We then get

$$\lambda_E(lm) = \frac{P_E(lm)}{\hbar\omega} = \frac{2(l+1)}{\hbar\epsilon_0 l[(2l+1)!!]^2} \left(\frac{\omega}{c}\right)^{2l+1} |Q_{lm}|^2, \tag{9–22}$$

$$\lambda_M(lm) = \frac{P_M(lm)}{\hbar\omega} = \frac{2(l+1)\mu_0}{\hbar l[(2l+1)!!]^2} \left(\frac{\omega}{c}\right)^{2l+1} |M_{lm}|^2. \tag{9–23}$$

(2) In Eq. (9–9), the charge density ρ should be replaced, for a quantum-mechanical system, by the unit charge times the probability density ψ_a^2 and summed over all charged particles. The quantum theory of radiation also shows that Q_{lm} in Eq. (9–22) is not the multipole moment element in the initial state ψ_a but rather is the *multipole matrix element* between the initial state ψ_a and the final state ψ_b:

$$Q_{lm}(ab) = e \sum_{k=1}^{Z} \int r_k^l Y_{lm}^*(\theta_k \phi_k) \psi_b^* \psi_a \, d\tau. \tag{9–24}$$

The corresponding expression for the magnetic multipole matrix element is

$$M_{lm}(ab) = -\frac{1}{l+1} \frac{e\hbar}{m_P} \sum_{k=1}^{Z} r_k^l Y_{lm}(\theta_k, \phi_k) \, \text{div} \, (\psi_b^* \mathbf{L}_k \psi_a) \, d\tau, \tag{9–25}$$

where $\hbar \mathbf{L}_k = -\hbar i \mathbf{r}_k \times \nabla_k$ is the angular momentum operator. This, as it stands, accounts only for the contribution to the magnetic field from the orbital motion of the protons. An additional term is needed to account for the intrinsic magnetic moments.

Another result of the wave-mechanical calculation is that in spite of the spontaneous nature of the transition, the natural width remains as calculated classically above. We introduce the natural width Γ measured in energy units rather than frequency units and obtain from Eq. (9–21):

$$\Gamma = \hbar \, \Delta\omega_{1/2} = \hbar\lambda = \hbar/\tau.$$

This is Eq. (9–7).

Finally, the wave-mechanical calculations relate the change of angular momentum and parity of the nucleus to the multipolarity, lm, of the transition, as discussed in the next section.

9–6 Selection Rules

The modes of electromagnetic radiation in the spherical cavity, referred to above, are quantized to $\Delta E = \hbar\omega$. Each mode is described by a vector function derived from the spherical harmonic functions $Y_{lm}(\theta, \phi)$. The multipole moments Q_{lm} and M_{lm} couple with the mode of order lm and with no others. Since one quantum in the mode lm carries an angular momentum $\sqrt{l(l+1)}\hbar$ and z-component $m\hbar$, radiation of multipolarity lm must remove from the nucleus a total angular momentum exactly equal to $\sqrt{l(l+1)}\hbar$, with z-component $m\hbar$, that is, the vector difference between the angular momenta $\mathbf{J}_a$ of the initial state and $\mathbf{J}_b$ of the final state must be $\sqrt{l(l+1)}$, and the z-component must change by $\Delta m_J = -m$. Reversing the argument, we find that the possible multipolarities of transitions between states J_a and J_b are given by

$$|J_a - J_b| \leq l \leq J_a + J_b. \tag{9–26}$$

Table 9–1. Selection rules for gamma-ray transitions

Type	Symbol	Angular momentum change, l	Parity change
Electric dipole	$E1$	1	yes
Magnetic dipole	$M1$	1	no
Electric quadrupole	$E2$	2	no
Magnetic quadrupole	$M2$	2	yes
Electric octupole	$E3$	3	yes
Magnetic octupole	$M3$	3	no
Electric 16-pole	$E4$	4	no
Magnetic 16-pole	$M4$	4	yes

The parity of the nucleus may or may not change in a multipole transition, and the rules are simple enough to derive so that we can do it here. Consider the definition of the electric multipole matrix element (Eq. 9–24). The integral is a product of four functions, of which the first, r^l, is always positive. The other three functions are either symmetric or antisymmetric, that is, their numerical values do not change by a reflection through the origin, but they may change sign. For the integral to give a result different from zero, the product of these three functions must be symmetric, because an antisymmetric function integrated over the whole nucleus yields as many negative contributions as positive. For even values of l, the spherical harmonic function is even; therefore the product of ψ_b and ψ_a must be even. For odd values of l, the product of ψ_b and ψ_a must be odd. We therefore get the following rule for the combination of parities of the initial and final state in an electric multipole transition:

$$\pi_a \pi_b = (-1)^l. \tag{9–27}$$

By a similar argument, we find that for a magnetic multipole transition the relationship between the parities of the initial and final state is

$$\pi_a \pi_b = (-1)^{l+1}. \tag{9–28}$$

The rules given above for the angular momentum and parity changes resulting from a transition of a given multipolarity are summarized in Table 9–1. These rules are called *selection rules* for gamma-ray transitions. Note that, in general, more than one type of multipole transition is possible between two states. For instance, if the angular momenta and parities of the initial and final states are $J_a = 1^+$ and $J_b = 2^-$, the possible l-values are 1, 2, and 3. Since the parity changes, the possible transitions are $E1$, $M2$, and $E3$. In general, however, the transition probability decreases very rapidly with increasing multipolarity l, so that for most practical purposes we can neglect all but the lowest possible

l-value. In the example above, therefore, the transition will be almost exclusively electric dipole radiation.

Equations (9–22) and (9–23) with the matrix elements (9–24) and (9–25) inserted give the decay constants for transitions of order lm from the state J_a, m_{Ja} to the state J_b, m_{Jb}. In addition to the selection rules (9–26) and (9–27) or (9–28), we have the following requirement for this partial transition:

$$m_{Ja} - m_{Jb} = m. \tag{9–29}$$

For each initial substate characterized by m_{Ja}, there is always one or more substates m_{Jb} that can be reached, provided Eq. (9–26) holds. Let us assume that we have calculated the matrix element $Q_{lm}(ab)$ for a given transition, $J_a \rightarrow J_b$, for a given l, and for all possibilities $m_{Ja} \rightarrow m_{Jb}$ with $|m| \leq l$. Since the components m_{Ja} and m_{Jb} are not usually measured, we must take an average over all possible transitions with given l in order to get the transition probability that can be directly compared with experiment. We define a *reduced transition rate* for electric transitions of order l as

$$B(El, J_a \rightarrow J_b) = \frac{1}{2J_a + 1} \sum_{m_{Ja}} \sum_{m_{Jb}} Q^2_{lm}(ab). \tag{9–30}$$

The double sum is taken with observance of the requirement that $|m| = |m_{Ja} - m_{Jb}| \leq l$. For magnetic transitions, of course, we replace $Q_{lm}(ab)$ with $M_{lm}(ab)$. Most often the wave functions are so inadequately known that a calculation of $Q_{lm}(ab)$ that is anywhere near exact is not possible. To take an average, as implied by (9–30), seems to be of academic interest only. However, since this same average appears in the theory of other processes, namely, internal conversion and Coulomb excitation, it can be determined *experimentally* in one process and checked in another.

We can now write for the decay constants for electric and magnetic transitions

$$\lambda_E(l, J_a \rightarrow J_b) = \frac{2(l+1)}{\hbar\epsilon_0 l[(2l+1)!!]^2} \left(\frac{\omega}{c}\right)^{2l+1} B(El, J_a \rightarrow J_b), \tag{9–31}$$

$$\lambda_M(l, J_a \rightarrow J_b) = \frac{2(l+1)\mu_0}{\hbar l[(2l+1)!!]^2} \left(\frac{\omega}{c}\right)^{2l+1} B(Ml, J_a \rightarrow J_b). \tag{9–32}$$

9–7 *Angular Correlation*

There is no experimental way to discriminate directly between the different types of multipole radiation by observations on gamma quanta emitted from nonoriented nuclei. However, if the nuclei can be oriented so that the direction, m_J, of the angular momentum is known, the angular distribution of the emitted gamma rays is no longer spherically symmetric, and the shape of this distribution reveals the multipolarity l. For both electric and magnetic transitions, the angular distribution is proportional to*

$$S_{lm} = \frac{1}{2l(l+1)} \{[l(l+1) - m(m+1)]|Y_{lm+1}|^2 + [l(l+1) - m(m-1)]|Y_{lm-1}|^2 + 2m^2|Y_{lm}|^2\}. \quad (9\text{–}33)$$

For instance, for $l = 1$, $m = 0$, we get

$$S_{10} = \frac{3}{8\pi} \sin^2 \theta,$$

and for $l = 1$, $m = 1$, we get

$$S_{11} = \frac{3}{16\pi} (1 + \cos^2 \theta).$$

To align nuclei with the aid of magnetic fields is difficult, but it can be done in special cases (see Section 11–8). A more convenient way of aligning nuclei, or rather of obtaining information about the direction of the angular momentum of a given state, is to record the direction of the particle or gamma ray emitted in the formation of this state. If the state is short-lived and decays by gamma emission, there will be an observable correlation between the directions of the initial radiation and the secondary gamma rays. Figure 9–12 shows two cascading gamma rays in an energy-level diagram and, schematically, the experimental arrangement for measuring gamma-gamma correlation. Coincidences between the two counters are observed as a function of the angle θ between them. This angular correlation function $W(\theta)$ depends on the angular momenta J_i, J, and J_f in a fairly complicated way, but the theory has been worked out and tabulations of $W(\theta)$ exist.† In the particularly simple case $J_i = J_f = 0$ and $J = 1$ (both transitions dipole), we have

$$W(\theta) \sim 1 + \cos^2 \theta.$$

Angular-correlation experiments of various kinds have proved very useful in aiding the assignment of J-values for nuclear energy levels.

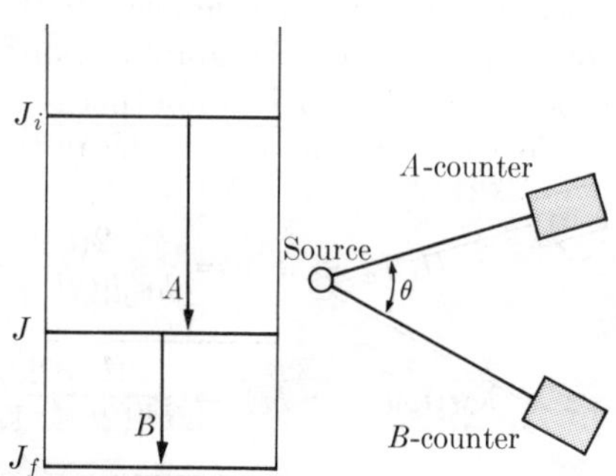

Fig. 9–12. Two gamma rays in cascade and an apparatus to measure the angular correlation between them.

* See, for instance, M. A. Preston, *Physics of the Nucleus*, Reading, Mass.: Addison-Wesley Publishing Company, 1962, p. 315.

† L. C. Biedenharn and M. E. Rose, *Rev. Mod. Phys.* **25,** 729 (1953).

9–8 Estimates of Transition Rates and Comparison with Experiment

The transition probability for a given type of multipole radiation can, in principle, be calculated from Eqs. (9–31) and (9–32). However, in order to find the multipole matrix elements, we have to know the wave functions of the initial and final states. Shell-model wave functions may be used, but, as we have seen before, the shell model does not really give a good description of excited states. In general, therefore, we do not know the nuclear wave functions with any kind of precision. However, for the purpose of making order-of-magnitude estimates of the transition probabilities, we may be justified in using a simple shell-model picture. Following Weisskopf,* we assume the following:

(1) The wave function of the initial state is given by a single-particle function of the form $\psi_a = R_a(r)Y_{lm}(\theta, \phi)$, describing an odd proton. The other nucleons, by assumption, do not contribute to the matrix element (spherically symmetric charge distribution, i.e., closed shells).

(2) The final state is given by the single-particle proton function $\psi_b = R_b(r)/\sqrt{4\pi}$, that is, the final state is assumed to be an S-state.

(3) For the purpose of making a crude estimate, we can assume that the radial wave functions R_a and R_b are constants inside the nucleus ($r < R$) and zero outside.

According to the two first conditions above, we assume that one proton jumps from a state with orbital angular momentum l to a state where the orbital angular momentum is zero. The other particles do not take part in the transition. In accordance with the third condition, we set up the normalizing integral for the radial wave function $R_a(r)$:

$$\int_0^R |R_a|^2 r^2\, dr = 1$$

and a similar integral for $R_b(r)$. Since these functions are regarded as constants within the range of integration, we get $R_a(r) = R_b(r) = \sqrt{3/R^3}$. By inserting the expressions for ψ_a and ψ_b into the formula for the matrix element for an electric multipole transition (Eq. 9–24), we get

$$Q_{lm}(ab) = \frac{e}{\sqrt{4\pi}} \int r^l \frac{3}{R^3}\, Y^*_{lm}(\theta, \phi) Y_{lm}(\theta, \phi) r^2 \sin\theta\, dr\, d\theta\, d\phi.$$

Since the spherical harmonic function is normalized, the angular part of the integral above gives a factor unity. By performing the radial integration, we get

$$Q_{lm}(ab) = \frac{e}{\sqrt{4\pi}} \frac{3R^l}{l+3}.$$

---

* V. F. Weisskopf, *Phys. Rev.* **83,** 1073 (1951).

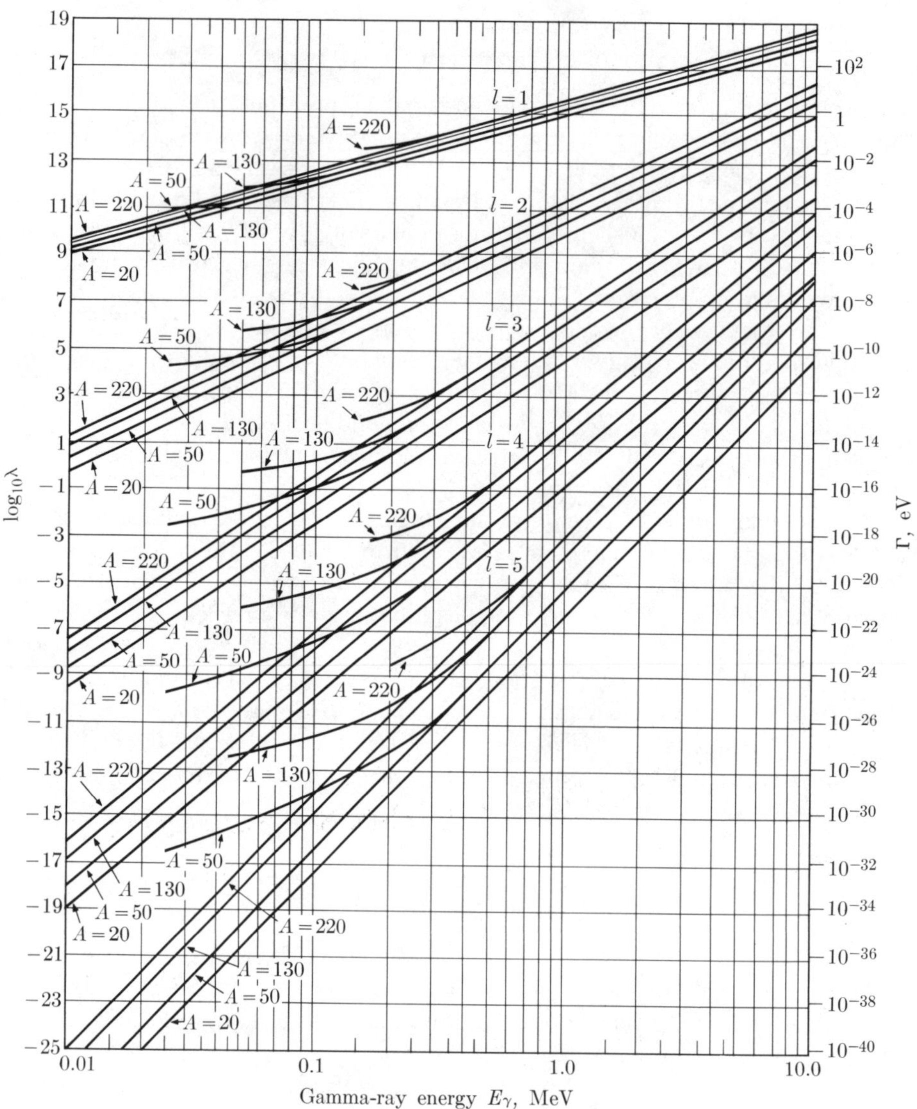

Fig. 9–13. Probability for electric multipole transition based on Weisskopf's and Moszkowski's single-proton estimates. The curved lines indicate the total transition probabilities with internal conversion included. (From E. U. Condon and H. Odishaw, *Handbook of Physics*, New York: McGraw-Hill Book Company, 1958, pp. 9–109. Reproduced by permission.)

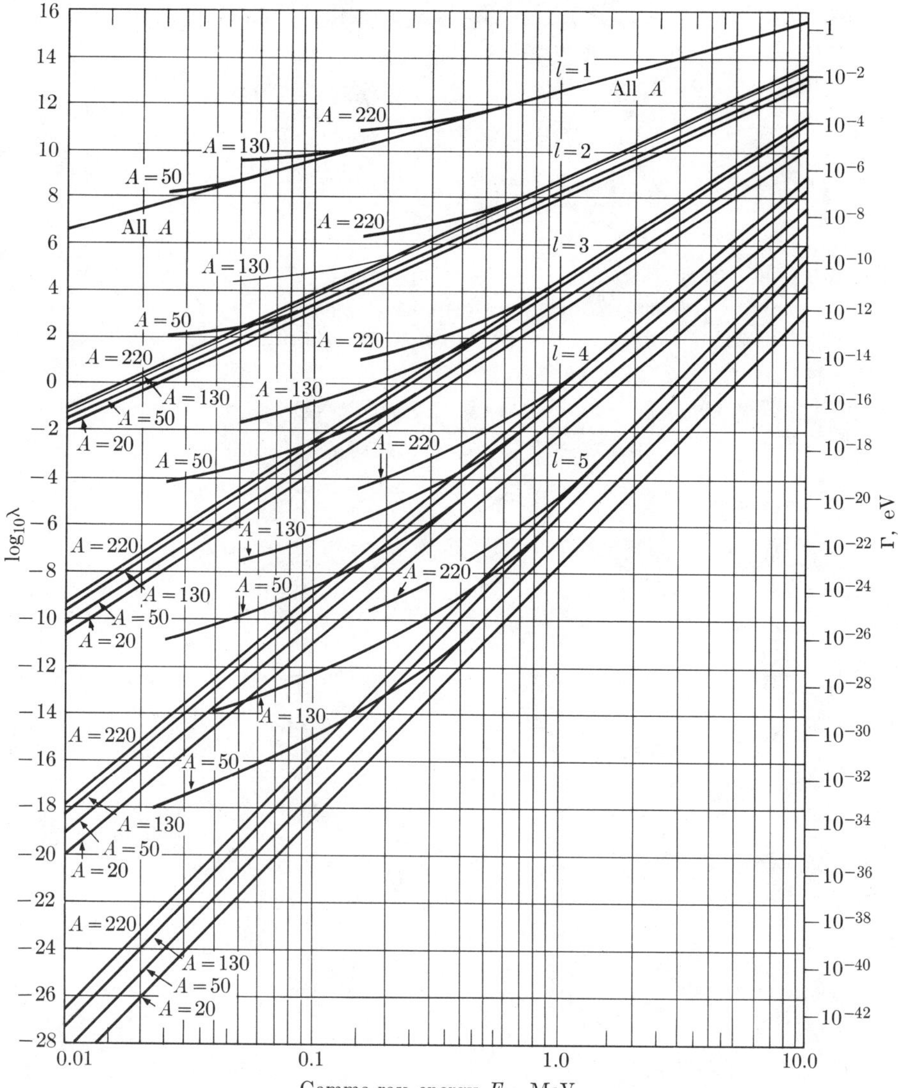

Fig. 9–14. Probability for magnetic multipole transitions based on Moszkowski's single-proton estimates. Weisskopf's formula (Eq. 9–35) gives only slightly different transition rates. The curved lines indicate the total transition probabilities with internal conversion included. (From E. U. Condon and H. Odishaw, *op. cit.*, pp. 9–110. Reproduced by permission.)

Inserted into Eq. (9–22) this gives for the so-called Weisskopf estimate of the electric multipole-transition probability

$$\begin{aligned}\lambda_E(l) &= \frac{2(l+1)}{l[(2l+1)!!]^2}\left(\frac{3}{l+3}\right)\frac{e^2R^{2l}}{4\pi\epsilon_0\hbar}\left(\frac{\omega}{c}\right)^{2l+1}\ \text{sec}^{-1} \\ &= \frac{4.4(l+1)10^{21}}{l[(2l+1)!!]^2}\left(\frac{3}{l+3}\right)^2\left(\frac{E_\gamma}{197}\right)^{2l+1} R^{2l}\ \text{sec}^{-1},\end{aligned} \tag{9–34}$$

where, in the last expression, the transition energy $E_\gamma = \hbar\omega$ is to be inserted in MeV and the nuclear radius R in fermis.

A similar calculation can be made for a magnetic multipole transition. The result is

$$\begin{aligned}\lambda_M(l) &= \frac{20(l+1)}{l[(2l+1)!!]^2}\left(\frac{3}{l+3}\right)^2\frac{e^2\mu_0c\omega}{4\pi\hbar}\left(\frac{\hbar}{McR}\right)^2\left(\frac{\omega R}{c}\right)^{2l}\ \text{sec}^{-1} \\ &= \frac{1.9(l+1)10^{21}}{l[(2l+1)!!]^2}\left(\frac{3}{l+3}\right)^2\left(\frac{E_\gamma}{197}\right)^{2l+1} R^{2l-2}\ \text{sec}^{-1}.\end{aligned} \tag{9–35}$$

In the first expression, M is the nucleon mass, and the units are MKS. In the second expression, the units are MeV and fermis.

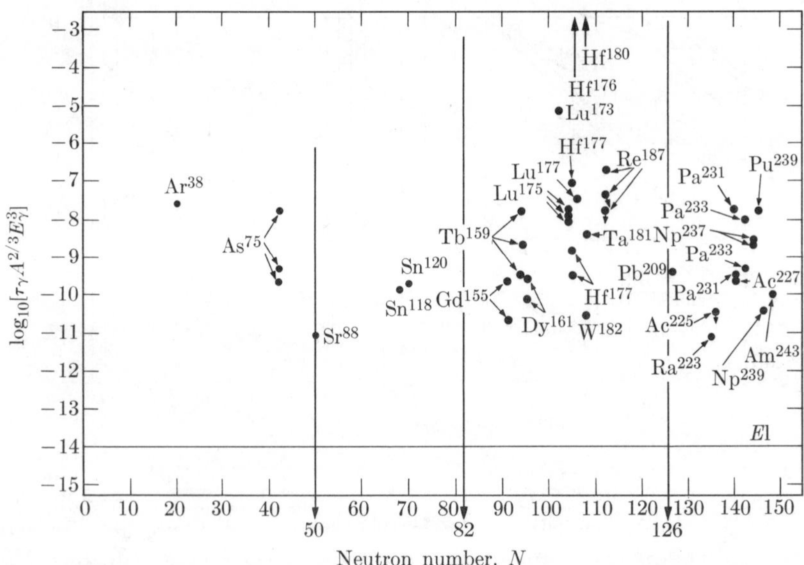

Fig. 9–15. Comparative mean lives for electric dipole ($E1$) transitions vs. neutron number N. The straight line is the Weisskopf and Moszkowski estimate. (From M. Goldhaber and A. W. Sunyar in *Alpha-, Beta-, and Gamma-Ray Spectroscopy*, Kai Siegbahn, ed., Amsterdam: North-Holland Publishing Company, 1965. Reproduced by permission.)

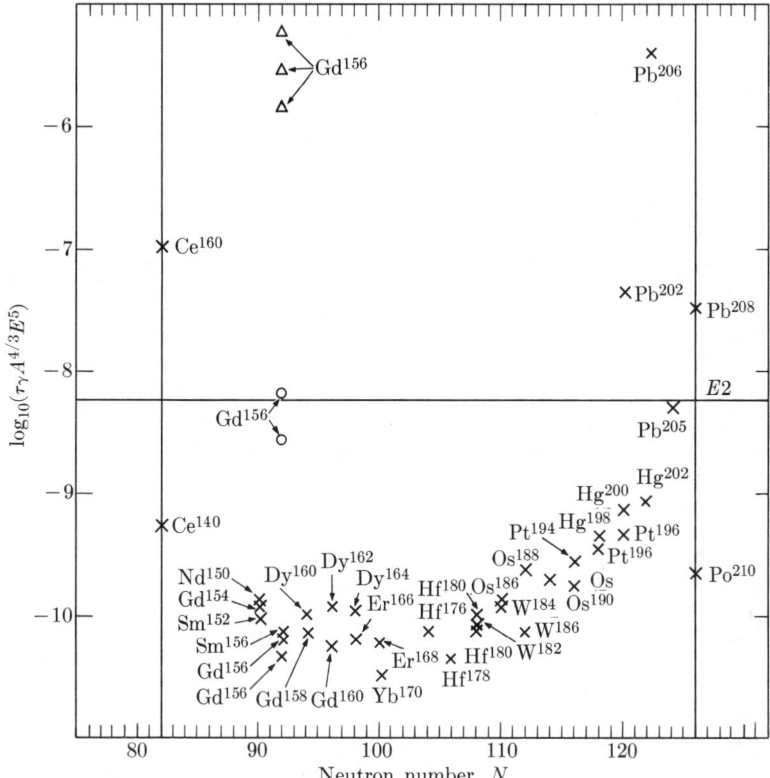

Fig. 9–16. Comparative mean lives for electric quadrupole ($E2$) transitions vs. neutron number N. The straight line is the Weisskopf and Moszkowski estimate. [From W. M. Currie, *Nucl. Phys.* **32,** 574 (1962).]

Moszkowski* has made estimates similar to those given above, based on essentially the same assumptions, but carried out in more detail. For instance, he has averaged over substates (Eq. 9–30) and, in the magnetic case, separated the effects of orbital magnetic moments and spin magnetic moments. Moszkowski's estimates are less than an order of magnitude different from Weisskopf's estimates given above.

Figures 9–13 and 9–14 are plots of Moszkowski's formulas with $R = 1.4A^{1/3}$ and without the factor arising from averaging over substates (since this depends upon J_a and J_b). This makes the formula for electric transitions identical with Eq. (9–34). The straight lines give the decay constant λ_γ for gamma emission. The curved lines give the total decay constant with internal conversion included (Section 9–9). Scales for the natural level width Γ, as computed from Eq. (9–7) are also given in the two figures.

---

* S. A. Moszkowski, *Phys. Rev.* **89,** 474 (1953).

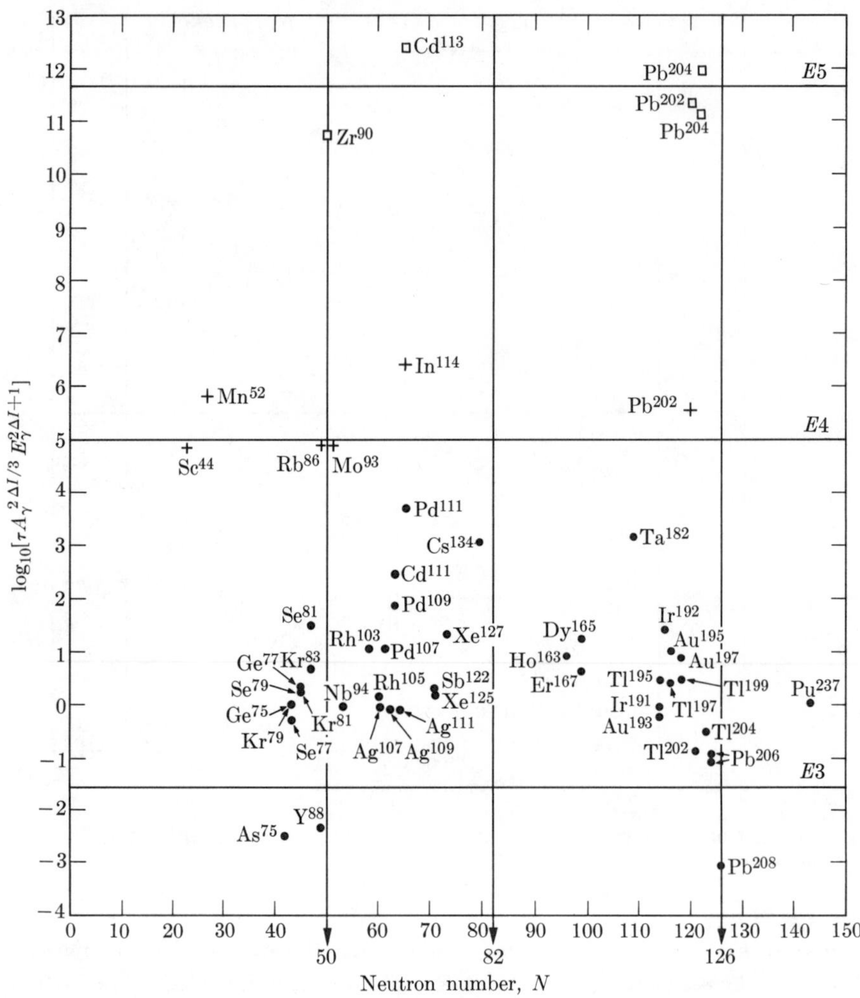

Fig. 9–17. Comparative mean lives for $E3$, $E4$, and $E5$ transitions vs. neutron number N. The straight line is the Weisskopf and Moszkowski estimate. (From M. Goldhaber and A. W. Sunyar, *op. cit.* Reproduced by permission.)

The basis for the various theoretical estimates of gamma-ray decay constants is so uncertain that not even an order-of-magnitude agreement with experimental values should be expected. In general, because of the idealized assumptions made, the theoretical formulas are expected to overestimate λ_γ.

Figures 9–15 to 9–18 give comparisons of experimentally determined mean lives τ_γ with Weisskopf's as well as Moszkowski's single-proton estimates. The experimental lifetimes have been corrected for internal conversion and multiplied with $A^{2\Delta I/3}E_\gamma^{2\Delta I+1}$ for electric transitions and with $A^{(2\Delta I-2)/3}E_\gamma^{2\Delta I+1}$ for

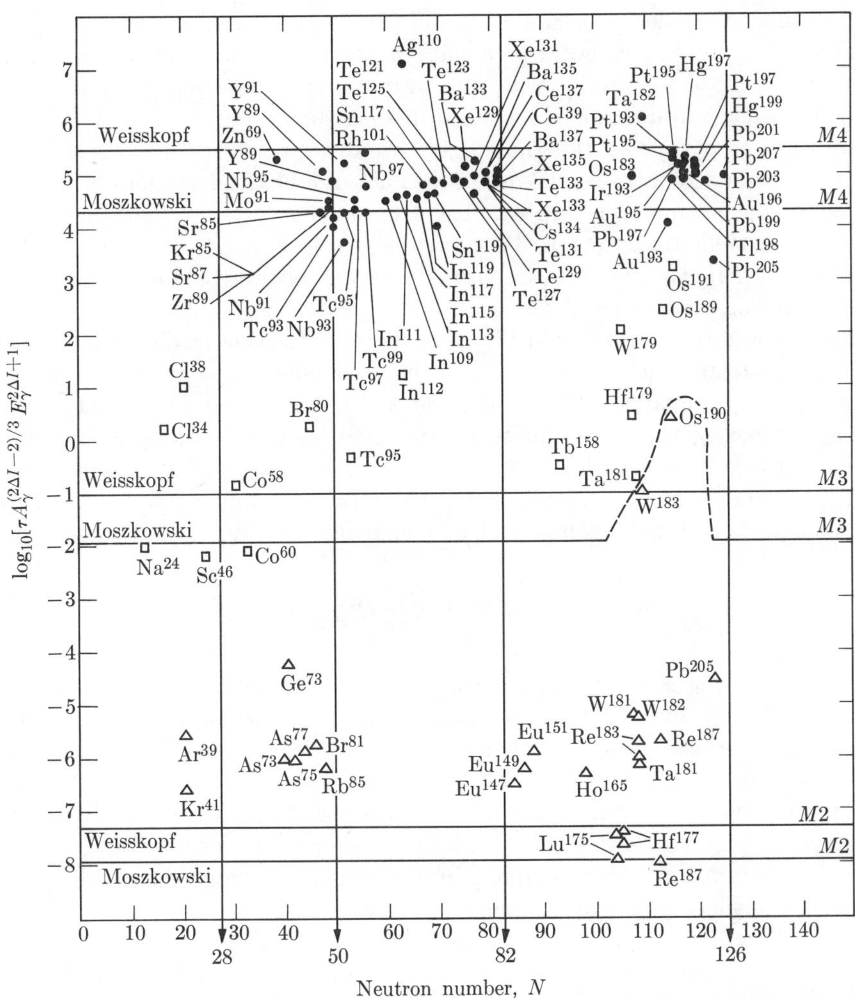

Fig. 9-18. Comparative mean lives for $M2$, $M3$, and $M4$ transitions vs. neutron number N. The straight lines are the Weisskopf and Moszkowski estimates. (From M. Goldhaber and A. W. Sunyar, *op. cit.* Reproduced by permission.)

magnetic transitions. According to Eqs. (9-34) and (9-35), this should remove the energy- and size-dependence so that the figures give comparisons of reduced transition rates (B-values, Eq. 9-30). The multipolarity order l has been assumed to be as small as possible, i.e., $l = \Delta I = |J_b - J_a|$. The reduced transition rates are seen to range over several orders of magnitudes for the various types of transitions. They are, as expected, in general smaller than the estimates (lifetime longer), except in the case of some $E2$ transitions, as further discussed below.

The single-particle formulas (9–34) and (9–35) were based on the assumption that a single proton changes from a state lm to an S-state. In about half of the examples in Figs. 9–15 to 9–18, a neutron rather than a proton changes state if and when one can describe the change in such simple terms. For the electric transitions, in particular, this should give rise to a much smaller reduced transition rate—not zero, because the rest of the nucleus is charged and moves opposite to the single neutron, but reduced. The experimental facts are that there seems to be no systematic difference between the two sets of cases. This indicates again that excited states of nuclei cannot very well be described in terms of pure single-particle excitations.

Some of the $E2$ transitions in Fig. 9–16, notably those of nuclei in the regions of large quadrupole moments, are more than one hundred times faster than the single-proton estimates. The explanation for this is that these nuclei display collective excitations, i.e., rotation or vibration, so that more than one single unit of charge takes part in the transition. For the 2^+ to 0^+ rotational transitions, one finds that the reduced $E2$ transition rate is simply equal to the square of the static quadrupole component Q_{20}, as defined by Eq. (9–12). This gives

$$B(E2) = \frac{5e^2}{16\pi} Q_{\text{int}}^2, \tag{9–36}$$

where Q_{int} is the static quadrupole moment defined by Eq. (1–14) with the z-axis being the nuclear symmetry axis. Equation (9–36) inserted into Eq. (9–31) gives a transition rate in good agreement with experiments for these deformed nuclei.

The overall result of the comparisons with the single-particle estimates for gamma-ray transition rates is that, although the assumptions underlying these estimates are rather special, empirically the formulas give good enough results to be of considerable use in assigning J-values.

9–9 Internal Conversion

As mentioned earlier, a nucleus in a bound excited state can pass to a lower state either by gamma emission or by internal conversion. In the internal-conversion process, the available energy and the angular momentum changes are transferred to an orbital electron which is thereby ejected. Since the internal-conversion electrons can be studied directly by electron spectrometers, they are more convenient to observe than are gamma rays. The instruments most often used for studies of conversion electrons are magnetic beta-ray spectrometers, some types of which are described in Chapter 11. Indeed, conversion electrons are very often observed superimposed on beta spectra, because a beta emitter often leaves the residual nucleus in an excited state that subsequently decays by internal conversion. Figure 9–19 is an example of how complex these electron spectra may be. The source is ThB (Pb^{212}), a β^- emitter, in equilibrium with

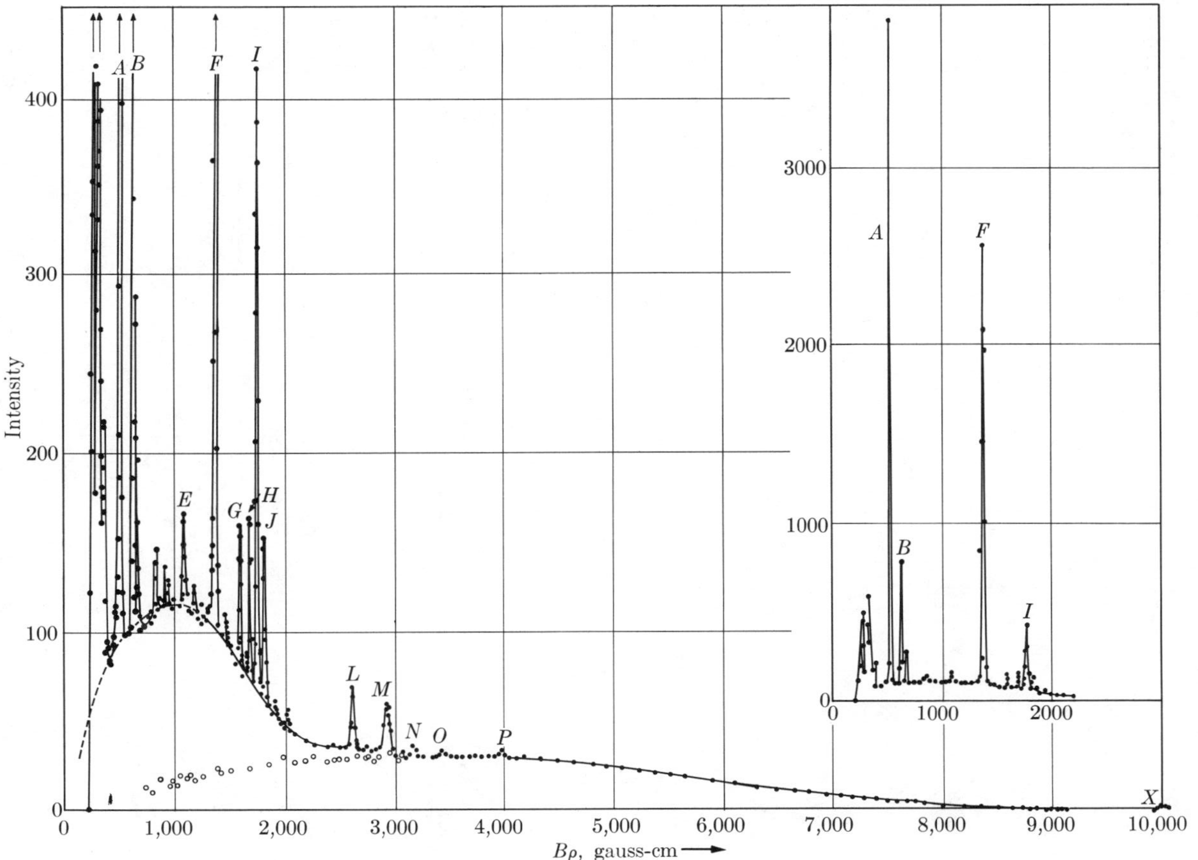

Fig. 9–19. Electron spectrum from Pb^{212} and daughter products. [From A. Flammersfeld, *Z. Physik* **114**, 227 (1939).]

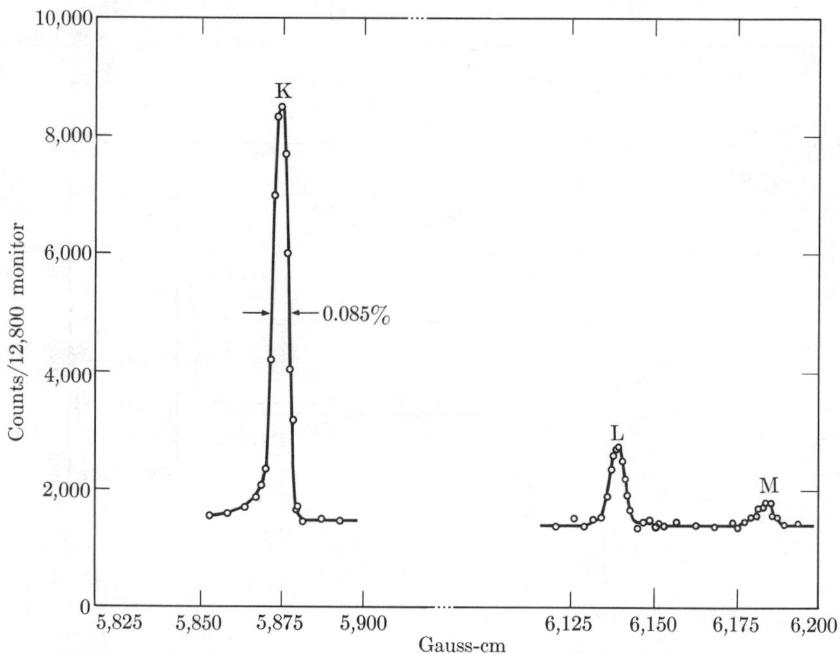

Fig. 9–20. Internal conversion lines from the 1.4158-MeV zero-to-zero ($E0$) transition in Po^{214}. [From D. E. Alburger and A. Hedgran, *Arkiv Fysik* **7**, 424 (1953–54).]

its daughter products, among which are two other β^- emitters and two α emitters. Four of these five disintegrations branch to excited states, as well as to the ground states of the daughter nuclei. The result is a profuse display of conversion lines superimposed on the continuous β^- spectra. The abscissa in Fig. 9–19 is magnetic rigidity $B\rho$ which is proportional to the electron momentum.

Figure 9–20 gives an example that is simpler to analyze. It is the spectrum of conversion electrons resulting from a 1.4158-MeV transition in RaC′ (Po^{214}), a $J_a = 0$ to $J_b = 0$ transition for which gamma-ray emission is completely forbidden. We see three conversion lines, arising from total energy transfer to electrons in the K-, L-, and M-shells. In general, we can write for the kinetic energy of the ejected electron

$$T_x = E_\gamma - E_x, \tag{9–37}$$

where E_γ is the available transition energy and E_x is the binding energy for K-, L-, and M-electrons, etc. In polonium, the binding energy for a K-electron is $E_K = 93.1$ keV; for an L_I-electron, $E_L = 16.9$ keV; and for an M_I-electron, $E_M = 4.2$ keV. The characteristic spread in energies, as well as intensity ratios, simplifies the identification of conversion lines for a given transition. Zero-to-zero conversion, as represented in Fig. 9–20, takes place only inside the nucleus, and therefore only S-electrons take part in the process to any measurable extent.

For all electromagnetic transitions, except the zero-to-zero transitions, gamma-ray emission and internal conversion compete. Excluding other possible modes of decay, for instance β-decay, we write

$$\lambda = \lambda_\gamma + \lambda_c, \tag{9–38}$$

where λ_γ is the probability for emission of a gamma ray per second, and λ_c is the probability for emission of a conversion electron per second. As we shall see shortly, the ratio between the two decay constants

$$\alpha = \lambda_c/\lambda_\gamma \tag{9–39}$$

is an important observable. The quantity α is called the *conversion coefficient*, and it is measured as the ratio between the total number of conversion electrons emitted over a given time divided by the number of gamma rays emitted in the same transition over the same time. The total probability for internal conversion λ_c can also be broken up into partial probabilities for ejection of K-, L-, and M-electrons, etc. We can therefore write

$$\alpha = \alpha_K + \alpha_L + \alpha_M + \cdots, \tag{9–40}$$

which is a rapidly converging series, because the outer electrons do not normally get close enough to the nucleus to have strong enough interactions with the dipole, quadrupole, and octupole fields from the nucleus.

The theory of internal conversion is straightforward but too lengthy to be included here. One important result is that in the expression for the decay constant λ_c, exactly the same matrix elements enter as in the expression for λ_γ (Eqs. 9–24 and 9–25). This means that the conversion coefficients α_K, α_L, and α_M, etc. depend only on the type of transition (electric or magnetic), the multipolarity, the atomic number Z, and the energy of the transition. Blatt and Weisskopf* give an approximate formula for the K-conversion coefficient in transitions for which the binding energy of the K-electron is small compared with the transition energy. Their formula is

$$\alpha_K \approx Z^3 \left[\frac{e^2}{4\pi\epsilon_0\hbar c}\right]^4 \frac{l}{l+1} \left[\frac{2m_0c^2}{\hbar\omega}\right]^{l+5/2}. \tag{9–41}$$

The factor inside the bracket that is raised to the fourth power is the fine-structure constant, $\frac{1}{137}$. As indicated by the formula, the conversion coefficient becomes large only for low-energy transitions in heavy nuclei. For these transitions, however, the formula (9–41) is no longer accurate. Much more elaborate

---

* J. M. Blatt and V. F. Weisskopf, *op. cit.*, p. 618.

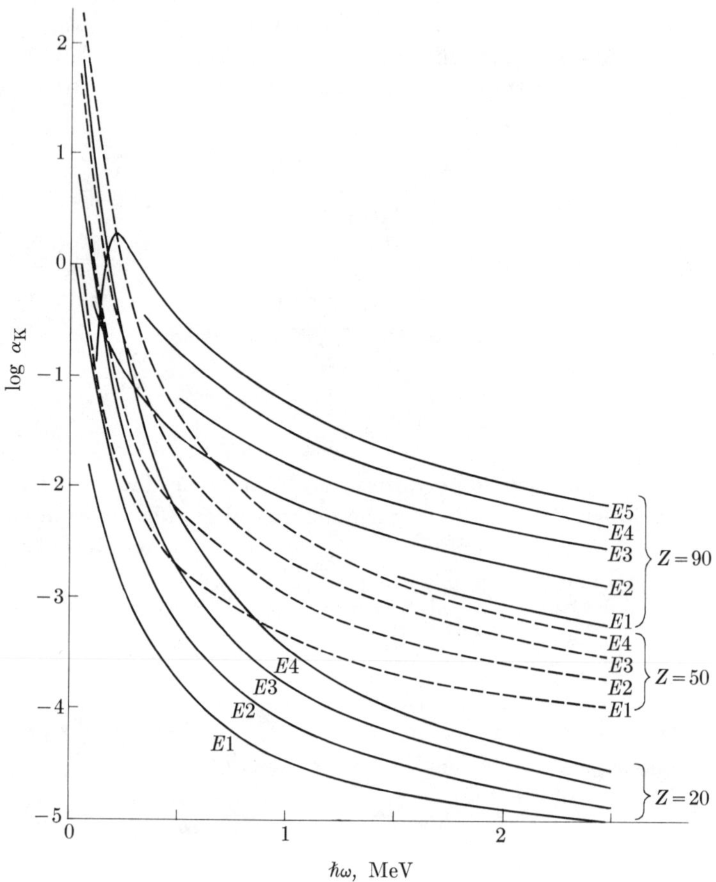

Fig. 9–21. The K-shell conversion coefficient α_K for electric multipole transition with $Z = 20, 50$, and 90. (From M. A. Preston, *Physics of the Nucleus*, Reading, Mass.: Addison-Wesley Publishing Company, 1962, p. 307.)

calculations of conversion coefficients have been performed by Rose*, as well as others. Figure 9–21 shows the K-conversion coefficient for electric transitions for $Z = 20$, 50, and 90 as a function of the energy and multipolarity. Figure 9–22 gives the same for magnetic transitions. Unlike the estimates of transition rates given in Section 9–8, these calculations of conversion coefficients are, if not exact, at least accurate enough so that a measurement of α_K, for instance, will pinpoint the multipolarity order l. It is sometimes simpler to measure the ratio α_L/α_K, and this too can be used for determining l.

---

* M. E. Rose, *Internal Conversion Coefficients*, Amsterdam: North-Holland Publishing Company, 1958.

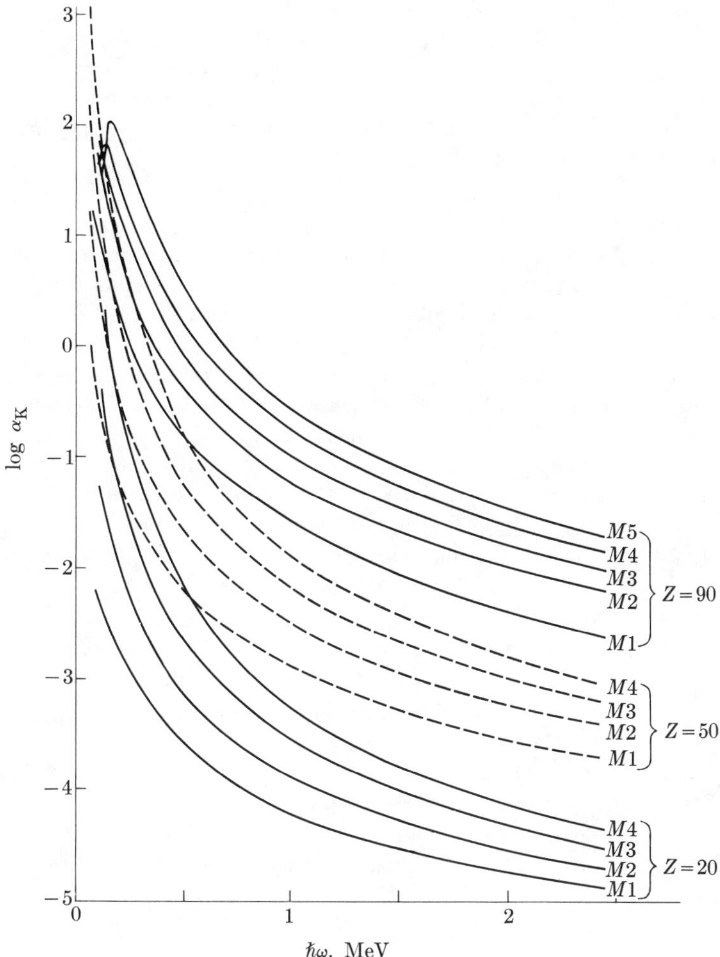

Fig. 9–22. The K-shell conversion coefficient α_K for magnetic multipole transition with $Z = 20$, 50, and 90. (From M. A. Preston, *op. cit.*, p. 308.)

PROBLEMS

9–1. In a bent-crystal spectrometer, the quartz crystal has an interplanar spacing of 1.1776×10^{-8} cm. The radius of the focal circle is 2 m. The source is a thin wire emitting gamma rays of energies 1.33 and 1.17 MeV. Assuming that the source is in a position where it gives first-order Bragg reflection for the 1.33-MeV gamma ray, calculate the distance it has to be moved to obtain first-order reflection for the 1.17-MeV gamma ray.

9–2. In a pair spectrometer with infinitesimal radiator thickness, counter separation $2r$, and magnetic induction B, a gamma ray strikes the radiator in the center (distance r to either counter). (a) Develop the formual for its energy, assuming that it gives rise to a coincidence count. (b) What is the energy of the gamma ray giving rise to a count, but striking the radiator at a distance $r/3$ from the center? (c) Use the above results to estimate the resolution of the instrument for 4-MeV gamma rays, assuming that the total radiator length is $2r/3$ and that the counter slit openings are very small.

9–3. Prove Eq. (9–5).

9–4. A photon of energy E_γ strikes an electron at rest and rebounds directly backward. The electron moves in a magnetic field of induction B. The radius of curvature of the orbit is observed to be ρ. Develop a formula for the energy of the photon expressed as a function of B, ρ, and fundamental constants.

9–5. Young's modulus for iron is about 2×10^{11} newtons/m^2. The density of iron is 7.8 gm/cm^2. From this information, calculate the effective spring constant acting on an iron atom in the lattice and its vibrational frequency. Is the vibrational quantum $\hbar\omega_{\text{vibr}}$ smaller or larger than the recoil energy a free Fe^{57} atom receives when emitting its 14.4-keV photon in the decay of the first excited state? Is this transition suitable for a study of the Mössbauer effect?

9–6. The elements of an electric multipole are defined by Eq. (9–9). Find the elements of the dipole and quadrupole moments of two positive point charges $+q$, one at $z = +a/2$ and the other at $z = -a/2$.

9–7. Go over the Fourier analysis on p. 254 in more detail. Write $\mathcal{E}_\omega = A(\omega)e^{-i\omega t}$ and calculate $A(\omega)$. Add to the spectrum for $\omega > 0$ the spectrum obtained by changing the sign of ω, i.e., $\mathcal{E}_{-\omega} = A(-\omega)e^{i\omega t}$. Reduce the result.

9–8. A fictitious nuclide has a $J = 1/2^+$ ground state and approximately evenly spaced excited states with $J = 9/2^+, 3/2^-, 1/2^+, 5/2^+, 7/2^-$ in order of ascending energy. Draw an energy-level diagram for this nuclide and indicate on this diagram the most likely gamma transition (down) from each level (five lines in all). Write beside the lines their multipolarity ($E1$, $M2$, etc.).

9–9. The three lowest states of the nuclide S^{34} have the characteristics shown in the table below.

Level	Excitation energy	Angular momentum and parity
Ground state	0	0^+
1	2.13 MeV	2^+
2	3.30 MeV	2^+

(a) When the nuclide is produced in its 3.3-MeV level, three gamma-ray energies are observed in the ensuing de-excitation process. List their energies and radiation type (electric dipole, etc.). Show the transitions in an energy-level diagram. (b) Compute the predicted intensities of the two lowest energy gamma lines relative to the highest energy line by using the Weisskopf formulas. Don't get trapped; remember the nuclide is produced only in the 3.3-MeV level.

9–10. Calculate the angular distribution of photons from a source emitting radiation with $l = 2$, $m = 0$.

9–11. The nuclide $_{49}In^{113}$ has a stable $J = 9/2^+$ ground state and an isomeric first excited state with half-life $t_{1/2} = 104$ m. This excited state decays to the ground state partly by internal conversion. The K-conversion electrons have $B\rho = 2370$ gauss-cm, and the K-conversion coefficient is measured as $\alpha_K = 0.5$. The binding energy for K-electrons in indium is 28 keV. Find the excitation energy of this state, and, if you have enough information, its angular momentum and parity.

*9–12. Select ten examples of experimental mean lives or natural widths of bound energy levels found in the literature. Correct for internal conversion to obtain the decay constant for gamma emission. Compute the corresponding theoretical decay constants using Weisskopf's formulas with $r_0 = 1.2$ F. Compare the theoretical and experimental results and comment on any major discrepancies. (For reference use *Alpha-, Beta-, and Gamma-Ray Spectroscopy*, Kai Siegbahn, Ed. Amsterdam: North-Holland Publishing Company, 1965, p. 1599ff.)

*9–13. Design a Compton spectrometer for γ-rays in the energy range 100 keV to 10 MeV. Specify magnetic field strength, magnet configuration, counter geometry, and the converter material and thickness. Estimate efficiency and resolving power. Use either two electron counters (as Groshev) or one electron detector in coincidence with a detector for the back-scattered gamma ray.

*9–14. Review recent literature for work on gamma-ray distributions from polarized targets. Describe techniques and simple results. Possible sources are *Reviews of Modern Physics*, *The Physical Review*, *Nuclear Physics*, *Annual Review of Nuclear Science*, and *Progress in Nuclear Physics* (annual).

10 Alpha Decay

10–1 Stability of Heavy Nuclei Against Breakup

In Section 9–1, we discussed the fact that heavy nuclei break up by emitting an alpha particle. We now raise the question: Why are four nucleons emitted together in the form of an alpha particle, rather than one proton or one neutron at a time? In this section, we shall answer that question.

In the treatment of the semiempirical mass formula (Section 4–6), we discussed the binding energy of the nucleons in the nucleus. Because of the Coulomb effect, the binding energy per new added particle decreases slightly with increasing A for heavy nuclei. This is illustrated in Fig. 10–1, which shows the range of the binding energy of the last nucleon added for beta-stable nuclei. The binding energy of the last nucleon fluctuates rapidly with A, and only the limits on this fluctuation are shown in the figure. For no nuclide found in nature is the binding energy of the last nucleon anywhere close to zero. They are, therefore, all stable against nucleon breakup.

The reason that many of these heavy nuclei are unstable for alpha-particle breakup is the following. The total binding energy of the alpha particle is 28.3 MeV (Table 1–3). If in a heavy nucleus the binding energy of the last four nucleons (the last two protons and the last two neutrons) averages about 7 MeV, then it will require 28 MeV to remove them from the nucleus. If these four nucleons afterward combine to form an alpha particle, the binding energy of the alpha particle (28.3 MeV) is released. In the complete process, then, the total expenditure of energy is less than the gain. Alpha decay is therefore energetically possible. We have to think of the process as one in which four nucleons combine at the surface of the nucleus to form an alpha particle which then escapes from the nucleus.

In general, we may say that the binding energy of an alpha particle in a nucleus is 28.3 MeV less than the sum of the binding energies of the two last protons and the two last neutrons. In Fig. 10–1 the range of the binding energy of an alpha particle is shown as a function of A for beta-stable nuclides. At about $A = 140$ the points fall below zero, and the indication is that most of the heavier nuclei are alpha unstable. Why, then, are not practically all nuclei

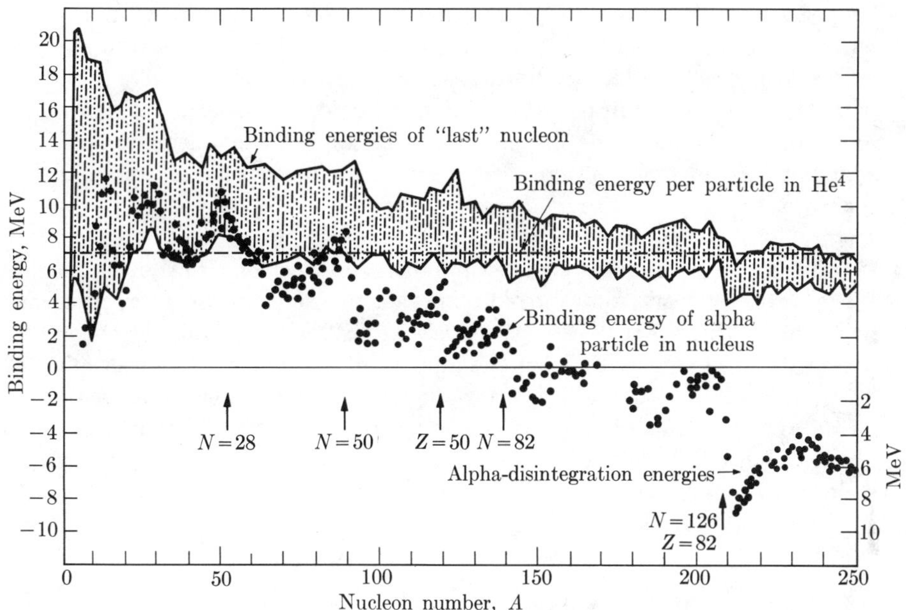

Fig. 10–1. Minimum and maximum binding energy for "last" nucleon and binding energies of "last" alpha particle for beta-stable nuclei.

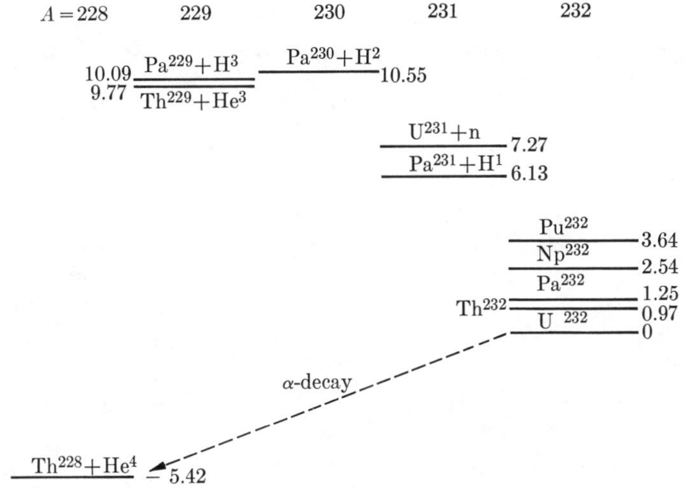

Fig. 10–2. Ground states of nucleus-plus-particle systems with 232 nucleons.

above $A = 140$ observed to be radioactive; indeed, why do we find these nuclides in nature at all? The answer is that in order to reach the state of increased entropy, the higher disorder toward which nature moves, the alpha particle has to pass a hurdle—the Coulomb barrier. Unless the energy available is sufficiently high, the lifetime of the unstable state will be longer than the age of the universe; in many cases, so long that it becomes impossible or impractical to observe the radioactivity.

Figure 10–2 shows an energy-level diagram with the ground state of U^{232} and other states involving the same number of nucleons. Clearly, the nuclide U^{232} is stable against proton breakup and against neutron breakup. It is also beta stable. However, it can release about 5.42 MeV in kinetic energy by alpha breakup. In Fig. 10–2, A is the nucleon number of the daughter nucleus, that is, the nucleus that is left after the α-particle has been removed. For beta decay, of course, A does not change; hence, beta decay is indicated by a vertical line when the energy levels are arranged as they are in this figure. All the nuclei involved in the diagram have low-lying excited states, but only the ground states are indicated in this figure.

10–2 Measurement of Alpha-Particle Energies

Early measurements of alpha-particle energies were performed by determining the range of the particles in air. The accuracy of these measurements was limited by straggling (Section 7–1). Modern measurements of alpha-particle energies are performed either with the aid of a solid-state counter (Section 7–6) or, preferably, by a magnetic spectrograph. Some of the properties of magnetic fields as momentum analyzers are discussed in Section 4–2 and in Appendix 2. Briefly stated, the most important features are the following. The momentum of a charged particle can be determined as $p = qB\rho$, where q is the charge of the particle ($2e$ for the alpha particle), B is the magnetic induction assumed to represent a homogeneous field, and ρ is the radius of curvature of the particle orbit in this field (Appendix 2). If enough intensity were available, it would, in principle, be possible to determine accurately the radius of curvature of the circular path by locating three points on the circular orbit. For instance, this could be done by the use of three fine slits through which the alpha particles would have to pass. In practice, this procedure is not very feasible, mainly because the solid angle into which the alpha particles are accepted in such an arrangement would be extremely small. In general, alpha particles emitted from a natural radioactive source have an isotropic distribution. In order not to make the exposure times for an energy-measuring device excessively long, one always makes use of the focusing abilities of the magnetic field. The focusing properties of a sector magnet with normal entrance and exit angles for the central ray are described in Appendix 2.

One member of the family of homogeneous magnetic-field instruments suited for absolute measurements of alpha-particle momenta is the 180° spectrograph.

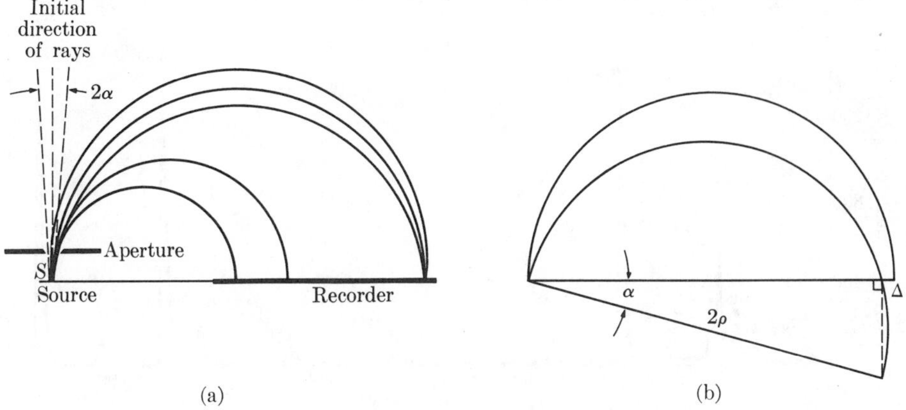

Fig. 10–3. Focusing action of a 180° spectrograph.

This may be thought of as a sector magnet with deflecting angle $\phi = 180°$ and object and image distances $l = l' = 0$. (Compare Eqs. A2–26 and A2–27 with $k_M = 1/r_0$.) That is, both the source and the image (detector) can actually be inside the magnetic field. Figure 10–3 illustrates the focusing action of this spectrograph. The source S can be assumed to be a thin wire coated with a very thin layer of the alpha-emitting material. When alpha particles of different momenta are emitted from the source, they will travel in orbits of different radii of curvature and hit the recorder (e.g., a photographic plate) at different positions. Particles of the same momenta travel along circles of the same radius of curvature. When they are emitted in different, but not in greatly different, directions, their orbits will cross again after approximately 180° deflection, that is, at or close to the photographic plate. The width of the image formed on the plate depends on the width of the source S and also on the angle of acceptance, 2α. If 2α is very small, the width of the image will simply be $\Delta = S$, that is, the magnification of the instrument is unity. If, on the other hand, the source width is very small, then the aberration (error in focusing) will produce an image width (Fig. 10–3b)

$$\Delta = 2\rho(1 - \cos\alpha) \approx \rho(\alpha^2 - \alpha^4/12 + \cdots). \tag{10–1}$$

When two groups of alpha particles have very similar momenta, the image width Δ may prevent the groups from being resolved. The image width Δ corresponds to a momentum change Δp, which we can find by noting that the distance along the photographic plate in Fig. 10–3(a) is the diameter of the particle orbit. We can then write

$$\Delta p/p = \Delta\rho/\rho = \Delta/2\rho \approx \alpha^2/2. \tag{10–2}$$

If, for instance, $\alpha = 0.05$ rad, two groups of momenta p and $p + \Delta p$ will be

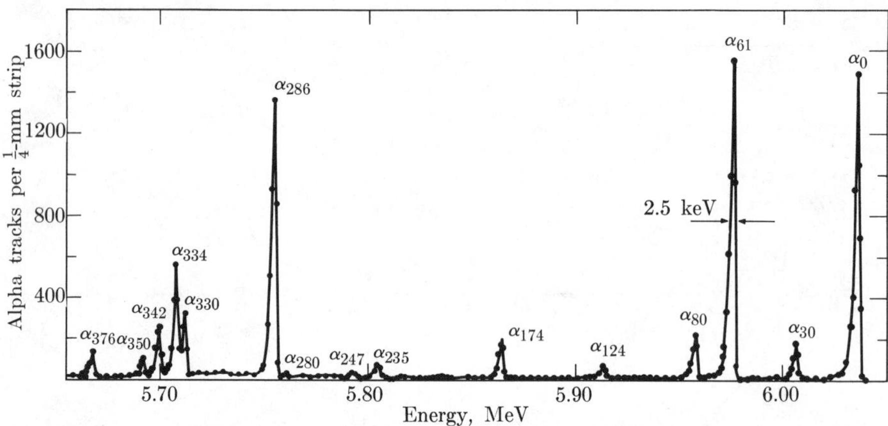

Fig. 10–4. Alpha-particle spectrum of Th^{227} taken by Pilger *et al.* [R. C. Pilger, Ph.D. thesis, University of California Radiation Laboratory Report UCRL-3877 (1957)]. The subscripts on the alpha peaks indicate the excitation energies of the corresponding levels in the daughter nucleus Ra^{223}.

completely separated if $\Delta p/p = \alpha^2/2 = 1.25 \times 10^{-3}$. It has become standard practice to define the resolving power of an instrument as

$$R = p/\Delta p_{1/2}. \tag{10–3}$$

Here $\Delta p_{1/2}$, rather than being the total width of a peak measured at its base, is the total width measured at one-half of the full amplitude. This is illustrated in an example below.

The great advantage of the 180° instrument for absolute energy measurement is that the diameter of the particle orbits can be determined by one simple measurement. It is the distance from the right-hand edge of the source (Fig. 10–3a) to the right-hand edge of the image. When the accuracy of momentum determination is not the principal aim, other spectrographs may give equal or better performance (resolving power and intensity). These spectrographs are usually calibrated with alpha particles whose energy has been measured in a 180° instrument.

Figure 10–4 shows an example of an alpha-particle spectrum obtained with a 60° sector magnet at the University of California Radiation Laboratory. The abscissa, which was originally the distance along the photographic plate, has been converted to radius of curvature, then to momentum, and finally to kinetic energy of the alpha particle. The ordinate is the number of alpha-particle tracks counted in a quarter-millimeter strip across the photographic plate. The full width at half-maximum for one of the peaks, as indicated in Fig. 10–4, is 2.5 keV. This indicates that the energy resolving power R_E is $E/\Delta E_{1/2} = 5970/2.5 = 2400$. The momentum resolving power is then $R_p = 4800$, because for nonrelativistic particles, $\Delta E/E = 2\,\Delta p/p$. The highest energy alpha group in Fig. 10-4 results from a transition from the ground state of Th^{227} to the ground state of Ra^{223}. The lower energy groups result from transitions to excited states of Ra^{223}. Hence, the alpha-particle spectrum reflects the position of energy levels in the daughter nucleus. Information of this type obtained from alpha-disintegration studies will be discussed in Section 10-7.

Very long half-life alpha emissions are difficult to study in a magnetic spectrograph because of intensity problems. The requirement of a high resolving power limits the source area to about 0.1 cm^2 for existing spectrographs. The thickness of the radioactive layer in the source is limited to an order of magnitude of 10 $\mu gm/cm^2$ because of the stopping power of the material and the resulting energy spread of particles leaving the source. The total amount of radioactive material in the source may therefore be of the order of magnitude of 1 μgm. Let us assume that the nucleon number is $A \approx 240$. We then get a total number of radioactive atoms in the source:

$$N = (6.025 \times 10^{23} \times 10^{-6})/240 = 2.5 \times 10^{15}.$$

If the total solid angle of acceptance of the spectrograph is 10^{-4} of the total sphere, or about 10^{-3} sterad, then the total recorded number of disintegrations per second will be

$$-dN/dt = N\lambda = 10^{-4} \times 2.5 \times 10^{15}\lambda.$$

If we set $-dN/dt = 10^{-3}$ (one count per thousand seconds) as a practical lower limit, we get from the above equation that λ must be larger than $\lambda_{\min} = 4 \times 10^{-15}\ \text{sec}^{-1}$. This corresponds to a half-life of 5.5 million years. For longer half-life alpha emitters, that is, for weaker sources, it is more feasible to use solid-state counters or gas counters which permit the use of larger solid angles and larger source areas.

10-3 Experimental Decay Constants; the Geiger-Nuttal Law

The measured half-lives of natural alpha emitters range from 0.3 μs to about 10^{17} y. There is every reason to believe that alpha emitters with much longer half-lives exist; however, the activity is then so weak that it becomes extremely difficult to detect.

The longest lifetimes have been measured by counting the total number of disintegrations per second from a sample of known number of nuclei. As an example, we will discuss briefly the measurement by Beard and Wiedenbeck* of the Sm^{147} half-life. The sample was a layer of samarium chloride, about 100 $\mu gm/cm^2$ thick on a thin film of Zapon lacquer. The sample was mounted inside a gas counter in such a way that alpha particles emitted in any direction

---

* G. Beard and M. L. Wiedenbeck, *Phys. Rev.* **95,** 1245 (1954).

would be recorded in the counter; in other words, the solid angle of acceptance for this experiment was 4π sterad. The number of counts per unit time was measured, and the total amount of samarium in the sample was determined by spectroscopic methods after the counting experiment. The activity was found to be 719 ± 3.6 counts per second per gram of Sm^{147}. From this, we find that the disintegration constant is

$$\lambda = \frac{-dN/dt}{N} = \frac{719 \times 147}{6.025 \times 10^{23}}$$

$$= 1.75 \times 10^{-19}\ \text{sec}^{-1}.$$

This corresponds to a half-life of $(1.25 \pm 0.06) \times 10^{11}$ years.

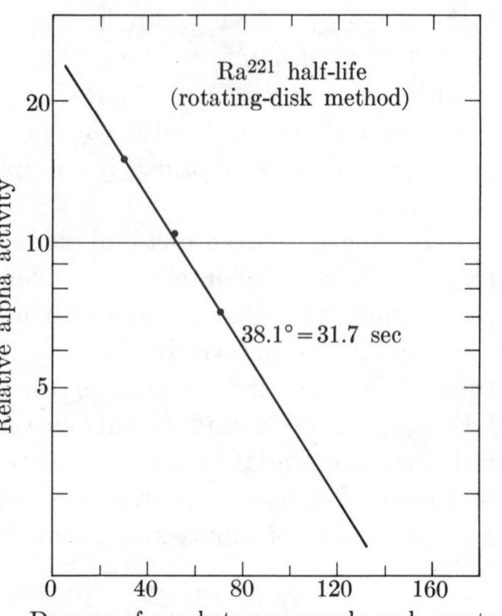

Fig. 10–5. Determination of the half-life of Ra^{221} by the rotating-disk recoil method. [From Meinke *et al.*, *Phys. Rev.* **81,** 782 (1951).]

When the half-life is less than a few years, it becomes practical to measure it directly by observing the decrease in counting rate. If the nuclide is a member of a radioactive chain, the counting experiment has to be preceded by a chemical separation from the parent and daughter products. When separation is necessary, it is hardly feasible to use this method for measuring half-lives that are less than about 1 min.

Nuclides with shorter half-lives can sometimes be separated mechanically from their parents. As an example, we will discuss briefly the method employed by Meinke, Ghiorso, and Seaborg* for measuring the half-minute activity of Ra^{221}. The parent nucleus (Th^{225}) is placed close to the outer (cylindrical) surface of a rotating disk of 13-in. diameter. When Th^{225} decays, the alpha particle may be emitted into the sample, and the daughter nucleus Ra^{221} may be ejected by recoil from the sample. It can then be collected by the rotating disk. During the ejection through a thin layer of solid matter and by motion through the air, the Ra^{221} atom usually loses electrons. The rotating disk is therefore negatively charged with respect to the sample in order to help pull the positive Ra^{221} ions through the air. A counter is facing the rim of the disk downstream from the place where the sample is collected. The angular distance to the counter can be varied, and this then represents a varying time lag from production to observation. Figure 10–5 shows the counting rate vs. angular displacement for the Ra^{221} experiment; 38.1° dis-

* W. W. Meinke, A. Ghiorso, and G. T. Seaborg, *Phys. Rev.* **81,** 782 (1951).

placement decreases the counting rate by a factor of two. Since the angular velocity was 1.20°/sec, the measured half-life is

$$38.1/1.20 = 31.7 \text{ sec.}$$

Very short alpha lifetimes can be measured with a delay coincidence technique, discussed briefly in Section 9-3. This technique has been used, for instance, to measure the shortest alpha half-life known for ground-state decay: 3×10^{-7} sec (Po^{212}).

Long before the theory of alpha decay had evolved, Geiger and Nuttal had noticed a striking dependence of the half-life on the alpha-particle energy. This empirical relationship can be expressed as

$$\log_{10} \lambda = C - D/\sqrt{E_\alpha}, \tag{10-4}$$

where the energy E_α is measured in MeV, and C and D are slowly varying functions of Z, but are independent of the neutron number N. For $Z \approx 90$, these parameters are $C \approx 52$ and $D \approx 140$. The theory of alpha decay, which will be developed in the next two sections, leads to a formula for the decay constant

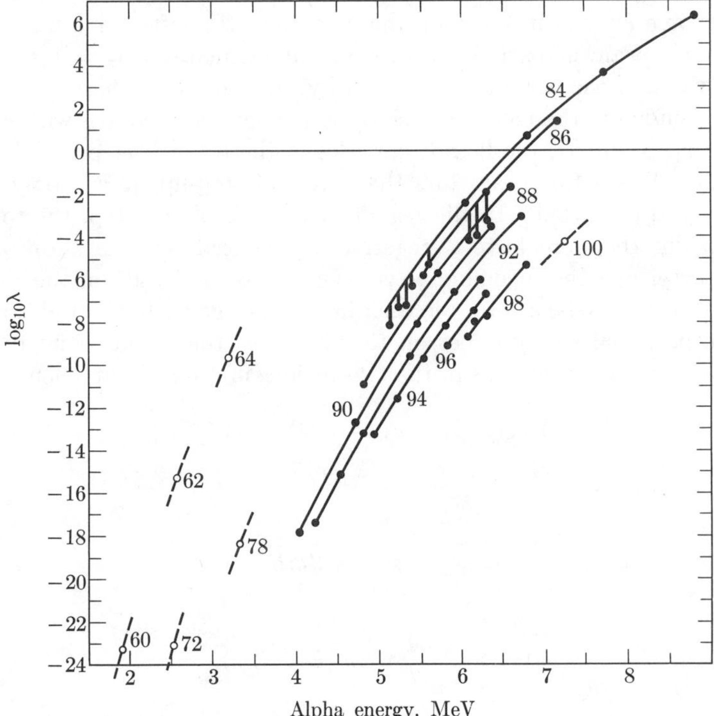

Fig. 10-6. Logarithm of decay constant λ vs. alpha-particle energy for ground-state-to-ground-state decay of even-even nuclei.

which is more complex than Eq. (10–4). The latter apparently just happens to be a fairly good approximation for the correct formula.

The smooth relationship between energy and decay constant is apparent in the so-called Geiger-Nuttal plot, Fig. 10–6. In this figure, only ground-state–to–ground-state transitions of even-even nuclei have been included. In cases where the alpha decay also leaves the daughter nucleus in higher excited states, the fraction of the total decay probability that is associated with the ground-state–to–ground-state transition has been plotted. The striking systematic relationship between λ, E, and Z that is evident in Fig. 10–6 suggests a simple theoretical interpretation. The theory, the gist of which is quantum-mechanical tunneling, or barrier penetration, is given below.

10–4 Barrier Penetration

As a prelude to the discussion of the theory of alpha decay, we will here discuss briefly the transmission of a plane wave past a potential step and through a potential barrier.

Consider first the potential step shown in Fig. 10–7(a). We assume that a plane wave e^{ik_1x} is incident on the step from the left. This wave function represents a beam of particles with constant momentum $p_x = k_1\hbar$. The numerical value of the wave function is unity, meaning that there is one particle per unit volume in the beam, and since all particles are moving with a uniform velocity, $v_1 = k_1\hbar/m$, the flux of particles in the beam is v_1 per unit area and unit time. When this beam hits the potential step-up, it is partly reflected and partly transmitted. In the region to the left of the step, the total wave function will therefore have a negative exponential term in addition to the term representing the incoming wave. On the other hand, on the right-hand side there will only be a term representing a wave going to the right, assuming that the potential step-up goes on to infinity so that there is no further reflection. The wave functions in the two regions of 10–7(a) can then be written

$$\begin{aligned} \text{Region I,} \quad u_1 &= e^{ik_1x} + Re^{-ik_1x}, \\ \text{Region II,} \quad u_2 &= Te^{ik_2x}, \end{aligned} \tag{10–5}$$

where

$$k_1 = \frac{1}{\hbar}\sqrt{2mE}$$

and

$$k_2 = \frac{1}{\hbar}\sqrt{2m(E - V_0)}.$$

The coefficients R and T are to be determined by the use of boundary conditions at $x = 0$. These boundary conditions are: $u_1 = u_2$ and $du_1/dx = du_2/dx$ for $x = 0$.

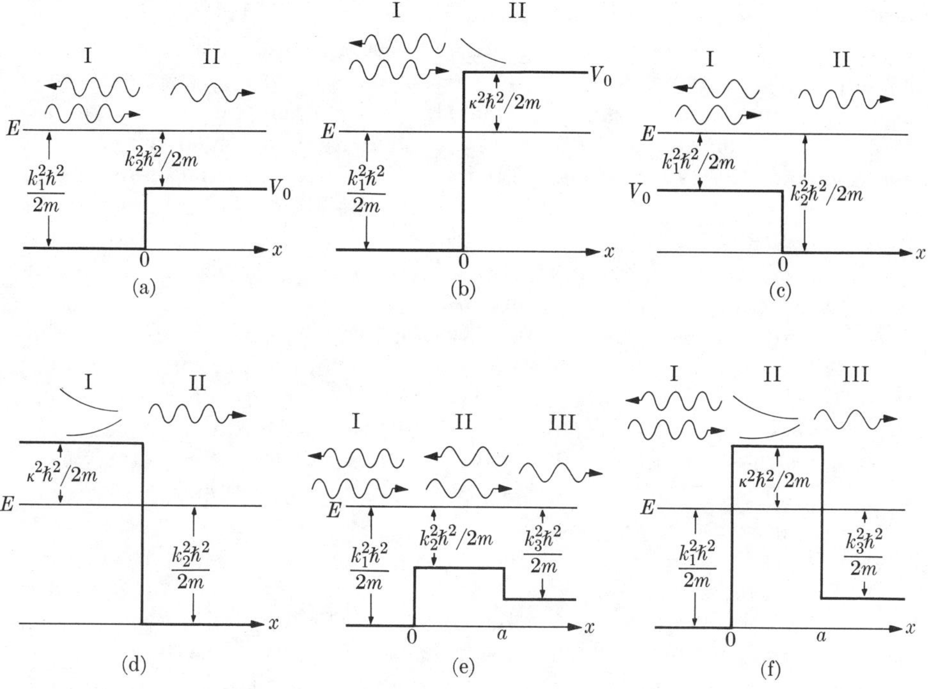

Fig. 10–7. Potential steps and barriers.

When we apply these boundary conditions to Eq. (10–5), we obtain

$$1 + R = T, \qquad k_1(1 - R) = k_2 T,$$

with solutions

$$T = \frac{2k_1}{k_1 + k_2}, \tag{10–6}$$

$$R = \frac{k_1 - k_2}{k_1 + k_2}. \tag{10–7}$$

As a second example, consider the case in Fig. 10–7(b). It is similar to the example we have discussed except that k_2 now is imaginary ($V > E$). Then, the second equation in (10–5) will be of the form $Te^{-\kappa x}$. A wave function of the form $e^{\kappa x}$ is also a solution of Schrödinger's equation in this region, but this solution must be rejected for physical reasons, because it will go to infinity when x goes to infinity. Since, for this case, the last equation of (10–5) can be changed to the desired form by replacing k_2 with $i\kappa$, the correct solutions for the transmission and reflection coefficients can also be found by replacing k_2 in Eqs. (10–6) and (10–7) by $i\kappa$. It is important to note that in the two cases shown in Fig. 10–7(a) and (b), only one term in the wave function has been included for region II (Eq. 10–5). In both cases, the second term was rejected for physical reasons, and in both cases Schrödinger's equation including the boundary conditions at $x = 0$ can be fulfilled mathematically also if we include two terms in region II. It is also important to note that Schrödinger's equation is a linear differential equation, so that if two solutions can be found, the sum of these solutions or any linear combination of them is also a solution. For instance, in Fig. 10–7(a) in addition to the wave coming from the left and being partially reflected and partially transmitted at $x = 0$, we can have, superimposed on it, a wave coming from the right which also is partially reflected and partially transmitted.

As a third example, consider the situation depicted in Fig. 10–7(c). Obviously, this represents a possible physical situation in which a wave is coming from the left, and again it is partially reflected and partially transmitted through $x = 0$. Equations (10–5), (10–6), and (10–7) therefore apply equally well to this situation. If we put the wave number $k_1 = i\kappa$, we get the situation depicted in Fig. 10–7(d). Again the solutions of Eqs. (10–6) and (10–7) apply, but the situation is no longer a physical one (particles coming out of a barrier that extends to $x = -\infty$). Mathematically, however, it again represents a possible solution of Schrödinger's equation.

Consider now the potential function shown in Fig. 10–7(e), in which, again, the plane wave moving in from the left will be partially transmitted and partially reflected. We assume, as before, that the amplitude of the wave falling in on the barrier from the left is known and that the wave in region III consists of one term only describing particles moving to the right. Our objective is to calculate what fraction of the number of particles in the incident beam is transmitted through the region of the potential step-up. There are four unknown amplitudes; namely, for the wave that is reflected, for the wave that is transmitted, and for the two partial waves inside the potential step-up. These amplitudes can be determined by the four boundary conditions imposed on the wave function at the two discontinuities in the same manner as above. The solution of the problem is therefore unique, and it can be found by writing the partial wave functions ($e^{\pm ikx}$) in each region and the boundary conditions. These calculations are carried out in most textbooks on wave mechanics. We shall here take a slightly different approach, actually the approach of the electrical engineer who is to study the amplitudes and phases of signals on a transmission line with two mismatched joints. By considering the total transmitted wave as being built up of waves that have been either transmitted directly or have been reflected a multitude of times inside the potential step-up, we can write the following expression directly for the resulting amplitude transmission factor for the wave function:

$$T = T_{12}e^{ik_2a}T_{23}[1 + R_{23}R_{21}e^{i2k_2a} + (R_{23}R_{21}e^{i2k_2a})^2 + \cdots]. \quad (10\text{–}8)$$

Here T_{12} is the amplitude change in going from region I to region II, and

R_{23} is the amplitude change for the reflected wave at boundary II–III, etc. These coefficients are given by Eqs. (10–6) and (10–7) with appropriate subscripts. In Eq. (10–8) the factor in front of the brackets combined with the 1 inside the brackets gives the amplitude and phase shift of the part of the wave that is directly transmitted without reflections. The second term inside the brackets represents a correction caused by a wave that has been bounced back and forth once inside the step-up, and the third term inside the brackets represents the correction for a wave that has been bounced back and forth twice, etc. The series inside the parentheses is a simple geometric series of the form

$$S = 1 + y + y^2 + y^3 + \cdots = 1/(1 - y).$$

By applying this sum formula and inserting the values for the individual coefficients, we get for the amplitude transmission factor

$$T = \frac{4k_1k_2e^{ik_2a}}{(k_1 + k_2)(k_2 + k_3) - (k_3 - k_2)(k_1 - k_2)e^{i2k_2a}}. \tag{10–9a}$$

The probability density in region III is equal to $|T|^2$.

In the examples of single step-ups and step-downs, we found that the calculations made for cases where $E > V$ in both regions could be carried over to cases where $E < V$ in one of the regions by replacing k with $i\kappa$. We make this substitution in region II and find from Eq. (10–9a) the amplitude transmission factor for the case of Fig. 10–7(f):

$$T = \frac{4ik_1\kappa e^{-\kappa a}}{(k_1 + i\kappa)(k_3 + i\kappa) - (k_1 - i\kappa)(k_3 - i\kappa)e^{-2\kappa a}}. \tag{10–9b}$$

For the electrical engineer, this is a reasonably close analogy of two transmission lines joined over an attenuator.

When the potential barrier has such dimensions that $2\kappa a \gg 1$, the second term in the denominator becomes negligible compared with the first term. We now define the barrier-penetration factor as the ratio of the flux of particles on the right-hand side to the flux of particles falling in on the barrier on the left-hand side. This is equal to the ratio of the square of the numerical values of the corresponding wave functions multiplied by the ratio of the velocities:

$$\begin{aligned} B = |T|^2\,\frac{k_3}{k_1} &\approx \frac{16k_1\kappa^2k_3}{(k_1^2 + \kappa^2)(k_3^2 + \kappa^2)}\,e^{-2\kappa a} \\ &= \frac{16}{(k_1/\kappa + \kappa/k_1)(k_3/\kappa + \kappa/k_3)}\,e^{-2\kappa a}. \end{aligned} \tag{10–10a}$$

When $2\kappa a \gg 1$, the most important factor in Eq. (10–10a) obviously is the exponential, which then will be extremely small. The factor in front of the exponential, which usually is of the order of magnitude of unity (its maximum value is 4), is then unimportant by comparison. For order-of-magnitude calculations, we can therefore write

$$B \approx e^{-2\kappa a}. \tag{10–10b}$$

This then represents the fraction of the particles that will penetrate the barrier of width a and of constant potential energy $V_0 > E$, so that it produces a constant imaginary wave number $i\kappa$.

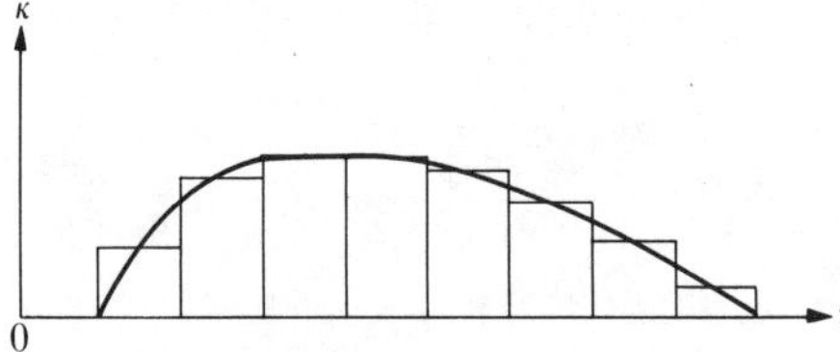

Fig. 10–8. Approximation to smoothly varying wave number κ by step functions.

If the potential is not constant in the region $0 < x < a$, we can always approximate it with a series of small steps, each with constant potential (Fig. 10–8). It is easy to see that when we multiply the barrier-penetration factors for all these intervals together, we get a sum in the exponent of the exponential (Eq. 10–10b). By making the intervals smaller and smaller, this sum goes over into an integral, so that we end up with

$$B \approx e^{-2\int \kappa\, dx}, \tag{10–11}$$

where now

$$\kappa = (1/\hbar)\sqrt{2m[V(x) - E]}.$$

The integral is taken through the complete barrier, which means between the two points for which $V = E$. It is not easy to see without a further mathematical discussion what happens to the factor in front of the exponential in Eq. (10–10a) in going through such an infinite number of steps as the integration implies. This discussion is carried out in Appendix 3, and the result of the discussion is that when the potential is a smoothly varying function of x, that is, when there are no discontinuous steps, the so-called WKB approximation gives exactly the result shown in Eq. (10–11). For alpha decay, which we are going to discuss in the next section, there is a rather sharp step-up of the potential barrier, and the WKB approximation may be off by as much as a factor of 2. Since, however, we are calculating penetration factors which are of the order of magnitude of 10^{-20} to 10^{-40}, we are not going to be particularly concerned about a factor of 2.

10–5 Barrier Penetration as Applied to Alpha Decay

Rutherford, in a sense, performed the reverse experiment to alpha decay by bombarding nuclei with alpha particles. He found that his experimental data indicated that the positive charge of the atom was concentrated in a tiny nucleus, so that the alpha particle moved in the Coulomb potential $V = Zze^2/4\pi\epsilon_0 r$ for $r > 10^{-12}$ cm. Rutherford also found that this potential function, as probed by the alpha particles, broke down at smaller distances from the center of the nucleus.

Recent experimental data on alpha-particle scattering from various nuclei have been studied by G. Igo.* In this work, it is concluded that the experimental data are consistent with a potential which, at large distances from the nucleus, is given by the Coulomb potential, and that at and around the nuclear surface an additional attractive potential of a specified form rapidly compensates for the repulsive Coulomb potential. From the nuclear surface and out, the complete potential seen by an alpha particle is approximately

$$V(r) = \frac{2.88Z}{r} - 1100 \exp\left[-\frac{r - 1.17A^{1/3}}{0.574}\right] \text{MeV}, \qquad (10\text{–}12)$$

with r in fermis. This function is plotted in Fig. 10–9. The first term is the Coulomb potential in which numerical values have been inserted, including $z = 2$ for the alpha particle. Equation (10–12) is only valid from the nuclear surface and outward. Inside the nucleus, the alpha particle is assumed to be absorbed by the nucleus, that is, the identity of the alpha particle is lost, and the four constituent nucleons go into single-particle orbits.

In the alpha-decay problem, we assume, as previously mentioned, that four nucleons go together to form an alpha particle at the nuclear surface. The combined momentum of these nucleons is such that we can carry out the calculations under the assumption that an alpha particle is moving toward the barrier from inside, and we will then try to carry out the calculations of pene-

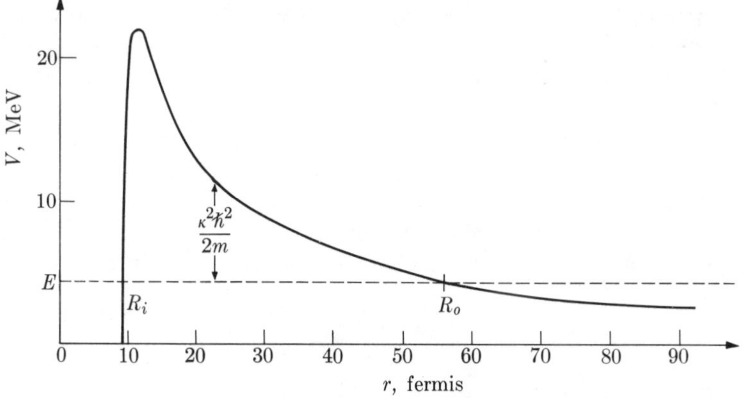

Fig. 10–9. Potential barrier between the nucleus $_{90}Th^{230}$ and an alpha particle as given by Eq. (10–12). The total energy of decay is $E = 4.76$ MeV.

---

* G. Igo, *Phys. Rev. Letters* **1,** 72 (1958).

trability to estimate the chance of this particle's actually escaping through the barrier.

In Fig. 10–9, the dashed line indicates the energy of the system, that is, the kinetic energy of the daughter nucleus and the alpha particle after the decay. Since the momentum of the alpha particle and the daughter nucleus is the same, the total energy can be expressed as

$$E = \frac{p^2}{2m_\alpha} + \frac{p^2}{2m_D} = E_\alpha\left(1 + \frac{m_\alpha}{m_D}\right) \approx E_\alpha\left(1 + \frac{4}{A}\right), \tag{10–13}$$

where A is the nucleon number of the daughter nucleus.

If the barrier were not present, the individual nucleons would still be bound to the nucleus, since each has a positive binding energy. However, as discussed in Section 10–1, if four nucleons combine to form an alpha particle, the energy available for escape may be present. Since nuclear dimensions are not very much larger than the diameter of an alpha particle, we must assume that four nucleons get close enough together to form an alpha particle rather frequently. It is reasonable to expect that the number of alpha-particle escape trials per second is somehow related to the frequency of oscillation of a single nucleon in the nucleus. This relationship is further discussed in Section 10–6. For the moment, assume that the number of alpha-particle escape trials per second is λ_0. The total decay constant is then

$$\lambda = \lambda_0 B, \tag{10–14}$$

where B is the barrier-penetration factor. We will first concentrate on deriving a formula for B. In these calculations we will assume that the alpha particle does not necessarily leave the nucleus in a zero orbital angular-momentum state. If the potential is spherically symmetric, we can, as before, write the wave function for the alpha particle as a product of a radial function and a spherical harmonic function

$$\psi = (u/r)Y_{lm}(\theta, \phi). \tag{10–15}$$

This must be a solution of Schrödinger's equation for the alpha particle through the barrier and outside the barrier. The function u is a solution of the radial wave equation

$$\frac{d^2u}{dr^2} + k^2(r)u = 0, \tag{10–16}$$

where the wave number k is given by

$$k^2(r) = \frac{2m}{\hbar^2}\left[E - V(r) - \frac{l(l+1)\hbar^2}{2mr^2}\right]. \tag{10–17}$$

Here l is the relative orbital angular momentum of the alpha particle and the daughter nucleus, and m is the reduced mass

$$m = \frac{m_\alpha m_D}{m_\alpha + m_D} \approx \frac{4}{1 + 4/A} \text{ mass units.} \tag{10-18}$$

The potential to be inserted in Eq. (10-17) is the one given by Eq. (10-12).

To find the penetration factor B, we assume that the alpha particle impinging on the barrier from the inside can be represented by a radial wave function u_i^+ which contains e^{ik_ir} as a factor. Outside the barrier, we are looking for a solution u_f which contains e^{ik_fr} as a factor. The penetration factor is the ratio between the integrated flux outside the barrier to the integrated flux impinging on the barrier from the inside. We integrate in both cases over the total sphere with $r^2\, d\Omega$ as the surface element

$$B = \frac{k_f \int |\psi_f|^2 r_f^2\, d\Omega}{k_i \int |\psi_i|^2 r_i^2\, d\Omega} = \frac{|u_f|^2 k_f \int |Y_{lm}(\theta, \phi)|^2\, d\Omega}{|u_i^+|^2 k_i \int |Y_{lm}(\theta, \phi)|^2\, d\Omega} = \frac{|u_f|^2 k_f}{|u_i^+|^2 k_i}.$$

This shows that the three-dimensional barrier-penetration problem in the case where the potential is spherically symmetric is exactly equivalent to the one-dimensional barrier-penetration problem when we use, instead of the one-dimensional wave function, the solution of Eq. (10-16). This means that in calculating the barrier-penetration factor, we must use a potential which includes the centrifugal barrier, as indicated in Eq. (10-17). We therefore write for the barrier-penetration factor

$$B = \exp\left(-2 \int_{R_i}^{R_0} \kappa\, dr\right), \tag{10-19}$$

where κ is given by

$$\kappa = \frac{(2m)^{1/2}}{\hbar} \left[V(r) + \frac{l(l+1)\hbar^2}{2mr^2} - E\right]^{1/2}. \tag{10-20a}$$

The two limits of the integral R_i and R_0 are the so-called classical turning points (see Fig. 10-9) where $\kappa = 0$.

With numerical values inserted, the formula for κ becomes

$$\kappa = \frac{0.437}{(1 + 4/A)^{1/2}} \left[\frac{2.88Z}{r} + \frac{5.23(1 + 4/A)l(l+1)}{r^2} - 1100 \exp\left(-\frac{r - 1.17A^{1/3}}{0.574}\right) - E\right]^{1/2}. \tag{10-20b}$$

Eq. (10-19) has been evaluated numerically for a large number of cases with $l = 0$ and $60 \lesssim Z \lesssim 100$. The results of these calculations have been

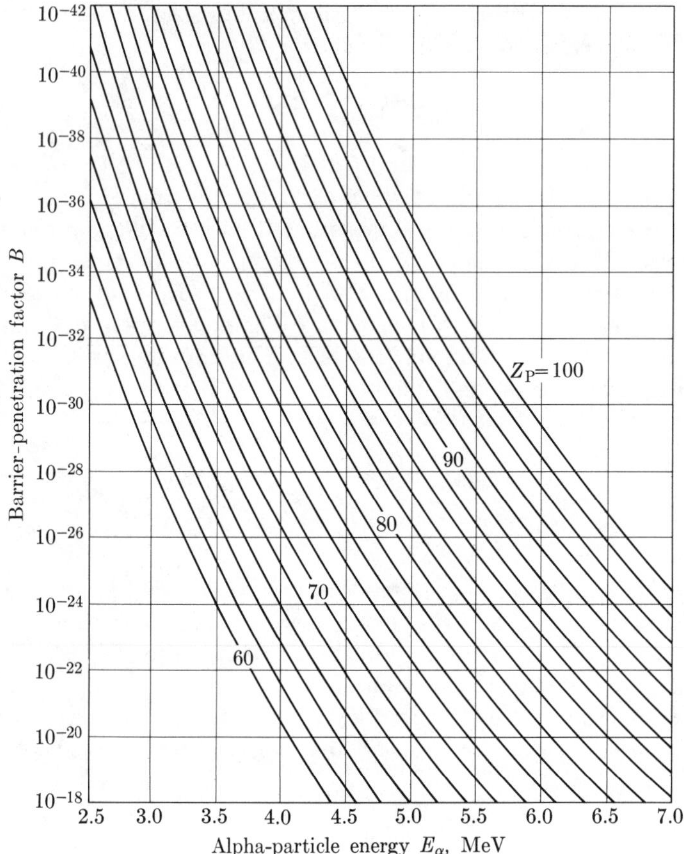

Fig. 10–10. Barrier-penetration factor calculated by use of Eqs. (10–19) and (10–20b) with $l = 0$. For the equation, Z is the element number of the daughter nucleus. For the graph, for convenience, the element number Z_P of the parent is given.

plotted in Fig. 10–10.* Since the barrier-penetration factor, relatively speaking, is not very sensitive to changes in A, the calculations were carried out with a single value of A for each element, namely, the mean value for the alpha-decaying isotopes of that element. For an increase in A of one unit, the change in B is about four percent.

When an alpha particle is emitted with an orbital angular momentum $l = 0$, the change in angular momentum of the nucleus is of course zero, since the alpha particle itself has no internal angular momentum. The parity of the

---

* A major part of the results presented in Fig. 10–10 and in Table 10–2 in the next section has been taken from a paper by John O. Rasmussen, *Phys. Rev.* **113,** 1593 (1959).

Table 10–1. Barrier-penetration factors for higher orbital angular momentum states, $Z = 90$, $E = 4.5$ MeV

l	0	1	2	3	4	5	6
B_l/B_0	1	0.84	0.60	0.36	0.18	0.078	0.028

nucleus is then unchanged. When the transition takes place between nuclear states of different angular momenta and/or different parities, the alpha particle is emitted in a higher orbital angular momentum state. In this case, the centrifugal barrier term in Eq. (10–20a) must be included in the barrier-penetration calculations. For small l-values, the term is not very important as seen from the example given in Table 10–1. Listed are the ratios of the barrier-penetration factors in an orbital angular momentum state l to the barrier-penetration factor in the state $l = 0$ for $Z = 90$ and $E = 4.5$ MeV.

10–6 Reduced Widths of Alpha-Unstable States

Equation (10–14) gives a relationship between the decay constant λ, the barrier-penetration factor B, and the so-called reduced decay constant λ_0, that is, the decay constant in the absence of a barrier. In the past it has been customary in discussions of alpha decay to use Eq. (10–14) and the available experimental data for a determination of the nuclear radius. The decay constant λ is, in general, accurately known; the reduced decay constant λ_0 can be estimated. The nuclear radius, which is essentially the lower limit of integration in Eq. (10–19), is then adjusted to produce a penetration factor in agreement with Eq. (10–14). Since the analysis of alpha-particle scattering data by Igo has enabled us to calculate B without any arbitrary assumptions, we will follow Rasmussen in using Eq. (10–14) to determine λ_0. We can then discuss the significance of the values of λ_0 thus obtained.

Table 10–2, selected from a table in the paper by Rasmussen, gives, among other information, the experimental half-life, the barrier-penetration factor, and the calculated reduced decay constant for ground-state–to–ground-state transitions of even-even nuclei. In cases where β decay competes with α decay, the total decay constant is

$$\lambda = \lambda_\alpha + \lambda_\beta.$$

The branching ratio $\lambda_\alpha/\lambda_\beta$, as well as the total decay constant λ, has been experimentally determined. From this, one gets an experimental value for λ_α and the partial half-life for alpha decay $t_{1/2} = 0.693/\lambda_\alpha$. Column 5 gives the percentage of alpha particles from a given nuclear species that leads to the formation of the daughter nucleus in its ground state. In column 6 we find R_i, the distance between the center of mass of the daughter nucleus and the center of mass of the alpha particles for which the kinetic energy is zero. This number is somewhat larger than the nuclear radius. For the last column in

Table 10–2. Ground-state alpha transitions of even-even nuclei, $l = 0$

Atomic number Z	Mass number A	α-particle energy E_α, MeV	Particle half-life for α-decay, $t_{1/2}$, sec*	Ground-state group intensity, percent	Inner turning point R_i, fermis	Barrier penetration factor B*	Reduced decay constant λ_0, sec*	Reduced width ΔE_0, keV
60	144	1.90	1.58 (23)	100	8.44	2.18 (−42)	2.02 (18)	1.33
64	148	3.16	4.47 (9)	100	8.50	7.52 (−30)	2.06 (19)	13.6
72	174	2.50	9.5 (22)	100	8.77	5.44 (−43)	1.34 (19)	8.85
84	208	5.108	9.24 (7)	100	9.17	2.96 (−27)	2.54 (18)	1.67
84	212	8.780	3.04 (−7)	100	9.35	1.32 (−13)	1.73 (19)	11.4
84	218	5.996	1.827 (2)	100	9.32	1.31 (−22)	2.90 (19)	19.1
86	208	6.141	6.90 (3)	100	9.19	4.35 (−23)	2.31 (18)	1.52
86	218	7.130	1.90 (−2)	99.8	9.34	4.67 (−19)	7.82 (19)	51.5
88	224	5.680	3.15 (5)	94.8	9.34	5.91 (−26)	3.52 (19)	23.4
90	230	4.682	2.528 (12)	74	9.37	6.61 (−33)	3.07 (19)	20.3
92	234	4.768	7.83 (12)	72	9.40	2.34 (−33)	2.73 (19)	18.0
94	238	5.493	2.822 (9)	72	9.44	9.30 (−30)	1.90 (19)	12.5
96	242	6.110	1.404 (7)	73.7	9.49	2.16 (−27)	1.69 (19)	11.1
98	250	6.024	3.45 (8)	83	9.56	1.16 (−28)	1.44 (19)	9.5
100	254	7.200	1.150 (4)	83	9.62	4.09 (−24)	1.23 (19)	8.1

* The number in parentheses is the power of 10 by which the preceding number is to be multiplied.

Table 10–2, a quantity called the reduced width is given. This is the natural width* that the level will exhibit in the absence of a barrier

$$\Delta E_0 = \hbar/\tau_0 = 6.59 \times 10^{-16}\lambda_0 \text{ eV}. \tag{10–21}$$

The reduced widths of Table 10–2 and others given in Rasmussen's paper are plotted in Fig. 10–11 vs. the neutron numbers of the parent nucleus. It is interesting to note that nuclei with neutron numbers close to the magic 126 have significantly lower reduced widths (reduced decay constant) than have other nuclei.

It remains now to calculate or estimate theoretically the reduced widths or reduced decay constants and to compare these estimates with the results quoted above. Many attempts have been made in this direction, and the consensus is that the mechanism of breakup is qualitatively understood. However, quantitatively perfect agreement is not easy to obtain. Part of the reason for this is that the nucleus is not spherically symmetric, as we have assumed here. More important, maybe, is the fact that neither the shell model nor the collective model appears to describe correctly the phenomena in the nuclear surface. In particular, there is considerable evidence of fleeting formations of nucleon clusters in the surface, a feature that is particularly important for the rate of alpha decay.

---

* In the paper by Rasmussen, the reduced width is defined slightly differently. The relationship between the two definitions is $\delta^2 = 2\pi\,\Delta E_0$.

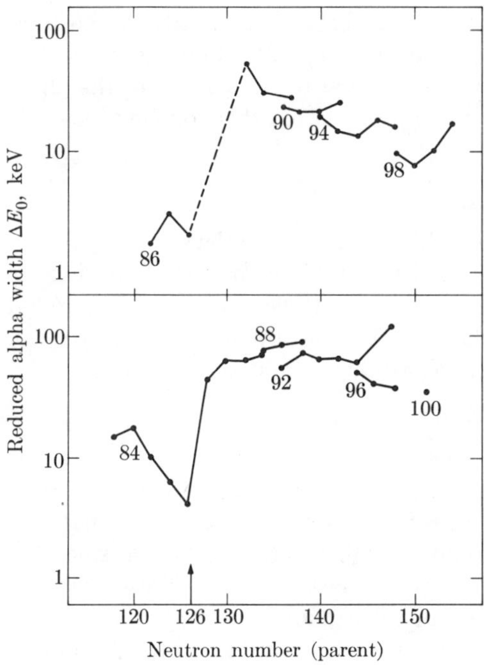

Fig. 10–11. Reduced width ΔE_0 for ground-state–to–ground-state alpha transitions in even-even nuclei. The number beside each curve is Z for the parent nucleus. [Adapted from J. O. Rasmussen, *Phys. Rev.* **113,** 1593 (1959).]

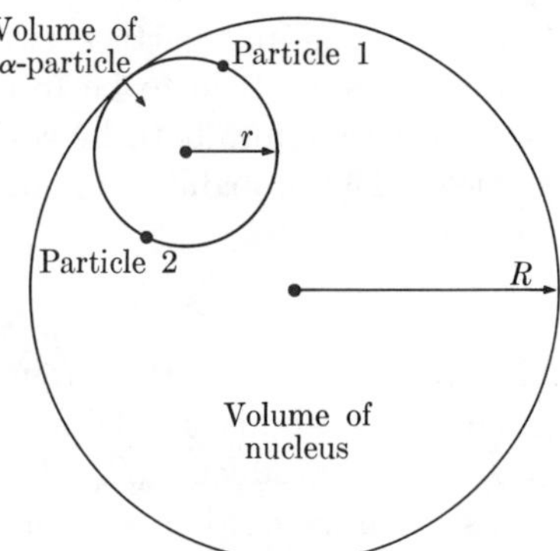

Fig. 10–12. Aid used for theoretical estimate of the reduced decay constant λ_0.

We will here make a crude estimate of the reduced decay constant, based on independent particle motion in the nucleus. Consider two neutrons and two protons in the highest occupied states in the nucleus. One of them (either one) oscillates through the nucleus with a velocity $v \approx (2T/m)^{1/2}$, where T is the average value of the kinetic energy. It therefore appears at or near the nuclear surface approximately $v/2R$ times per second. If the three other particles are close enough when the first particle appears at the nuclear surface, an alpha particle can be formed. We will consider such an event as an escape trial. The probability that a given nucleon is within a distance d from the first nucleon is approximately

$$P_1 \approx \frac{\text{Volume of sphere of radius } d}{\text{Volume of nucleus}} = \left(\frac{d}{R}\right)^3,$$

assuming that the probability density is more or less uniform within the nuclear volume. An alpha particle can be formed if particle one and particle two are separated by less than $d = 2r$, where r is the radius of the alpha particle (see Fig. 10–12). The probability for this to occur at a given instant is

$$P_{12} = 8(r/R)^3.$$

If particle one and particle two are exactly a distance $2r$ apart, the position of the alpha particle to be formed is fixed (Fig. 10–12). Particles three and four must therefore both be within a volume equal to the volume of the alpha particle. The probability for particle three to be within this volume at a given instant is

$$P_3 = (r/R)^3.$$

The probability for particle four to be within the volume is the same, $P_4 = P_3$, and the probability for finding both particle three and particle four there is given by the product P_3P_4. If particle one and particle two are not separated by as much as $2r$, there is more freedom for particles three and four. We can therefore say that a lower limit for the probability sought is

$$P_{\text{min}} = P_{12}P_3P_4 = 8(r/R)^9.$$

Tolhoek and Brussaard* calculate the probability for three particles to be within a distance r from the center of mass for those three plus a fourth particle. This gives an estimate for the probability sought that is too large, since the stated condition does not guarantee that the fourth particle is also within a distance r from the center of mass, although it cannot be very far away.† We can therefore take the estimate by Tolhoek and Brussaard as an upper limit,

$$P_{\text{max}} = 64(r/R)^9.$$

Both estimates of the alpha-formation probability given above are based on constant-probability densities of the individual particles. The oscillations of actual single-particle wave functions may reduce or increase the alpha-formation probability, depending on which states the particles are in. For the purpose of making an order-of-magnitude estimate of the reduced decay constant, we will take 25 as a compromise between the factors 8 and 64 appearing in the formulas for P. Let us assume that the formula for the nuclear radius $R = r_0A^{1/3}$ also applies to the alpha particle. We then get

$$P \approx 25(4/A)^3. \tag{10–22}$$

For $A = 230$, for example, we get $P \approx 1.3 \times 10^{-4}$.

The number of times per second a single nucleon appears at the nuclear surface is approximately

$$v/2R \approx (1/2R)\sqrt{2T/m} = (c/R)\sqrt{T/2mc^2}.$$

---

* H. A. Tolhoek and P. J. Brussaard, *Physica* **21,** 449 (1955).

† If all the other three particles are close together and at a distance r from the center of mass (not very probable, though), the fourth particle must be at a distance $3r$ from the center of mass.

As an example, if we insert $R = 8$ F and $T = 30$ MeV, we obtain

$$\frac{v}{2R} = \frac{3 \times 10^8}{8 \times 10^{-15}} \sqrt{\frac{30}{1878}} = 4.75 \times 10^{21} \text{ sec}^{-1}.$$

Multipled with the alpha-formation probability, this yields for our estimate of the reduced decay constant

$$\frac{v}{2R} P \approx 6.2 \times 10^{17} \text{ sec}^{-1}.$$

This is about a factor of 3 lower than the lowest reduced decay constant in Fig. 10-11, and a factor of 125 lower than the largest. Three important facts may be invoked to explain this discrepancy.

(1) If there are in the highest occupied levels more than four nucleons that can form an alpha particle with total energy E, the probability P for alpha formation will be larger than estimated, by a sizable factor.

(2) Distortions of the shell-model wave functions causing fleeting formations of nucleon clusters in the surface are likely to occur. Again, this will increase the value of P.

(3) In calculating the values for λ_0 in Table 10-2, we have assumed a spherically symmetric nucleus. In fact, above Pb^{208} the nuclei have quite large quadrupole moments. The electrostatic potential at the poles of a prolate nucleus is lower than at the surface of a spherical nucleus of the same volume and charge. The width of the barrier from the pole and out is also smaller than from the surface of a sphere. This will increase the barrier-penetration factor from the poles where the density of outer nucleons is highest. The effect of this will be to reduce the values of λ_0 in Table 10-2.

Since these three factors work in the direction of reducing the discrepancy found above, we dare to conjecture that proper account of them will bring the theoretical estimates of λ in accord with measured values.

10-7 Nuclear Energy Levels as Deduced from Alpha-Decay Data

In Fig. 10-4, we gave an example of an alpha-particle spectrum (Th^{227}) measured with the aid of a magnetic spectrograph. As shown earlier, the relation between the alpha-particle energy and the total disintegration energy is $E = (1 + m_\alpha/m_D)E_\alpha$. This equation is not relativistically correct, but it can be shown (Problem 10-1) that the relativistic correction is so small that it can be neglected. When the alpha particle is emitted with the highest possible energy (the group α_0 in Fig. 10-4), the daughter nucleus is left in its lowest possible state, the ground state. When, however, the alpha particle is emitted with a lower energy, the daughter nucleus is left with more energy, that is, in an excited state. The excitation energy for a given level is simply:

$$E_x = E_0 - E_i, \tag{10-23}$$

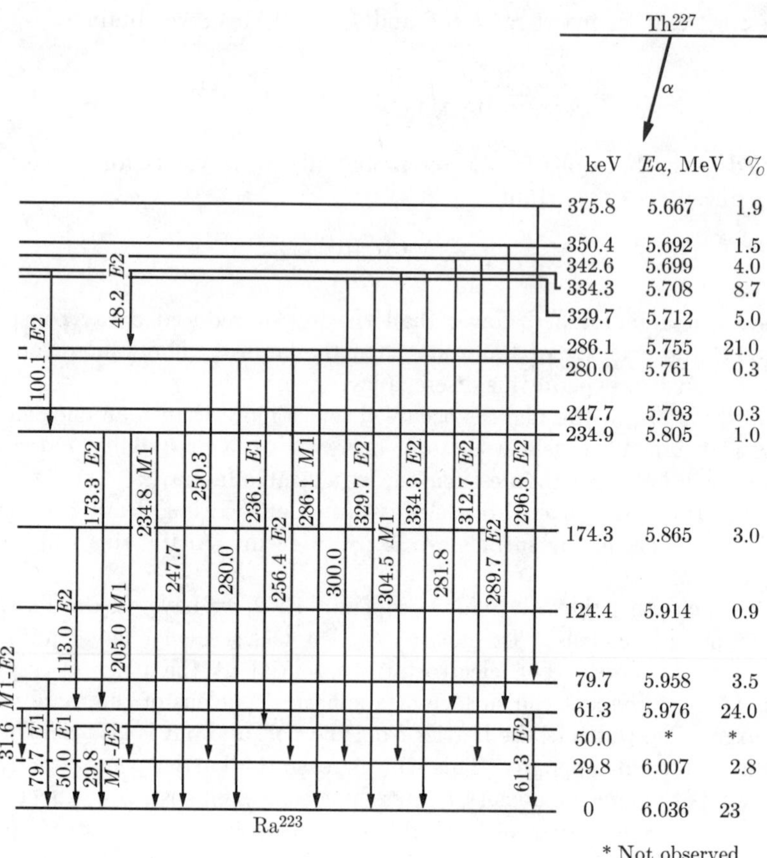

Fig. 10–13. Energy-level diagram of Ra^{223} derived from the alpha-particle spectrum of Th^{227} shown in Fig. 10–4. Also shown are observed electromagnetic transitions. (From F. S. Stephens in *Nuclear Spectroscopy*, Part A, Ed. Fay Ajzenberg-Selove. New York: Academic Press, 1960, p. 202. Reproduced by permission.)

where E_0 is the total disintegration energy for the ground-state case, and E_i is the total disintegration energy when the daughter nucleus is left in level i.

From the data in Fig. 10–4, an energy-level diagram of the daughter nucleus Ra^{223} has been constructed (Fig. 10–13). Also shown in the diagram are lines indicating electromagnetic de-excitation of the various levels. The transition types indicated (e.g., $M1$, $E2$, etc.) are assigned on the basis of measured conversion coefficients. Interpretation of the level scheme of Ra^{223} appears to be quite difficult. Closer to the doubly magic nucleus Pb^{208}, the shell model is quite successful in describing at least the lowest excited states. The nuclei in this region have very low quadrupole moments, and the spherical shell model therefore gives a good approximation to the actual states of the nuclei. For nuclei with nucleon number $A > 230$, on the other hand, the quadrupole

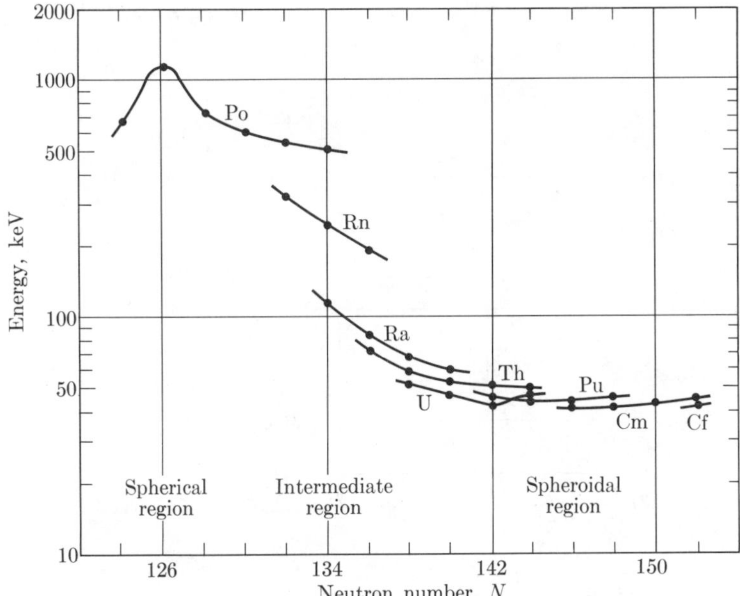

Fig. 10–14. The first excited-state energy of even-even nuclei vs. neutron number. The lines connect the points for each element. The spherical, intermediate, and spheroidal regions of the heavy elements are indicated. (From F. S. Stephens, *op. cit.*, p. 189. Reproduced by permission.)

moments are quite large, and the energy levels can be interpreted in terms of rotational sequences (Section 6–9). The nuclide Ra^{223} falls between these two regions of simple models. The systematic change in the structure as the neutron number is increased is demonstrated very clearly in Fig. 10–14. This is a semilogarithmic plot of the excitation energy of the first excited state of nuclei in this region. According to Fig. 10–14, the level spacings of the shell-model states and the occupancy of these states apparently have no effect on the excitation energy of the first excited state in these even-even nuclei. The only influence of the shell model seems to be to make the nuclei spherical in the magic-number region $N = 126$ ($Z \sim 82$).

In the spheroidal region where the quadrupole moments of the nuclei are quite large, the energy levels exhibit typical rotational bands. An example of such an energy-level diagram for an even-even nucleus with large quadrupole moment was shown in Fig. 6–17. Figure 10–15 illustrates as an example a typical energy-level diagram of an odd nucleus, Np^{237}, displaying rotational band structure. The experimental information consists of an energy spectrum of alpha particles and an energy spectrum with relative intensities of electromagnetic transitions. Two different rotational bands, built on two different intrinsic states, are indicated in Fig. 10–15; one built on the ground state, for which the odd proton is assumed to be in the $5/2^+$ (642) state (Section 6–8),

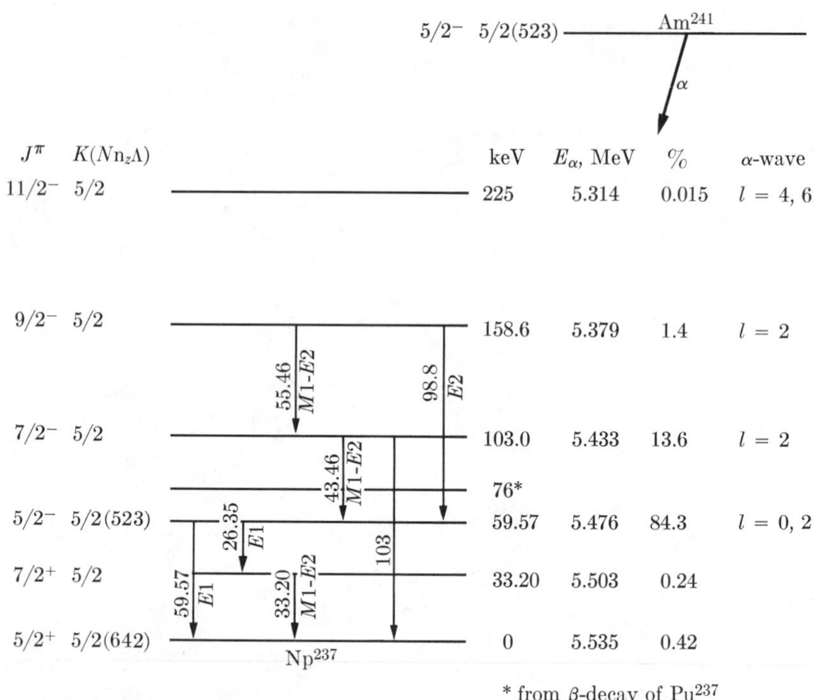

Fig. 10–15. Decay scheme of Am^{241}, illustrating particularly the favored alpha decay to the $5/2^-$ band. The l-values are the alpha waves believed to contribute to the population of each member of the favored rotational band. (From F. S. Stephens, *op. cit.*, p. 198. Reproduced by permission.)

and one built on the $5/2^-$ (523) second excited state. The appropriate section of the diagram of single-proton levels in distorted nuclei is shown in Fig. 10–16. The justification for the separation of the Np^{237} levels into two bands is the agreement between theoretical and experimental level separations and angular momenta, and the appreciable difference in alpha-particle intensity between the two classes of levels.

It is a curious fact that the intensity of alpha particles leading to the ground state is much lower than the intensity of those leading to the second excited state, which is the lowest member of the other band. The explanation for this is that the second excited state and the band built on the second excited state have the same intrinsic configuration as the Am^{241} ground state. The alpha decay will therefore proceed unhindered by any configuration change. In the transition to the ground state, however, the odd proton has to change from $5/2^-$ (523) to $5/2^+$ (642). This inhibits transitions to the ground state and to the rotational band built on the ground state. The ground-state rotational band is, of course, expected to have more members than are shown in Fig. 10–15; these are not seen, however, because of experimental intensity problems. The separation between the lowest member of a rotational band and any other

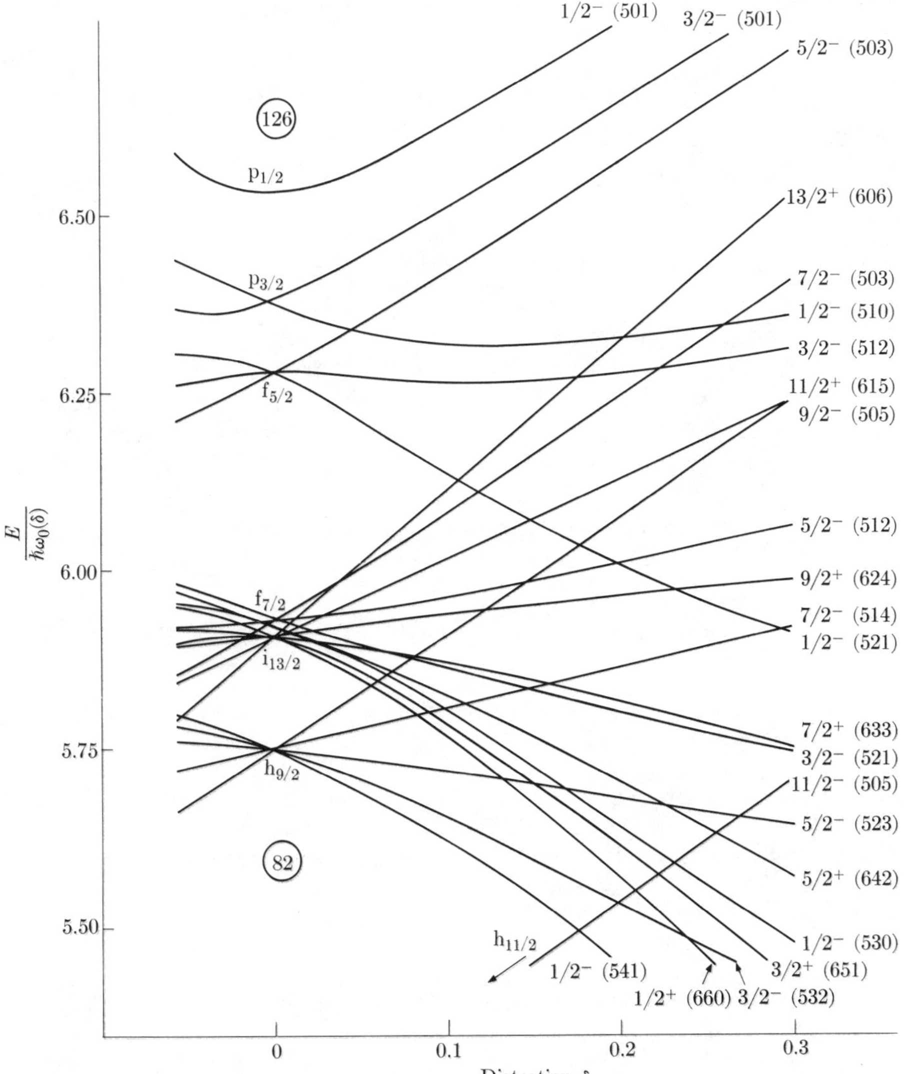

Fig. 10-16. Single proton levels for $Z > 82$. [Adapted from B. R. Mottelson and S. G. Nilsson, *Mat. Fys. Skr. Dan. Vid. Selsk.* **1,** No. 8 (1959).]

member is expected to follow the formula

$$\Delta E = (\hbar^2/2\mathcal{I})[J(J+1) - J_0(J_0+1)], \tag{10-24}$$

where $J_0 = K$ is the component of the angular momentum about the symmetry axis (Fig. 6-15). For simple rotational excitation of odd nuclei, we have in general $K = \Omega$.

Table 10–3. Level spacings in rotational band in Np^{237}

Level, MeV	Spacing ΔE Experimental, MeV	Predicted, MeV
59.57	0	0
103.0	43.43	(43.43)
158.6	99.0	99.2
225	165.4	167.6

Four members of the rotational band built on the $J_0 = 5/2^-$ second excited state are seen in the alpha-particle spectrum. We can use the moment of inertia in Eq. (10–24) as an adjustable parameter, and, for instance, select the value that gives correct level spacing between the two lowest levels 3 and 5. Table 10–3 shows a comparison between these predictions and the observed spacings. The agreement is quite good, and it would have been still better if allowance had been made for the slight increase in moment of inertia with increasing angular momenta (Section 6–9).

PROBLEMS

10–1. (a) Calculate what resolving power is needed to measure with a spectrograph the natural line width of the alpha particles from $_{84}Po^{212}$ (use the uncertainty principle). (b) Estimate the contribution to the experimentally observed line width of $_{84}Po^{212}$ alpha particles from heat motion of the source. (Calculate the energy of the alphas when the nucleus is moving with energy $3kT/2$ in the direction of the emitted alpha particle and when it is moving in the opposite direction.)

10–2. The wave function in the region $R_i < r < R_0$ of Fig. 10–9 is of a form similar to $e^{-\kappa x}$ but κ is not constant. Try the following solution for Schrödinger's equation in this region:

$$\psi = A(r)e^{-\int \kappa\, dr},$$

where κ is given by Eq. (10–20a). Insert this trial solution into Schrödinger's equation and find the form of $A(r)$, assuming that d^2A/dr^2 is negligible compared with the other terms in the differential equation for A. (This is the WKB approximation mentioned on p. 286.)

10–3. The ground state of Po^{211} may decay by alpha emission to the ground state of Pb^{207}. A metastable (isomeric) state of Po^{211} may also decay by alpha emission to the ground state of Pb^{207} ("long-range" alpha particles). (a) Draw an energy-level diagram showing these processes. (b) The two alpha-particle groups are observed simultaneously in a homogeneous-field 180° magnetic spectrograph. The radii of curvatures of their trajectories are r_1 and r_2 (longest). What is the ratio between their energies? (c) Given the excitation energy of the metastable state E in addition to the information above, find an expression for the magnetic induction B in the spectrograph. Use nonrelativistic mechanics.

10–4. The alpha emitter Ra^{226} has a half-life of 1622 y, and the alpha-particle energy is 4.791 MeV. Use Fig. 10–10 to determine the barrier-penetration factor for this decay, and determine the reduced width.

10–5. Calculate the barrier-penetration factor for a triangular barrier (see Fig. 10–17), using Eq. (10–11). Use the result to estimate the barrier-penetration factor for $l = 0$ alpha particles from a $Z = 70$ nucleus on the assumption that the potential-energy curve between R_i and R_0 approximates a straight line. Take $E = 5$ MeV, $R_i = 9$ F, and calculate R_0 as the point where the actual potential energy $V = Zze^2/4\pi\epsilon_0 r$ is equal to E. Use the same formula to find V_0. Compare the result of the calculation with Fig. 10–10.

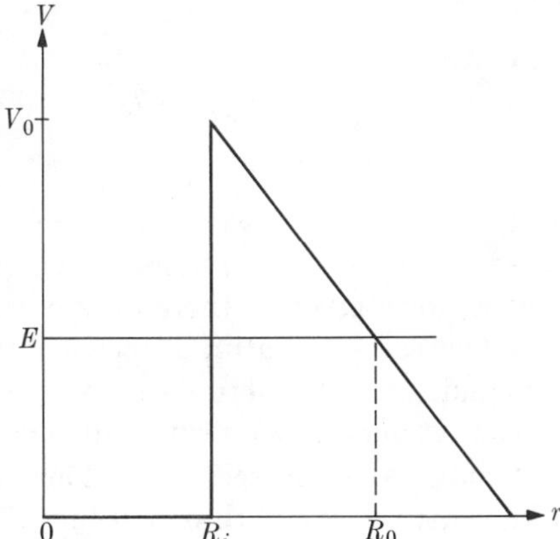

Figure 10–17

10–6. Show that the relativistic correction to the equation

$$E = \left(1 + \frac{m_\alpha}{m_D}\right) E_\alpha$$

in Section 10–7 is negligibly small in terms of the accuracies normally claimed for alpha-energy measurements ($\Delta E > 1$ keV).

10–7. The following are the energies of ten low-lying levels in Cm^{245}, as determined from the alpha decay of Cf^{249}: 0, 55, 124, 207, 257, 301, 357, 394, 450, and 511. Organize these states into three rotational bands, one with $K = 7/2^+$ (four states), one with $K = 5/2^+$ (three states), and one with $K = 9/2^-$ (three states). [*Hint:* $\mathcal{J}$ does not have to be identical for different bands.]

*10–8. Find an approximation method (graphically or otherwise) to estimate the ratio between the barrier-penetration factors for $l = 1$, 2, or 3 and $l = 0$. Note that the change in magnitude of the integral in Eq. (10–11) is small. Assume that the potential energy is given by $V = Zze^2/4\pi\epsilon_0 r$ with a sharp cutoff at $r = R_i$. Examples: $E = 4, 5, 6, 7, 8$; $R_i = (1.4A^{1/3} + 1)$ F; $(Z, A) = (80, 200), (85, 210), (90, 225), (95, 240)$. (Select one set.)

*10–9. Study the probability of forming an alpha particle on the nuclear surface (Eq. 10–22) in more detail, but classically only.

11 Beta Decay

11-1 Introduction

A perusal of the Chart of the Nuclides or a table of nuclides reveals that among the nuclear species that are found in nature, there are very many with identical nucleon numbers A, that is, for a given A there may be several stable isobars. However, there are very few cases of naturally occurring *neighbor* isobars, or pairs of the type ${}_{50}\text{Sn}^{115}$ and ${}_{49}\text{In}^{115}$, where Z differs by one unit only. There are good reasons to believe that in every case where such pairs exist, one member is actually unstable, but may have an exceedingly long lifetime. In the case mentioned, ${}_{49}\text{In}^{115}$ is known to decay with a half-life of 6×10^{14} years into ${}_{50}\text{Sn}^{115}$.

In contrast to the situation for neighbor isobars, there is an abundance of cases of apparently stable isobars separated by two units of Z (and N). The observations are that between two neighbor isobars the one with the larger *atomic* mass will decay by a beta process to the lighter one, but that apparently there is no process which, with sufficient speed, can change the nuclear charge by two units.

We may think of the Chart of the Nuclides as a three-dimensional plot with mass being the quantity plotted in the third dimension. The stable nuclei will then represent the bottom of a valley. All neutron-rich nuclides will decay by β^- emission along its isobar line toward the bottom of the valley, and all proton-rich nuclides will decay similarly with β^+ emission or electron capture. A cross section of the valley, along an isobar line, may exhibit local minima (Fig. 11–1). The naturally occurring isobars are located at the minima.

In the beta-decay process a positive or negative electron is emitted from the nucleus, or an orbital electron is captured by the nucleus. In all cases, a neutrino or an antineutrino is simultaneously emitted.

The electron and positron are antiparticles, i.e., they can annihilate each other when brought in close contact. Correspondingly, there are two kinds of neutrinos involved in beta decay, the neutrino emitted in β^+ (positron) decay and the antineutrino emitted in β^- (negatron) decay. All four belong to a class of particles called leptons (Chapter 15), which, according to observations, are always created or annihilated in pairs. For instance, the creation of an electron in β^- decay is always accompanied by the creation of an antineutrino, and in β^+ decay a positron and a neutrino are created. These observations can be formulated into a physical law expressing conservation of lepton number. (Compare with conservation of charge.) That is, we give the electron and the neutrino lepton number 1 and the positron and antineutrino lepton number -1. The sum of these numbers is then always constant in any reaction (beta decay, pair production, etc.).

The neutrino and the antineutrino were postulated by Pauli in 1931 to explain an otherwise unaccountable loss of energy and angular momentum in the β-decay process. Consider a simple example, the decay of a free neutron:

$$\mathrm{n} \rightarrow \mathrm{p} + \beta^- + \bar{\nu}.$$

The neutron has half-integer spin quantum number and so has the proton as well as the electron. Without the antineutrino on the right-hand side of the equation, angular momentum cannot be conserved, since a possible *orbital* angular momentum of the electron relative to the proton must have integer quantum number. The other argument in favor of a two-particle emission stems from the fact that the energy of the emitted electron displays a broad continuous spectrum with a maximum energy that corresponds to the neutron-proton mass difference (Fig. 11-2). Clearly, this agrees with the view that the energy is shared in a random fashion between two particles. This point is discussed in detail in Section 11-4.

Neutrino detection is possible, if difficult, with present-day techniques, so that the existence of these elusive particles is firmly established. A further discussion of the neutrino and antineutrino is given in Section 11-9.

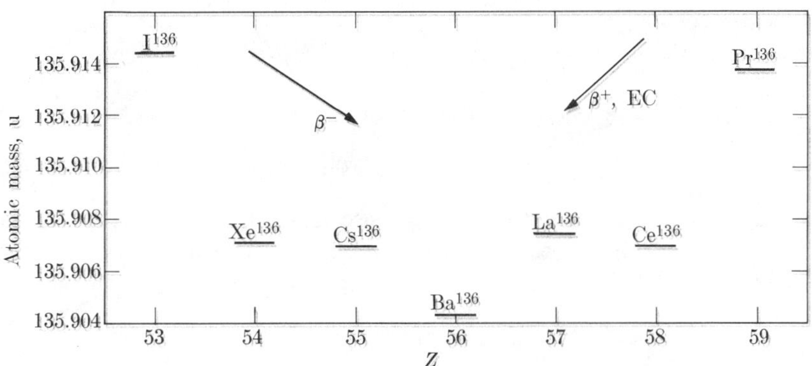

Fig. 11-1. Cross section of the valley of nuclides at isobar line, $A = 136$.

For a beta process to take place there must be energy available for the creation of the leptons. The basic processes are

$$\mathrm{n} \to \mathrm{p} + \beta^- + \bar{\nu}, \qquad \beta^- \text{ decay}; \tag{11-1}$$

$$\mathrm{p} \to \mathrm{n} + \beta^+ + \nu, \qquad \beta^+ \text{ decay}; \tag{11-2}$$

$$\mathrm{p} + \mathrm{e}^- \to \mathrm{n} + \nu, \qquad \text{Electron capture (EC)}. \tag{11-3}$$

Clearly, in these processes, both charge and lepton number are conserved. The symbol ν indicates the neutrino, and the symbol $\bar{\nu}$, the antineutrino. The symbol β^- is used to represent an electron created in a β-decay process, and the symbol e^- is used for an atomic (orbital) electron. They are, of course, identical particles. Process (11–1) is energetically possible for a free neutron which has a 0.78-MeV 12-m (half-life) decay. The processes (11–2) and (11–3) are then, of course, not possible without an extra supply of energy which may be present in the field of other nucleons inside the nucleus.

The maximum kinetic energy available for the decay products in a beta process can be found from the following balance sheet between the *atomic* rest energies of two members of an isobaric pair.

Process	Before	After
β^-	${}_ZM^Ac^2$	${}_{Z+1}M^{A+}c^2$ (positive ion) $+ m_0c^2 + Q_{\beta^-}$
β^+	${}_{Z+1}M^Ac^2$	${}_ZM^{A-}c^2$ (negative ion) $+ m_0c^2 + Q_{\beta^+}$
EC	${}_{Z+1}M^Ac^2$	${}_ZM^{A*}c^2$ (neutral but excited) $+ Q_{\mathrm{EC}}$

The energy Q released in the process in the form of kinetic energy of the decay products must, of course, be equal to the reduction in rest energy. This is essentially what the balance sheet expresses.

The β^- process increases the nuclear charge by one unit but leaves the number of atomic electrons unchanged. Since the energy of the neutral daughter atom is

$${}_{Z+1}M^Ac^2 = {}_{Z+1}M^{A+}c^2 + m_0c^2 - I,$$

where I is the binding energy of the last atomic electron, we get

$$Q_{\beta^-} = {}_ZM^Ac^2 - {}_{Z+1}M^Ac^2 - I. \tag{11-4}$$

The binding energy I (ionization energy) is so small that it is usually neglected.

The β^+ process decreases the nuclear charge by one unit and hence leaves a negative ion. The rest energy of this negative ion can be written:

$${}_ZM^{A-}c^2 = {}_ZM^Ac^2 + m_0c^2 - I.$$

From the balance sheet, we then get

$$Q_{\beta^+} = {}_{Z+1}M^Ac^2 - {}_ZM^Ac^2 - 2m_0c^2 + I. \tag{11-5}$$

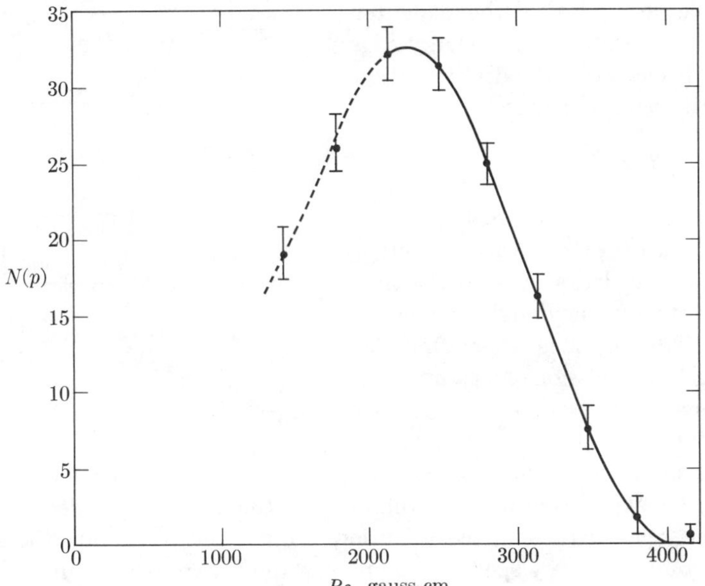

Fig. 11-2. Beta-minus spectrum from the decay of free neutrons. [From J. M. Robson, *Phys. Rev.* **83,** 349 (1951).]

The electron-capture process reduces the number of elementary charges by one unit, and at the same time removes one electron from one of the atomic shells. Most often this is one of the innermost shells, for instance, the K-shell. The process therefore leaves the atom excited, and a cascade of photons will, in general, follow the capture. The rearrangement energy is equal to the binding energy, E_B, of the captured electron minus the binding energy, I, of an electron in the lowest orbit that is not occupied when the daughter atom is in its ground state.

From the balance sheet, we get

$$Q_{\text{EC}} = {}_{Z+1}M^A c^2 - {}_Z M^A c^2 - E_B + I. \tag{11-6}$$

The binding energy for a K-electron in heavy elements is over 100 keV, but the L- and M-electrons are bound by only about 20 and 5 keV, respectively. If ${}_{Z+1}M^A$ is larger than ${}_Z M^A$, electron capture is therefore, in practice, possible. Equations (11-4) and (11-6) show that between two neighbor isobars, in practice, one has enough energy to decay into the other. This explains the observations made in the first paragraph of this section about neighbor isobars. For β^+ decay, Eq. (11-5) shows that an excess energy of $2m_0c^2 = 1.022$ MeV must be available for the process to go.

The masses entering into Eqs. (11-4) and (11-6) are atomic masses for the neutral species with both the nuclei and the atoms in the ground states. Very often beta decay leaves the daughter nucleus in an excited state (energy E_x). The kinetic energy of the disintegration products is then, of course:

$$T = Q - E_x. \qquad (11\text{-}7)$$

Figure 11–3 shows an example, the decay scheme of Au^{198}. A large fraction (98.6%) of the decay goes to the first excited state of the daughter nucleus Hg^{198}. This nucleus thereafter de-excites itself by emission of a gamma ray or conversion electron leading to the ground state.

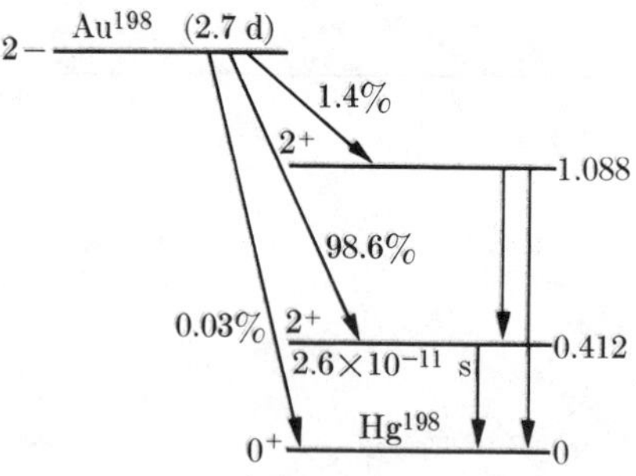

Fig. 11–3. Decay scheme of Au^{198} showing branching to the ground state and first two excited states of Hg^{198}.

In beta decay, as in other decay processes, the most important parameters that can be experimentally determined are the half-life or decay constant and the energies of the emitted radiation. In β^- and β^+ decay, the endpoint of the continuous energy spectrum represents the energy released in the process, and this of course is an important parameter. In addition, the shape of the continuous energy spectrum provides important information (Sections 11–3 and 11–4). At this point, therefore, a discussion of experimental methods for studying electron energy spectra is in order.

11–2 Instruments of Beta Spectroscopy

Early measurements of the energies of beta particles were performed with the use of aluminum and/or air absorbers followed by a gas counter. The amount of absorber needed to cut off the count completely gave information about the maximum energy in the beta spectrum, but very little detail as to the shape of the spectrum. This method is now used only in very special cases, and we will not discuss it further here.

Some excellent work in beta spectroscopy has been done with three types of particle counter spectrometers discussed in Chapter 8: the proportional gas counter, the solid-state counter, and the scintillation counter. In all cases the pulse height from the counter is a measure of the energy absorbed in the counter, and if the counter volume is large enough so that most of the beta particles are stopped in the counter material, the pulse height spectrum is a good representation of the energy spectrum. The condition of a sufficeintly large volume has so far been most difficult to achieve with the solid-state counter, which consequently has been used as a spectrometer only for low-energy betas.

Undoubtedly the most exact methods of measuring beta-ray spectra utilize deflection of the particles in magnetic fields. The different types of magnetic spectrographs devised can be rather arbitrarily classified into two groups: flat types, in which the particles move in plane orbits, and lens types, in which the particles move in spiral-shaped orbits.

As in alpha spectroscopy, it is important to have a good resolving power and at the same time a sufficiently high counting rate. The latter requirement is particularly important when samples with very low activity are being studied (long-lived nuclides). High counting rates can be obtained by using large source areas and counter slit openings, moderately thick sources, and a large solid angle of acceptance to the spectrograph for the particles emitted from the source. Since the attainment of a high resolving power requires that the source area and thickness, solid angle, etc., be small, it is necessary to compromise between yield and resolving power.

(*a*) *Flat-type spectrometers.* The 180° spectrograph, which was discussed in Section 10–2, has high resolving power and the additional advantage that it is possible to make absolute determination of particle momenta with the instrument by measuring the magnetic field and the diameter of the circular orbit. This means that no secondary standard, that is, a source with particles of known momentum, need be used for calibrating the instrument. The 180° instrument has the disadvantage that focusing takes place only in one plane, the median plane of the instrument. Particles that have a momentum component normal to the median plane, that is, parallel to the direction of the field, will diverge from the median plane of the instrument, and they are not brought back to a focus at the median plane since there are no magnetic forces acting in that direction. A point source will therefore give a line image at the position of the recorder. Most of the other types of magnetic instruments of beta spectroscopy are double focusing, which in the simplest cases means that a point source produces a point image on the recorder (ideally).

As a second example of a beta spectrometer which has been extensively used, we shall here discuss an instrument originally devised by Svartholm and Siegbahn.* Figure 11–4 shows the magnet, with a sector cut out, and particle trajectories from the source S to the recorder C. The particles travel in an evacuated annular region where the magnetic field is not homogeneous but varies with radius r approximately according to the relationship

$$B_z = B_0\left(\frac{r}{r_0}\right)^{-n}. \tag{11-8}$$

Here B_0 is the magnetic induction on a circular orbit defined as the central orbit, with radius r_0. The field exponent is $n = \frac{1}{2}$. The source S and the detector C are both located on the central orbit. Particles diverging from the source are focused in both directions and converge toward the detector (point-to-point focusing).

---

* N. Svartholm and K. Siegbahn, *Ark. för Mat. Astr. och Fysik* **33A**, No. 21.

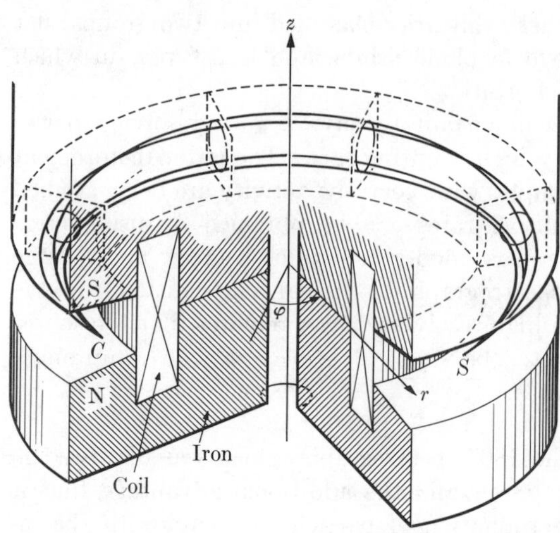

Fig. 11–4. Sketch showing operating principle of a double-focusing beta spectrometer. (From N. Svartholm and K. Siegbahn, *Ark för Mat. Astr. och Fysik* **33A,** No. 21. Reproduced by permission.)

To calculate the focusing properties of this type of field, we use cylindrical coordinates r, ϕ, and z and introduce the displacement y from the central orbit, given by

$$r = r_0 + y. \tag{11-9}$$

We consider particles of momentum $p = eB_0r_0$, for which the magnetic force balances the centrifugal force on the central orbit. It is shown in Appendix 2 that particles emitted from the source but diverging from the central orbit will experience horizontal and vertical forces directed toward the central orbit and of magnitude proportional to the distance from the central orbit. The equations of motion of these particles can, in cases of small deviations only from the central orbit, be written in the form (Appendix 2):

$$\ddot{y} + \omega^2(1 - n)y = 0, \tag{11-10}$$

$$\ddot{z} + \omega^2 nz \qquad = 0. \tag{11-11}$$

The double-dot symbol, as usual, indicates the double derivative with respect to time, and $\omega = eB_0/m$ is the cyclotron frequency of a particle moving on the central orbit. For $n = \frac{1}{2}$, the two harmonic differential equations (11–10) and (11–11) will have identical form with solutions of the type y or $z = A \sin \Omega t$, where $\Omega^2 = \omega^2/2$. The half period for the motion, that is, the time t_c of excursion from the axis is given by $\Omega t_c = \pi$. During this time, the particles move around the spectrometer through an angle $\phi_c = \omega t_c = \sqrt{2}\pi = 254.5°$. This is therefore the angular distance from object to image. Particles with higher momenta will be focused to a point outside r_0, and particles with lower momenta to a point inside r_0. A momentum spectrum of the particles therefore appears at position C.

The preceding paragraph represents a simple first-order theory of focusing in the Svartholm-Siegbahn spectrograph. Several approximations were applied

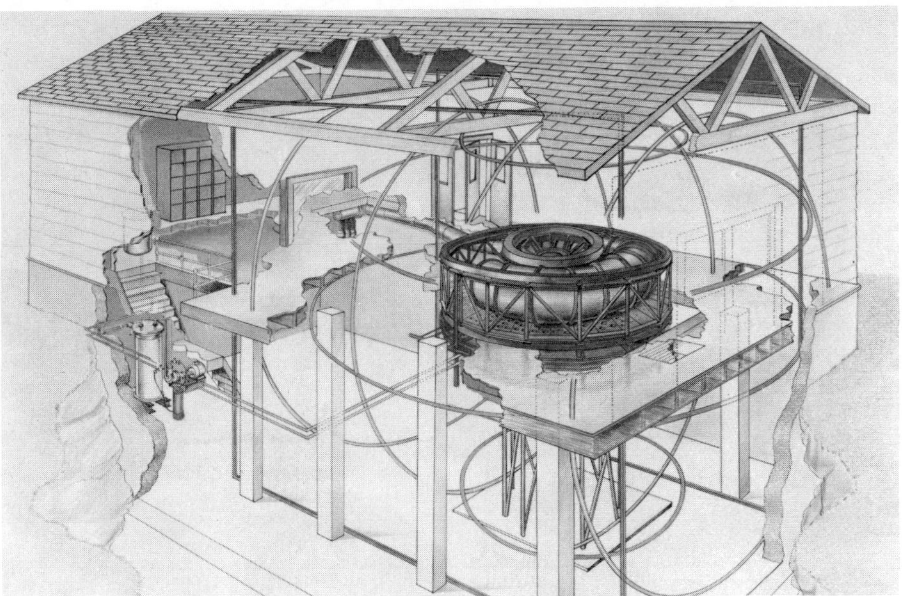

Fig. 11–5. Iron-free spectrograph of the Svartholm-Siegbahn type. Note the large Helmholtz coils surrounding the spectrograph. The purpose of these is to compensate for the earth's magnetic field. (Courtesy of R. L. Graham.)

in Appendix 2 when deriving Eqs. (11–10) and (11–11), and the theory is therefore good only for small angles of divergence of the rays from the central orbit. For larger angles of divergence, the image will be distorted, and there are, naturally, limits to how far one can go with the solid angle before distortion imposes too serious a limitation on the resolving power of the instrument. The resolving power also depends on the area of the source and the area of the detector slit. A closer study of these problems indicates that for a desired momentum resolving power, $R = p/\Delta p$ (see Section 10–2), the source area that can be tolerated is approximately $S = 5.5r_0^2R^{-3/2}$ and the total transmission that can be used is of the order of magnitude $T = 0.27/R$. The transmission T is defined as the fraction of the particles emitted from a given source in all directions (4π sterad) that will be collected by the detector when the momentum of the particles is $p = eB_0R_0$. Other causes of line widening in beta spectroscopy are scattering and energy loss of the particles in the source material and substrata on which it is supported and also scattering from the walls of the vacuum chamber.

Iron-free spectrographs of the double-focusing type have the advantage that they are free of hysteresis effects and therefore are more accurate.* Figure 11–5 is a sketch of such an instrument built at the Chalk River Laboratories in

---

* K. Siegbahn, *Physica* **18,** 1043 (1952); R. L. Graham, G. T. Ewan, and J. S. Geiger, *Nucl. Instr. Methods* **24,** 81 (1963).

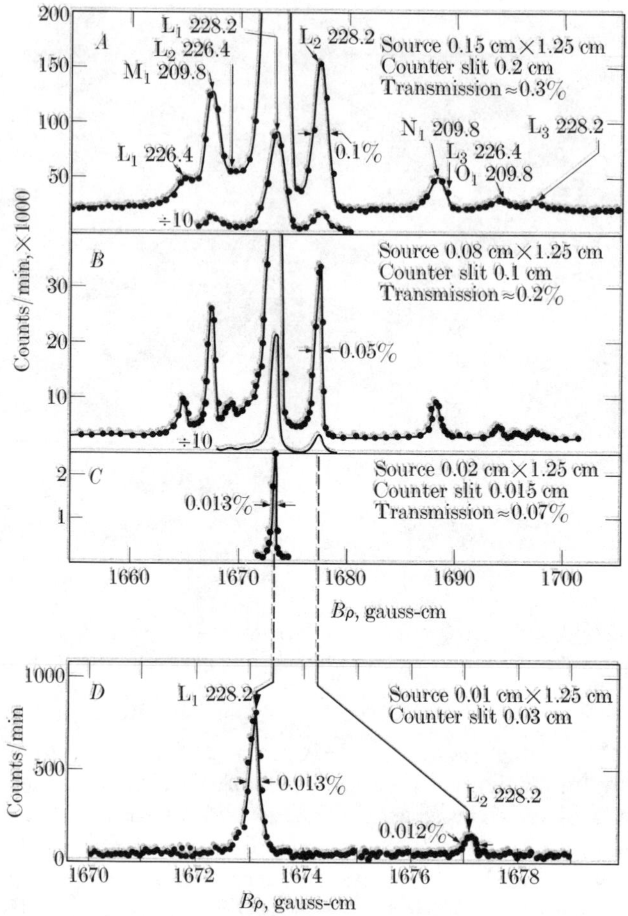

Fig. 11–6. A portion of the conversion-electron spectrum taken with the Chalk River air-core spectrometer set for different resolving powers. (From G. T. Ewan and R. L. Graham in *Alpha-, Beta-, and Gamma-Ray Spectroscopy*, ed. by K. Siegbahn. Amsterdam: North-Holland Publishing Company, 1965, p. 962. Reproduced by permission.)

Canada. Figure 11–6 shows an example of the outstanding work done with the Chalk River instrument, a portion of the conversion-electron spectrum from Np^{239}. Note the severe loss of counting rate as the resolution is improved by the closing down of slits and apertures.

(*b*) *Lens-type spectrometers.* Another type of beta spectrometer that enjoys a certain popularity operates on the same principle as a magnetic lens, familiar from electron microscopes, television tubes, etc. An instrument of this class, which is particularly easy to analyze, is the longitudinal type homogeneous-

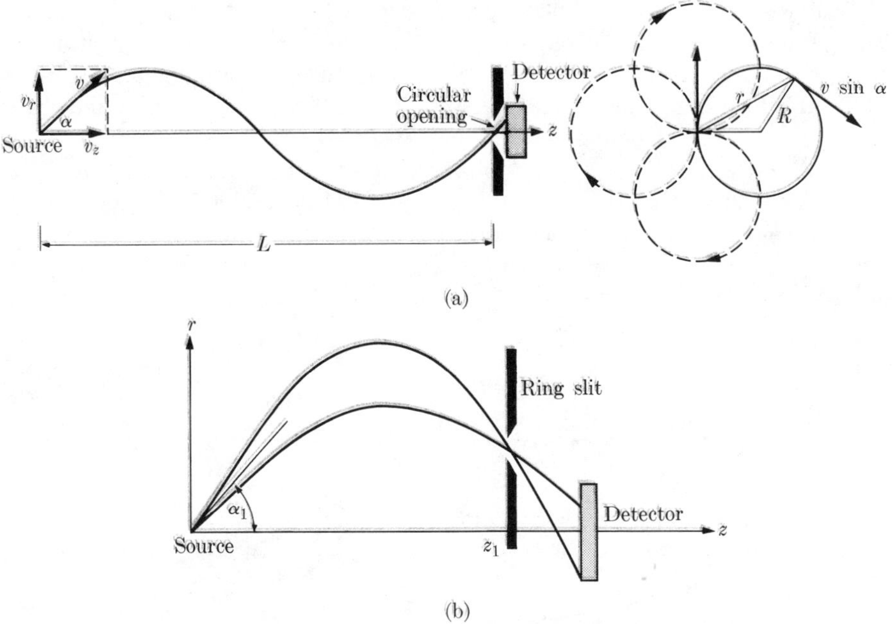

Fig. 11-7. (a) Principle of operation of the longitudinal type homogeneous-field beta spectrometer with circular detector window on the axis (single focusing). (b) Principle of operation of the longitudinal type homogeneous-field beta spectrometer with ring-shaped detector slit (double focusing).

field spectrometer, shown in Fig. 11-7(a). For calculating the electron orbits in this instrument, we use a cylindrical coordinate system with the z-direction along the instrument axis, which is also the direction of the magnetic induction B. We consider a particle emitted with a velocity v from a point on the axis, its direction forming an angle α with the axis. The component of this velocity in the z-direction $v_z = v \cos \alpha$ is unaffected by the magnetic field, so that the equation of motion in the z-direction is simply

$$z = vt \cos \alpha.$$

In the $r\phi$ plane, the motion is circular with a period $T = 2\pi/\omega$, where $\omega = eB/m$ is the cyclotron frequency for the particle in the field B. When the particle returns to the axis after the period T, it has traveled in the z-direction a distance

$$L = vT \cos \alpha = 2\pi mv (\cos \alpha)/eB.$$

Hence, if a detector is placed on the axis at a distance L from the source, the relationship between the momentum p of the recorded particles and the magnetic induction B is given by

$$BL = 2\pi p (\cos \alpha)/e. \tag{11-12}$$

This shows that there is a linear relationship between the magnetic induction and the momentum of the particle, but that the proportionality constant relating them depends on the angle of ejection α. The spectrometer is therefore not double focusing, which would imply that the relationship between induction and momentum must be independent of the direction of emission, that is, independent of α and ϕ over a range of these angles. Because of the cylindrical symmetry, the relationship (Eq. 11–12) is clearly completely independent of the angle ϕ. A ring-shaped acceptance aperture can be inserted, limiting the range of ejection angles α to such an extent that the resolving power is not seriously affected.

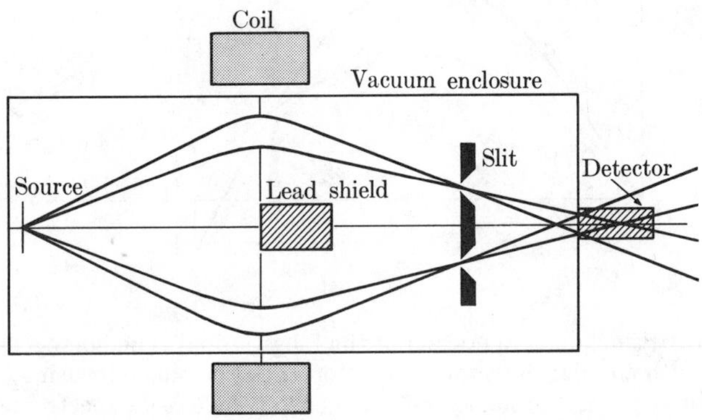

Fig. 11–8. Short-lens beta spectrometer with ring slit as in Fig. 11–7(b); the lead shield is designed to stop direct gamma rays from the source.

In the preceding paragraph, we have assumed that the source is a small object, for instance a circular disk, on the axis and that the recorder is an electron counter with a small hole in front, also located on the axis. It turns out that it is possible to improve the instrument, to make it double focusing, by using a ring-shaped counter slit that is not located immediately adjacent to the counter, but in the position indicated in Fig. 11–7(b). As indicated on that figure, two particles having different angles of ejection α, but having the same momentum, can both pass through the narrow energy-defining slit. The position at which this energy-defining slit should be placed can be found by describing the particle orbit in the rz plane as $r = f(z, \alpha, p)$ and putting the first-order derivative $\partial f(z, \alpha, p)/\partial \alpha = 0$. This yields, with the use of Eq. (11–12):

$$\tan \pi \frac{z_1}{L} = -\pi \frac{z_1}{L} \tan^2 \alpha_1. \tag{11–13}$$

If the ring-shaped slit is placed at the position $z = z_1$, given by Eq. (11–13), then particles of the same momentum emitted in directions centered around the angle $\alpha = \alpha_1$ will pass through the slit independent of α.* As indicated in Fig. 11–7(b), the detector needs to be larger than the one shown in Fig. 11–7(a) to collect all particles passing through the ring slits.

As another example of a lens-type spectrometer, Fig. 11–8 shows a so-called "short-lens" instrument. The construction and operating principles are somewhat similar to the homogeneous-field longitudinal spectrometer, but the instrument has the advantage of greater accessibility to the source and detector areas. Since it contains no iron, it is free of hysteresis effects; however, as in any iron-free spectrometer, the earth's magnetic field needs to be compensated for by extra coils, properly oriented.

Before we discuss examples of beta spectra observed with the instruments described in this section, it will be advantageous to be familiar with the theory of beta decay and with the methods used for analyzing the data (e.g., Kurie plots, Section 11–4).

11–3 Simple Theory of Beta Decay

The following discussion gives a simplified derivation of the momentum spectrum for electrons emitted in an *allowed beta transition.* This is a transition in which the two leptons are both emitted with zero angular momentum with respect to the nucleus. For more refined treatments of the beta-decay process for allowed as well as so-called "forbidden" transitions (Section 11–6), consult textbooks in theoretical nuclear physics.†

From perturbation theory (Appendix 4), one has the following formula for the disintegration constant associated with the transition of a system from an initial state i to a final state f:

$$\lambda = \frac{2\pi}{\hbar} |H'_{if}|^2 \frac{dN}{dE_0}, \tag{11–14}$$

where dN/dE_0 is the number of quantum-mechanical states of the final system per unit interval of the total energy E_0. The matrix element H'_{if} of the interaction is defined as

$$H'_{if} = \int \psi_f^* H' \psi_i \, d\tau, \tag{11–15}$$

where ψ_f is the wave function of the final state of the complete system, ψ_i is the wave function of the initial system, H' is the energy operator that describes the (weak) coupling between the two states, and $d\tau$ is the volume element.

---

* Since it is only the first-order derivative $\partial f/\partial \alpha$ that is equal to zero, the radial distance r at $z = z_1$ is not independent of α, except in an infinitesimally small range of that angle. This condition is called *first-order* focusing.

† For example, J. M. Blatt and V. F. Weisskopf, *Theoretical Nuclear Physics*, New York: John Wiley and Sons, 1952; or M. A. Preston, *Physics of the Nucleus*, Reading, Mass.: Addison-Wesley Publishing Co., 1962.

The physical situation to which Eq. (11–14) is applied in the case of beta decay is the following: the parent nucleus in a given quantum-mechanical state can change to a daughter nucleus in a given state plus two leptons, through the action of a perturbing potential. The two particles can travel in any direction from the nucleus, and they can share the available energy between them in a large number of different ways. Consequently, there is a very large number of different quantum-mechanical states for the total system after the decay, since the state of the daughter nucleus can be combined with a large number of combinations of states of the two leptons. The energy of the unstable parent state is not perfectly sharp, so that it will overlap a certain number of states of the system after decay (Fig. 11–9). The decay can therefore take place to any one of a large number of states with slightly different energies without violation of the energy conservation law. We assume that the state of the daughter nucleus is sharp so that the uncertainty in energy results in an uncertainty in the sum of the energies of the leptons. In Eq. (11–14), then, we take E_0 to mean this sum.*

We will first look into the matrix element (Eq. 11–15). We do not know the form of the interaction operator H', but Fermi suggested trying the simplest possible operator he could think of, namely, a constant, which we will call G. We now write for the final state of the total system a product consisting of three factors: the normalized wave function $\psi_{f\mathrm{N}}$ for the daughter nucleus and ψ_{e} and ψ_{ν}, the normalized wave functions for the electron (positron) and the antineutrino (neutrino). We then get

$$H'_{if} = G \int \psi^*_{f\mathrm{N}} \psi^*_{\mathrm{e}} \psi^*_{\nu} \psi_{i\mathrm{N}}\, d\tau. \tag{11–16}$$

where $\psi_{i\mathrm{N}}$ is the normalized wave function of the parent nucleus. As mentioned

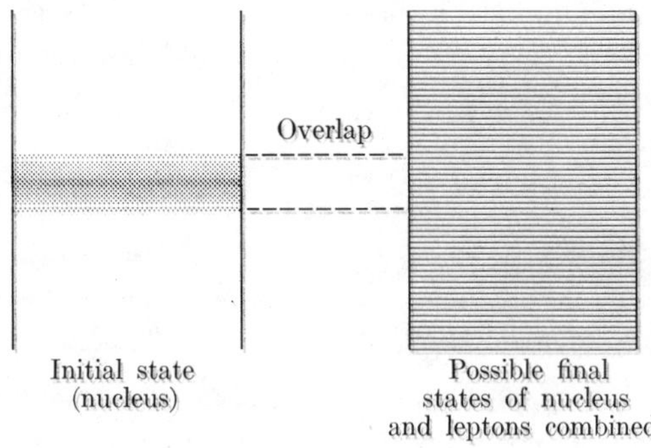

Fig. 11–9. The width of an unstable level overlaps a number of possible levels of the nucleus-plus-lepton system.

---

* Several previous elementary texts incorrectly state that the sum of the energies of the two leptons is sharp.

earlier, both leptons can be in any of a large number of states with different momentum vectors. The validity of Eq. (11–16) requires that these states be normalized. This can be done by introducing an artificial volume V, in which the system is contained.

Now it can easily be shown that the wavelengths of the leptons at the energies considered are substantially longer than the nuclear dimensions. We can therefore, at least to a first approximation, replace the lepton wave functions in Eq. (11–16) with their constant value at the nuclear center. Neglecting for a moment the distortion of the electron (positron) wave function caused by the charge on the nucleus, we can assume that both lepton wave functions are free-particle wave functions and will fill the whole volume V. Since they are normalized, their numerical value will be equal to

$$\begin{aligned} |\psi_{\mathrm{e}}^*(r)| &= |V^{-1/2}e^{i\mathbf{k}_{\mathrm{e}}\cdot\mathbf{r}}| = V^{-1/2}, \\ |\psi_{\nu}^*(r)| &= |V^{-1/2}e^{i\mathbf{k}_{\nu}\cdot\mathbf{r}}| = V^{-1/2}. \end{aligned} \tag{11–17}$$

Coming back to the electrostatic distortion of the electron (positron) wave function, we simply quote without proof that the effect can be taken into account by multiplying $|\psi_{\mathrm{e}}|^2$ with a factor sometimes called the Coulomb factor and sometimes called the Fermi function:

$$F(Z, E_{\mathrm{e}}) \approx \frac{2\pi\eta}{1 - \exp(-2\pi\eta)}, \tag{11–18}$$

where

$$\eta = \pm \frac{Ze^2}{4\pi\epsilon_0\hbar v}. \tag{11–19}$$

The positive sign is used for electrons; the negative sign, for positrons. Equation (11–18) is based on nonrelativistic calculations that are of course not very accurate, except in the range where $v \ll c$. Figure 11–10 is a graph of the relativistically correct Coulomb factor.

Assembling Eqs. (11–16), (11–17), and the Coulomb factor, we obtain for the square of the matrix element:

$$|H'_{if}|^2 = \frac{G^2}{V^2} |M_{if}|^2 F(Z, E_{\mathrm{e}}), \tag{11–20}$$

where M_{if} is the overlap integral of the final and initial wave functions of the nucleus

$$M_{if} = \int_{\text{nucleus}} \psi_{f\mathrm{N}}^* \psi_{i\mathrm{N}} \, d\tau. \tag{11–21}$$

This nuclear matrix element or overlap integral between the wave functions of the parent and daughter nuclei can only be computed in a few cases where the structure of the nuclei is reasonably well known. For the neutron decay, for instance, it is simply unity (see Section 11–5).

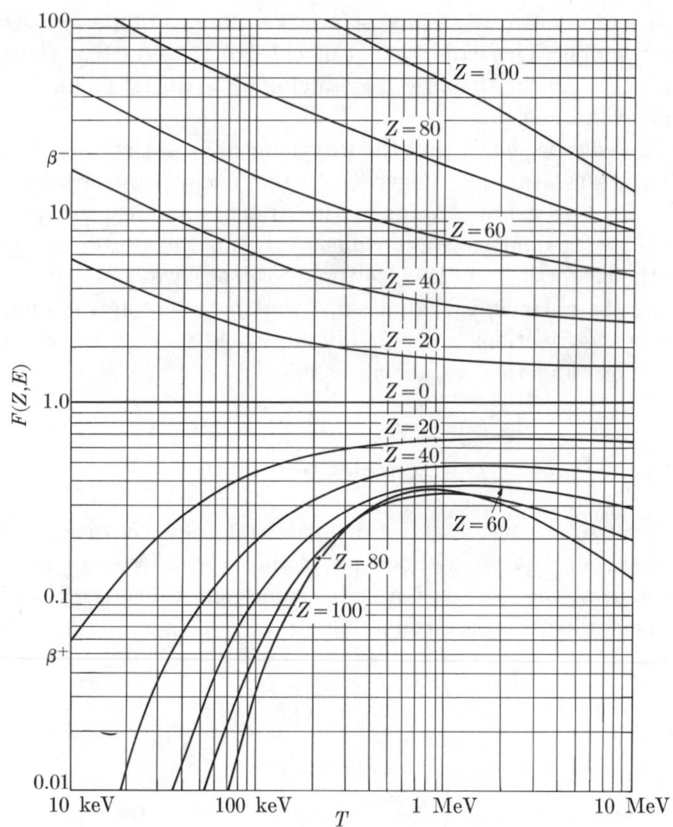

Fig. 11–10. The Coulomb factor (Fermi function) $F(Z, E)$ plotted vs. T, the kinetic energy of the electron or positron. (Prepared from *Tables for the Analysis of Beta Spectra,* National Bureau of Standards, Applied Mathematics Series, 13.)

We now proceed to calculate the last factor, dN/dE_0 in Eq. (11–14). For simplicity of calculation, assume that the volume V in which our system is enclosed is a cubical box with side L and with one corner at the origin of a cartesian coordinate system. We are going to count the number of states that each lepton can occupy in a given momentum interval, and we should, by rights, use the momentum wave functions (11–17) with periodic boundary conditions. Since the standing wave type functions for a particle in a box are more familiar to some readers, we shall use them, remembering that we can always construct standing waves from traveling waves. We consequently make the walls of the box impenetrable. The nucleus is inside the box, but its volume is small compared with the volume of the box, so that its presence can be neglected for the computations to follow. A set of eigenfunctions for a particle in a cubical box can be written in the form

$$\psi = A \sin k_x x \sin k_y y \sin k_z z, \tag{11–22}$$

in which the values of k_x, k_y, and k_z are restricted by the boundary conditions at $x = L$, $y = L$, and $z = L$, such that

$$k_x L = n_x \pi, \quad \text{etc.} \qquad n_x = 1, 2, 3, \ldots$$

The square of the total momentum of the particle is given by

$$p^2 = (k_x^2 + k_y^2 + k_z^2)\hbar^2 = (\pi^2\hbar^2/L^2)(n_x^2 + n_y^2 + n_z^2). \tag{11-23}$$

Each set of integral values of n_x, n_y, and n_z clearly gives one state for the particles with an associated value of p^2. We now ask how many different sets of n_x, n_y, and n_z give a numerical momentum below a certain value p. The answer can be found most easily by plottine, in a cartesian coordinate system the values of n_x, n_y, and n_z along the three axes (Fig. 11–11). Each unit volume in the first quadrant of this coordinate system then contains one point, corresponding to one state of the particle. The positive numbers n_x, n_y, and n_z are components of a vector $\mathbf{n}$, the maximum length of which is limited when there is a limit for the momentum p. The relationship between the two is given by Eq. (11–23) as

$$n_{\max} = \frac{pL}{\pi\hbar}.$$

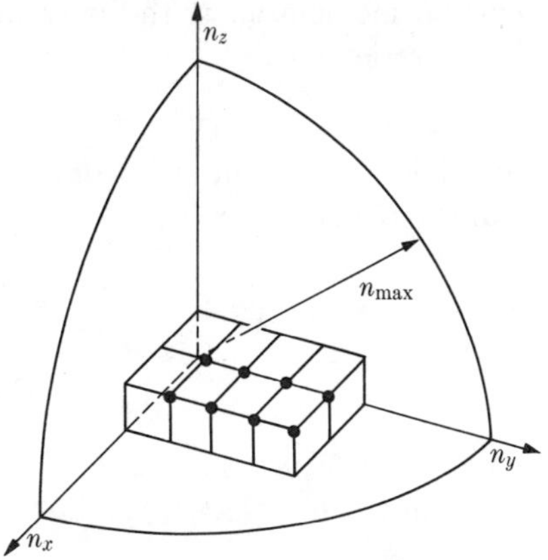

Fig. 11–11. Each point in this diagram represents a possible set of integers n_x, n_y, and n_z, and therefore a possible lepton state.

The total number of points, each of which represents a lepton state, can then be found by counting the number of unit volumes in the first quadrant within the distance $n_{\max}$ from the origin. This is equal to one-eighth the volume of a sphere with radius $n_{\max}$. The number of states with momenta lower than p is therefore

$$N = \frac{1}{8}\,\frac{4}{3}\,\pi\left(\frac{pL}{\pi\hbar}\right)^3 = \frac{Vp^3}{6\pi^2\hbar^3},$$

where $V = L^3$ is the volume of the box. The number of states in the momentum interval dp between p and $p + dp$ is found by differentiation:

$$dN = Vp^2\,dp/2\pi^2\hbar^3. \tag{11-24}$$

Now let us stop to find our bearings before we proceed. What we are seeking initially is not the total disintegration constant λ, but the shape of the momentum spectrum of the electrons. This can be called the partial disintegration constant or the probability for decay into the momentum interval between p_e and

$p_e + dp_e$. In terms of the formula for λ (Eq. 11–14), we can express this partial probability as

$$P(p_e)\,dp_e = \left(\frac{d\lambda}{dp_e}\right) dp_e, \tag{11–25}$$

where λ is regarded as a function of p_e. We will, however, compute $P(p_e)$ directly and not as a derivative of λ. We shall later integrate $P(p_e)$ to find λ.

How do we compute $P(p_e)$ from Eq. (11–14)? First, we imagine that our experimental apparatus is so outstanding that we can actually determine into which state the electron is emitted. Let us label this state k. What is the probability for decay with the electron going into state k? This is given by Eq. (11–14) with dN/dE_0 now being the density of neutrino states, since the neutrino momentum is the only momentum that is free to vary. The total disintegration energy is

$$E_0 = E_e + E_\nu \tag{11–26}$$

and E_e is constant in our gedanken experiment so that $dE_0 = dE_\nu$. Further, from the relativistic relationship

$$E_\nu^2 = (m_\nu c^2)^2 + (p_\nu c)^2 \tag{11–27}$$

we obtain

$$dp_\nu = \frac{E_\nu}{p_\nu c^2}\,dE_\nu = \frac{E_\nu}{p_\nu c^2}\,dE_0. \tag{11–28}$$

Combining Eqs. (11–24), (11–26), (11–27), and (11–28), we find

$$\frac{dN_\nu}{dE_0} = \frac{V}{2\pi^2\hbar^3c^3}\,(E_0 - E_e)[(E_0 - E_e)^2 - (m_\nu c^2)^2]^{1/2}. \tag{11–29}$$

The reason why we have taken such pains in substituting functions of E_e for E_ν and p_ν is that we want our final expression in terms of measurable quantities.

The probability per unit time for decay leaving the electron in the specified state k can now be found by combining Eqs. (11–14), (11–20), and (11–29):

$$\lambda_k = \frac{G^2|M_{if}|^2}{\pi V\hbar^4c^3}\,F(Z, E_e)(E_0 - E_e)[(E_0 - E_e)^2 - (m_\nu c^2)^2]^{1/2}. \tag{11–30}$$

The total probability per unit time for decay into any one of the electron states in the momentum interval dp_e is now found simply by multiplying (11–30) by the number of electron states in the interval. This is given by Eq. (11–24). We find that

$$\begin{aligned} P(p_e)\,dp_e &= \lambda_k\,dN_e \\ &= \frac{G^2|M_{if}|^2}{2\pi^3\hbar^7c^3}\,p_e^2F(Z, E_e)(E_0 - E_e)[(E_0 - E_e)^2 - (m_\nu c^2)^2]^{1/2}\,dp_e. \end{aligned} \tag{11–31}$$

This is the theoretical prediction for the spectrum of electrons observed in an allowed beta transition. It is expressed in terms of both the electron momentum and its total energy because this gives a somewhat simpler expression. Of course we use the relativistic relationship,

$$E_e^2 = (m_0c^2)^2 + (p_ec)^2, \tag{11–32}$$

to substitute energy for momentum or vice versa. As usual, m_0 is the electron rest mass.

The neutrino rest mass m_ν has been left in the calculations to enable us to demonstrate through a comparison between Eq. (11–31) and experimental data that m_ν is zero or very small (Section 11–4). Other evidence is given in Section 11–9 to the effect that the neutrino (antineutrino) rest mass must be exactly zero. With $m_\nu = 0$, Eq. (11–31) becomes

$$P(p)\,dp = \frac{G^2|M_{if}|^2}{2\pi^3\hbar^7c^3}\,p^2(E_0 - E)^2F(Z, E), \tag{11–33}$$

where we now have dropped the subscript e for the electron momentum and energy.

The shape of the beta spectrum is mainly determined by the factors p^2 and $(E_0 - E)^2$. The first of these factors makes a spectrum which, when not corrected for the Coulomb effect $F(Z, E)$, approaches zero as a parabola for zero momentum. The second factor makes it approach zero for $E = E_0$. This is called the *endpoint* of the beta spectrum, and it is related to the total kinetic energy released, T_0 or Q, by the equation

$$E_0 = E_{\text{max}} = T_0 + m_0c^2 = Q + m_0c^2. \tag{11–34}$$

11–4 Kurie Plots; Example of Beta Spectra

Equation (11–33) gives the form of the momentum spectrum of the electrons emitted in an allowed beta transition. We can, of course, compare this formula directly with any experimental spectrum for the purpose of

(1) testing the theory of the beta process,
(2) possibly gaining information about whether the process is allowed or forbidden,
(3) finding the value of the matrix element $|M_{if}|$.

Point 3 assumes that the factor G^2 is known and that the absolute value of the decay probability $P(p)$ is determined. Most often, only relative values are measured, partly because the samples used are so small (a few micrograms) that it is difficult to determine the number of unstable atoms in the sample, but also because the matrix element can be extracted more directly from the measured half-life (see Section 11–5).

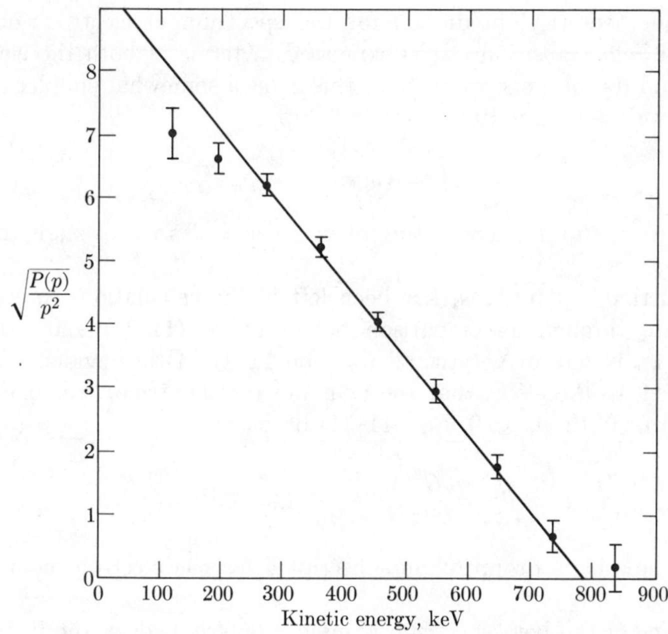

Fig. 11–12. Kurie plot of the $n(\beta^-)H^1$ spectrum (Fig. 11–2). [From J. M. Robson, *Phys. Rev.* **83,** 349 (1951).]

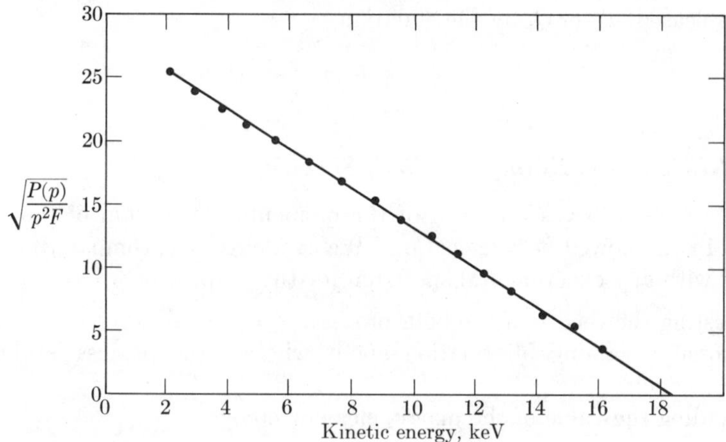

Fig. 11–13. Kurie plot of the $H^3(\beta^-)He^3$ spectrum. [From S. C. Curran, J. Angus, and A. L. Cockroft, *Phil. Mag.* Ser. 7, **40,** 53 (1949).]

To deal with points 1 and 2, and also to allow a more precise determination of the endpoint E_0, instead of plotting the experimental spectrum $P_{\text{exp}}(p)$ directly, we plot the quantity

$$\sqrt{P_{\text{exp}}(p)/F(Z, E)p^2} \quad \text{vs.} \quad E \quad \text{or} \quad T.$$

As can easily be seen from Eq. (11–33), this so-called Kurie plot should, if the theory is right, be a straight line intersecting the energy axis at $E = E_0$.

Figure 11–12 shows as an example the neutron spectrum (Fig. 11–2) replotted as outlined in the preceding paragraph. In this case ($Z = 1$), the factor $F(Z, E)$ is so nearly constant over the extent of the spectrum that it has been neglected. The plot is linear above 300 keV, but the points break away from the straight line at lower energies. This is presumably caused by an instrumental error. The measurement of the beta spectrum from neutron decay is complicated by the fact that the source is a beam of neutrons rather than a solid, liquid, or containable gas.

As a second example, we show in Fig. 11–13 a Kurie plot for the beta spectrum of H^3 obtained by S. C. Curran *et al.** The sample is tritium gas, and the spectrometer used in this case is a proportional gas counter. Because of its low endpoint ($T_0 = 18$ keV), the H^3 spectrum shape is particularly sensitive to the value of the neutrino rest mass m_ν (see Eq. 11–31). It has been possible to set an upper limit of 250 eV for the neutrino rest energy from a study of the straightness of the Kurie plot for the H^3 spectrum.

Figure 11–14 shows, as a third example, a Kurie plot of β^- data for Sc^{47} taken by the aid of a scintillation spectrometer.† This shows a composite spectrum of two beta transitions, the highest energy member with an endpoint $T_0 = 600$ keV. A straight line is drawn from this endpoint following the high-energy part of the plot. Assuming that this represents an allowed transition, the line can be extrapolated to lower energies, and the difference between $P(p)$ represented by this line and the observed spectrum can be calculated. When a new Kurie plot is made of this difference, a second straight line is obtained with an endpoint at 440 keV. This, then, represents another branch of the beta transition, also with an allowed-shape spectrum and going to an excited state at 160 keV in the daughter nucleus Ti^{47}. The observation of a 160-keV gamma line from the Sc^{47} source supports this view. As a further check, Graves and Suri measured the spectrum of only those beta particles that were observed in coincidence with a 160-keV gamma quantum. This spectrum is also shown in Fig. 11–14. Within the limits of error, it is also straight, and with an endpoint coinciding with the endpoint of the low-energy component of the composite spectrum, as expected.

---

* S. C. Curran, J. Angus, and A. L. Cockroft, *Phil. Mag.* Ser. 7, **40,** 53 (1949). See also S. C. Curran, *Physica* **18,** 1161 (1952).

† W. E. Graves and S. K. Suri, *Phys. Rev.* **101,** 1368 (1956).

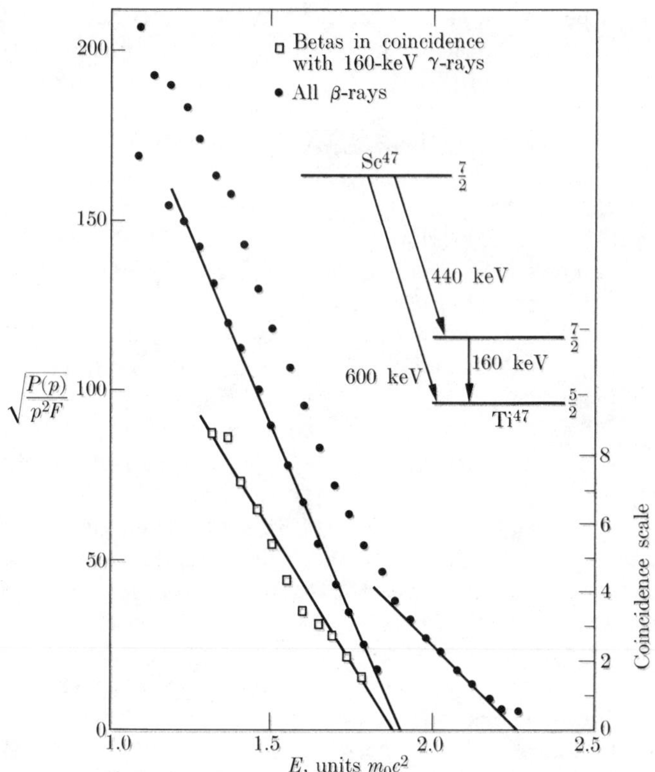

Fig. 11–14. Kurie plots of the beta spectrum from the $Sc^{47}(\beta^-)Ti^{47}$ decay resolved into its one component with endpoint at 600 keV and another with endpoint at 440 keV. Also Kurie plot of beta spectrum in coincidence with a 160-keV gamma ray. [From W. E. Graves and S. K. Suri, *Phys. Rev.* **101,** 1368 (1956).]

As a final example, we show in Fig. 11–15 a standard Kurie plot of the *forbidden* beta spectrum (Section 11–6) of Y^{91} measured with a lens spectrometer.* This plot is not straight, but by applying a special correction factor which is applicable to this kind of transition, it can be made straight (Section 11–6, see also Fig. 11–18).

A very large number of beta spectra have been carefully measured and analyzed in the same way as described above for the examples chosen. From the straightness of the Kurie plots, it can be concluded that the Fermi theory of an allowed beta transition is essentially correct. It should be mentioned that the simple theory presented here requires some minor modifications in order to give perfect agreement with experiments; notably, at low energies a correction to the electron wave function is necessitated by the presence of atomic electrons around the nucleus.

---

* L. M. Langer and H. C. Price, Jr., *Phys. Rev.* **75,** 1109 (1949).

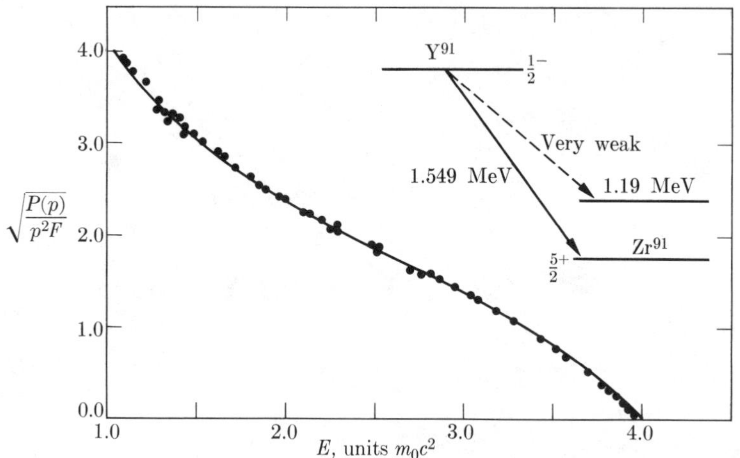

Fig. 11-15. Standard Kurie plot of the forbidden $Y^{91}(\beta^-)Zr^{91}$ spectrum. [From L. M. Langer and H. C. Price, Jr., *Phys. Rev.* **75,** 1109 (1949).]

11-5 Comparative Half-Lives

Equation (11-33) gives the decay probability per second and per unit momentum interval for an allowed beta transition. Clearly, if we integrate the spectrum from 0 to $p_{\max}$, we get a formula for the total decay probability, that is, the disintegration constant λ. Performing this integration, we obtain

$$\lambda = \frac{\ln 2}{t_{1/2}} = \int_0^{p_{\max}} P(p)\, dp$$
$$= \frac{m_0^5 G^2 c^4 |M_{if}|^2}{2\pi^3\hbar^7} \int_0^{p_{\max}} F(Z, E)\, \frac{p^2}{m_0^2c^2}\, \frac{(E_0 - E)^2}{m_0^2c^4}\, \frac{dp}{m_0c} \cdot \tag{11-35}$$

The integrand is a function of p, E_0, and Z and has been made nondimensional by division with the factor $m_0^5c^7$. The integral

$$f(Z, E_0) = \int_0^{p_{\max}} F(Z, E)\, \frac{p^2}{m_0^2c^2}\, \frac{(E_0 - E)^2}{m_0^2c^4}\, \frac{dp}{m_0c} \tag{11-36}$$

has been evaluated numerically by Feenberg and Trigg* for the ranges of Z and E_0 which are of practical interest. These results are shown in Fig. 11-16 for both β^- and β^+ decay. By combining Eqs. (11-35) and (11-36), we get

$$f(Z, E_0)t_{1/2} = \frac{2\pi^3 \ln 2\hbar^7}{m_0^5 G^2 c^4 |M_{if}|^2} \cdot \tag{11-37}$$

---

* E. Feenberg and G. Trigg, *Rev. Mod. Phys.* **22,** 399 (1950).

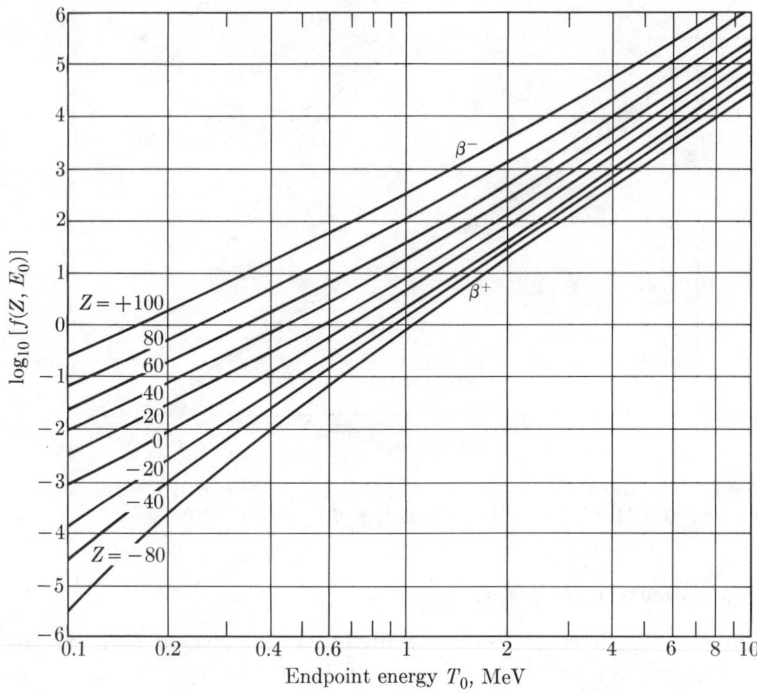

Fig. 11–16. Integral function $f(Z, E_0)$. (From R. D. Evans, *The Atomic Nucleus*, New York: McGraw-Hill Book Company, 1955 p. 560. Reproduced by permission.)

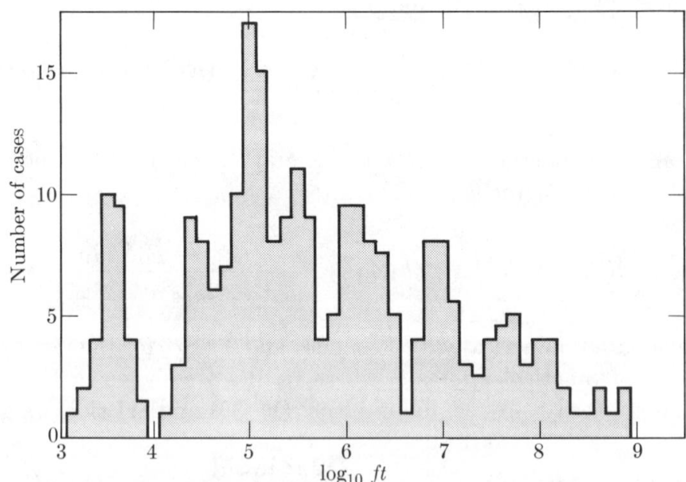

Fig. 11–17. Histogram showing number of β^- radioactive nuclides vs. their comparative half-life ft. [Adapted from E. Feenberg and G. Trigg, *Rev. Mod. Phys.* **22,** 399 (1950).]

The product $f(Z, E_0)t_{1/2}$ is called the *comparative half-life*, because the energy-dependent part of the half-life or decay constant has been divided out. Equation (11–37) shows that the comparative half-life, also called the *ft*-value, is proportional to the inverse square of the matrix element $|M_{if}|$. Assuming that the value of the constant G is known and that the transition is allowed, we can determine $|M_{if}|$ simply from a measurement of the half-life $t_{1/2}$.

In some transitions where a neutron changes into a proton or vice versa but otherwise the structure of the nucleus remains practically unchanged, the nuclear overlap integral is approximately unity. The sum over different combinations of spin states may give an additional integer factor for $|M_{if}|^2$. For beta transitions between $J = 0$ states of similar structure, the total matrix element is $|M_{if}|^2 \approx 2$. The *ft*-values for these transitions can be used to estimate the magnitude of the coupling constant G. We use the $O^{14}(\beta^+)N^{14}$ decay as an example. The important parameters are:

$$t_{1/2} = 72.5 \text{ s}, \qquad T_0 = 1.810 \text{ MeV},$$
$$f(Z, E_0) = 42.8, \qquad ft = 3103 \text{ s}.$$

With these numbers inserted into Eq. (11–37), we obtain

$$G \approx 1.4 \times 10^{-62} \text{ J-m}^3 \approx 0.9 \times 10^{-4} \text{ MeV-F}^3.$$

It is customary in beta spectroscopy to quote the value of $\log ft$ for a decay rather than the matrix element. Equation (11–37), which gives the relationship between ft and M_{if}, is, of course, only valid for allowed transitions, but this does not deter beta spectroscopists from using the same formula (11–36) for f in cases where the process is suspected of being forbidden. Since the lifetimes for comparable Z and $E_{\max}$ are much longer for forbidden transitions, the $\log ft$-values will then, naturally, be much higher. Figure 11–17 shows a histogram of the frequency of observed $\log ft$-values.

One would perhaps expect, or hope, that the $\log ft$-value would clearly separate allowed and forbidden transitions. Such is not the case, however. The group of decays included in Fig. 11–17 with $\log ft$-values between 3 and 4 are definitely allowed, but so are many of the others with higher *ft*-values. The group between 3 and 4 has indeed been called *superallowed* transitions, characterized by an overlap integral of the nuclear wave functions close to unity. The neutron decay and the H^3 decay (Fig. 11–13) are included in this group, together with the decays of all known mirror nuclei (Section 1–13). A typical beta decay involving a mirror pair is

$${}_7N^{13}(\beta^+){}_6C^{13}.$$

The structures of the two nuclides are practically identical, except for the fact that the odd particle is a proton in one case and a neutron in the other.

11-6 Allowed and Forbidden Transitions; Selection Rules

The theory developed in Section 11–3 is applicable when the electron and neutrino both leave the nucleus with zero orbital angular momentum. The nuclear angular momentum will then be unchanged if the spin vectors of the neutrino and the electron are antiparallel (singlet), and it may or may not change by one unit if they are parallel (triplet). Accordingly, we get the following selection rules for allowed transitions:

Singlet: $\Delta J = 0$, no parity change;

Triplet: $\Delta J = 0, \pm 1$ (but no $J_i = 0$ to $J_f = 0$), no parity change.

The singlet and triplet cases are called beta decays by Fermi and Gamow-Teller interactions, respectively. The two types of decay are observed to proceed with approximately, but not exactly, the same speed. The O^{14} decay discussed above is an example of Fermi interaction, and consequently the calculated coupling constant G is the appropriate constant for the purely singlet transitions.

Entering now on the subject of forbidden transitions, we recall that in Section 11–3, we treated the neutrino and electron wave functions as plane waves, except for the relatively minor Coulomb correction factor $F(Z, E)$. The plane waves can be expanded in a series with terms having characteristic values of the orbital angular momentum l, as in Chapter 3, and it is only the $l = 0$ term that carries the full amplitude of the plane wave at the origin (nucleus). The higher orbital angular momentum waves have very small amplitudes inside the nuclear volume. Hence, the overlap integral (11–16) will be very small when the leptons are emitted with orbital angular momentum different from zero. The effect, of course, is to make the lifetimes for these forbidden transitions

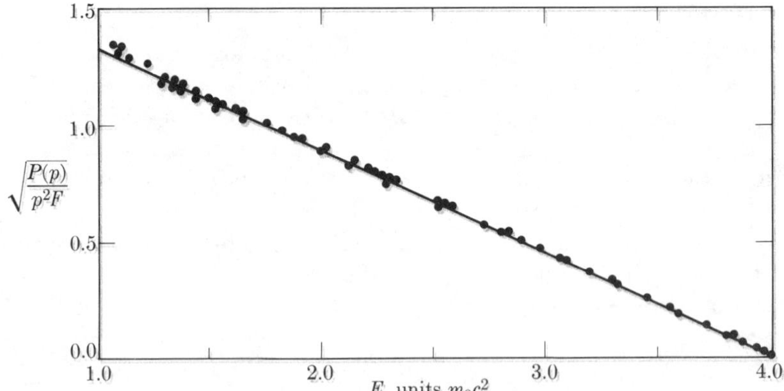

Fig. 11-18. Corrected Kurie plot of the forbidden $Y^{91}(\beta^-)Zr^{91}$ spectrum. [From L. M. Langer and H. C. Price, Jr., *Phys. Rev.* **75**, 1109 (1949).]

Table 11-1. Classification of beta transitions according to *ft*-values

Type of transition	Selection rules	*ft*
Superallowed	$\Delta J = 0, \pm 1$ (no)	1000–4000
Allowed	$\Delta J = 0, \pm 1$ (no)	2×10^4–10^6
First forbidden	$\Delta J = 0, \pm 1$ (yes)	10^6–10^8
Unique first forbidden	$\Delta J = \pm 2$ (yes)	10^8–10^9
Second forbidden	$\Delta J = \pm 2$ (no)	2×10^{10}–2×10^{13}
Unique second forbidden	$\Delta J = \pm 3$ (no)	10^{12}
Third forbidden	$\Delta J = \pm 3$ (yes)	10^{18}
Unique third forbidden	$\Delta J = \pm 4$ (yes)	4×10^{15}
Fourth forbidden	$\Delta J = \pm 4$ (no)	10^{23}
Unique fourth forbidden	$\Delta J = \pm 5$ (no)	10^{19}

much longer, on the average, than for allowed transitions. In general, there will also be some effects on the shape of the spectrum.

The formal theory of beta decay employing relativistic wave mechanics gives relatively simple expressions for the shape of the spectra in some of the cases of forbidden transitions, called *unique* forbidden transitions. The selection rules applying to these unique forbidden transitions, as well as to all other beta transitions, are given in Table 11-1, together with the ranges of *ft*-values normally observed for each class. Approximate correction factors a_n to be applied to Eq. (11-33) for unique forbidden transitions are given by the following formulas:

$$\text{First} \qquad a_1 = \frac{1}{(m_0c)^2}\,[p_e^2 + p_\nu^2], \tag{11-38}$$

$$\text{Second} \qquad a_2 = \frac{1}{(m_0c)^4}\,[p_e^4 + p_\nu^4 + \tfrac{10}{3}p_e^2p_\nu^2], \tag{11-39}$$

$$\text{Third} \qquad a_3 = \frac{1}{(m_0c)^6}\,[p_e^6 + p_\nu^6 + 7p_e^2p_\nu^2(p_e^2 + p_\nu^2)]. \tag{11-40}$$

These expressions are written in terms of the electron and neutrino momenta to keep them simple. For the neutrino momentum we can, as before, substitute $p_\nu = (E_0 - E)/c$.

In Fig. 11-15 we showed a standard Kurie plot of the unique first forbidden spectrum of Y^{91}. In Fig. 11-18, this spectrum is replotted with the factor a_1 (Eq. 11-38) included. We see from Fig. 11-18 that this modified Kurie plot is straight, indicating that the theory of beta decay is also correct for these forbidden transitions.

11-7 Electron Capture

In electron capture, an orbital electron, venturing inside the nuclear volume, reacts with a proton to form a neutrino and a neutron. The theory of electron capture is similar to that of ordinary beta decay, except that the electron is now in a definite energy state and the electron wave function is the atomic wave function of a K- or an L-electron, etc. The neutrino, of course, receives all the available energy in the decay, except for the negligible portion given to the recoiling nucleus.

The total decay probability $\lambda = \ln 2/t_{1/2}$ for electron capture can be found from Eq. (11–14), where now dN/dE refers to the density of neutrino states only. This is found from Eq. (11–24) to be

$$\frac{dN}{dE} = \frac{Vp_\nu^2\,dp_\nu}{2\pi^2\hbar^3\,dE} = \frac{VE_{0c}^2}{2\pi^2\hbar^3c^3},$$

where we have substituted $E_\nu = E_{0c}$, the energy released in electron capture (Q_{EC} of Eq. 11–6), and $dE = dE_\nu = c\,dp_\nu$. Following essentially the same development as in Section 11–3, we replace the amplitude $V^{-1/2}$ for the plane electron wave with the wave amplitude of an atomic electron in a K- or L-shell, etc. Since K-capture represents the case of highest actuality, we write for the electron wave amplitude at the origin

$$\psi_{\mathrm{e}} = \psi_{\mathrm{K}}(0)$$

and obtain, using Eq. (11–14):

$$\lambda = 2\,\frac{2\pi}{\hbar}\,G^2|M_{if}|^2|\psi_{\mathrm{K}}(0)|^2\,\frac{E_{0c}^2}{2\pi^2\hbar^3c^3}. \tag{11–41}$$

The first factor 2 in this expression results from the fact that there are two electrons in the K-shell. The amplitude of the K-electron wave function at the origin is* approximately

$$\psi_{\mathrm{K}}(0) = \pi^{-1/2}\left(\frac{Zm_0e^2}{4\pi\epsilon_0\hbar^2}\right)^{3/2}. \tag{11–42}$$

With this inserted into Eq. (11–41), we obtain

$$\lambda_{\mathrm{K}} = \frac{G^2Z^3m_0^3e^6|M_{if}|^2E_{0c}^2}{32\pi^5\epsilon_0^3\hbar^{10}c^3}. \tag{11–43}$$

The nuclear matrix element for electron capture is the same as for β^+ decay. We can therefore find a formula for the branching ratio $\lambda_{\mathrm{K}}/\lambda_{\beta^+}$, which is

---

* See, for instance, R. B. Leighton, *Principles of Modern Physics*, New York: McGraw-Hill Book Company, 1959, p. 183.

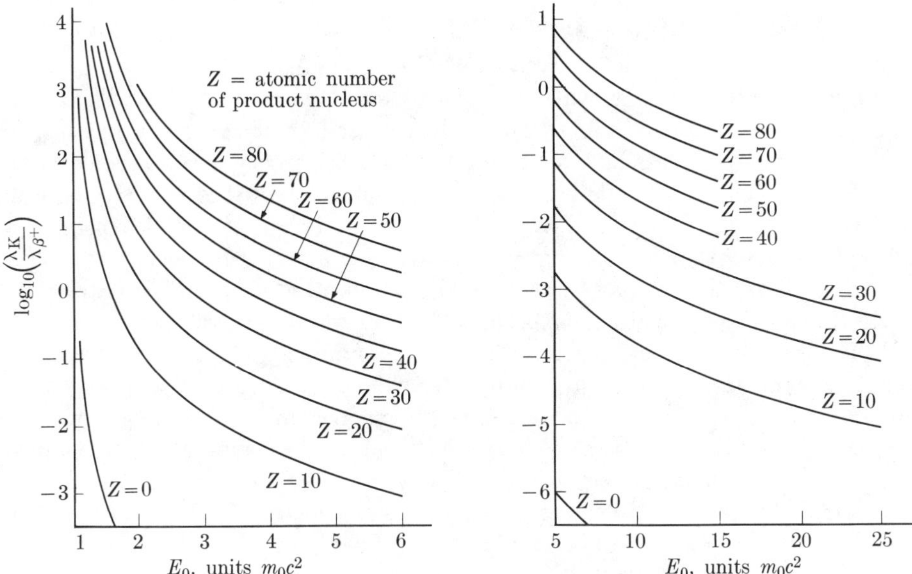

Fig. 11–19. Logarithmic plot of K-capture to β^+ branching ratio vs. disintegration energy. (From M. A. Preston, *Physics of the Nucleus*, Reading, Mass.: Addison-Wesley Publishing Company, 1962, p. 441.)

independent of M_{if}. Dividing Eq. (11–43) by (11–35), we obtain

$$\frac{\lambda_K}{\lambda_{\beta^+}} = \frac{e^6 Z^3 E_{0c}^2}{16\pi^2 \epsilon_0^3 \hbar^3 c^7 m_0^2 f(Z, E_0)}. \tag{11–44}$$

Figure 11–19 is a plot of this branching ratio vs. the total energy of the emitted positron. In the range where only electron capture is energetically possible, the branching ratio is, of course, infinite.

Experimental study of the electron-capture process is not quite so convenient as β^- and β^+ spectroscopy. The neutrino is practically unobservable, so that the only way to detect electron capture in practice is to observe the atomic processes following the disappearance of a K- (or an L-) electron. For K-capture, one can observe the K-lines in the x-ray spectrum, and for L-capture, the L-lines. It is also usually possible to observe Auger electrons following K-capture. An Auger electron is an atomic electron receiving enough kinetic energy to be ejected, usually from the L-shell, when another electron falls from the same shell to fill a vacancy in the K-shell. The process competes with photon (x-ray) emission and may be more convenient to observe experimentally.

If the daughter *nucleus* is left in an excited state after electron capture, the emission of a subsequent gamma ray, of course, is a detectable sign of the total process.

11–8 Parity Violation in Beta Decay

The theory of macroscopic physics includes a number of conservation laws, notably the laws of conservation of energy, linear momentum, and angular momentum. In atomic and nuclear physics, the same laws apply; and in addition, we also have a law expressing the fact that parity is conserved. That a system possesses a definite parity essentially means that it is equal to its own mirror image. If parity is conserved, the mirror image of a real experiment should also correspond to an experiment that can actually be performed. The law of conservation of parity rests on the assumption that the potentials involved in a nuclear or atomic experiment are mirror-symmetric. In the macroscopic world, systems of course are not mirror-symmetric in general; a human being, for instance, is not equal to his own mirror image. A helix is not equal to its own mirror image, and for this reason systems that are not mirror-symmetric are said to possess helicity. Even systems as small as organic molecules possess helicity; all life on this planet consists of organic material with one kind of helicity. Molecules of the opposite helicity could form living organisms with the same properties, and it is possible that such life exists on other planets.

As an example of a macroscopic experiment that apparently violates the parity law, we study the deflection of a compass needle under the influence of a magnetic field from a current conductor (Fig. 11–20a). The north pole of the compass needle in the real experiment, which is shown to the left, will deflect in the direction toward the reader. We recognize the north pole on the needle in the real experiment and in the mirror as the tip which is painted black, for instance. In the mirror we also see this tip being deflected toward the reader. If, however, the experiment we see in the mirror were a real experiment, the north pole of the compass needle would deflect in the opposite direc-

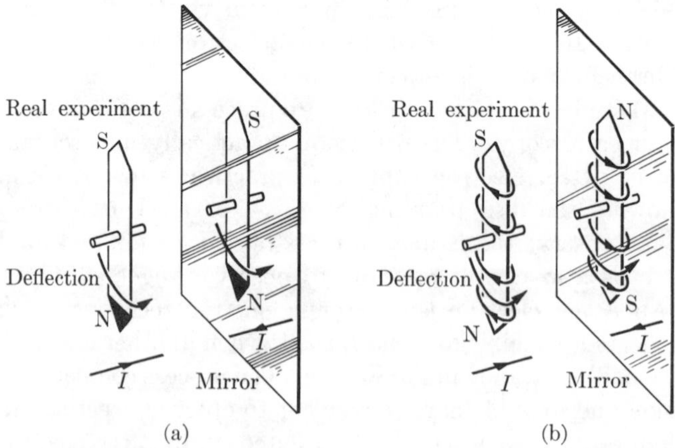

Fig. 11–20. Study of parity conservation in a magnetic-deflection experiment.

tion. It appears then as if parity is violated in this experiment. However, if we look at the same experiment on the atomic scale, as in Fig. 11–20(b), the situation is different. Here, in the real experiment, the currents (spinning electrons) producing the magnetic field in the compass needle are indicated, and in the mirror we see the images of these currents. The north pole of the compass needle in this *true mirror image* on the atomic scale is pointing up. Therefore the experiment seen in the mirror can actually be performed; that is, the deflection will be in the direction out of the plane of the paper just as seen in the mirror. The law of conservation of parity is therefore not violated on the atomic scale.

The conclusion to be drawn from this and a vast number of other experiments on the atomic scale is that, on this scale, nature appears to be perfectly symmetric, or, expressed differently, the systems appear to have definite parities. However, it is perfectly possible for us to combine atoms into molecules and more complicated bodies that are not like their own mirror images, that is, they possess helicity (right-handedness or left-handedness), which means that they do not have a definite parity.

Strong indications of parity violation in a process governed by the so-called weak interaction, of which beta decay is an example, came first from elementary-particle physics. Two particles called the τ^+ and θ^+ mesons had been observed to have, within experimental errors, identical masses and identical lifetimes. The only thing that distinguished them from each other was the fact that one decays into three π-mesons, which represent a negative parity state, and the other decays into two π-mesons, which represent a positive parity state. Therefore, if parity was to be conserved, the particles could not be identical. We now believe that they are identical, and we have given the same label, K^+, to these mesons (see Chapter 15).

In 1956 T. D. Lee and C. N. Yang* pointed out that there existed no experimental proof of parity conservation in weak interactions. They also suggested several experiments to test whether or not parity is conserved. The first of these experiments to be carried out concerns the angular distribution of beta particles emitted from aligned Co^{60} nuclei.† The sample is actually a nitrate in which a high degree of alignment of the *atomic* angular momentum vectors can be achieved by an external field at very low temperatures. This produces an internal magnetic field which is strong enough to align a large percentage of the nuclear angular momentum vectors.

In Fig. 11–21, the C. S. Wu experiment is sketched to the left of our imaginary mirror. Assume that there is an anistropy in the intensity of the emitted β^- radiation such that there are more electrons emitted upward, that is, in a

* T. D. Lee and C. N. Yang, *Phys. Rev.* **104**, 254 (1956).
† C. S. Wu, E. Ambler, R. W. Hayward, D. D. Hoppes, and R. P. Hudson, *Phys. Rev.* **105**, 1413 (1957).

direction opposite to the direction of the angular momentum vector, than in any other direction. Look in the mirror. The predominant direction of beta radiation is seen to be up, as in the real experiment, but the angular momentum vector has changed direction. In the mirror we therefore see the electrons being predominantly emitted in the direction of the angular momentum vector. Obviously then, the experiment that we see in the mirror cannot be performed in reality because the predicted results contradict the results we have assumed for the original experiment. Therefore observation of an asymmetry of the kind assumed for the real experiment would constitute a proof of parity violation.

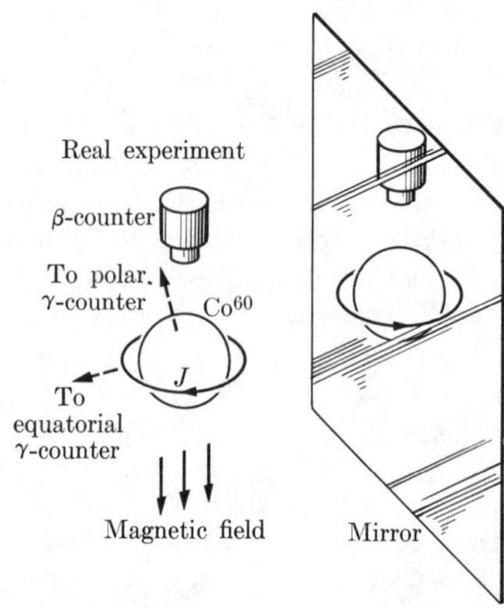

Fig. 11–21. Parity violation experiment. [From C. S. Wu *et al.*, *Phys. Rev.* **105,** 1413 (1957).]

If, instead of assuming a single direction of predominance, we had assumed two, namely parallel and antiparallel to the angular momentum vector, the experiment would be identical to its own mirror image. The parity law would then presumably rest in peace. It was known to Wu and coworkers that the latter kind of anisotropy could be detected in the gamma radiation from aligned Co^{60} nuclei (see Section 9–7). They therefore used two gamma counters to check the alignment. The sample was cooled to 4.2°K by liquid helium and further cooled to below 0.01°K by adiabatic demagnetization.* The Co^{60} nuclei were then aligned by an external field, as indicated, and the counting rates observed as a function of time as the sample warmed up again. The experiment was then repeated with the magnetic field in the opposite direction.

Figure 11–22 shows the results. To the left is plotted the counting rate in the two gamma counters. The polar counter read lower than the equatorial counter for both field directions, as expected for $E2$ radiation (Section 9–7). The beta counter, however, indicated that more electrons were emitted in the direction antiparallel to the angular momentum vector than parallel to it. This is proof of parity violation in the beta process.

* The sample is an anisotropic crystal. With the aid of an external magnetic field, electron spins are oriented in the direction of maximum susceptibility while the crystal is in thermal contact with the liquid helium. The heat of orientation is absorbed by the helium. The sample is thereafter isolated from the helium, and the magnetic field is removed. The electrons then again become randomly oriented, and in the process absorb energy from the crystal lattice which thereby is cooled. The magnetic field needed for the parity experiment is applied in the direction of minimum susceptibility. This prevents excessive heating of the crystal again.

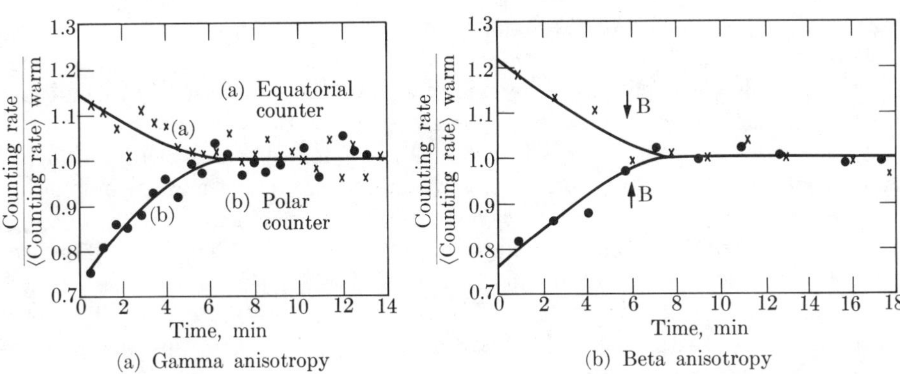

Fig. 11-22. Results of parity violation experiment. [From C. S. Wu *et al.*, *Phys. Rev.* **105,** 1413 (1957).]

The results of the experiment described here and of others involving helicity in weak interactions point to the neutrino (antineutrino) as the culprit of parity violation. The antineutrino involved in the β^- decay is presumed to have its angular momentum vector aligned with its momentum vector; it moves as a right-handed screw, whereas the neutrino moves as a left-handed screw (Section 11-10). In the Co^{60} decay, the transition is from a 5^+ state to a 4^+ (Gamow-Teller transition). To conserve angular momentum, the spin vectors of both the electron and the antineutrino must be aligned with the angular momentum vector of the nucleus. The antineutrino, because it behaves as a right-handed screw, will be ejected predominantly in the direction of the angular momentum vectors. Because in the Gamow-Teller type decay there is a correlation (or rather, an anticorrelation) between the direction of motion of the electron and the antineutrino, the experiment yields the results described above. Note that there is no change in parity of the nuclear state in this allowed transition. The neutrino violates the parity law, and the electron compensates for it.

11-9 Neutrinos

As mentioned earlier in this chapter, the existence of neutrinos was first postulated to bring the observations of beta decay into accord with the conservation laws of energy and angular momentum. The beautiful agreement between Fermi's theory of beta decay and the observed spectra provided further credulence to the neutrino hypothesis. The straightness of the Kurie plots for low-energy beta transitions, particularly the 18-keV decay of H^3, is evidence of zero or very low rest mass for the neutrino.* Further indirect evidence that the rest mass is indeed exactly zero is discussed in Section 11-10.

---

* L. M. Langer and R. J. D. Moffat, *Phys. Rev.* **88,** 689 (1952); and D. R. Hamilton, W. P. Alford, and L. Gross, *Phys. Rev.* **92,** 1521 (1953).

Several measurements of the balance of linear momentum in beta processes have been performed, again demonstrating that an undetected particle is being emitted and that this particle is carrying away linear momentum of magnitude E_ν/c. For example, Kofoed-Hansen, with a specially designed recoil spectrometer,* measured a recoil energy of 9.58 ± 0.18 eV for Cl^{37} ions being produced by electron capture in Ar^{37}. From this we can calculate the momentum of the recoiling nucleus. Equating it with the neutrino momentum and putting $E_\nu = p_\nu c$, we obtain a neutrino energy of 812 ± 8 keV. The mass difference between Ar^{37} and Cl^{37} corresponds to 816 ± 2 keV, and the binding energy of a K-electron in Ar^{37} is 2.8 keV. This gives (Eq. 11–6) a predicted energy release available to the neutrino of 813 ± 2 keV, in excellent agreement with Kofoed-Hansen's measurements.

The elusiveness of the neutrino is caused by the fact that the interaction potential, *the weak interaction*, responsible for beta decay is so small (G, small). Consider the interaction between a proton and an antineutrino in the reaction

$$\bar{\nu} + \mathrm{H}^1 \rightarrow \mathrm{n} + \mathrm{e}^+. \tag{11–45}$$

This reaction is similar to an electron-capture process, except that the electron and the neutrino have changed places and that the probability density for the particle initiating the reaction is given by the density in the beam instead of in an atomic state (ψ_K^2).

To estimate the reaction cross section, we again use Eq. (11–14) for the transition probability. The factor dN/dE is now the density of electron states, given by Eq. (11–24) with $dp_\mathrm{e}/dE_\mathrm{e}$ calculated from the relativistic relationship

$$E_\mathrm{e}^2 = (m_0c^2)^2 + (p_\mathrm{e}c)^2. \tag{11–46}$$

Differentiation yields

$$\frac{dp_\mathrm{e}}{dE_\mathrm{e}} = \frac{E_\mathrm{e}}{p_\mathrm{e}c^2}\cdot \tag{11–47}$$

By combining Eqs. (11–14), (11–24), (11–47), and

$$\psi_\mathrm{e}^2 = V^{-1}F(Z, E),$$

we obtain

$$\lambda = \frac{2\pi}{\hbar}\, G^2\, \frac{1}{V}\, F(Z, E)|\psi_\nu|^2|M_{if}|^2\, \frac{Vp_\mathrm{e}E_\mathrm{e}}{2\pi^2\hbar^3c^2}\cdot$$

The probability of decay per second can also be expressed in terms of the neutron flux $\Phi = |\psi_\nu|^2c$ and the reaction cross section σ as

$$\lambda = \sigma\Phi = \sigma|\psi_\nu|^2c.$$

---

* O. Kofoed-Hansen, *Phys. Rev.* **96,** 1046 (1954).

Equating these two expressions for λ, we find that

$$\sigma_\nu = \frac{G^2|M_{if}|^2F(Z, E)p_eE_e}{\pi\hbar^4c^3}. \tag{11-48}$$

For the reaction (11–45), $|M_{if}|^2 = 1$ and $F(Z, E) = 1$, so that we get

$$\sigma_{\nu\mathrm{H}} = \frac{G^2p_eE_e}{\pi\hbar^4c^3}. \tag{11-49}$$

This reaction is endoergic, requiring neutrinos with minimum energies of 1.29 MeV. As an example, assume that the neutrino energy is of such a magnitude (1.5 MeV) that the electron momentum is $p_e = m_0c$, which gives $E_e = \sqrt{2}\, m_0c^2$ by Eq. (11–46). By inserting this into Eq. (11–49), we obtain

$$\sigma_{\nu\mathrm{H}} = \frac{G^2m_0^2}{\pi\hbar^4} \approx 0.42 \times 10^{-48}\ \mathrm{m}^2 = 0.42 \times 10^{-44}\ \mathrm{cm}^2$$

for 1.5-MeV neutrinos. This is truly a small cross section. To get a feeling for how tiny it is, we calculate the mean free path of 1.5-MeV neutrinos through water. We can neglect the presence of the oxygen atoms, since higher neutrino energies are required to induce reactions in them. The mean free path is given by

$$L_\nu\sigma_\nu N = 1,$$

where N is the number of nuclei per unit volume in the target. For H_2O we get

$$L_\nu = \frac{18}{2\sigma_\nu N_A} = 3.4 \times 10^{21}\ \mathrm{cm} = 3600\ \text{light years}.$$

The cross section increases rapidly with increasing neutrino energy, because of the factor p_eE_e in Eq. (11–49), but for neutrinos produced in beta decays this increase is hardly enough to produce much more than an order of magnitude change.

In spite of the obvious difficulties of observing these particles, some neutrino detectors have been devised, first by Reines and Cowan* in 1953. These researchers mounted a large (10 ft^3) liquid scintillator, viewed by ninety photomultiplier tubes and shielded by thick layers of paraffin and lead, outside a large nuclear reactor at Hanford. Events of the type (11–45) were detected and identified by measuring output pulses characteristic of 2- to 5-MeV positrons followed a few microseconds later by a pulse characteristic of a gamma ray from the reaction $\mathrm{Cd}^{113}(\mathrm{n}, \gamma)\mathrm{Cd}^{114}$ produced in cadmium dissolved in the liquid scintillator. Cadmium was chosen as the converter for the neutrons because of the enormous cross section for slow neutron capture in Cd^{113}.

---

* F. Reines and C. L. Cowan, *Phys. Rev.* **92,** 830 (1953).

Reines and Cowan detected 2.55 ± 0.15 delayed coincidences per minute with the reactor operating and 2.14 ± 0.13 background events per minute, the latter probably arising from energetic cosmic-ray events (not neutrinos) in which a slow neutron is produced in the scintillator. The 0.41 ± 0.20 difference attributable to reactor-produced radiation is consistent with the reaction cross section (11–49) and proved not to be produced by other known types of particles (as, for instance, neutrons) by auxiliary techniques.

Another very elaborate experiment to detect free neutrinos was performed at the Brookhaven 30-MeV proton synchrotron by Danby *et al.** The objective of the experiment was to determine whether the neutrinos and antineutrinos released in beta decay, and hence associated with electrons, are the same particles as those associated with muons (also called heavy electrons). The muons, earlier called μ-mesons, are charged leptons with the same characteristic properties as electrons, except for the mass which is $m_\mu = 206.84m_0$. The muons are decay products of the charged π-mesons encountered in Section 3–11. The process is

$$\pi^\pm \to \mu^\pm + \nu \quad (\text{or } \bar{\nu}) \tag{11–50}$$

with a reaction energy $Q = 33.9$ MeV.

Danby *et al.* mounted a 10-ton spark chamber behind 13.5 meters of steel shielding in the neutrino beam produced by decay-in-flight pions from the proton-synchrotron target. The spark chamber with associated electronics could detect and discriminate between electrons and muons produced in the chamber through interactions between the nucleons and the neutrinos. If the muon-associated neutrino is identical to the electron-associated neutrino, equal amounts of muons and electrons should be produced. The result: Only muons seemed to be produced by those neutrinos with muon-associated origin. The conclusion: There are apparently two classes of neutrinos differing in some characteristic feature which so far has not been discovered.

11–10 Measurement of the Neutrino Helicity

In Section 11–8, we indicated that the observed anisotropy of the beta radiation from a source of aligned Co^{60} nuclei could be explained on the basis that the antineutrino possesses an inherent helicity. Another necessary condition is that the directions of motion of the two leptons are correlated. Further light was thrown on the subject by Goldhaber, Grodzins, and Sunyar† who found an ingenious method by which to measure the helicity of the neutrino. For this experiment, they used radioactive Eu^{152} produced by bombarding 10 mg of Eu_2O_3 in the Brookhaven reactor. The important branch of the decay

* G. Danby, J. M. Gaillard, K. Goulianos, L. M. Lederman, N. Mistry, M. Schwartz, and J. Steinberger, *Phys. Rev. Letters* **9,** 36 (1962).
† M. Goldhaber, L. Grodzins, and A. W. Sunyar, *Phys. Rev.* **109,** 1015 (1958).

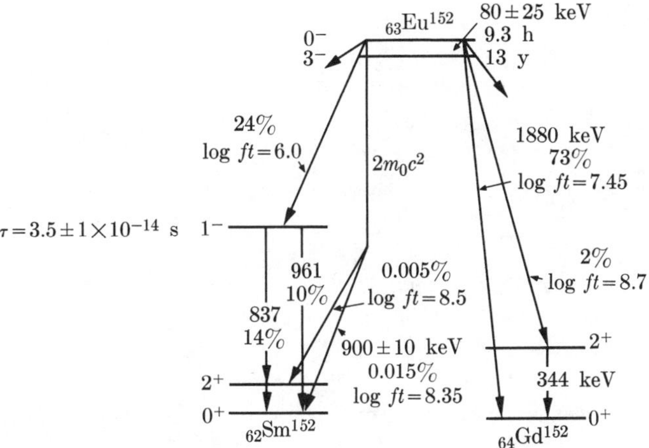

Fig. 11–23. A portion of the decay scheme of Eu^{152m}. [From L. Grodzins, *Phys. Rev.* **109,** 1014 (1958).]

scheme (Fig. 11–23) is the K-capture decay of the metastable 0^- state of Eu^{152} to the 1^- state of Sm^{152} and the 961-keV $E1$ gamma transition to the 0^+ ground state. The J-values of the three states are important, as we shall see, and so is the fact that the neutrino energy, 840 keV, is quite close to the gamma-ray energy, 961 keV.

A determination of the neutrino helicity constitutes the measurements of (a) its direction of motion and (b) its spin direction. Let us look first at point (a). Goldhaber *et al.* determined the direction of motion of the neutrino by devising a scheme to detect preferentially gamma rays that are emitted in the opposite direction. Thereby they ascertained in which direction the neutrino was emitted without having a neutrino counter. The trick was to make use of resonance scattering, also called nuclear-resonance fluorescence radiation (Section 9–3). The 961-keV gamma rays *emitted from the source* in a transition to the ground state of Sm^{152} will normally be scattered by another sample of Sm^{152}, *the scatterer*, very much like other gamma rays of arbitrary energy. The 961-keV quanta have slightly less energy ($\Delta E \approx 6.5$ eV) than the excitation energy of the 1^- state because of the recoil loss (Doppler shift) in the source, and the width of the state is not large enough to permit more than a negligible amount of resonance absorption in the scatterer. If, however, the emitting nucleus in the source has been given a forward momentum prior to gamma emission by a neutrino of energy close to that of the gamma ray, then the Doppler shift at emission cancels the Doppler shift at absorption so that resonance absorption can occur. This greatly enhances scattering of the 961-keV line in the samarium scatterer. The neutrino energy does not have to match the gamma-ray energy perfectly, because heat motion of the emitter as well as of the absorber broadens the lines.

Figure 11–24 depicts the apparatus used by Goldhaber *et al.* and Fig. 11–25 shows a pulse-height spectrum of gamma rays scattered into the scintillation counter. Most of the events recorded are Compton-scattered gamma rays originating, for a large part, in the bremsstrahlung spectrum of the 1880-keV β^- transition (Fig. 11–23). The dashed curve represents the spectrum taken with a scatterer not containing Sm^{152} and the full curve with peaks at 837 keV, and 961 keV represents the spectrum with a Sm_2O_3 scatterer. Only the 961-keV line connecting with the ground state is absorbed, but in re-emission both lines occur (see the decay scheme in Fig. 11–25). From the preceding discussion, we conclude that the counts represented by the two peaks in the spectrum result from events in which the neutrino is emitted upward in Fig. 11–24.

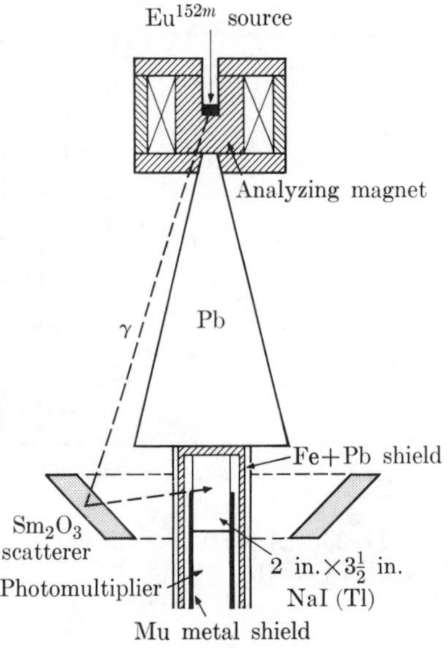

Fig. 11–24. Apparatus used by Goldhaber *et al.* to measure the helicity of the neutrino. [From M. Goldhaber, L. Grodzins, and A. W. Sunyar, *Phys. Rev.* **109,** 1015 (9158).]

Now we return to point (b), the measurement of the spin direction of the neutrino. Consider the sequence of events depicted in Fig. 11–26. In (A) the electron with spin up is being captured by the $J = 0^-$ nucleus. In (B), the neutrino is leaving the nucleus in the upward direction, but with spin down (an assumption of negative helicity). In (B) the nucleus is left with angular momentum $J = 1^-$, as it should be, according to the decay scheme. In the $E1$ transition to the 0^+ ground state, the gamma ray takes this angular momentum with it so that its helicity is negative when emitted downward (left-handed, circularly polarized). If we had assumed positive helicity for the neutrino, it is easy to see that the gamma ray would have positive helicity when emitted in the direction opposite to the neutrino. The important fact is clearly that the gamma ray being emitted in the direction opposite to the neutrino has the same helicity as the neutrino. Of course, gamma rays are emitted in all directions, but we are preferentially detecting those that are emitted opposite to the neutrino, as explained above.

The problem now is reduced to one of measuring the helicity of a gamma ray. This is done by introducing a magnetized iron absorber in the path of the gammas. The absorption coefficient is larger for right-handed polarization than for left-handed, when the gamma ray is moving in the direction of the field.

Goldhaber *et al.* measured the effect of magnetic-field reversal on the counting rate in channel B (Fig. 11–25). The result was a higher counting rate with the

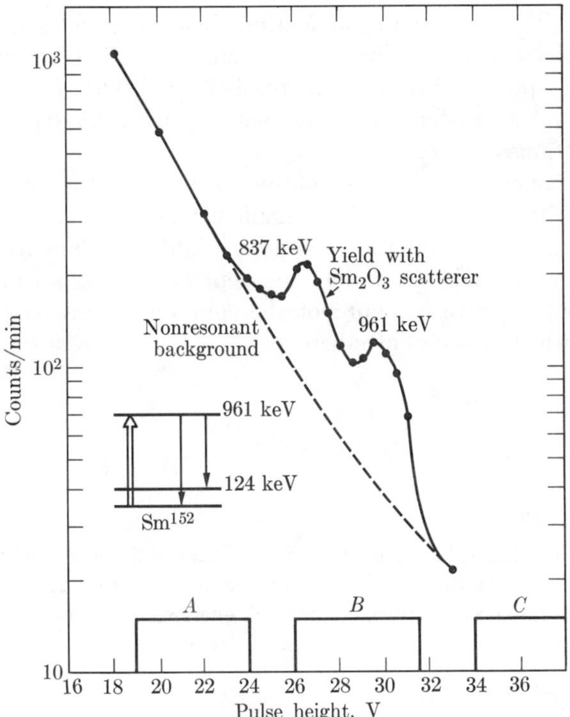

Fig. 11–25. Pulse-height spectrum of gamma rays scattered into the scintillation spectrometer of Fig. 11–24. [From M. Goldhaber, L. Grodzins, and A. W. Sunyar, *Phys. Rev.* **109,** 1015 (1958).]

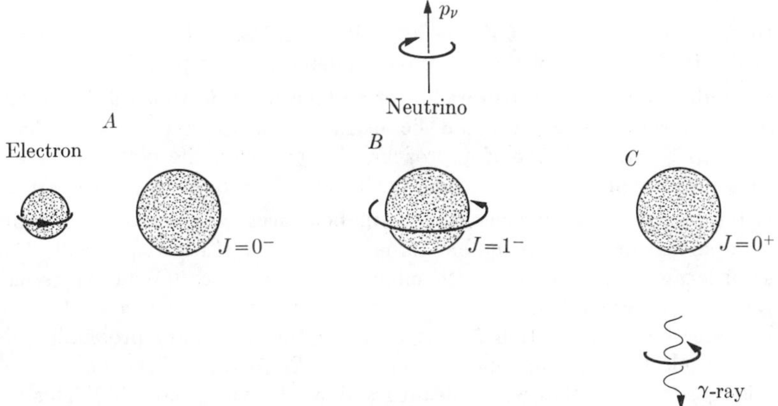

Fig. 11–26. Sequence of events leading to emission of a circularly polarized gamma ray from the second excited state of Sm^{152}.

field down than with the field up, indicating that the gamma rays had left-handed polarization. The neutrino has therefore negative helicity, and the antineutrino, then, presumably has positive helicity. The magnitude of the effect measured was consistent with complete polarization (spin component in direction of motion $= -\frac{1}{2}$).

One important aspect of the now-confirmed helicity of the neutrino is that the neutrino velocity must be c, which again means zero rest mass, exactly. If, namely, the velocity is not the velocity of light, it is always possible to conceive of a frame moving faster than the neutrino. In this frame, the momentum vector will be reversed but not the spin vector, giving the neutrino positive helicity, which is self-contradictory.

PROBLEMS

11–1. Prove Eq. (11–13).

11–2. (a) In the following table of isobars, *atomic* mass differences between element $Z + i$ and Z are given in MeV (i is an integer from -3 to $+2$, as shown). Find the possible beta-decay modes and the total energies of the emitted particles in each case, assuming only ground-state transitions.

Element number	$(m_{Z+i} - m_Z)c^2$	Ground-state J^π
$Z - 3$	3.57	$1/2^+$
$Z - 2$	1.12	$3/2^+$
$Z - 1$	1.97	$5/2^+$
Z	0	$5/2^+$
$Z + 1$	2.27	$1/2^+$
$Z + 2$	5.15	$7/2^+$

(b) Assume that element $Z + 1$ has a low-lying excited state with $J^\pi = 9/2^+$. Will this change any of the decay modes determined in part (a)?

11–3. Show that if $m_\nu > 0$, a Kurie plot for an allowed transition will be an approximately straight line that can be extrapolated to zero at $E = E_0$, when $E_0 - E \gg m_\nu c^2$. When E approaches E_0, however, the plot will curve away from the straight line, intercepting the axis at $E = E_0 - m_\nu c^2$ (see Eq. 11–31).

11–4. If the parity of the nucleus changes in beta decay, or if $|\Delta J| > 1$, either the beta particle or the neutrino has to be emitted in a state with $l > 0$. Consider as an example an electron with momentum $p = m_0 c$. (What is its energy?) Calculate classically its impact parameter or orbit radius in an $l = 1$ state. Use the theory of Section 6–2 to estimate the maximum probability density of this electron at the nuclear surface. ($R_0 = 5$ F. Take $k\hbar = p = m_0 c$. Disregard the fact that we are dealing with a relativistic particle.) This example illustrates the difficulty for the nucleus to emit an electron in a first forbidden transition.

11–5. The irradiation of $_{27}Co^{59}$ with neutrons produces a mixture of two isomers of $_{27}Co^{60}$, one with a half-life of 10.4 m, the other with a half-life of 5.27 y. The latter decays by the emission of beta rays with a maximum energy of 0.31 MeV, followed by the emission of two gamma rays with energies of 1.17 and 1.33 MeV. The 10.4-m activity produces a mixture of low-energy internal conversion electrons and a continuous β^- spectrum with a maximum energy of 1.56 MeV, followed by emission of a 1.33-MeV gamma ray. Each gamma ray corresponds to an electric quadrupole transition. (a) Construct a nuclear energy-level diagram for $_{27}Co^{60}$ and its beta-decay product (nickel). Indicate the transitions mentioned and the spin and parity of the levels in the daughter nucleus. (b) What is the difference in energy between the two states of $_{27}Co^{60}$?

11–6. The atomic weight of the isotope $_{41}Nb^{95}$ is higher than that of $_{42}Mo^{95}$ by 0.995×10^{-3} atomic mass units (1 u = 931 MeV). The beta decay of Nb^{95} leads to an excited state at 768 keV in Mo^{95}. This excited state decays to the ground state partly by internal conversion (total conversion coefficient = 1.6×10^{-3}). (a) Sketch an energy-level diagram showing the decay scheme. (b) Find the endpoint energy of the continuous beta spectrum and the energy of the K-conversion line when the binding energy for a K-electron in molybdenum is 20 keV. (c) Sketch the beta spectrum (counts vs. energy), including the conversion lines (no calculations are needed). Indicate the approximate positions of the L- and M-lines without calculating their energies.

11–7. Three points from an experimental momentum spectrum of electrons from a radioactive sample are as follows:

$$p = \sqrt{8}\, m_0c, \qquad p = \sqrt{24}\, m_0c, \qquad p = \sqrt{48}\, m_0c;$$
$$P(p) = 288, \qquad P(p) = 384, \qquad P(p) = 192.$$

(a) Make a Kurie plot of these data, neglecting the Coulomb factor $F(Z, E)$. Determine the endpoint of the β spectrum (maximum *kinetic* energy of the electrons in terms of m_0c^2). (b) The comparative half-life is given by $\log(ft) = 4.1$. The daughter state is known to be 2^+. Determine the possible values of the angular momentum and parity for the parent (β-unstable) state.

11–8. The β^- emitter Na^{24} has a half-life $t_{1/2} = 15.0$ h. Below is a table of counts per unit momentum interval vs. $B\rho$ of the β spectrometer. (a) Make a Kurie plot of these data. (b) Compute the ft-value for Na^{24}. (Use Figs. 11–10 and 11–16.)

Na^{24} spectrum

$B\rho$	5950	5600	5280	4950	4600	4280	3950	3600	
$P(p)$	0.7	4.0	9.3	15.5	23.0	29.9	34.6	39.7	
$B\rho$	3280	2950	2600	2280	1950	1600	1280	950	600
$P(p)$	42.0	41.1	39.7	37.8	32.1	26.2	22.2	16.0	7.8

PART 5

Nuclear-Reaction Studies, Nuclear Energy, Elementary Particles

12 Accelerators and Sources of Atomic Particles

12–1 Ion Sources

Every accelerator for atomic particles consists of an ion source and a means for producing electric fields to accelerate the charged particles produced in the source. The ion source for an electron machine is very simple: It is a hot filament. The intensity of the beam can be regulated by regulating the filament temperature or the voltage on a grid structure similar to the one used in electronic tubes or cathode-ray oscilloscope tubes. Here, we shall concentrate on a description of sources used to produce positive or negative ions of the hydrogen or helium isotopes or isotopes of heavier atoms. Although ions can in many cases be produced directly from a solid or liquid, we shall only describe sources in which they are formed in one or another kind of gas discharge.

The first ion sources utilized a dc gas discharge between two electrodes. A hole in the cathode allowed positive ions to emerge from the region of the gas discharge into a region of lower pressure and accelerating electric fields. The next step in the development was the hot cathode-arc sources. In these sources, copious amounts of electrons were produced by thermionic emission from a hot cathode, and it was possible to sustain a very intense arc with a fairly low voltage between the cathode and anode. In capillary-arc sources, the arc was restrained to a smaller region by forcing it through an insulating tube. Positive ions could be pulled out of the arc in the axial or radial direction.

The quality of an ion source can be measured in terms of the amount of ions of the desired kind it emits into a given solid angle per unit time. The area of the extraction hole, or rather the minimum diameter of constriction of the stream of ions, is also important, since this ultimately determines the minimum cross section of the beam after acceleration. Finally, the percentage of the desired ions to the neutrals and other components is important. Particularly, since the region of the accelerator into which the ion source opens has to be kept at high vacuum, leakage of a large amount of neutral gas cannot be tolerated.

Figure 12–1 shows a very efficient ion source called the Duoplasmatron, originally devised by M. von Ardenne.* This ion source can, according to the inventor, give 500 mA of protons through a 1-mm diameter hole. The output of the source is practically 100% H^+ with very few H_2^+ and neutral atoms. The anode structure in this hot cathode-arc source forms the pole pieces of an electromagnet that produces an intense axial magnetic field in the discharge region. This field allows the source to operate at lower gas pressure since it coils up the orbits of the electrons; therefore it enhances the probability of an electron's colliding with a gas molecule before striking the anode. The field also has a focusing effect on the ions produced.

Very efficient ion sources have been produced that operate on the principle of electrodeless gas breakdown in a radiofrequency field. Figure 12–2 shows an example of such an ion source. The gas is enclosed in a Pyrex® tube, and the radiofrequency field inside the tube is produced by the two ring-shaped electrodes outside the tube. At a pressure of about 2×10^{-2} mm Hg, about

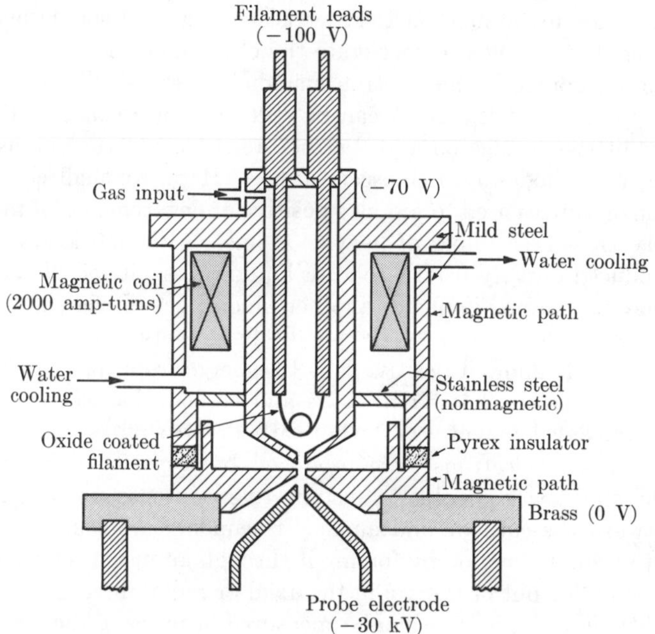

Fig. 12–1. Duoplasmatron ion source. [Adapted from C. D. Moak, H. E. Banta, J. N. Thurston, J. W. Johnson, and R. F. King, *Rev. Sci. Instr.* **30,** 694 (1959).]

---

* M. von Ardenne, *Tabellen der Elektronenphysik und Übermikroskopie,* Berlin: Deutscher Verlag der Wissenschaften, 1956.

® Corning Glass Works, Corning, New York.

60 watts of radiofrequency power at 100 Mc/sec is needed to produce a breakdown in the gas. The ions are extracted from the source by a superimposed dc field between the extraction canal and the metallic electrode at the top of the source. An axial magnetic field produced by an external solenoid increases the efficiency of this source.

The violent gas breakdown in the two ion sources described produces positive ions and electrons. In the Tandem accelerator (Section 12–2), as well as in some cyclotrons, negative ions are accelerated and later stripped of two or more electrons to become positive ions. For these machines, therefore, negative-ion sources are needed. Some of the electrons released in the gas breakdown in a source for positive ions actually attach themselves to gas molecules and produce negative ions which could be extracted by reversing the extraction potential. The intensity of such a beam would, however, be very low. In most Tandem machines, therefore, the negative ions are not produced directly in the ion source,

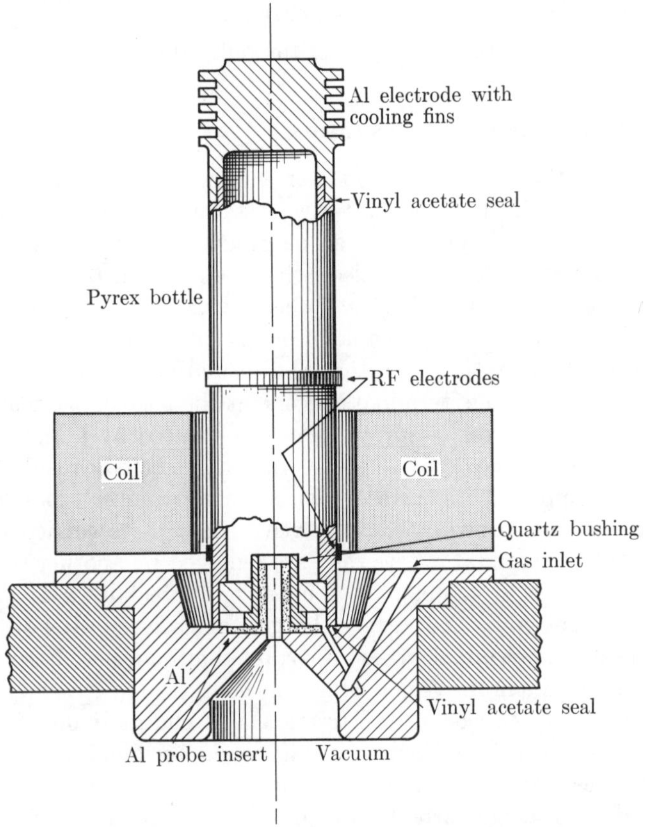

Fig. 12–2. Radiofrequency ion source. (Courtesy of High Voltage Engineering Corporation, Burlington, Mass.)

but rather are formed by charge exchange from a beam of positive ions of about 50 keV passing through an "adder" gas. The speed of 50-keV hydrogen ions, for instance, is of the order of magnitude of the speed of electrons in the outer shells of atoms. When these hydrogen ions pass through the gas, the probability of pickup of one or more electrons from the gas molecules is reasonably large. The efficiency for converting positive ions into negative ions by such an arrangement is of the order of magnitude of 1%.

For some applications, in particular for the time-of-flight studies to be discussed in Section 13–4, it is required that the ion source give off very short bursts of ions rather than a continuous stream. Pulses of duration as short as one nanosecond (10^{-9} sec) are required. Such pulses can be produced by sweeping the ion beam very rapidly across a fine slit by electric deflection at a very high frequency. A method used for packing more ions into these short pulses is to produce initially pulses of about 10-nsec duration and then, by application of a small radiofrequency accelerating voltage, speed up the ions in the back part of the pulse so that by the time they reach the target, they have caught up with the ions in the front part of the pulse (klystron bunching).

12–2 Direct-Current Accelerators

In principle, the simplest method for accelerating ions is to inject them into a region over which a constant electrostatic potential is maintained. This constant electrostatic potential can be produced by rectification of ac voltages or by mechanical transport of electricity from ground potential to the terminal of high tension (e.g., Van de Graaff accelerator).

Figure 12–3 shows the principle of operation of the Van de Graaff generator, also called electrostatic generator. An insulating belt runs over two pulleys: one in the high-voltage terminal and one at the base of the machine. A corona breakdown from a row of spray points is produced by a high voltage between these points and the lower pulley. Since the belt is insulating, the corona current is stopped at its surface, which therefore collects positive charges produced in the breakdown. These positive charges are carried mechanically by the belt to the terminal, where they are removed by another corona breakdown to another set of needlepoints. The second breakdown is produced by the electric field set up by the surface charges themselves in the otherwise field-free region inside the terminal. It is important that no other sharp points be facing the belt anywhere in the region where the charges are carried up to the terminal.

The electricity carried to the terminal will charge it up to the point where a balance is reached between the drain on the terminal in the form of current through a resistor column to ground (not shown), the current in the accelerating tube, and the leakage current through the insulating gas. If too much current is transported by the belt into the terminal, the terminal potential will increase until electric breakdown occurs either in the form of a sparkover from terminal to tank through the gas or by a surface flashover along the column insulators

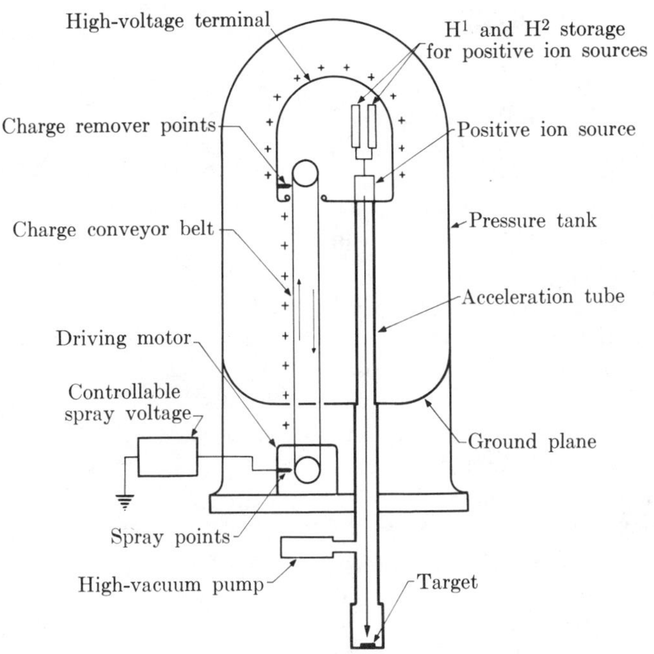

Fig. 12-3. Schematic diagram of a Van de Graaff accelerator. The insulating column supporting the high-voltage terminal is not shown. (From I. Kaplan, *Nuclear Phsyics*, Reading, Mass.: Addison-Wesley, 1962.)

supporting the high-voltage terminal or along the belt or tube. The structural parts of the Van de Graaff accelerator are made of materials that can bear a fair amount of such breakdowns without being damaged. Most of these machines are in fact operated at potentials where they are continuously on the verge of breakdown.

For most experiments a concentrated spot of radiation on the target is desired. Focusing of the ion beam before, during, and after acceleration is therefore of utmost importance. In the Van de Graaff accelerator, the entrance aperture to the accelerating tube acts as a strong lens. Figure 12-4 shows the upper section of a modern accelerating tube with electric field lines and equipotentials drawn in. It is quite clear from the direction of the field lines above the upper aperture that there is a funneling effect acting on the ions entering this region; that is, in addition to the axial accelerating forces, there are radial forces pointing inward which will produce a focusing effect. It can be shown that the focal length of the aperture lens is of the order of magnitude

$$F = 4V/E, \tag{12-1}$$

where V is the potential through which the ions have been accelerated before entering this region, and E is the more or less uniform electric field in the tube below the entrance aperture. Typically, we may have $V = 60$ kV, and $E = 1500$ kV/m. This gives a focal length of approximately 16 cm. If the ion-source outlet is placed 16 cm above the entrance aperture, the particles will move in approximately parallel paths down the tube; if the source is placed a little bit farther away, particles can be made to converge at a point past the exit of the tube. In practice, the ion-source distance is kept fixed, and the focal properties are varied by varying the preaccelerating voltage V.

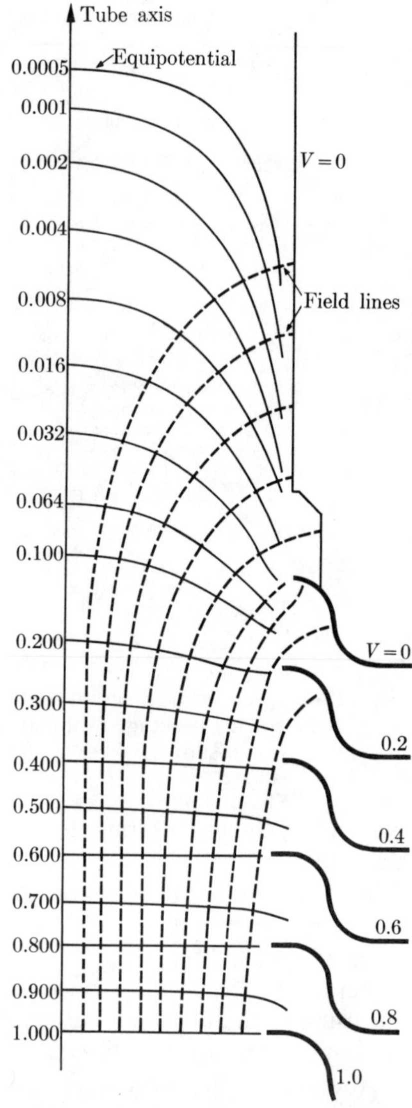

Fig. 12–4. The upper section of an accelerator tube for a dc generator. (Courtesy of High Voltage Engineering Corporation.)

Single-stage Van de Graaff accelerators have been built for terminal voltage up to approximately 10 MV. The bulk and cost of the machine increase very rapidly with maximum voltage, and it is therefore very desirable, when possible, to use a given potential V to accelerate particles to energies $T = nVe$, where n is larger than 1. One obvious suggestion is to produce multiply charged ions by removing two or more electrons from helium and heavier atoms. A more elegant method which is applicable also to hydrogen isotopes is to produce negative ions at ground potential, to let these ions accelerate in the vacuum tube to the terminal, then to strip off two electrons while the ions are inside the positive terminal, and to let them accelerate again from terminal to ground.

Figure 12–5 is a schematic drawing of a two-stage Tandem generator operating on this principle. Positive ions are produced in the ion source and accelerated to approximately 50 keV. In passing through the electron-adding gas, approximately 1% of the positive ions are converted into negative ions by pickup of two electrons. These negative ions are deflected into the accelerating tube of the first stage of the accelerator. As negative ions, they are attracted

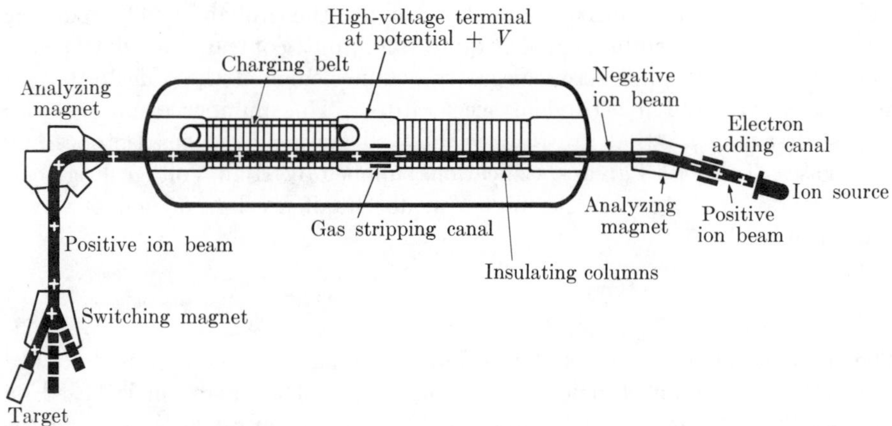

Fig. 12–5. A two-stage Tandem accelerator. [From R. J. Van de Graaff, *Nucl. Instr. Methods* **8,** 195 (1960).]

toward the positive terminal and gain an energy of V electron volts. In the terminal they pass through a gas stripper canal or a thin carbon-foil target. At this high velocity, practically all the ions emerging from the stripper will have lost both electrons. Because they are positively charged, they will gain another V electron volts in passing from terminal to ground potential in the accelerator tude of the second stage. For atoms heavier than hydrogen, more than one electron can be removed in the stripper. Clearly if the charge of the ion emerging from the stripper canal is $+ne$, the total energy of the particles reaching the high-energy end of the machine is $(1 + n)V$ electron volts plus the small energy the beam had at injection. For a Tandem machine with 10 MV on the terminal, oxygen ions may be stripped of seven of the eight electrons, for instance, and the total energy gained in the accelerator will be 80 MeV. Hydrogen ions will gain an energy of 20 MeV in the same machine,

Table 12–1. Specifications for a single-stage Van de Graaff generator and a Tandem generator, both with beam-analyzing magnets*

	Single-stage, type CN	Tandem, type MP
Energy range for hydrogen ions	1 to 5.5 MeV	6 to 20 MeV
Energy stability (90% of time)	$< \pm 2$ keV	$< \pm 2$ keV
Beam current, analyzed	$> 35\ \mu$A	$> 10\ \mu$A
Total length of pressure tank	6.1 m	27 m
Diameter of pressure tank	2.4 m	6 m
Insulating gas	$N_2 + CO_2$ 14 atm	$N_2 + CO_2$ 14 atm
Beam diameter, analyzed	<5 mm	<5 mm

* Data from High Voltage Engineering Corporation, Burlington, Mass.

and helium ions will gain 30 MeV. For helium, the probability of producing negative ions in the adding canal is quite small, but, contrary to what is commonly believed, it is not zero. Negative helium beams of the order of 0.2 μA have been produced for Tandem accelerators. This number compares with beams of several μA that are readily obtained for the hydrogen isotopes and other gases. Table 12–1 gives specifications supplied by High Voltage Engineering Corporation, for one single-stage Van de Graaff accelerator and one two-stage Tandem.

12–3 The Cyclotron

The principle of operation of the cyclotron-resonance accelerator is described in most textbooks on electricity and magnetism. The operation is based on the fact that the frequency of circulation of ions in the magnetic field in the nonrelativistic range is independent of the energy of the ion. We assume that the ion of charge q and mass m is moving in a plane perpendicular to the magnetic field B. Newton's Second Law then gives

$$qvB = \frac{mv^2}{\rho}, \tag{12–2}$$

where ρ is the orbit radius and v is the velocity of the ion. Equation (12–2) is relativistically correct, since v^2/ρ is the centripetal acceleration and since the mass of the ion does not change (no energy gain) by motion in the magnetic field. We solve Eq. (12–2) for the angular frequency $\omega = v/\rho$ and obtain

$$\omega = \frac{qB}{m}. \tag{12–3}$$

To the extent that the mass m can be regarded as a constant when an ion is accelerated in a cyclotron, Eq. (12–3) shows that the frequency of circulation is a constant.

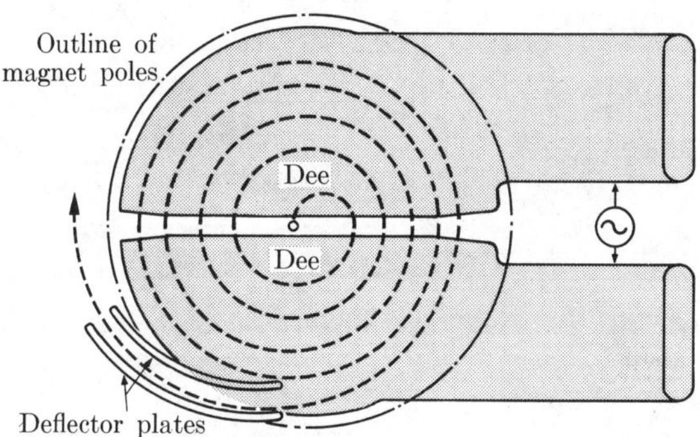

Fig. 12–6. The principal elements of a cyclotron.

Figure 12–6 shows the operating principle of a cyclotron. A radiofrequency voltage is applied to the two dees, as shown in the figure. Ions produced in the center of the machine will be accelerated across the gap in the direction shown when the electric field has the appropriate direction. After describing a half-circle, the ions will cross the gap again, now in the opposite direction. However, if the applied radiofrequency field is in resonance with the cyclotron frequency (12–3) for the ions, the field also has changed direction, so that the ions are again accelerated. After another half-period, the ions again cross the gap and are again accelerated. If the frequency of the applied field exactly matches the cyclotron frequency, the ions will clearly stay in phase and gain energy every half-period. Since the momentum is continuously increasing, the radius of curvature of each half-circle will increase until eventually the ions reach the periphery of the pole pieces. The momentum is then, by Eq. (12–2):

$$p = qBr. \tag{12–4}$$

For example, for protons accelerated in a cyclotron with $B = 16{,}000$ gauss and $r = 50$ cm, the total energy will be approximately 31 MeV (see Fig. A1–2). The frequency, as given by Eq. (12–3) is $f = \omega/2\pi = 24.3$ Mc/sec.

On reaching the periphery of the magnet, the high-energy ions may enter a deflection channel (Fig. 12–6) across which a constant electric field is maintained. This forces a large fraction of the spiraling ions out of the magnetic field in one place so that they exit as a somewhat diverging beam. The beam can be focused, deflected, and brought to impinge on external targets by auxiliary deflecting magnets and lenses.

Of utmost importance for the proper operation of a cyclotron is the magnetic focusing that takes place inside the main magnet. Figure 12–7 illustrates this. The magnet is designed so that the field in the center is higher than the field along the periphery. The magnetic field lines will then curve as indicated in Fig. 12–7. An ion moving in the central plane of the magnet will experience only radial forces from the magnetic field; an ion moving above the central

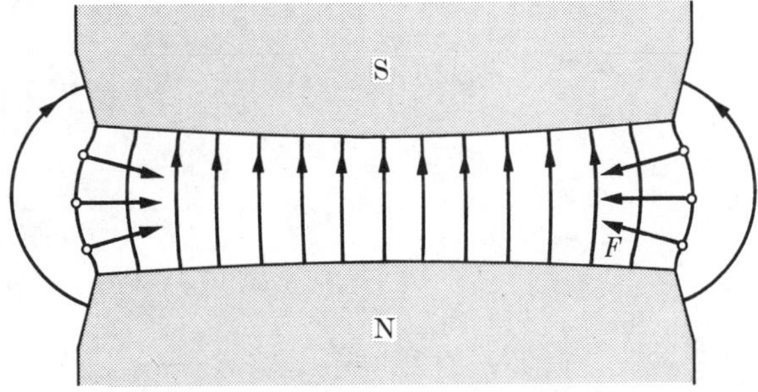

Fig. 12–7. The curvature of the magnetic field lines in a cyclotron results in vertical focusing forces (as for a ball racing around inside a barrel).

plane, however, will experience forces which, in addition to the radial component, have a vertical component directed toward the central plane. An ion that starts out with a slight vertical component of velocity will, because of these vertical restoring forces, execute harmonic motion about the central plane. Without such restoring forces, of course, it would be likely to drift toward the inside of the dees and be lost. Since the total spiral path length of an ion from ion source to extraction canal may be several hundred meters, it is clear that this vertical focusing action is vital for the operation of the cyclotron. When this vertical focusing action is accomplished by a design of cylindrical symmetry, as in Fig. 12–7, the field will decrease with increasing radius of curvature, in conflict with the requirement of synchronism, as discussed above. As a matter of fact, if we also consider the relativistic increase of mass, Eq. (12–3) expresses the fact that, in order for the ions to stay in synchronism with the accelerating field, the induction B should increase with the radius, since the mass (energy) increases. In the first generation of cyclotrons, this dilemma was solved by shaping the field as in Fig. 12–7 and by using such a high radiofrequency voltage between the dees that the total number of revolutions could be limited to the order of one hundred. The cumulative error in phase could then be kept small enough so that the ions stayed in phase until maximum energy was obtained. For this reason it was impractical to design a cyclotron of this first-generation type to deliver beams of much more than 30 MeV.

An entirely practical scheme of reaching higher energies is to vary the radiofrequency in accordance with Eq. (12–3) by following a bunch of ions out from the center to the maximum radius of curvature with an increase in ω as m increases. A machine that incorporates such a feature is called a synchrocyclotron, or a frequency-modulated cyclotron. Energies of the order of 1 BeV

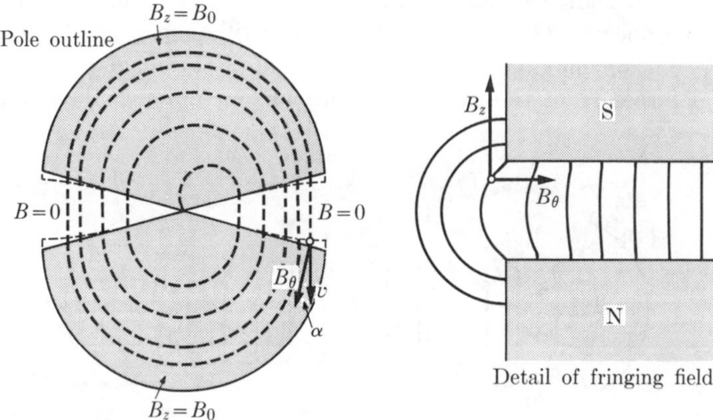

Fig. 12–8. Principle of vertical focusing in sector-focused cyclotron. In practice, the field seen by the ion in one revolution never goes to zero but varies from $B_{\max}$, to say, $0.7B_{\max}$.

Table 12-2. Characteristics of two cyclotrons

	University of Pittsburgh conventional	University of Michigan sector focused
Energy	8-MeV protons 16-MeV deuterons 32-MeV alphas	7 to 35-MeV protons 15 to 50-MeV deuterons 30 to 80-MeV alphas
Internal beam current	300 μA	1 mA
External beam, analyzed	$<1\ \mu$A	$<1\ \mu$A
Energy stability, analyzed half-width	0.3%	0.012%
Maximum magnetic induction	16 kG	16 kG at hill 14 kG at valley
Frequency	12 Mc/sec	variable
Maximum orbit, radius	0.50 m	0.84 m
Magnet air gap	12 cm	18 cm (min)
Total weight	180 tons	350 tons
Magnet power	16 kW	75 kW

(thousand MeV) have been attained with such machines. Clearly, the ions from such a machine can only come out in relatively short bursts and not quasi-continuously, as in the regular cyclotron. This is sometimes a disadvantage, but sometimes it is a desired feature, for instance, for time-of-flight studies.

The highest energy synchrocyclotrons have been used and are being used mostly for elementary-particle research. For nuclear-structure research, the energy range from 10 to 50 MeV with the highest possible energy resolution is more in demand. In recent years, a new generation of very versatile cyclotrons has emerged in this general range of energies. These machines employ a new method of focusing called "sector" focusing, proposed by L. H. Thomas in 1938.* The sector-focused cyclotron has a field which varies with azimuthal angle. For the purpose of explaining the focusing action, we exaggerate this field variation to an on-off situation, as depicted in Fig. 12-8. A particle that moves *above* the central plane of the cyclotron will, in passing through the entrance fringing field as indicated in the figure, move through a region where there is a horizontal field component B_θ. Since the particle is not moving normal to the pole boundary, that is, it is not moving parallel to B_θ, there is a resulting focusing force $F_z = -qvB_\theta \sin \alpha$. Similarly, when it moves through the exit fringing field, there is a focusing force. The net focusing in the case shown may be quite strong in spite of the short duration of these forces. For constant mass, the frequency of circulation is again independent of ρ if the field boundaries are straight. For the machine as outlined in Fig. 12-8, it is therefore possible

* L. H. Thomas, *Phys. Rev.* **54,** 580 (1938).

to retain synchronism while accomplishing vertical focusing as required. It is even possible to increase the average field integral seen by the particle faster than linearly with ρ (shown dashed in the figure), so that it is possible to retain both synchronism and z-direction focusing while m is increasing. In practice, the arrangement of Fig. 12–8 gives stronger focusing than is actually needed, and in machines that have been built, the sectors are merely shims on circular pole pieces. Whereas the maximum field may be 18,000 gauss, the field in the split between the sectors may be, for instance, 12,000 gauss. Also, instead of two sector-shaped areas of maximum field, the magnet may have three or more maxima, and the same number of minima, of field strengths. Table 12–2 gives the main characteristics of two cyclotrons, one with homogeneous field and one with sector focusing.

12–4 *The Linear Accelerator* (*Linac*)

The idea of accelerating positive ions by the aid of an alternating radiofrequency field was first published by Ising* in 1925, and the first working accelerator was reported by Wideröe† in 1928. The principle of operation of an early linear accelerator will be explained with reference to Fig. 12–9. The ions to be accelerated are injected into a series of electrodes connected alternately to one or the other of the two poles of a radiofrequency oscillator. Assume that an ion moves across the gap between two of these coaxial cylinders while the radiofrequency voltage between them is approximately at the maximum and accelerating. If the length of the following electrode is such that the ion moves across the next gap after exactly one half-period, it will again be accelerated. Since the velocity now has increased, the next electrode needs to be longer in order for the ion to spend another half-period between the gaps. Clearly, the condition for synchronism is, in general,

$$\text{Half-period} = 1/2f = L_n/v_n. \tag{12–5}$$

Here L_n is the length of the nth electrode plus a gap, v_n is the velocity of the ions inside the nth electrode, and f is the frequency of the radiofrequency oscillator.

If the average potential drop that the particle sees in passing a gap is V_0, we find the velocity in the nth electrode from the nonrelativistic energy equation

$$neV_0 + C = \tfrac{1}{2}mv_n^2. \tag{12–6}$$

The constant C allows for the fact that the injection energy is different from zero and for the fact that the first gap has only half the accelerating voltage V_0

---

* G. Ising, *Ark. Math. Astron. Phys.* **18,** 30, Heft 4, p. 45 (1925).
† R. Wideröe, *Arch. Elektrotech* **21,** 387 (1928).

if the oscillator is balanced with respect to ground. By combining Eqs. (12-5) and (12-6), we obtain for the length of the nth electrode:

$$L_n = (1/2f)\sqrt{2(neV_0 + C)/m} = \lambda\sqrt{(neV_0 + C)/2mc^2}. \qquad (12\text{-}7)$$

It is clear from Eq. (12-7) that the length of each section, and therefore the total length of the accelerator, is proportional to the wavelength λ of the radiofrequency signal. With pre-World War II radiofrequency power sources, the wavelengths were too large to be practical, except for accelerators designed for heavy ions such as mercury. Mercury ions with a kinetic energy of 2 MeV are of no use in studying nuclear reactions, but these experiments in the early 1930's demonstrated the feasibility of the linear accelerator and gave impetus to the development of very high-frequency power sources. After the end of World War II, when such power sources were available, a number of linear accelerators were designed for both protons and electrons. When the frequency barrier had been broken, this method of acceleration turned out to be more attractive for electrons than for heavier ions, because the electrons are very rapidly brought up into the highly relativistic range where the velocity is practically constant ($v \approx c$). The electron tube therefore has uniform dimensions all the way through, and the energy of the electron linear accelerator can easily be varied.

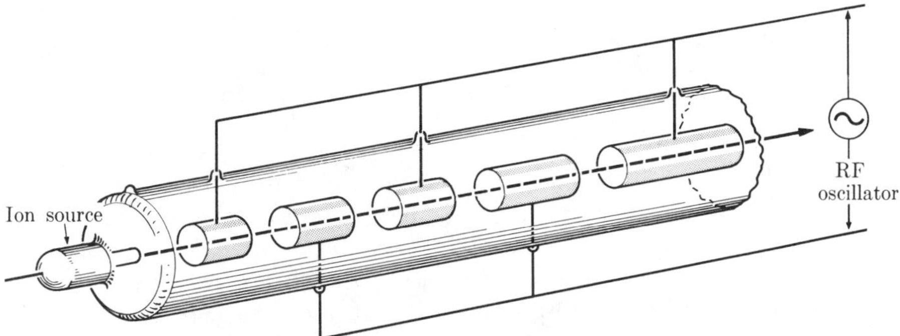

Fig. 12-9. Schematic drawing of an early linear accelerator for heavy ions.

The heavy-ion linear accelerator shown in Fig. 12-9 is a standing-wave device, and electron linear accelerators can also be made to operate on the same principle. A wave guide is filled with standing waves of electromagnetic radiation in a mode which has an axial electric field and an azimuthal magnetic field. The relationship between frequency and wavelength is such that the electron moves half a wavelength during half a period. If the field is then accelerating, it will be accelerating during the next half-cycle as well, since the electron has moved past a node. Such a standing wave can be thought of as two traveling waves going in opposite directions. Both waves move with the velocity of light, and the electron rides on or near the crest of one of the waves, experiencing a constant accelerating field from it. The other wave, moving against the electron, will exert alternately accelerating and decelerating forces on it, so that the effect from this partial wave averages to zero.

All modern electron linear accelerators are traveling-wave devices. Power is fed into the wave guides at regular intervals through directional couplers which send it in the direction of motion of the electron. The radiofrequency signal is produced by a master oscillator and amplified at each feeding station by klystrons. The phase of the signal at each station can be adjusted so that the electron sees a continuous traveling wave, and it can ride on a crest of this wave from one end of the wave guide to the other, thus being continuously accelerated. Because of the very high field strength in the wave guide, power losses are high. All Linacs are therefore pulsed with duty cycles of the order of 0.1 to 1%.

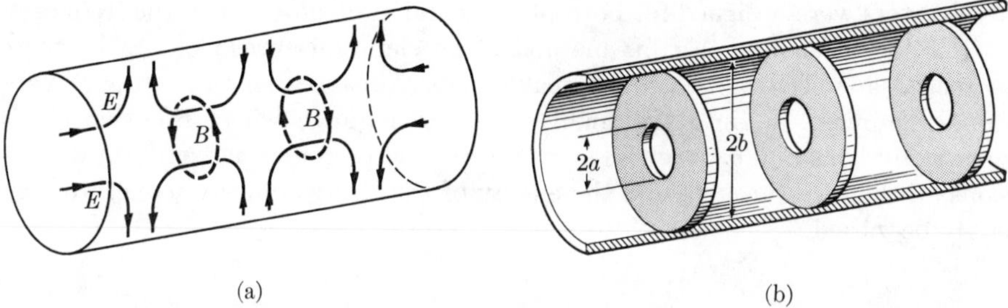

Fig. 12–10. (a) Field pattern in a wave guide excited in the TM_{01} mode (transverse magnetic field). (b) Disk loading of the wave guide to reduce the phase velocity to the velocity of light.

Figure 12–10(a) shows schematically the field pattern in a wave guide operated in the TM_{01} mode, with TM meaning transverse magnetic field. In a cylindrical wave guide, the phase velocity is always greater than the velocity of light. It can be slowed down to the velocity of light by inserting conducting disks,* as shown in Fig. 12–10(b).

Many electron linear accelerators are presently in operation in the energy range 10 to 1000 MeV. Characteristic parameters for one of these, built for Rensselaer Polytechnic Institute by Applied Radiation Corporation, are given in Table 12–3. Also shown in this table are the parameters for the "two-mile Linac" under construction at Stanford University.

The linear accelerator is used for electron-scattering experiments and for studies of photonuclear reactions, either by using the electron beam directly, or by converting it into an x-ray beam by inserting a high Z target in which bremsstrahlung is produced. The spectrum of x-rays produced is continuous and therefore not so convenient for studies of nuclear reactions as is a charged-particle

---

* J. C. Slater, *Rev. Mod. Phys.* **20,** 473 (1948).

Table 12–3. Characteristics of two linear accelerators

	Rensselaer Polytechnic Institute	Stanford University (design objectives)
Maximum electron energy	35 MeV	40 BeV
Energy stability, unanalyzed half-width	6%	$\approx$1%
Peak electron current	0.8 A	0.2 A
Pulse duration	0.1 to 4.5 μsec	2 μsec
Repetition rate	7 to 700 pulses/sec	360 pulses/sec
Beam diameter	$<$2 cm	$<$2 cm
Frequency	L-band (1300 Mc/sec)	S-band (2856 Mc/sec)
Peak radiofrequency power input	50 MW	13,000 MW
Wave guide diameter	18 cm	8.2 cm
Total length of accelerating tube	8.9 m	3050 m

beam from a Van de Graaff accelerator, for instance. However, high-intensity linear accelerators can be used for production of gamma rays of nearly constant energy by use of an interesting process to be described in Section 13–14. Briefly, the process involves converting the electron beam to positrons by a two-step process: bremsstrahlung and pair production. After the positrons have been deflected through a magnet for momentum analysis, they are made to impinge on a thin target in which a certain fraction of them will annihilate with an electron while in flight. A beam of gamma rays with a narrow energy spectrum and a relatively small angular divergence results.

Focusing the beam in the electron linear accelerator is accomplished by axial magnetic fields produced by solenoids outside the wave guide. The principle of operation is exactly parallel to the principle of longitudinal beta spectrometers described in Section 11–2.

12–5 The Betatron

The betatron is an electric transformer in which, instead of a secondary winding, we place a doughnut-shaped vacuum chamber and let electrons be subjected to the force exerted by the induced electric field. Figure 12–11 shows a schematic diagram of such a device. Two important requirements have to be fulfilled for this machine to work. One is that as the electrons gain momentum, the magnetic field on the orbit must always be of such a magnitude that the familiar requirement $p = eB\rho$ (Eq. A1–9) is fulfilled. This leads to a very simple design requirement which was recognized by Wideröe* in 1928 and is discussed below. The second requirement is that there must be a stable orbit for the

---

* R. Wideröe, *Arch. Elektrotech* **21,** 400 (1928).

electron inside the vacuum chamber; that is, the magnet must provide focusing forces both in the radial direction and in the vertical direction. This is an obvious necessity, since the electrons make of the order of a million turns before gaining full energy. The correct design of a magnet that will focus the electrons in both planes was found by Kerst,* who was able to produce 2.3-MeV electrons from a betatron in 1940.

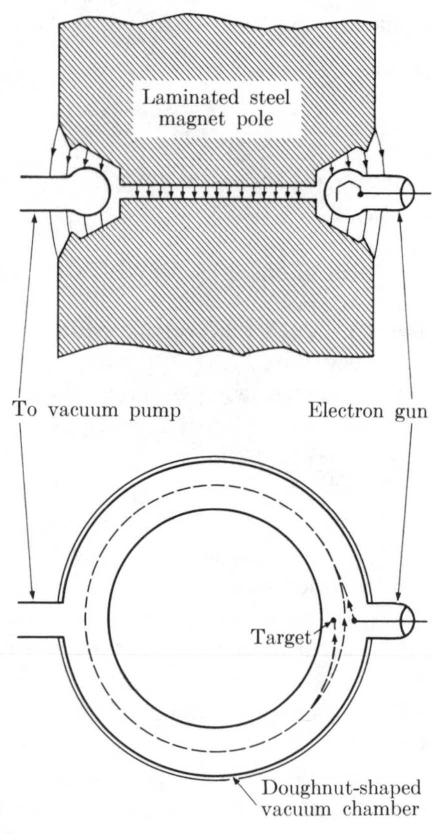

Fig. 12–11. Schematic diagram of a betatron, without the coils and magnetic return yoke.

We shall first develop the orbit field condition as given by Wideröe. The induced electric field $\mathcal{E}$ at the orbit is given by

$$2\pi\rho\mathcal{E} = \frac{d}{dt}\,(\pi\rho^2 B_{\mathrm{av}}), \qquad (12\text{–}8)$$

where ρ is the radius of the orbit, and B_{av} is the average field enclosed by the orbit. By using Newton's Second Law, $dp/dt = \mathcal{E}e$, we obtain

$$\frac{dp}{dt} = \frac{e\rho}{2}\,\frac{dB_{\mathrm{av}}}{dt},$$

which, integrated, yields:

$$p = \frac{e\rho B_{\mathrm{av}}}{2} + p_0. \qquad (12\text{–}9)$$

By balancing the magnetic force and the centrifugal force, we get the familiar

$$p = e\rho B_{\mathrm{orb}}. \qquad (12\text{–}10)$$

When comparing the two equations for p, we see that in order to keep the electron on the orbit of radius ρ, it must be injected at such a time of the cycle that Eq. (12–9) is fulfilled with $p_0 = 0$; and the machine has to be designed such that

$$B_{\mathrm{av}} = 2B_{\mathrm{orb}}. \qquad (12\text{–}11)$$

As indicated in Fig. 12–11, the second condition is fulfilled by making the air

---

* D. W. Kerst, *Phys. Rev.* **58,** 841 (1940); *Phys. Rev.* **60,** 47 (1941). See also D. W. Kerst and R. Serber, *Phys. Rev.* **60,** 93 (1941).

gap in the central part of the magnet smaller than the air gap enclosing the orbit. Thereby the average field inside the orbit can be made equal to twice the field strength on the orbit. Equations (12-9) and (12-10) show that the momentum is at any time proportional to the field B, which is in phase throughout the magnetic circuit.

Theoretically, it should be possible to inject electrons of zero energy when the field strength is zero. Because it is impossible in practice to make the field along the orbit uniform enough at very low field strengths, the electrons are injected into orbit with the appropriate momentum at a later instant. At the end of the acceleration period when the field has reached maximum, the orbit can be made to contract or expand by sending a short current pulse in an auxiliary turn near the doughnut. This will make the electrons strike a properly placed target from which an x-ray beam will emerge.

Magnetic focusing in the betatron is very similar in principle to the focusing action in the Svartholm-Siegbahn type beta spectrometer described in Section 11-2. Equations (11-10) and (11-11) show that when the field gradient n defined by Eq. (11-8) is in the range $0 < n < 1$, focusing takes place both in the radial and vertical planes. This means that a particle starting from a point on the central orbit, but in a direction diverging from the central orbit, will return to the central orbit, cross it, and in effect execute harmonic oscillations about the central orbit. This theory applies to stationary fields. It is also essentially correct for time-varying fields, since the variation is relatively small for each revolution of the electron. The detailed theory shows that the amplitudes of oscillations will diminish as the particle is accelerated. This is because the accelerating force is directed parallel to the central orbit so that the electron picks up more and more tangential momentum without a corresponding increase in radial and vertical momentum.

Table 12-4. Characteristics of the 300-MeV betatron at the University of Illinois

Maximum electron energy	315 MeV
Orbit radius	122 cm
Maximum orbit field	9.2 kG
Weight	340 tons
Energy stored in capacitors	170,000 J
Injection energy	80 to 135 keV
Pulse repetition rate	6 pulses/sec
X-ray output at 1 m from target	14,000 R/min

Table 12-4 gives the characteristic parameters for a 300-MeV betatron, the largest ever built. As a source for intense beams of electrons or x-rays, the betatron has been all but replaced by the linear accelerator. Historically, however, the betatron was of enormous importance as a forerunner for the two machines to be described in the following two sections.

12-6 The Electron Synchrotron

The betatron described in the previous section is relatively bulky, since it requires an iron core with an air gap filling the volume enclosed by the orbit. As we have seen, this iron is necessary to provide enough flux lines inside the orbit so that the momentum gained in the acceleration process stays in step with the field in the orbit. Betratons are most often designed to operate at power-line frequencies (50 or 60 c/sec). Because of the large air gap, the reactive power can run into thousands of kilowatts for large betatrons. For good power economy, it is therefore necessary to connect the betatron to a capacitor bank tuned to resonance with the inductance of the magnet. Only losses in the circuit are then provided by the power line.

Since the bulk of the iron is required for accelerating purposes and a relatively minor part of it is required to provide a guiding field for the particle, it is logical to look for other means of accelerating the electrons. A solution to this problem was found independently by MacMillan* and by Veksler.† Their idea was to accelerate the electrons by use of a radiofrequency cavity; in other words, the principle is the same as the one used both in the cyclotron and in the linear accelerator. The important discovery was that such acceleration could take place over a very large number of cycles without loss of synchronism. This synchrotron phase stability is explained below.

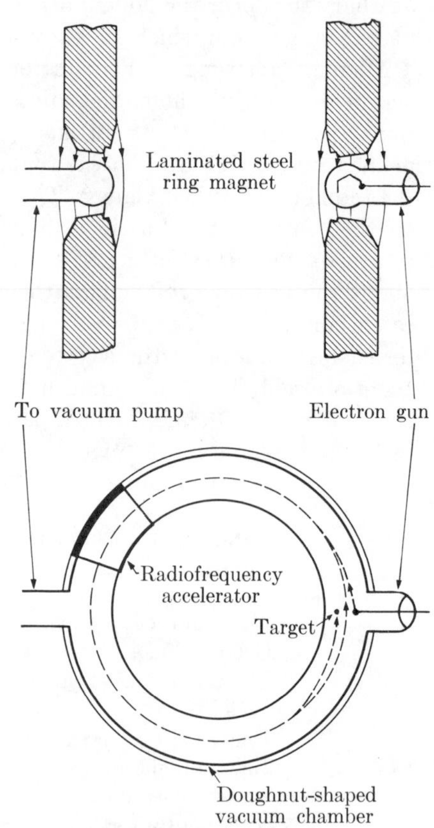

Fig. 12–12. The principal elements of a synchrotron.

Figure 12–12 shows schematically the poles of a synchrotron magnet and the doughnut-shaped vacuum chamber. In the annular region where the electrons are moving, the magnetic field varies with radius in the same way as in the betatron. We therefore have orbit stability in the synchrotron in exactly the same fashion as in the betatron. At one or more places along the orbit, the

* E. M. MacMillan, *Phys. Rev.* **68,** 143 (1945). † V. Veksler, *J. Phys.* (*USSR*) **9,** 153 (1945).

electrons pass through radiofrequency cavities in which there are standing waves of electromagnetic radiation with the electric field directed along the orbit of the electron. The frequency of these oscillations is chosen so that when the electron moves on its equilibrium orbit with a velocity that for all practical purposes can be assumed to be equal to c, it passes through the cavity or cavities every time at a given phase of the electromagnetic radiation. We need not go into the details of the cavity construction; just note that, as the electrons pass a given point in their orbit, they receive an energy gain ΔE, which depends on their time of passage, as illustrated in Fig. 12–13. Assume that a bunch of electrons passes at a time $t = t_1$ and again, one cycle later, at $t = t_1 + T$. The condition for this synchronism is that the frequency of the accelerating field is

$$\omega = \frac{v}{r_0} \approx \frac{c}{r_0}, \tag{12-12}$$

where r_0 is the radius of the central orbit. To keep the electron on this orbit, the field B must increase proportionally to the mass m in accordance with Eq. (12–3).

Assume for a moment that the increase in magnetic field is too slow to keep up with the increase in momentum received per revolution. The electrons will then move out toward a larger radius, their angular frequency will be smaller (as by Eq. 12–12), and they will arrive later at the accelerating gaps (time t_2). According to Fig. 12–13, then, they will receive less increase in energy, the field B can catch up with the mass increase, and the orbit will again contract. If the field strength increases too rapidly, that is, if the increase is more than proportional to the increase in m, the radius will decrease and the angular frequency will increase so that the electrons will arrive at the accelerating gap earlier for each revolution. They will therefore, according to Fig. 12–13, receive more energy increase per turn, resulting in an expansion of the orbit. Clearly, there is a stable equilibrium in radius and phase about which the electrons will

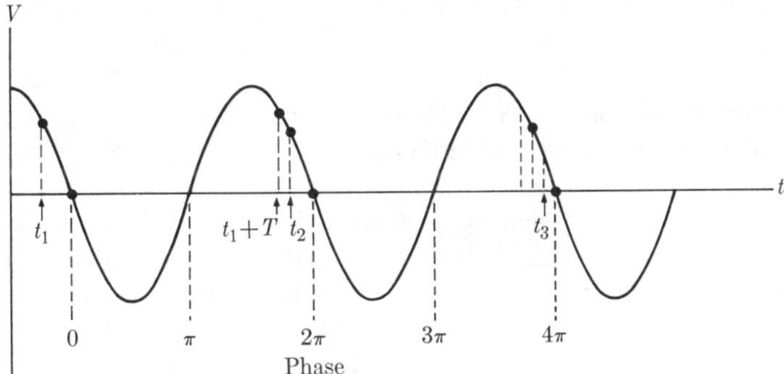

Fig. 12–13. Phase relationship in the synchrotron.

Table 12–5. Characteristics of two electron synchrotrons

	General Electric, 70 MeV	Cambridge Electron Accelerator
Maximum electron energy	70 MeV	6 BeV
Mean orbit radius	0.3 m	36 m
Maximum orbit field	8100 gauss	7600 gauss
Energy at synchrotron takeover	2 MeV	25 MeV
Injector	Betatron action	Linac
Pulse repetition rate	60/sec	60/sec
Radiofrequency cavities	1	16
Frequency of cavities	163 Mc/sec	475.8 Mc/sec
Harmonic or orbital frequency	1st	360th
Magnet power consumption	10 kW	1100 kW

oscillate, provided the maximum available energy increase per turn is large enough.

As we have seen, the phase oscillations and radial oscillations are coupled together in a synchrotron. As in the betatron, radial oscillations will always occur because the electrons are never injected exactly on the equilibrium orbit. Also, scattering by the residual gas in the vacuum system will introduce radial oscillations and, coupled to them, phase oscillations.

Most synchrotrons are operated at line frequency, 50 or 60 c/sec, with the acceleration taking place over a quarter-period every cycle. In some machines, the electrons are injected into orbit from a pre-accelerator external to the synchrotron. This may be a high-voltage rectifier unit (Cockcroft-Walton generator) or a Van de Graaff accelerator. Once inside the magnetic field, the electrons are steered into orbit by the aid of an electrostatic deflector. In other machines, they are injected at low energy from an electron gun inside the dough-nut vacuum system, as in the betatron, and pre-accelerated by betatron action to velocities close to the velocity of light, at which point the synchrotron action takes over. For the betatron phase of the acceleration period, it is necessary to have a relatively large number of flux lines enclosed by the orbit, as required by the betatron condition (Eq. 12–11). This field is produced in an iron core of relatively small cross section. At the end of the betatron cycle, this iron core saturates.

An important factor influencing the operation of any high-energy orbital machine for electrons is the radiation loss caused by the fact that the electrons are subject to a centripetal acceleration. This loss is given by Eq. (9–16) and can be rewritten as

$$\Delta T = 8.85 \times 10^4 \frac{E^4}{r_0} \text{ eV/turn}, \tag{12–13}$$

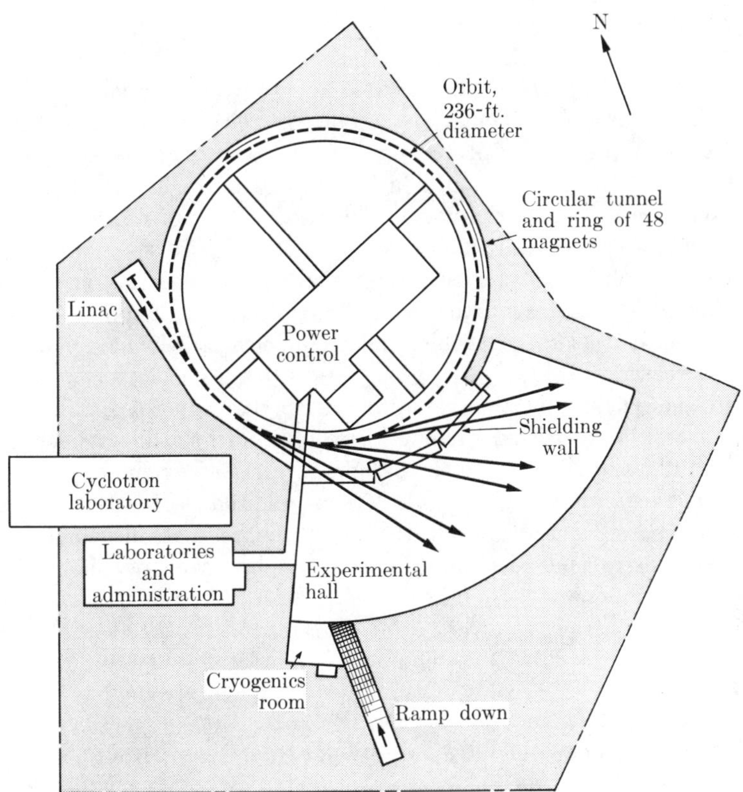

Fig. 12–14. Plan for the Cambridge Electron Accelerator, a 6-BeV synchrotron. (Adapted by permission from M. S. Livingston and J. P. Blewett, *Particle Accelerators*, New York: McGraw-Hill Book Company, Inc., 1962.)

where the total energy of the electrons E is in BeV (1000 MeV), and the radius r_0 is in meters. For instance, the 6-BeV Cambridge Electron Accelerator, a joint Harvard University-Massachusetts Institute of Technology machine, has effective orbit radii of 26 m in the magnets and therefore a total loss of 4.4 MeV/turn. This loss must, of course, be made up for every turn by the energy supplied to the electrons in the accelerating cavities.

The Cambridge Electron Accelerator utilizes the alternating-gradient focusing principle, to be described in the next section. Figure 12–14 shows the building layout for this machine which is used principally for investigations of interactions of high-energy electrons or gamma rays with matter. Table 12–5 shows the principal characteristics of the Cambridge Electron Accelerator, as well as of a smaller conventional electron synchrotron built by The General Electric Corporation.

12–7 The Proton Synchrotron

In the electron synchrotron described in the previous section, the frequency of the accelerating field is kept constant because electrons with energies above a couple of MeV move with practically constant velocity. As explained above, the electrons are pre-accelerated to a few MeV, at which energy there will be a synchronous orbit inside the vacuum chamber. In a proton synchrotron the energy at which the protons get close enough to the velocity of light so that a constant frequency can be used is several BeV. The proton synchrotron, which otherwise operates on the same principle as the electron synchrotron, therefore needs accelerating fields, the frequency of which increases as the velocity increases.

The proton synchrotron was first proposed in 1943 by M. L. Oliphant, then at the University of Birmingham in England. After the war, construction was started at the University of Birmingham, and the machine was completed in 1953. Its maximum energy is 1.0 BeV. Design studies of proton synchrotrons in the United States were started in 1947, and the first machine, the Brookhaven Cosmotron, was in operation in 1952 at a maximum energy of 2.3 BeV. In 1954, a maximum energy of 3.0 BeV was attained. At the University of California in Berkeley, the Bevatron, a 5.7-BeV proton synchrotron, was put into operation in 1954. A 10-BeV machine was completed at Dubna near Moscow in 1957. Several other conventional proton synchrotrons have since been built in England, France, and the United States. Characteristic of all these machines is a relatively low pulse-repetition rate, associated with the fact that the total magnetic energy stored in these machines is very large. To let the energy oscillate between the magnetic field and a bank of capacitors is impractical; it is therefore stored in a flywheel running on the shaft of a large alternator. The alternator supplies the increasing current to the magnet through high-power rectifiers. After the acceleration cycle, the energy built up in the magnetic field is delivered back to the alternator through grid-controlled rectifiers. The energy lost during the cycle is made up by a motor running on the same shaft as the alternator and connected to the power line.

A very exciting development in high-energy accelerator technique came in the early 1950's with the discovery of the alternating-gradient focusing principle. Equations (11–10) and (11–11), which govern the orbital oscillations in the conventional synchrotron as well as in the betatron, show that very strong focusing is obtained in the z-direction by making n very large. However, this results in a loss of focusing in the radial direction. On the other hand, by making n negative and numerically very large, it is possible to obtain a strong radial focusing with simultaneous loss of z-direction focusing. It turns out that strong focusing can be accomplished in both planes by using a large number of magnets around the circumference of the machine, each having the same field strength at the equilibrium orbit but with alternately positive and negative n-values. For example, we recall that for $n = \frac{1}{2}$ (the Svartholm-Siegbahn

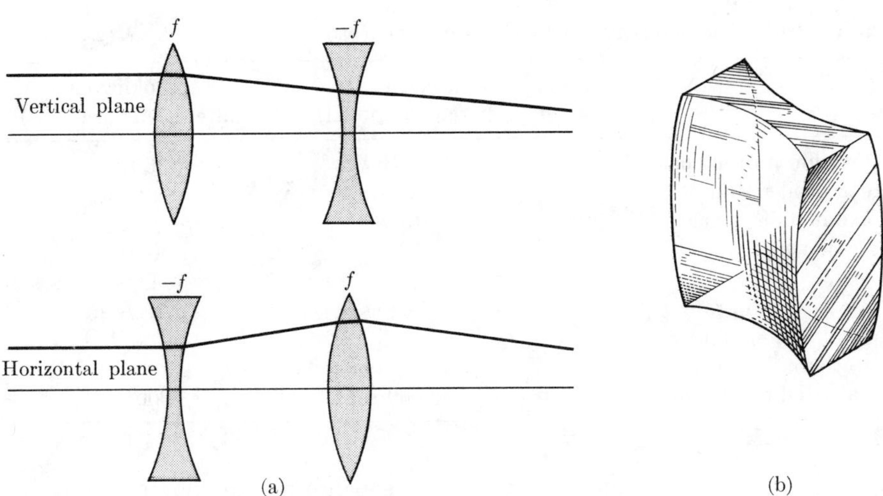

Fig. 12–15. (a) Optical analog of two of the magnets in an alternating-gradient synchrotron. (b) Shape of lens with focusing action analogous to high-n magnet.

spectrometer), particles diverging in both directions from a point on the central orbit will converge toward another point on the central orbit after going through an angle of 254.5°. With alternating-gradient magnets, the particles will experience alternately focusing and defocusing forces in both planes, but the net effect is a return to the central orbit after a much shorter flight distance than 254.5°. This means that a vacuum chamber with a much smaller aperture can be used, assuming a given initial angle of divergence for the injected particles. This means a tremendous saving in the costs of both magnet and power supply.

The principle of alternate-gradient focusing can best be understood in terms of a very simple optical analog. Figure 12–15(a) shows two optical lenses, one convex and one concave, but both with the same numerical focal length. Offhand, one might think that parallel light falling on the first lens will experience no net focusing. This is not so, however. In any lens, whether optical or ion optical, the angle of deflection experienced by a given ray is proportional to the distance from the central ray. Therefore the rays experience a larger angle of deflection in the focusing lens than in the defocusing lens for both cases shown in Fig. 12–15(a). A net focusing effect always results. The action of the alternating-gradient magnets on the particles in the proton synchrotron is the same as the action on the light ray by a series of lenses which are alternately focusing and defocusing. The n-values for the magnets are made very large and alternately negative and positive. The magnets with positive n are focusing in the vertical direction and defocusing radially. The complete optical analog for such a magnet is therefore the lens shown in Fig. 12–15(b) combined with a prism that deflects and disperses the beam.

Table 12–6. Characteristics of two proton synchrotrons

	Dubna, U.S.S.R. (conventional)	Brookhaven (alternating gradient)
Maximum proton energy	10 BeV	33 BeV
Mean orbit radius	30.5 m	128 m
Maximum orbit field	13 kG	13 kG
Injection energy	9 MeV	50 MeV
Injector	Linac	Linac
Pulse repetition rate	5/sec	2.4/sec
Aperture (doughnut cross section)	150 × 40 cm	18 × 8 cm
Total weight of magnets	35,000 tons	4000 tons

The first two alternating-gradient proton synchrotrons to be put into operation were the 28-BeV machine at CERN (European Council for Nuclear Research), Geneva, Switzerland and the 33-BeV machine at Brookhaven National Laboratory. The doughnut of the Brookhaven machine has an elliptic cross section with an 18-cm horizontal axis and 7.5-cm vertical axis. For comparison, the 10-BeV Dubna machine, which does not have alternating-gradient focusing, has a total aperture width of 150 cm and height of 40 cm (see Table 12–6). Figure 12–16 shows the cross section of a magnet with positive n-value; the outline of the pole pieces for the following magnet, which has negative n-value, is shown by dashed lines.

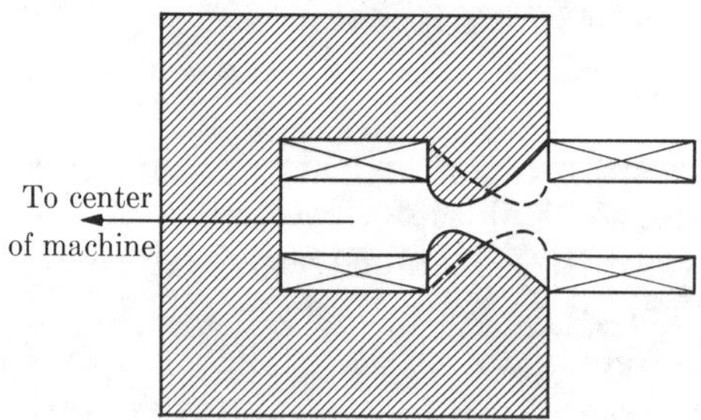

Fig. 12–16. Pole shapes of magnets used in the Brookhaven 33-BeV proton synchrotron. (From Livingston and Blewett, *op. cit.*)

Proton synchrotrons for energies higher than 33 BeV are being planned. At these highly relativistic energies, however, a substantial increase in energy is needed to produce an appreciable amount of new information. As will be further discussed in Section 15–2, a highly relativistic proton colliding with another nucleon represents a heavy particle colliding with a light particle. Therefore a very large fraction of the energy is simply kinetic energy of center-of-mass motion. The total energy in the center-of-mass system, which is the energy that can be utilized for exciting the nucleons or for creating new particles, is a smaller fraction. It would be better, then, to accelerate both particles and let them collide head on. This turns out to be feasible to do in practice, by utilizing two magnetic storage rings with crossing particle orbits. The beam from a proton synchrotron can be injected alternately into these storage rings in which the particles can coast around for relatively long periods of time. At the cross-over point for the two orbits, very energetic collisions will take place, and the radiation emanating from these collisions can be studied with detecting equipment such as spark chambers and bubble chambers surrounding the target area.

12–8 Neutron Sources

Credit for the discovery of the neutron goes to J. Chadwick,* although several other researchers had already studied the effects of neutron radiation without being able to clarify the nature of it. Chadwick and early researchers used a natural radioactive alpha emitter, as for instance Po^{210}, placed adjacent to or surrounded by beryllium. This we know now yields neutrons through the reaction $Be^9(\alpha, n)C^{12}$ with a Q-value of 5.708 MeV. Chadwick elucidated the nature of the neutron by studying the recoil protons from a paraffin layer bombarded with the radiation from the Po-Be source.

Portable neutron sources are still being made from finely divided beryllium and natural alpha emitters, as for instance, radium. The alpha particles from the radium itself and all its decay products produce a wide spectrum of neutrons from the $Be^9(\alpha, n)C^{12}$ reaction, leaving C^{12} in its ground state or in excited states. One curie (1 gm) of radium produces approximately 1.7×10^7 neutrons/sec, and the half-life of the source is the half-life of Ra^{226}, that is, 1622 y.

Other neutron sources have been made with a radioactive nuclide providing the primary radiation. For instance, the binding energy of the last neutron in Be^9 is only 1.67 MeV. Neutrons can therefore be released from Be^9 by photodisintegration, that is, by bombardment with gamma rays of energy 1.67 MeV or more. A large number of radioactive nuclides are available that give off such gamma radiation following beta decay.

More intense neutron radiation can be obtained by bombarding various targets with charged particles from a Van de Graaff accelerator or from a cyclotron. For instance, the following reactions have been used extensively for this purpose: $Li^7(p, n)Be^7$ ($Q = -1.646$ MeV), $Be^9(d, n)B^{10}$ ($Q = 4.35$ MeV), $H^3(p, n)He^3$ ($Q = -0.765$ MeV), and $H^3(d, n)He^4$ ($Q = 17.6$ MeV). The first of these reactions was used by Storrs and Frisch in the low-energy neutron-proton scattering experiment described in Section 3–3. The last reaction gives relatively high-energy neutrons even at low bombarding energies because of

* J. Chadwick, *Proc. Roy. Soc.* (*London*) **A136,** 692 (1932).

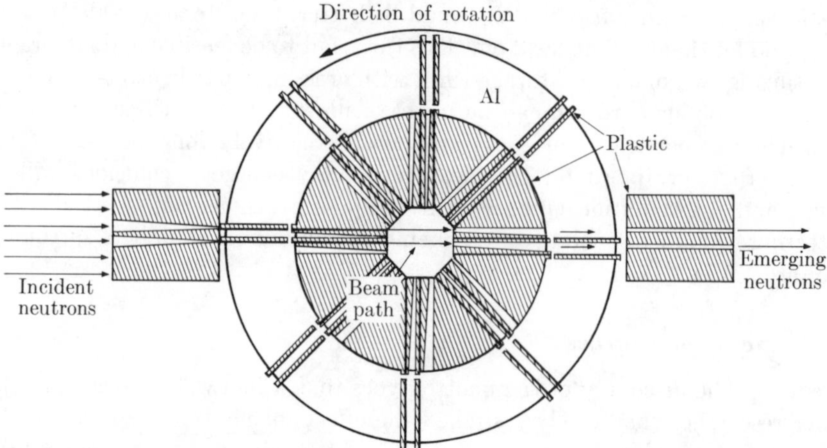

Fig. 12–17. Neutron chopper used to produce microsecond bursts of neutrons from a reactor. [From Seidl *et al.*, *Phys. Rev.* **95,** 476 (1954).]

the large Q-value. At moderate deuteron energies, the neutrons emitted from thin H^3 targets are virtually monoenergetic, because the first excited state of the residual nucleus (He^4) is at approximately 20 MeV, so that all transitions go to the ground state. The neutron energy from this reaction, as well as from the others listed, can be varied by varying either the energy of the incident particles or the reaction angle θ (see Section 13–2).

For experiments where a wide energy spectrum of neutrons is not a disadvantage, a very prolific source is a thick beryllium target struck by the internal deuteron beam in a cyclotron or synchrocyclotron. With such a neutron source, measurements of total cross sections can be performed by use of the absorber method discussed in Section 3–3. The energies of the individual neutrons recorded by the detector are determined by use of time-of-flight techniques (Section 13–4). The same technique can also be employed with neutrons produced by the very intense pulsed beams from modern electron Linacs.

The nuclear fission reactor, described in Section 14–3, has a very high intensity of neutrons in the core. Activation studies can be performed by placing the sample inside this core, and high-intensity beams of neutrons can also be channeled out through the reactor's shielding for experiments outside. It is possible to convert the continuous flux of neutrons into a pulsed beam by letting them pass through a collimator and chopper. In its simplest embodiment, the chopper is a rotating cylinder with a diametrical slot through which the neutrons pass when the slot is oriented in the beam direction. The chopper produces bursts of neutrons with duration as short as a microsecond. The energies of the neutrons are determined by measuring the time of flight from the chopper to the detector.

For neutron energies below 0.5 eV, cadmium is used for lining the slot or slots in the chopper. The cadmium cross section is very large for slow neutrons, but above 1 eV, hydrogenous materials are more effective. Figure 12–17 is a schematic drawing of such a "fast chopper" at Brookhaven National Laboratory.* Eight pairs of slots are made by blocks of plastic material which are held between two forged aluminum wheels. The slots on the entrance side of the wheel are so narrow (a fraction of a millimeter) that they are drawn as single lines. Adjacent to them are two wider slots which will be the "exit" slots four pulses later, when the wheel has turned 180 degrees. At 6000 rpm the pulse duration is about 1 μsec, and the time between pulses is 1.25 msec. The Brookhaven chopper has been used for determining neutron cross sections in the energy range 2 to 200 eV. The energy of the neutrons emerging through the chopper is measured by timing their arrival at a counter placed 20 m away. More details of time-of-flight measurements are given in Section 13–4.

PROBLEMS

12–1. What is the gas consumption (in cm^3/hr at standard pressure) of an ion source that delivers 1 mA H^+ ions with 10% efficiency (85 atom-percent neutrals and 5 atom-percent H_2^+)? If the pumping speed of the accelerating tube is 100 liter/sec, what is the gas pressure at the top of the tube? Assume that the pressure at the bottom of the tube is zero. (Pumping speed, 100 liter/sec means: 100 liters of gas at the higher pressure, not atmospheric pressure, is removed per second.)

12–2. The belt of a Van de Graaff accelerator is 50 cm wide and it moves with a linear velocity of 10 m/sec. Calculate how much current it can carry to the high-voltage terminal when the surface charge is limited by gas breakdown. The gas (at 15-atm pressure) can withstand a field strength of 2×10^7 V/m. Disregard end effects.

12–3. Assume that a cyclotron has a perfectly homogeneous field B and that the applied frequency is $\omega = eB/m_p$, where m_p is the proton rest mass. For simplicity, assume that the radiofrequency voltage is a square wave with amplitude 100 keV. What is the maximum attainable energy of the protons, i.e., the energy gained before they have shifted phase by 180° relative to the radiofrequency voltage because of mass increase? Does it help to lower the frequency of the applied voltage?

12–4. Estimate the total electromagnetic energy in the accelerating tube of the SLAC two-mile Linac during the acceleration pulse when it is operated to give 40-BeV electrons. The diameter of the wave guide is 8.2 cm. What is the total energy in joules of the electrons in one pulse after acceleration? (Use Table 12–3.)

---

* F. G. P. Seidl, D. J. Hughes, H. Palevsky, J. S. Levin, W. Y. Kato, and N. G. Sjöstrand, *Phys. Rev.* **95**, 476 (1954).

12–5. An electron synchrotron has a doughnut of aperture 10×5 cm (elliptic) with a radius of the central orbit $R = 1$ m. Assume that the radiofrequency voltage has frequency $\omega = c/R$. What is the absolute minimum energy of injection, i.e., the energy at which the electrons scrape the inside radius of the doughnut? Discuss injection problems and associated radial oscillations.

*12–6. Design a conventional cyclotron for 15-MeV protons. Give maximum radius, magnetic induction, air-gap dimension, frequency and voltage of radiofrequency power, yoke and coil design. Estimate the weights of iron and copper and the power delivered by the dc supply. Must the current in the coils be stabilized?

13 Nuclear Reactions

13–1 Introduction

A nuclear reaction is a process in which a change in the composition and/or energy of a target nucleus is brought about through bombardment with a nuclear particle or gamma ray. The objectives of experimental nuclear-reaction studies are twofold: (1) The experimental data obtained about the reaction mechanism itself can be compared with the predictions of theories about the process; and (2) nuclear reactions constitute one of the most powerful tools of nuclear spectroscopy, i.e., the mapping of nuclear energy levels. The level schemes, with all the pertinent information about each state, of course, constitute the most valuable data for testing theories of nuclear structure.

When a given target nucleus interacts with a particle of sufficient kinetic energy, there are, in general, many ways for the reaction to proceed. As an example, let us study what possible end products may result from reactions initiated by 6-MeV deuterons on a ${}_{19}K^{39}$ target. In a nuclear reaction of transmutation or scattering process, the number of protons and the number of neutrons are conserved. We therefore make an energy-level diagram containing nuclei and nuclear particles with a total proton number of 20 and a total neutron number of 21. All such systems of interest in this connection are shown in Fig. 13–1. The total energy in the center-of-mass system equals the sum of the rest energies of K^{39} and H^2 plus the 6-MeV kinetic energy reduced from laboratory to center-of-mass coordinates, as follows (nonrelativistic):

$$\begin{aligned} &\text{CM velocity,} \qquad V = \frac{mv}{m+M}, \\ &\text{KE in CM,} \qquad T_{\mathrm{CM}} = \tfrac{1}{2}m(v-V)^2 + \tfrac{1}{2}MV^2 = \frac{T_{\mathrm{lab}}}{1+m/M}, \end{aligned} \tag{13–1}$$

where m is the mass of the incident particle, the deuteron, and M is the mass of the target nucleus, K^{39}. With $m = 2$, $M = 39$, and $T_{\mathrm{lab}} = 6.00$ MeV, we get $T_{\mathrm{CM}} = 5.71$ MeV.

In Fig. 13–1, the top dashed horizontal line at 20.18 MeV above the ground state of Ca^{41} represents the total energy of the system. The following reactions

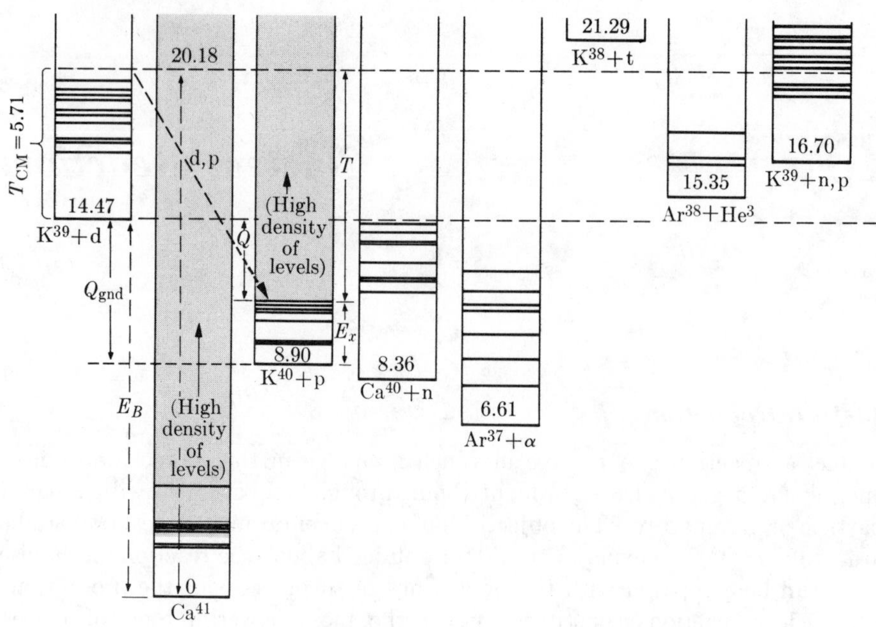

Fig. 13–1. Energy diagram of nucleus plus particle systems with 20 protons and 21 neutrons.

are all seen to be energetically possible (with one exception):

$K^{39}(d, d)K^{39}$	elastic scattering or inelastic scattering, leaving K^{39} in any state below 5.71-MeV excitation
$K^{39}(d, \gamma)Ca^{41}$	deuteron capture at an excitation energy of $E_x = 20.18$ MeV in Ca^{41} with gamma-ray cascades to the ground state
$K^{39}(d, p)K^{40}$	leaving K^{40} in any state below 11.28-MeV excitation
$K^{39}(d, n)Ca^{40}$	leaving Ca^{40} in any state below 11.82-MeV excitation
$K^{39}(d, \alpha)Ar^{37}$	leaving Ar^{37} in any state below 13.57-MeV excitation
$K^{39}(d, He^3)Ar^{38}$	leaving Ar^{38} in any state below 4.83-MeV excitation
$K^{39}(d, np)K^{39}$	leaving K^{39} in any state below 3.48-MeV excitation
$K^{39}(d, t)K^{38}$	not energetically possible at 6-MeV bombarding energy

When a residual nucleus is formed in the ground state, the available energy $Q_{gnd} + T_{CM}$ is given off as kinetic energy of the reaction products (in the center-of-mass system). When the residual nucleus is formed in an excited state, this energy is shared between the internal excitation E_x and the kinetic energy of the reaction products [see example indicated for the (d, p) transition in Fig. 13–1].

All reactions that are energetically possible are likely to occur, for instance those mentioned in the specific example above, but all reactions involving charged particles are subject to the sometimes prohibitively large reduction in cross section imposed by the Coulomb barrier. Reactions involving very high angular-momentum transfer are also inhibited, but there are no angular-momentum or parity-selection rules that completely prohibit certain final states.* As an example, consider the reaction $K^{39}(d,p)K^{40}$. The angular momenta of the target nucleus and the deuteron are $\frac{3}{2}^+$ and 1^+. Assume that the orbital angular momentum of the particle-nucleus system can have the values $l = 0, 1, 2$, and 3 without serious reduction of intensity (see Problem 13–2). Intermediate states with angular momenta up to $J = \frac{11}{2}$ can then be formed. If the proton, with spin $\frac{1}{2}$, can leave the nucleus also with $l = 0, 1, 2$, and 3, we see that final states with angular momenta in the ranges 0^+ to 9^+ or 0^- to 8^- can be formed.

The tools of nuclear-reaction studies can be classified into (1) instruments that provide the projectiles for the reaction, i.e., accelerators and reactors; (2) instruments used for detecting and energy analyzing the reaction products, i.e., counters and spectrographs; and (3) equipment for producing thin targets, preferably monoisotopic.

The preceding chapter was devoted entirely to nuclear accelerators, and some of the most important detectors were discussed in Chapter 7. Spectrographs for charged particles emitted in nuclear reactions are similar to the ones that are used for alpha-particle studies (Section 10–2). Another example of a spectrograph which has the focusing properties of a sector magnet but is of rather special design is described in Section 13–3. Time-of-flight neutron spectroscopy is treated in Section 13–4.

The energy region of greatest interest for nuclear spectroscopy is the 0 to 10 MeV range. As seen in the example (Fig. 13–1), this range of excitation

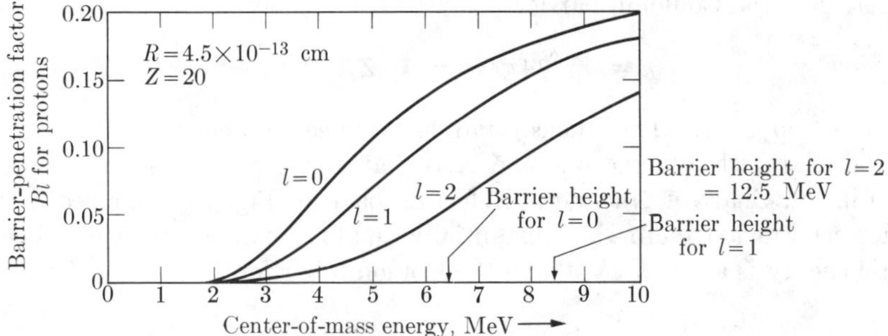

Fig. 13–2. Barrier-penetration factor for protons on a $Z = 20$ nucleus. (From J. M. Blatt and V. F. Weisskopf, *Theoretical Nuclear Physics*, New York: John Wiley and Sons, Inc., 1952, p. 323, reproduced by permission.)

---

* There exists a theoretical isospin selection rule, which in the idealized case of completely Coulomb-independent nuclear states would prohibit reactions for which isospin is not conserved. In practice, this rule has some inhibiting rather than prohibiting effects. See R. K. Adair, *Phys. Rev.* **87,** 1041 (1952) and C. P. Browne, *Phys. Rev.* **104,** 1598 (1956).

energies can be reached for a number of reactions with very modest bombarding energies, at least in deuteron-induced reactions. However, the Coulomb barrier is another factor that needs to be considered. Wave-mechanical barrier penetration can be utilized to some extent, but yield is at a premium in high-resolution work, and it is not usually desirable to take more than a factor of 10 loss in intensity from the barrier-penetration factor.

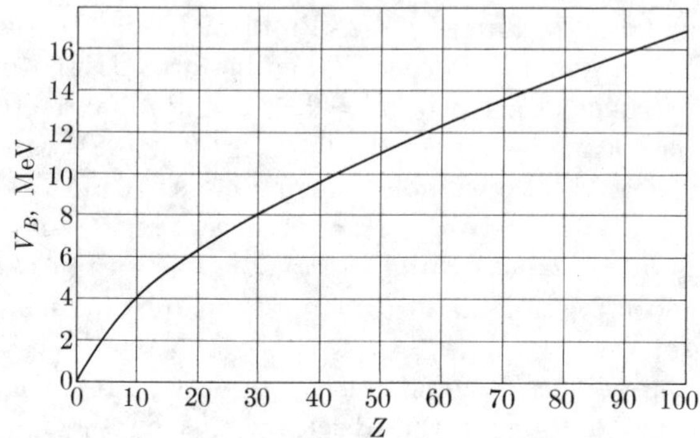

Fig. 13–3. Height of the Coulomb barrier for protons, deuterons, and tritons as a function of Z.

Figure 13–2 shows as an example the barrier-penetration factor (Eq. 10–19) for protons on a $Z = 20$ nucleus with a radius $R = 4.5$ F. The potential utilized in the calculations in Eq. (10–20) is the Coulomb potential $V = Ze^2/4\pi\epsilon_0 r$ with a sharp cutoff at the nuclear radius R. Figure 13–3 shows the height of the Coulomb barrier

$$V_B = Ze^2/4\pi\epsilon_0 r = 1.1ZA^{-1/3} \text{ MeV} \tag{13–2}$$

as a function of Z. The nuclear radius has been taken as $R = 1.3A^{1/3}$ F, and the relationship between Z and A is that given by the line of most stable nuclei in the Chart of Nuclides. Referring back to Fig. 13–2, we see that the barrier-penetration factor is substantially smaller than unity even when the kinetic energy is a few MeV above the Coulomb barrier.

13–2 Reaction Dynamics; the Q-equation

An important part of nuclear-reaction experiments is the measurement of the energy released in the reaction, the Q-value (compare Section 4–5). Here, we will study a single event, a particle-particle reaction, in the light of the elementary conservation laws of mechanics in order to calculate the relationship between particle energies and Q.

We are concerned with a reaction initiated by an *incident particle* of mass M_I and kinetic energy T_I in a collision with a *target nucleus* with mass M_T

and energy $T_T \approx 0$. After the reaction, an emitted particle with mass M_E and kinetic energy T_E leaves the *residual nucleus* with mass M_R and kinetic energy T_R (Fig. 13–4). We are not at this time concerned with exactly what takes place at the moment of collision, whether M_I and M_T actually fuse to form a short-lived intermediate nucleus (compound nucleus) or whether a transfer of nucleons or energy takes place at the surface of the nucleus (direct reaction).

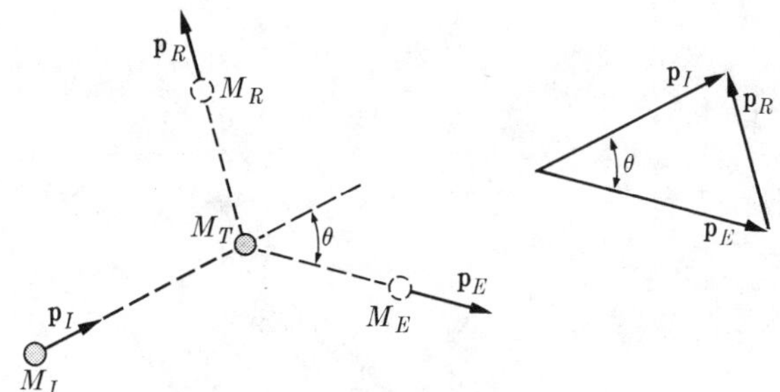

Fig. 13–4. Nuclear reaction; schematic of a single event.

The Q-value is defined as

$$Q = (M_I + M_T)c^2 - (M_E + M_R)c^2, \tag{13–3}$$

which by conservation of energy can be rewritten

$$Q = T_E + T_R - T_I - T_T. \tag{13–4}$$

If our measurements took place in the center-of-mass system, it would suffice to measure T_I and T_E, since T_T and T_R could then be determined very simply by invoking momentum conservation. However, our equipment is earthbound, and the experimental observables that are simplest to record are the values of T_I, T_E, and the reaction angle θ, all in the laboratory system. Fortunately, we normally have $T_T \approx 0$ in the laboratory system. We must therefore find an expression for T_R in terms of measured quantities (see Eq. 13–4). We use the law of conservation of momentum (Fig. 13–4):

$$\mathbf{p}_I = \mathbf{p}_R + \mathbf{p}_E, \tag{13–5}$$

together with the general (relativistic) relationship between momentum and kinetic energy

$$p^2 = 2MT + T^2/c^2. \tag{13–6}$$

By applying the law of cosines to the momentum triangle (Fig. 13–4), we obtain

$$2M_RT_R + T_R^2/c^2 = 2M_IT_I + T_I^2/c^2 + 2M_ET_E + T_E^2/c^2 \\ - 2\cos\theta\sqrt{(2M_IT_I + T_I/c^2)(2M_ET_E + T_E^2/c^2)}. \tag{13–7}$$

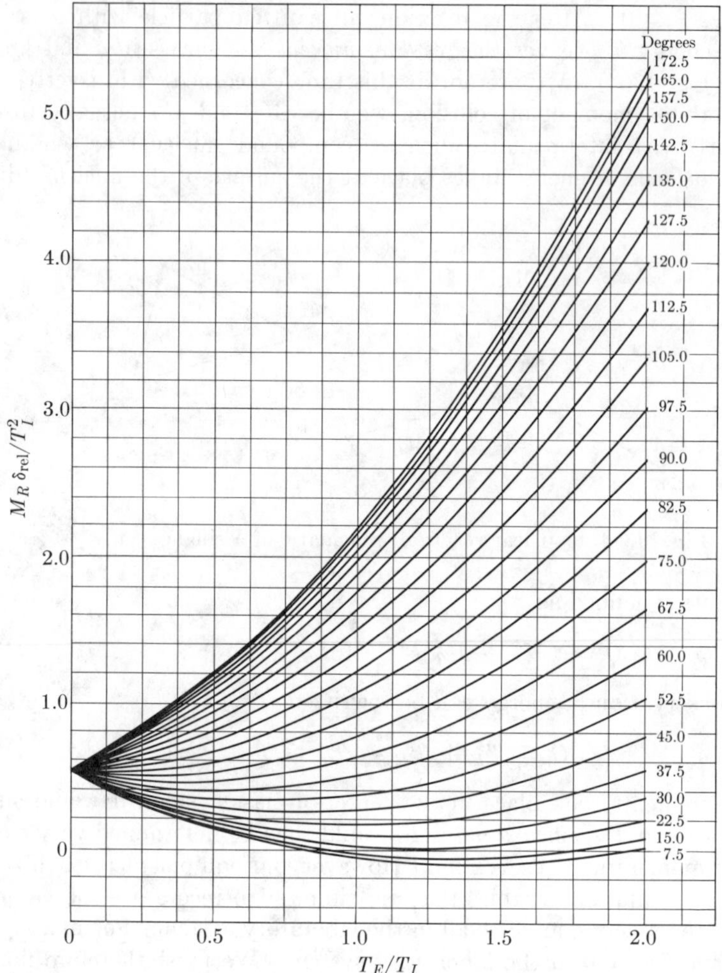

Fig. 13–5. Relativistic correction to the Q equation for (d, p) reactions; M_R = residual mass in mass units, u, T_I = incident kinetic energy in MeV, T_E = emitted energy in MeV, δ_{rel} = relativistic correction in keV.

Since the second-order terms, T_I^2/c^2, etc., are small compared with their neighbors for nuclear reactions in the binding energy range, we do not need to write out the exact solution of the second-order equation (13–7). Instead we expand the square root and obtain

$$T_R = \frac{M_I}{M_R}\,T_I + \frac{M_E}{M_R}\,T_E - 2\cos\theta\,\frac{\sqrt{M_I M_E T_I T_E}}{M_R} + \delta_{\text{rel}}, \tag{13–8}$$

where the relativistic correction term is

$$\delta_{\text{rel}} \approx \frac{1}{2M_R c^2}\left[T_I^2 + T_E^2 - T_R^2 - \cos\theta\sqrt{M_I M_E T_I T_E}\left(\frac{T_I}{M_I} + \frac{T_E}{M_E}\right)\right]. \tag{13-9}$$

Most often T_R is so small compared with T_I and T_E that for the purpose of calculating the relativistic correction, δ_{rel}, we can set $T_R = 0$ in Eq. (13–9) or we can use the classical expression (Eq. 13–8 without δ_{rel}). The latter approach then represents a solution by successive approximations.

Since we usually prefer to work with MeV and mass units rather than with joules and kilograms, we can substitute $1863M_R$ (with M_R in mass units u) for $2M_R c^2$ to get δ_{rel} in MeV with T in MeV.

Equation (13–8) inserted into (13–4) with $T_T = 0$ yields

$$Q = \frac{M_R + M_E}{M_R} T_E - \frac{M_R - M_I}{M_R} T_I - 2\cos\theta \frac{\sqrt{M_I M_E T_I T_E}}{M_R} + \delta_{\text{rel}}. \tag{13-10}$$

This is what nuclear-reaction physicists refer to as the Q-value equation. It gives the desired relation between the energy release Q and the measured quantities T_I, T_E, and θ. The masses entering into the formula are nuclear rest masses. When the residual nucleus is left in an excited state, M_R is, of course, the rest mass of the nucleus in that state. As shown by the example in the problem section (Problem 13–3), the errors introduced by using the ground-state rest masses, or even integral mass numbers, in Eq. (13–10) are very small, except for cases where a very light residual nucleus is left at a high excitation energy.

Figure 13–5 is a plot of Eq. (13–9) for the relativistic correction as calculated for a (d, p) reaction. The term T_R^2 in Eq. (13–9) has been neglected. With $T_I = 10$ MeV and $M_R = 10$ u, as an example, we obtain $\delta_{\text{rel}} \approx 10$ keV (order of magnitude), depending on T_E and θ. For higher residual mass M_R, the correction is smaller.

13–3 Charged-Particle Reaction Spectroscopy

The problems of measuring the energy of charged particles from nuclear reactions are very much the same as those encountered in alpha-particle spectroscopy, except that the source, instead of being a radioactive substance, is a target bombarded with a beam of incident particles. The instruments most often used are the scintillation counter, the proportional gas counter, the solid-state counter, and magnetic spectrographs.

The scintillation counter, or scintillation spectrometer (Section 7–7), has proved very useful when a resolving power that is not too high is required. The scintillation crystal can be mounted quite close to the target to yield a large solid angle of acceptance. Because the charged particles in low-energy nuclear-reaction spectroscopy have a relatively small range in solid materials (less than 1 mm), the scintillator can be quite thin. This helps to cut down the background from gamma rays, neutrons, and cosmic rays. The resolving power attained with scintillation spectrometers is typically $E/\Delta E = 20$ to 30. One can do much better than this with other types of instruments, but the scintillation spectrometer is still useful in nuclear-reaction work, especially when coincidences are being studied between the charged particles and gamma rays de-exciting the state formed in the reaction.

In recent years, the solid-state spectrometer (Section 7–6) has been used extensively in charged-particle spectroscopy. Resolving powers of the order of $E/\Delta E = 200$ to 300 have been obtained, and initial difficulties in producing sufficiently thick active layers to stop, for instance 20-MeV protons, seem to have been overcome. A pulse-height spectrum from the $Ni^{64}(p, p)Ni^{64}$ scattering process taken with a solid-state spectrometer is shown in Fig. 13–6. The incident energy is $T_I = 11$ MeV, and the scattering angle $\theta = 60°$. The peak half-widths are about $\Delta E \approx 40$ keV, giving a resolving power $E/\Delta E \approx 250$ for the highest energy peaks. The numbered peaks in Fig. 13–6 refer to levels in Ni^{64} and peaks arising from elastic or inelastic scattering from contaminants are labeled accordingly. The general background of some 10 to 20 counts per channel is caused mostly by elastically scattered protons that somehow do not deliver their full energy to the counter [notice the high intensity of the $Ni^{64}(0)$ peak].

For high-resolution work, the magnetic spectrograph or spectrometer is unquestionably the right instrument to use in nuclear-reaction studies. Two homogeneous-field spectrographs are described in Section 10–2; they are both single focusing. This means that particles diverging from a point source located in the median plane of the magnet will converge after deflection toward a line image perpendicular to the median plane at some distance from the exit of the magnet. The reason why the image is a line rather than a point is that there are no focusing forces acting perpendicular to the median plane. Therefore the particles having velocity components perpendicular to the median plane will keep diverging in this direction, and the result is, of course, that a point object will produce a line image. Double-focusing instruments, i.e., instruments that produce a point image of a point source, can be designed in various ways. A very popular spectrometer of this kind utilizes a magnet with an inhomogeneous field similar to the Svartholm-Siegbahn instrument used in beta spectroscopy, except that it is a sector magnet with both the source and the detector outside the field.*

We shall now describe in somewhat more detail a complex instrument which is used in nuclear-reaction studies in association with an 8-MeV Van de Graaff

* C. W. Snyder, S. Rubin, W. A. Fowler, and C. C. Lauritsen, *Rev. Sci. Instr.* **21,** 852 (1950).

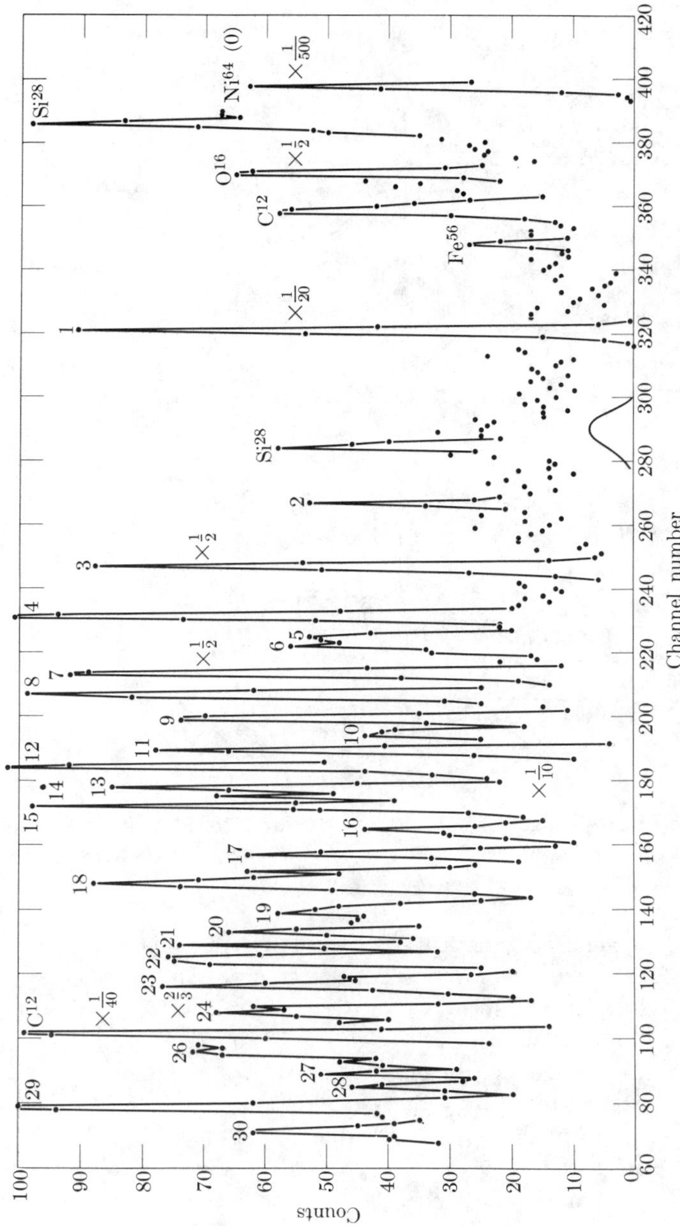

Fig. 13–6. Pulse-height spectrum of protons elastically and inelastically scattered from a thin (1 mg/cm^2) Ni^{64} target. Incident proton energy T_I = 11 MeV. Reaction angle θ = 60°. [From J. K. Dickens, F. G. Percy, and R. J. Silva, *Phys. Rev.* **132,** 1190 (1963).]

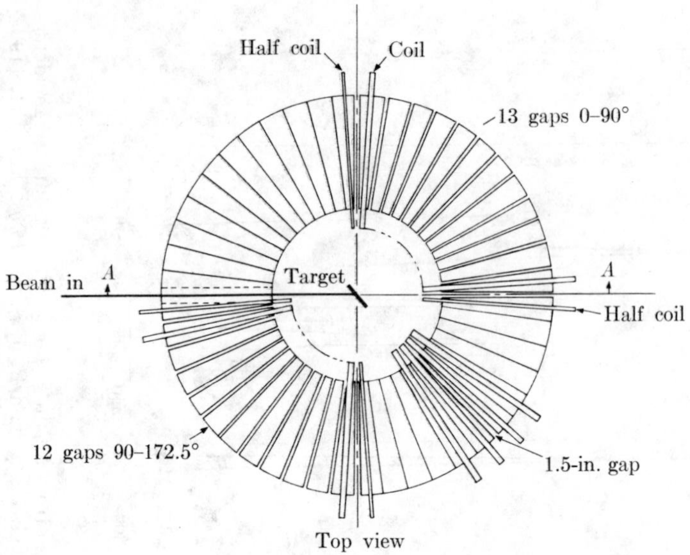

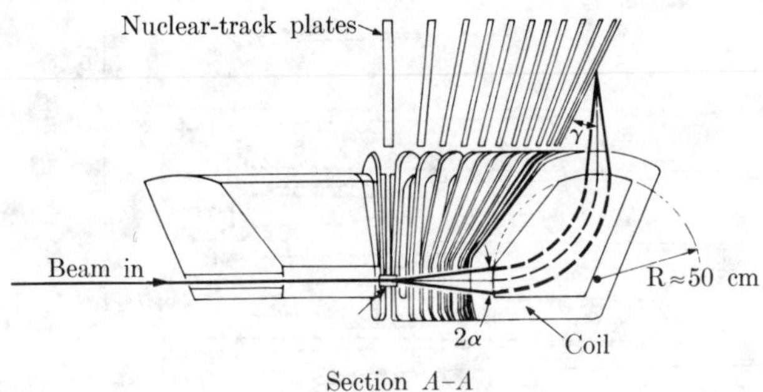

Fig. 13–7. Simplified drawing of the Massachusetts Institute of Technology multiple-gap spectrograph. [From H. A. Enge and W. W. Buechner, *Rev. Sci. Instr.* **34,** 155 (1963).]

machine at the Massachusetts Institute of Technology.* This spectrograph is actually twenty-four instruments in one large vacuum enclosure, each spectrograph recording a broad-range spectrum of particles emitted at a given angle θ from the incident beam. The range of angles is 0° to 172.5° in steps of 7.5°. The reason for wanting to record the emitted particles throughout such a large angular range will be made evident in Section 13–12. Figure 13–7 is a simplified drawing of the spectrograph illustrating its principles of operation. The toroidal magnetic circuit comprises forty-eight 7.5° cast-iron wedges, some of which are thinner than others so that gaps are left between them. The wedges are clamped

* H. A. Enge and W. W. Buechner, *Rev. Sci. Instr.* **34,** 155 (1963).

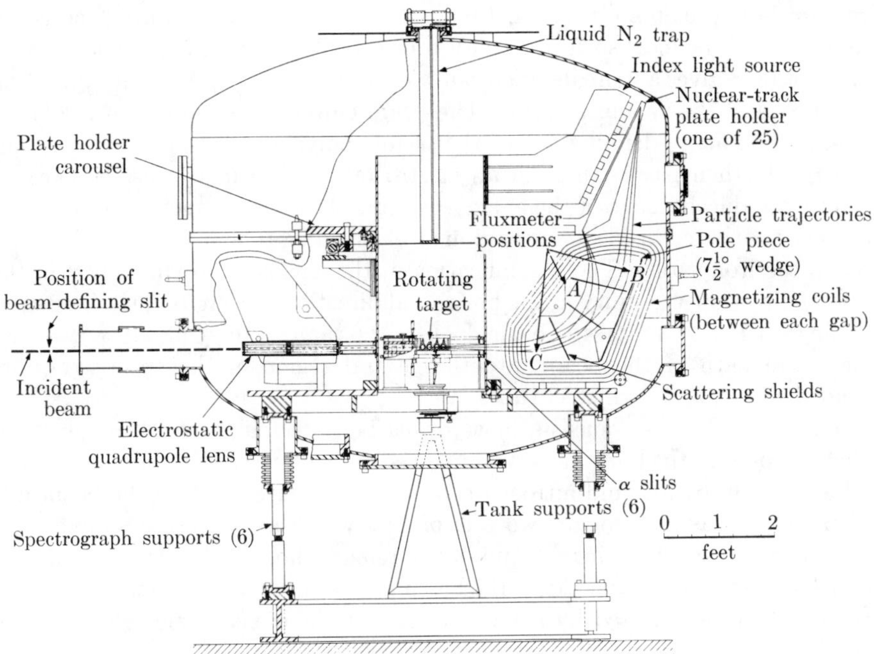

Fig. 13-8. Cross-sectional view of the Massachusetts Institute of Technology multiple-gap spectrograph. (From H. A. Enge and W. W. Buechner, *op. cit.*)

rigidly together with stainless-steel spacers defining the gaps. Twenty-five of the gaps are $\frac{3}{8}$ in. wide, and one gap is 1.5 in. wide.* The magnetic reluctance of the iron between the gaps is very small compared with the reluctance in the gap, and practically no magnetomotive force is required to drive the flux in the iron. In order to minimize the effects of stray fields, the coils have been placed so as to achieve balance between the reluctance and the magnetomotive force throughout the magnetic circuit. Each $\frac{3}{8}$-in. gap is magnetized by five turns on each of the two pole pieces adjacent to the gap. The 1.5-in. gap is magnetized by twenty turns on each side of the gap. The target is placed in the center of the torus, and the beam reaches the target region by passing through a field-free hole through the iron.

The lower part of Fig. 13-7 shows a cross-sectional side view of the spectrograph with the beam-entering hole, the target, and the particle trajectories in the 0° gap (if used). The pole-face geometry and focal surface geometry are identical for all gaps and also very nearly the same as in a similar single-gap spectrograph built earlier at M.I.T.† The range of energy covered in one

---

* The 1.5-in. gap is intended for large solid-angle spectrometry in conjunction with a quadrupole lens. See H. A. Enge, *Rev. Sci. Instr.* **29,** 885 (1958).
† C. P. Browne and W. W. Buechner, *Rev. Sci. Instr.* **27,** 899 (1956).

exposure is approximately 2.3:1, that is, if 11.5-MeV protons are focused to the top end of the focal surface, 5-MeV protons will be focused to the lower end.

Figure 13–8 gives a more detailed side view of the spectrograph, its supporting structure, and the vacuum vessel. The beam enters from the left in Fig. 13–8 through the energy-defining slit of the beam-analyzing magnet (the latter not shown). It then passes through an electrostatic quadrupole lens designed to produce a reduced image of the energy-defining slit on the target. This quadrupole lens is situated inside a low-carbon steel shielding tube in the 3-in. diameter hole in the iron torus. The magnification of the lens is approximately $\frac{1}{3}$ in the vertical direction and unity in the horizontal direction. Therefore, if the energy-defining slit is 1×3 mm, the beam spot on the target will be about $\frac{1}{3} \times 3$ mm. The entire path of the beam into the central region of the spectrograph is shielded with low-carbon steel tubes.

The target chamber consists of a low-carbon steel pipe of 24-in. diameter which is closed at the bottom by a stainless-steel plate used as a reference surface and at the top by a liquid-nitrogen cooled copper plate. Before the beam hits the target, it passes through two sets of slits which are adjusted so as not to intercept any part of the main beam but to remove most of the cone of scattered particles around the beam. After the beam passes through the thin solid, or gas, target, it can be collected by a Faraday cup at the opposite end of the target chamber.

The reaction products are recorded on nuclear-track plates mounted in rigid holders above each gap. Three 2×10-in. plates are used in each holder to cover the 30 in. long part of the focal surface which is used. After the exposure, the plates are developed and scanned under microscopes in half-millimeter strips across the plate. The number of tracks having the correct length and correct direction are counted. Spurious events arising from cosmic rays or neutrons colliding with a proton in the emulsion can usually be eliminated on the basis of track length and direction. The number of half-millimeter strips in 30 in. is about 1500. This quantity multiplied by the number of angles normally utilized, 24, gives 36,000 data points obtainable with this instrument in one single exposure. The exposure time for most applications is typically of the order of 1 to 10 hrs.

Figure 13–9 shows an example of a spectrum recorded at a reaction angle of 37.5° in the multiple-gap spectrograph.* The reaction is $Sc^{45}(d,p)Sc^{46}$ and the various peaks in the spectrum, of course, correspond to various states in Sc^{46}. These states are labeled "0" for the ground state, "1" for the first excited state, etc., and the corresponding excitation energies can be found on the scale at the top of the figure. The scandium target had a certain amount of contaminant elements and also was supported by a film made from an organic compound. The peaks resulting from (d, p) reactions in these other elements are labeled accordingly in Fig. 13–9. They have been identified on the basis

* J. Rapaport, A. Sperduto, and W. W. Buechner (to be published).

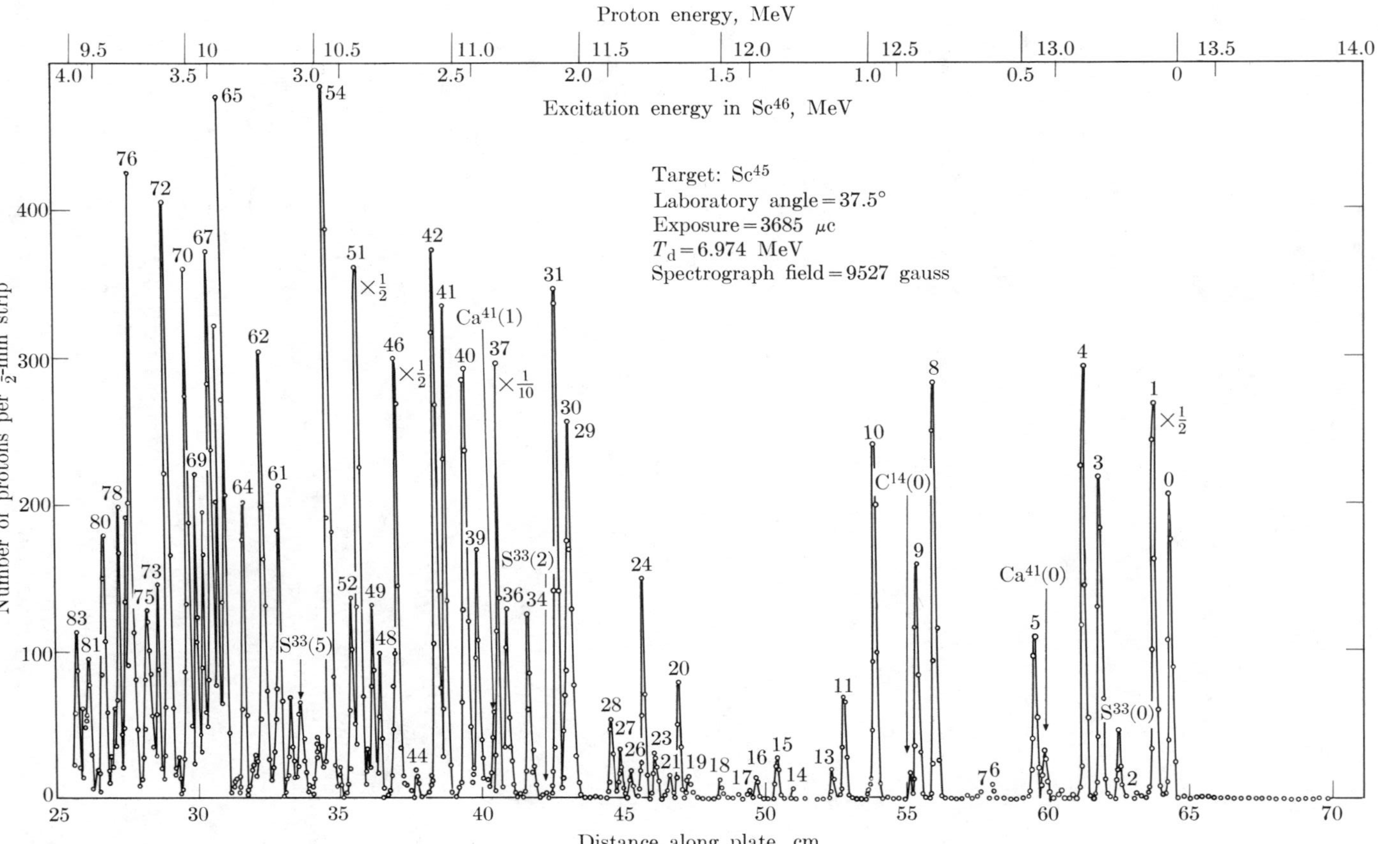

Fig. 13–9. Part of the energy spectrum of protons from the $Sc^{45}(d,p)Sc^{46}$ reaction recorded at $\theta = 37.5$ in the multiple-gap spectrograph. (From J. Rapaport, A. Sperduto, and W. W. Buechner (to be published).

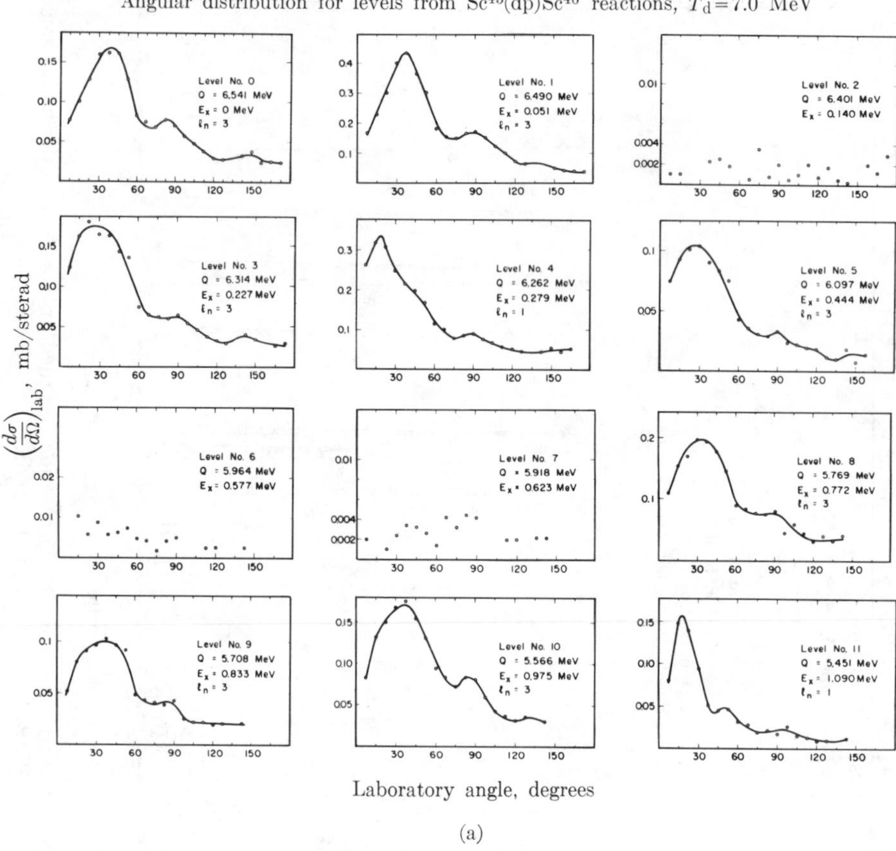

Fig. 13–10. Examples of angular distributions of protons for the Sc^{45}(d, p)Sc^{46} reaction leaving the residual nucleus in the level numbers indicated on each little graph. (From J. Rapaport *et al., op. cit.*)

of the shift in proton energy for a given change in reaction angle θ (see Problem 13–4 and Eq. 13–10).

Spectra similar to the one shown in Fig. 13–9 were obtained for all angles of the spectrograph. The differential cross section for each individual peak at each angle was determined and plotted as a function of θ. Figure 13–10 shows some of these so-called angular-distribution curves. Almost all of these curves show pronounced forward maxima. We shall see in Section 13–11 that the position of the maximum in the proton distribution reflects the value of the orbital angular-momentum quantum number l_n of the state into which the neutron has been captured.

The overall resolving power of an instrument like the one described above, when used in conjunction with a Van de Graaff accelerator, is not determined

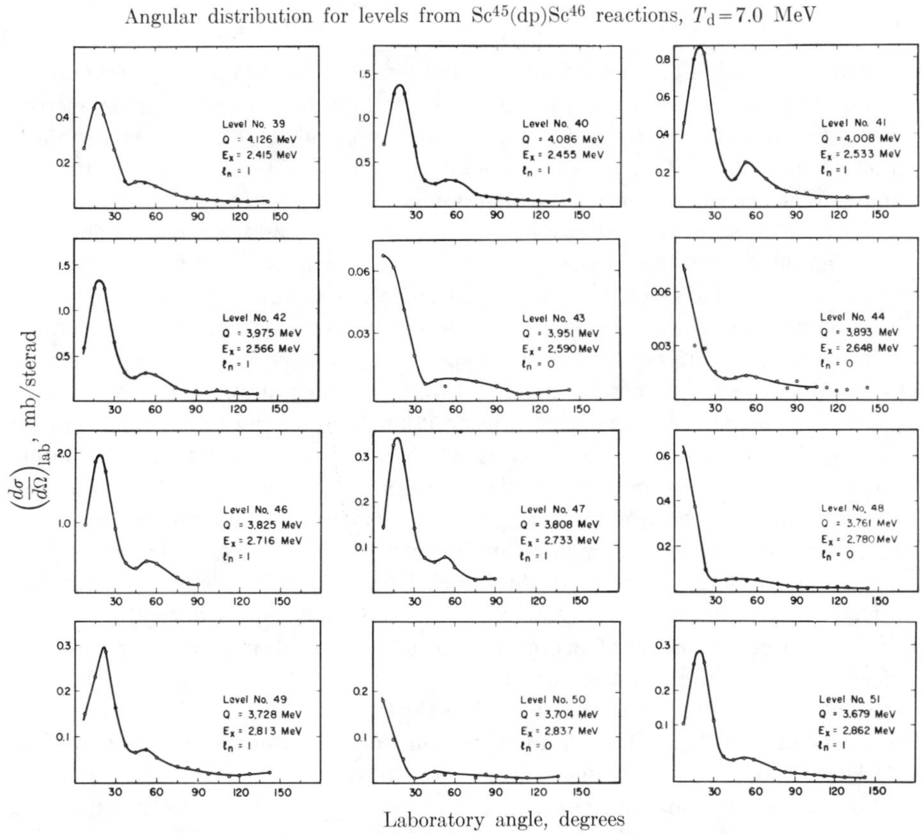

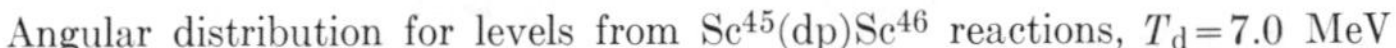

Angular distribution for levels from Sc^{45}(dp)Sc^{46} reactions, $T_d = 7.0$ MeV
Level No. 39 Q = 4.126 MeV Ex = 2.415 MeV ℓn = 1
Level No. 40 Q = 4.086 MeV Ex = 2.455 MeV ℓn = 1
Level No. 41 Q = 4.008 MeV Ex = 2.533 MeV ℓn = 1
Level No. 42 Q = 3.975 MeV Ex = 2.566 MeV ℓn = 1
Level No. 43 Q = 3.951 MeV Ex = 2.590 MeV ℓn = 0
Level No. 44 Q = 3.893 MeV Ex = 2.648 MeV ℓn = 0
Level No. 46 Q = 3.825 MeV Ex = 2.716 MeV ℓn = 1
Level No. 47 Q = 3.808 MeV Ex = 2.733 MeV ℓn = 1
Level No. 48 Q = 3.761 MeV Ex = 2.780 MeV ℓn = 0
Level No. 49 Q = 3.728 MeV Ex = 2.813 MeV ℓn = 1
Level No. 50 Q = 3.704 MeV Ex = 2.837 MeV ℓn = 0
Level No. 51 Q = 3.679 MeV Ex = 2.862 MeV ℓn = 1
$\left(\frac{d\sigma}{d\Omega}\right)_{lab}$, mb/sterad
Laboratory angle, degrees

Figure 13–10 *(cont.)* (b)

by the instrument alone but, in general, by the following factors: (1) the energy stability of the beam of the Van de Graaff generator, (2) the vertical dimension of the beam spot on the target (since this influences the size of the image on the nuclear-track plate), (3) the width of the strips scanned with the microscope across the nuclear-track plates (usually 0.5 mm), (4) the effective target thickness, and (5) the aberration of the spectrograph. If one desires to increase the resolving power, for instance by a factor of 2, then, of course, improvements corresponding to about a factor of 2 are required in all five areas mentioned above. Such improvement will always entail a loss in yield from the reaction. What this means in practice is that one can have an improvement of the resolving power by a factor of 2 only at the expense of a decrease in the yield or an increase in the exposure time by about a factor of 10. The resolving power for the experiment described above was $E/\Delta E \approx 1000$. It can easily be appreciated then that resolving powers of the order of $E/\Delta E = 10^4$ are quite difficult to attain with existing instruments. They are needed, however, for precision energy-level studies on heavy elements where the density of levels is very high.

13–4 Neutron Spectroscopy

In order to reach a given residual nucleus one often has to employ a reaction in which the emitted particle is a neutron. Since they have no charge, the neutrons are harder to detect than protons, deuterons, etc. and their energy is also more difficult to analyze. One must always introduce an additional step in which the neutron, either through a second reaction or an elastic-scattering process, produces a detectable charged particle. Most often this additional step entails a considerable reduction of the yield, a reduction which can only be compensated for by increases in target thickness, solid angles, etc., which, again, are reflected in a reduction in the resolving power (see the previous section).

The simplest example of a neutron spectrometer is perhaps the thick photographic emulsion. Neutrons passing through the emulsion may collide with protons in the emulsion and give up a fraction or practically all of their kinetic energy. The direction of the entering neutron (from the target) is presumably known, so that when the track of the recoil proton in the emulsion is measured under the microscope, the scattering angle θ between the neutron direction and proton direction can be found. The energy of the proton is determined by measuring its range in the emulsion (track length), and the neutron energy can then be computed as $T_{\mathrm{n}} = T_{\mathrm{p}}(\cos\theta)^{-2}$. This equation is derived by using the laws of conservation of energy and of conservation of momentum and neglecting the neutron-proton mass difference (Problem 13–5). Figure 13–11 is an example of a neutron spectrum from the $\mathrm{Be}^9(\mathrm{d,n})\mathrm{B}^{10}$ reaction.* The resolving power $E/\Delta E \approx 20$ is limited by straggling of the protons in the emulsion, thereby making the track lengths uncertain by about 5%.

Scintillators containing hydrogen can be used to detect the protons recoiling from neutron-proton collisions in the scintillator material. The scintillation counter is not, however, very well suited for neutron spectroscopy because the recoil angle between the neutron direction and the proton direction cannot be determined. Unless the scintillator is very large, the neutron usually gives up only a fraction of its energy in the scintillator.

Solid-state detectors have recently come into use in neutron spectroscopy in the so-called sandwich counters. A thin film containing Li^6 is sandwiched between two solid-state counters. In passing through the sandwich, neutrons in the energy range 1 to 10 MeV will, relatively speaking, have a reasonably high probability of initiating the reaction $\mathrm{Li}^6(\mathrm{n,t})\mathrm{He}^4$. If the triton enters one of the solid-state counters and the alpha particle enters the other, a coincidence can be registered, and the sum of the pulse heights from the two counters is a measure of the energy of the neutron initiating the reaction. Practical sandwich counters have a detection efficiency of the order of 10^{-6} or 10^{-7}, and the half-width of a peak in the pulse-height spectrum arising from monoenergetic neutrons may be of the order of 300 keV.

---

* Fay Ajzenberg, *Phys. Rev.* **88,** 298 (1952).

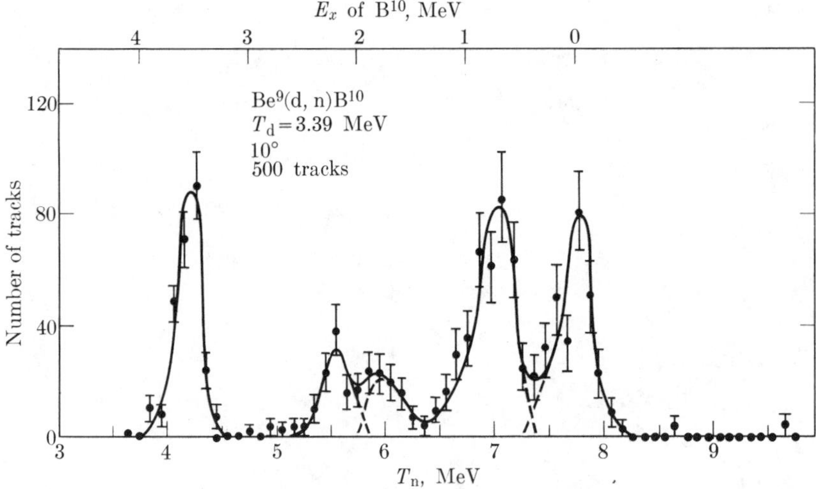

Fig. 13-11. Neutron spectrum from the $Be^9(d, n)B^{10}$ reaction at $\theta = 10°$. The spectrum is derived from analysis of proton recoil tracks in Eastman Kodak NTA emulsions. [From Fay Ajzenberg, *Phys. Rev.* **88,** 298 (1952).]

The most exact work in neutron spectroscopy has undoubtedly been performed with pulsed accelerators and devices to measure the time of flight of neutrons over a certain path length L from target to detector. Essentially, then, the energies of the neutrons are determined through a measurement of their velocities. The accelerator may be a Van de Graaff generator delivering the beam to the target in bunches of approximately 1 nsec (10^{-9} sec) duration about 1 μsec apart. The detector may be a scintillation counter with associated electronic equipment designed, not to measure the pulse-height spectrum, but to measure the time-delay spectrum, with the reference being the time a pulse strikes the target. The flight time for neutrons over a path length L in meters depends on the neutron energy as

$$t = L/v = L\sqrt{m/2T} = (L/c)\sqrt{mc^2/2T} = 72.3L/\sqrt{T}\ \text{nsec}, \quad (13\text{–}11)$$

where T is the kinetic energy of the neutron in MeV. For instance, if the flight path L is 5 m, the flight time for a 1-MeV neutron is 361.5 nsec. Typically, the time resolution of such equipment may be of the order of 2 nsec. This means that because of the duration of the beam pulse, the size of the detector, and the time uncertainties in the electronic equipment, the flight time for a neutron of a given energy is uncertain to approximately 2 nsec. For the example of the 1-MeV neutron, this gives a time resolving power of $t/\Delta t = 180$, but since $\Delta T/T = 2\,\Delta t/t$, the energy resolving power for this example will be about $R = T/\Delta T = 90$. For neutron spectroscopy, this is quite good but, of course, the resolving power decreases with increasing energies as t diminishes

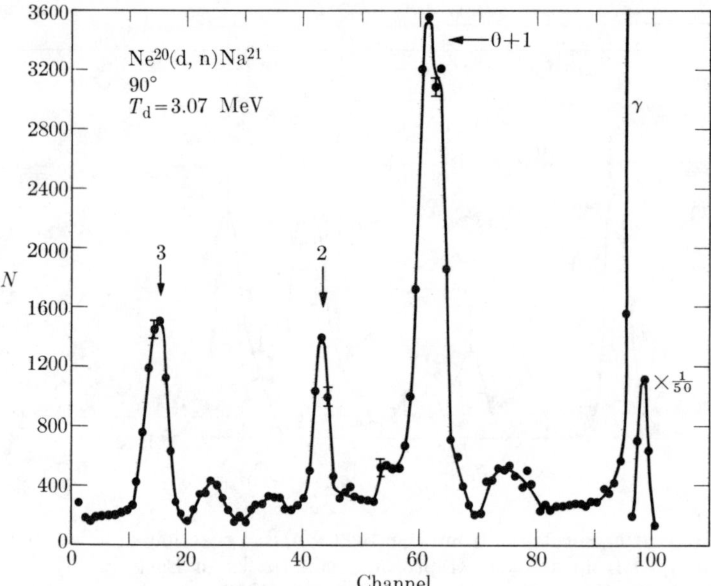

Fig. 13–12. Time-of-flight spectrum. The target-to-counter distance was L = 2.02 m. The time difference between channels was approximately 2.3 nsec with zero time at about channel 102. [From Fay Ajzenberg-Selove, L. Cranberg, and F. S. Dietrich, *Phys. Rev.* **124,** 1548 (1961).]

(Eq. 13–11) while Δt stays approximately constant. Obviously, increasing the flight time by making the flight path longer will improve the resolving power. Figure 13–12 is an example of a time-of-flight spectrum of neutrons from a Ne^{20} gas target bombarded with 3.07-MeV deuterons. The intense peak to the far right arises from gamma rays arriving first ($v = c$).

13–5 Theories of Nuclear Reactions

It has been the policy in previous chapters of this book first to present well-established experimental facts, then to develop theories that might illuminate the particular facts presented, and finally to make the comparison between experiments and theories. In this chapter, we shall deviate somewhat from this procedure. This is because nuclear reactions cover a much wider area and present a much more complex picture than, for instance, alpha decay. A unified theory of nuclear reactions exists but it is sufficiently abstract so that we shall have to forego a discussion of it in this text and rather concentrate on simpler, more to-the-point discussions of particular aspects of the reactions. In the following sections we will therefore develop some seemingly widely different theories, each applicable to a particular area, and then illustrate the particular aspect covered by examples of experimental data.

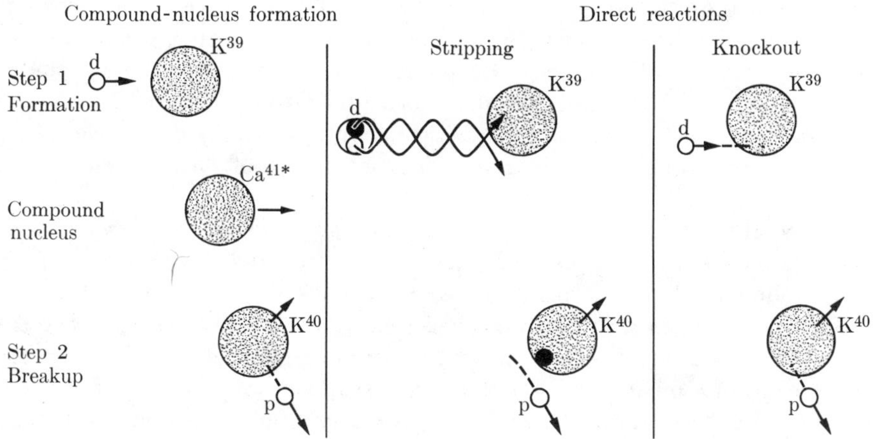

Fig. 13–13. Example of a reaction that can proceed along different lines, all of which lead to the same result.

We consider first only particle-induced reactions, but we will come back to reactions induced by electromagnetic interactions in the last two sections of this chapter. The particle-induced reactions are classified as *compound-nucleus reactions* or *direct processes* (Fig. 13–13). The experimental arrangement for the example chosen is such that we know that a target of K^{39} nuclides is being bombarded with 6-MeV deuterons. We observe scattered deuterons and other kinds of particles emerging from the target region, among them protons. We have no way of telling, by observing the direction and kinetic energy of a single proton, what exactly took place at the moment of collision between the deuteron and the K^{39} target nucleus. Of the large number of possibilities, we single out three processes that represent two extreme points of view concerning the chain of events resulting in the emission of a proton. These three processes are depicted in Fig. 13–13. To the left is illustrated an event in which the reaction proceeds through the formation of a compound nucleus, a concept introduced by Niels Bohr. According to Bohr's ideas, when the bombarding particle has sufficiently low energy, it will be absorbed by the target nucleus, and the kinetic energy, as well as the binding energy, of the incoming particle will represent an excitation energy of the compound nucleus (Ca^{41} in Fig. 13–1). Because of collisions between the incoming nucleon or nucleons and the target nucleons, this energy will be rapidly shared between a number of particles. Therefore none of them will have sufficient energy to escape immediately. The compound nucleus will then stay together until, by chance, enough energy is concentrated on one nucleon or an assembly of nucleons (e.g., an alpha particle) for escape to occur.

A reaction that proceeds by way of compound-nucleus formation is regarded as a two-step process: the formation process and the breakup. It is assumed that the time lapse between the two events is sufficiently long (several times the period of oscillations of a nucleon) so that at the time of breakup no trace is left that identifies the particular process of formation; the compound nucleus does not break up until it has forgotten how it was formed. The second step, the decay by particle emission, is then simply the decay of a nucleus in a highly excited state, very similar to the alpha decay of natural radioactive isotopes.

The second reaction mechanism indicated in Fig. 13–13, the *stripping process*, represents another extreme point of view. The neutron and the proton are quite loosely bound in the deuteron (binding energy, 2.226 MeV). It is therefore quite likely that when the deuteron comes close to the target nucleus, either the neutron or the proton may be captured by the target nucleus while the other particle continues on its path relatively undisturbed. Stripping belongs to a class of reactions called direct reactions, which are instantaneous processes that usually take place at the nuclear surface. The inverse of a stripping reaction would be a pickup reaction, for instance $K^{40}(p, d)K^{39}$.

The final example illustrated in Fig. 13–13 is a *knockout reaction* in which, for our particular example, the deuteron imbeds itself in the target nucleus K^{39}, but in the process it collides with a proton, which is knocked out. This is again a direct reaction, an instantaneous process quite different in the theory from the compound-nucleus process.

We see that in the examples covered in Fig. 13–13, the initial stage and the end stage are always the same. Can it then be possible to determine by which process the reaction goes? To some extent it can be determined what the prevalent mechanism is because the theories of compound-nucleus formation and, for instance, stripping give different predictions for the magnitude of the cross sections; in particular, different predictions are given for the angular distributions of the differential cross sections $d\sigma/d\omega = f(\theta)$.

In Section 13–6 we start the theoretical treatment of nuclear reactions by developing general formulas for the scattering and absorption cross sections, following essentially the same procedure as that used in Section 3–4 for neutron-proton scattering. This partial-wave method is particularly useful for compound-nucleus theories, and further elaborations follow two different avenues. One is applicable to nuclear reactions induced by low-energy particles, especially on light nuclei; the other applies to reactions in which a compound nucleus is formed at a relatively high excitation, in the continuum. In this region, beyond a few MeV above the dissociation energy* of the compound nucleus, the density of levels and the width of the individual levels become so large that they overlap to a very great extent. The continuum theory is treated in Section 13–7, and the resonance theory, applicable to cases where the bombarding energy is low

---

* Dissociation energy = minimum excitation energy needed to release a nucleon ≈ 5 to 8 MeV.

enough to correspond to individual resolved levels in the compound nucleus, is treated in Section 13–8.

In compound-nucleus theories, the assumption is made that once the incident particle has passed through the nuclear surface, it is completely absorbed, and it can only be emitted again with its full energy in competition with all the other modes of decay of the compound nucleus. In the treatment of the *optical model* (Section 13–10), a less extreme point of view is taken. In optical terms the nucleus is treated as being translucent to the incoming wave. This model, which is most applicable to scattering phenomena, is sometimes called a cloudy crystal-ball model. Part of the wave can be reflected from the surface, part can be absorbed inside the nucleus, and part can be transmitted through the nucleus. The optical model is applicable to energies which put the compound nucleus into the continuum as well as into the region where sharp resonances occur. In the latter region, however, it is expected to give only average cross sections and not the fine details of the resonance theory.

Stripping processes have proved to be a very efficient tool in nuclear spectroscopy, in particular for determining the properties of the ground state and low-lying excited states (below the dissociation energy). The theory of stripping is discussed in Section 13–11, and an example illustrating the usefulness of stripping reactions in probing the nucleus is given in Section 13–12.

13–6 Partial-Wave Analysis of Reaction Cross Sections

Consider a plane wave representing a particle beam incident on a nucleus located at the origin. To keep the mathematics reasonably simple, we will assume that the particles are neutrons, but the results are, in principle, the same for charged particles as well. The expansion in partial waves (Eq. 3–11) can then be written in the following "asymptotic" form for large values of r:

$$\exp(ikr\cos\theta) \rightarrow \frac{\pi^{1/2}}{kr}\sum_{l=0}^{\infty}\sqrt{2l+1}\, i^{l+1}\left\{\exp\left[-i\left(kr-\frac{\pi}{2}l\right)\right] - \exp\left[i\left(kr-\frac{\pi}{2}l\right)\right]\right\} Y_{l,0}(\theta). \tag{13–12}$$

This is the undistorted wave, that is, it describes the situation without the nucleus in place. The two terms in the braces describe waves coming in toward the origin and waves going out, respectively.

We now turn on the interaction. The outgoing waves can change in phase and amplitude, but the incoming waves cannot. When we studied scattering (Chapter 3), we only introduced a phase change. Now we also assume that the incoming wave can be reduced in amplitude, indicating a possibility for absorption of the incoming particle by the nucleus. This is the first part of a reaction. Let the outgoing part of the partial wave with orbital angular momentum l

be changed by a factor η_l. This may be a complex number (Fig. 13–14), and since the number of particles coming out must be equal to or smaller than the number of particles moving in toward the nucleus in a given angular momentum state, we have

$$|\eta_l| \leq 1.$$

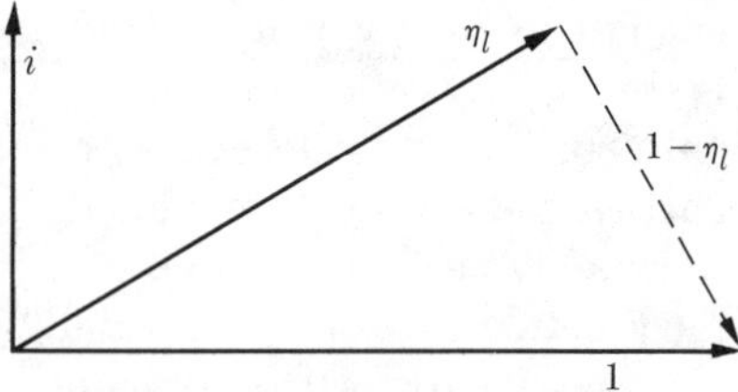

Fig. 13–14. The complex number η_l which is the ratio between the amplitudes of the outgoing wave with and without interaction turned on.

The wave of scattered particles will, as for n-p scattering, be equal to the difference between the new total wave function and the original wave (Eq. 13–12). At large distances, this becomes

$$\psi_{\text{sc}} = \psi - \exp(ikr\cos\theta) \rightarrow$$
$$\frac{\pi^{1/2}}{kr}\sum_{l=0}^{\infty}\sqrt{2l+1}\,i^{l+1}(1-\eta_l)\exp\left[i\left(kr-\frac{\pi}{2}l\right)\right]Y_{l,0}(\theta). \tag{13–13}$$

Since all particles in the scattered wave have the same radial velocity, we find that the flux of particles in the wave is $|\psi_{\text{sc}}|^2 v$, where v is the velocity of the particles. When integrating this flux over all angles, the integration of the spherical harmonics over the angles gives unity, since the Y's are normalized. The total number of particles per second in the scattered wave moving out through a shell of radius r in angular momentum state l is therefore

$$\begin{aligned} N_{\text{sc},l} &= \frac{\pi}{(kr)^2}(2l+1)|1-\eta_l|^2 v\int_{\text{angles}}|Y_{l,0}(\theta)|^2 r^2\sin\theta\,d\theta\,d\phi \\ &= \frac{\pi}{k^2}(2l+1)|1-\eta_l|^2 v. \end{aligned}$$

The "partial" scattering cross section in this angular momentum state is then

$$\begin{aligned} \sigma_{\text{sc},l} &= \frac{\text{number of particles scattered per second}}{\text{number of particles per unit area per second in beam}} \\ &= \frac{\pi}{k^2}(2l+1)|1-\eta_l|^2. \end{aligned} \tag{13–14}$$

We have made use of the fact that our incoming beam is normalized to have a flux of v particles per unit area per second.

Note that the plane wave, as we have written it, actually represents a beam extending to infinity in all directions. In practice, the beam cross section is always large compared with the wavelength $\lambda = 2\pi/k$, but it is usually small compared with the target-to-counter distance (Fig. 13–15). We can therefore always integrate over a shell with radius r that is much larger than the beam diameter. Over most of the integration surface there is no interference between

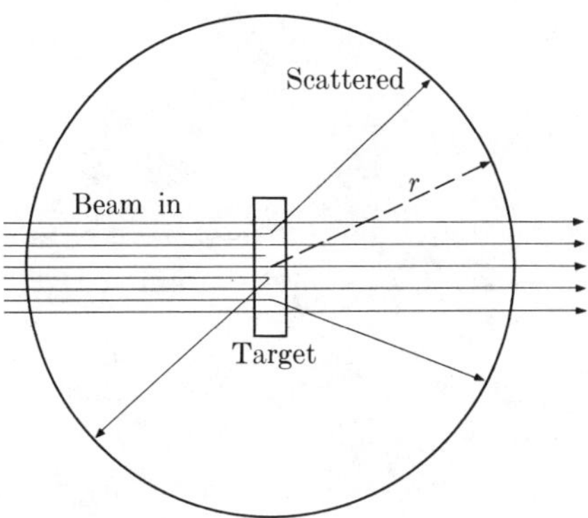

Fig. 13-15. A spherical shell through which the flux of scattered particles is determined has radius r much larger than the beam diameter. In the integration, the angles covering the part of the shell where the beam enters and exits may be considered omitted.

the scattered wave and the beam, so that the integration preceding Eq. (13-14) is justified. In the forward direction, however, the wave amplitude within the beam cross section changes by interference, and the number of particles in this part of the beam is reduced to make up for the scattered and absorbed particles.

If $|\eta_l| < 1$, the number of particles coming out is less than the number going in. The number of particles with a given l that are absorbed is obviously proportional to $1 - |\eta_l|^2$, and by an integration similar to that performed above, we find a difference

$$N_{\mathrm{r},\,l} = \frac{\pi}{k^2}(2l + 1)(1 - |\eta_l|^2)v.$$

The partial absorption (reaction) cross section is therefore

$$\sigma_{\mathrm{r},\,l} = \frac{\pi}{k^2}(2l + 1)(1 - |\eta_l|^2). \tag{13-15}$$

The cross sections, Eqs. (13-14) and (13-15), are valid for neutron scattering and absorption only, since the plane-wave expansion, Eq. (13-12), even at large distances from the nucleus is not valid for particles affected by the $1/r$-type Coulomb field. To simplify the discussion further, we consider now only $l = 0$ neutrons. We can then express the total wave function as

$$\psi_0 = \frac{\pi^{1/2}}{kr} i[e^{-ikr} - \eta_0 e^{ikr}]Y_{0,0} = \frac{u_0}{r} Y_{0,0}$$

and this formula is applicable, not only at large radii, but also all the way in to the nuclear surface. The radial wave function u_0 is

$$u_0 = (\pi^{1/2}/k)i[e^{-ikr} - \eta_0 e^{ikr}]. \tag{13-16}$$

We now introduce a factor f_0, as defined by

$$f_0 \equiv \left[\frac{r}{u_0}\frac{du_0}{dr}\right]_{r=R}. \tag{13–17}$$

This is the logarithmic derivative of the radial wave function u_0 times r, as measured at the surface of the nucleus. By combining Eqs. (13–16) and (13–17), we get

$$f_0 = \frac{-ikRe^{-ikR} - ik\eta_0 Re^{ikR}}{e^{-ikR} - \eta_0 e^{ikR}},$$

which, solved for η_0, yields

$$\eta_0 = \frac{f_0 + ikR}{f_0 - ikR}\, e^{-2ikR}. \tag{13–18}$$

Equation (13–18) inserted into Eqs. (13–14) and (13–15) yields the scattering and reaction cross sections. This shows that these cross sections for $l = 0$ are uniquely determined by the logarithmic derivative f_0 of the radial wave function at the nuclear surface, or, for that matter, at any radius R outside the range of the nuclear forces. This statement is true also for higher l-values.

13–7 Compound-Nucleus Formation and Breakup

We will now derive and discuss expressions for the cross section of a reaction that proceeds in accordance with the compound-nucleus concept, which was introduced in Section 13–5. Since the breakup process of the compound nucleus is independent of the formation process, we can write in general

$$\sigma(\alpha, \beta) = \sigma_C(E_C, \alpha)G_C(E_C, \beta), \tag{13–19}$$

where $\sigma_C(E_C, \alpha)$ is the cross section for formation of a compound nucleus at an excitation energy E_C with particle a, and $G_C(E_C, \beta)$ is the branching ratio, that is, the relative probability for the compound nucleus at excitation energy E_C to break up by emitting particle b. It is implied that particle a and the target nucleus are in a given total angular momentum state specified by the symbol α, and that particle b leaves the residual nucleus in a given state specified by the symbol β. Total angular momentum and parity must, of course, be conserved in the reaction. The specified entrance and exit states are called *channels;* the reaction is initiated through channel α, and the compound nucleus breaks up through channel β.

We will first calculate the formation cross section, limiting the discussion again to $l = 0$ neutrons. For a more rigorous treatment of the theory, including higher orbital angular momentum states and charged particles, the reader is referred to textbooks in theoretical nuclear physics. We use Eq. (13–15) for the compound-nucleus formation cross section with η_0 given by Eq. (13–18).

We make the assumption that the nucleus has a well-defined surface with radius R and that inside this surface an incident particle will be subjected to a negative potential and, hence, will move with an increased kinetic energy, characterized by the wave number K. We further assume that the particle rapidly shares its energy with the other nucleons so that the amplitude of the outgoing wave for $r < R$, representing the probability of the particle's being re-emitted without loss of energy, is negligible. These assumptions may be reasonably well founded in the region of very high excitation energy of the compound nucleus where the density of levels is so high and the level widths are so large that the levels completely overlap. Absorption can then take place at any energy, in contrast to the situation in the next section in which we assume well-separated levels for the compound nucleus (resonance absorption). To assume that there is no outgoing wave of particle a with full energy (elastic scattering) can never be strictly correct because even if there are many different ways for the compound nucleus to break up, it will always be possible for it to break up by emitting the incident particle again with full energy. This process is called *compound elastic scattering*, as opposed to the scattering which takes place at the surface. The latter process, in which the particle never actually enters the nucleus, is called *potential scattering*. Nevertheless, if the number of ways for the compound nucleus to break up is sufficiently large, we may assume that compound elastic scattering is negligible. Immediately within the surface of the nucleus we then have an incoming wave of the form

$$u_0 = e^{-iKr}, \qquad \text{for} \quad r \lessapprox R \tag{13–20}$$

and no corresponding outgoing term. From Eq. (13–17), we get

$$f_0 = -iKR, \tag{13–21}$$

which, combined with Eq. (13–18), yields

$$|\eta_0| = \frac{K - k}{K + k}. \tag{13–22}$$

With this value of η_0, the compound-nucleus formation cross section (Eq. 13–15) for $l = 0$ neutrons becomes

$$\sigma_{r,0} = \frac{4\pi K}{k(K + k)^2}. \tag{13–23}$$

According to this formula the cross section becomes infinite for neutron energies approaching zero, but as stated above, this simple theory is not valid for that case, and the resonance theory given in the next section should be used.

The wave number K can be determined from the assumed kinetic energy $T = V_0 + E$ inside the nuclear surface, where V_0 is the depth of the potential well representing the nuclear forces. If we use $V_0 = 40$ MeV, in accordance with the shell-model calculations (Chapter 6), we get $K \approx 0.2187\sqrt{40 + E}\ \mathrm{F}^{-1}$

and $k = 0.2187\sqrt{E}\,\mathrm{F}^{-1}$. For $E = 5$ MeV, for example, Eq. (13–23) yields $\sigma_{r,0} = 99$ mb (1 mb = 1 millibarn = 10^{-27} cm^2).

The reaction cross sections for higher l-values and for charged particles are calculated along the same lines, but the actual wave functions have much more complex forms. Assuming that the partial-reaction cross sections have been computed, we can find the total cross section for compound-nucleus formation as

$$\sigma_C = \sum_{l=0}^{\infty} \sigma_{r,l}. \tag{13–24}$$

For moderately low energies and for exactly the same reason as given in Section 3–4, the l-values which we need to consider are limited. Equation (13–24) therefore represents a rapidly converging series.

Figure 13–16 gives the total compound-nucleus formation cross section for incident protons and alpha particles computed in the same way as outlined for $l = 0$ neutrons above, but, of course, with wave functions appropriate for charged particles and summed over l.

We now consider the decay of the compound nucleus in an attempt to get an idea about the factor $G_C(E_C, \beta)$ in Eq. (13–19). In the example depicted in Fig. 13–1, assuming that this reaction proceeds via the compound nucleus Ca^{41}, there are hundreds of different ways for this nucleus to break up, i.e., hundreds of different exit channels. Each channel is characterized by a given particle emitted with a given energy E_β and in a given angular-momentum state. In the example of Fig. 13–1, the entrance channel has the target nucleus K^{39} in its ground state, and with a specified direction of its angular momentum, it has an incoming deuteron in a given angular-momentum state and a total kinetic energy in the center-of-mass system of $E_\alpha = 5.71$ MeV.* Let us assume that the compound nucleus formed in a given angular-momentum state can break up through channel β with a decay constant λ_β. The level width associated with this decay constant is given by

$$\Gamma_\beta = \hbar\lambda_\beta = \hbar/\tau_\beta. \tag{13–25}$$

When we add all the decay constants for all possible exit channels, we get, of course, the total decay constant for the compound nucleus; hence, the total width of the compound level is

$$\Gamma = \sum_{\beta} \Gamma_\beta. \tag{13–26}$$

The individual decay constant λ_β and, therefore, also the partial level width Γ_β are strongly influenced by the barrier-penetration factor (as in alpha decay).

---

* The energy E_α is the eigenvalue in Schrödinger's equation representing the motion of the deuteron before the reaction. It is equal to the kinetic energy of the deuteron *and* the target nucleus (in CM) while they are far away from each other and therefore is denoted by T_{CM} in Fig. 13–1.

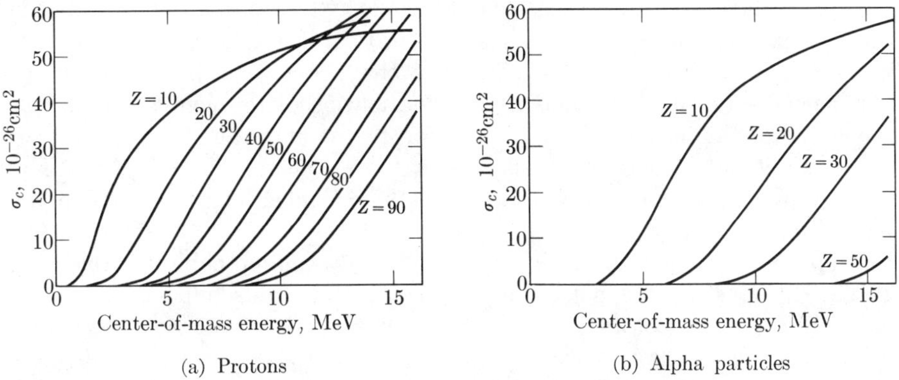

Fig. 13–16. Total compound-nucleus cross sections for protons and alpha particles. (Prepared from tables in J. M. Blatt and V. F. Weisskopf, *Theoretical Nuclear Physics*, New York: John Wiley and Sons, 1952, p. 352.)

The same barrier-penetration factor, of course, also affects the formation of the compound nucleus through the entrance channel. Indeed, it can be shown* that there is a very simple relationship between Γ_β and the cross section for forming the compound nucleus through the channel β, assuming that this is possible. If, for instance, the channel β leads to an excited level in K^{40} by the emittance of a proton from the compound nucleus in our example, then we can, at least in principle, consider the formation of the compound nucleus by bombarding K^{40}, which has previously been brought up into this excited state, by protons with the appropriate energy. Let us assume that the cross section for compound-nucleus formation in this process is $\sigma_C(\beta)$. The relationship mentioned, called the *reciprocity theorem*, can then be expressed as follows for spinless particles:

$$k_\alpha^2 \frac{\sigma_C(\alpha)}{\Gamma_\alpha} = k_\beta^2 \frac{\sigma_C(\beta)}{\Gamma_\beta} = \cdots = U(E_C), \tag{13-27}$$

where k_α and k_β are wave numbers associated with the energies E_α and E_β. The proportionality coefficient $U(E_C)$ is a function of the excitation energy E_C of the compound nucleus only. Equation (13–27) shows that there is a simple proportionality relationship between the probability for breakup into a given channel, expressed by Γ, and the cross section for forming the compound nucleus through the same channel. Using Eq. (13–27), we find that the probability for decay into channel β is

$$G_C(\beta) = \frac{\lambda_\beta}{\sum_\gamma \lambda_\gamma} = \frac{\Gamma_\beta}{\sum_\gamma \Gamma_\gamma} = \frac{k_\beta^2 \sigma_C(\beta)}{\sum_\gamma k_\gamma^2 \sigma_C(\gamma)}. \tag{13-28}$$

---

* J. M. Blatt and V. F. Weisskopf, *Theoretical Nuclear Physics*, New York: John Wiley and Sons, 1952, p. 344.

The sum is taken over all open channels (index γ). Consider an example in which an emitted charged particle has an energy far below the Coulomb barrier. Obviously, decay through that particular channel will be inhibited by the barrier-penetration factor. Similarly, the formation of the compound nucleus through that channel will be inhibited for the same reason. In particular, heavy compound nuclei with moderate excitation energies will preferentially break up by neutron emission because of the high Coulomb barrier that inhibits charged-particle decay.

Except for such general insights into the breakup probabilities that Eq. (13–28) can give us, it is not of very high quantitative usefulness. There are too many unknown factors in it for detailed cross-sectional calculations. There is, however, one other important observation that we shall make about compound-nucleus reactions. This is that if the total wave function for the reaction has a definite parity, the angular distribution of reaction products will be symmetric around 90° in the center-of-mass system. In other words,

$$\frac{d\sigma}{d\Omega}(\theta) = \frac{d\sigma}{d\Omega}(\pi - \theta). \tag{13–29}$$

Parity, of course, is conserved in nuclear reactions, but in the continuum region it is quite possible that odd and even parity levels overlap to a great extent. The incoming particle can have odd and even l-values; hence, compound levels of both parities can be reached. The outgoing particle can also have odd and even l-values; hence, a definite state of the residual nucleus can be reached from both parity states in the compound nucleus. In general, Eq. (13–29) will not hold in such cases. Indeed, for stripping reactions (Sections 13–11 and 13–12), the angular distributions of reaction products are very far from being symmetric around 90°. On the other hand, if the compound nucleus is formed by very slow neutrons, which necessarily have to be $l = 0$ neutrons, the rule will definitely apply. Also, when the compound nucleus is formed through a level that is an isolated resonance (Section 13–8), the single compound-nucleus level formed, of course, has definite parity, and the rule will again hold. The reason behind the rule (13–29) is very simple to understand. The beam direction that we chose as the z-direction is a symmetry axis for the total wave function. If the wave function has definite parity, its square will not change when we change the sign of z. This applies to the total wave function for the reaction and therefore also includes the part of it which describes outgoing particles. Equation (13–29) follows from this.

13–8 Resonance Scattering and Reactions

We are now going to study compound-nucleus formation in the region where separated levels exist. The theory of the breakup of the compound system is essentially the same as described in the previous section. However, the formation cross section, as well as the scattering cross section, will go through sharp resonances when the bombarding energy is varied. This is, of course, one feature that can be studied experimentally and will then, among other things, yield information about the positions of the levels in the compound nucleus. Again we limit the discussion to $l = 0$ neutrons and start by considering the scattering of these neutrons by an attractive well.

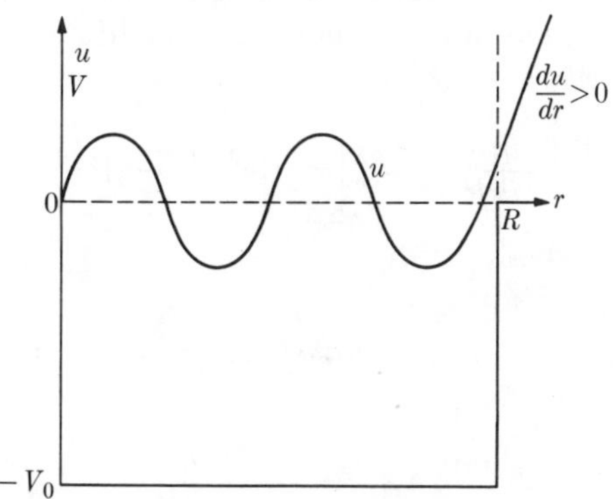

Fig. 13–17. The radial wave function $u(r)$ for an $l = 0$ neutron in a spherically symmetric square-well potential.

Figure 13–17 shows the radial wave function for a neutron in a square well. The logarithmic derivative is positive, but it will decrease for increasing energy as more of the wave is packed into the well. It will go smoothly through zero, become negative, and go to $-\infty$ as u becomes zero. For the square well, this behavior is expressed analytically very simply as

$$f_0 = -KR \cot KR,$$

but even for any other conceivable type of attractive well, the behavior will be qualitatively the same. We are going to be particularly interested in the energy regions close to the energies at which f_0 goes through zero.

In general, we do not know the behavior of f_0 to any high degree of accuracy. However, it turns out that we can learn a great deal just by knowing that f_0 goes smoothly through zero at a given energy E_s, so that we can write, for a limited region of E,

$$f_0 = -a(E - E_s), \tag{13–30}$$

where a is considered to be a constant.

Before we insert this expression into Eq. (13–18) and further into the cross-section equation, we should make one more observation: If f_0 is a real quantity, Eq. (13–18) gives $|\eta_0| = 1$, and therefore $\sigma_{r,0} = 0$. To produce an absorption cross section, the logarithmic derivative needs to have an imaginary term. Since obviously $\sigma_{r,0} \gtreqless 0$, we must have $|\eta_0| \lesseqgtr 1$, which according to Eq.

(13–18) means that the imaginary term always has negative sign. Therefore we replace Eq. (13–30) with

$$f_0 = -a(E - E_s) - ib, \tag{13–31}$$

where both a and b are considered constants. This expression, we assume, represents adequately the behavior of f_0 in a narrow region around $E = E_s$.

Using Eq. (13–18), we now calculate the amplitude factor $|1 - \eta_0|$ of the scattered wave

$$|1 - \eta_0| = \left|1 - \frac{f_0 + ikR}{f_0 - ikR}\, e^{-2ikR}\right| = \left|e^{2ikR} - 1 - \frac{2ikR}{f_0 - ikR}\right|$$
$$= |A_{\text{pot}} + A_{\text{res}}|, \tag{13–32}$$

where

$$A_{\text{pot}} = e^{2ikR} - 1 = e^{ikR}(e^{ikR} - e^{-ikR}) = 2ie^{ikR}\sin kR \tag{13–33}$$

and

$$A_{\text{res}} = \frac{-2ikR}{f_0 - ikR}\cdot \tag{13–34}$$

We have split the amplitude into A_{pot} and A_{res} to get the most important term A_{res} in a more elegant form later. The other term A_{pot} without interference from A_{res} turns out to represent scattering from a perfectly reflective nucleus (hard-sphere scattering). As we will see, the term A_{res} can get to be enormously larger than A_{pot}.

With Eq. (13–31) inserted, the "resonance" amplitude becomes

$$A_{\text{res}} = -\frac{2ikR}{-a(E - E_s) - ib - ikR} = \frac{2i(kR/a)}{(E - E_s) + i(b/a + kR/a)}\cdot \tag{13–35}$$

If we neglect A_{pot} compared with A_{res}, the $l = 0$ neutron scattering cross section becomes

$$\sigma_{\text{sc},0} \approx \frac{\pi}{k^2}\,|A_{\text{res}}|^2 = \frac{\pi}{k^2}\,\frac{4(kR/a)^2}{(E - E_s)^2 + (b/a + kR/a)^2}\cdot \tag{13–36}$$

Clearly, a plot of Eq. (13–36) will show the behavior of a resonance curve. If the resonance is narrow, we can disregard the fact that k varies with the energy over the interval considered. Assume also for the moment that $b = 0$ (no absorption). We then see that kR/a is equal to half the width of the resonance peak at half-amplitude. The full width at half-maximum, the *width of the resonance* is

$$\Gamma_{\text{sc},0} = 2kR/a. \tag{13–37}$$

The constant a can be expressed as (from Eq. 13–31):

$$a = -(df/dE)_{E_s}. \tag{13–38}$$

The capture or reaction cross section is found in similar fashion by combining Eqs. (13–15), (13–18), and (13–31):

$$\sigma_{\mathrm{r},0} = \frac{\pi}{k^2}\left(1 - \left|\frac{-a(E - E_s) - ib + ikR}{-a(E - E_s) - ib - ikR}\, e^{-2ikR}\right|^2\right)$$

$$= \frac{\pi}{k^2}\,\frac{4(b/a)(kR/a)}{(E - E_s)^2 + (b/a + kR/a)^2}. \qquad (13\text{–}39)$$

When capture takes place ($b > 0$), the width of the resonance peak increases by $2b/a$. It is therefore natural to call this quantity the reaction width:

$$\Gamma_{\mathrm{r},0} = 2b/a.$$

We can then write (again neglecting A_{pot}) for $l = 0$ neutrons:

$$\sigma_{\mathrm{sc},0} = \frac{\pi}{k^2}\,\frac{\Gamma^2_{\mathrm{sc},0}}{(E - E_s)^2 + (\Gamma_{\mathrm{sc},0} + \Gamma_{\mathrm{r},0})^2}, \qquad (13\text{–}40)$$

$$\sigma_{\mathrm{r},0} = \frac{\pi}{k^2}\,\frac{\Gamma_{\mathrm{sc},0}\Gamma_{\mathrm{r},0}}{(E - E_s)^2 + (\Gamma_{\mathrm{sc},0} + \Gamma_{\mathrm{r},0})^2}. \qquad (13\text{–}41)$$

It is evident from these equations that resonance reaction is always accompanied by resonance scattering ($\sigma_{\mathrm{r},0} = 0$ if $\Gamma_{\mathrm{sc},0} = 0$).

To be able to trace the resonance curve for the scattering cross section in detail, we reinstate the "potential scattering" term A_{pot}, and we get

$$\sigma_{\mathrm{sc},0} = \frac{\pi}{k^2}\left|\frac{\Gamma_{\mathrm{sc},0}}{(E - E_s) + \frac{1}{2}i(\Gamma_{\mathrm{sc},0} + \Gamma_{\mathrm{reac},0})} + 2e^{ikR}\sin kR\right|^2. \qquad (13\text{–}42)$$

Assume for simplicity that a resonance displays only scattering, that is, $\Gamma_{\mathrm{r},0} = 0$. Further, we assume that the energy is low so that $kR \ll 1$. We can then write approximately

$$\sigma_{\mathrm{sc},0} = \frac{4\pi}{k^2}\left|\frac{\Gamma}{2(E - E_s) + i\Gamma} + kR\right|^2.$$

Far away from the resonance, where $2|E - E_s| \gg \Gamma/kR$, the term kR will dominate, and we get the hard-sphere scattering formula

$$\sigma_{\mathrm{sc},0} \approx 4\pi R^2.$$

For negative values of $E - E_s$, the first term will have a negative real component, partly canceling the term kR. As resonance is reached, the first term will be $-i$, completely dominating the expression, but for increasing positive values of $E - E_s$, this term will again diminish, bringing the cross section back down again. Figure 13–18 is a sketch of the expected behavior of $\sigma_{\mathrm{sc},0}$ vs. E.

The formulas given above for resonance scattering and absorption of $l = 0$ neutrons were developed without regard to spin, and they apply without modification when the target nucleus has angular momentum $J = 0$. In general,

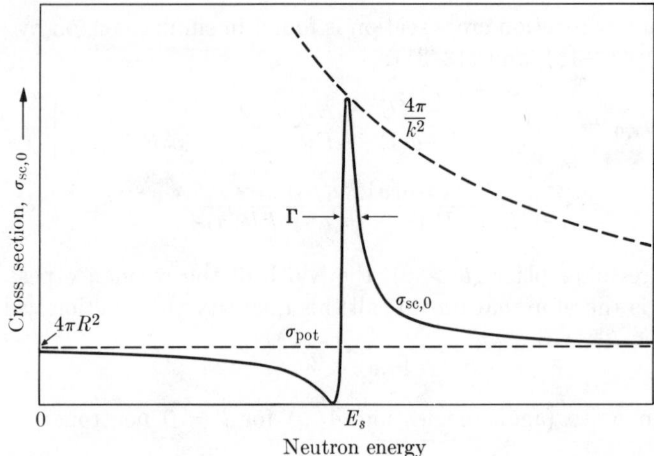

Fig. 13–18. Elastic scattering cross section for $l = 0$ neutrons near a resonance in the compound nucleus. The angular momentum of the target nucleus is $J = 0$ and the reaction width $\Gamma_{r,0} = 0$, in which case the maximum scattering cross section $\sigma_{sc,0} = 4\pi/k^2$.

the compound nuclear states that can be reached with $l = 0$ neutrons have angular momenta $J_C = J \pm \frac{1}{2}$. To reach a given level with a given J_C, the neutron spin and the angular momentum of the nucleus have to have the right relative orientation. The cross-section formulas should accordingly be multipled by a statistical weight factor, which turns out to be

$$g(J_C) = \frac{2J_C + 1}{2(2J + 1)}, \qquad \text{where} \quad J_C = J \pm \tfrac{1}{2}. \tag{13–43}$$

For charged particles, the theory of resonances is more complex because of the existence of the Coulomb field. However, the results are essentially the same as for neutrons. Of course, the nuclear effects will be superimposed on the cross section for Rutherford (Coulomb-field) scattering. Examples of charged-particle resonances are given in the next section.

Before we discuss experimental results of resonance reactions, we shall make some general remarks concerning resonance widths. Consider again an $l = 0$ neutron in the square well (Fig. 13–17). Resonances occur when the logarithmic derivative is $f_0 \approx 0$, that is, when

$$KR = (n + \tfrac{1}{2})\pi, \qquad n = 0, 1, 2, 3, \ldots$$

The distance in energy between resonances is therefore given by

$$\Delta K = \pi/R.$$

To introduce a distance D between the resonances in energy units, we use

$K^2\hbar^2 = 2mE$, which gives

$$D = \Delta E = K\,\Delta K\hbar^2/m = (K\hbar/m)\,(\pi/R)\hbar.$$

But $K\hbar/m$ is simply the velocity v of the particle in the well, and $2R/v \approx t_0$, the approximate transit time of the particle in the nucleus. Introducing this quantity, we get

$$D\,t_0 \approx 2\pi\hbar. \tag{13–44}$$

Further, we have the following relationship between the level width Γ and the lifetime τ of a state formed by the neutron in the well $\Gamma\tau = \hbar$. Combined with Eq. (13–44), this yields

$$\Gamma \approx (D/2\pi)(t_0/\tau). \tag{13–45}$$

The last factor, the transit time t_0 divided by the lifetime τ, is simply equal to the barrier-penetration factor, which for the square-well case is (compare Section 10–4)

$$t_0/\tau = P = 4kK/(k+K)^2.$$

For slow neutrons ($k \ll K$), this can be written

$$P \approx 4k/K = 4\sqrt{E_n/V_0},$$

where $E_n = T_n$ is the kinetic energy of the neutron outside the nucleus and V_0 is the depth of the well, which also is approximately the kinetic energy of the neutron in the well. Equation (13–45) now becomes

$$\Gamma \approx (D/2\pi)P \approx (2D/\pi)\sqrt{E_n/V_0}. \tag{13–46}$$

This is the predicted width of a virtual level formed by a neutron in a square-well potential. For an actual nucleus, the situation is of course not so simple, although some levels that are formed without appreciable reorientation of the target nucleons have measured widths in qualitative agreement with Eq. (13–46). Interspersed between these "single-particle" resonances are, however, many narrower resonances in which the corresponding compound-nuclear state is formed by internal reorientation simultaneously with the addition of a neutron. The transition probability for formation, as well as for decay, then becomes much smaller, and the width therefore is also smaller.

13–9 Nuclear Resonance Spectroscopy

A great amount of experimental data has been collected on nuclear resonances, in particular with slow neutrons as bombarding particles. Some of these data exist in the form of curves for the total cross section, that is, the sum of the elastic scattering and the reaction cross section. This is what is measured in a transmission experiment of the type discussed in Section 3–3. In other cases,

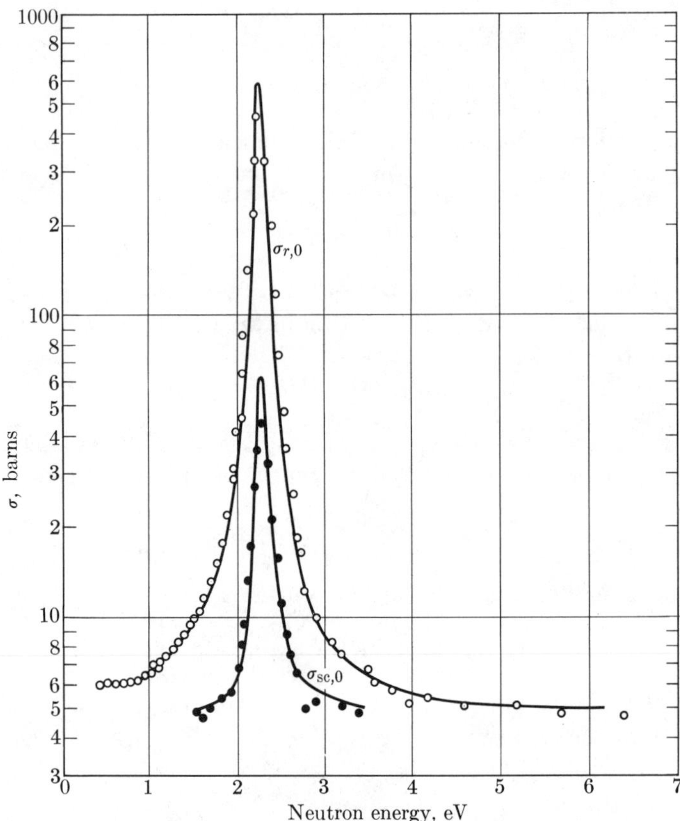

Fig. 13–19. Neutron resonance in tellurium ascribed to the Te^{123} ($J = \frac{1}{2}$) isotope. Open circles are measured reaction cross sections, and closed circles are scattering cross sections. (From D. J. Hughes and J. A. Harvey, *Neutron Cross Sections*, New York: McGraw-Hill Book Company, 1955. Reprinted by permission.)

the elastic-scattering and reaction cross sections have been measured separately, thus yielding material for testing both Eq. (13–41) and Eq. (13–42). Time-of-flight methods are usually employed for determining the neutron energy. Figure 13–19 shows as an example the elastic-scattering cross section (filled circles) and the reaction cross section (open circles) measured in the electron-volt range for natural tellurium. The resonance shown occurs in the isotope Te^{123} which has only 0.85% abundance. In calculating the experimental cross section for the data taken, the yield has been divided over all the tellurium atoms in the target, giving an average of about 600 barns at maximum for the reaction cross section. The actual maximum reaction cross section in Te^{123} is therefore $600/0.0085 \approx 70{,}000$ barns.

The curves in Fig. 13–19 are theoretical curves obtained from Eqs. (13–41) and (13–42) with $\Gamma_{sc,0} = 0.0104$ eV and $\Gamma_{r,0} = 0.104$ eV. The angular

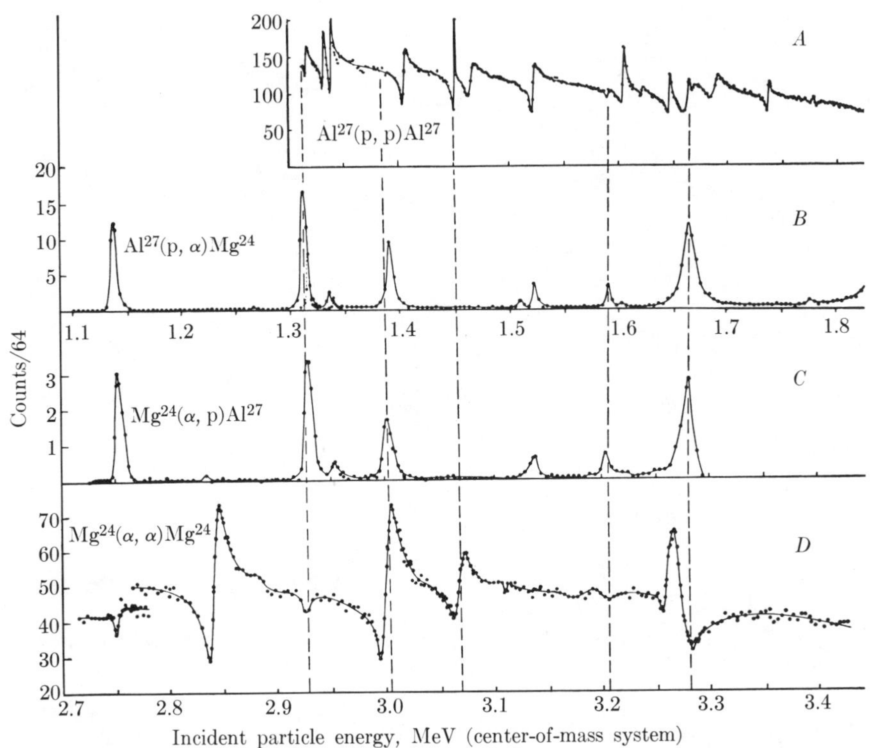

Fig. 13–20. Excitation curves for the Al^{27} + p and $Mg^{24} + \alpha$ systems displaying several resonances in the compound nucleus Si^{28}. [From Kaufmann *et al.*, *Phys. Rev.* **88,** 675 (1952).]

momenta of the target and compound states are $J = \frac{1}{2}$ and $J_C = 1$, giving a weight factor $g(J_C) = \frac{3}{4}$ (Eq. 13–43). A constant background from the other tellurium isotopes has been added to the theoretical yield from Te^{123}.

As a second example, we show the result of work done on compound levels in Si^{28} by Kaufmann *et al.** Very thin aluminum targets were bombarded with protons from the Van de Graaff generator at the University of Wisconsin. The excitation curves, i.e., the relative cross sections vs. bombarding energy, were measured for elastic scattering of protons on aluminum and for the $Al^{27}(p, \alpha)Mg^{24}$ reaction. These excitation curves are shown in the upper part of Fig. 13–20 for the proton energy ranges 1.3 to 1.8 MeV and from 1.1 to 1.8 MeV, respectively. The resonances shown correspond to levels in the compound nucleus Si^{28} at about 12.7 to 13.4 MeV, since the binding energy for

* S. G. Kaufmann, E. Goldberg, L. J. Koster, and F. P. Mooring, *Phys. Rev.* **88,** 675 (1952); and F. C. Shoemaker, J. E. Faulkner, G. M. B. Bouricius, S. G. Kaufmann, and F. P. Mooring, *Phys. Rev.* **83,** 1011 (1951).

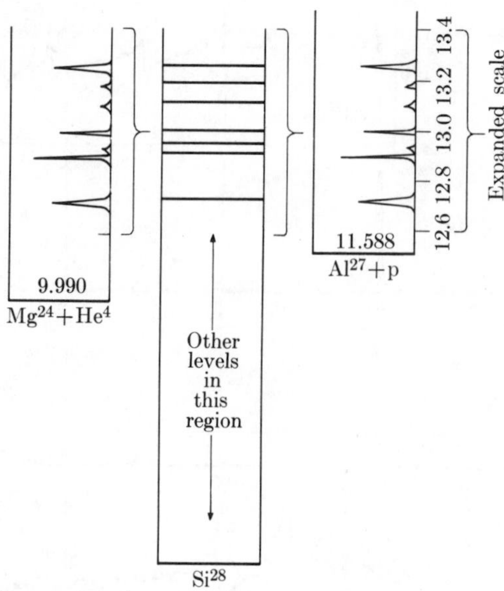

Fig. 13–21. Energy levels in the compound nucleus Si^{28} formed by bombarding Al^{27} with protons or Mg^{24} with alpha particles.

the last proton in Si^{28} is 11.588 MeV. This is illustrated in the energy-level diagram for Si^{28} in Fig. 13–21.

The (p, α) reaction in Al^{27} leads to Mg^{24} as the residual nucleus. This is a stable isotope, so it is therefore possible to reverse the reaction and to reach exactly the same compound-nucleus levels in Si^{28} by way of the $Mg^{24}(\alpha, p)Al^{27}$ reaction and the $Mg^{24}(\alpha, \alpha)Mg^{24}$ scattering process. This was done in the work by Kaufmann *et al.* and the result is shown in the two lower excitation curves in Fig. 13–20. The binding energy for an alpha particle in Si^{28} is about 1.6 MeV lower than the binding energy for a proton. To reach the same region of levels, the alpha-particle bombarding energy in the center-of-mass system must be 1.6 MeV higher than the proton energy as shown in Fig. 13–20 (see also Fig. 13–21). The fact that the cross section for the $Al^{27}(p, \alpha)Mg^{24}$ reaction varies in the same fashion as for the inverse reaction is a beautiful demonstration of the reciprocity theorem (13–27).

Because of the low barrier-penetration factor, the actual widths of the resonances in Fig. 13–20 are very small; the experimental peak widths are often determined by the resolving power of the apparatus rather than by the natural width of the level.

The natural level width is an important parameter to measure, since it reveals some of the character of the excited state. Extensive work in this area has been carried out with neutrons as well as with charged particles, the latter mostly in the region of the light elements. Figure 13–22 shows some examples of level

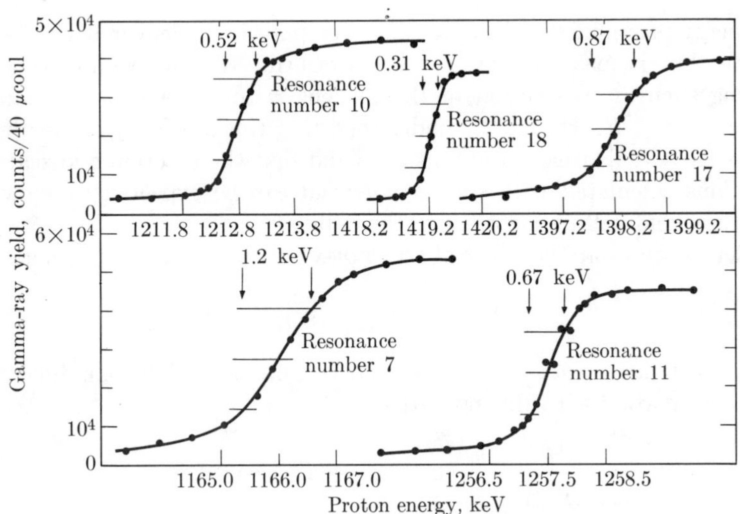

Fig. 13–22. Thick-target γ-ray yield curves taken over five $Na^{23}(p, \gamma)Mg^{24}$ resonances. The indicated widths are measured between the one-quarter and three-quarter points on the rising curve. [From P. H. Stelson and W. M. Preston, *Phys. Rev.* **95,** 974 (1954).]

widths in the compound nucleus Mg^{24} formed by bombarding Na^{23} with protons.* The technique used was to measure the gamma-ray yield from a thick Na^{23} target bombarded by protons. Since consecutive layers of the target are struck by protons of lower and lower energies, an integrated excitation curve results. The slope of the yield curve at a resonance is then a measure for the width of the level. Resonance number 18 with an experimental width of 0.31 keV is believed to be much narrower. The 0.31 keV is therefore the experimental resolution, i.e., energy spread of the proton beam. Assuming that both this energy spread and the natural resonance curve can be approximated with gaussian curves, the natural width of, for instance, level number 10 (Fig. 13–22) is

$$\Gamma = \sqrt{0.52^2 - 0.31^2} = 0.42 \text{ keV}.$$

13–10 The Optical Model

In the previous section, we assumed that the incoming particle, once it had penetrated the nuclear surface, was absorbed by the nucleus. In the mathematical treatment we accounted for this fact by completely deleting any outgoing part of the wave function inside the nuclear surface. In the optical model we do not take such an extreme point of view, but rather we assume that the nucleus is translucent to the particle waves. In effect, a given particle of a given

---

* P. H. Stelson and W. M. Preston, *Phys. Rev.* **95,** 974 (1954).

kinetic energy is assumed to have a mean free path in nuclear matter of such a magnitude that it may or may not be absorbed. The conventional way of introducing such an absorption in the nucleus is to use a complex potential for the region $r < R$. It must be understood that this is a fairly crude approximation to the actual situation in a nucleus and that the reaction and scattering cross sections calculated with such a potential can be expected to show only gross features and will be incorrect in the details.

First, let us see what the effect of a complex potential will be in general. We write

$$V = -(V_0 + iW), \tag{13–47}$$

where V_0 and W are presumed to be positive real numbers. The one-dimensional Schrödinger equation with this potential is

$$\frac{d^2\psi}{dx^2} + \frac{2m}{\hbar^2}(E + V_0 + iW)\psi = 0.$$

We find plane wave solutions of the form

$$\psi = e^{\pm iK_c x}, \tag{13–48}$$

where the complex wave number K_c is given by

$$K_c = (1/\hbar)\sqrt{2m(E + V_0 + iW)}. \tag{13–49}$$

Obviously, this wave number can be expressed as

$$K_c = K + i\kappa,$$

where K and κ can be found readily from Eq. (13–49). When W is small compared with $E + V_0$, we can expand the square root and find, approximately

$$K \approx (1/\hbar)\sqrt{2m(E + V_0)}, \tag{13–50}$$

$$\kappa \approx \frac{WK}{2(E + V_0)}\cdot \tag{13–51}$$

When we substitute K_c into Eq. (13–48) and use the plus sign describing a wave moving in the positive x-direction, we find that

$$\psi = e^{iKx}\, e^{-\kappa x}.$$

This obviously represents an exponentially decaying wave with a mean decay length for $|\psi|^2$ (mean free path) of

$$L = \frac{1}{2\kappa} = \frac{E + V_0}{WK} = \frac{E + V_0}{2\pi W}\,\lambda \tag{13–52}$$

with the wavelength $\lambda = 2\pi/K$.

As an example, consider a neutron with $E = 10$ MeV moving in a potential with $V_0 = 40$ MeV and $W = 10$ MeV. The real part of the wave number is, according to Eqs. (13–50) and (2–14)

$$K = 0.2187\sqrt{50} = 1.55\ \mathrm{F}^{-1}.$$

The mean free path is then

$$L = \frac{50}{10 \times 1.55} = 3.23\ \mathrm{F}.$$

The physical significance of the decaying wave function is that, as far as the world outside the nucleus is concerned, the particle may disappear into the nucleus. What exactly goes on inside the nucleus, of course, is not correctly described by a decaying wave function. If the particle is a nucleon, for instance, it stays intact, but it may collide with other nucleons and share its energy with them. Even if it has enough energy left to escape, it is then no longer identifiable as a particle in the beam or as an elastically scattered particle.

The one-dimensional problem with the plane-wave solution was chosen for the discussion above in order to limit the mathematical complexity. However, it is clear from this discussion what the general features of a complex potential will be for the spherical problem as well. Mathematically, the solutions of the radial wave equation for a constant complex potential will be of the form discussed in Chapter 6 (Eq. 6–3), except that the wave number is now complex. The logarithmic derivative of these inside wave functions can be matched at the boundary to the logarithmic derivative of the outside wave functions. This

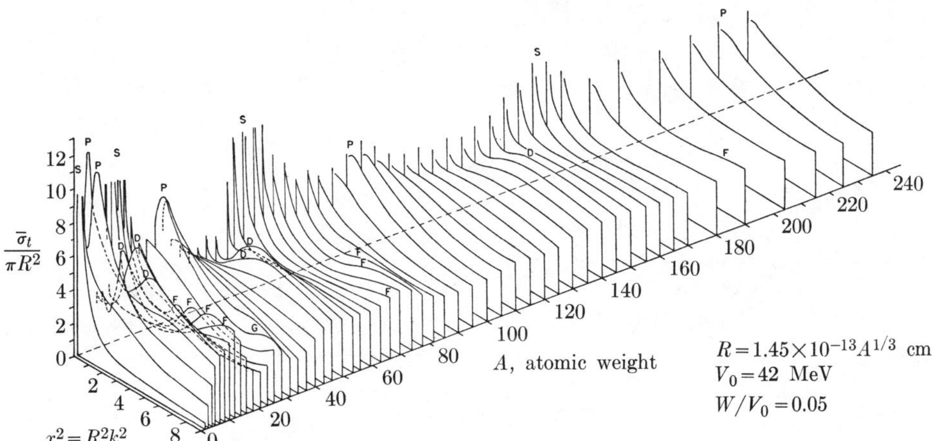

Fig. 13–23. Calculated "gross structure" of total neutron cross section, as a function of the energy parameter x^2 and A. [From H. Feshbach, C. E. Porter, and V. F. Weisskopf, *Phys. Rev.* **96,** 448 (1954).]

yields the complex numbers η_l, which determine the partial reaction and scattering cross sections, Eq. (13–14) and Eq. (13–15).

The first work on the optical model* consisted of calculation of the total cross section (scattering plus reaction cross section) for neutrons of various energies on a large number of nuclei. Figure 13–23 shows some of the results of the calculations for a number of nuclei throughout the list of elements. The parameters of the well were $R = 1.45A^{1/3}$ F, $V_0 = 42$ MeV, and $W/V_0 = 0.05$. The abscissa x^2 is proportional to the neutron energy and is given by

$$x^2 = R^2k^2 = \frac{0.101A^{5/3}E_n}{A+1}.$$

Wide resonances are predicted at certain energies and A-values, and the cross section in general decreases with increasing energy, as for neutron-proton scattering. The l-values of the partial waves that are responsible for the various resonances are indicated in Fig. 13–23 with the standard letter symbols s, p, d, etc.

Figure 13–24 gives the corresponding experimental results plotted in the same fashion. The data have been compiled by Feshbach, Porter, and Weisskopf from published works originating at the University of Wisconsin and other laboratories. The total cross sections were measured by transmission experiments, and the neutrons were produced in nuclear reactions initiated by charged-particle beams from Van de Graaff accelerators. Where the resolution was adequate to separate individual compound-nucleus levels, these have been smoothed out in Fig. 13–24 for comparison with the results of the optical-model theory which does not produce such fine details.

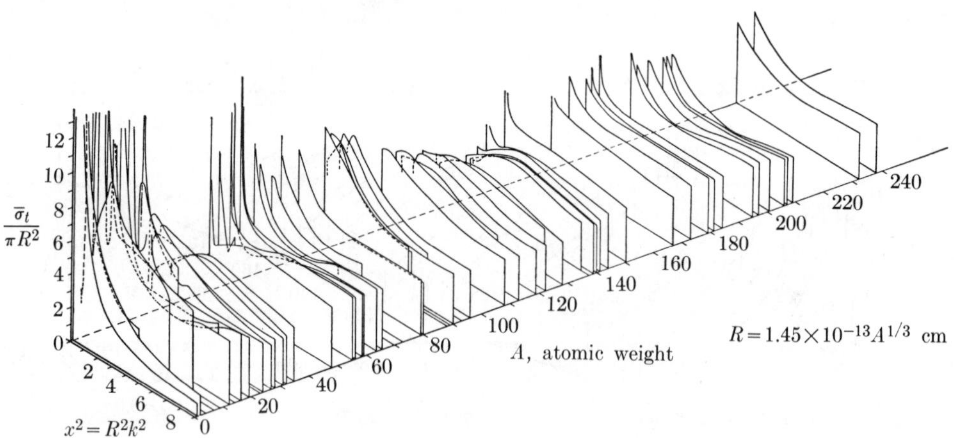

Fig. 13–24. Observed "gross structure" of total neutron cross section. (Compiled by Feshbach *et al.*, *loc. cit.*)

---

* H. Feshbach, C. E. Porter, and V. F. Weisskopf, *Phys. Rev.* **96,** 448 (1954).

With the rapid increase in the speed of electronic computers, it has been possible in recent years to make more and more sophisticated optical-model calculations. Coulomb forces can be included for charged-particle interactions; nuclear potentials other than the square well can be used; spin-orbit effects can be introduced, as required by the shell model; and the absorption effect, (W), can be concentrated in the nuclear surface when this seems warranted.

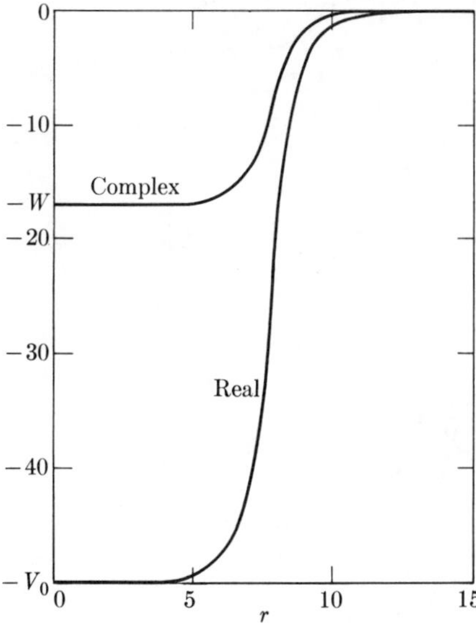

Fig. 13–25. Optical-model potential used by A. E. Glassgold and P. J. Kellogg.

Figure 13–25 shows the real and imaginary parts of the nuclear well used in some optical-model calculations performed by Glassgold and Kellogg.* These are to be compared with proton-scattering experiments performed by N. Hintz.† The total potential used was

$$V = \frac{Ze^2}{4\pi\epsilon_0 r} - (V_0 + iW)\,\frac{\frac{1}{2}\exp[-(r-R)/a]}{1-\frac{1}{2}\exp(-R/a)} \qquad \text{for} \quad r > R,$$

$$V = \frac{Ze^2 r}{4\pi\epsilon_0 R^2} - (V_0 + iW)\,\frac{1-\frac{1}{2}\exp[(r-R)/a]}{1-\frac{1}{2}\exp(-R/a)} \qquad \text{for} \quad r < R. \tag{13–53}$$

The nuclear radius was given by

$$R = r_0 A^{1/3}\ \mathrm{F}, \tag{13–54}$$

and the quantities V_0, W, r_0 and the surface thickness a were used as adjustable

---

* A. E. Glassgold and P. J. Kellogg, *Phys. Rev.* **109,** 1291 (1958).
† N. Hintz, *Bull. Am. Phys. Soc.* **2,** 14 (1957).

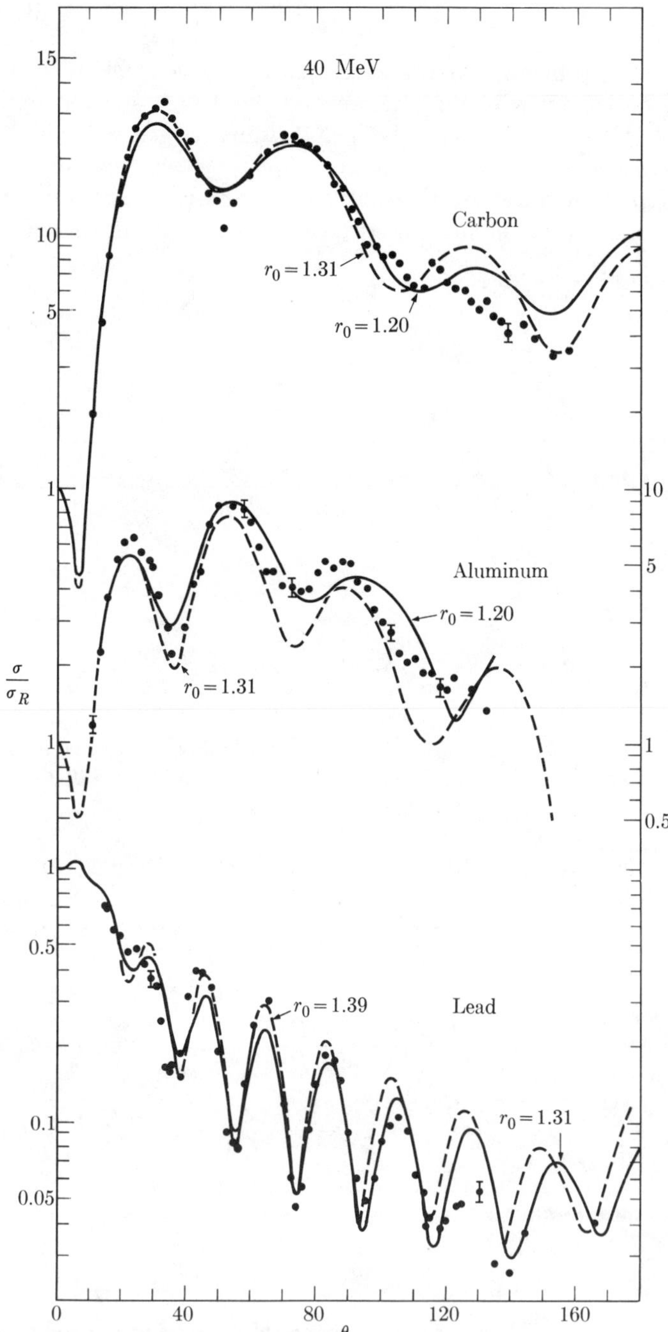

Fig. 13–26. Elastic scattering cross sections for 40-MeV protons on various targets. Theoretical curves by A. E. Glassgold and P. J. Kellogg, *Phys. Rev.* **109,** 1291 (1958) and experimental points by N. Hintz, *Bull. Am. Phys. Soc.* **2,** 14 (1957).

parameters. Figure 13–26 shows a comparison between the experimental and theoretical values of the elastic-scattering cross section of 40-MeV protons on three different elements. The ordinate is the ratio between the actual cross section and the Rutherford (pure Coulomb-scattering) cross section. The curves display a diffraction pattern that is remarkably similar to the scattering pattern of light from a translucent obstacle. Hence, the term "optical model" has been applied.

Glassgold and Kellogg also compared available data on elastic scattering of protons at other energies with calculations. They arrived at the set of "best-fit" optical parameters for proton scattering given in Table 13–1, all based on $r_0 = 1.3$ F.

Table 13–1. Best-fit optical parameters for proton scattering

Energy, MeV	V_0, MeV	W, MeV	a, F
10	53	7	0.7
17	50	8	0.7
40	36	15	0.9
95	26	10	0.9

In other optical-model calculations, particularly at lower energies, it has been found that an imaginary part of the potential concentrated in the surface of the nucleus gives better agreement with experimental results. The assumption is that the nucleons in the surface are more easily excitable by collision with the incoming particle than those in the interior. Qualitatively speaking, the inner nucleons, being tightly bound, need more energy to be excited into an unoccupied state. At low and moderate energies, the probability of inelastic scattering for an incoming particle is therefore smaller in the middle of the nucleus than it is at the surface. At higher energies, for example 40 MeV as in Fig. 13–26, this argument does not hold, and Eq. (13–53) as used by Glassgold and Kellogg gives the same shapes for the real and imaginary parts.

13–11 Theory of Stripping Reactions

The term "stripping" is used for a type of direct reaction in which the incoming compound particle is split into two fragments, one of which is absorbed by the target nucleus while the other continues more or less undisturbed. The inverse of a stripping reaction is called a "pickup" reaction; an example is $Ne^{20}(He^3, \alpha)Ne^{19}$. The theories of stripping and pickup reactions are very similar, and the angular distributions, with the characteristic forward maxima, are also quite similar. As an example here, we shall discuss deuteron stripping and, in particular, study the angular distribution of the emitted deuteron fragments (neutrons or protons).*

(*a*) *Semiclassical description.* For the sake of simplicity we will refer to a (d, p) process in this description, but since we will ignore the Coulomb interaction, the arguments are equally valid for a (d, n) process.

In Fig. 13–27(a), the deuteron, consisting of a neutron and a proton, moves from the left toward the target nucleus which is, for the present, regarded as being very heavy compared with the deuteron. In Fig. 13–27(b), the neutron has joined the target nucleus to form a residual nucleus in a specific state. The proton is moving away from the region with a kinetic energy equal to the Q-value for the state in question plus the kinetic energy of the deuteron (Eq. 13–4 with $T_R \approx 0$ and $T_T \approx 0$). In the momentum diagram, Fig. 13–27(c), $\mathbf{K}_d\hbar$ is the momentum of the deuteron, and $\mathbf{K}_p\hbar$ is the momentum of the proton; hence, $\kappa\hbar$ is the momentum imparted to the residual nucleus. When $\mathbf{K}_d\hbar$, $\mathbf{K}_p\hbar$, and θ_p are known, $\boldsymbol{\kappa}\hbar$ is given by the cosine rule applied to the momentum triangle. The vector $\mathbf{k}_i\hbar$ in Fig. 13–27(c) is the momentum of the proton relative to the center of mass of the deuteron (internal momentum).

The assumption is now made that the proton does not come within the range of nuclear forces from the target nucleus and is not significantly deflected by the Coulomb forces from the nucleus. The linear momentum $\boldsymbol{\kappa}\hbar$ imparted to the nucleus is then the momentum that the neutron brings with it. The *orbital angular momentum* that the neutron brings with it into the nucleus can also be estimated if a reasonable assumption can be made about the magnitude of the impact parameter of the neutron with respect to the center of mass. If we assume that the impact parameter is approximately equal to R, the nuclear

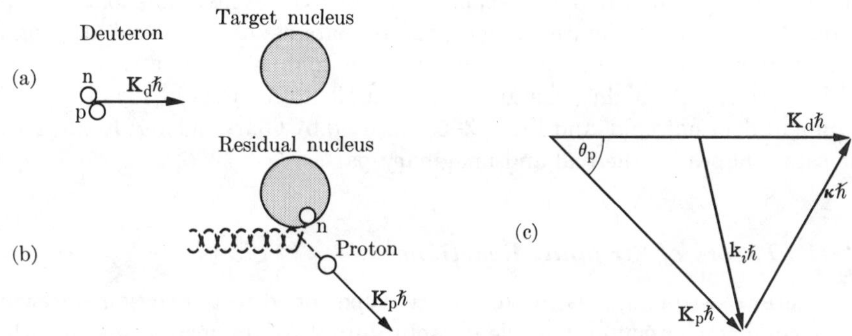

Fig. 13–27. Deuteron stripping; (a) before the collision, and (b) after the reaction has taken place. (c) Diagram used to illustrate conservation of momentum.

* For more details, see S. T. Butler, *Nuclear Stripping Reactions*, New York: John Wiley and Sons, Inc., 1957.

radius (the neutron goes into an outer orbit), then the orbital angular momentum is $\kappa\hbar R$. This orbital angular momentum is quantized, i.e., it is equal to $\sqrt{l(l+1)}\hbar$, where l is an integer. This gives

$$\kappa R \approx \sqrt{l(l+1)}. \tag{13–55}$$

If our model of the process is not too crude, Eq. (13–55) essentially expresses the fact that it is possible to determine the orbital angular momentum quantum number of the neutron by determining κ. As discussed above, κ is given when the reaction angle and the kinetic energies of the deuteron and the proton are given. The reasoning can be reversed, and we reach the conclusion that when, for stripping to a certain level, only one value of l occurs, the wave number κ must satisfy Eq. (13–55), and the geometry of the process is thereby fixed. In other words, the proton must come out at a given reaction angle θ, which is found by applying the cosine rule to the triangle in Fig. 13–27(c).

Obviously, the results of such a crude theory should not be taken too literally. It seems reasonable, however, to expect a maximum in the differential cross section for an angle that leads to the fulfillment of Eq. (13–55). This is, indeed, in accordance with the results of the wave-mechanical treatment.

The prediction of Eq. (13–55) can be tested on the angular distributions of Fig. 13–10. The wave number for a 7-MeV deuteron is $K_{\rm d} = 0.82\ {\rm F}^{-1}$, and for a 13-MeV proton it is $K_{\rm p} = 0.79\ {\rm F}^{-1}$. Choosing a radius $R = 6$ F and applying the cosine rule to the momentum triangle (Fig. 13–27c), we get the following predictions:

$$l = 1, \qquad \theta_{\rm max} \approx 16°;$$
$$l = 2, \qquad \theta_{\rm max} \approx 29°;$$
$$l = 3, \qquad \theta_{\rm max} \approx 42°.$$

For $l = 0$, the predicted angle for maximum cross section is imaginary ($\cos\theta > 1$), but $\theta = 0$ comes nearest to satisfying the equation.

The majority of the angular distributions shown in Fig. 13–10 display strong forward maxima, in general agreement with the predictions made above. Specifically, there are many levels with maxima around 17° to 18° and others with maxima around 40°, suggesting stripping with neutrons going into $l = 1$ and $l = 3$ orbits (p- and f-state stripping). As elaborated in Section 13–12, this is what would be expected from shell-model ideas in this region of the nucleon number A.

(*b*) *Wave-mechanical description.* Now let us consider the wave-mechanical treatment of stripping. The differential cross section for the reaction can be computed by use of perturbation theory in which the reaction signifies that the system is transferred from a state ψ_i to a state ψ_f by action of a perturbing potential. As usual, the transition probability (cross section) will be proportional to the square of a matrix element of the form

$$H'_{if} = \int \psi_f^* H' \psi_i \, d\tau,$$

where H' is the perturbing part of the total Hamiltonian. The initial wave function ψ_i describes a deuteron with initial wave number $\mathbf{K}_\mathrm{d}$ moving toward the nucleus. The internal motions of the proton and the neutron in the deuteron are also described by ψ_i, but the internal motions of the nucleons in the target nucleus are of no concern to us in the simple stripping theory. The target nucleus is therefore treated as a potential well. The center-of-mass motion of the deuteron is represented in ψ_i by a wave distorted by the combined Coulomb field and nuclear field, as described in the discussion of the optical model. This part of the wave function ψ_i is therefore a complete optical-model wave function consisting of a sum of partial waves with orbital momenta l_d and different spin directions. The final state ψ_f describes a proton with wave number $\mathbf{K}_\mathrm{p}$ moving away from the nucleus and a neutron in a state with orbital angular momentum l added to the target nucleus. The proton part is equivalent to an optical-model wave function for a proton moving toward the final nucleus and being scattered by it, except that the direction of motion is reversed. The perturbing potential which produces the transfer of the system from state ψ_i to state ψ_f can be found by comparing the total Hamiltonian H_t with the Hamiltonian of which the final state ψ_f is an eigenfunction. With reference to Fig. 13–27, we write:

$$H_t = T_{\mathrm{d}T} + T_{\mathrm{pn}} + V_{\mathrm{pn}} + V_{\mathrm{p}T} + V_{\mathrm{n}T} = T_{\mathrm{p}R} + T_{\mathrm{n}T} + V_{\mathrm{pn}} + V_{\mathrm{p}T} + V_{\mathrm{n}T}, \tag{13–56}$$

where $T_{\mathrm{d}T}$ is the operator for the relative kinetic energy of the deuteron-target system, $V_{\mathrm{p}T}$ is the relative potential energy of the proton-target system, etc. The final wave function ψ_f is an eigenfunction of the Hamiltonian

$$H_f = T_{\mathrm{p}R} + T_{\mathrm{n}T} + V'_{\mathrm{p}R} + V_{\mathrm{n}T}, \tag{13–57}$$

where $V'_{\mathrm{p}R}$ is not the true potential acting between the proton and the residual nucleus, but is the simpler optical-model potential (Eq. 13–53). By comparing Eq. (13–57) with Eq. (13–56), we find the perturbing potential

$$H' = H_t - H_f = V_{\mathrm{pn}} + V_{\mathrm{p}T} - V'_{\mathrm{p}R}.$$

We now make the simplifying assumption that the optical-model potential $V'_{\mathrm{p}R}$ is not very much different from the proton-target potential $V_{\mathrm{p}T}$. To make the calculations manageable, we can therefore put $V_{\mathrm{p}T} = V'_{\mathrm{p}R}$ and then obtain

$$H' \approx V_{\mathrm{pn}}(r_{\mathrm{np}}), \tag{13–58}$$

where r_{np} is the neutron-proton separation. For simplicity, the neutron-proton potential is considered a function of the separation r_{np} only (central force).

It is shown in Appendix 4 that the differential cross section for a (d, p) reaction from the initial state α (entrance channel) to the final state β is given by the formula

$$\frac{d\sigma(\alpha, \beta)}{d\Omega} = \frac{M_d M_p}{(2\pi\hbar^2)^2} \frac{K_p}{K_d} |A_{\alpha,\beta}(\mathbf{K}_d, \mathbf{K}_p)|^2, \tag{13–59}$$

where the reaction amplitude $A_{\alpha,\beta}$ is given by

$$A_{\alpha,\beta}(\mathbf{K}_d, \mathbf{K}_p) = \int \psi_f^* V_{np} \psi_i \, d\tau_n \, d\tau_p. \tag{13–60}$$

The wave functions are

$$\psi_f^* = \Phi_p^{(-)}(\mathbf{K}_p, \mathbf{r}_p)\phi_R^*(r_{nT}),$$

$$\psi_i = \Phi_d^{(+)}(\mathbf{K}_d, \mathbf{r}_d)\phi_d(r_{np}),$$

where $\mathbf{r}_d = (r_p + r_n)/2$.

Here, the final wave function is written as a product of an optical-model wave function $\Phi_p^{(-)}$, describing a proton moving outward, asymptotically in direction $\mathbf{K}_p$, and a function $\phi_R(r_{nT})$, describing the neutron bound to the target nucleus (shell-model wave function). The initial wave function is written as a product of an optical-model wave function $\Phi_d^{(+)}$ for the center-of-mass motion of the deuteron times a function ϕ_d describing the internal motion in the deuteron. The target nucleus is thought of as a particle, the internal structure of which is irrelevant. Equation (13–59) gives the differential cross section for a given entrance channel α and exit channel β. For both channels, all angular momenta and their directions are specified. By adding the contributions from all values of l_d, l_p, and spin orientations consistent with a given neutron l-value, we get the total differential cross section.

Two approaches can be taken for solving Eq. (13–60). The first is to make a sufficient number of simplifying assumptions so that the integral can be worked out analytically. In particular, the optical-model wave functions $\Phi_d^{(+)}$ and $\Phi_p^{(-)}$ can be replaced by plane waves. The second approach is to use a high-speed computer and more realistic wave functions.

An analytic expression for the differential cross section of stripping was worked out by Butler* and, independently, by Bhatia *et al.*† Computer calculations of stripping cross sections were pioneered by Tobocman.‡ Figure 13–28§ shows some examples of experimentally determined angular distributions and

---

* S. T. Butler, *Proc. Roy. Soc.* (*London*) **A208,** 559 (1951).

† A. B. Bhatia, K. Huang, R. Huby, and H. C. Newns, *Phil. Mag.* **43,** 485 (1952).

‡ See, for instance, W. Tobocman, *Phys. Rev.* **115,** 98 (1959).

§ J. Rapaport, A. Sperduto, and W. W. Buechner, to be published.

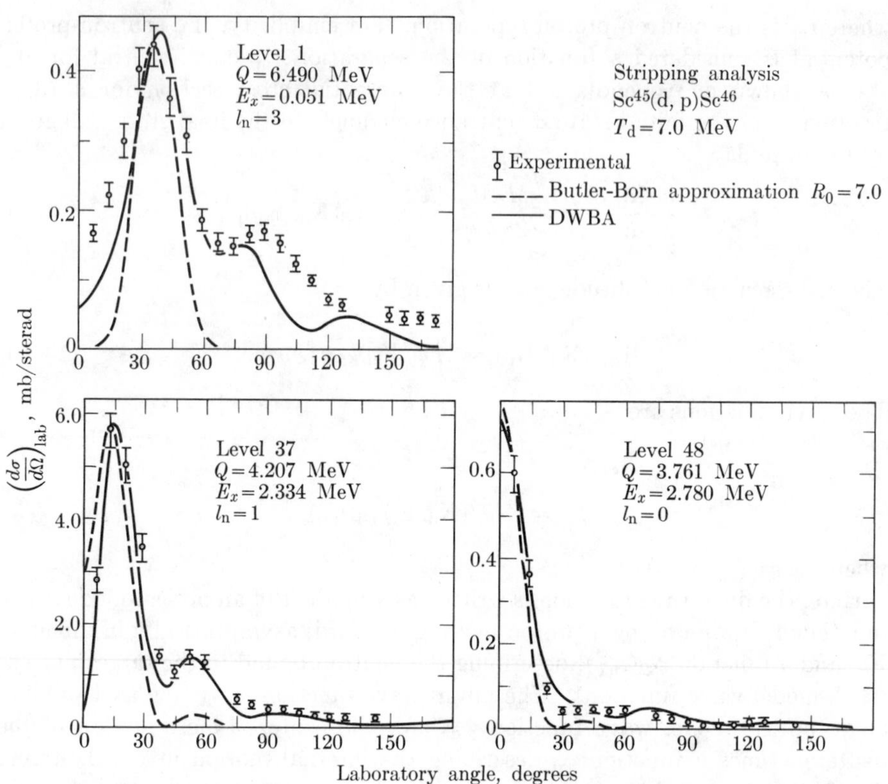

Fig. 13–28. Experimental stripping cross sections compared with distorted-wave Born approximation, (DWBA) calculations as well as plane-wave (Butler) calculations. (From J. Rapaport, A. Sperduto, and W. W. Buechner, to be published.)

corresponding theoretical curves. The dashed curves are calculated from Butler's analytical formula and the solid curves are evaluated using a computer program written by Tobocman and coworkers. The abbreviation DWBA stands for "distorted-wave Born approximation" and refers to the method using optical-model wave functions described above. There are a number of adjustable parameters in the DWBA calculations, and it is very likely that a better fit could be obtained, particularly for level number 1 through further work.

Aside from the interesting result that the stripping mechanism seems to be adequately described by the wave-mechanical methods we have used, the greatest significance of the analysis is that it can yield the orbital angular momentum of the captured neutron. This gives us, so to speak, a direct handle on the wave function for the "last" neutron in a given state, particularly for nuclei in which the neutron is expected to fall directly into a practically pure shell-model state. As discussed earlier (e.g., Section 6–5), most nuclear states are not pure shell-model states, but the total wave function can be thought of as a sum of shell-model terms, all having the same resulting angular momentum and parity. In general, the following model-independent selection rules can be used to determine the change of angular momentum and parity in a stripping process:

$$|(|J_i - l| - \tfrac{1}{2})| \lesssim J_f \lesssim J_i + l + \tfrac{1}{2}, \qquad \pi_i\pi_f = (-1)^l. \tag{13–61}$$

If the angular momentum of the target nucleus is 0^+, the final state will have angular momentum $J_f = l \pm \frac{1}{2}$ and parity $\pi_f = (-1)^l$.

The ordinates for the theoretical curves in Fig. 13–28 have been adjusted so as to make them match the data at the principal maximum. The DWBA calculations are based on the assumption that the neutron goes into a single-particle state, i.e., a shell-model state. If this is not the case, the experimental cross section, of course, will be lower than the calculated one. In general, one can write

$$\left(\frac{d\sigma}{d\omega}\right)_{\text{exp}} = S\left(\frac{d\sigma}{d\omega}\right)_{\text{th}} = S(2J_f + 1)\left(\frac{d\sigma}{d\omega}\right)_0, \tag{13–62}$$

where a factor $(2J_f + 1)$, which appears in the theoretical calculations, has been pulled out, and $(d\sigma/d\omega)_0$ contains the rest of the terms in the cross-section formula. The reason why $(2J_f + 1)$ has been factored out is that it is not known in general. It is indeed one of the objectives of stripping-reaction studies to determine J_f. The factor S, called the *spectroscopic factor*, measures the ratio of the observed cross section to the cross section expected for a single-particle state. Put differently, it measures the percentage contribution of a single-particle state or states with given l to the total wave function describing the residual state.

13–12 Stripping Reactions and the Shell Model

It was pointed out first by Bethe and Butler* that stripping reactions in some cases could be used to measure the purity of shell-model states. For instance, in the reaction P^{31}(d,p)P^{32}, the target nucleus has angular momentum $J_i = 1/2^+$ (an odd $2s_{1/2}$ proton), and the ground state of P^{32} is expected to be formed by adding a neutron in a $d_{3/2}$ state. The two j-values, $j_p = 1/2$ and $j_n = 3/2$, can combine to $J_f = 1^+$ or 2^+. The 1^+ state happens to be the ground state. If we apply the model-independent selection rule (13–61), we find that the 1^+ state can be reached both by an $l = 0$ and an $l = 2$ neutron, whereas the shell-model state $d_{3/2}$, of course, requires that $l = 2$. The question raised by Bethe and Butler was: Will a stripping experiment yield an angular distribution consistent with $l = 2$, with $l = 0$, or with a mixture of these cases?

---

* H. A. Bethe and S. T. Butler, *Phys. Rev.* **85**, 1045 (1952).

The experiment was performed by Parkinson *et al.** They found an angular distribution consistent with $l = 2$ and very little, if any, trace of $l = 0$ contribution. In the particular example chosen, the test is a very sensitive one because $l = 0$ stripping gives a cross section that is one order of magnitude larger at the maximum than does $l = 2$ stripping under similar circumstances. The result is therefore a great tribute to the shell model.

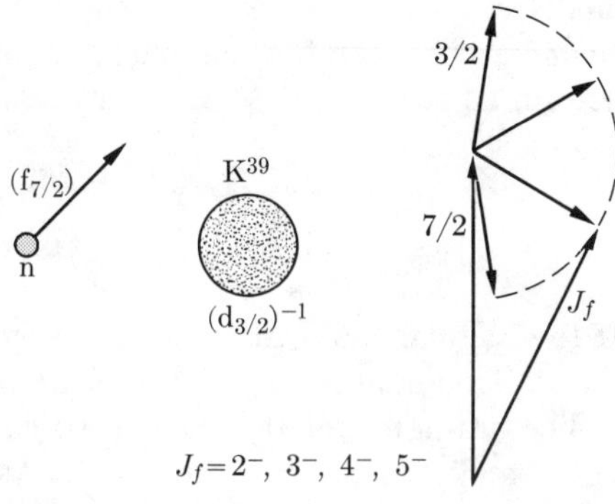

Fig. 13–29. The addition of an $f_{7/2}$ neutron to a $d_{3/2}$ target nucleus.

As a second example, we shall discuss in somewhat more detail the results of stripping analysis of the reaction $K^{39}(d, p)K^{40}$. The experiment† was performed on the broad-range magnetic spectrograph, the forerunner of the multiple-gap spectrograph at the Massachusetts Institute of Technology (Section 13–3). The spectrum of protons from a thin potassium-iodide target bombarded by 6-MeV deuterons was measured at fifteen different reaction angles from 10°

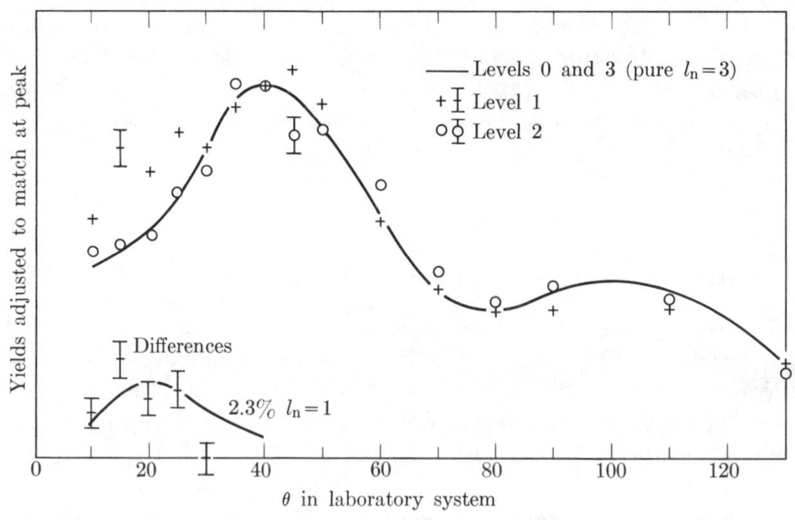

Fig. 13–30. Angular distributions of protons for the $K^{39}(d, p)K^{40}$ reaction leaving the residual nucleus in level 0, 1, 2, and 3 with angular momentum $J = 4^-, 3^-, 2^-,$ and 5^-.

* W. C. Parkinson, E. H. Beach, and J. S. King, *Phys. Rev.* **87,** 387 (1952).
† H. A. Enge, E. J. Irwin, and D. H. Weaner, *Phys. Rev.* **115,** 949 (1959).

to 130°. The angular distributions for over fifty levels were studied, and neutron l-values were determined for thirty-nine of them.

The residual nucleus in this reaction is again an example of an odd-odd nucleus in which j_p and j_n can combine in $2j_{min} + 1$ different ways, where j_{min} is the smaller of j_p and j_n. The lowest states are expected to be formed by adding an $f_{7/2}$ neutron ($l = 3$) to a core containing an odd $d_{3/2}$ proton (Fig. 13–29). This leads to a quadruplet with $J_f = 2^-, 3^-, 4^-$, and 5^-. Two of the states, the 2^- and 3^- states, can also be reached with $l = 1$ stripping without violating Eq. (13–61). Again we ask the question: Do the experimental data indicate that $l = 3$ stripping takes place, as predicted by the shell model; and, if so, is there any contamination of $l = 1$ stripping to the 2^- and 3^- states?

The answer to the first question is that the angular distributions for the four lowest states show clearly $l = 3$ stripping. To answer the second, we need to assign J-values to the four levels. This has been done on the basis of the amplitude factor $(2J_f + 1)$ appearing in Eq. (13–62), and the result is that the ground state has $J = 4^-$, and the three excited states have $J = 3^-, 2^-$, and 5^-, in order of ascending excitation.

The angular-distribution data are shown in Fig. 13–30, in which the fully drawn curve represents the average of the experimental cross sections of the two states for which $l = 1$ is forbidden by Eq. (13–61). This therefore represents an empirical, pure $l = 3$, angular distribution for this reaction and energy. The experimental yields for the two levels for which $l = 1$ is not forbidden are also shown in Fig. 13–30 as open circles for the 2^- level and crosses for the 3^- level. Both sets of data have been normalized so that the principal maxima are equal to that of the fully drawn curve. As can be seen from Fig. 13–30, the circles follow the curve very closely, indicating that the 2^- level is formed by very pure $l = 3$ stripping. The differential cross section for the 3^- level is, however, systematically higher at forward angles, and this may be interpreted as a small contribution from $l = 1$ stripping. On the basis of relative intensities of $l = 1$ and $l = 3$ stripping, it is found that the contribution does not exceed a few percent (2.3% indicated on the figure). Thus the 3^- level also is formed predominantly by adding an $l = 3$ neutron to the core, as predicted by the shell model.

The final results of the stripping analysis of the $K^{39}(d, p)K^{40}$ data are shown in Fig. 13–31, together with similar results from the $Ca^{40}(d, p)Ca^{41}$ reaction.* The ground state of Ca^{41} is formed by adding an $f_{7/2}$ neutron to Ca^{40} which has doubly closed shells ($Z = N = 20$). This singlet ground state of Ca^{41} splits into the quadruplet $(d_{3/2})^{-1}(f_{7/2})$ for K^{40} which has one proton hole.†

---

* T. A. Belote, A. Sperduto, and W. W. Buechner, *Phys. Rev.* **139,** B80 (1965).

† The notation $(d_{3/2})^{-1}$ is commonly used for cases such as this where one particle is needed to complete the shell.

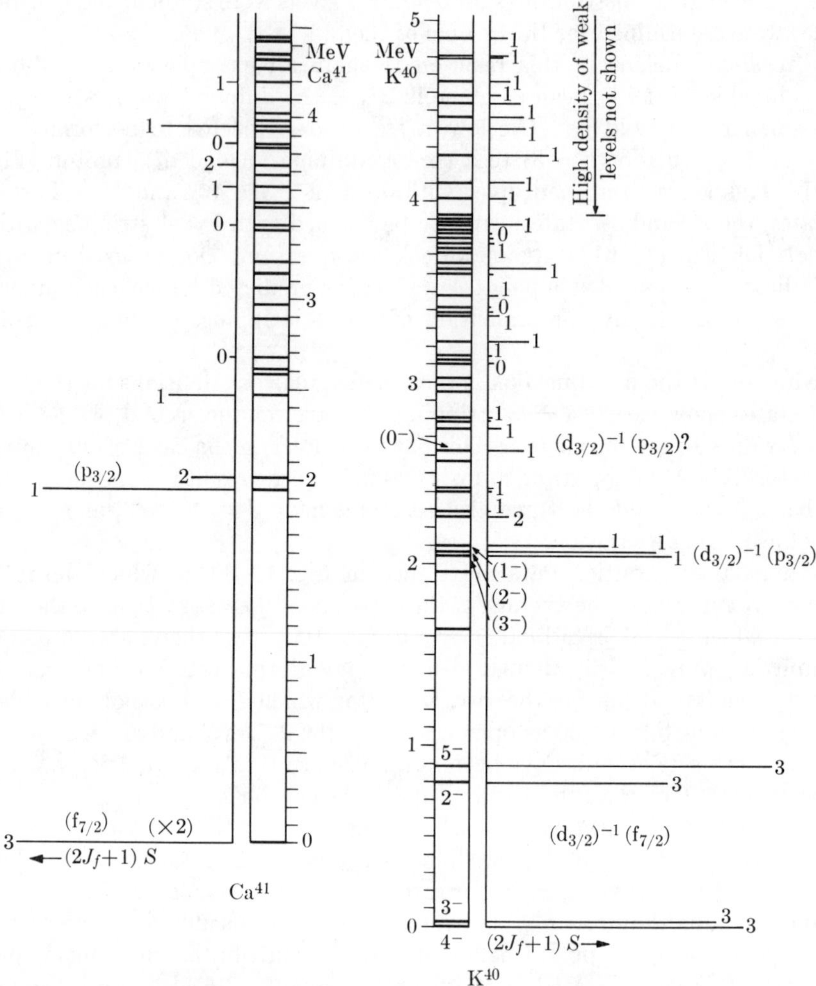

Fig. 13–31. Energy levels of the odd-odd nucleus K^{40} compared with the odd neutron nucleus Ca^{41}. The numbers beside the lines indicating stripping strength are the l-values.

Similarly, the first excited state in Ca^{41}, a $p_{3/2}$ state, splits into a $(d_{3/2})^{-1}(p_{3/2})$ quadruplet in K^{40}. There is also a second low-lying $p_{3/2}$ state in Ca^{41}, presumably formed by adding a $p_{3/2}$ neutron to a small $(d_{3/2})^{-2}(f_{7/2})^2$ term in the Ca^{40} ground-state wave function. This and higher excited states in Ca^{41} all split into multiplets in K^{40} when the proton number is also odd. However, the members of the multiplets are so close that they overlap and mix and are therefore hard to identify.

13–13 Coulomb Excitation

One of the more fruitful approaches to the study of nuclear energy levels in the last decade has been to produce electromagnetic excitations of the nucleus through bombardment with charged particles. Coulomb excitation is an inelastic scattering process in which the bombarding particle is charged and brings about an excitation of the target nucleus from the ground state to a higher state through the intermediary of the electromagnetic field. Consider a proton, for instance, which is being deflected by the Coulomb field of the nucleus and, hence, experiences an acceleration near the nucleus. It can create an electromagnetic field quantum which is absorbed by the nucleus. The bombarding energy may be so low that the proton cannot penetrate the Coulomb barrier with any significant probability. Direct nuclear force interactions can therefore be neglected.

The theory of Coulomb excitation, involving the well-known electromagnetic type of interaction, is exact, but quite complex mathematically. We can, however, get considerable insight into the process through rather simple calculations. Our mathematical treatment will be subject to the following restrictions.

(1) We calculate, as the simplest possible example, the differential cross section for Coulomb excitation at a scattering angle of $\theta = 180°$.

(2) The bombarding particle is assumed to be spinless, and the target nucleus is assumed to have angular momentum $J_i = 0$. This restriction is designed to leave sums and quantum-mechanical vector addition coefficients out of our calculations, but the restriction is otherwise unimportant.

(3) The quantum-mechanical state of the particle is, in these calculations, represented by a classical Rutherford orbit. In other words, the finite size of the wave packet describing the motion of the particle is neglected.

(4) The excitation energy $\Delta E = E_f - E_i$, imparted to the nucleus, is assumed to be small; how small and why will be discussed later.

(5) As a specific example of multipole moment excitation, we chose the type which has been most studied, electric quadrupole excitation. Since we have already introduced the restriction $J_i = 0$, this means that $J_f = 2$.

We shall study first the particle motion for classical head-on collision ($\theta = 180°$). The equation describing the position of the particle vs. time can be found by using the law of conservation of energy

$$\tfrac{1}{2}mv^2 + \frac{zZe^2}{4\pi\epsilon_0 r} = \tfrac{1}{2}mv_0^2. \qquad (13\text{–}63)$$

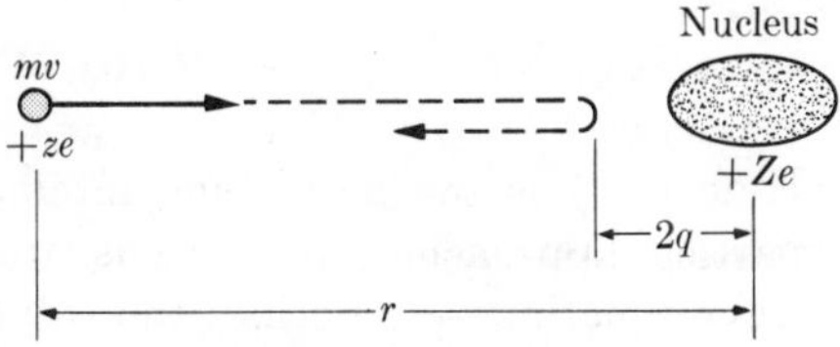

Fig. 13–32. Head-on collision between a charged particle and a nucleus resulting in 180° scattering and possibly Coulomb excitation of the nucleus.

Figure 13–32 defines the symbols used. We introduce the distance of closest approach $2q$, given by

$$2q = \frac{zZe^2}{4\pi\epsilon_0(\frac{1}{2}mv_0^2)} \tag{13–64}$$

and solve Eq. (13–63) for the velocity v. We obtain

$$v = dr/dt = \pm v_0\sqrt{1 - 2q/r}. \tag{13–65}$$

This is a differential equation which gives the relationship between time and position of the particle. It turns out that we do not have to solve this equation, but can use it as it stands in the calculation of the reaction cross section.

The differential cross section for the inelastic scattering process involving Coulomb excitation will now be calculated as a product of the Rutherford elastic scattering cross section $d\sigma_R/d\omega$ times the probability P that the particle will Coulomb-excite the nucleus from somewhere in its orbit:

$$\frac{d\sigma}{d\omega} = P\frac{d\sigma_R}{d\omega}. \tag{13–66}$$

The Rutherford cross section is*

$$\frac{d\sigma_R}{d\omega} = \frac{q^2}{4\sin^4\theta/2}. \tag{13–67}$$

The probability P for excitation of the nucleus through the electromagnetic interaction can be calculated by the aid of perturbation theory (Appendix 4). We have

$$P = |a_{if}|^2, \tag{13–68}$$

where

$$a_{if} = \frac{1}{i\hbar}\int_{-\infty}^{\infty} H'_{if}(t)e^{i\omega t}\,dt. \tag{13–69}$$

The matrix element $H'_{if}(t)$ is given by

$$H'_{if}(t) = \int \psi_f^* H'(t)\psi_i\,d\tau. \tag{13–70}$$

Here $H'(t)$ is the perturbing interaction energy. It varies with time as the particle approaches the nucleus, turns around, and moves away again. The wave function ψ_f describes the total final state in which the nucleus is in the excited state and the particle energy is correspondingly reduced. The initial wave function ψ_i describes the particle in the original Rutherford orbit and the

---

* See any textbook on modern physics, for instance F. K. Richtmeyer, E. H. Kennard, and T. Lauritsen, *Introduction to Modern Physics*, New York: McGraw-Hill, 1956, p. 145.

nucleus in the ground state. The last term in the integrand of Eq. (13–69) is the phase factor required by perturbation theory. The angular frequency ω is

$$\omega = (E_f - E_i)/\hbar, \tag{13–71}$$

where E_f and E_i are the energies of the final and initial nuclear states, respectively.

The interaction energy between a quadrupole Q_{20} and a particle of charge ze at a distance $r(t)$ from the center of the quadrupole is for $\theta = 0$ or π (see Problem 13–12):

$$H'(t) = \sqrt{\frac{4\pi}{5}}\,\frac{ze}{4\pi\epsilon_0 r^3}\,Q_{20}. \tag{13–72}$$

The quadrupole moment Q_{20} is given by (see Eq. 9–9):

$$Q_{20} = \int_{\mathrm{N}} r^2 Y^*_{20}(\theta, \varphi)\rho\, d\tau, \tag{13–73}$$

where the integration is performed over the nuclear volume (indicated by N). This quadrupole moment is part of the perturbing Hamiltonian which is bracketed between ψ_f^* and ψ_i in Eq. (13–70). It is therefore regarded as an operator, but since it contains no momentum coordinates, it does not change form, except that ρ is replaced by e and a summation over protons is performed. The static quadrupole moment in this formalism becomes, as before:

$$Q_{20} = e\sum_{k=1}^{k=Z}\int_{\mathrm{N}} r_k^2 Y^*_{20}(\theta_k, \phi_k)\psi^2\, d\tau, \tag{13–74}$$

and the quadrupole matrix element between the initial state ψ_i and final state ψ_f is

$$Q_{20}(if) = e\sum_{k=1}^{k=Z}\int_{\mathrm{N}} r_k^2 Y^*_{20}(\theta_k, \phi_k)\psi_f^*\psi_i\, d\tau, \tag{13–75}$$

where index k stands for the kth proton.

By combining Eqs. (13–70) and (13–72) and the operator form of Q_{20}, we get

$$H(t) = \sum_{k=1}^{k=Z}\int_{\mathrm{p}}\int_{\mathrm{N}} \psi^*_{f\mathrm{p}}\psi^*_{f\mathrm{N}}\sqrt{\frac{4}{5}}\,\frac{ze^2}{4\pi\epsilon_0 r^3}\, r_k^2 Y^*_{20}(\theta_k, \phi_k)\psi_{i\mathrm{p}}\psi_{i\mathrm{N}}\, d\tau_{\mathrm{p}}\, d\tau_{\mathrm{N}}.$$

The final wave function has been replaced by a product of a wave function for the particle (subscript p) and a wave function for the nucleus. The integration over the nucleus is carried through as an integration over the coordinates of each particle (subscript k) and a summation over protons only, since the neutrons do not carry charge. The integration and summation over the nucleons yield the quadrupole matrix element (Eq. 13–75), which is independent of time. The integration over particle coordinates yields

$$\int_{\mathrm{p}} \psi_{f\mathrm{p}}^{*} \frac{1}{r^{3}(t)} \psi_{i\mathrm{p}}\, d\tau_{\mathrm{p}} = \langle r^{-3} \rangle,$$

which is the expectation value for the inverse cube of the position of the particle as a function of time. Assembling this information, we obtain

$$H_{if}(t) = \sqrt{\frac{4\pi}{5}} \frac{ze}{4\pi\epsilon_0} \langle r^{-3} \rangle Q_{20}(if).$$

The integration over time indicated in Eq. (13–69) will now be performed with consideration for the restrictions listed above. In particular, we are assuming that the motion of the particle is adequately described by a classical Rutherford orbit. This means replacing $\langle r^{-3} \rangle$ with r^{-3}. Also we shall assume that ω is so small that $e^{i\omega t}$ does not change appreciably during the time the particle is close enough to the nucleus to interact with it. This means that

$$\frac{E_f - E_i}{\hbar} \frac{q}{v_0} \ll 1, \tag{13–76}$$

since q/v_0 is a measure of the time the particle is close to the nucleus. With these approximations, we get, since $|e^{i\omega t}| = 1$:

$$a_{if} = \frac{2}{i\hbar} \sqrt{\frac{4\pi}{5}} \frac{ze}{4\pi\epsilon_0} Q_{20}(if) \int_0^\infty \frac{dt}{r^3} \cdot$$

Because of the symmetry of the orbit, we integrate from $t = 0$ at which time the particle is at $r = 2q$, to ∞ and multiply by a factor of 2 instead of integrating from $-\infty$ to $+\infty$. We now use Eq. (13–65) to substitute dr for dt. The result is

$$a_{if} = \frac{2}{i\hbar v_0} \sqrt{\frac{4\pi}{5}} \frac{ze}{4\pi\epsilon_0} Q_{20}(if) \int_{2q}^\infty \frac{dr}{r^3\sqrt{1 - 2q/r}} \cdot \tag{13–77}$$

The integral can be solved easily by using the substitution $u = 1 - 2q/r$. The result is

$$\int_{2q}^\infty \frac{dr}{r^3\sqrt{1 - 2q/r}} = \frac{1}{3q^2} \cdot \tag{13–78}$$

By combining Eqs. (13–66), (13–67), (13–68), (13–77), (13–78), and, finally, (13–64), we get

$$\frac{d\sigma}{d\omega}(180^\circ) = \frac{4\pi m^2 v_0^2}{45\hbar^2 Z^2 e^2} |Q_{20}(if)|^2. \tag{13–79}$$

In the complete theory of Coulomb excitation, where a summation over angular-momentum directions is performed, the same reduced transition rate $B(E2)$ that was introduced in Section 9–8 replaces the square of the matrix element in Eq. (13–79). It is therefore possible to measure widths (lifetimes) of excited states by measuring the cross section for Coulomb excitation to these states. A large number of such measurements have been performed and reported in the literature.

Now we will further assume that the 2^+ excited state can be described as a collective state, for instance, a member of the 0^+, 2^+, 4^+, ... rotational band built on the 0^+ state. In this case, the two wave functions ψ_f and ψ_i overlap almost completely, and the quadrupole matrix element is simply equal to the intrinsic quadrupole moment, as defined by Eq. (13–74). This again is

$$Q_{20}(if) = Q_{20} = e\sqrt{4/16\pi}\, Q_{\text{int}},$$

where Q_{int} is the more commonly used form of the quadrupole moment, as defined in Eq. (1–14). With this inserted into Eq. (13–79), we get for the 0^+ to 2^+ electric quadrupole excitation

$$\begin{aligned}\frac{d\sigma}{d\omega}(180^\circ) &= \frac{m^2 v_0^2}{36Z^2\hbar^2}\, Q^2 \\ &= 0.133\, \frac{mE}{Z^2}\, Q_{\text{int}}^2 \text{ barn/sterad,}\end{aligned} \qquad (13\text{–}80)$$

with m given in mass units (u), E (the particle energy) in MeV, and Q_{int} in barns. Note that the cross section as it is given by Eq. (13–80) is independent of z.

This example illustrates some important features of Coulomb excitation. One is that the cross section increases linearly with energy. This is strictly true only for the example chosen, but qualitatively it expresses the trend in general. The result is in striking contrast with the results of the calculations of compound-nucleus cross sections (Fig. 13–16). Because of the absence of a barrier, Coulomb excitation of energy levels in heavy nuclei can be executed by quite low-energy particles. The second feature that should be mentioned is the appearance of m in the numerator of Eq. (13–80). Heavy particles, for instance oxygen ions, are quite effective for Coulomb-excitation experiments. Finally, for the particular type of excitation studied, the collective $E2$ excitation, the quadrupole moment appears in the cross-section formula. A measurement of the cross section therefore is a measure of Q. The cross section is particularly large in the rare-earth region of elements where Q is large.

Experimentally, Coulomb excitation can be observed either by detecting the inelastically scattered incident particle or by detecting the gamma ray or conversion electron emitted by the nucleus in the transition back to the ground state.

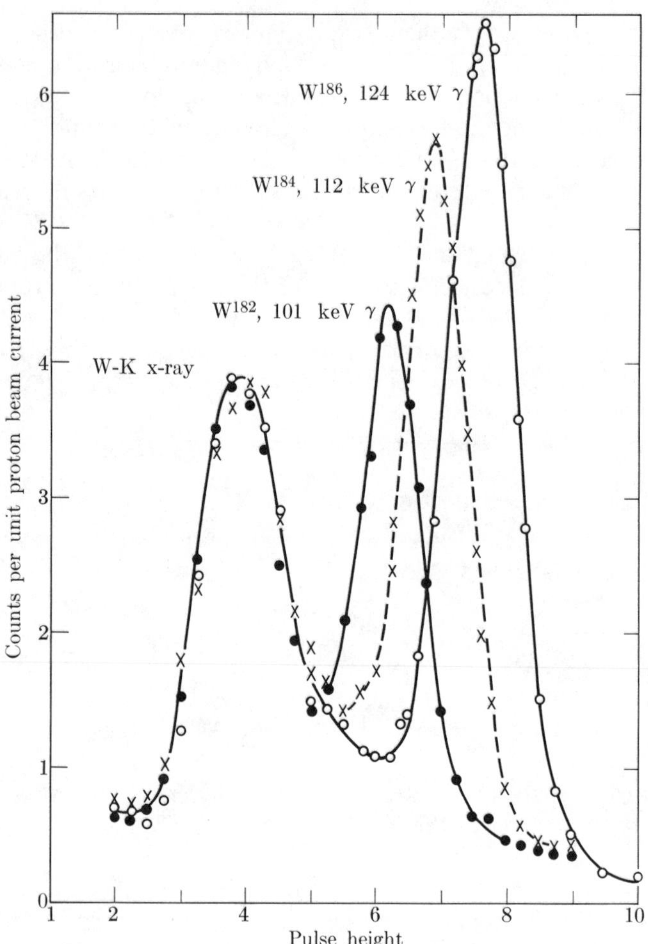

Fig. 13–33. Pulse-height spectra produced by gamma rays following Coulomb excitation of thin targets of separated tungsten isotopes. [From C. L. McClelland, H. Mark, and C. Goodman, *Phys. Rev.* **93,** 904 (1953).]

Figure 13–33 shows pulse-height spectra from a scintillation counter, exposed to gamma rays from three targets consisting of separated tungsten isotopes.* The spectra were recorded while the targets were bombarded by 2.5-MeV protons from a Van de Graaff generator. In addition to the gamma rays following Coulomb excitation of the 2^+ rotational states in the W nuclei, all three spectra showed a peak resulting from the characteristic x-ray emitted by the W atom. This is a result of the ionization of the atoms by the proton beam.

---

* C. L. McClelland, H. Mark, and C. Goodman, *Phys. Rev.* **93,** 904 (1953).

13–14 Photonuclear Reactions

At various times in earlier chapters and in this chapter we have discussed radiative-capture reactions, which involve compound-nucleus formation by particle bombardment and decay by gamma emission. At sufficiently low excitation, the compound-nucleus formation displays resonances in the cross section $\sigma(E)$, corresponding to excited states of the nucleus. These virtual states vary in width because their lifetimes vary in accordance with the complexity of the excitation. For instance, a state that can be formed by adding a neutron in a pure shell-model orbit, with no changes of the states of the other nucleons, will have a large half-width. If a complex rearrangement of the target nucleons is involved in order to reach the excited state, the width will be very small.

The photodisintegration process is the inverse of the radiative-capture reaction. A nucleus in the ground state absorbs a photon of sufficient energy to excite it above the dissociation energy for a neutron, proton, or other particle. The process shows the same resonances in the cross section as seen in the inverse reaction, although the experimental resolving power, in general, does not permit such a detailed study as in, for instance, the case of a (p, γ) process.

The simplest photodisintegration process is clearly that of the deuteron. The binding energy of the deuteron is 2.225 MeV, and gamma rays exceeding this energy can break it up into a neutron and a proton. The process can be thought of as a transition from the ^{3}S ground state to the ^{1}S virtual state by magnetic-dipole absorption, or as a transition from the ^{3}S to a ^{3}P state by electric-dipole absorption. The cross section for this process, as a function of photon energy, is fairly simple to calculate, but we shall not take space to do it here. The result is shown in Fig. 13–34, separately for the $M1$ and $E1$ transitions. The total cross section is the sum of these two contributions.

In the deuteron the two unbound states in question are so broad that no typical resonance structure is seen. In more complex nuclei, particularly in light nuclei just above the dissociation energy for a neutron or a proton, the presence of sharp resonances characterizes the photodisintegration cross section. However, more attention has been given to a very large increase in the photonuclear cross section, the *giant dipole resonance*, appearing at approximately 14 MeV for heavy nuclei and 20 to 25 MeV for light nuclei. These giant resonances have been studied in past years mostly by use of bremsstrahlung photons produced in linear accelerators or betatrons. A difficulty with the bremsstrahlung spectrum is that it is continuous and increasing in intensity from the maximum energy down to zero energy. A technique is therefore employed to simulate a monoenergetic gamma-ray beam by measuring the difference in yield between two exposures taken at two different electron energies $E + \Delta E$ and E. The contribution in particle yield resulting from gamma rays from the low-energy part of the spectrum can thereby, in principle, be subtracted out. In practice, it is difficult to obtain very good resolution with this technique, particularly because of problems involving counting statistics. Two other methods have

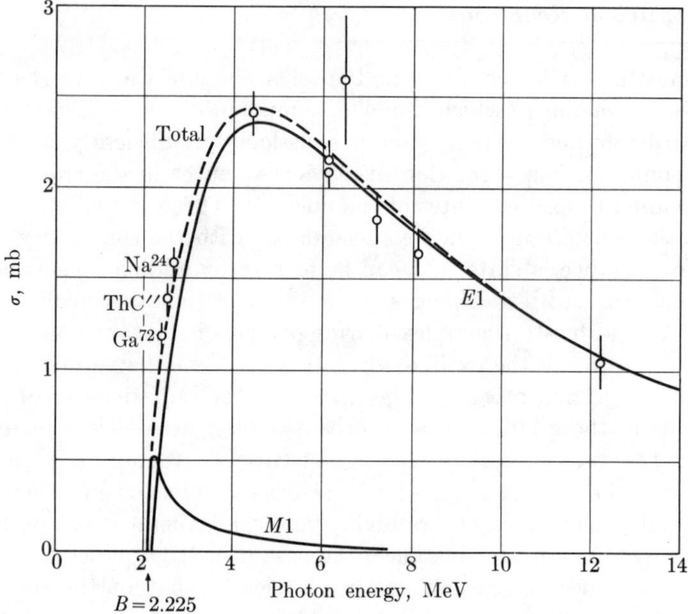

Fig. 13–34. Cross section for the photodisintegration of the deuteron. The points represent experimental data; the three first were obtained by use of gamma rays from radioactive nuclides. (Reproduced by permission from R. D. Evans, *The Atomic Nucleus*, New York: McGraw-Hill Book Company, 1955.)

proved more satisfactory: one involves production of monoenergetic gamma rays by positron annihilation in flight; the other involves measurement of the energy of the emitted particle rather than of the incident gamma ray. We discuss both these methods only briefly.

Figure 13–35 shows the experimental apparatus used by Fultz *et al.** for photonuclear studies with monoenergetic gamma rays. Electrons are accelerated to about 10 MeV in a linear accelerator and strike a tungsten target 2.5 mm thick. In this target they will produce gamma rays by bremsstrahlung, and the gamma rays in turn produce positrons in the same target. The positrons are focused (collected) by a magnetic lens and further accelerated in the second stage of the Linac to an energy that can be varied from 8 to 28 MeV. They are thereafter magnetically analyzed and focused onto a LiH target 1.5 mm thick, where some of them annihilate in flight, producing nearly monoenergetic gamma rays. The positrons passing through the target are deflected out of the photon beam by another magnet. The photon beam, which of course is not affected by the magnetic field, passes through a set of lead collimators and a xenon ion chamber

---

* S. C. Fultz, R. L. Bramblett, J. T. Caldwell, and N. A. Kerr, *Phys. Rev.* **127,** 1273 (1962).

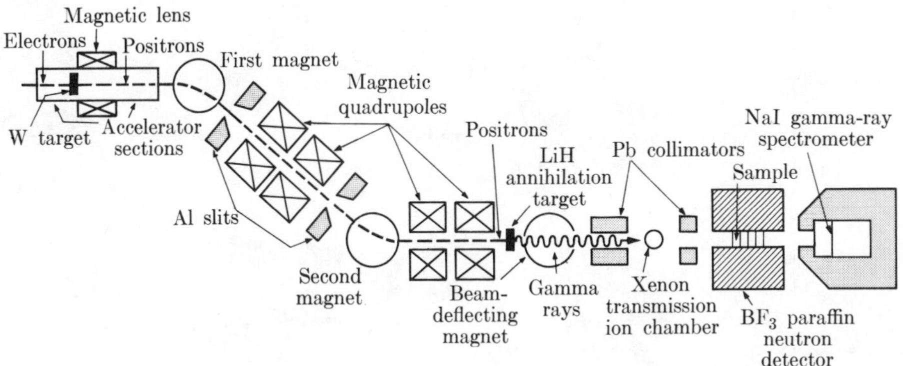

Fig. 13–35. Experimental apparatus for photoneutron cross-section measurements. The drawing is not to scale. Neutron shields and some gamma-ray shielding have been omitted. [From Fultz *et al.*, *Phys. Rev.* **127,** 1273 (1962).]

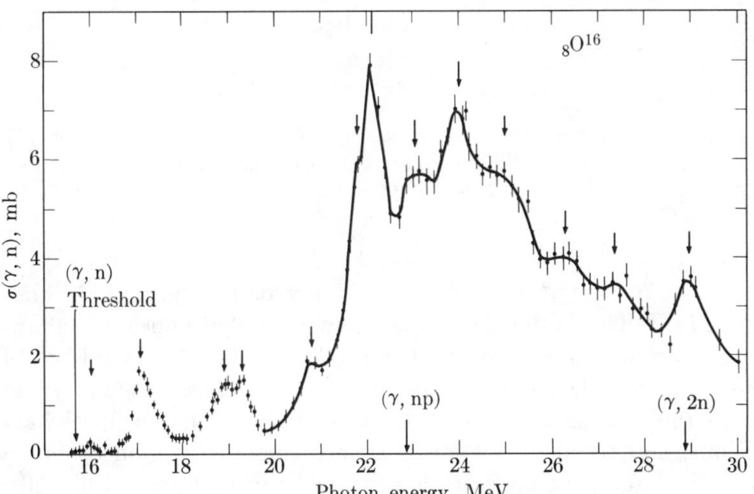

Fig. 13–36. Photoneutron cross section of O^{16} up to 30 MeV, showing resonances from levels in O^{16}. [From R. L. Bramblett, J. T. Caldwell, R. R. Harvey, and S. C. Fultz, *Phys. Rev.* **133,** B869 (1964).]

used for monitoring purposes. The sample to be studied is placed in a well-type BF_3 paraffin detector for fast neutrons and irradiated with the monoenergetic gamma-ray beam.

Figure 13–36 shows the results of a photodisintegration experiment on O^{16}. The arrows above the spectrum indicate positions of individual states in O^{16}, and the thresholds for (γ, n), (γ, np), and $(\gamma, 2n)$ reactions are indicated on the

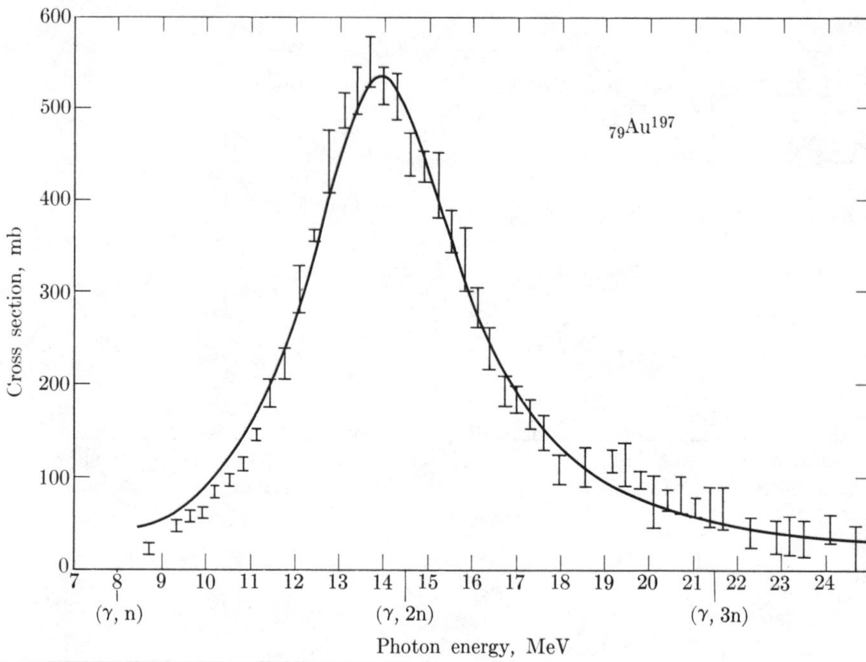

Fig. 13–37. The photonuclear cross section for gold, consisting of $\sigma(\gamma, \text{n}) + \sigma(\gamma, 2\text{n}) + \sigma(\gamma, \text{np})$. The solid line is a resonance curve with a peak cross section of 535 mb at 13.90 MeV and a width of 4.2 MeV. [From Fultz *et al.*, *Phys. Rev.* **127,** 1273 (1962).]

abscissa. The most interesting feature is the wide and large peak centered at about 25 MeV. This is the giant dipole resonance that appears in all nuclei at an energy varying only slowly with nucleon number A (roughly as $A^{-1/6}$). Figure 13–37 shows the giant resonance in Au^{197}. Because of the very high level density in this heavier nucleus, all traces of individual resonances have been washed out, and the cross section is a very smooth function of energy. As shown in the figure, the cross section for gold can be fitted quite well with a theoretical curve which is a simple resonance function (Eq. 13–36), with a maximum cross section of 535 mb at 13.90 MeV and a width $\gamma = 4.2$ MeV.

The other method mentioned above for precise photonuclear studies utilizes the fact that in many cases the state of the residual nucleus is known or can be inferred, and therefore the energy of the compound state can be determined by measuring the energy of the emitted particle. Figure 13–38 shows the situation for the $O^{16}(\gamma, \text{n})O^{15}$ reaction. The first excited state of O^{15} is at 5.18 MeV. If we bombard O^{16} with photons having a continuous energy spectrum with 25 MeV maximum, the spectrum of neutrons emitted in the 4- to 9-MeV range (approximately) uniquely determines the resonances in O^{16} in the range 20 to 25 MeV. Subsequently, the maximum photon energy is raised to 30 MeV,

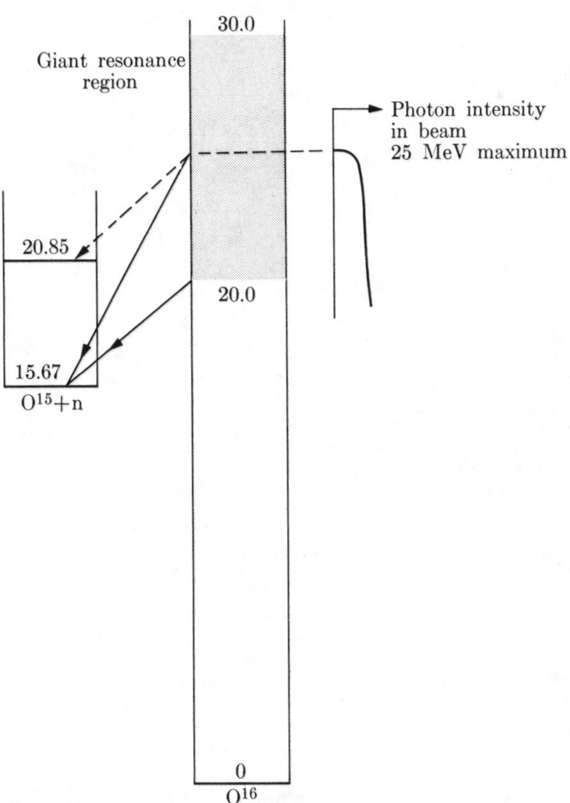

Fig. 13–38. Energy-level diagram showing how the giant resonance region can be mapped with a continuous bremsstrahlung spectrum by determining the energies of neutrons emitted in the reaction $O^{16}(\gamma, n)O^{15}$.

and the range 25 to 30 MeV is investigated by studying the neutron spectrum from approximately 9 to 14 MeV. Figure 13–39 shows two time-of-flight neutron spectra with the energy scale converted into gamma-ray energies assuming ground-state transitions only. The figure should be compared with Fig. 13–36.

Goldhaber and Teller explained the giant resonance in terms of a collective model. According to their explanation, the giant resonance excitation is one in which all protons collectively execute harmonic motion relative to all neutrons. The assemblies of protons and of neutrons are regarded as two interpenetrating, incompressible fluids that can be set in motion relative to each other. A restoring harmonic force is estimated by calculating the energy needed to move part of the proton fluid out of the neutron fluid, and vice versa. Combined with the reduced mass of the two assemblies of nucleons, this gives a frequency of oscillation, or quantum energy $\hbar\omega$, in fair agreement with observations. In particular,

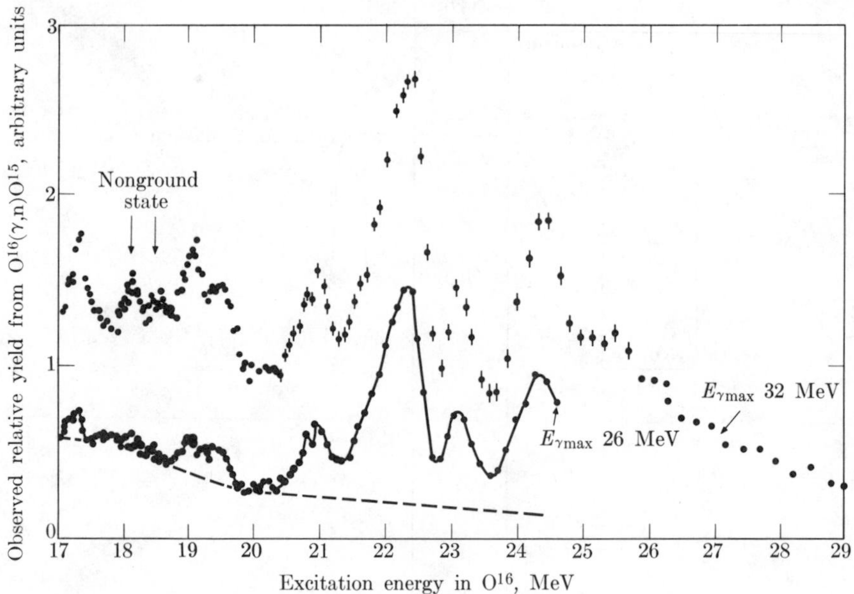

Fig. 13–39. The observed yield of photoneutrons from the reaction $O^{16}(\gamma, n)O^{15}$. The energy scale has been changed from neutron energy to gamma-ray energy on the assumption that all transitions go to the ground state of O^{15}. [From F. W. K. Firk, *Nucl. Phys.* **52,** 437 (1964).]

the calculations yield a resonance, the energy of which varies as $A^{-1/6}$, in rough accordance with the experimental results. More sophisticated calculations have been made using shell-model considerations, again yielding fair agreement with observed facts. One should not be surprised that two such widely different models can yield substantially the same result. Collective excitations can, in principle, be expressed in terms of expansion in shell-model wave functions. However, the expansions often will have to include such a large number of terms that they are impractical.

A theorem exists concerning the integral over all energies of the absorption cross section for dipole photons. The theorem, called the *dipole sum rule,* states that

$$\int_0^\infty \sigma_{\text{abs}}(E_\gamma)\, dE_\gamma = \frac{\pi\hbar e^2}{2\epsilon_0 mc}\,\frac{NZ}{A} = 0.058\,\frac{NZ}{A}\ \text{MeV-barns.} \qquad (13\text{–}81)$$

It can be proved from basic principles by use of simple time-dependent perturbation theory. The contributions to the integral from the region of bound states are small, but the giant dipole resonance practically exhausts the sum rule. The contributions from higher energies must, therefore, also be small.

PROBLEMS

13–1. Derive Eqs. (13–9) and (13–10).

13–2. Calculate the classical impact parameter for an $l = 3$ deuteron with $T = 6$ MeV incident on a heavy target nucleus.

13–3. Use the mass table (Appendix 6) to find the appropriate masses for calculating the Q-value of the $Al^{27}(d, p)Al^{28}$ reaction. If Al^{27} is bombarded with 6-MeV deuterons, what is the energy of the protons emitted at $\theta = 90°$ and leaving the residual nucleus in the ground state? Is δ_{rel} important in these calculations for slide-rule accuracy? Does it make much difference in Eq. (13–10) whether one uses the atomic mass, nuclear mass, or mass number for M_R?

13–4. In Fig. 13–9, there is a proton peak identified as arising from the $Ca^{40}(d, p)Ca^{41}$ reaction adjacent to peak number 5. Use the Q-equation (13–10) to calculate by how many keV one of them moves relative to the other as the reaction angle increases from 7.5° to 172.5°. Neglect δ_{rel}.

13–5. Show by classical calculations that when a neutron collides with a proton at rest, the relationship between the neutron energy T_n and the recoil proton energy T_p is $T_p = T_n(\cos\theta)^2$. Here θ is the angle between trajectories of the proton and the incident neutron.

13–6. Neutrons of mass m and kinetic energy T_1 are incident on a monoisotopic target of nuclear mass M. The neutrons are inelastically scattered from the target nuclei in such a way that they have zero energy (in the laboratory system) after the collision. Find the corresponding excitation energy E for the state to which the target nuclei are being excited. Use *nonrelativistic* formulas.

13–7. Repeat Problem 13–6, using *relativistic* formulas.

13–8. The reaction $Na^{23}(d, p)Na^{24}$ for 7-MeV deuterons has a total cross section $\sigma = 0.44 \times 10^{-24}$ cm^2. If a sodium target has a thickness of 0.1 mg/cm^2, what fraction of the number of deuterons hitting this target interacts with it to form Na^{24}?

13–9. Estimate by the aid of the semiclassical stripping theory the angles at which the (d, p) differential cross section has its maximum for the following l-values: $l = 0, 1, 2, 3, 4$. Use $R = 5$ F and deuteron energy $T_d = 10$ MeV. The proton energy is 14 MeV.

13–10. One of the higher energy proton groups observed when Ca^{40} ($J = 0^+$) is bombarded with 7-MeV deuterons is strongly peaked in the forward direction (maximum cross section at $\theta = 0°$). (a) What is the angular momentum and parity of the corresponding level? (b) In which nucleus is this level?

13–11. Calculate the element Q_{20} of the quadrupole moment for a system of three point charges, $+e$ at $z = \pm a$ and $-2e$ at the origin (Eq. 13–74)

$$Y_{20}(\theta, \phi) = \sqrt{\frac{5}{16\pi}}\,(3\cos^2\theta - 1).$$

13–12. Calculate the Coulomb potential energy between a test charge e on the z-axis at a distance r from the center of the quadrupole of Problem 13–11 and show that this energy can be expressed as in Eq. (13–72) for $r \gg a$.

13–13. The $Be^9(p, n)B^9$ reaction has a negative reaction energy, $Q = -1.851$ MeV. What is the minimum kinetic energy (laboratory system) of protons that can make this reaction go? Use integral masses.

13–14. Show that the Goldhaber-Teller model described in Section 13–14 yields a giant resonance energy proportional to $A^{-1/6}$ and estimate this energy for $A = 200$. Assume that the neutron and proton fluids are spheres of radius $R = r_0 A^{1/3}$, with $r_0 = 1.2$ F. Assume further that to remove a proton from the neutron fluid or vice versa requires a separation of 20 MeV/F.

*13–15. Use the optical model to calculate the total reaction and scattering cross sections for $l = 0$ neutrons on a heavy nucleus (reduced mass $m = 1$ u). Parameters $R = 5, 6, 7, 8$ F; $V_0 = 40$ MeV; $W = 10$ MeV; $E = 1, 2, 4, 8$ MeV.

14 Nuclear Energy

14–1 The Fission Process

O. Hahn and F. Strassemann discovered in 1939 that alkaline earth metals are produced when uranium is irradiated with neutrons.* Lise Meitner and O. R. Frisch† suggested that by absorption of a neutron, the uranium nucleus becomes sufficiently excited to split into two fragments of approximately equal mass. That such a process is energetically possible can easily be seen from a study of atomic masses or binding energies. In Fig. 14–1 the average binding energy per particle in beta-stable nuclei is plotted as a function of the mass number A. In the intermediate mass range ($A \approx 120$), the binding energy per particle is approximately 8.5 MeV; in the uranium region, however, it is only 7.6 MeV. If a heavy nucleus is split into two fragments, the increased binding energy per particle will be released in the form of kinetic energy of the fragments and in the form of various other types of radiation. The total energy released in a fission process should, in accordance with these considerations, be approximately

$$240(8.5 - 7.6) = 220 \text{ MeV}.$$

Since heavier nuclei are richer in neutrons, relatively speaking, than are intermediate-mass nuclei, two to three neutrons are released in each fission process. This costs energy, and after allowing for this, we find that about 200 MeV is released. Table 14–1 shows how this energy is distributed between the various types of radiation.

Shortly after the discovery by Hahn and Strassemann, Bohr and Wheeler‡ worked out a theory of the fission process based on considerations similar to those presented in the discussion of the semiempirical mass formula. The pertinent terms in the mass formula are the surface energy and the Coulomb

---

* O. Hahn and F. Strassemann, *Die Naturwissenschaften* **27,** 11 (1939).
† Lise Meitner and O. R. Frisch, *Nature* **143,** 239 (1939).
‡ N. Bohr and J. A. Wheeler, *Phys. Rev.* **56,** 426 (1939).

Table 14–1. Distribution of fission energy

	MeV
Kinetic energy of fission fragments	165 ± 5
Instantaneous gamma-ray energy	7 ± 1
Kinetic energy of fission neutrons	5 ± 0.5
Beta particles from fission products	7 ± 1
Gamma rays from fission products	6 ± 1
Neutrinos from fission products	10
Total energy per fission	200 ± 6

energy. For a spherical nucleus the sum of these two terms can be written as

$$E = 4\pi R^2 s + \tfrac{3}{5}(Ze)^2/4\pi\epsilon_0 R, \tag{14–1}$$

where s is the surface tension, that is, the surface energy per unit area, and R is the nuclear radius. If the nucleus is deformed, as indicated in Fig. 14–2(b), the surface energy will increase, but the Coulomb energy will decrease because the repulsive charges are moved farther apart. Whether the sum of the two terms will increase or decrease depends on the value of Z^2/R^3 or Z^2/A.

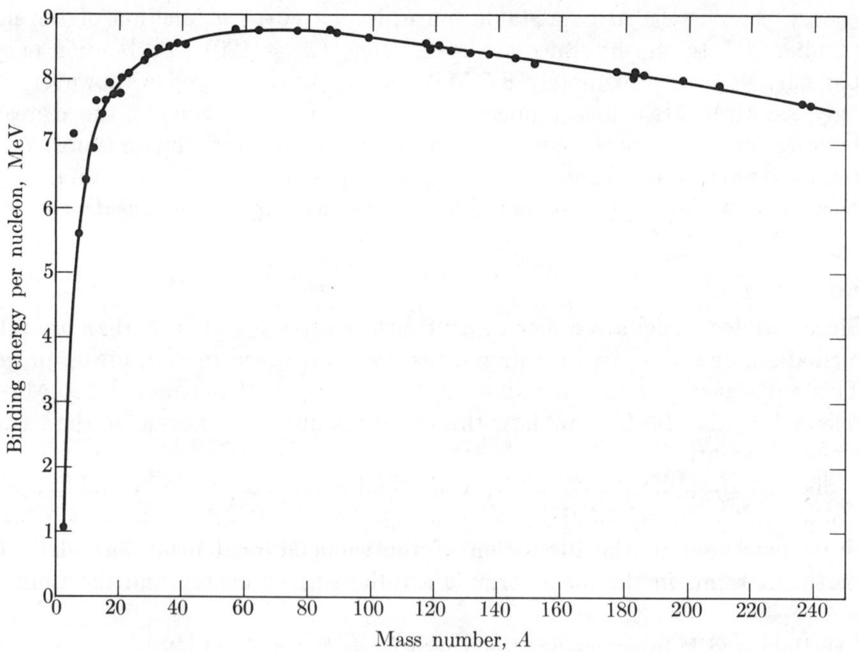

Fig. 14–1. Binding energy per nucleon vs. nucleon number A in beta-stable nuclei.

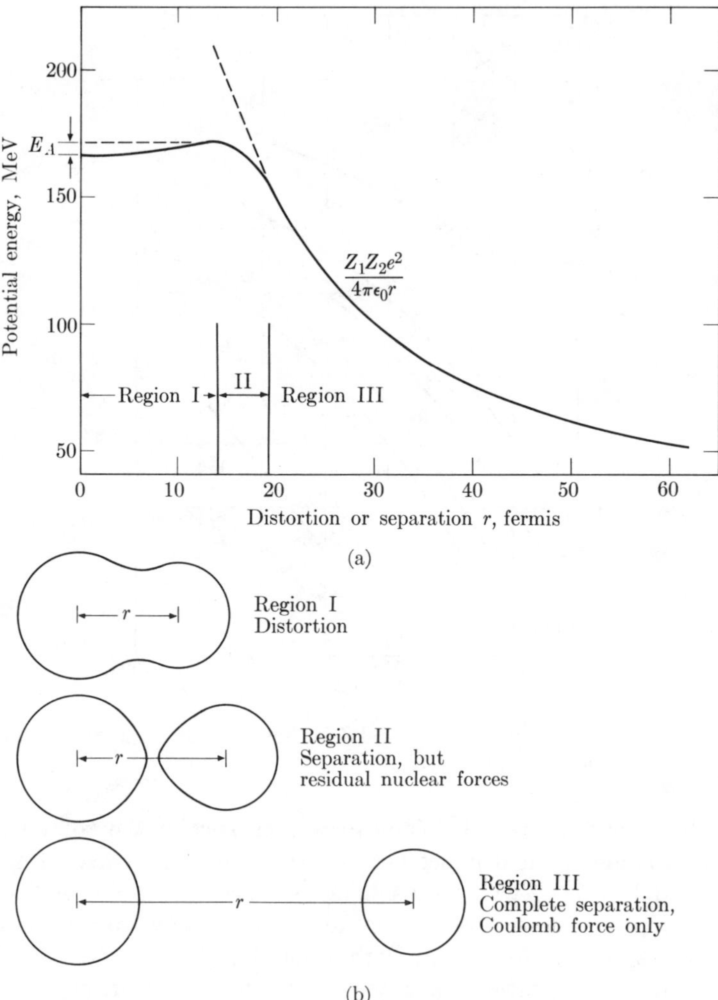

Fig. 14–2. Potential energy of a deformed nucleus and of fission fragments vs. separation or distortion.

By using the constants of the semiempirical mass formula, Bohr and Wheeler found that for $Z^2/A > 47.8$, the sum of the surface and Coulomb energy decreases by distorting the nucleus. There are therefore no forces that can stop such a nucleus from becoming more and more distorted, and the final result is that it splits into two or more fragments while releasing approximately 200 MeV, as calculated above. When $Z^2/A < 47.8$, distortion causes a change in surface energy that is larger than the change in Coulomb energy. The nucleus therefore resists distortion. This resistance, however, must have the character of a barrier only, since the total separation of two fragments leads to a state with lower rest

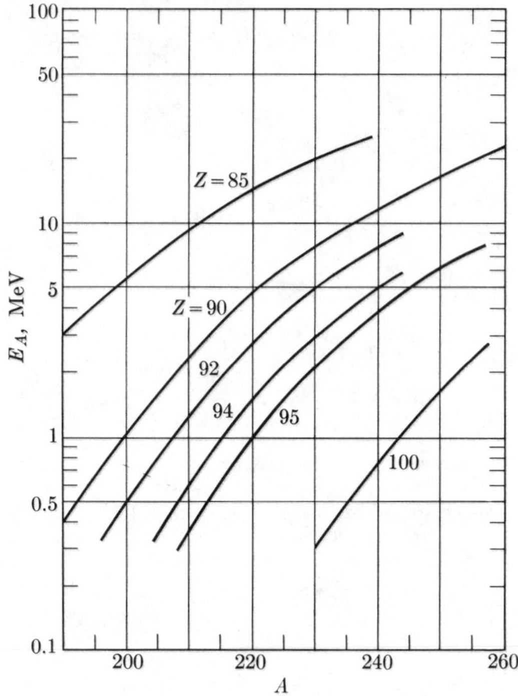

Fig. 14–3. Activation energy E_A vs. A and Z for heavy nuclei. [From S. Frankel and N. Metropolis, *Phys. Rev.* **72,** 914 (1947).]

energy. The curve in Fig. 14–2 indicates schematically the total potential energy as a function of the distance between the centers of the two fragments. Except for details, this curve is very similar to the curve showing the potential energy of an alpha particle as a function of its separation from the daughter nucleus in alpha decay. In analogy with alpha decay, the fission process can proceed by barrier penetration when $Z^2/A < 47.8$. However, because of the large masses of the fission fragments, the height of the barrier must be much smaller than for alpha decay in order to produce observable decay rates. The process described is called *spontaneous fission*, and the height of the barrier is called the *activation energy* (E_A in Fig. 14–2).

Bohr and Wheeler showed that the activation energy could be written as

$$E_A = 4\pi R^2 s\, f(x), \tag{14–2}$$

where

$$x = \frac{Z^2/A}{Z^2/A_{\text{cr}}} = \frac{Z^2/A}{47.8}\,.$$

The function $f(x)$ in Eq. (14–2) is quite difficult to evaluate with any high degree of accuracy. By using relatively simple arguments, however, Bohr and Wheeler were able to estimate the function for a few points so that an approximate curve could be drawn for $f(x)$ from $x = 0$ to $x = 1$. Frankel and Metropolis* have made somewhat more sophisticated calculations of the activation energy, using an electronic computer to carry out the numerical work. Figure 14–3 shows their results.

For U^{236} the activation energy is only 6.4 MeV. This happens to be approximately the binding energy for the last neutron in U^{236}, so that when this nucleus is formed by slow neutron capture in U^{235}, it is formed in an excited state at about 6.4 MeV. From this excited state, it can then decay to the ground state by gamma emission, or it can decay by fission. Experimentally, it has been shown that in about 85% of the cases, it does decay by fission. The fission lifetime is so short that other processes, such as alpha and beta decay from the excited state, that are energetically possible cannot compete to any significant degree.

14–2 Neutrons Released in the Fission Process; Cross Sections

We write the fission reaction initiated by slow neutrons on U^{235} as

$$U^{235} + \underset{\text{(slow)}}{n} \rightarrow U^{236} \rightarrow X + Y + \underset{\text{(fast)}}{\nu n}, \tag{14–3}$$

where X and Y stand for two intermediate-mass nuclides and ν is the *average* number of neutrons released in each process. This number is $\nu = 2.47$ for the reaction (14–3); Table 14–2 lists the value of ν for other possible target nuclides.

Table 14–2. Characteristics of fissionable materials bombarded with thermal neutrons, $v_n = 2200$ m/sec

Target nucleus	σ_F, barns	σ_γ, barns	ν	η
U^{233}	524	69	2.51	2.29
U^{235}	590	108	2.47	2.08
Natural uranium	–	–	2.47	1.33
Pu^{239}	729	300	2.91	2.08

A necessary condition which must be fulfilled for a chain reaction to take place is clearly $\nu > 1$. For instance, in a sufficiently large piece of U^{235}, the neutrons that are released in a first fission process will eventually be absorbed by other uranium nuclei and produce new processes which in turn emit new neutrons. It is clear that the density of neutrons will increase from generation to generation in a catastrophic fashion. If the sample of U^{235} is not large enough, a number of neutrons escape before they can initiate new processes,

* S. Frankel and N. Metropolis, *Phys. Rev.* **72,** 914 (1947).

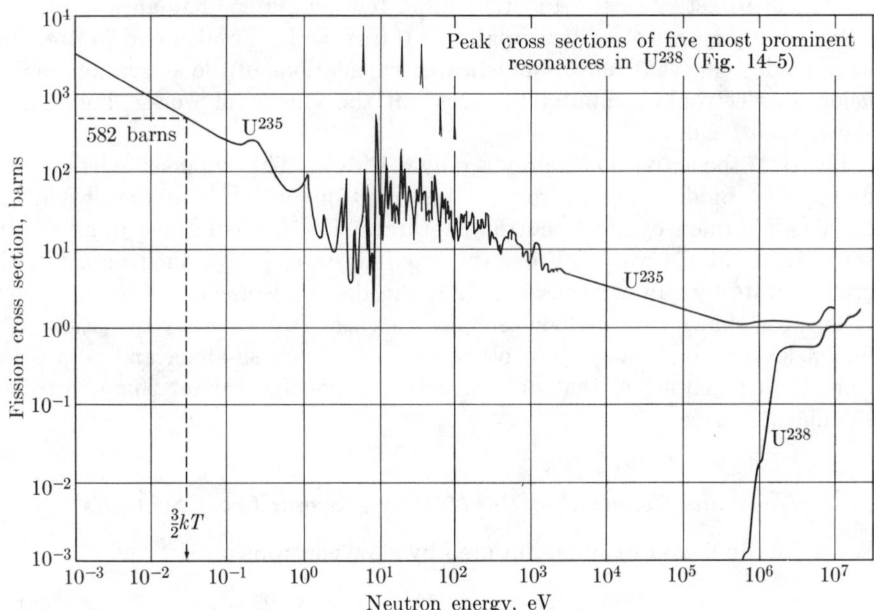

Fig. 14–4. Fission cross section in U^{235} and U^{238} vs. neutron energy E_n. [Replotted from several charts in D. J. Hughes and R. B. Schwartz, *Neutron Cross Sections*, Brookhaven National Laboratory Report 325, 2nd. ed. (1958).]

and a chain reaction will not take place. In the fission bomb, two or more pieces of U^{235} or Pu^{239}, each slightly smaller than the *critical size,* are rapidly brought together so that they become one sample larger than the critical size. The buildup of neutron intensity proceeds exponentially with a time constant of the order of magnitude of 10^{-8} sec. In less than a microsecond, therefore, a large fraction of the available energy is expended. The fission products that carry most of the released energy as kinetic energy have extremely short ranges in the bomb material. They are therefore rapidly slowed down, and the energy is converted into heat. Let us now turn to a more detailed discussion of the neutron population and to the aspects of fission which are of importance for the peaceful use of nuclear energy.*

The coefficient ν in Eq. (14–3) gives the average number of fast neutrons released in each fission process. What is actually of greater interest is the number of fast neutrons released *per slow neutron absorbed* by the fissionable material. This is of course smaller than ν, since, as explained above, some of the compound nuclei decay to the ground state by gamma emission, rather than by fission.

* The term "atomic energy" applied to fission or to fusion is a misnomer. Ordinary chemical energy, resulting from changes in the molecular structure, is of atomic character according to present-day terminology.

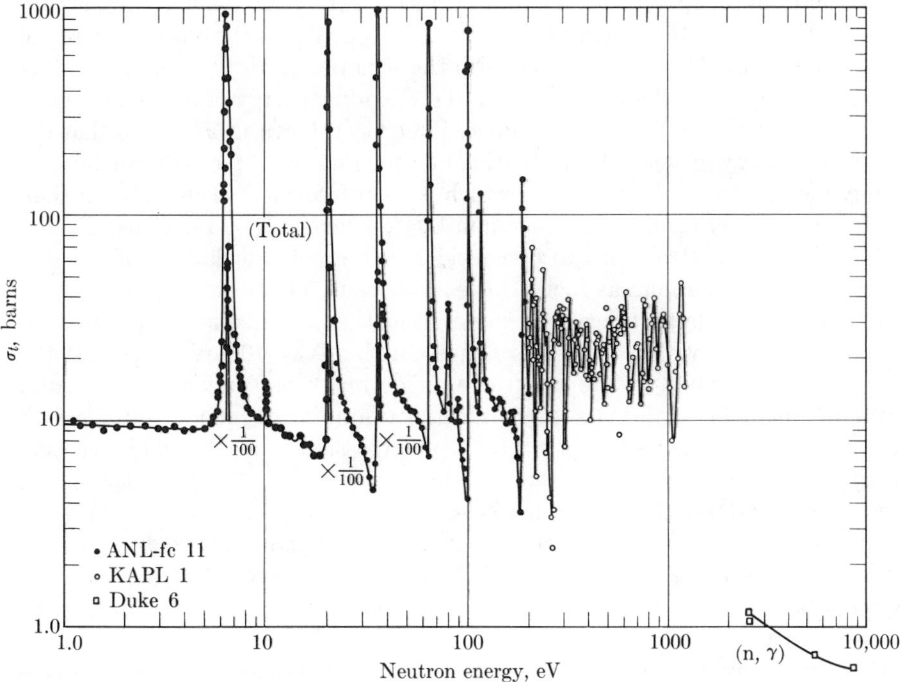

Fig. 14–5. The total cross section of U^{238} vs. neutron energy. The cross section between resonances is mostly due to elastic scattering. (From D. J. Hughes *et al.*, *op. cit.*)

We define a factor η, which is the number of fast neutrons released per neutron absorbed. It is given by

$$\eta = \frac{\nu\sigma_F}{\sigma_F + \sigma_\gamma}, \tag{14–4}$$

where σ_F and σ_γ are the cross sections for fission and gamma emission at the incident neutron energy considered. These cross sections are given for thermal neutrons ($v_n = 2200$ m/sec) on U^{233}, U^{235}, and Pu^{239} in Table 14–2, together with measured values of ν. The values of η calculated from Eq. (14–4) are given in the last column.

A second point of interest when we are dealing with natural uranium, rather than U^{235}, is the relative magnitudes of the absorption cross sections in the two isotopes. In U^{235}, as we have seen, fission dominates the absorption cross section, and the magnitude of the cross section at thermal energies is very large. In U^{238} the fission cross section is entirely negligible below 1 MeV, but there are resonances in the 5- to 100-eV range for which the (n, γ) cross section is very large. Figure 14–4 shows the fission cross sections in U^{235} and U^{238} vs. neutron energy, and Fig. 14–5 shows the total cross section in U^{238}.

The onset of an appreciable amount of fission in U^{238} at about 1.4 MeV indicates that the activation energy E_A in U^{239} is 1.4 MeV plus the binding energy of the last neutron. This is contrasted with the situation in U^{236}, for which the activation energy is smaller than or equal to the binding energy of the last neutron. The reason for this difference is twofold: First, it is shown in Fig. 14–3 that the activation energy increases for increasing nucleon number A; second, the binding energy for the last neutron in U^{236}, which is an even-even nucleus, is larger than the binding energy for the last neutron in U^{239}, which is an odd nucleus. Fission of U^{238} by fast neutrons has to be considered in exact calculations of reactors utilizing natural uranium as fuel. However, because of the small cross section, it is not of great importance. Of more crucial importance is the (n, γ) cross section, particularly the strong resonances in the 5- to 100-eV range. If the large (n, γ) probability were not there to detract from fission, pure natural uranium would be explosive. Since natural uranium has about 140 times as much U^{238} as U^{235}, at first sight it may seem impossible to make a chain reaction based on U^{235} fission operate with natural uranium as fuel. The trick is to make use of the very large thermal-fission cross section in U^{235} by slowing down the neutrons to thermal energies *outside* the uranium fuel and thus avoiding capture by U^{238}. The slowing-down process takes place by elastic collisions in a *moderating* material filling the space between the fuel rods in a natural uranium reactor. More about this later.

Of extreme importance for the orderly control of a fission reactor is a process called *delayed neutron emission.* As discussed above, the fission products X

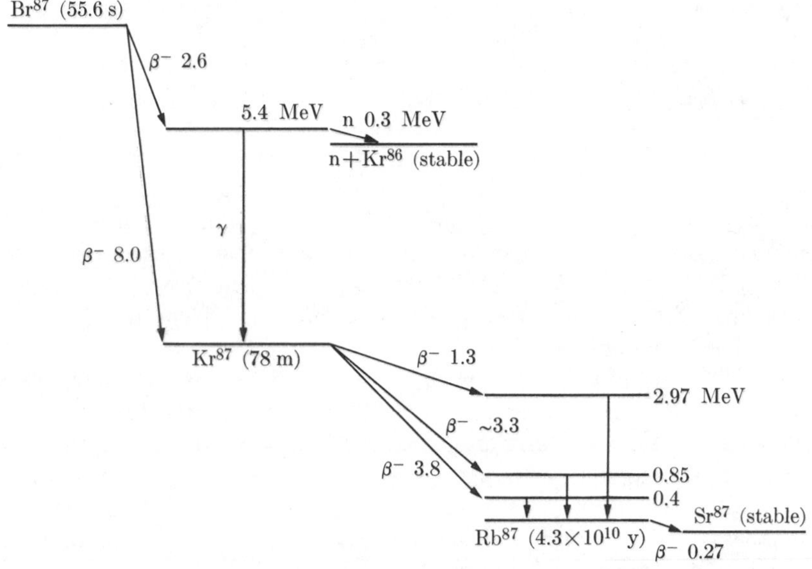

Fig. 14–6. Decay scheme for Br^{87}; a delayed neutron emitter.

and Y in Eq. (14-3) are very neutron-rich nuclides. They therefore decay by β^- emission toward the line of stable nuclides. If one fission product is so neutron rich that it is unstable against neutron emission, a prompt neutron is emitted within 10^{-20} sec. The right-hand side of Eq. (14-3) is supposed to represent the situation after such processes have taken place. There is, of course, no barrier for the neutrons that can keep them in the nucleus for any length of time if the energy is available for neutron emission. Yet, delayed neutrons with measurable lifetimes are emitted from some fission products. The explanation is quite simple. The neutron emission is a secondary process, and it is the lifetime of the primary process that is measured.

Figure 14-6 shows as an example the decay scheme of Br^{87}. In its ground state, this nucleus is neutron stable, but it is beta unstable and decays to either the ground state of Kr^{87} or to an excited state at 5.4 MeV. This excited state is above the dissociation energy for a neutron from Kr^{87}; it can therefore decay by neutron emission to Kr^{86}. In fact, 2% of all the Br^{87} decays follow this route. The neutron emission is very rapid, but since Br^{87}, the parent nucleus, is neutron stable, the neutron activity has the half-life of the primary process, the beta decay, which of course is a relatively slow process. Many other delayed neutron emitters have been found, and altogether 0.7% of all neutrons emitted in U^{236} fission are delayed.

14-3 The Fission Reactor Operating with Natural Uranium as Fuel

The first condition that has to be met for a fission reactor to operate is that the factor η given in Table 14-2 must be larger than 1. In U^{235}, this factor is 2.08; in natural uranium, it is 1.33. This is the number of fast neutrons produced in natural uranium per slow neutron absorbed. As explained earlier, the fast neutrons produced must be slowed down to thermal velocities outside the fissionable material to avoid nonfission capture in U^{238}. For this reason, a fission reactor operating on natural uranium consists of a lattice of uranium rods embedded in a moderating material in which the neutrons can slow down

Table 14-3. Properties of materials used as moderators

Material	Absorption cross section for thermal neutrons, barns	Average scattering cross section in resonance region, barns	Average change in natural logarithm of energy per collision	Average slowing down length from "fast" to thermal, cm
H_2O	0.664	44.8	0.926	5.3
D_2O	0.001	10.4	0.508	11.2
C	0.0045	4.7	0.158	19.1

without being captured. Figure 14–7 shows schematically the cross section of a natural uranium reactor with carbon (graphite) used as moderator. Table 14–3 gives the properties of some moderating materials. As can be seen from this table, ordinary water is very efficient for slowing down the neutrons; however, the absorption cross section of hydrogen for thermal neutrons is too large to make water a feasible moderator in natural uranium reactors. Therefore heavy water, D_2O, or carbon is used.

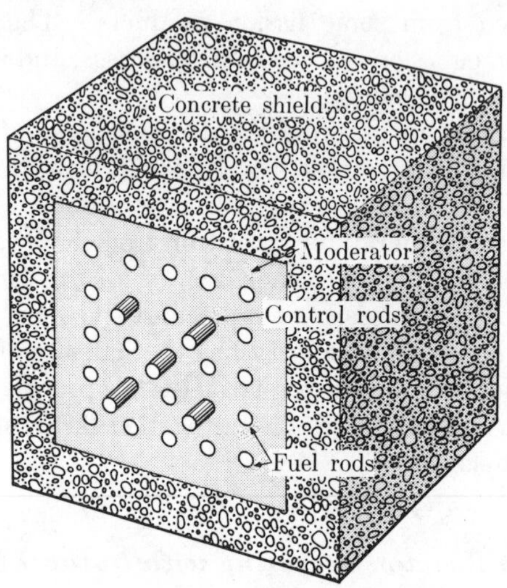

Fig. 14–7. Cross section of a natural uranium reactor showing the fuel rods, control rods, moderator, and concrete shielding.

Figure 14–8 shows schematically the neutron cycle from thermal neutron absorption in the fuel element, through fast neutron production, to slow down and absorption again. In reactor theory, standardized notation is used for the efficiency coefficients of the various parts of the cycle. This nomenclature is shown in Fig. 14–8. We assume that N slow neutrons are originally absorbed in the fuel, and we calculate the number kN of neutrons that are produced and survive the various competing processes so that they again are absorbed by the fuel as slow neutrons. Obviously, to make the reactor operate, it must be possible to make k larger than 1.

As we already discussed above, when N slow neutrons are absorbed in the fuel, ηN fast neutrons are produced. Of these fast neutrons, a few initiate fission in U^{238}, thereby increasing slightly the number of released fast neutrons by a factor ϵ, the *fast-fission factor*. From a finite-size reactor core, some fast neutrons will leak out and be lost. To account for this, we introduce the *leakage factor* l_f *for fast neutrons* and find that the number of fast neutrons remaining in the core long enough for slowdown is $\eta\epsilon(1 - l_f)N$. In the slowing-down process in the moderator, of course, quite a few neutrons will drift into the fuel elements again and will be absorbed without fission in U^{238}, particularly at energies in

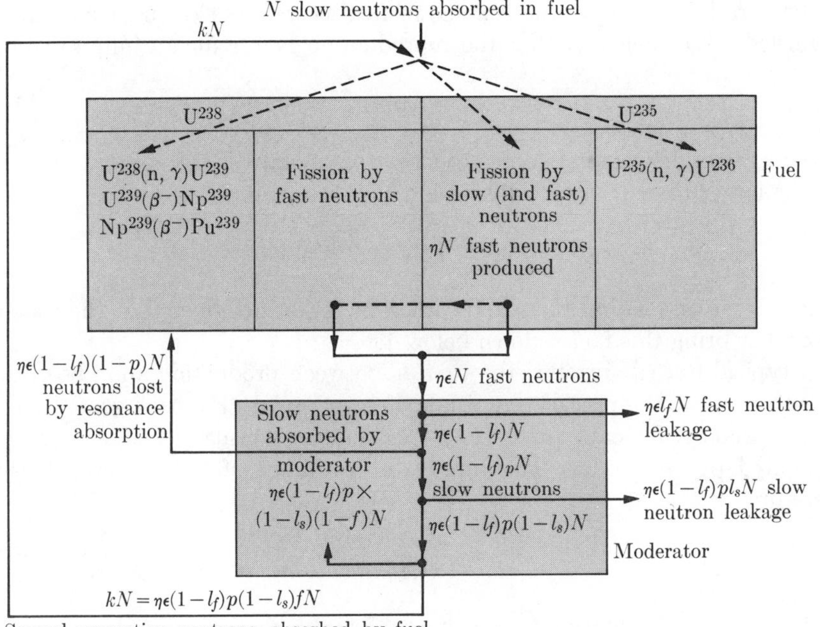

Fig. 14–8. The neutron cycle in a natural uranium reactor.

the region of strong resonances. We introduce the *resonance escape probability* p and find that the original N neutrons absorbed in the fuel have produced $\eta\epsilon(1 - l_f)pN$ thermal neutrons in the reactor core. Again, some of these thermal neutrons will leak out of the core, and we take care of this effect by introducing the *leakage factor* l_s *for slow neutrons.* The number of thermal neutrons remaining is $\eta\epsilon(1 - l_f)p(1 - l_s)N$. Finally, some of these thermal neutrons are absorbed by the moderator or structural elements in the core, such as aluminum fuel capsules. The fraction of thermal neutrons that escape this fate is given by the *thermal utilization factor*

$$f = \frac{N_{235}\sigma_A(235) + N_{238}\sigma_A(238)}{\sum_i N_i\sigma_A(i)}, \tag{14-5}$$

where $\sigma_A(i)$ is the absorption cross section for nuclide "i," and N_i is the relative abundance of such nuclei in the core. The thermal utilization factor decreases for increasing moderator-to-fuel ratio. On the other hand, the resonance escape probability p increases, so that the product pf is a maximum at a certain moderator-to-fuel ratio. The final number of second-generation neutrons absorbed in the fuel is now

$$kN = \eta\epsilon pf(1 - l_f)(1 - l_s)N. \tag{14-6}$$

If the core is very large, the leakage of fast as well as slow neutrons can be disregarded. We then find that the reproduction factor for an infinite core is

$$k_\infty = \eta \epsilon p f. \tag{14-7}$$

A necessary condition for making the reactor operate is, of course, that this factor be larger than 1. Typically we might have

$$k_\infty = \eta \epsilon p f = 1.33 \times 1.02 \times 0.9 \times 0.9 = 1.10.$$

The next condition is that the reactor must be large enough so that the leakage rates do not bring this factor down below 1.

In a typical nuclear reactor, the time t_0 between production and absorption of a neutron is of the order of magnitude of 1 to 2 msec. For each generation of neutrons, that is, for each interval t_0, the neutron density ρ in the reactor is incremented by $(k - 1)\rho$. The time rate of change of the neutron density is therefore

$$\frac{d\rho}{dt} = \frac{\rho(k-1)}{t_0}. \tag{14-8}$$

The solution of this equation is an exponential with time constant

$$\tau = t_0/(k-1). \tag{14-9}$$

If, for instance, $k = 1.01$, the time constant for the increase of neutron flux (and power) is approximately 0.1 sec, which is awkwardly short for the safe control of reactor power. We have, however, so far disregarded any effect of the delayed neutrons discussed in the previous section. When k is made so small that the buildup of neutron density depends on the delayed neutrons, the time constant for the buildup rate will, of course, be strongly influenced by the half-life of the delayed neutrons.

Control of the neutron density is, in practice, accomplished by the insertion of rods of cadmium or another efficient slow-neutron absorber into the core. By withdrawing the rods, k can be made larger than 1, and when the reactor has reached the desired power level, the rods are reinserted sufficiently far into the core so that k is made equal to 1. The time rate of change of the neutron density is then, according to Eq. (14-8), equal to 0, so that the reactor will operate at the selected level. To slow down or to stop the operation of the reactor, the rods are pushed farther into the core so that k is made smaller than 1. The time rate of change of the neutron density will then be negative.

Very many different types of reactors have been built and are in operation throughout the world. Natural uranium reactors have been made with graphite and heavy-water moderators. Reactors using uranium fuel enriched in U^{235} can use ordinary water as a moderator, and several research reactors of this type have been built.

The neutrons absorbed in U^{238} in the reactor fuel produces U^{239} which is beta radioactive and decays to Np^{239} and further to Pu^{239}. As indicated by Table 14–2, Pu^{239} is another possible fuel for a slow-neutron reactor. Therefore, as far as overall power economy is concerned, the neutron absorption in U^{238} does not represent a loss. In the process of burning U^{235}, the natural uranium reactor actually produces new fuel from the hard-to-burn U^{238}. It has indeed been possible to design reactors in which more fuel is produced (converted) than burned. This is of far-reaching consequences for the world energy economy. Such a reactor is called a *breeder* reactor.

14–4 Fusion; Thermonuclear Energy

It is clear from a glance at Fig. 14–1 that energy can also be gained by building up an intermediate-mass nuclide from lighter ones. The nuclei of the iron group are most tightly bound, but even heavier elements can be formed in exoergic reactions by successive absorption of very light particles, e.g., nucleons. In the two main cosmological theories currently being discussed, all elements are assumed to be formed or to have been formed by successive fusion of nucleons to heavier nuclei with release of energy.

According to the original *Big Bang* theory of George Gamow, the universe was at one time an extremely densely packed assembly of neutrons, so densely packed that the neutrons were stable, which, of course, the free neutron is not. In Gamow's view, the universe was formed in a gigantic explosion, in which the elements were formed by consecutive absorptions of neutrons, interspersed with beta decays toward the line of highest beta stability in the Chart of the Nuclides. This explosion could, in Gamow's view, have been preceded by an implosion.

Another main cosmological theory describes the universe as existing in a *steady state*, in which matter is continuously created in interstellar space.* To conserve energy, it is assumed that the rest energy and kinetic energy of the particles created are equal in magnitude to their negative gravitational energy in the universe. According to this theory, the rate at which mass is produced is exactly equal and opposite to the rate at which it is diluted by the observed expansion of the universe. One difficulty with this theory is that according to present views, matter cannot be created without simultaneous creation of antimatter. It is, of course, quite posible that half of the universe consists of matter and the other half of antimatter, but it is difficult to understand the mechanism of separation of the two factions. Also, certain recent observations, demonstrating that the gamma-ray intensity in interstellar space is extremely low, seem to indicate that the requisite mixture of matter and antimatter is not present.

Other recent observations concerning the rate of expansion of the universe and the acceleration of this rate point toward modifications of the steady-state theory

---

* See, for instance, F. Hoyle, *Frontiers of Astronomy*, New York: Harper & Brothers, 1955, p. 320.

in the direction of a pulsating universe. Maybe the truth lies somewhere between the two extreme views, the Big Bang and the Steady State.

In the theory of Hoyle *et al.*, the creation of stars and the synthesis of elements start from the extremely thin hydrogen gas that is known to exist in interstellar space. The manner in which this hydrogen gas is originally created is actually irrelevant to the discussion of the theory of synthesis, which is based on careful measurements and calculations.* Because of statistical fluctuations in the density of the gas, it condenses into clusters under the influence of gravitational forces. Once a cluster is formed, it will grow in mass, extracting more and more hydrogen from the surroundings. As the cluster grows heavier and contracts more and more, the temperature inside rises because of conversion of the gravitational potential energy into kinetic energy. Eventually, it becomes hot enough for the nuclear burning process to start. This sets in at a temperature of about 10^7 degrees ($\frac{3}{2}kT \approx 1.3$ keV) at which temperature the penetration of Coulomb barriers is not completely negligible. Two protons combine to a mass 2 nucleus, and since He^2 is not stable, the only process that must be considered is

$$H^1 + H^1 \rightarrow H^2 + e^+ + \nu + 0.42 \text{ MeV}. \tag{14–10}$$

The positron annihilates with an electron thereby releasing an additional energy of 1.02 MeV.

The burning of light hydrogen (Eq. 14–10) goes by way of the weak interaction and is therefore a very slow process. The cross section is so small that the process has not been observed in the laboratory even at higher bombarding energies, but the reaction rate in a hydrogen gas of given temperature and density can be calculated accurately and it agrees with astronomical observations. Once heavy hydrogen is formed, the synthesis of the heavier nuclides can go by way of the strong interaction with relatively large cross sections. For instance, He^3 can be formed through the reaction

$$H^2(p, \gamma)He^3, \qquad Q = 5.49 \text{ MeV} \tag{14–11}$$

and two He^3 atoms can combine to form He^4 and two protons through the following process:

$$He^3(He^3, pp)He^4, \qquad Q = 12.86 \text{ MeV}. \tag{14–12}$$

This shows one possible chain of events that can lead to the fusion of hydrogen atoms into helium with the release of a considerable amount of energy.

In the continued synthesis of the elements beyond He^4, a difficulty arises in that no stable elements with mass 5 or 8 exist. However, two alpha particles can combine to Be^8, which stays together for approximately 10^{-15} sec. In a sufficiently high density of helium, this will result in an adequately high con-

---

* E. M. Burbidge, G. R. Burbidge, W. A. Fowler, and F. Hoyle, *Revs. Mod. Phys.* **29**, 547 (1957).

centration of Be^8 so that by combination with a third alpha particle, the nucleus C^{12} is formed. As shown by Cook *et al.*,* the reaction has a resonance which strongly enhances the production rate of C^{12} in a helium gas of 10^8 °K.

The production of free neutrons can take place through the following chain of events

$$\begin{aligned} &C^{12}(p, \gamma)N^{13}, && Q = 1.94 \text{ MeV}; \\ &N^{13}(\beta^+)C^{13}, && Q = 1.20 \text{ MeV and } 1.02 \text{ MeV}; \\ &C^{13}(\alpha, n)O^{16}, && Q = 2.21 \text{ MeV}. \end{aligned} \tag{14–13}$$

The existence of free neutrons is necessary to explain the synthesis of the neutron-rich isotopes of the heavier elements in Hoyle's theory.

Once carbon has been formed, the burning of four protons to form He^4 can go through a sequence of reactions in which carbon and nitrogen serve as catalysts. The main branch of this cycle starts with the first two reactions in Eq. (14–13) and continues with the reactions

$$\begin{aligned} &C^{13}(p, \gamma)N^{14}, && Q = 7.55 \text{ MeV}; \\ &N^{14}(p, \gamma)O^{15}, && Q = 7.29 \text{ MeV}; \\ &O^{15}(\beta^+)N^{15}, && Q = 1.74 \text{ MeV plus } 1.02 \text{ MeV}; \\ &N^{15}(p, \alpha)C^{12}, && Q = 4.96 \text{ MeV}. \end{aligned}$$

The total energy released in the process is about 26.73 MeV, of which about 6% is lost from the star by the neutrinos emitted in the two beta decays.

Although the sequences of events that we have described in this section appear to be the main sources of stellar energy, the complete picture of stellar evolution and synthesis of elements is much more complex than we can describe here. The main objective of this description has been to look at these sources of stellar energy with a view toward possibly utilizing the same or similar processes in self-sustained, earth-bound energy production. This, of course, has already been accomplished in an uncontrolled manner in the hydrogen bomb. To do the same in a controlled manner seems to be at least one order of magnitude more difficult.

14–5 Prospect of Controlled Fusion Energy

In the stars, the burning of hydrogen and of helium takes place at a noncatastrophic rate which is determined by the density and temperature of the gas and of the cross sections or lifetimes of the reactions involved. The gas is contained because of the action of the gravitational force. In the fusion bomb, the temperature needed for the reaction to start is attained by using a fission bomb as

---

* C. W. Cook, W. A. Fowler, C. C. Lauritsen, and T. Lauritsen, *Phys. Rev.* **107,** 508 (1957).

a trigger. The containing forces are inertial forces of the reacting gases themselves, as well as of the mantle containing the gases. Since the total process takes only about a microsecond, inertial containment is possible.

On a very large scale, it is possible to use the catastrophic process in a semicontrolled manner, and this possibility has been seriously looked into. A large canyon could be lined with concrete and fitted with a concrete roof so as to produce a giant steam boiler. Once every hour or so, a hydrogen bomb could be detonated inside the boiler so as to produce enough steam for an hour's consumption. This may be a last-resort scheme for the peaceful use of fusion energy; it obviously would be much more attractive if the gas in which the fusion reaction takes place could be contained in a controlled manner at the high temperatures involved. It appears to be a fair possibility that this can be accomplished by use of the focusing action on ions by magnetic fields.

The most attractive reactions for use in a thermonuclear fusion reactor appear to be the D-D reaction

$$H^2(\mathrm{d,n})He^3, \qquad Q = 3.27 \text{ MeV},$$

$$H^2(\mathrm{d,p})H^3, \qquad Q = 4.03 \text{ MeV},$$

and the D-T reaction

$$H^3(\mathrm{d,n})He^4, \qquad Q = 17.59 \text{ MeV}.$$

At the very high temperatures considered, these gases are completely dissociated into interpenetrating gases of nuclei and electrons, called a *plasma*. The plasma is electrically neutral so that in the absence of electric or magnetic fields, there are no external forces acting on it except gravity, which is negligible on the laboratory scale. Because of the internal pressure, the plasma would expand in a vacuum to fill the container in which it is kept. When it comes in contact with the walls, it cools off and in the process, of course, heats up the walls. The problems to be solved are therefore: First, how to bring a plasma up to sufficient temperature and density; and second, how to contain this plasma for a sufficiently long time to produce a net energy gain. Before we discuss any of the solutions that have been suggested, let us look a little closer at these requirements.

The power produced in a fusion reactor will depend on the plasma density and temperature. Knowing the cross sections for the D-D and D-T processes as a function of temperature (energy), we can easily calculate $P = f(T)$, the power density (energy released per unit time per unit volume) vs. temperature for a given particle density (see Problem 14–8). The results of such calculations are shown in Fig. 14–9. Also shown in this figure is the power loss by bremsstrahlung emitted by the electrons colliding with the nuclear particles. For the D-T reactions the bremsstrahlung loss equals the power produced at 3-keV plasma temperature, and for the D-D reactions the corresponding temperature is 35 keV. This does not necessarily mean that the plasma temperature for a D-D reactor has to be higher than 35 keV to produce a net power gain. The

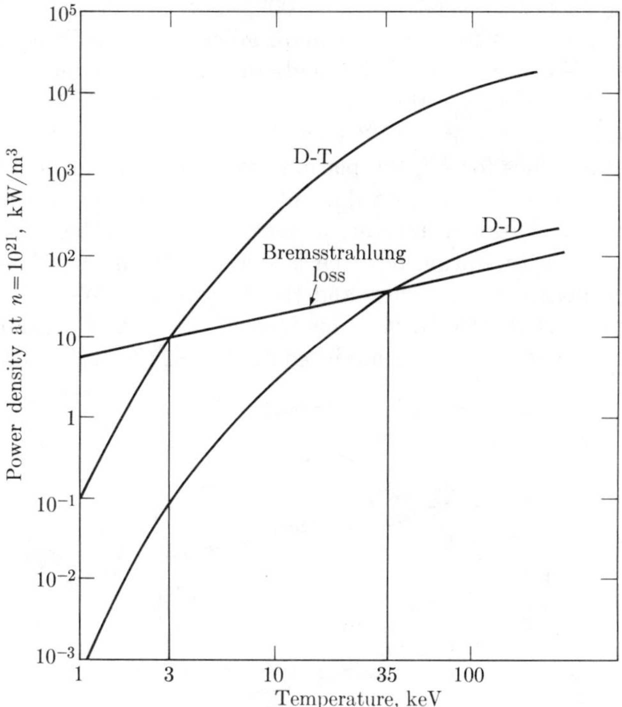

Fig. 14-9. Energy produced in plasma per m^3 and sec vs. plasma temperature at $n = 10^{21}$ particles/m^3. Reproduced from T. S. Green, *Thermonuclear Power*, London: George Newnes Limited, 1963, p.9.

reason is that the bremsstrahlung is not lost but absorbed by the walls of the plasma container and therefore converted into heat in the same way as is the kinetic energy of the reaction products. The minimum operating temperature for a given reactor will therefore depend on the efficiency with which heat can be converted into other forms of energy, part of which has to be put back into the plasma again to keep it at the operating level. We assume then that the energy developed in the nuclear processes is not retained in the plasma, but is more or less fully absorbed by the walls of the container and the coolant surrounding these walls. In particular, the neutrons emitted will contribute very little to the heating of the plasma.

Most of the schemes that have been discussed for plasma heating and containment assume that the reactor will be pulsed; in particular the *theta pinch*, discussed below, is inherently a pulsed device. Assuming that the energy conversion efficiency is less than 100%, we find that there is a minimum value for the product Nt of plasma density and containment time for which a useful energy gain can be obtained (see Problem 14-9). This is so because the plasma has a heat capacity. It therefore costs energy to bring it up to full temperature, and when the energy conversion is not 100%, part of this energy is lost. It is consequently important to keep the reactor going for a sufficiently long time so that at least this energy loss can be made up. The minimum value of Nt for an assumed efficiency of one-third is approximately 2×10^{16} particles-sec/cm^3 for the D-D reactor and 9×10^{13} particle-sec/cm^3 for the D-T reactor. At these minimum values for Nt, the plasma temperature must be approximately 100 keV for net gain; for larger values of Nt, the plasma temperature can be somewhat lower. The D-T reactor, in fact, can operate below 10 keV. The goals toward which the fusion research is striving are the attainments of these values for the plasma temperature and the Nt product. We shall now discuss various suggestions that have been made for heating and containing the hot plasma, such that it does not come in contact with the walls of the enclosure for the gas.

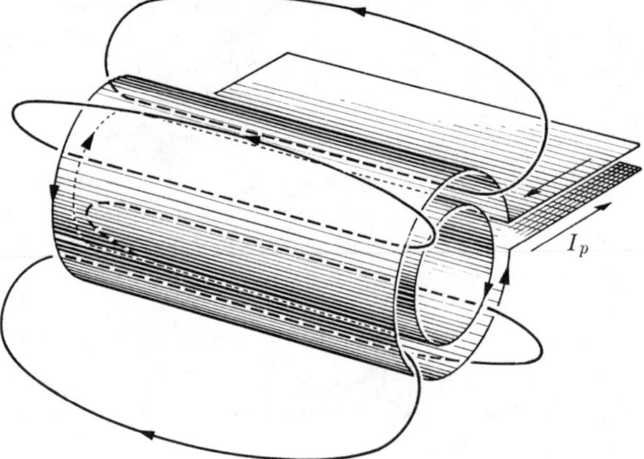

Fig. 14–10. Theta-pinch apparatus; schematic.

(*a*) *The pinch.* In principle the simplest way of heating and containing the plasma is to make use of a phenomenon, called the *pinch*, that long has been known in gas-discharge physics. If the current density in straight-line (axial) gas discharge is extremely high, the magnetic field produced by the current and surrounding it will be sufficiently intense to compress the discharge and confine it to a thin filament. The temperature in this filament will rise to very high levels, but the hot plasma is contained, and heat exchange with the surrounding gas can be kept low enough so that, in principle, fusion temperatures and containment times should be obtainable. The apparatus for the axial pinch is very simple, and for this reason the scheme is very attractive. However, the difficulty is that a straight-line current passing through the gas does not represent a stable situation. Instabilities very rapidly occur in which the current filament develops kinks and disrupts. Therefore the axial pinch does not at the moment show very great promise for use in a practical fusion reactor.

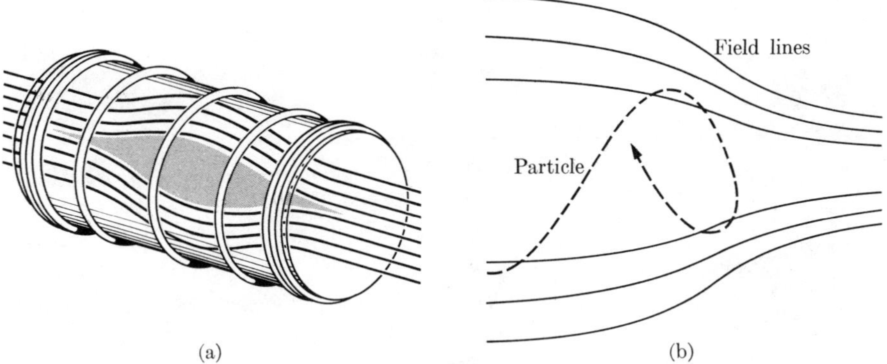

Fig. 14–11. (a) The pyrotron. (b) Reflection of an ion from a magnetic mirror.

More promising results have been obtained with the so-called *theta pinch*, illustrated in Fig. 14–10. In this scheme a very heavy current is suddenly passed through a single loop made of a conducting sheet surrounding the gas. An equal and opposite current is developed by induction in the gas in the discharge chamber. The magnetic field produced between the two currents compresses the gas discharge to the axial region and heats the plasma by the work done on it during the compression by the magnetic field.

(*b*) *The pyrotron.* The pyrotron shown in Fig. 14–11(a) has an axial magnetic figuration but with a higher concentration of field lines toward the ends, such that *magnetic mirrors* are produced here. The principle of such a magnetic mirror is shown in Fig. 14–11(b). The ions move in spiral orbits with radii of curvature inversely proportional to the field strength. When they move into regions of higher field strengths, they are therefore reflected, since the orbits will be more sharply bent. Because of the inward radial component of the field at the ends of the pyrotron, a component of the reflecting force will be axial, back toward the center of the machine. It can be shown that particles which move in the center of the pyrotron at an angle $\theta > \arcsin (B_{\text{min}}/B_{\text{max}})$ with the axis will be reflected back and forth between the mirrors indefinitely, or until, by scattering, their direction is changed toward a more axial one. The heating of the plasma in the pyrotron is accomplished by increasing the magnetic field relatively slowly (in about one millisecond) such that the plasma is compressed. This compression can be carried out in several stages and after each stage the compressed plasma is transferred from one magnetic bottle to a smaller one in which it is further compressed.

(*c*) *The stellarator.* In this device the gas is contained in a racetrack-shaped bottle, and the plasma-containing magnetic field, which follows the axis of the bottle, is produced by current-carrying conductors wrapped around the outside

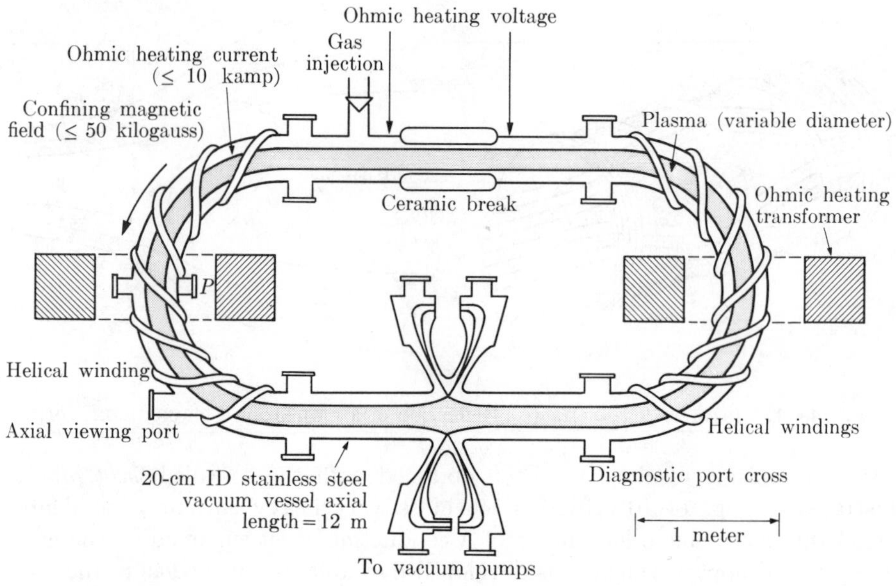

Fig. 14–12. The stellarator, Model C. (Adapted from A. S. Bishop, *Physics Today*, March, 1964, p. 19.)

(Fig. 14–12). The initial heating of the plasma is accomplished by ohmic currents produced·by alternating magnetic fields in a transformer core. The ions of the plasma spiral around lines of the main (dc) field but will, of course, diffuse toward the wall because of collisions with other ions. Most of these ions are directed into a pump-out device before they reach the walls.

So far, the stellarator has been used for studying the containment problems of a plasma, and it is clear from the outset that ohmic heating with the transformer method will not be sufficient to bring the plasma temperature up to the thermonuclear range. More sophisticated heating methods are being studied. One of these is a radiofrequency cyclotron-resonance method; another is a more complex process called magnetic pumping which we shall not discuss in this text.

(*d*) *Beam-injection methods.* One possible method for producing a plasma at thermonuclear temperature is to accelerate ions to the required energy, direct them into a magnetic bottle, and trap them there so as to build up a sufficiently high density. The principal difficulty with this scheme is that an ion cannot be trapped in any configuration of stationary magnetic fields unless it changes its charge or mass after having entered into the field or unless it collides with a gas molecule inside the region of the field. Attempts have been made to solve this problem in two different ways. One is to inject a beam of molecular ions which may dissociate by action of the magnetic force or by collision with other particles. Another method is to inject a beam of neutral but excited atoms which may be ionized inside the magnetic field by action of the magnetic force. The required plasma temperature (particle energy) is, of course, easily attained in the beam-injection devices. But so far the attainment of sufficiently high containment time, Nt, seems to be a long way off.

PROBLEMS

14–1. About 6-eV energy is released when an atom of carbon combines with two oxygen atoms. Calculate the energy in joules released by (a) the burning of 1 gm carbon; (b) the fission of 1 gm U^{235}; (c) the fusion of 1 gm deuterium; (d) the annihilation of 1 gm antimatter with 1 gm matter.

14–2. (a) Calculate the barrier-penetration factor (Eq. 10–19) for fission of $U^{238} + n$, assuming that the barrier is $V - E = 1.4$ MeV high and $\Delta r = 10$ F wide. Assume further that the nucleus splits into two approximately equal parts. (b) Show that the barrier-penetration factor becomes larger when the nucleus splits into two fragments of unequal mass, assuming that $V - E$ and Δr are constant.

14–3. The 5.4-MeV state in Kr^{87} (Fig. 14–6) is a $J = 3/2^-$ or $1/2^-$ state, and the Kr^{86} ground state is a $J = 0^+$ state. The emitted neutron must therefore pass a centrifugal barrier. Estimate the barrier-penetration factor for this case, and state whether or not the delay in the actual neutron emission is significant compared with the half-life of the preceding beta decay.

14–4. The abundance ratio of U^{238} to U^{235} in natural uranium is 140. Together with the data in Table 14–2, this is enough information for calculating the (n, γ) cross section for thermal ($v_n = 2200$ m/sec) neutrons on U^{238}. What is this cross section?

14–5. Use the information in Table 14–3 to calculate the average number of collisions needed to slow a neutron down from $T = 1$ MeV to thermal energy ($v_n = 2200$ m/sec) in H_2O, D_2O, and C moderators. What is the mean free path between collisions in each of these three moderators?

14–6. Assume that the average time t_0 between production and absorption of a neutron in a reactor is 10^{-3} sec. Compute the total number of free neutrons present at any time in the core when the reactor is operating at a power level of 10^6 watts.

14–7. Calculate k_∞ for a homogeneous mixture of natural uranium and graphite for the following ratios of carbon to uranium atoms near optimum.

N_C/N_U	= 200	300	400	500	600
p	= 0.896	0.852	0.812	0.775	0.742

Use $\eta = 1.33$; $\epsilon = 1$; $\sigma_A(U) = 7.68$ barns; $\sigma_A(C) = 0.0045$ barn. Is such a mixture feasible for use in a reactor?

14–8. In a deuterium plasma the average velocity of the deuterons is v m/sec, and their reaction cross section at this velocity is σ m^2. The deuteron density is n deuterons/m^3. (a) Show that the reaction rate is $n^2\sigma v/2$ reactions-m^{-3}-sec^{-1}. (b) Calculate the power density at a temperature of 100 keV where the reaction cross section is $\sigma \approx 0.1$ barn. The average energy released per reaction is 3.6 MeV. Compare with Fig. 14–9.

14–9. Suppose that you could devise a magnetic method for containing one liter (10^{-3} m^3) deuterium plasma containing 10^{18} deuterons and 10^{18} electrons at a temperature of 100 keV. Assume that the plasma can somehow be injected into the magnetic container by deuteron and electron accelerators operating at 100 keV. (a) What is the total injection energy? (b) How long a time does the plasma have to burn to regain the injection energy? (c) What is the pressure on the container? (d) What is the minimum induction B of the magnetic field needed to contain the plasma (pressure $= B^2/2\mu_0$)?

*14–10. Design a homogeneous reactor operating on enriched uranium in the form of a water-soluble compound and using ordinary water as moderator. Maximum power: 100 kW. Cooling: coiled pipes for cooling water in the core. Determine degree of enrichment needed, size of core, control rods, shielding, etc.

15 Elementary Particles

15–1 Introduction

One of the most exciting areas of research in physics and chemistry has always been the study of how matter can be subdivided into smaller and smaller particles. The existence of atoms and molecules was firmly established in the nineteenth century, and the first particle that still is classified as an elementary particle was discovered by J. J. Thomson in 1897. Early in the twentieth century, the experiments and ideas of Rutherford, Bohr, and others put the nuclear atom on a rather firm basis. The early experiments on radioactivity by the Curies and by Rutherford indicated that the nucleus could be subdivided. The first nuclear reaction, studied by Rutherford in 1919, supported this view, and the discovery of the neutron by Chadwick in 1932, ended the discussion concerning the kind of particles the nucleus contains.

In the 1930's, the picture of the world appeared quite satisfactory to the physicists. Matter could be built up of a limited number of different species of atoms, and each atom consisted of a nucleus with a cloud of electrons around it. The nucleus consisted of protons and neutrons held together by a strong force that needed further investigation but which did not necessarily need to be very complex in nature. One apparently superfluous particle, the neutrino, had already started to cast its shadow over this idyllic picture—but there was more to come!

Many discoveries of new so-called "elementary" particles have been made through the studies of cosmic rays. This is the penetrating radiation which mostly originates outside our solar system, but which changes character through interactions in the earth's atmosphere. In later years, however, most of the discoveries and all of the detailed studies of these particles have been made by the use of radiations produced in man-made machines. For the production of elementary particles, excluding the electron and the positron, very high energies, above 140 MeV, are needed. Figure 15–1 is a semilogarithmic plot of the energies attained by man-made machines over three decades. If we make the assumption, not necessarily valid, that the magnetic induction at the beam orbit in future circular machines will stay at about 15 kG, the orbit radius will have to be increased proportionally to the maximum particle energy wanted. It is therefore quite clear that the curve in Fig. 15–1 eventually will have to flatten off; otherwise, by 1990, we shall have a machine running around the earth!

This chapter is intended to present some of the most important information so far obtained about the elementary particles and their excited states and to point out some of the systematics of this information. No basic theoretical interpretation of these data exists to date, although relatively simple mathematical laws have been found, which on occasion have predicted correctly the exact properties of new particles.

In classifying the various particles, several discrete quantum numbers are used. First, we have the intrinsic spin and parity J^{π}, as well as the isospin T and its component T_3, which we discussed in Section 6–7. Second, some completely new quantum numbers have made their appearance in elementary-particle research. Best known is the strangeness quantum number S, which was introduced to resolve the puzzle of anomalously long lifetimes of certain excited states of the nucleons. These long-lived or metastable states, called *hyperons*, their production, and decay are discussed further below.

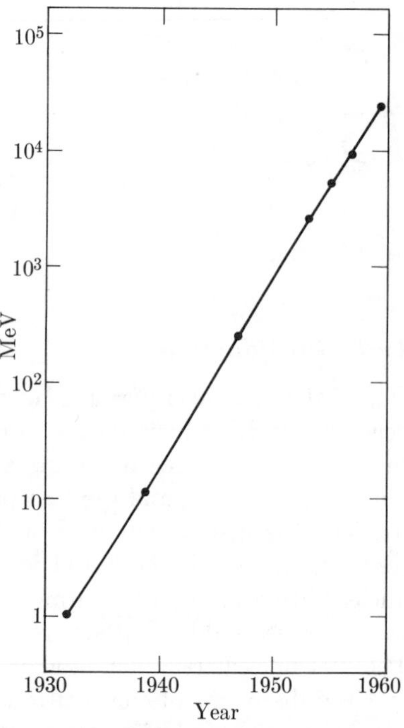

Fig. 15–1. Energies attained by man-made nuclear accelerators over three decades. (From C. N. Yang, *Elementary Particles*, Princeton, N.J.: Princeton University Press, 1962. Reproduced by permission.)

The positron and the electron are said to be antiparticles. They have the same mass and the same spin but opposite charge, and they annihilate each other with the emission of photons when they come in contact with each other. The existence of an antiparticle for the electron was actually predicted by Dirac because of a symmetry of the equations of the relativistic quantum theory of the electron. It has been found that this symmetry of matter persists throughout the list of particles; for instance, the proton has an antiparticle, the negative proton, which was found in 1955 by Chamberlain *et al.** (see below).

15–2 Experimental Techniques

As we mentioned earlier, the high-energy cosmic radiation reaching the earth from outer space has provided an excellent source of high-energy particles for elementary-particle studies. The primary radiation hitting the earth's atmosphere consists of nuclei, mostly protons. In colliding with other nucleons, mostly

* O. Chamberlain, E. Segrè, C. Weigand, and T. Ypsilantis, *Phys. Rev.* **100,** 947 (1955).

in the top layer of the earth's atmosphere, this primary radiation produces a variety of other particles, some of which can be studied at the surface of the earth, but most of which have to be studied by the aid of nuclear-track plates or other devices carried up to the upper atmosphere by balloons.

For extremely high-energy events, cosmic radiation is still the only source of primary particles. In the range of tens of BeV, however, man-made machines take over. They are much more convenient to work with because of the high concentration of radiation and because of the fact that experiments can be set up in a laboratory where heavier counter equipment, bubble chambers, cloud chambers, and heavy shielding materials, can be used. The machines presently being used in this high-energy range accelerate either protons or electrons. Since a large fraction of the research at the moment is carried out on particles or their resonance states having a total energy in the 1- to 3-BeV range, one might ask why it is necessary to use machines for accelerating protons up to, for instance, 30 BeV. The reason is partly that, in order to create new particles through a nucleon-nucleon collision, a certain amount of energy, say 2 BeV, must be available as kinetic energy in the center-of-mass system. However, since the accelerated particle has increased in mass and the target particle has not, as viewed in the laboratory frame, a good deal of the energy provided by the accelerator goes into center-of-mass motion. As will be shown through a few simple calculations below, the kinetic energy in the center-of-mass system increases only proportionally with the square root of the laboratory energy of the accelerated particle at extreme relativistic energies.

Assume that a nucleon of rest mass M_0 collides with another nucleon of rest mass M_0. The former has a velocity v, and the latter is at rest in the laboratory system (Fig. 15–2). The accelerated particle has a total energy $E = \gamma M_0 c^2$, where $\gamma = (1 - v^2/c^2)^{-1/2}$ (Appendix 1). The center-of-mass velocity, as measured in the laboratory system, will be given by

$$V = \frac{\gamma M_0 v}{\gamma M_0 + M_0} = \frac{\gamma v}{\gamma + 1}. \qquad (15\text{–}1)$$

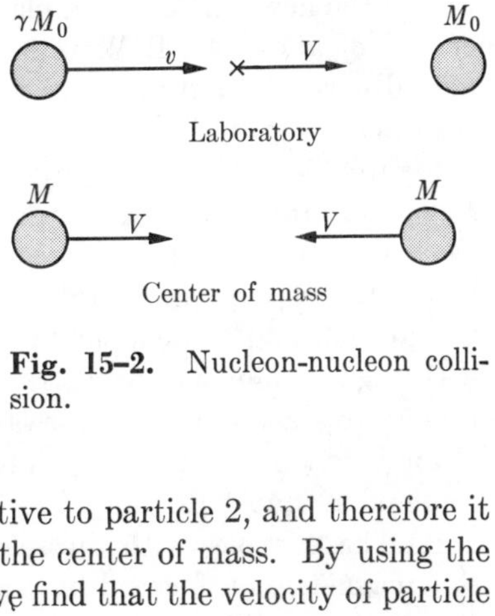

Fig. 15–2. Nucleon-nucleon collision.

This is the velocity of the center of mass relative to particle 2, and therefore it must be the velocity of particle 2 relative to the center of mass. By using the Lorentz transformation formula for velocity, we find that the velocity of particle 1 in the center-of-mass system is also given by Eq. (15–1). In the center-of-mass system, therefore, both particles have the same velocity and the same mass (naturally). The total energy for the collision, as measured in the center-of-mass system is therefore

$$E_{\rm CM} = \frac{2M_0c^2}{\sqrt{1 - V^2/c^2}} = M_0c^2\sqrt{2(\gamma + 1)}. \qquad (15\text{–}2)$$

The kinetic energy, as measured in the center-of-mass system, is therefore given by

$$T_{CM} = M_0c^2[\sqrt{2(\gamma + 1)} - 2]. \tag{15–3}$$

Consider as an example the creation of a nucleon pair through the reaction

$$\mathrm{p} + \mathrm{p} = \mathrm{p} + \bar{\mathrm{p}} + \mathrm{p} + \mathrm{p}, \tag{15–4}$$

where the symbol $\bar{\mathrm{p}}$ stands for the antiproton, or negative proton. Assuming that the antiproton has a rest mass equal to the rest mass of the proton, we need a kinetic energy in the center-of-mass system of $2M_0c^2$. By inserting this into Eq. (15–3) and solving for γ, we find $\gamma = 7$. In the laboratory system, therefore, the accelerated proton has to have a total energy of $7 \times 938 = 6580$ MeV $=$ 6.58 BeV, or a kinetic energy of about 5.6 BeV. If we assume that particle 2 is not at rest but is executing its normal oscillatory motion inside a nucleus with a kinetic energy of about 30 MeV, it turns out that under favorable circumstances, namely when the particle is moving against particle 1, the kinetic energy of particle 1 need be only about 4.3 BeV.

The antiproton was produced and detected in copious quantities at the Bevatron (proton synchrotron) at the University of California at Berkeley, in 1955. Before that time, a few cosmic-ray events that had been carefully studied gave strong indication of the existence of an antiproton. The Bevatron experiment, however, is much more convincing because not only were particles of the correct charge and mass produced in quantities, but also it was shown that the production of the new particle took place only when the synchrotron was run above an energy of about 4.3 BeV, which agrees with the discussion above. We shall now discuss the antiproton experiment in some detail, as an example of the very many careful investigations that are being made in this area of physics.

Figure 15–3 shows the physical layout of the antiproton experiment. The Bevatron proton beam impinges upon a copper target, in which it produces a shower of negative, positive, and neutral particles of various kinds. At these high energies, the interactions between the nucleons in the copper nucleus is immaterial, and the copper target is simply a target of protons and neutrons with a given momentum distribution. The negative particles produced in the target are scattered in the forward direction and deflected outward by the field of the Bevatron. Particles within an arbitrarily selected small range of momenta centered around 1.19 BeV/c* are deflected approximately 21° and enter magnet $M1$. The particles with the selected momenta will be deflected about 32° by this magnet, then focused by the three-element quadrupole lens $Q1$ to a small spot at the scintillation counter $S1$. Negative particles having different momenta will be deflected through different angles and will not hit $S1$. After passing

* The unit BeV/c for momentum is frequently used in high-energy physics. It equals the momentum of a particle with zero rest mass and kinetic energy 1 BeV.

through counter $S1$, experiencing only a slight loss of energy in the process, the particles are further deflected and focused by the combination $Q2$-$M2$. Thereafter, they pass through counters $S2$, $C1$, $C2$, and $S3$, in succession.

The difficult part of this experiment is to separate out negative particles with a rest mass approximately equal to the rest mass of the proton from an extremely heavy background of negative pi mesons produced in the target. Particles of momentum 1.19 BeV/c and with a rest mass equal to the rest mass of the proton have $v/c = \beta = 0.78$. For pi mesons of momentum 1.19 BeV/c, $\beta = 0.99$. What is needed, then, in addition to the momentum selection provided by the magnets, is a velocity-selection mechanism. Chamberlain *et al.* used two methods of velocity selection, one of which was to measure the time of flight of the particles between counters $S1$ and $S2$. The separation between these two counters was 40 ft, giving a flight time of 40 nsec for pi mesons and 51 nsec for proton-mass particles. A delayed coincidence technique was used to select particles with the appropriate flight time for proton-mass particles.

Because of the tremendously high background of negative pi mesons (about 40,000 per observed antiproton), it was necessary to take further precautions. The reason for this is that two pi mesons traveling reasonably close together can give rise to an accidental coincidence; that is, they can trigger pulses in counters $S1$ and $S2$ which are 51 nsec apart. A second velocity-selection mechanism was provided by the counters $C1$, $C2$, and $S3$, which were, respectively, two Cerenkov counters (Section 7–10) and another scintillation counter. The

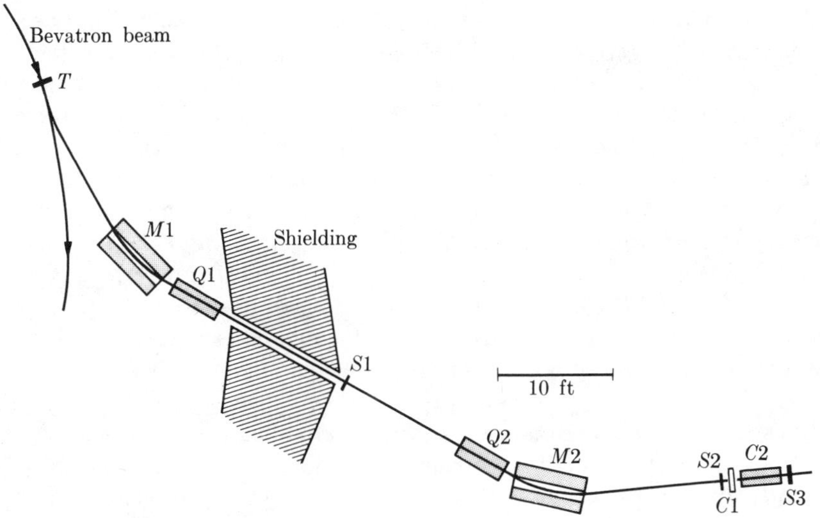

Fig. 15–3. Experimental setup for the antiproton experiment by Chamberlain *et al.* [*Phys. Rev.* **100,** 947 (1955).]

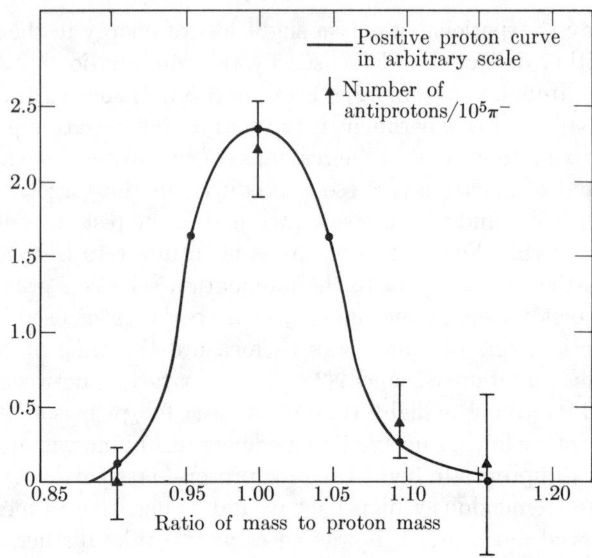

Fig. 15–4. Crude mass measurement of negative particles observed by Chamberlain *et al., op. cit.*

counter $C1$ was constructed so that it was triggered by a particle with $\beta > 0.79$, thereby indicating that the particle was not a proton-mass particle, but a lighter one. The counter $C2$ was triggered by particles with β in the interval 0.75 to 0.78. This is the right range for a proton-mass particle at this position, since ionization energy losses in traversing counters $S2$, $C1$, and $C2$ reduce the velocity of antiprotons from $\beta = 0.78$ to $\beta = 0.765$. Since it was possible to get a count in the Cerenkov counter, $C2$, from a particle of different velocity, provided that it was scattered in that counter, a third scintillation counter, $S3$, was included to check that a given particle had not been scattered.

In summary: a particle was accepted as a negative proton-mass particle if it had a correct flight time of 51 nsec between counters $S1$ and $S2$, if it did not give rise to a count in $C1$, but was detected in counters $C2$ and $S3$. The result of the experiment by Chamberlain *et al.* was that one negative particle of proton mass was detected per approximately 40,000 negative pi mesons recorded.

A crude measurement of the mass of the detected particles was performed by Chamberlain *et al.* in the following way. First, the target was placed in a different position in the Bevatron beam so that positive protons scattered from the target would enter magnet $M1$ after deflection in the Bevatron field. The polarity of $M1$, $Q1$, $Q2$, and $M2$ was reversed so that the positive protons were further deflected and focused as described above for negative particles. The number of counts registered by the equipment for a given exposure was then measured as a function of field strength in the string of magnets. The resulting curve, which indicates the mass-resolving power of the equipment, is shown in Fig. 15–4.

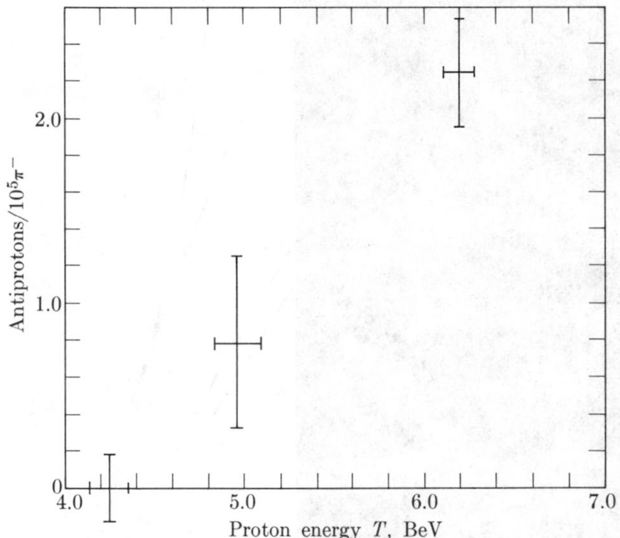

Fig. 15–5. Excitation function for production of antiprotons as observed by Chamberlain *et al.*, *op. cit.*

The abscissa has been converted from field strength to mass of the selected particle. The circular points and the solid curve represent the measurement with positive protons; the triangles with error bars represent the measurement on the detected negative particles. These measurements demonstrate in a convincing way that the mass of the negative particles observed corresponds quite closely to the mass of protons. The only previously known particle with this mass and charge is the negative hydrogen ion. The possibility that the particles detected by Chamberlain *et al.* could have been negative hydrogen ions is ruled out, because the probability that a proton with this velocity would pick up two electrons and retain them while penetrating all the counters and the air between the counters is completely negligible.

As a final test, Chamberlain *et al.* measured the excitation function for the new particles, that is, the number of particles produced in a given exposure as a function of the Bevatron energy. The result of these measurements is shown in Fig. 15–5. The excitation function appears to go to zero at approximately 4.3 BeV, as predicted. The experiments described indicated that negatively charged particles of rest mass equal to, or approximately equal to, the proton rest mass were produced in energetic proton-nucleon collisions and that the threshold energy was approximately that predicted from calculations on the process given by Eq. (15–4). We conclude that these particles must have been antiprotons.

Since the original work by Chamberlain *et al.*, antiprotons have been produced in large quantities at the new large proton synchrotrons. Figure 15–6

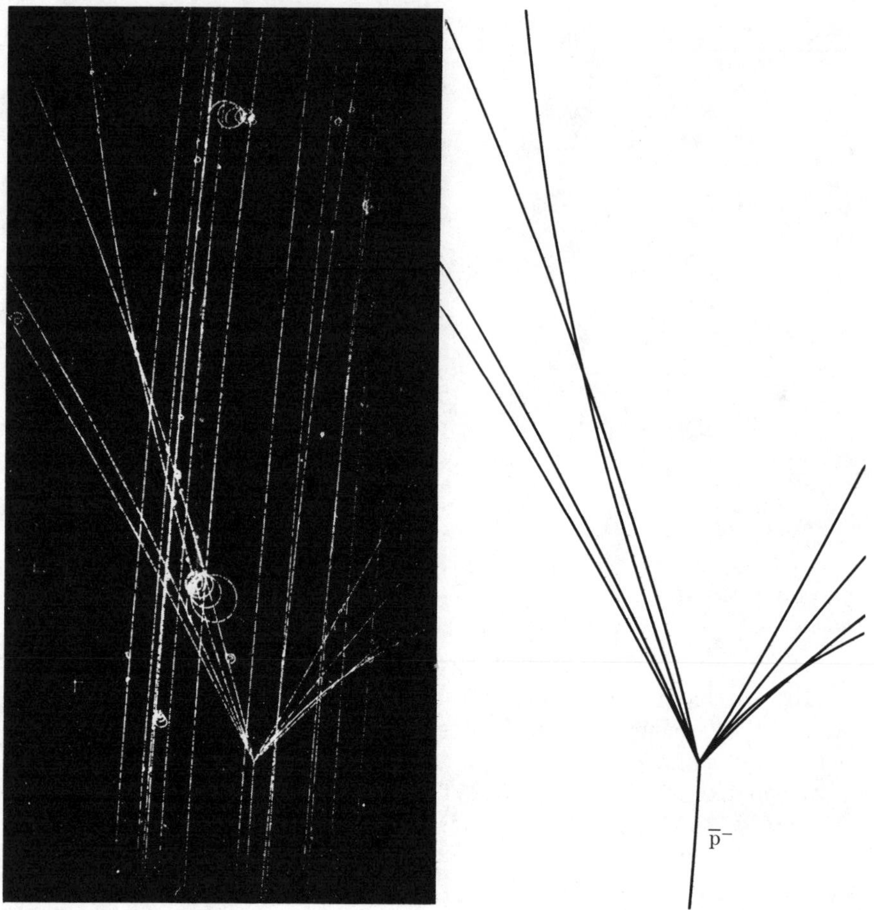

Fig. 15-6. Annihilation of an antiproton with a proton in a hydrogen bubble chamber (Courtesy of Brookhaven National Laboratory).

shows an example of the annihilation in flight of an antiproton in a hydrogen bubble chamber. The reaction is

$$p + \overline{p} = 4\pi^+ + 4\pi^- + x\pi^0.$$

The pions subsequently decay through several steps such that the final results are gamma rays, electrons, and positrons. In matter, these forms of radiation ultimately are degraded to heat and chemical dissociation energy.

The antiproton experiment has been described in some detail here because it is a good example of a thoroughly planned and carefully executed experiment. In this case, the investigators knew exactly what they were looking for. Very often this has not been the case in elementary-particle physics; or, for that

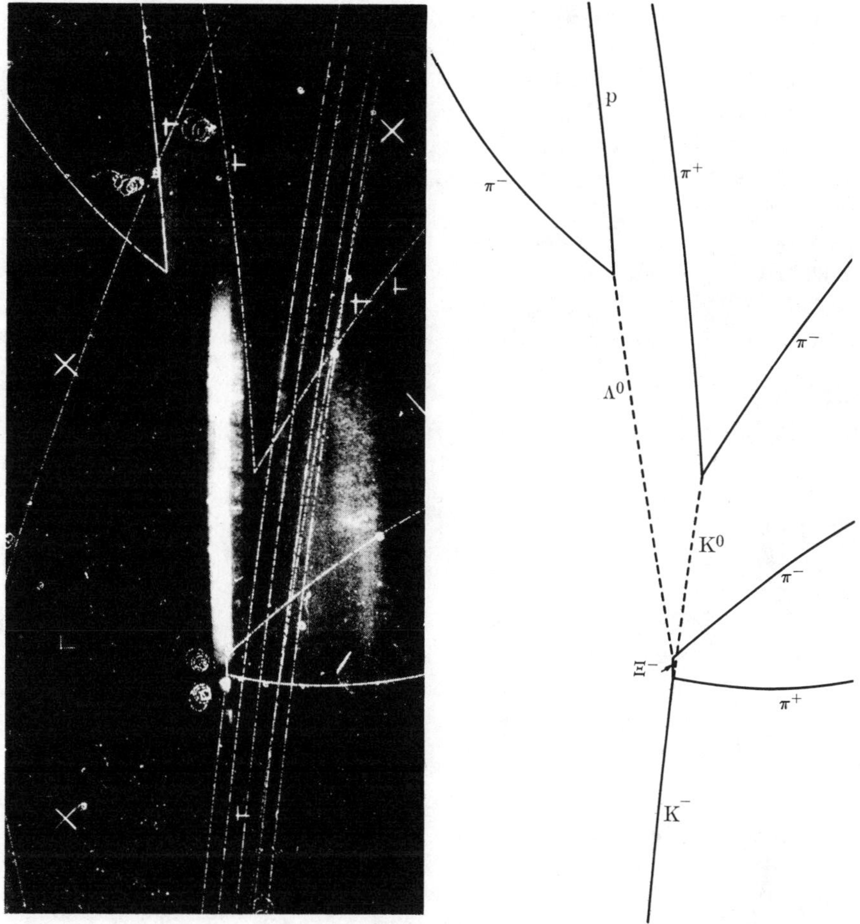

Fig. 15–7. Production and decay of Ξ and Λ hyperons in a hydrogen bubble chamber (Courtesy of Brookhaven National Laboratory).

matter, in any part of physics during the first one or two decades after the opening of that particular area. Sometimes new discoveries are made by accident, while the investigators are looking for something else. Sometimes new techniques are developed that enable physicists to go exploring, so to speak. For instance, one research team may decide to shoot a beam of K^- mesons into a hydrogen bubble chamber to "see what happens."

Figure 15–7 is an example of what might happen. The K^- mesons (kaons), the properties of which will be discussed later, are produced in the proton-synchrotron targets, together with a large number of other particles. They can be separated from these other particles if they are allowed to pass through a chain of magnets and velocity selectors (crossed electric and magnetic fields). Such a beam was directed through a bubble chamber at Brookhaven National

Laboratory, and one of the resulting pictures is shown in Fig. 15–7. The bubble chamber is immersed in a magnetic field and stereoscopic pictures are taken of the events. This enables the investigators to measure with fairly high precision the momenta of all charged particles involved. A careful study of the density of the bubble tracks gives a crude measurement of the velocities of the particles, and this helps to identify them, if they are known particles ($m = p/v$). By using the laws of conservation of energy and conservation of momentum at each vertex or star, one can check these identity assignments and also find the masses of new particles. For instance, the two-prong event in the upper left-hand corner of Fig. 15–7 is coplanar with the starting point of the π^- track in the lower part of the picture. This makes it likely that it is caused by a neutral particle, which takes a straight-line path between the two points. Checking that the sum of the transverse momenta of the two decay products balance confirms this. The sum of the longitudinal momenta of the decay products gives the momentum of the neutral particle. From track-density studies, we find that the negative decay product is a pion and the positive product is a proton. Knowing the identities and momenta of the two particles, we can calculate their energies, and the sum is, of course, the energy of the neutral particle (Λ^0). Since both the total energy of the Λ^0 and its momentum are determined, we can calculate its rest mass. The particles involved in the sequence of events depicted in Fig. 15–7 are further discussed in the following sections.

The experimental study of the elementary particles is a fascinating area of research, but it is not the primary topic of this text. We must therefore limit any further treatment to merely listing the principal results of these studies.

15–3 Physical Properties of the Elementary Particles

Table 15–1, from a paper by Rosenfeld *et al.*,* gives the most important physical properties of the elementary particles or long-lived particles, as known today. The table has been somewhat abbreviated, and all error limits have been left out to keep it short. In column 1 the particles are classified as photons, leptons, mesons, and baryons. The term *baryon* is used for the nucleons and higher excited states that decay to nucleons by emission of mesons. Only the long-lived or metastable states of the baryons are listed in Table 15–1. Other short-lived states are discussed in Section 15–6.

Column 2 gives the symbol of the particle, in accordance with presently accepted, but rapidly changing, convention. Note that two pairs of neutrinos are listed: the electron neutrinos and the muon neutrinos. One class is associated with normal beta decay; the other class (also called neutretto), with decay of the muon. Columns 3 and 4 give the isospin T and the ordinary spin and parity J^π whenever observable and observed. For leptons, for instance, the isospin T, or its component T_3, cannot be defined, nor can the parity. For mesons, a new

---

* A. H. Rosenfeld, A. Barbaro-Galtieri, W. H. Barkas, and P. L. Bastien, *Rev. Mod. Phys.* **36,** 977 (1964).

type of parity, *G-parity,* can be defined, but we are not going into a discussion of that rather intricate concept here. Column 5 gives the strangeness quantum number, which is discussed in more detail in the next section. This quantum number again cannot be defined for leptons.

The mass, or the rest energy, of the particles in Table 15-1 is given in MeV, and the mean lives are given in seconds. The particles in this table have been called long-lived particles because their mean lives are long compared with a unit appropriate for decay by the strong (nuclear) interaction

$$\tau_0 = \hbar/m_\pi c^2 = 4.7153 \times 10^{-24} \text{ sec.}$$

This is approximately the lifetime of a virtual pion produced in nuclear encounters (see Section 3-11).

Most of the baryon resonance states discussed in Section 15-6 have lifetimes that are of the order of magnitude unity on this scale. The particles or states listed in Table 15-1 are all stable against decay by the strong interaction because of the operation of selection rules. The last column of the table gives the common decay modes for the unstable particles, the relative rate of occurrence, and the energy released in the various modes.

A further discussion of the baryon states, including the metastable hyperons listed in Table 15-1, is given in Sections 15-6 and 15-8. A discussion of the mesons and their excited states is given in Section 15-7. The leptons, the behavior of which is governed by the so-called weak interaction, are the least understood of the elementary particles. No further discussion of them will be attempted here.

15-4 Associated Production and Strangeness

For some time the hyperons and K-mesons were classified as "strange" particles. They are indeed strange in several respects. First, they seem to be completely superfluous in the theory of matter; another, and maybe stranger, aspect of these particles concerns their comparatively long lifetimes. The fact that they are produced in copious quantities in nucleon-nucleon collisions of sufficiently high energy indicates that they interact very strongly with the nuclear field. The theory then predicts that they should decay to nucleons and pions or only to pions, as the case may be, very rapidly; in fact, their decay time should be of the order of magnitude of unity on the τ_0 scale. Table 15-1 indicates that their lifetimes are of orders of magnitude 10^{13} to 10^{16} times this unit. It is possible to explain this strange behavior in terms of a new *ad hoc* conservation law: the conservation of strangeness, as further described below.

It was pointed out first by Pais* and by Y. Nambu† that the strange particles are always produced in pairs. A beam of pions, for instance, colliding with a

---

* A. Pais, *Phys. Rev.* **86,** 663 (1952).

† Y. Nambu, *Progress of Theoretical Physics* (Kyoto) **6,** 615, 619 (1951).

Table 15–1. Elementary (long-lived) particles*

Class	Symbol and charge	T	J^{π}	S	Mass, MeV	Mean life, sec	Principal decays: Partial mode	Principal decays: Fraction	Q, MeV
PHOTON	γ		1		0	Stable	Stable		
LEPTONS	ν_e		1/2		$0(<2 \times 10^{-4})$	Stable	Stable		
	ν_μ				$0(<4)$				
	$e^{\mp}$		1/2		0.511006	Stable	Stable		
	$\mu^{\mp}$		1/2		105.659	2.2001×10^{-6}	$e\nu\bar{\nu}$	100%	105.15
MESONS	$\pi^{\pm}$	1	0^-	0	139.580	2.551×10^{-8}	$\mu\nu$	$\approx$100%	33.94
							$e\nu$	1.24×10^{-4}	139.09
							$\mu\nu\gamma$	1.24×10^{-4}	33.94
							$\pi^0 e\nu$	1.13×10^{-8}	4.08
	π^0			0	134.974	1.78×10^{-16}	$\gamma\gamma$	98.8%	135.00
							$\gamma e^+ e^-$	1.19%	133.98
	$K^{\pm}$	1/2	0^-	$\pm$	493.78	1.229×10^{-8}	$\mu\nu$	63.1%	388.1
							$\pi^{\pm}\pi^0$	21.5%	219.2
							$\pi^{\pm}\pi^-\pi^+$	5.5%	75.0
							and other		
	K^0			1	497.7	50% K_1, 50% K_2			
	K_1			$\pm$1		0.909×10^{-10}	$\pi^+\pi^-$	68.9%	218.8
							$\pi^0\pi^0$	31.1%	228.0
	K_2			$\pm$1		5.70×10^{-8}	$\pi^0\pi^0\pi^0$	26.5%	93.0
							$\pi^+\pi^-\pi^0$	11.4%	83.8
							$\pi\mu\nu$	26.9%	252.7
							$\pi e\nu$	35.3%	357.9
							$\pi^+\pi^-$	2.1×10^{-3}	218.8

	η	0	0^-	0	548.7	$>10^{-22}$	$\gamma\gamma$ $3\pi^0$ or $\pi^0\,2\gamma$ $\pi^+\pi^-\pi^0$ $\pi^+\pi^-\gamma$	38.6% 30.8% 25.0% 5.5%	548.8 143.7 134.5 269.5
BARYONS	p	1/2	$1/2^+$	0	938.256	Stable			
	n			0	939.550	1.01×10^3	$pe^-\nu$	100%	0.78
	Λ	0	$1/2^+$	−1	1115.44	2.61×10^{-10}	$p\pi^-$ $n\pi^0$ and others	66.9% 33.1%	37.5 40.9
	Σ^+	1	$1/2^+$	−1	1189.39	0.794×10^{-10}	$p\pi^0$ $n\pi^+$ and others	51.0% 49.0%	116.13 110.26
	Σ^0			−1	1192.3	$<1.0 \times 10^{-14}$	$\Lambda\gamma$	100%	77.0
	Σ^-			−1	1197.20	1.58×10^{-10}	$n\pi^-$ and others	$\approx$100%	117.94
	Ξ^0	1/2	$1/2^+$	−2	1314.3	3.05×10^{-10}	$\Lambda\pi^0$ and others	$\approx$100%	63.9
	Ξ^-			−2	1320.8	1.75×10^{-10}	$\Lambda\pi^-$ $\Lambda e^-\nu$ $n\pi^-$	$\approx$100% $\leq 1.7 \times 10^{-3}$ $<5 \times 10^{-3}$	65.8 204.9 241.7
	Ω^-	0	$3/2^+$	−3	1675	1.3×10^{-10}	$\Xi\pi$ ΛK	? ?	221 66

* Reprinted in abbreviated form from A. H. Rosenfeld, A. Barbaro-Galtieri, W. H. Barkas, P. L. Bastien, J. Kirz, and M. Roos, *UCRL-8030*, Part I (March, 1965 edition).

nucleon target produces lambdas and kaons, according to the reaction

$$\pi + \mathrm{N} = \Lambda + \mathrm{K}. \tag{15–5}$$

The fact that two strange particles are produced simultaneously is called "associated production." According to the reciprocity theorem, the reaction (15–5) can go both ways, with comparable cross sections. However, the reaction has not been observed to go from right to left, for the obvious reason that no lambda targets can be provided for a K beam to collide with, or vice versa. According to Table 15–1, the Λ decays to a nucleon and a pion, but with a long lifetime. Does it need to find the "mate," the K-meson, to go with high probability (short life) back to $\pi + \mathrm{N}$?

These observations led Gell-Mann and, independently, K. Nishijima to introduce a new conservation law connected with a new quantum number, the strangeness, which is a discrete number, just as is the spin, assigned to each elementary particle.* It is postulated that the total strangeness is conserved in a reaction governed by the strong (nuclear force) interaction.

The process given by Eq. (15–5), it is said, can go by the strong interaction because, for the two particles on the left-hand side of the equation, the strangeness is zero, and on the right-hand side one particle has strangeness +1 and the other has strangeness −1. The sum is therefore conserved in the reaction. In the decay processes, however, both the lambda and the kaon leave daughter products with strangeness zero (Table 15–1). In these reactions, then, strangeness is not conserved. Consequently, they cannot go by the way of the strong interaction, but it is assumed that they can go by way of the weak interaction (beta-decay interaction), for which strangeness presumably need not be conserved. The reactions that proceed by way of the weak interaction are very slow, and this explains the long lifetimes of kaons and hyperons.

15–5 Fundamental Particles and Interactions

In Section 15–3, we listed some measured properties of what we called elementary particles. Included are the photon and several mesons, all of which are called *field quanta*, rather than particles, by some experts. The term "elementary," as applied to the listed particles, has also come into some disrepute lately. There is general agreement about the status of the hyperons (Λ, Σ, Ξ, and Ω). They are excited baryon states that happen to be metastable because of the action of selection rules for their decays. Aside from this, they are no more elementary than the more than one hundred other excited states of the baryon that have been discovered so far. With regard to the proton, which is the only completely stable baryon (when free), the opinion is that it is, by accident, the lowest state of the baryon, in much the same way as the $(\mathrm{d}_{3/2})^{-1}(\mathrm{f}_{7/2})^1$, $J = 4^-$ state happens to be the ground state of K^{40}. The similarity does not stop there. Transitions between baryon states take place by emission of a meson

* See M. Gell-Mann and A. H. Rosenfeld, *Ann. Rev. Nucl. Sci.* **7**, 407 (1957).

Table 15-2. Force fields and field quanta

Interaction	Source	Quantum	Spin J	Charge Q	Isospin T	Strangeness S	Mass m
Gravity	Mass	Graviton	2	0	–	–	0
Electro-magnetic	Charge	Photon	1	0	–	–	0
Strong	Baryon	Pion	0	0, ± 1	1	0	m_π
(Nuclear)	Baryon	Kaon	0	0, ± 1*	$\frac{1}{2}$	± 1	m_K
Weak (Beta)	Baryon Lepton	Intermediate Boson	1?	1	–	–	?

* See Eq. (15-9).

"quantum," which like the photon is a boson, an entity with integral spin. We cannot, however, from this similarity draw the conclusion that the baryon is a composite particle.

One might ask why the proton does not decay, since there clearly are a number of lower mass particles into which it could conceivably be converted. One could argue that among the decay products, there would have to be an odd number of particles of spin $\frac{1}{2}$, and this means leptons. This would violate the law of conservation of lepton number, which was formulated in Chapter 11. Whatever the reason, we formulate another *ad hoc* law: the law of conservation of baryon number. According to all observations, a baryon can only be created and annihilated together with an antibaryon. The baryon number is $A = 1$ for the nucleon and other baryons, $A = 0$ for mesons, and $A = -1$ for antibaryons. Mesons, which have integral spin, can be created in any number, and they do decay to lepton pairs.

It is believed that there is a very intimate connection between the properties of the various particles and the properties of the force fields (interactions). We mentioned in Section 3-11 that the electromagnetic interaction is carried by virtual photons, and the nuclear (strong) interaction is carried by virtual π-mesons (and other mesons). Table 15-2 completes the list of known forces and the field quanta that carry them. The list starts with the gravitational field, which is the weakest of the known force fields.

The source of the gravitational field is the mass of the particle or particles that produce it, and the source for the next entry on the list, the electromagnetic field, is the charge. Since the baryon always has mass and sometimes charge, it can obviously be the source both of gravitational and electromagnetic fields. The baryon is also listed as the source of the nuclear field, but it is not known what particular property or quality of the baryon is really the source for this field. The field quantum for gravitational fields is called the *graviton,* which is a postulated quantum that so far has not been detected; free gravitons would be emitted only by large masses (stars) subject to very large accelerations. The field quantum for the electromagnetic field is the photon, and for the nuclear field there are at least two different field quanta, the pion and the kaon, with strangeness 0 and +1 (−1 for the antikaon), respectively. The final entry in the column for field quanta, the intermediate boson, is again a postulated quantum that has not so far been detected.

The fields are stationary when the source is at rest, and free field quanta are formed only when the source is accelerated; the field is left behind as the particle is jerked away from it. The number of field quanta, or the probability for a field quantum to be left behind, is a measure of the strength of the interaction. If a momentum p is given to the source in the electromagnetic case, the number of photons produced is approximately equal to $(e^2/4\pi\epsilon_0\hbar c)\ln(p/mc)$. Since the fine-structure constant that appears in front of the logarithm is a small number ($\frac{1}{137}$), the probability of photon emission is small for reasonable values of p/mc. For nuclear fields, the corresponding number is very much larger, of the order of magnitude of unity when the momentum imparted to the source is a few BeV/c. This is partly the reason why we call the nuclear interaction a strong interaction.

15–6 Baryon Spectroscopy

The hyperons, whose properties are discussed above, are long-lived states of the baryon, so long-lived that they can produce tracks of measurable lengths in bubble chambers, for instance. The many other excited states of the baryon are so short-lived that they travel only a few fermis before decay. Their observation, therefore, requires some changes in the techniques. As an example, we shall discuss briefly the study of a resonance or excited state at 1385-MeV total energy with $S = -1$ and $T = 1$. This is a charge triplet with the same strangeness as the Σ-hyperons, but unlike the Σ-hyperons, it has enough energy to decay by pion emission to the Λ-hyperon.

The work to be described briefly here was carried out at the Lawrence Radiation Laboratory, Berkeley, by M. H. Alston and M. Ferro-Luzzi.* A hydrogen-filled bubble chamber was irradiated with a separated K^- beam from the Berkeley Bevatron. This beam was magnetically analyzed, and five different exposures were made with kaon momenta $p_{K^-} = 510, 620, 760, 850$, and 1150 MeV/$c$. About 1000 pictures showing production of two charged particles plus one neutral particle were analyzed. The following reactions were found to occur in these events:

$$\begin{aligned} K^- + p &\rightarrow \Lambda + \pi^+ + \pi^- \\ &\rightarrow \Sigma^0 + \pi^+ + \pi^- \\ &\rightarrow (\Lambda \text{ or } \Sigma^0) + \pi^+ + \pi^- + \pi^0 \\ &\rightarrow \overline{K}^0 + p + \pi^-. \end{aligned} \tag{15–6}$$

* M. H. Alston and M. Ferro-Luzzi, *Revs. Mod. Phys.* **33**, 416 (1961).

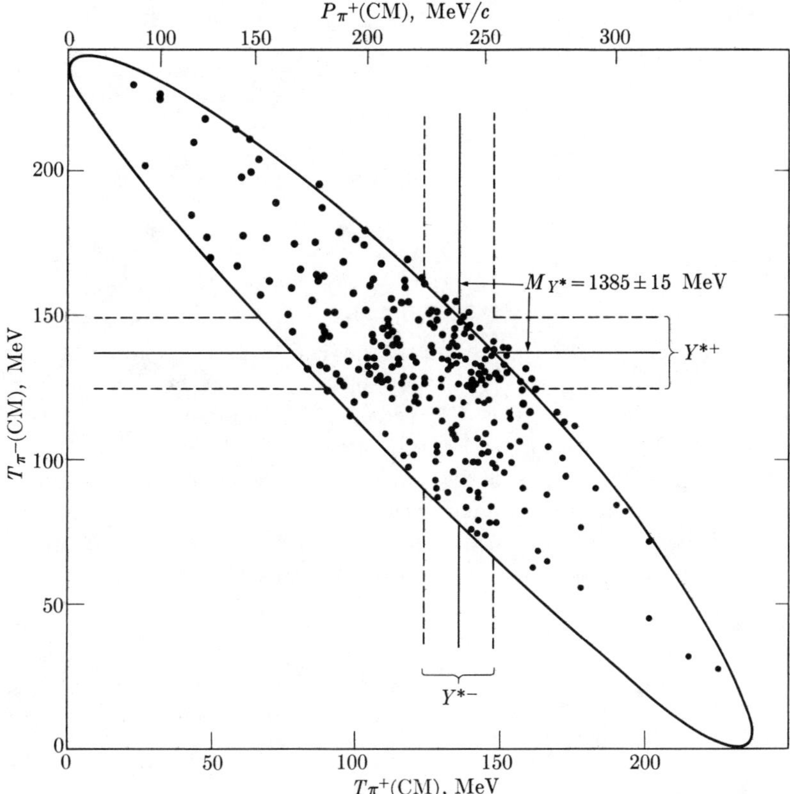

Fig. 15-8. Dalitz plot of the reaction $K^- + p \rightarrow \Lambda + \pi^+ + \pi^-$ at $p_{K^-} = 760$ MeV/c (262 events). [From M. H. Alston and M. Ferro-Luzzi, *Revs. Mod. Phys.* **33**, 416 (1961).]

The data from the reaction on the top line were singled out for further study. For each event, the momenta of both pions were recorded and for each incident energy, plots were made as shown in Figs. 15-8 and 15-9. These are called Dalitz plots, after the originator.

In any three-body breakup there are infinitely many ways in which the total energy released can be distributed between the three particles. In the particular case studied, one of the particles is much heavier than the other two. If the Λ had been infinitely heavy, the pions would have shared the available energy and the Dalitz plot would have been a straight line expressing $T_{\pi^+} + T_{\pi^-} =$ constant. Since Λ has a finite rest mass, the kinetic energy imparted to it will depend on the relative directions of emission of the two pions. The boundaries of the Dalitz plot can easily be calculated (Problem 15-5), and the detailed theory shows that the density of points should be constant over the allowed area if the reaction is a true three-body breakup, but not if it is a two-step process. The two plots shown here clearly put the reaction studied in the latter category. We can rewrite the top line of (15–6) as follows:

$$\begin{aligned} K^- + p &\rightarrow Y^{*+} + \pi^-, \\ Y^{*+} &\rightarrow \Lambda + \pi^+, \end{aligned} \tag{15–7a}$$

or

$$\begin{aligned} K^- + p &\rightarrow Y^{*-} + \pi^+, \\ Y^{*-} &\rightarrow \Lambda + \pi^-. \end{aligned} \tag{15–7b}$$

The resonance states Y^{*-} and Y^{*+} are the two charge members of an isospin triplet state which has the same strangeness and isospin as the Σ-hyperons. If the state were sharp, the points in the Dalitz plots should fall along two straight lines, as indicated in Figs. 15–8 and 15–9. The distribution of the points about these lines gives the width of the resonance. This is plotted separately in Fig. 15–10 for the data taken at $p_{K^-} = 1150$ MeV/c. The smooth curve fitted to the data is a standard resonance curve with natural width $\Gamma = 64$ MeV. Some intricate corrections have to be applied to this measurement, and the true natural width is found to be about $\Gamma = 53$ MeV, corresponding to a mean life of the resonance equal to

$$\tau = \hbar/\Gamma = 1.2 \times 10^{-23} \text{ sec.}$$

The example discussed here may be typical of the large amount of careful work that has been produced in recent years on the excited states of the baryon

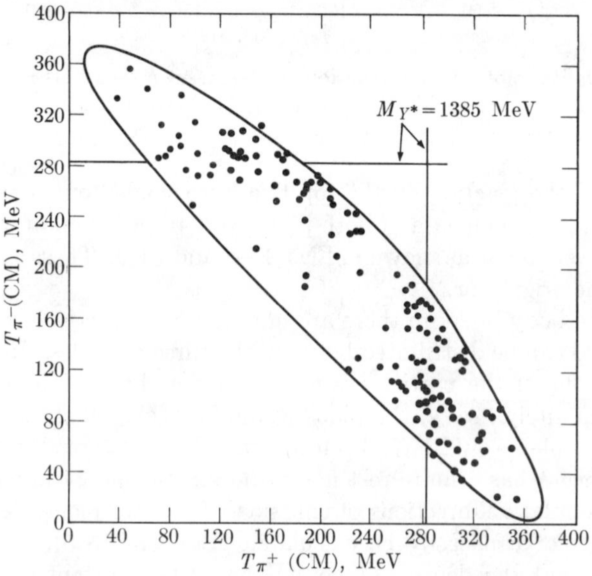

Fig. 15–9. Dalitz plot of the reaction $K^- + p \rightarrow \Lambda + \pi^+ + \pi^-$ at $p_{K^-} = 1150$ MeV/c (141 events). (From Alston and Ferro-Luzzi, *Ibid.*)

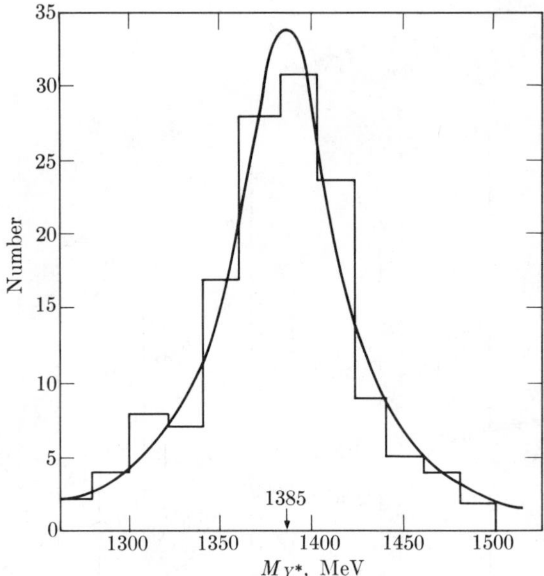

Fig. 15–10. Mass spectrum for the charged members of an isospin triplet with strangeness $S = -1$. (From Alston and Ferro-Luzzi, *Ibid.*)

system. The lowest lying states that are well established at this writing are plotted in Fig. 15–11. The information for this figure is taken from the paper by Rosenfeld *et al.** and the system of labeling follows a proposal by Chew *et al.*† The states are ordered in a three-dimensional coordinate system according to strangeness from $S = 0$ to -3, isospin from $T = 0$ to $\frac{3}{2}$, and energy mc^2 from 939 MeV and up. Each set of states with identical S and T is given a symbol which is an upper-case Greek letter, except for the nucleons (N) and the other states with $S = 0$ and $T = \frac{1}{2}$. The splitting of the various states into $2T + 1$ substates with different isospin projection (charge) is somewhat exaggerated. The relation between the isospin projection T_3 and the charge Q (or Z) in units of e was given in Section 6–7 as

$$Q = T_3 + A/2, \tag{15–8}$$

where A, as before, is the nucleon number. In elementary-particle physics it is called the baryon number and has a somewhat broader application; it is 0 for mesons and -1 for antibaryons. (Sometimes the symbol B is used for the baryon number.) For particles with strangeness $S \neq 0$, we find that Eq. (15–8)

---

* Rosenfeld, *et al.*, *loc. cit.*

† G. F. Chew, M. Gell-Mann, and A. H. Rosenfeld, *Scientific American*, February, 1964, p. 74.

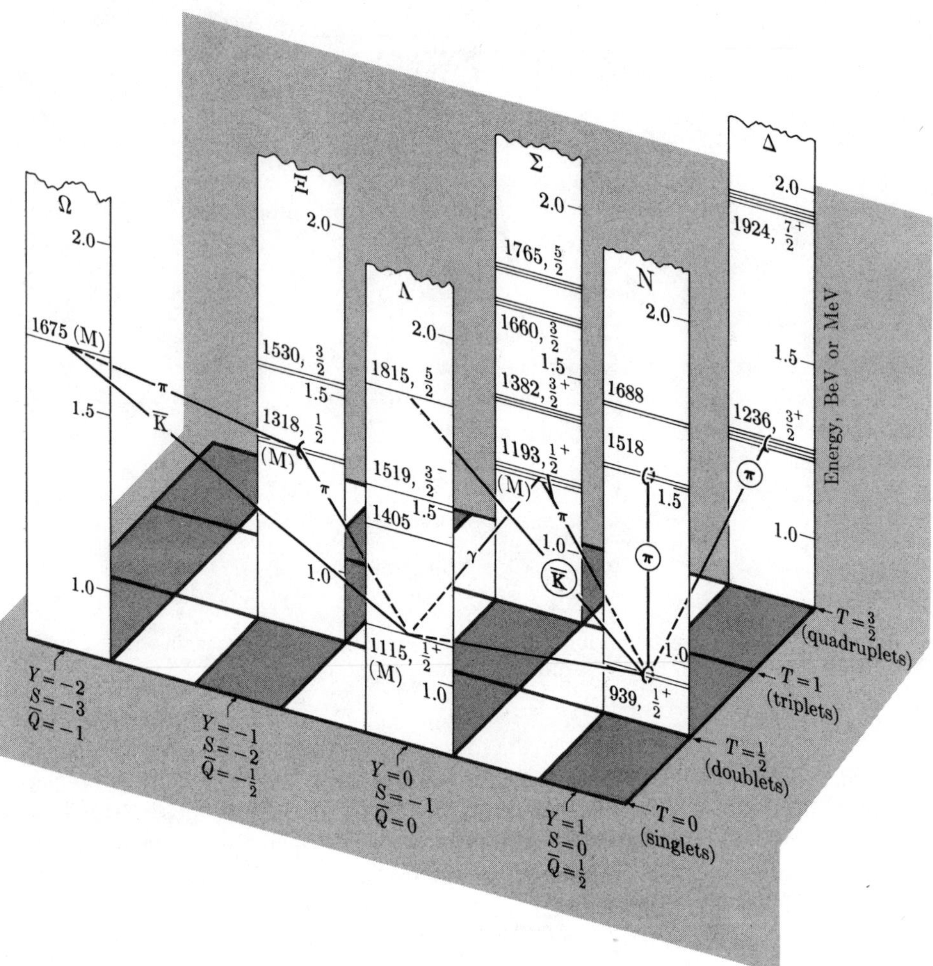

Fig. 15–11. Baryon states ($A = 1$) plotted vs. isospin and hypercharge. Only selected decays are indicated, and strong decays are encircled. The symbol (M) stands for metastable. (Data from Rosenfeld *et al., loc. cit.*)

has to be modified (extended) to agree with observations. We now write

$$Q = T_3 + A/2 + S/2 = T_3 + Y/2, \tag{15–9}$$

where we have introduced another quantum number, the hypercharge Y, which from now on we shall use instead of S. Since, for any charge multiplet, the average of T_3 is zero, we see that the average charge of a multiplet is

$$\overline{Q} = Y/2. \tag{15–10}$$

Each state of the baryon system has a corresponding antibaryon state with opposite baryon number A, hypercharge Y, isospin projection T_3, and charge Q. In some cases these antistates have been observed; however, more energy is required to produce them than the baryon states (compare Section 15–2).

The transition from a baryon state to a lower state usually goes by pion emission, when hypercharge does not change, and by kaon or antikaon emission, when hypercharge changes by one unit.

In these strong-interaction, or "allowed," transitions, all total quantum numbers are conserved (angular momentum, parity, isospin, isospin projection, and hypercharge). In Fig. 15–11, some examples of strong-interaction transitions are indicated by an encircled bold-face $\boldsymbol{\pi}$ or $\overline{\mathbf{K}}$. One electromagnetic transition is shown; it is the decay of the Σ^0-hyperon to the Λ^0-hyperon. This is a slower transition, and still much slower are the weak-interaction transitions indicated by a light-face π or $\overline{\mathrm{K}}$. These "forbidden" transitions violate conservation of hypercharge, and strong decay is therefore not possible. For example, the Ω-hyperon decays to the Ξ-hyperon with pion emission and with a change of hypercharge of one unit. Since the pion has hypercharge zero, the conservation law is violated. It cannot go by a $\overline{\mathrm{K}}$-transition, because there is not enough energy available to create a kaon. It is clear then that the hyperons or metastable states owe their long mean lives to the fact that the kaon and, for $\Sigma^{\pm}$, the pion have rest masses different from zero.

The lifetimes of the baryon states that can decay by way of the strong interaction are of the order of magnitude of 10^{-23} sec with natural widths in the range 10 to 200 MeV. The hyperons, or metastable states, that decay by way of the weak interaction have lifetimes of the order of magnitude of 10^{-10} sec, corresponding to widths of about 10^{-5} eV.

15–7 Meson Spectroscopy

The previous section dealt with excited states of the baryon and the de-excitation of those states by the emission of field quanta, pions or kaons. This situation is somewhat analogous to an atomic system where internal-structure changes give rise to excited states, and these excited states can decay to lower states by emission of photons. In the present section, we deal with excited states of the field quanta, pions and kaons. At first sight, this does not seem to have any counterpart in the atomic system; that is, we never talk about excited states of a photon. Weisskopf* has pointed out, however, that we can reestablish the analogy by introducing into the discussion the properties of positronium.

The positronium is a hydrogenlike atom consisting of an electron and a positron instead of an electron and a proton. We have previously mentioned

* V. F. Weisskopf, *Physics Today*, **16,** No. 6, 26 (June 1963).

that when a positron is slowed down in matter, it will eventually pair with one of the electrons within its range, and the two particles will annihilate each other, disposing of their rest energy by the emission of two or three gamma rays. Before annihilation takes place, however, the system exists for a short while as a positronium atom, which may be formed in an excited (hydrogenlike) state and subsequently de-excite itself by the emission of long wavelength light quanta. The ground-state configuration can be either $^1S_0$ or $^3S_1$, both with negative parity, since a fermion has intrinsic parity opposite to its antiparticle. The annihilation process is different for the two states because of the operation of selection rules. The singlet state decays with a mean lifetime of 8×10^{-9} sec into two quanta, each of energy m_0c^2. The triplet state decays with a mean lifetime of 7×10^{-6} sec into three quanta, with a total energy of $2m_0c^2$.*

Since the positronium is unstable, the wave function for the ground state is not a pure particle-particle function but contains a component that describes it as a pure field (the electromagnetic field after annihilation). Weisskopf writes this in the following way:

$$\text{Positronium} = a(e^+ + e^-) + b(\text{field}). \tag{15–11}$$

In this equation b is very much smaller than a, since the annihilation radius is very small compared to the Bohr radius, so that the two particles, in general, perform many rotations about each other before annihilation. Since the positronium has definite states, the field *communicating* with it has the same definite states.

We now return to the strong interaction between baryons and the associated field quanta, pions and kaons. The analog to the positronium is the nucleonium, which is formed by a nucleon and an antinucleon. This quantum-mechanical system can exist for a very short time before it annihilates, emitting meson field quanta (Fig. 15–6). For the nucleonium, the annihilation radius is of the order of magnitude of the nuclear "Bohr radius," so that if we write an equation similar to Eq. (15–11) for the nucleonium, the two constants a and b will be of the same order of magnitude. This strong mixture of field states into the two-particle states makes it more difficult to compute the level scheme for nucleonium. However, some qualitative understanding of the observed levels seems to be emerging.

Figure 15–12 shows the well-established meson states,† again plotted vs. hypercharge and isospin. The mesons have integer spins (they are bosons), and there is no law requiring that they be created and annihilated in pairs. All

---

* Strictly speaking, the total energy available is less than $2m_0c^2$, since a small part of this energy already has been given up in the emission of long wavelength light quanta when the positronium decayed to the ground state. However, the binding energy of the ground state is only 6.76 eV, which for the present discussion is negligible compared with $2m_0c^2 = 1.022$ MeV.

† Data taken from the paper by Rosenfeld, *et al.*, *loc. cit.*

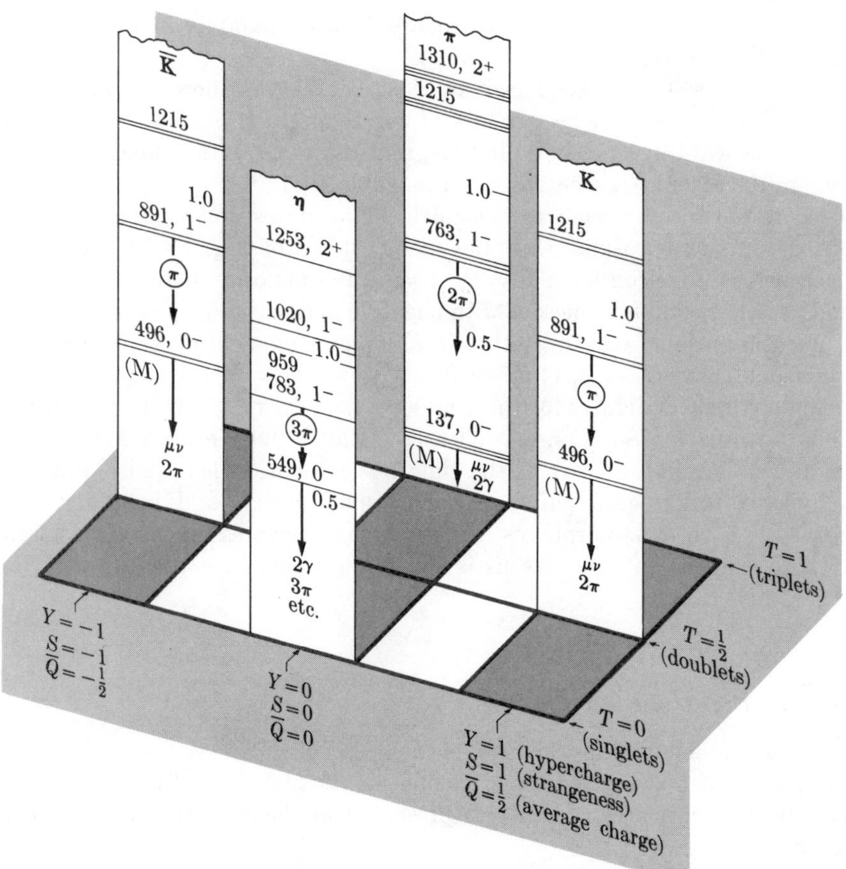

Fig. 15-12. Meson states ($A = 0$) plotted vs. isospin and hypercharge. Only selected decays are indicated, and strong decays are encircled. (Data from Rosenfeld *et al., loc. cit.*)

mesons are unstable, but the lowest members (multiplets) of the four columns are stable against strong decay. For kaons and antikaons, which can decay into two pions without violating any of the common conservation laws, hypercharge conservation dictates weak decay. In the case of η (549), the reason why it cannot strong-decay is more subtle. It turns out that this will violate G-parity, the new quantum number for mesons that was mentioned earlier.

In Fig. 15-12, both states and antistates are shown. In Fig. 15-11, only states with $A = 1$ are shown, and the antistates have $A = -1$. For the mesons, both states and antistates have $A = 0$, and this has some peculiar consequences. First, all singlets, that is, all states in the η column are their own antiparticles. The same applies for the neutral numbers of the states in the π column. The π^+ and the π^-, however, form a particle-antiparticle pair.

They therefore have identical mass but are drawn separately in Fig. 15–12 to show that the π-states are triplets.

For the kaons, the consequences of $A = 0$ are even more peculiar. The K^0 and $\overline{K}^0$ are not observed separately. Instead, mixtures of state and antistate are seen, one with a very short lifetime, and the other with a longer lifetime. These are the K_1 and K_2 mesons listed in Table 15–1.

We now must come back to the nucleonium states and compare possible resulting spins and isospins with the meson states of Fig. 15–12. Since the nucleon and antinucleon have $T = \frac{1}{2}$, $J = \frac{1}{2}$ and opposite intrinsic parity, we should be able to find four mesons with negative parity that can part of the time be a nucleon-antinucleon pair with orbital angular momentum zero (S-states). These should have $T = 0, 1$; $J^\pi = 0^-, 1^-$; and $Y = 0$. In Fig. 15–12 we immediately find candidates for these mesons, namely π (137, 0^-), π (763, 1^-), η (549, 0^-), and η (783, 1^-), as well as η (1020, 1^-). We must assume that these mesons are indeed part of the time nucleon-antinucleon pairs, probably also hyperon-antihyperon pairs, whenever spin, parity, and isospin can be conserved in such metamorphoses. Another way of expressing this Dr. Jekyll–Mr. Hyde existence of the mesons is to say that they *communicate* with, for instance, a N–$\overline{\text{N}}$ pair.

15–8 The Eightfold Way

Theoretical understanding of the elementary particles is increasing very rapidly, and what is written about it one month may be outdated the next. Hopefully, the simple considerations presented in the following will prove to have some lasting value.

Some light was thrown on the structure of baryons and mesons from a theory developed by the Italian physicist Regge. He predicted that a given baryon or meson state (an *occurrence*) should have companions (*recurrences*) at higher energies with spins increased by 2, 4, 6 units, etc. This is somewhat similar to the rotational bands encountered among nuclear energy levels. Three such Regge recurrences are shown in Fig. 15–11. They are Δ(1924, $7/2^+$), N(1688, $5/2^+$), and Λ(1815, 5/2). The corresponding Regge occurrences are the lowest states in the Δ, N, and Λ columns.

Undoubtedly, the most important contribution made in recent years to the understanding of the particles came from M. Gell-Mann and, independently, from Y. Ne'eman, when they introduced the *eightfold way*.* The mathematical basis for the eightfold way is group theory of a kind called SU(3). This stands for "special unitary group for arrays of size 3×3," with a special condition that reduces the number of components from nine to eight.

---

* The early literature on this subject is compiled in M. Gell-Mann and Y. Ne'eman, *The Eightfold Way*, New York: W. A. Benjamin, Inc., 1964.

The SU(3) theory is a generalization of the theory of isospin which is treated with the Pauli spin matrices. In group-theoretical language, isospin can be classified as an SU(2) theory, dealing with three dimensions (the three components of isospins), while SU(3) deals with eight dimensions which can be chosen to be the three dimensions of isospin, hypercharge, and four new "spin" dimensions or operators.

The isospin formalism is based on charge independence of nuclear forces, and the splitting of an isospin multiplet into $2T + 1$ states is caused by the isospin-violating electromagnetic interaction. Correspondingly, in SU(3) theory, *supermultiplets* of baryons or mesons can be formed containing 1, 8, 10, or 27 states, all with the same spin and parity. These supermultiplets are assemblies of isospin multiplets; for instance, the decuplet (ten states) contains a singlet, a doublet, a triplet, and a quadruplet, all with different hypercharge. In the pure SU(3) formalism, all ten states should have the same energy. Turning on the electromagnetic interaction causes the splitting within the individual isospin multiplets, and turning on some other kind of interaction (part of the strong interaction?) causes a splitting between the various multiplets.

Now let us look at some examples. As mentioned above, the theory allows for singlets, octets, and decuplets (ten members), and a supermultiplet with 27 members. The singlets are trivial and provide no test for the theory. Two of the octet states are mixed, and this complicates the discussion slightly. We shall therefore look at a decuplet first. The only example known at present is a family of $3/2^+$ states with the following members (Fig. 15–11):

$$\Delta(1236),\quad \Sigma(1382),\quad \Xi(1530),\quad \text{and}\quad \Omega(1675).$$

At the time the SU(3) theory was introduced, the Ω-hyperon had not been observed experimentally. Its existence and its properties were predicted by the theorists, and an intense search was started, leading to its discovery by a group of experimenters at Brookhaven National Laboratory. The spin and parity of $\Omega(1675)$ have not yet (1966) been measured, but energy, charge, and hypercharge agree with predictions, so that it would be extremely surprising if the other quantum numbers were found to be in disagreement.

Figure 15–13(a) is a plot of hypercharge vs. isospin projection for the ten individual states formed by the four isospin multiplets mentioned above. The energy given beside each multiplet is the average energy for that multiplet, the internal splitting being relatively small. We see that the energy distance between the multiplets is remarkably constant, about 146 MeV. The SU(3) theory allows for this new splitting roughly in the following way. We rotate the plot in Fig. 15–13(a) through 120° and obtain a diagram as shown in Fig. 15–13(b). Here ordinary charge Q has replaced hypercharge Y as the ordinate, and as abscissa we have a new "spin" component, U_3, which has replaced T_3. We can rotate the diagram by another 120° and call the new abscissa the third component of V-spin. Four operators, U^+, U^-, V^+, and V^-, are indeed the four new spin

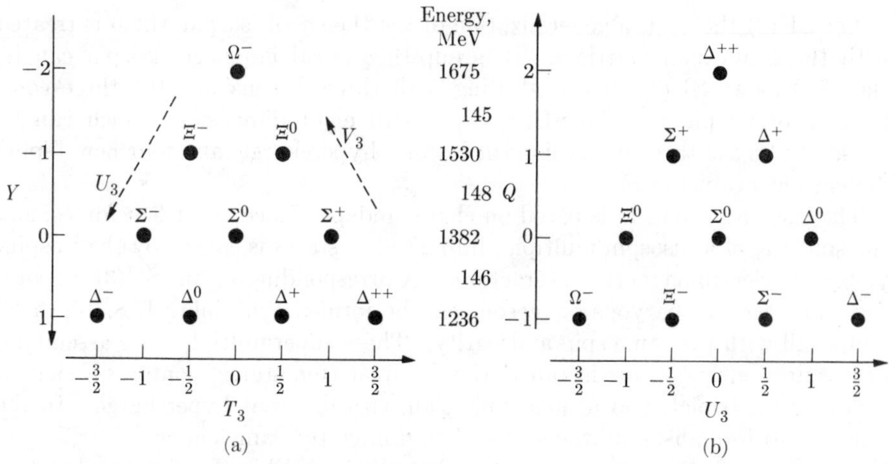

Fig. 15–13. Decuplet of $3/2^+$ baryon states in representations (a) Y vs. T_3; (b) Q vs. U_3. The energy splitting in a U-multiplet is approximately 146 MeV for $\Delta U_3 = \frac{1}{2}$.

dimensions referred to earlier. From Fig. 15–13 we see that charge does not change when U_3 goes up or down by one unit within a U-spin multiplet. The electromagnetic interaction has therefore no effect on the splitting of the states in a U-spin multiplet. Some other interaction or field **M** gives rise to an energy term of the form MU_3, and this causes the splitting.

Figure 15–14(a) shows, as a second example, the members of a baryon octet consisting of the neutron-proton doublet and the Λ-, Σ-, and Ξ-hyperons. In the representation Y vs. T_3, the octet is a hexagon with two particles Λ^0 and Σ^0 in the center. These two particles are isospin eigenstates ($T = 0$ and 1, $T_3 = 0$ for both). In the world of U-spin, they are not eigenstates, but U-spin eigenstates can be found by making two simple linear combinations of the isospin eigenstates* Λ^0 and Σ^0. The correct mixing is shown in Fig. 15–14(b) and corresponds to the following values of the U-spin and the component U_3:

$$Y^0 = \tfrac{1}{2}(-\Sigma^0 + \sqrt{3}\Lambda^0), \qquad \text{for} \quad U = 1, \qquad U_3 = 0; \qquad (15\text{–}12)$$

$$Z^0 = \tfrac{1}{2}(\sqrt{3}\Sigma^0 + \Lambda^0), \qquad \text{for} \quad U = 0, \qquad U_3 = 0. \qquad (15\text{–}13)$$

Equations (15–12) and (15–13) are written in the form of wave functions. We calculate the squares in order to obtain probabilities and find that the "particle" Y^0 is one-quarter Σ^0 and three-quarters Λ^0 (remembering that Σ^0 and Λ^0 are orthogonal). Correspondingly, "particle" Z^0 is three-quarters Σ^0 and one-quarter Λ^0. Now we turn on the energy-splitting interaction that is proportional to U_3. This produces for the $U = 1$ triplet an energy difference

* See, for instance, H. J. Lipkin, "Unitary Symmetry for Pedestrians (U-Spin, I-Spin, V-All Spin for I-Spin)," *Argonne National Laboratory Informal Report* (1963).

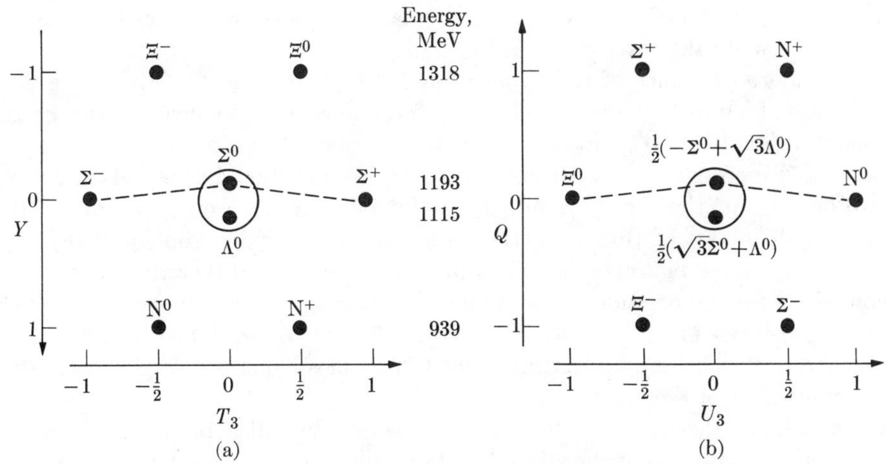

Fig. 15–14. Octet of $1/2^+$ baryon states in representations (a) Y vs. T_3 (b) Q vs. U_3. Since Σ^0 and Λ^0 are not eigenstates of U-spin, the peculiar mixing of states shown in (b) occurs in this representation.

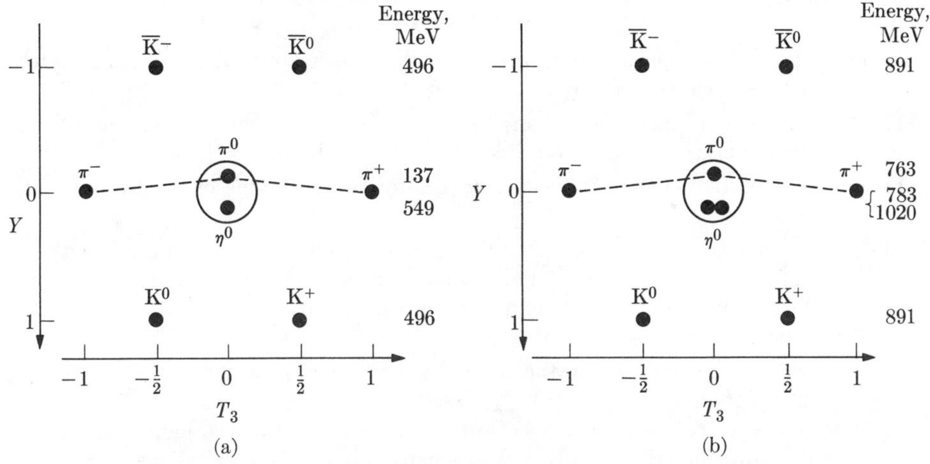

Fig. 15–15. (a) Octet of 0^- meson states; (b) octet plus singlet of 1^- meson states.

between Ξ^0 and Y^0 equal to the difference between Y^0 and n, since ΔU_3, in both cases, is equal to 1. We thereby arrive at the following prediction for the rest masses: $M_Y^0 = (M_N^0 + M_\Xi^0)/2$, or

$$(M_\Sigma^0 + 3M_\Lambda^0)/4 = (M_N^0 + M_\Xi^0)/2. \tag{15–14}$$

Plugging in the known masses for these particles, we find that

$$1134.6 \text{ MeV} \stackrel{?}{=} 1126.9 \text{ MeV}.$$

The discrepancy is 7.7 MeV, which is small compared with the difference in energy between the states of different U_3.

Two more examples of the application of SU(3) to strongly interacting particles are given in Fig. 15–15. The first example covers the lowest states of the pseudoscalar ($J = 0^-$) mesons and the second shows an octet of vector ($J = 1^-$) mesons. The same mass formula (15–14) should apply also to these two octets, but the theory requires that for mesons, we use the *squares* of the masses. The test of this prediction is left as a problem (Problem 15–8).

For the vector mesons (Fig. 15–15b), there are three rather than two states competing for the position in the center of the hexagon. One linear combination of these states must have $U = 1$, $U_3 = 0$, two other linear combinations have $U = 0$. Of the two last-mentioned "particles," one is a singlet, the other is the member of the octet.

The SU(3) algebra predicts not only masses, but also branching ratios in decay and production of the strongly interacting particles. As the accumulation of experimental data increases and the theoretical insight deepens, this theoretical tool may be modified and extended, but probably not replaced.

PROBLEMS

15–1. With reference to Fig. 15–2, prove that the velocity of particle 1 in the center-of-mass system is given by Eq. (15–1).

15–2. Calculate the kinetic energy in the center-of-mass system for a system of two protons, one with $T_{\text{lab}} = 30$ MeV, the other with $T_{\text{lab}} = 4.3$ BeV.

15–3. Calculate the kinetic energies for antiprotons and π-mesons with momenta 1.19 BeV/c.

15–4. Study the sequences of events following the annihilation of a proton with an antiproton. If a supply of antiprotons somehow could be produced cheaply and kept in a container, would it be a convenient source of energy for, say, ship propulsion?

15–5. Calculate the position of the following four points on the boundary of the Dalitz plot in Fig. 15–9: (a) $T_{\pi^+} = 0$ (b) $T_{\pi^-} = 0$ (c) and (d) $T_{\pi^+} = T_{\pi^-}$, with $T_{\pi^+} + T_{\pi^-} =$ min or max, respectively. In (c) the two pions are emitted in the same direction; in (d) they are emitted in opposite directions.

15–6. List some channels open for strong decay of $\Delta^\circ(1925, 7/2^+)$.

15–7. A K^- beam is incident on a target of nucleons. List the two reactions in which Ω^- is produced with a minimum beam energy. Calculate the beam energy needed, assuming that the target nucleon is at rest.

15–8. Apply the mass formula Eq. (15–14) (with the masses squared) to the mesons of Fig. 15–15.

*15–9. Design an experiment to study the lifetime of the Λ-hyperon.

APPENDIX 1 *Brief Review of the Mechanics of Atomic Particles*

A1–1 The mks System of Units

In the rationalized system of mks units, the primary units are kilogram for mass, meter for length, second for time, and coulomb for electric charge. All other units are derived from these primary units. For example, the unit of force is the newton. This is defined through Newton's Second Law as 1 kg-m-sec^{-2}. The unit of energy then becomes 1 kg-m^2-sec^{-2}; this is called 1 joule. The unit of power, the watt, becomes 1 kg-m^2-sec^{-3}. The unit for electrical potential is 1 volt = 1 kg-m^2-sec^{-2}-coul^{-1}. The electrical units, the amp, the volt, and the watt, are thus the ones used in practice. The only exception is the unit for magnetic induction. In the mks-system this is the weber/m^2, which is equal to 10,000 gauss. Some of the important mks units are listed in Table A1–1.

The great advantage of the mks-system over the cgs-system is that the electrical units used are the same as those used in practice. However, this advantage is purchased at the expense of introducing two new constants. One is the *permeability* constant that appears in Ampère's law

$$\oint \mathbf{B} \cdot d\mathbf{l} = \mu_0 i. \tag{A1–1}$$

The permeability of free space is

$$\mu_0 = 4\pi \times 10^{-7} \text{ kg-m-coul}^{-2} \quad \text{(or henry/m)}.$$

The other is the *permittivity constant* that appears in Coulomb's force law

$$F = \frac{1}{4\pi\epsilon_0} \frac{q_1 q_2}{r^2}. \tag{A1–2}$$

The permittivity of free space is

$$\epsilon_0 = 1/c^2\mu_0 = 8.85415 \times 10^{-12} \text{ coul}^2\text{-sec}^2\text{-m}^{-3}\text{-kg}^{-1} \quad \text{(or farad/m)},$$

where c is the velocity of light.

Table A1-1. mks units

Quantity	Unit	Abbreviation	Usual symbol	Dimension	Derivation
Length	Meter	m	l	L	Basic unit
Mass	Kilogram	kg	m	M	Basic unit
Time	Second	sec	t	T	Basic unit
Charge	Coulomb	coul	q	Q	Basic unit
Velocity		m/sec	v	LT^{-1}	$\mathbf{v} = d\mathbf{s}/dt$
Momentum		kgm/sec	p	MLT^{-1}	$\mathbf{p} = m\mathbf{v}$
Force	Newton	N	F	MLT^{-2}	$\mathbf{F} = d\mathbf{p}/dt$
Energy, work	Joule	J	E, V, T, W	ML^2T^{-2}	$\Delta F = W = \int \mathbf{F} \cdot d\mathbf{s}$
Angular velocity		rad/sec	ω	T^{-1}	$\omega = d\theta/dt$
Angular momentum		kgm^2/sec	L	ML^2T^{-1}	$\mathbf{L} = \mathbf{r} \times \mathbf{p}$
Current	Ampere	A	I	QT^{-1}	$I = dq/dt$
Voltage, emf	Volt	V	U or V	$ML^2T^{-2}Q^{-1}$	$U = \Delta E/q$
Resistance	Ohm	Ω	R	$ML^2T^{-1}Q^{-2}$	$R = U/I$
Capacitance	Farad	F	C	$M^{-1}L^{-2}T^2Q^2$	$Q = CU$
Inductance	Henry	H	L	ML^2Q^{-2}	$U = -L dI/dt$
Magnetic flux	Weber	Wb	ϕ	$ML^2T^{-1}Q^{-1}$	$U = -\partial\phi/\partial t$
Magnetic induction	(Tesla)	Wb/m^2	B	$MT^{-1}Q^{-1}$	$\phi = \int \mathbf{B} \cdot d\mathbf{S}$

In nuclear physics, it has become standard practice to use as a secondary unit of length, the fermi (1 fermi $= 10^{-15}$ m). Somewhat inconsistently, the barn (1 barn $= 10^{-28}$ m^2) is used as a secondary unit for cross section. As an alternative unit for mass, the mass unit, u, is used; as an alternative unit for energy, the electron volt is used.

A1–2 Relativistic Particle Dynamics

The laws of classical dynamics do not apply directly to systems in which particles are moving relative to each other or relative to the frame of reference with velocities approaching the velocity of light. All standard texts of modern physics demonstrate how one can retain most of the concepts of classical physics by assuming that the mass of a moving particle increases with its velocity as

$$m = m_0/\sqrt{1 - \beta^2}. \tag{A1-3}$$

Here, m_0 is the rest mass and $\beta = v/c$, the velocity of the particle relative to the observer divided by the velocity of light. Some of the basic laws and formulas of mechanics now are:

(1) Linear momentum is conserved for a system on which no external forces are acting. The linear momentum of a particle is defined as $\mathbf{p} = m\mathbf{v}$, where the mass m is given by Eq. (A1–3).

(2) The angular momentum of a system with respect to a given reference point is conserved when there are no external torques acting on the system. The angular momentum of a particle is defined as $\mathbf{L} = \mathbf{r} \times \mathbf{p}$, where $\mathbf{r}$ is the radius vector from the reference point to the particle.

(3) The total energy of an isolated system is conserved. The total energy of a free particle is $E = mc^2$. The kinetic energy is $T = mc^2 - m_0c^2$. By inserting Eq. (A1–3) we can show that for *low velocities* the kinetic-energy formula becomes $T \approx \frac{1}{2}mv^2$.

(4) The force is defined as $\mathbf{F} = d\mathbf{p}/dt$.

(5) Work is defined as the increase in energy and the familiar work law $\Delta W = \int \mathbf{F} \cdot d\mathbf{s}$ holds.

Equation (A1–3) can be rearranged to

$$(mc^2)^2 = (m_0c^2)^2 + (pc)^2. \tag{A1–4}$$

This equation gives the relation between the total energy, the rest energy, and the momentum. By substituting $mc^2 = m_0c^2 + T$, we obtain the relationship between the kinetic energy and the momentum:

$$p = \sqrt{2m_0T + T^2/c^2}. \tag{A1–5}$$

Except for the last term under the square root, Eq. (A1–5) is identical with the classical formula for momentum. This last term is therefore called the *relativistic correction term.*

As an aid for the memory, Eq. (A1–4) is represented graphically in Fig. A1–1. The figure has no real meaning, but is merely given as a mnemonic device.

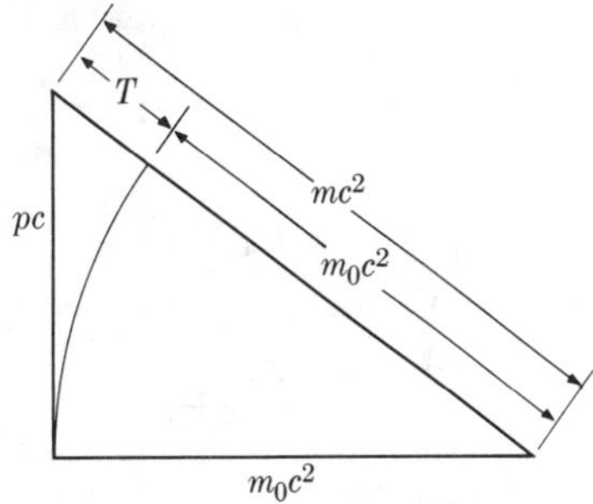

Fig. A1–1. Mnemonic triangle for the relationship $(mc^2)^2 = (m_0c^2)^2 + (pc)^2$.

A1–3 Motion of Charged Particles in Magnetic Fields

A charged particle moving in a static magnetic field will be deflected if the magnetic induction B has a component perpendicular to the direction of the particle. Newton's Second Law applied to this motion gives

$$q\mathbf{v} \times \mathbf{B} = d\mathbf{p}/dt. \tag{A1–6}$$

The component of the velocity, or momentum, parallel to the magnetic induction will remain unchanged. The component of the velocity perpendicular to the magnetic induction will give rise to a centripetal force, and the motion in this plane will be circular. Since the speed of the particle does not change, the mass also remains the same so that

$$\left|\frac{d\mathbf{p}}{dt}\right| = m\left|\frac{d\mathbf{v}}{dt}\right| = m\frac{v^2}{\rho}, \tag{A1-7}$$

just as in classical mechanics (ρ is the radius of curvature of the circle). By substituting Eq. (A1–7) into Eq. (A1–6), we get, when v is perpendicular to B,

$$qvB = m(v^2/\rho). \tag{A1-8}$$

The product $B\rho$ is called the *magnetic rigidity* of the particle. Equation (A1–8) yields for the magnetic rigidity

$$B\rho = p/q. \tag{A1-9}$$

The magnetic rigidity is therefore simply the momentum of the particle divided by its charge.

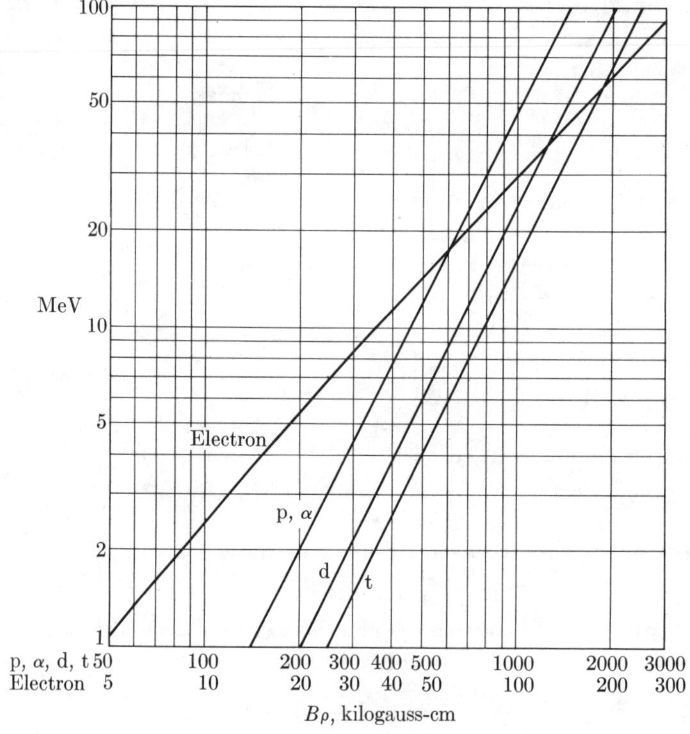

Fig. A1–2. Magnetic rigidity for electrons, alpha particles, protons, deuterons, and tritons.

If the kinetic energy and the rest mass of the particle are given, rather than the momentum, the magnetic rigidity can be found by substituting Eq. (A1–5) into Eq. (A1–9). The resulting formula can be written in the form

$$B\rho = \frac{1}{cz}\sqrt{\frac{2m_0c^2}{e}\frac{T}{e} + \left(\frac{T}{e}\right)^2}. \tag{A1–10}$$

Here z is the number of elementary charges carried by the particle, and e is the elementary charge measured in Coulombs. Since the energy in joules divided by the elementary charge is equal to the energy in electron volts, Eq. (A1–10) can also be written

$$B\rho = \frac{1}{cz}\sqrt{2(m_0c^2)T + T^2}, \tag{A1–10a}$$

where the energies are now inserted in electron volts. The answer is expressed in units of weber/meter. In practice, the magnetic rigidity is measured in kilogauss-centimeters, and the rest energy and kinetic energy are measured in MeV. The final version of the formula then becomes

$$B\rho = \frac{3.334}{z}\sqrt{2(m_0c^2)T + T^2} \text{ kilogauss-cm}, \tag{A1–10b}$$

with m_0c^2 and T measured in MeV. The rest energies of the particles most often encountered in low-energy nuclear physics are given in Table 1–2. The magnetic rigidity is plotted vs. the kinetic energy for the electron, proton, deuteron, triton, and alpha particle in Fig. A1–2.

A1–4 Wave-Particle Duality

The German physicist, Max Planck (1900), in a study of the black-body radiation discovered that harmonic oscillators can only absorb and emit energy in discrete quanta. The energy of a quantum is $E = h\nu$, where h is called Planck's constant. Albert Einstein (1905) carried this important observation a great step further. He was able to explain photoemission of electrons by assuming that the energy in the radiation field is embodied in discrete particles, or quanta, and not continuously distributed through the field as classical electrodynamics suggests. Compton (1923) demonstrated that these quanta (photons) carry a momentum equal to $p = h\nu/c$. This is indeed what one would expect for a particle with zero rest mass traveling with the velocity of light (Eq. A1–4). By 1923, therefore, the particle nature of the photons, the carriers of light, was well established; and yet, nothing had been brought out that disproved the conclusion drawn from a great mass of experiments that light behaves as waves. The fact had to be accepted that light sometimes behaves as particles and sometimes as waves.

DeBroglie (1924), speculating about the symmetry of nature, argued that, since light sometimes behaves like waves and sometimes like particles, then material particles sometimes possibly behave like waves. He postulated that the relationship between energy and frequency and between wavelength and momentum that holds for photons also would hold for material particles. Consequently, with the motion of material particles, there will be associated a frequency

$$\nu = E/h \tag{A1–11}$$

and a wavelength (the deBroglie wavelength)

$$\lambda = h/p. \tag{A1–12}$$

Both these equations have proved to be correct and are used in Schrödinger's nonrelativistic wave mechanics. The energy E in Eq. (A1–11) is the sum of kinetic and potential energy. The rest energy is not included. The wave nature of particles was demonstrated in 1927 by Davisson and Germer by diffraction of low-energy electrons by a nickel crystal.

A1–5 The Uncertainty Principle

Heisenberg's uncertainty principle states that it is inherently impossible to measure simultaneously the exact position and the exact momentum of a particle. This follows directly from the wave properties of the particle, and is closely related to the observation from optics that a high resolving power of a microscope requires a small wavelength (high momentum). If the uncertainty, or indeterminacy, in the position measurement is Δx and the uncertainty in the momentum measurement is Δp, then the following inequality holds:

$$\Delta x \, \Delta p \geq h/2\pi = \hbar. \tag{A1–13}$$

For instance, if one attempts to measure the exact position of an electron by letting the electron hit a scintillating screen and observing the light flash, this act will make the electron scatter from the atoms in the screen, and thereby introduce a great uncertainty in its momentum. Similarly, if one invents an experiment to determine the momentum of a particle with great accuracy, automatically the act of performing the experiment will introduce a great uncertainty in the position. The uncertainty principle applies to any conjugate variables in Hamiltonian mechanics, for example, time and energy. If the observation is carried out over a time Δt, then an energy can be measured only to the accuracy ΔE, related to Δt through the uncertainty relation

$$\Delta t \, \Delta E \geq \hbar. \tag{A1–14}$$

A1–6 Wave Functions

In quantum mechanics all information about physical variables of a particle or a system of particles, such as their positions, momenta, angular momenta, and energies, is contained in the probability amplitude, or wave function. In the following, we will restrict the discussion to a one-body system, but all formulas given can be generalized so as to encompass many-particle systems. The wave function can be expressed in terms of space coordinates and time, or in terms of momentum coordinates and time. In the former notation, the one-particle wave function is written as $\Psi(x, y, z, t)$, or simply Ψ. The probability of finding the particle inside a volume element $dx\,dy\,dz$ around the position (x, y, z) at time t is then given by

$$W\,dx\,dy\,dz = \Psi^*\Psi\,dx\,dy\,dz. \tag{A1–15}$$

The wave function Ψ is in general complex, and the notation Ψ^* is used for the complex conjugate of Ψ. The product of Ψ^* and Ψ is a real quantity equal to the square of the numerical value of Ψ. The probability of finding the particle at a given position within a given volume element is of course proportional to the volume element, as expressed in Eq. (A1–15). The probability per unit volume or the probability density is $W = \Psi^*\Psi$. Since Eq. (A1–15) expresses probability, which is a dimensionless quantity, the dimension of the wave function must be $(\text{length})^{-3/2}$.

The total probability of finding a given particle somewhere within the constraints of a given system (possibly all space) must of course be unity. This is expressed mathematically through the normalizing integral

$$\int \Psi^*\Psi\,d\tau = 1, \tag{A1–16}$$

where $d\tau$ denotes the volume element in whatever coordinate system is used, and the integral is taken over the full range of coordinates over the volume in which the particle is restricted to move.

When the value of a physical quantity P is known as a function of position [e.g., in cartesian coordinates: $P(x, y, z)$], the *average value*, also called *expectation value*, of this quantity can be found as

$$\langle P\rangle = \int P(x, y, z)W\,dx\,dy\,dz = \int \Psi^*P(x, y, z)\Psi\,d\tau. \tag{A1–17}$$

Since W is a function of the time t, the expectation value $\langle P\rangle$ will in general be a function of t. The expectation values of the coordinates $\langle x\rangle$, $\langle y\rangle$, and $\langle z\rangle$ as functions of t can be considered to be a description of a particle's trajectory.

A1–7 Operators

If the wave function, instead of being written in terms of position coordinates, is expressed in terms of momenta as $\phi(p_x, p_y, p_z)$, then $\phi^*\phi$ expresses the probability of finding a given set of momentum components. In further analogy, one can find the expectation value for the momentum of a particle or for any quantity which can be expressed as a function of the momentum through an equation similar to Eq. (A1–17). The momentum wave function ϕ and the position wave function Ψ are related to each other mathematically through a Fourier transformation. As a consequence of this, the expectation value of the momentum, of any function of the momentum, or of any quantity that is a mixed function of position and momentum can be found by replacing all terms of the momentum components with the operator

$$p_x \rightarrow \frac{\hbar}{i}\frac{\partial}{\partial x}; \tag{A1–18}$$

and similar expressions for p_y and p_z. For instance, the expectation value, or average value of p_x, is simply

$$\langle p_x \rangle = \int \Psi^* \left(\frac{\hbar}{i}\frac{\partial}{\partial x}\right) \Psi \, d\tau. \tag{A1–19}$$

As a further example we consider the orbital angular momentum of a particle with respect to the origin of the coordinate system. Classically, this can be expressed as $\mathbf{L} = \mathbf{r} \times \mathbf{p}$ with components

$$L_z = xp_y - yp_x, \quad \text{etc.}$$

The corresponding quantum-mechanical operator, for instance for the z-component of the orbital angular momentum, is

$$L_{z\,\mathrm{op}} = x\left(\frac{\hbar}{i}\frac{\partial}{\partial y}\right) - y\left(\frac{\hbar}{i}\frac{\partial}{\partial x}\right). \tag{A1–20}$$

Another important example is the kinetic energy. In classical nonrelativistic theory, the kinetic energy can be written in terms of the momenta as

$$T = \frac{p^2}{2m} = \frac{p_x^2 + p_y^2 + p_z^2}{2m}.$$

The corresponding quantum-mechanical operator is

$$T_{\mathrm{op}} = -\frac{\hbar^2}{2m}\left(\frac{\partial^2}{\partial x^2} + \frac{\partial^2}{\partial y^2} + \frac{\partial^2}{dz^2}\right). \tag{A1–21}$$

Note that the differential operator is squared and then applied to the wave function as $\partial^2/\partial x^2$, for instance, rather than $(\partial\Psi/\partial x)^2$. The expectation value for kinetic energy can be found by an equation similar to Eq. (A1–19). In general, the expectation value for a physical quantity represented by a quantum-mechanical operator expressed in terms of coordinates and momenta is

$$\langle Q \rangle = \int \Psi^* Q \Psi \, d\tau. \tag{A1–22}$$

Equation (A1–22) is a generalization of Eq. (A1–17).

As a final example of a quantum-mechanical operator, we construct the operator for total energy, the *Hamiltonian:*

$$H = T + V = -\frac{\hbar^2}{2m}\left(\frac{\partial^2}{\partial x^2} + \frac{\partial^2}{\partial y^2} + \frac{\partial^2}{\partial z^2}\right) + V(x, y, z). \qquad \text{(A1–23)}$$

This is formed by adding to the kinetic-energy operator (A1–21) the potential energy expressed as a function of the position of the particle. A shorter way of writing (A1–23) is

$$H = -\frac{\hbar^2}{2m}\nabla^2 + V(\mathbf{r}), \qquad \text{(A1–24)}$$

where the *Laplacian* operator "del square" is defined as

$$\nabla^2 \equiv \frac{\partial^2}{\partial x^2} + \frac{\partial^2}{\partial y^2} + \frac{\partial^2}{\partial z^2}. \qquad \text{(A1–25)}$$

In certain cases, a differential operator operating on the wave function will give as a result a constant times the wave function

$$Q\Psi = q\Psi. \qquad \text{(A1–26)}$$

This equation is called an *eigenvalue equation.* The constant q is called an *eigenvalue,* and Ψ is an eigenfunction for the operator Q. By combining Eqs. (A1–22), (A1–26), and (A1–16), we find that the expectation value for the operator Q is $\langle Q\rangle = q$. The expectation value, therefore, is a constant (independent of time). A closer study, indeed, reveals that the eigenvalue q is not only the average value of a large number of measurements, but also that each individual measurement yields the same value q for this physical quantity. The eigenvalue q is also called a *sharp value.* That a physical quantity possesses a sharp value in a given experimental situation corresponds classically to conservation of this physical quantity.

In general, a given operator Q can by Eq. (A1–26) produce an infinite set of eigenfunctions Ψ_n with corresponding eigenvalues q_n. Depending on the form of Q, the numbers q_n may constitute a discrete or a continuous set of eigenvalues or a combination of both. If it can be shown that two or more solutions of Eq. (A1–26) have the same eigenvalue ($q_n = q_m$, etc.), then the solutions are said to be degenerate.

All operators used in quantum mechanics are Hermitian. This means that the following equality holds:

$$\int \Psi_n^* Q \Psi_k \, d\tau = \int \Psi_k Q^* \Psi_n^* \, d\tau. \qquad \text{(A1–27)}$$

Here, Ψ_n and Ψ_k are two arbitrary functions in space, capable of being normalized.

When two eigenfunctions Ψ_n and Ψ_k are not degenerate ($q_n \neq q_k$), it follows from Eq. (A1–27) that

$$\int \Psi_n^* \Psi_k \, d\tau = 0. \tag{A1–28}$$

This property, which is called *orthogonality* of the eigenfunctions, is extremely important in quantum mechanics. The property is well known from Fourier analysis, and the eigenfunctions of a given operator form a set that can be used for expansion of any arbitrary function in space, exactly as is done with the trigonometric functions in Fourier analysis.

A1–8 The Schrödinger Equation

In the previous discussion, it was assumed that the wave function Ψ is known. In this section, we discuss how the wave function for a single particle can be determined when the potential-energy function $V(\mathbf{r})$ is known.

Erwin Schrödinger found in 1926 that the equation

$$-\frac{\hbar^2}{2m} \nabla^2 \Psi + V\Psi = i\hbar \frac{\partial}{\partial t} \Psi \tag{A1–29}$$

gives as solutions wave functions that correctly describe the behavior of an atomic particle in a potential field $V(\mathbf{r})$. By making use of the abbreviation (A1–24), we can rewrite Schrödinger's equation as

$$H\Psi = i\hbar \frac{\partial}{\partial t} \Psi. \tag{A1–29a}$$

We will restrict the discussion here to cases in which the space-dependent part and the time-dependent part of the wave function can be separated. In this case, the total wave function can be written as

$$\Psi = \psi(\mathbf{r})\eta(t). \tag{A1–30}$$

By inserting this into Eq. (A1–29a), we obtain

$$\eta H \psi = \psi i\hbar \frac{d\eta}{dt}.$$

Division with the total wave function $\Psi = \psi\eta$ yields

$$\frac{1}{\psi} H\psi = \frac{1}{\eta} i\hbar \frac{d\eta}{dt}. \tag{A1–31}$$

Since the left-hand side depends only on the space coordinates and the right-hand side depends only on time, the only way in which (A1–31) can be satisfied for all values of x, y, z, and t is by making both sides equal to the same constant.

If we call this separation constant E, the left-hand side of (A1–31) yields

$$H\psi = E\psi. \tag{A1–32}$$

The right-hand side of (A1–31) yields

$$i\hbar \frac{d\eta}{dt} = E\eta. \tag{A1–33}$$

Equation (A1–32) is called *Schrödinger's time-independent equation.* The solutions of this equation depend on the potential that the particle is moving in, since this is included in the Hamiltonian. Equation (A1–33), on the other hand, can readily be integrated. The result is

$$\eta = e^{-iEt/\hbar}, \tag{A1–34}$$

which is a cyclic function of time with angular frequency

$$\omega = E/\hbar. \tag{A1–35}$$

The expression for η (A1–34) can be multiplied by an arbitrary constant and η will still satisfy Eq. (A1–33). However, in the form in which we have left it, the time-dependent part of the total wave function is numerically equal to unity. If we normalize ψ, the total wave function Ψ will then be automatically normalized.

The separation constant E is equal to the total energy $E = T + V$. This can be seen from Eq. (A1–32), which has the form of an eigenvalue equation with H as the total energy operator and E as its eigenvalue. The separation of Schrödinger's equation is therefore possible only when the total energy is constant. Equation (A1–35) agrees with deBroglie's relationship $\nu = E/h$.

A1–9 Spherical Coordinates and Spherical Harmonic Functions

In very many important problems in quantum mechanics, the potential-energy function possesses a spherical symmetry. Such problems can be much better handled in spherical coordinates than in cartesian coordinates. The relationships between the spherical coordinates r, θ, and ϕ, and the cartesian coordinates x, y, and z can be read directly from Fig. A1–3. They are

$$x = r\sin\theta\cos\phi, \qquad y = r\sin\theta\sin\phi, \qquad z = r\cos\theta. \tag{A1–36}$$

We use these transformation equations to find the Hamiltonian operator (A1–24) in spherical coordinates. Schrödinger's time-independent equation in spherical coordinates then takes the form

$$-\frac{\hbar^2}{2m}\left[\frac{1}{r^2}\frac{\partial}{\partial r}\left(r^2\frac{\partial\psi}{\partial r}\right) + \frac{1}{r^2\sin\theta}\frac{\partial}{\partial\theta}\left(\sin\theta\frac{\partial\psi}{\partial\theta}\right) + \frac{1}{r^2\sin^2\theta}\frac{\partial^2\psi}{\partial\phi^2}\right] + V\psi = E\psi. \tag{A1–37}$$

When the potential energy is spherically symmetric, we can write

$$V = V(r), \qquad \text{(A1–38)}$$

and we will see that Eq. (A1–37) is separable; that is, the angular dependence of the wave function can be found by solving one differential equation, and the radial dependence can be found by solving another. We write the total wave function as a product,

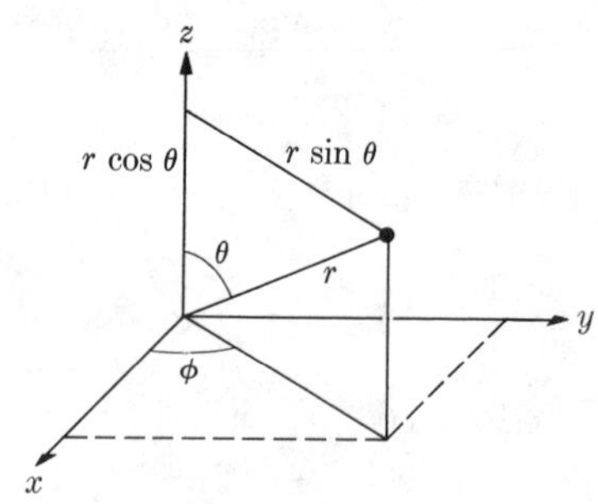

Fig. A1–3. Relationship between cartesian and spherical coordinates.

$$\psi = R(r)Y(\theta, \phi), \qquad \text{(A1–39)}$$

and substitute this into (A1–37). After arranging the terms so that all quantities that are functions of r are on the left-hand side and all functions of θ and ϕ are on the right-hand side, we obtain

$$\frac{1}{R}\frac{d}{dr}\left(r^2\frac{dR}{dr}\right) + \frac{2mr^2}{\hbar^2}(E - V) = -\frac{1}{Y}\left[\frac{1}{\sin\theta}\frac{\partial}{\partial\theta}\left(\sin\theta\frac{\partial Y}{\partial\theta}\right) + \frac{1}{\sin^2\theta}\frac{\partial^2 Y}{\partial\phi^2}\right]. \qquad \text{(A1–40)}$$

The only way in which this equation can be satisfied for all values of r, θ, and ϕ is to make both sides of the equation equal to the same constant, called the separation constant. Concentrating first on the right-hand side, we obtain

$$\frac{1}{\sin\theta}\frac{\partial}{\partial\theta}\left(\sin\theta\frac{\partial Y}{\partial\theta}\right) + \frac{1}{\sin^2\theta}\frac{\partial^2 Y}{\partial\phi^2} = -CY, \qquad \text{(A1–41)}$$

where C is the separation constant. We note that Eq. (A1–41) does not contain the total potential energy. It is therefore completely general. In other words, if we solve it once, we have solved it for all cases where V does not depend on θ or ϕ. Several solutions of (A1–41) exist that satisfy the general requirements of a wave function; namely, finiteness, single-valuedness, and continuity of the function itself as well as of its first derivative. These solutions are called *spherical harmonic functions* and are denoted by $Y_{l,m}(\theta, \phi)$. To each solution is associated a value of the constant C. A general expression for C is

$$C = l(l + 1), \qquad \text{(A1–42)}$$

where $l = 0, 1, 2, 3 \ldots$ For each possible value of C, there are $2l + 1$ solutions. The first few solutions are:

For $l = 0$ $(C = 0)$:

$$Y_{0,0} = 1/\sqrt{4\pi}.$$

For $l = 1$ $(C = 2)$:

$$Y_{1,1} = \sqrt{3/8\pi}\sin\theta e^{i\phi},$$
$$Y_{1,0} = \sqrt{3/4\pi}\cos\theta,$$
$$Y_{1,-1} = \sqrt{3/8\pi}\sin\theta e^{-i\phi}.$$

The second index, m, runs in integers from $-l$ to $+l$. The functions $Y_{l,m}(\theta, \phi)$ are already normalized; that is, the angular part of the normalizing integral (A1–16) has already been performed.

With the separation constant $C = l(l+1)$ inserted, the left-hand side of (A1–40) becomes

$$\frac{1}{R}\frac{d}{dr}\left(r^2\frac{dR}{dr}\right) + \frac{2mr^2}{\hbar^2}(E - V) = l(l+1). \tag{A1–43}$$

Instead of the variable R, it is convenient to introduce another dependent variable u, defined by

$$R(r) = u(r)/r. \tag{A1–44}$$

When this is substituted into (A1–43), we obtain

$$\frac{d^2u}{dr^2} + \frac{2m}{\hbar^2}\left(E - V - \frac{l(l+1)\hbar^2}{2mr^2}\right)u = 0. \tag{A1–45}$$

This is called the *radial wave equation*. It is identical with the wave equation written in cartesian coordinates in one dimension, except for the last term inside the parentheses. As will be shown in the next section, this term is equivalent to a centrifugal potential; that is, a potential whose first derivative with respect to r gives the centrifugal force.

Since the spherical harmonic functions are normalized over the angular coordinates and the time-dependent part of the wave function has a numerical value of unity, the normalizing integral (A1–16) yields

$$\int_0^\infty R^2(r)r^2\,dr = \int_0^\infty u^2(r)\,dr = 1. \tag{A1–46}$$

The factor r^2 in the first integral arises from the form of the volume element in spherical coordinates $d\tau = r^2\sin\theta\,dr\,d\theta\,d\phi$.

A1–10 Parity and Orbital Angular Momentum

A wave function has positive (or even) parity π if it does not change sign by reflection through the origin

$$\psi(-\mathbf{r}) = \psi(\mathbf{r}) \quad \text{positive parity;} \tag{A1–47}$$

and negative (or odd) parity π if it does change sign

$$\psi(-\mathbf{r}) = -\psi(\mathbf{r}) \quad \text{negative parity.} \tag{A1–48}$$

When ψ is written in terms of r, θ, and ϕ, one can check whether it has positive or negative parity by replacing θ and ϕ with $(\pi - \theta)$ and $(\pi + \phi)$, respectively. The coordinate r, which in spherical coordinates only measures the distance to the point from the origin, does not change. In other words, in spherical coordinates, the parity of a wave function is determined only by the angular part of the function. When this is a spherical harmonic function, it turns out that the value of l uniquely determines the parity as

$$\pi = (-1)^l. \tag{A1–49}$$

Parity is also discussed in Sections 1–6 and 11–8.

In 1913 Niels Bohr made the important discovery that orbital angular momentum is quantized in atomic systems. In the new quantum mechanics of both Schrödinger and Heisenberg, this fact can be derived from the wave formalism without any extra postulates. To demonstrate this, we can derive the operators for the various components of the orbital angular momentum in terms of spherical coordinates. The operator for the z-component of the orbital angular momentum is given by Eq. (A1–21), and corresponding expressions exist for the y- and x-components. Transfer to spherical coordinates is made by aid of Eqs. (A1–36). The results are, for the square of the total orbital angular momentum:

$$L^2_{\text{op}} = L^2_{x\ \text{op}} + L^2_{y\ \text{op}} + L^2_{z\ \text{op}} = -\hbar^2\left[\frac{1}{\sin\theta}\frac{\partial}{\partial\theta}\left(\sin\theta\frac{\partial}{\partial\theta}\right) + \frac{1}{\sin^2\theta}\frac{\partial^2}{\partial\phi^2}\right], \tag{A1–50}$$

and for the z-component of the orbital angular momentum:

$$L_{z\ \text{op}} = \frac{\hbar}{i}\frac{\partial}{\partial\phi}. \tag{A1–51}$$

Since neither expression depends on r, the orbital angular momentum is obviously determined by the angular part of the wave function. By comparing Eqs. (A1–41) and (A1–50) and by making use of (A1–42), we obtain

$$L^2_{\text{op}}Y = l(l+1)\hbar^2 Y, \tag{A1–52}$$

where Y is any acceptable solution of Eq. (A1–41); that is, any of the spherical harmonics. Equation (A1–52) is an eigenvalue equation, and it shows that the eigenvalue for the square of the orbital angular momentum is equal to $l(l+1)\hbar^2$. The first index l in the subscript for a spherical harmonic $Y_{l,m}(\theta, \phi)$, therefore, immediately reveals what the orbital angular momentum is for the particle described by that function. The subscript l is therefore called the *orbital angular-momentum quantum number*.

The ϕ-dependence of the spherical harmonic function is always of the form $e^{im\phi}$. Therefore, if we apply the operator $L_{z\,\text{op}}$ (Eq. A1–51) to a spherical harmonic function, the result is

$$L_{z\,\text{op}} Y_{l,m}(\theta, \phi) = \hbar m Y_{l,m}(\theta, \phi). \tag{A1–53}$$

This shows that also the z-component of the orbital angular momentum is quantized and equal to $m\hbar$ when the angular part of the wave function is a spherical harmonic. The integer m is called the quantum number for the z-component of orbital angular momentum, or the *magnetic quantum number*.

It is clear from the discussion above that a choice of spherical harmonic uniquely determines the particle's orbital angular momentum, as well as the z-component. The z-direction here means any direction in which the angular-momentum component can be observed; for instance, the direction of a magnetic field.

A1–11 The Two-Body Problem in Wave Mechanics

Schrödinger's equation for a single-particle (A1–28) contains on the left-hand side the Hamiltonian operator, or operator for total energy. The logical extension of this theory, when several particles are involved, is to form the operator for the total energy of all particles. This Hamiltonian will be a function of the coordinates and momenta of all particles and will have to operate on a wave function that contains the coordinates of all particles. The probability of finding particle 1 in position x_1, y_1, z_1 within the volume element $d\tau_1 = dx_1\,dy_1\,dz_1$ and particle 2 at position x_2, y_2, z_2 within the volume element $d\tau_2 = dx_2\,dy_2\,dz_2$ is $\psi^*\psi\,d\tau_1\,d\tau_2$.

For the particular case of two particles interacting with each other through a potential energy that depends upon the distance r between the particles, the time-independent Schrödinger equation takes the form

$$\left(-\frac{\hbar^2}{2m_1}\nabla_1^2 - \frac{\hbar^2}{2m_2}\nabla_2^2\right)\psi + V(r_{12})\psi = E\psi. \tag{A1–54}$$

In this equation ∇_1^2 depends upon the coordinates x_1, y_1, and z_1, and ∇_2^2 depends upon the coordinates x_2, y_2, and z_2. It can easily be shown that Eq. (A1–54) can be separated into two equations if one introduces the center-of-mass coordinates and relative coordinates given by

$$\frac{\mathbf{r}_1 + \mathbf{r}_2}{2} = \mathbf{R}, \tag{A1–55}$$

$$\mathbf{r}_1 - \mathbf{r}_2 = \mathbf{r}_{12}. \tag{A1–56}$$

The total wave function is again written as a product:

$$\psi = \psi_{\text{CM}}\psi_{\text{rel}}. \tag{A1–57}$$

Substitution into Eq. (A1–54) yields

$$-\frac{\hbar^2}{2M}\nabla^2_{\text{CM}}\psi_{\text{CM}} = E_{\text{CM}}\psi_{\text{CM}} \tag{A1–58}$$

and

$$-\frac{\hbar^2}{2m}\nabla^2_{12}\psi_{\text{rel}} + V(r_{12})\psi_{\text{rel}} = E_{\text{rel}}\psi_{\text{rel}} \tag{A1–59}$$

Here M is the sum of the two masses $m_1 + m_2$, and m is the so-called *reduced mass*, equal to

$$m = \frac{m_1 m_2}{m_1 + m_2}. \tag{A1–60}$$

The total energy is the sum of the energy of center-of-mass motion and the energy of the relative motion, exactly as in classical mechanics:

$$E = E_{\text{CM}} + E_{\text{rel}}. \tag{A1–61}$$

Equation (A1–58) gives as a solution a plane-wave motion

$$\psi_{\text{CM}} = \text{const } e^{i(k_x X + k_y Y + k_z Z)} = \text{const } e^{i\mathbf{k}\cdot\mathbf{R}}, \tag{A1–62}$$

where the square of the wave number k is given by

$$k^2\hbar^2 = 2ME_{\text{CM}}. \tag{A1–63}$$

Schrödinger's equation for the relative motion (A1–59) contains only as independent variables the components of the relative vector $\mathbf{r}_{12}$. We see therefore that this separation and the introduction of a reduced mass m have reduced the Schrödinger equation (A1–54) from a two-particle equation to an equivalent one-particle equation (A1–59).

APPENDIX 2 Ion-Beam Focusing and Dispersion in Electric and Magnetic Fields

We will here derive the equations governing the focusing of charged particles in the electric and magnetic fields of the mass spectrometers and of other spectrometers for charged particles mentioned in Chapters 10, 11, and 13. The equations governing magnetic focusing are also referred to in the discussion of particle accelerators, particularly the betatron (Chapter 14).

A2–1 Equations of Motion

(*a*) *Magnetic field.* We shall first study the motion of a charged particle in a magnetic field, as shown in Fig. A2–1. The magnet is symmetric about a *median plane*, and the induction on the circular *central orbit* of radius r_0 in this median plane is B_0. A particle of charge q moving on the central orbit has momentum

$$p_0 = mv_0 = qB_0r_0. \tag{A2–1}$$

The angular velocity is $\omega = v_0/r_0 = qB_0/m$, the cyclotron frequency. We consider only small deviations from the central orbit. Specifically, we assume

$$y \equiv r - r_0 \ll r_0, \qquad z \ll r_0, \qquad \delta \equiv \frac{p - p_0}{p_0} < 1.$$

The z-direction is the third coordinate in the right-hand curvilinear system (s, y, z) and is therefore directed out of the plane of the paper in Fig. A2–1(a). We assume further that the field in the median plane varies with the radius r in accordance with the formula

$$B_z = B_0\left(\frac{r}{r_0}\right)^{-n}, \tag{A2–2}$$

where n is regarded as a constant. For a homogeneous field, the exponent is $n = 0$. On the median plane there is no other field component, but off the median plane there will be a radial component when $n \neq 0$ (see Fig. A2–1b).

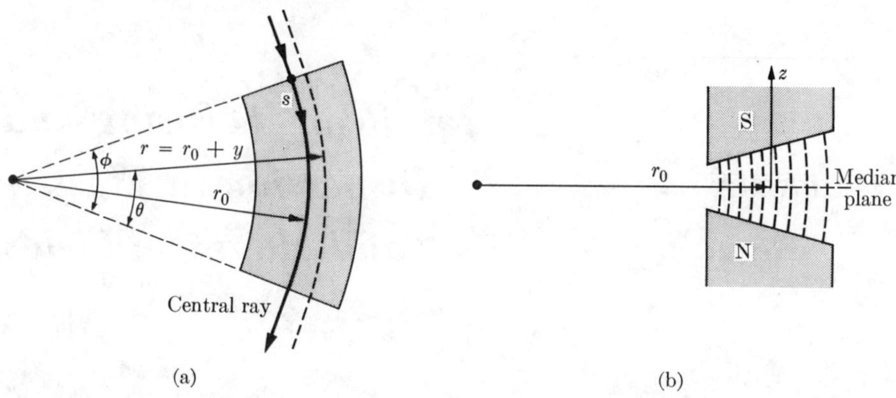

Fig. A2–1. Top view (a) and cross section (b) of a sector magnet of a type used to deflect and focus ion beams. The cross-sectional view also applies to the pole shapes of certain circular accelerators.

In general, we can express this component by a Taylor expansion

$$B_r = B_{r,0} + \frac{z}{1!}\frac{\partial B_r}{\partial z} + \frac{z^2}{2!}\frac{\partial^2 B_r}{\partial z^2} + \frac{z^3}{3!}\frac{\partial^3 B_r}{\partial z^2} + \cdots \tag{A2–3}$$

Since the field is symmetric about the median plane, all even-order derivatives will vanish such that only the first- and third-order terms, etc., are left in Eq. (A2–3). For small deviations we neglect all terms higher than first order, and we then get

$$B_r = z\frac{\partial B_r}{\partial z} = z\frac{\partial B_z}{\partial r} = -znB_0\left(\frac{r}{r_0}\right)^{-n-1}.$$

We have here made use of the fact that curl $\mathbf{B} = 0$. For $y/r_0 \ll 1$, we can write $r \approx r_0$, which leads to

$$B_r = -nB_0 z. \tag{A2–4}$$

To first order there is no coupling between the motion of the particle in the r-direction and the z-direction. We can therefore consider the equations of motion in these two directions separately. We start with the motion in the $r\theta$ plane and write Newton's Second Law as

$$\frac{d}{dt}(m\dot{r}) = mr\dot{\theta}^2 + qr\dot{\theta}B_z, \tag{A2–5}$$

$$\frac{d}{dt}(mr^2\dot{\theta}) = -qr\dot{r}B_z. \tag{A2–6}$$

where the dots indicate derivatives with respect to time.

We recall that m is constant for motion through static magnetic fields (and can also be regarded constant for "quasistatic" fields of circular accelerators). By inserting B_z from Eq. (A2–2) and substituting the cyclotron frequency

$\omega = qB_0/m$, we can rewrite Eqs. (A2–5) and (A2–6) as

$$\ddot{r} = r\dot{\theta}^2 + \omega\dot{\theta}r_0^n r^{1-n}, \tag{A2–7}$$

$$\frac{d}{dt}(r^2\dot{\theta}) = -\omega r_0^n r^{1-n}\dot{r}. \tag{A2–8}$$

Equation (A2–8) can be integrated directly, and by making use of the fact that $\dot{\theta} = -\omega$ for $r = r_0$, we get to first order in y/r_0:

$$\dot{\theta} = -\omega(1 - y/r_0). \tag{A2–9}$$

By inserting this into Eq. (A2–7), we get, again to first order in y/r_0,

$$\ddot{y} + (1 - n)\omega^2 y = 0. \tag{A2–10}$$

When $n > 1$, the solution of Eq. (A2–10) can be written as

$$y = y_0 \sin(\Omega_M t + \alpha_M), \tag{A2–11}$$

where the angular frequency Ω_M for median-plane focusing is given by

$$\Omega_M = \omega\sqrt{1 - n}, \tag{A2–12}$$

and α_M is a phase angle determined by initial conditions (injection position and angle).

This shows that, when $n < 1$, the particle executes harmonic motions in the r-direction about the equilibrium orbit. The resulting force in the $r\theta$ plane is therefore a restoring force, relative to the central orbit.

We can rewrite (A2–11) by introducing instead of the time t the path length s along the central orbit. This is $s = r_0\omega t$, which, together with (A2–11) and (A2–12), leads to

$$y = y_0 \sin(k_M s + \alpha_M), \tag{A2–13}$$

where the wave number for median-plane focusing is

$$k_M = \sqrt{1 - n}/r_0. \tag{A2–14}$$

For motion off the median plane, we consider again only small deviations from the central orbit (z small, $\dot{\theta} \approx -\omega$, and $r \approx r_0$). The equation of motion in the z-direction is

$$\frac{d}{dt}(m\dot{z}) = q\dot{\theta}rB_r, \tag{A2–15}$$

which, with Eq. (A2–4), yields

$$\ddot{z} + \omega^2 nz = 0. \tag{A2–16}$$

For positive field exponents n, the solution of Eq. (A2–16) can be written as

$$z = z_0 \sin(\Omega_T t + \alpha_T), \tag{A2–17}$$

where the angular frequency Ω_T for transverse focusing is given by

$$\Omega_T = \omega\sqrt{n}. \tag{A2–18}$$

The corresponding wave number is $k_T = \sqrt{n}/r_0$.

(*b*) *Electric field.* Figure A2–2 shows an electric cylinder capacitor such as is used for deflecting and dispersing ion beams, for instance, in mass spectrometers. The radial electric field is given by

$$E_r = -K/r, \tag{A2–19}$$

where K is a constant. We shall consider the motion of a *nonrelativistic* ion through this field. Since the force acting on the ion by the electric field is radial, there is no focusing action of the deflector in the axial direction (z-direction). An ion that initially has a z-direction velocity will continue to have this velocity during the motion through the deflector. In the following, we therefore ignore this part of the motion and the kinetic energy associated with it.

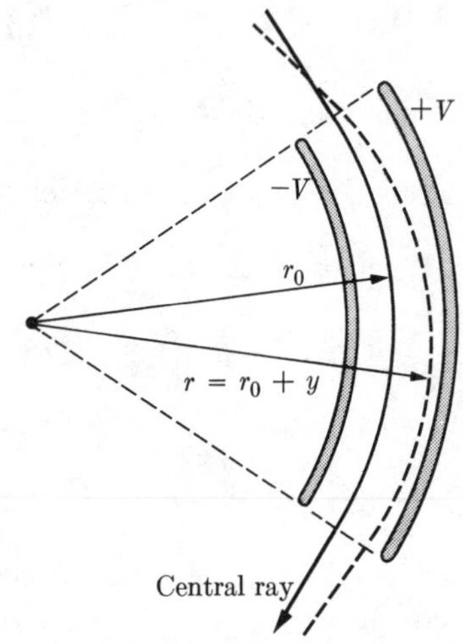

Fig. A2–2. Electrostatic deflector for ion beams.

The equations of motion in the $r\theta$ plane for a particle of charge q and mass m can be written as

$$m\ddot{r} = mr\dot{\theta}^2 - qK/r, \tag{A2–20}$$

$$mr^2\dot{\theta} = p_\theta, \tag{A2–21}$$

where p_θ is a constant of the motion. Substituting Eq. (A2–21) into Eq. (A2–20), we obtain

$$\ddot{r} - \frac{p_\theta^2}{m^2r^3} + \frac{qK}{mr} = 0. \tag{A2–22}$$

Again we introduce $y = r - r_0$ and assume that $y/r_0 \ll 1$. To first order in y/r_0, Eq. (A2–22) can be written as

$$\ddot{y} - \frac{p_\theta^2}{m^2r_0^3}\left(1 - 3\frac{y}{r_0}\right) + \frac{qK}{mr_0}\left(1 - \frac{y}{r_0}\right) = 0. \tag{A2–23}$$

We now assume that the field strength is adjusted so that

$$qK = p_\theta^2/mr_0^2. \tag{A2-24}$$

This condition ensures that a particle which initially moves on the center line will continue to move on the center line, since then in Eq. (A2-23) the acceleration is $\ddot{y} = 0$ if $y = 0$. Equation (A2-23) now becomes

$$\ddot{y} + 2\omega^2 y = 0, \tag{A2-25}$$

where we have again introduced the angular frequency on the central orbit $\omega = p_\theta/mr_0^2 = v_0/r_0$.

The solution of Eq. (A2-25) can be written in the form (A2-11) or (A2-13), in which $\Omega_M = \sqrt{2}\omega$ and $k_M = \sqrt{2}/r_0$ for the electrostatic deflector.

In the electrostatic deflector, the kinetic energy is not a constant of the motion, since the particle moves in an electrostatic scalar potential.

A2-2 Sector Fields

Figure A2-3 shows the orbit of a charged particle through a sector magnet or electrostatic deflector with central radius r_0 and deflection angle ϕ. The center line is folded out to a straight line. The motion inside the field is given by Eq. (A2-13), with α_M determined from the boundary condition at the origin

$$y = l\frac{dy}{ds} \qquad \text{at } s = 0.$$

This gives

$$\tan \alpha_M = k_M l. \tag{A2-26}$$

At the exit boundary, we require similarly that

$$y = -l'\frac{dy}{ds} \qquad \text{at } s = r_0\phi,$$

which leads to

$$\tan (k_M r_0 \phi + \alpha_M) = -k_M l'. \tag{A2-27}$$

By use of some trigonometry and algebraic rearrangement, we obtain from Eqs. (A2-26) and (A2-27):

$$\frac{1}{l+h} + \frac{1}{l'+h} = \frac{1}{f}, \tag{A2-28}$$

with

$$h = \frac{\tan (k_M r_0 \phi/2)}{k_M} \tag{A2-29}$$

and

$$f = \frac{1}{k_M \sin k_M r_0 \phi}. \tag{A2-30}$$

For the magnetic sector we have $k_M = \sqrt{n - 1}/r_0$, and for the electrostatic deflector, $k_M = \sqrt{2}/r_0$.

Equation (A2–28) shows that the magnetic sector and the electrostatic deflector act as lenses with principal planes located a distance h from the ends and with focal length f. Figure A2–3 shows only a single ray drawn from a point object to a point image. Other rays originating from the object point will also pass approximately through the same image point; approximately, because our deviation is valid for small displacements from the central ray only.

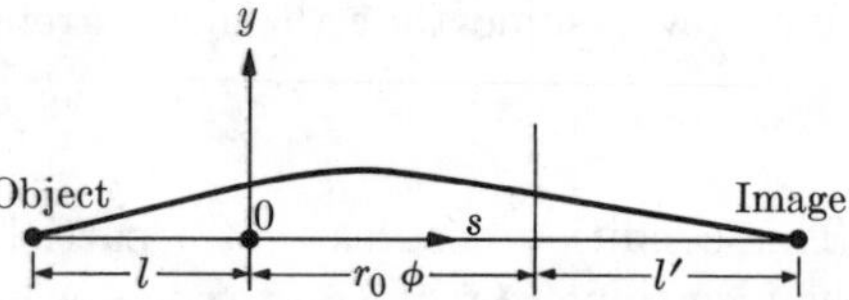

Fig. A2–3. Focusing action of a magnetic or electrostatic deflector. The central ray is folded out to a straight line.

As for any optical system, a finite-size object will produce a finite-size image, with a magnification given by

$$M = \frac{l' + h}{l + h}. \tag{A2–31}$$

As mentioned earlier, the electrostatic deflector has no focusing action in the z-direction. For the magnetic sector with $n \neq 0$, there is a transverse focusing action, and the theory of this section applies also to this. In all equations, k_M is then replaced by $k_T = \sqrt{n}/r_0$. For $n = \frac{1}{2}$, transverse focusing is identical with median-plane focusing. A point object forms a point image, rather than a line image. The magnet is then said to be *stigmatic*.

In the calculations made above on the sector magnet, we have assumed that the central ray enters and exits normal to the field boundary. If this is not the case, significant changes in the focusing properties result. Specifically, transverse focusing can also be attained with homogeneous-field magnets* ($n = 0$).

A2–3 Dispersion

In the previous discussion, we have considered only deflection and focusing of monoenergetic particles, i.e., particles that, outside the deflector, have the same energy. In the case of the electrostatic deflector, the kinetic energy is not a constant of the motion while the particle is in the field, but it emerges with the original kinetic energy. We have further assumed in the previous discussion that the magnetic or electric field strength is adjusted so that on a circle with radius $r = r_0$, the applied field balances the centrifugal force.

A higher-energy particle injected along the central orbit will, of course, not stay on this orbit, but will drift outward and emerge at a radius $r > r_0$ and

---

* See, for instance, S. Penner, *Rev. Sci. Instr.* **32,** 150 (1961) or H. A. Enge, "Deflecting Magnets" in *Focusing of Ion Beams*, ed. by A. Septier. New York: Academic Press, in press.

with a slope $dy/ds > 0$. It is the objective of this section to calculate the displacement (dispersion) of such a ray at the image location.

We determine first the radius of the equilibrium orbit for the higher energy particle. In the case of the sector magnet, we have $p = qBr = qB_0r_0^n r^{1-n}$, which, by differentiation, gives

$$\frac{\Delta p}{p} = (1 - n)\frac{\Delta r}{r} \cdot \qquad \text{(A2–32)}$$

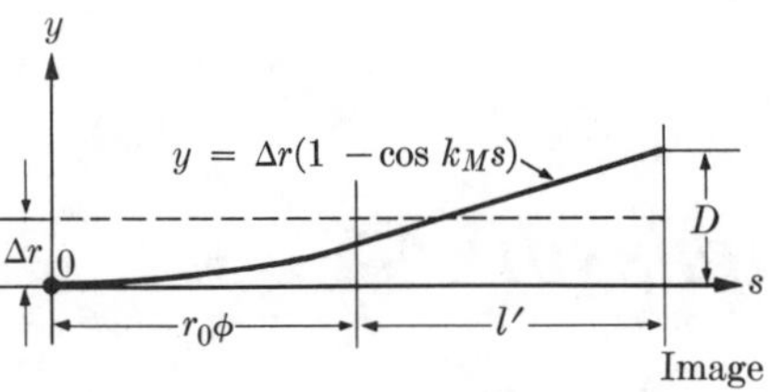

Fig. A2–4. Aid for calculating the dispersion of particles initially moving along the central ray.

In the case of the electrostatic deflector, kinetic energy is not conserved. We therefore have to be a little more careful while differentiating. For a particle injected on the central orbit with kinetic energy T_1, the kinetic energy at radius r is to first order in $\Delta r/r$:

$$T = T_1 - \frac{qK}{r_0}\Delta r. \qquad \text{(A2–33)}$$

The second term on the right-hand side represents the work done on the particle when it is displaced a radial distance Δr. On the equilibrium orbit, the centrifugal force equals the electrostatic force;

$$\frac{mv^2}{r} = \frac{qK}{r} \cdot$$

This shows that, for a given value of qK, the kinetic energy of any ray on its own equilibrium orbit is a constant: $T = \frac{1}{2}mv^2 = \frac{1}{2}qK$. The displacement Δr of the equilibrium orbit can therefore be found directly from Eq. (A2–33) by setting

$$\Delta T = \frac{qK}{r_0}\Delta r = \frac{2T}{r_0}\Delta r. \qquad \text{(A2–34)}$$

The particles with higher injection energy will execute harmonic motion about this new equilibrium orbit. For small values of Δp and ΔT, we need not consider any change in wavelength (or of k_M), since this will give rise to effects of second or higher order in small quantities. Figure A2–4 illustrates the motion of a higher-energy particle relative to the central orbit, which is folded out. From Eqs. (A2–32) and (A2–34), the displacement of the central orbit is

$$\Delta r = \frac{r_0}{1-n}\frac{\Delta p}{p}, \quad \text{magnetic}; \qquad \Delta r = \frac{r_0}{2}\frac{\Delta T}{T}, \quad \text{electrostatic.}$$

The total displacement D at the image position is readily seen to be

$$D = \Delta r(1 - \cos k_M\phi r_0 + k_M l' \sin k_M\phi r_0). \qquad \text{(A2–35)}$$

APPENDIX 3 Barrier Penetration

In Section 10–4 we discussed the transmission of momentum wave functions over single potential steps. We shall here derive the approximate transmission coefficient for a wave of initial form e^{ik_0x} moving over a *multiple* of small potential steps. Using Eqs. (10–5) and (10–6), we find in region 1 of Fig. A3–1 a forward-moving component

$$u_1^+ = \frac{2k_0}{k_0 + k_1} e^{ik_0a} e^{ik_1(x-a)}. \tag{A3–1}$$

If this wave encounters another step-up or step-down in potential such that the wave number changes to k_3 at position $x = b$, we find in region 2 a component

$$u_2^+ = \frac{2k_0}{k_0 + k_1} \frac{2k_1}{k_1 + k_2} e^{ik_0a} e^{ik_1(b-a)} e^{ik_2(x-b)}. \tag{A3–2}$$

The two factors in front give the amplitude ratios transmitted through the steps at a and b. The exponentials give the change of phase of the wave as a function of x. Because of multiple reflections between the steps, there will be other forward-moving components in every region except region 0. If the steps are very small, these components will be small. More exactly, we can neglect these multiple reflections in region 1, for instance, when

$$\left|\frac{k_1 - k_2}{k_1 + k_2} \frac{k_1 - k_0}{k_1 + k_0}\right| \ll 1. \tag{A3–3}$$

The reflection coefficients used are given by Eq. (10–7).

If the potential function varies smoothly with x, we can approximate it with a function with many small steps a distance Δx apart. It is then obvious, if we restrict the discussion to cases where k is always real, that Eq. (A3–2) can be extended to

$$u_N^+ \approx \frac{2k_0}{k_0 + k_1} \cdots \frac{2k_{n-1}}{k_{N-1} + k_N} e^{ik_0a} e^{ik_1\Delta x} \cdots e^{ik_{N-1}\Delta x} e^{ik_N(x-d)}. \tag{A3–4}$$

The step from k_0 to k_1 is at $x = a$; the step from k_{N-1} to k_N, at $d = a + (N - 1)\,\Delta x$. There are N steps from region 0 to region N. We introduce

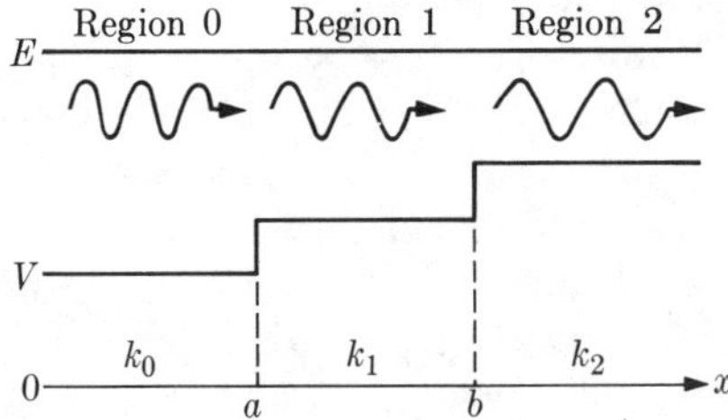

Fig. A3-1. The transmission of a plane wave over potential steps. In each region the kinetic energy is $T = k^2\hbar^2/2m$.

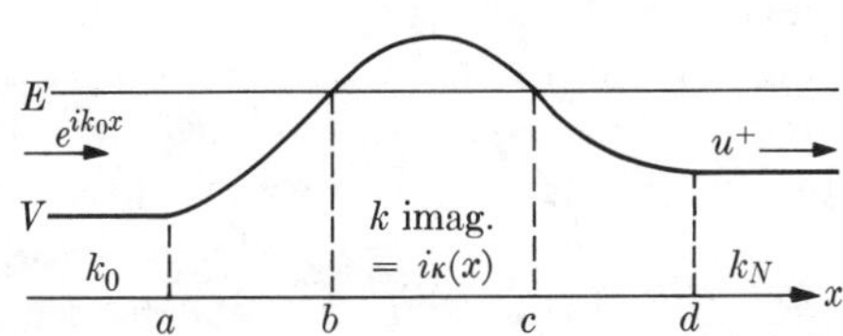

Fig. A3-2. The transmission of a plane wave through a potential barrier.

$k_n - k_{n-1} = \Delta k_n$, and take the logarithm of (A3-4):

$$\ln u_N^+ \approx -\sum_1^N \ln\left(1 + \frac{1}{2}\frac{\Delta k_n}{k_n}\right) + i\sum_1^{N-1} k_n\,\Delta x + ik_0a + ik_N(x - d).$$

When $\Delta k_n \ll k_n$, we can write

$$\ln\left(1 + \frac{1}{2}\frac{\Delta k_n}{k_n}\right) \approx \frac{1}{2}\frac{\Delta k_n}{k_n}. \tag{A3-5}$$

We now make the step width Δx infinitesimal and obtain at position x

$$\ln u^+ \approx -\int_a^x \frac{dk}{2k} + i\int_a^x k\,dx + ik_0a$$

$$\approx \frac{1}{2}\ln\frac{k_0}{k} + i\int_a^x k\,dx + ik_0a.$$

This gives

$$u^+ \approx \frac{k_0^{1/2}}{k^{1/2}}\exp(ik_0a)\exp\left(i\int_a^x k\,dx\right). \tag{A3-6}$$

The transmission coefficient from 0 to x is

$$\tau = \frac{|u^+|^2k}{|u_0^+|^2k_0} = 1. \tag{A3-7}$$

With the assumption that we have made, namely that the potential variations are so smooth that we can neglect reflections, clearly we should expect such a result.

Let us now study the more interesting case where k becomes imaginary. We have seen in Section 10-4 that the transmission formulas through step-ups and step-downs are equally valid for these cases, provided we use wave functions of the general form $e^{-\kappa x}$ in the region where $E < V$. In the derivation of

Eq. (A3–6), however, we have made approximations that break down when $k \to 0$ at $x = b$ and $x = c$ (Fig. A3–2). Condition (A3–3) becomes dubious when $k \to 0$, and Eq. (A3–5) clearly breaks down if the steps Δk_i are kept constant. If we insist upon keeping $\Delta k_i \ll k_i$, then k will never reach zero. In spite of these difficulties, it turns out that Eq. (A3–6) is valid in and out of the region of imaginary wave number, provided we do not ask for the value of u_+ at $x = b$ and $x = c$, where (A3–6) gives incorrectly $u_+ \to \infty$. Postponing the proof of the validity of (A3–6), we calculate the wave function for $x > c$ as

$$u^+ \approx \frac{k_0^{1/2}}{k^{1/2}} \exp(ik_0 a) \exp\left(i\int_a^b k\,dx\right) \exp\left(-\int_b^c \kappa\,dx\right) \exp\left(i\int_c^x k\,dx\right).$$

In region b to c, we have

$$\kappa = (1/\hbar)\sqrt{2m(V-E)}.$$

We can now find the barrier-penetration factor as

$$B = \frac{|u_N^+|^2 k_N}{|u_0^+|^2 k_0} = \exp\left(-2\int_b^c \kappa\,dx\right). \qquad \text{(A3–8)}$$

Now let us try to justify the use of Eq. (A3–6) through the classical turning points b and c. In the complex plane, the wave number varies, as indicated on Fig. A3–3, from k_0 to $i\kappa_{\max}$ back through zero to k_N. The integration preceding Eq. (A3–6) is straightforward whether k is real or imaginary, except through the origin, where the expression becomes infinite. We may avoid this difficulty by integrating along a circular arc with a small radius q (Fig. A3–3). This procedure should be acceptable if we can show that the exact solution of Schrödinger's equation is not radically changed by letting k vary in this manner instead of going through zero. We write Schrödinger's equation as

$$d^2u/dx^2 + k^2u = 0.$$

Clearly, when $k \approx 0$, whether real or imaginary, we get $d^2u/dx^2 \approx 0$, so that du/dx is approximately constant (and finite). The exact solution is therefore insensitive to the details of the variation of k near the origin in the complex plane.

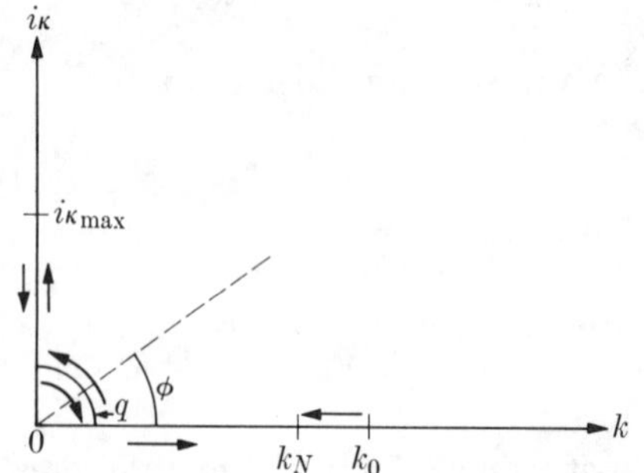

Fig. A3–3. The variation of the wave number of Fig. A3–2 from k_0 through imaginary values to k_N.

Along the arc shown in Fig. A3–3, we have

$$k = qe^{i\phi},$$

$$dk = iqe^{i\phi}\,d\phi,$$

where q is an arbitrarily small number. The integration of Eq. (A3–5) in this region therefore yields

$$-\int_0^{\pi/2} \frac{dk}{2k} = \frac{-i}{2} \int_0^{\pi/2} d\phi = -i\frac{\pi}{4}\cdot$$

This represents a change of phase of the wave function in moving through the classical turning point at $x = b$. Taking the exponential, we get

$$e^{-i\pi/4} = i^{-1/2}. \tag{A3–9}$$

This phase change is exactly what Eq. (A3–6) predicts when we substitute $k = i\kappa$ after passing the classical turning point. The same procedure can be used in justifying the transition through $x = c$. It appears, then, that in spite of the dubious approximations used when deriving Eq. (A3–6) and using it through the classical turning points, it is consistent with results of more acceptable methods.

The problem treated in this Appendix is usually solved in standard textbooks on wave mechanics by an approximation method called the *WKB approximation.* The result is identical to what has been obtained with our direct approach.

APPENDIX 4 Time-Dependent Perturbation Theory

A4–1 General First-Order Theory

Consider a quantum-mechanical system that can be described by a wave function written as a sum of two or more terms. Each term represents a physical description which, at least in principle, can be distinguished experimentally from that of other terms. Several examples of such systems are given in the main text. In particular, the results of this Appendix are used on three examples of theoretical calculations of reaction rates.

The first example is beta decay (Section 11–3). Here one part of the wave function describes a beta-unstable nucleus. The other part describes a daughter nucleus, an electron (or positron) and an antineutrino (or neutrino). There is a "coupling" between these parts of the system, which means that the probability for existence in one mode reduces while there is a build-up of probability for existence in the other. The coupling is the universal "weak interaction."

The second example is a deuteron-stripping reaction (Section 13–11). One part of the quantum-mechanical system describes a deuteron moving relative to a target nucleus. The other part describes a physical situation in which one of the nucleons in the deuteron has been absorbed by the target nucleus, and the other has a given momentum with respect to the nucleus. The coupling is the "strong interaction" that binds the stripped-off nucleon to the target nucleus or to the other nucleon.

The third example is Coulomb excitation (Section 13–13). In our semiclassical description, one part of the system consists of a target nucleus and a charged particle moving along a classical Rutherford orbit in the field of the nucleus. The second part describes the nucleus in a low-lying excited state and the particle in a Rutherford orbit with reduced kinetic energy.

In the two first examples, the "final" state is one of a large number of states; each of these states describes the particles moving in a given direction and having a given spin orientation. The third example represents, in our semiclassical description, a transfer between two states only.

Let us assume for a moment that we can turn off the interaction that brings about transfer from one physical description to another; in the case of beta decay, the weak interaction. We can then, in principle, write a Hamiltonian

H_0 which has as eigenfunctions a complete set ψ_n, including both types of physical descriptions. For beta decay, this means the various states of the parent nucleus and the various states of the daughter nucleus, the latter combined with lepton states describing the two decay products in standing-wave states or momentum eigenstates in a normalization box.

In general the initial state ψ_m is given by experimental conditions; in beta decay, for instance, it may be the parent nucleus in its ground state. At time $t = 0$, we can therefore write

$$\Psi = \psi_m e^{-iE_m t/\hbar} \qquad (\text{for } t = 0). \tag{A4–1}$$

We assume that the interaction that may bring about a change is turned on at $t = 0$. At a later time, we can expand the wave function in a set ψ_n:

$$\Psi = \sum_n a_n(t)\psi_n e^{-iE_n t/\hbar}. \tag{A4–2}$$

The individual functions ψ_n are orthonormal eigenfunctions of the Hamiltonian H_0. Thus

$$H_0\psi_n = E_n\psi_n. \tag{A4–3}$$

The total wave function Ψ must satisfy Schrödinger's time-dependent equation

$$H\Psi = \hbar i \frac{\partial \Psi}{\partial t}, \tag{A4–4}$$

where

$$H = H_0 + H'. \tag{A4–5}$$

Thus the total Hamiltonian includes a perturbing interaction H' which produces mixing of the states or, as expressed above, flow of probability from one state to another.

Inserting Eqs. (A4–5) and (A4–2) into (A4–4), and with further use of (A4–3), we obtain

$$\hbar i \sum_n \dot{a}_n\psi_n e^{-iE_n t/\hbar} = \sum_n H' a_n \psi_n e^{-iE_n t/\hbar}. \tag{A4–6}$$

We now multiply Eq. (A4–6) from the left with ψ_k^*, one of the other eigenfunctions of H_0, and integrate over ψ-space. We then get (remembering that the ψ_n's are orthonormal)

$$\dot{a}_k = \frac{1}{\hbar i} \sum_n a_n H'_{kn} e^{i\omega_{kn} t}, \tag{A4–7}$$

where we have introduced the matrix element

$$H'_{kn} \equiv \int \psi_k^* H' \psi_n \, d\tau \tag{A4–8}$$

and the frequency

$$\omega_{kn} \equiv \frac{E_k - E_n}{\hbar}. \tag{A4–9}$$

We now assume that the perturbation is very weak, so that the build-up of probability in other than the initial state ψ_m is very small over the time considered. We can therefore in the *first-order perturbation theory* put $a_m = 1$ and all other a_m's equal to zero on the right-hand side of Eq. (A4–7). We then obtain

$$a_k = \frac{1}{\hbar i} \int H'_{km} e^{i\omega_{km}t}\, dt\,. \tag{A4–10}$$

The probability of finding the system in state ψ_k is then at any time given by $|a_k|^2$. This result is used in Section 13–13.

A4–2 Transitions to the Continuum

For most examples in which perturbation theory is applied, the perturbing interaction H' is constant in time, and the states considered are stationary states.* There is, in general, an extremely large number of possible final states of decay, each describing an outgoing particle moving in a different direction or with a different momentum.

Experimentally, we cannot pinpoint the exact final state after the process. We can, however, calculate the total transition rate by summing over all possible final states. We assume that the constant perturbation H' is turned on at time $t = 0$ and off again at $t = t_1$, a short time later. We calculate the total probability as the sum of all $|a_k|^2$ at time t_1, and find the transition rate by dividing by t_1.

For simplicity, we assume that in a given small energy interval about E_m, the matrix element H_{km} is a constant for all states considered; that is, for all states that can be reached in a given type of transition subject to, for instance, conservation of angular momentum. We then get, by integrating Eq. (A4–10),

$$a_k = \frac{H'_{km}}{\hbar} \frac{e^{i\omega_{km}t_1} - 1}{\omega_{km}} = \frac{H'_{km}}{\hbar} e^{i\omega_{km}t_1/2} \frac{2 \sin \omega_{km}t_1/2}{\omega_{km}}. \tag{A4–11}$$

The total transition rate from state ψ_m to all other states is given by

$$\lambda = \frac{1}{t_1} \sum_k |a_k|^2 = \frac{1}{t_1} \int_{-\infty}^{\infty} |a_k|^2 \frac{dN}{dE}\, dE_k, \tag{A4–12}$$

where dN/dE is the number of accessible final states per unit energy. We write

---

* In the sense used here, a continuous beam of particles or a continuous stream of reaction products represents a stationary state.

$dE_k = \hbar\, d\omega_{km}$ (from Eq. A4–9) and get

$$\lambda = \frac{4}{\hbar t_1} |H'_{km}|^2 \int_{-\infty}^{\infty} \frac{\sin^2 \omega_{km} t_1/2}{\omega_{km}^2} \frac{dN}{dE}\, d\omega_{km}. \tag{A4–13}$$

Figure A4–1 shows that the most significant contribution to the integral comes from the region $-2\pi < \omega_{km} t_1 < 2\pi$. For any reasonable value of the observation time, this represents an extremely small energy interval $\Delta E_k = \hbar\, \Delta\omega_{km}$. In this interval we can, for practical applications, assume that dN/dE is a constant. We can therefore write

$$\lambda = \frac{2}{\hbar} |H'_{km}|^2 \frac{dN}{dE} \int_{-\infty}^{\infty} \frac{\sin^2 x}{x^2}\, dx$$

$$= \frac{2\pi}{\hbar} |H'_{km}|^2 \frac{dN}{dE}, \tag{A4–14}$$

where we have substituted $x = \omega_{km} t_1/2$.

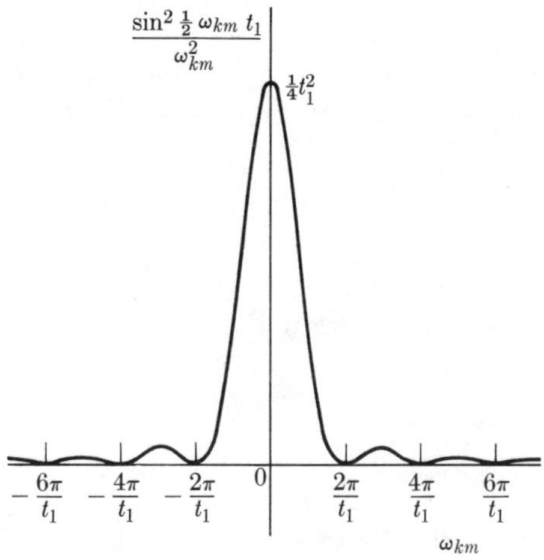

Fig. A4–1. A plot of the integrand of Eq. (A4–3), assuming constant dN/dE.

Equation (A4–14) is the starting point for quantum-mechanical calculations of transition rates such as, for instance, the transition rate per unit momentum in beta decay (the beta spectrum). It is sometimes called *the golden rule number two.**

---

* Curiously, golden rule number one applies to second-order perturbations for which the direct matrix elements H_{km} vanish between states that can communicate without violating a conservation law.

A4–3 Reaction and Scattering Cross Sections

Equation (A4–14) can be used in the following manner to derive theoretical formulas for reaction and scattering cross sections. Consider as the *initial* state a heavy target nucleus and an incoming beam with particles of mass M_i and wave number K_i (before interaction with the nucleus). The wave function is normalized so that, at large distances from the target, we have $|\psi_{ip}|^2 = 1$. The flux of particles in the beam is then $v = K_i\hbar/M_i$. The relationship between transition rate and cross section is clearly

$$\lambda = v\sigma = \sigma K_i \hbar / M_i.$$

We are interested in the differential cross section, and therefore write for the part of the cross section which leads to outgoing particles in the solid-angle element $d\Omega$:

$$d\sigma = \frac{M_i}{K_i\hbar}\, d\lambda = \frac{M_i}{K_i\hbar}\,\frac{2\pi}{\hbar}\,|H'_{fi}|^2\, d\left(\frac{dN}{dE}\right). \tag{A4–15}$$

The last factor is the number of *final* states which describe outgoing particles within the solid-angle element $d\Omega$.

Assuming that we are considering only one final nuclear state, the number of states is given by Eq. (11–24). With $p\,dp = M_f\,dE$, we get

$$\frac{dN}{dE} = \frac{VpM_f}{2\pi^2\hbar^3},$$

where M_f is the mass of the outgoing particles. The directions of the momentum vectors for these particle states are uniformly distributed over the total solid angle 4π steradians, so that we can write

$$d\left(\frac{dN}{dE}\right) = \frac{VpM_f}{2\pi^2\hbar^3}\,\frac{d\Omega}{4\pi} = \frac{VK_fM_f}{8\pi^3\hbar^2}\, d\Omega.$$

Combining this result with Eq. (A4–15), we obtain

$$\frac{d\sigma}{d\Omega} = \frac{VM_iM_fK_f}{4\pi^2\hbar^4K_i}\,|H_{fi}|^2. \tag{A4–16}$$

The matrix element is calculated for an initial state consisting of a target nucleus and an incoming beam, and a final state consisting of the residual nucleus and a beam going out in a given direction. The incoming beam is normalized as described above. The outgoing beam is described by states normalized in a box of volume V, which means that numerically we have $|\psi_{f\mathrm{p}}| = V^{-1/2}$ (Section 11–3). For convenience in calculating the matrix element, we introduce wave functions for the outgoing particles which are normalized in the same manner as the incoming beam; namely, such that $|\psi_{f\mathrm{p}}| = 1$. This takes out the factor V in Eq. (A4–16), and we get

$$\frac{d\sigma}{d\Omega} = \frac{M_i M_f K_f}{4\pi^2 \hbar^4 K_i} |A_{fi}|^2, \tag{A4–17}$$

where

$$A_{fi} = \int \psi_{f\text{p}}^* \psi_{f\text{N}}^* H' \psi_{i\text{p}} \psi_{i\text{N}} \, d\tau. \tag{A4–18}$$

The final and initial wave functions have both been written as products of nuclear wave functions (subscripts N) and particle wave functions (subscripts p) normalized to one particle per unit volume.

We started by assuming that the nucleus was heavy, implying that the center of mass was at rest. This assumption is not necessary. Equation (A4–17) applies for the center-of-mass system, with M_i and M_f being reduced masses and K_i and K_f representing energies in the center-of-mass frame.

APPENDIX 5 Matrix Diagonalization

The technique described in the following is used for calculating the coefficients a_n in the expansion

$$\psi = \sum_n a_n u_n, \tag{A5-1}$$

when ψ is not known but the Hamiltonian operator H is known. The functions u_n will initially be assumed to constitute a complete orthonormal set, but later we will recognize the fact that, for practical reasons, a truncated set of functions may be used. In most textbooks on wave mechanics the problem at hand is usually treated under the sections on matrix mechanics. Although the treatment here is in reality identical with these descriptions, we shall not use matrix formulation.

To find the coefficients a_n, we start by substituting Eq. (A5-1) into Schrödinger's equation, thus:

$$\sum_n a_n H u_n = E \sum_n a_n u_n. \tag{A5-2}$$

We now use the standard trick of multiplying with the complex conjugate u_k^* of one of the functions from the orthonormal set and integrating over all coordinates. We then get

$$\sum_n a_n H_{kn} = E a_k, \tag{A5-3}$$

with

$$H_{kn} \equiv \int u_k^* H u_n \, d\tau. \tag{A5-4}$$

The term H_{kn} is called a matrix element of the Hamiltonian H in the representation u_n. These matrix elements can of course be calculated when the set u_n is given and when H is known. By giving k all possible values from 1 and up, we get a series of equations from Eq. (A5-3). We can write them out as follows:

$$\begin{aligned}
a_1(H_{11} - E) + a_2 H_{12} + a_3 H_{13} + \cdots + a_N H_{1N} &= 0,\\
a_1 H_{21} + a_2(H_{22} - E) + a_3 H_{23} + \cdots + a_N H_{2N} &= 0,\\
a_1 H_{31} + a_2 H_{32} + a_3(H_{33} - E) + \cdots + a_N H_{3N} &= 0,\\
&\vdots\\
a_1 H_{N1} + a_2 H_{N2} + a_3 H_{N3} + \cdots + a_N(H_{NN} - E) &= 0.
\end{aligned} \tag{A5-5}$$

Equations (A5–5) form a set of homogeneous first-order equations for the coefficients a_n. Our derivation is based on the assumption that the set is complete, which implies $N = \infty$. When, for practical reasons, we have to limit the number of terms N, it is not obvious that the coefficients a_n resulting from a solution of Eqs. (A5–5) with finite N produces the best possible approximation for the wave function ψ (Eq. A5–1). However, this turns out to be the case, although we shall not take space to prove it here.* It is well known that such a set of homogeneous equations only possesses nontrivial solutions for the unknowns when the determinants of the coefficients disappear. We therefore get

$$\begin{vmatrix} (H_{11} - E) & H_{12} & H_{13} \ldots & H_{1N} \\ H_{21} & (H_{22} - E) & H_{23} \ldots & H_{2N} \\ \vdots & & & \vdots \\ H_{N1} & H_{N2} & H_{N3} \ldots & (H_{NN} - E) \end{vmatrix} = 0. \quad \text{(A5–6)}$$

Since all the matrix elements H_{kn} are presumed known, this is an Nth-order equation in E. It is called the *secular equation* and gives the eigenvalues E for N approximate solutions of Schrödinger's equation. For a given eigenvalue E, the set of N equations (A5–5) gives the N coefficients a_n and thereby the eigenfunctions ψ corresponding to E.

In the problem discussed in Section 6–8, the *base functions* u_n are harmonic-oscillator functions with a given principal quantum number and given projection Ω along the symmetry axis. The total number of functions used in each diagonalization is thus not very large. For instance, in the fifth harmonic-oscillator shell (3s, 2d, and 1g states), the state with $\Omega = \frac{1}{2}$ is composed of the base functions $3s_{1/2}$, $2d_{5/2}$, $1g_{9/2}$, and $1g_{7/2}$, each with a j-component of $\frac{1}{2}$ along the symmetry axis.

* For proof see, for instance, J. C. Slater, *Quantum Theory of Atomic Structure*, Vol. 1, New York: McGraw-Hill, 1960, p. 113ff.

APPENDIX 6 Table of Nuclides

The Table of Nuclides, starting on p. 527 presents the most important experimental information relating to the *ground states* of the known nuclides. In addition, it gives information of a somewhat more speculative nature about the quantum-mechanical states of the odd nucleons in the ground level or low-lying excited levels of these nuclides.

Following the identification of the nuclide in the first column of the table is the isospin projection $T_3 = \frac{1}{2}(Z - N)$. In general, the total isospin for the ground state is $T = |T_3|$, and for excited states it is $T = |T_3|, |T_3| + 1$, etc.

The mass excess $M - A$, given in column three, is taken directly from the 1965 mass table by Mattauch *et al.** The excess is given in micro mass units on the C^{12} scale. The uncertainties assigned to these figures by Mattauch *et al.* vary from a fraction of a micro mass unit for some light nuclides to about 1.5 milli mass units (1.4 MeV) for some more obscure nuclides for which the mass has been interpolated. The subscript on the mass excess gives the number of digits in the error quoted by Mattauch *et al.* when this error is written in whole micro mass units. Zero means error less than 1μu; one means 1 to 9 μu, etc.

The configurations for protons and neutrons given in columns 4 and 5 have been arrived at as follows: the terms for *even Z* or *even N* have been written down by following blindly sequences of shell-model states, which are those given in Section 6–4, with the following modifications. For neutron *pairs,* $1h_{11/2}$ fills before $3s_{1/2}$ and $2d_{3/2}$; $1i_{13/2}$ fills before $2f_{5/2}$ and $3p_{1/2}$; $1i_{11/2}$ fills before $3d_{5/2}$. These modifications are caused by the fact that the pairing energy increases with increasing l-value.

The shell-model terms for *odd Z* or *odd N* have been assigned according to the sequences of states given in Section 6–4, when no evidence indicates the choice of neighbor states.

In the regions of large deformations, the assignment of Nilsson orbits has been made on the basis of the work by Mottelson and Nilsson† with further extrap-

* J. H. E. Mattauch, W. Thiele, and A. H. Wapstra, *Nucl. Phys.* **67,** 1 (1965).
† B. R. Mottelson and S. G. Nilsson, *Mat. Fys. Skr. Dan. Vid. Selsk.* **1** No. 8 (1959).

Table A6–1. Approximate filling order of Nilsson orbits for deformed nuclei

Region $8 < (Z, N) < 20$ (Fig. 6–16)

Z, N	State	Parent	Z, N	State	Parent
9	$1/2^+$ (220)	$1d_{5/2}$	13	$5/2^+$ (202)	$1d_{5/2}$
11	$3/2^+$ (211)	$1d_{5/2}$	15	$1/2^+$ (211)	$2s_{1/2}$

Region $50 < Z < 104$

Z	State	Parent	Z	State	Parent	Z	State	Parent
51	$1/2^+$ (431)	$1g_{7/2}$	69	$1/2^+$ (411)	$2d_{3/2}$	87	$1/2^+$ (660)	$1i_{13/2}$
53	$3/2^+$ (422)	$1g_{7/2}$	71	$9/2^-$ (514)	$1h_{11/2}$	89	$3/2^+$ (651)	$1i_{13/2}$
55	$1/2^+$ (420)	$2d_{5/2}$	73	$7/2^+$ (404)	$1g_{7/2}$	91	$1/2^-$ (530)	$2f_{7/2}$
57	$1/2^-$ (550)	$1h_{11/2}$	75	$5/2^+$ (402)	$2d_{5/2}$	93	$5/2^+$ (642)	$1i_{13/2}$
59	$3/2^-$ (541)	$1h_{11/2}$	77	$11/2^-$ (505)	$1h_{11/2}$	95	$5/2^-$ (523)	$1h_{9/2}$
61	$5/2^-$ (532)	$1h_{11/2}$	79	$3/2^+$ (402)	$2d_{3/2}$	97	$3/2^-$ (521)	$1f_{7/2}$
63	$5/2^+$ (413)	$1g_{7/2}$	81	$1/2^+$ (400)	$3s_{1/2}$	99	$7/2^+$ (633)	$1i_{13/2}$
65	$3/2^+$ (411)	$2d_{5/2}$	83	$1/2^-$ (541)	$1h_{9/2}$	101	$7/2^-$ (514)	$1h_{9/2}$
67	$7/2^-$ (523)	$1h_{11/2}$	85	$3/2^-$ (532)	$1h_{9/2}$	103	$1/2^-$ (521)	$2f_{5/2}$

Region $82 < N < 158$

N	State	Parent	N	State	Parent	N	State	Parent
83	$1/2^-$ (541)	$2f_{7/2}$	109	$1/2^-$ (510)	$2f_{5/2}$	135	$3/2^-$ (761)	$1j_{15/2}$
85	$1/2^-$ (530)	$1h_{9/2}$	111	$3/2^-$ (512)	$3p_{3/2}$	137	$3/2^+$ (631)	$1i_{11/2}$
87	$3/2^-$ (532)	$2f_{7/2}$	113	$7/2^-$ (503)	$1h_{9/2}$	139	$5/2^-$ (752)	$1j_{15/2}$
89	$1/2^+$ (660)	$1i_{13/2}$	115	$9/2^-$ (505)	$1h_{9/2}$	141	$5/2^+$ (633)	$2g_{9/2}$
91	$3/2^+$ (651)	$1i_{13/2}$	117	$11/2^+$ (615)	$1i_{13/2}$	143	$7/2^-$ (743)	$1j_{15/2}$
93	$3/2^-$ (521)	$1h_{9/2}$	119	$13/2^+$ (606)	$1i_{13/2}$	145	$1/2^+$ (631)	$3d_{5/2}$
95	$5/2^+$ (642)	$1i_{13/2}$	121	$3/2^-$ (501)	$2f_{5/2}$	147	$5/2^+$ (622)	$1i_{11/2}$
97	$5/2^-$ (523)	$2f_{7/2}$	123	$5/2^-$ (503)	$2f_{5/2}$	149	$7/2^+$ (624)	$2g_{9/2}$
99	$7/2^+$ (633)	$1i_{13/2}$	125	$1/2^-$ (501)	$3p_{1/2}$	151	$9/2^-$ (734)	$1j_{15/2}$
101	$1/2^-$ (521)	$3p_{3/2}$	127	$1/2^+$ (651)	$2g_{9/2}$	153	$7/2^+$ (613)	$1i_{11/2}$
103	$5/2^-$ (512)	$1h_{9/2}$	129	$1/2^+$ (640)	$1i_{11/2}$	155	$11/2^-$ (725)	$1j_{15/2}$
105	$7/2^-$ (514)	$2f_{7/2}$	131	$1/2^-$ (770)	$1j_{15/2}$	157	$9/2^+$ (615)	$2g_{9/2}$
107	$9/2^+$ (624)	$1i_{13/2}$	133	$3/2^+$ (642)	$2g_{9/2}$			

olations. The approximate level sequences are given in Table A6–1. For the even values of Z or N, the shell-model notation has been retained, not because it is more appropriate, but because it makes it easier for the user of the table to compare the two models. The correct assignment in the distorted model for an even Z or even N is usually two nucleons in the orbit indicated as occupying one nucleon for proton number $Z - 1$ or neutron number $N - 1$.

Note that odd-odd nuclides in the regions of large deformations usually have $J = K = |\Omega_p \pm \Omega_n|$ in the ground state.

The angular momenta and parities J^π have been taken from the General Electric *Chart of the Nuclides* and from the *Nuclear Data Sheets.** Values in parentheses are uncertain, and some of these have been assigned partly on the basis of shell-model arguments. However, for the values quoted in this table, there is always some concrete experimental data supporting the assignments. When there is disagreement between J^π and the model terms given, an asterisk has been placed in front of the J^π-value.

The quoted half-lives apply to the nuclear ground state. Whenever a metastable state exists with longer half-life than the ground state, a *dagger* appears before the quoted value.

Abundances, decay modes, and energies have been taken from the *Chart of the Nuclides.* Some of the energy values have been left out because of space limitations. The energies listed are given in order of descending intensities. Three dots after the last number indicate other low-intensity transitions.

The total disintegration energies for beta decays have been taken directly from the mass table†. When, for some odd-odd nuclides, both modes are possible, both energies are quoted and labeled $-$ and $+$. The energies given are maximum energies for β^- and electron capture (atomic mass differences). For β^+ decay, $2m_0c^2 = 1.022$ MeV must be subtracted to get the maximum kinetic energy of the positron in a ground-state transition. For alpha decay, the total disintegration energy has been calculated from masses, and the value obtained should be $(1 + 4/A_D)$ times the alpha energy for a transition between ground states (A_D is the mass number for the daughter nucleus).

The magnetic moment and quadrupole moment have been taken directly from Appendix 1 to *Nuclear Data Sheets*, 1965.‡

---

* K. Way *et al.*, *Nuclear Data Sheets*, National Academy of Sciences-National Research Council, Oak Ridge, Tennessee.

† Mattauch *et al.*, *loc. cit.*

‡ G. H. Fuller and V. W. Cohen, "Nuclear Moments," Appendix 1 to *Nuclear Data Sheets*, National Academy of Sciences – National Research Council, Oak Ridge National Laboratory, May 1965.

Table of Nuclides

Table of Nuclides

Nuclide	T_3	Mass excess $M - A$, μu	Prominent terms for ground state or low-lying level: Proton	Neutron	J^π	Half-life, sec	**Abundance,** percent or decay modes with energies, MeV	Total disintegration energy, MeV	Magnetic moment, nm	Quadrupole moment, barns
$_0n^1$	$-\frac{1}{2}$	8665_0		$(1s_{1/2})^1$	$\frac{1}{2}+$	$.720 \times 10^3$	β^- .78	0.78	−1.9131	
$_1H^1$	$\frac{1}{2}$	7825_0	$(1s_{1/2})^1$		$\frac{1}{2}+$		**99.99**		2.7928	
$_1D^2$	0	14102_0		$(1s_{1/2})^1$	$1+$		**0.015**		0.8574	0.003
$_1T^3$	$-\frac{1}{2}$	16050_0		$(1s_{1/2})^2$	$\frac{1}{2}+$	$.387 \times 10^9$	β^- .0181	0.02	2.9789	
$_2He^3$	$\frac{1}{2}$	16030_0	$(1s_{1/2})^2$	$(1s_{1/2})^1$	$\frac{1}{2}+$		**0.0001**		−2.1276	
$_2He^4$	0	2603_0		$(1s_{1/2})^2$	$0+$		**100**			
$_2He^6$	−1	18893_1		$(1p_{3/2})^2$	$0+$	.810	β^- 3.51	3.51		
$_2He^7$	$-\frac{3}{2}$			$(1p_{3/2})^3$		$.500 \times 10^{-4}$	β^- ~10, . . .; γ			
$_3Li^6$	0	15125_1	$(1p_{3/2})^1$	$(1p_{3/2})^1$	$1+$		**7.42**		0.8220	−0.001
$_3Li^7$	$-\frac{1}{2}$	16004_1		$(1p_{3/2})^2$	$\frac{3}{2}-$		**92.58**		3.2564	−0.040
$_3Li^8$	−1	22487_1		$(1p_{3/2})^3$	$2+$	.850	β^- 13	16.00	1.6532	
$_3Li^9$	$-\frac{3}{2}$	26802_2		$(1p_{3/2})^4$		.170	β^- 11, 13	13.62		
$_4Be^7$	$\frac{1}{2}$	16929_1	$(1p_{3/2})^2$	$(1p_{3/2})^1$	$\frac{3}{2}-$	$.458 \times 10^7$	EC; γ .48	0.86		
$_4Be^9$	$-\frac{1}{2}$	12186_1		$(1p_{3/2})^3$	$\frac{3}{2}-$		**100**		−1.1776	±0.030
$_4Be^{10}$	−1	13534_1		$(1p_{3/2})^4$	$0+$	$.852 \times 10^{14}$	β^- .56	0.56		
$_4Be^{11}$	$-\frac{3}{2}$	21666_2		$(1p_{1/2})^1$	$(+)$	$.136 \times 10^2$	β^- 11.5, 9.3, . . . ; γ	11.51		
$_5B^8$	1	24609_1	$(1p_{3/2})^3$	$(1p_{3/2})^1$	$(2+)$	.780	β^+ 1.4	17.98		
$_5B^{10}$	0	12939_0		$(1p_{3/2})^3$	$3+$		**19.78**		1.8007	0.080
$_5B^{11}$	$-\frac{1}{2}$	9305_0		$(1p_{3/2})^4$	$\frac{3}{2}-$		**80.22**		2.6885	0.040
$_5B^{12}$	−1	14354_1		$(1p_{1/2})^1$	$1+$	$.200 \times 10^{-1}$	β^- 13.4, 9.0; γ 4.4	13.37		
$_5B^{13}$	$-\frac{3}{2}$	17780_1		$(1p_{1/2})^2$	$\frac{3}{2}-$	$.190 \times 10^{-1}$	β^- 13.4, 9.7; γ 3.68	13.44		
$_6C^{10}$	1	16810_2	$(1p_{3/2})^4$	$(1p_{3/2})^2$	$0+$	$.190 \times 10^2$	β^+ 1.9, . . . ; γ 7.2, 1.04	3.6		
$_6C^{11}$	$\frac{1}{2}$	11432_1		$(1p_{3/2})^3$	$\frac{3}{2}-$	$.123 \times 10^4$	β^+ .96	1.98	±1.0300	±0.031
$_6C^{12}$	0	0		$(1p_{3/2})^4$	$0+$		**98.89**			
$_6C^{13}$	$-\frac{1}{2}$	3354_0		$(1p_{1/2})^1$	$\frac{1}{2}-$		**1.11**		0.7024	
$_6C^{14}$	−1	3242_0		$(1p_{1/2})^2$	$0+$	$.181 \times 10^{12}$	β^- .156	0.16		
$_6C^{15}$	$-\frac{3}{2}$	10599_0		$1/2^+$ (220)	$\frac{1}{2}+$	$.225 \times 10^1$	β^- 4.5, 9.77; γ 5.30	9.77		
$_6C^{16}$	−2	14700_2		$(1d_{5/2})^2$	$0+$	.740	β^-	8.01		
$_7N^{12}$	1	18641_1	$(1p_{1/2})^1$	$(1p_{3/2})^3$	$1+$	$.110 \times 10^{-1}$	β^+ 16.4	17.36		
$_7N^{13}$	$\frac{1}{2}$	5738_1		$(1p_{3/2})^4$	$\frac{1}{2}-$	$.600 \times 10^3$	β^+ 1.19	2.22	±0.3223	
$_7N^{14}$	0	3074_0		$(1p_{1/2})^1$	$1+$		**99.63**		0.4036	0.010
$_7N^{15}$	$-\frac{1}{2}$	108_0		$(1p_{1/2})^2$	$\frac{1}{2}-$		**0.37**		−0.2831	
$_7N^{16}$	−1	6103_1		$(1d_{5/2})^1$	$2-$	$.735 \times 10^1$	β^- 4.3, 10.4, . . . ; γ 6.13, 7.12	10.42		
$_7N^{17}$	[illegible]	[illegible]		[illegible]		[illegible]	[illegible]	[illegible]		

$_{8}O^{15}$	$\frac{1}{2}$	3070_1		$(1p_{1/2})^1$	$\frac{1}{2}^-$	$.124 \times 10^3$	β^+ 1.74	2.70	±0.7189	
$_{8}O^{16}$	0	-5085_0		$(1p_{1/2})^2$	0^+		**99.76**			
$_{8}O^{17}$	$-\frac{1}{2}$	-867_1		$(1d_{5/2})^1$	$\frac{5}{2}^+$		**0.037**		−1.8937	−0.026
$_{8}O^{18}$	−1	-840_0		$(1d_{5/2})^2$	0^+		**0.204**			
$_{8}O^{19}$	$-\frac{3}{2}$	3578_1		$(1d_{5/2})^3$	$\frac{5}{2}^+$	$.290 \times 10^2$	β^- 3.25, 4.60; γ .20, 1.36, . . .	4.82		
$_{8}O^{20}$	−2	4079_1		$(1d_{5/2})^4$	0^+	$.140 \times 10^2$	β^- 2.69; γ 1.06	3.81		
$_{9}F^{17}$	$\frac{1}{2}$	2095_0	$(1d_{5/2})^1$	$(1p_{1/2})^2$	$(\frac{5}{2})^+$	$.660 \times 10^2$	β^+ 1.74	2.76		
$_{9}F^{18}$	0	937_0	or	$1/2^+ (220)$	1^+	$.660 \times 10^4$	β^+ .65; EC	1.65		
$_{9}F^{19}$	$-\frac{1}{2}$	-1595_0	$1/2^+ (220)$	$(1d_{5/2})^2$	$\frac{1}{2}^+$		**100**		2.6287	
$_{9}F^{20}$	−1	-13_1		$3/2^+ (211)$	2^+	$.110 \times 10^2$	β^- 5.40; γ 1.63	7.03	2.0940	
$_{9}F^{21}$	$-\frac{3}{2}$	-49_1		$(1d_{5/2})^4$		$.460 \times 10^1$	β^- 4.0, 5.4, . . . ; γ .35, 1.38	5.68		
$_{10}Ne^{17}$	$\frac{3}{2}$		$(1d_{5/2})^2$	$(1p_{1/2})^1$		.690	$\beta^+ >5$			
$_{10}Ne^{18}$	1	5711_1		$(1p_{1/2})^2$	0^+	$.146 \times 10^1$	β^+ 3.42, 2.37; γ 1.04	4.45		
$_{10}Ne^{19}$	$\frac{1}{2}$	1881_1		$1/2^+ (220)$	$\frac{1}{2}^+$	$.180 \times 10^2$	β^+ 2.23	3.24	−1.8870	
$_{10}Ne^{20}$	0	-7560_0		$(1d_{5/2})^2$	0^+		**90.92**			
$_{10}Ne^{21}$	$-\frac{1}{2}$	-6151_1		$3/2^+ (211)$	$\frac{3}{2}^+$		**0.257**		−0.6618	0.090
$_{10}Ne^{22}$	−1	-8615_0		$(1d_{5/2})^4$	0^+		**8.82**			
$_{10}Ne^{23}$	$-\frac{3}{2}$	-5527_1		$5/2^+ (202)$		$.380 \times 10^2$	β^- 4.4, 3.9, . . . ; γ .44, 1.65	4.38		
$_{10}Ne^{24}$	−2	-6387_2		$(1d_{5/2})^6$	0^+	$.203 \times 10^3$	β^- 1.98, 1.10; γ .47, .88	2.47		
$_{11}Na^{20}$	1	8880_3	$(1d_{5/2})^3$	$1/2^+ (220)$		.400	β^+	15.32		
$_{11}Na^{21}$	$\frac{1}{2}$	-2345_1	or	$(1d_{5/2})^2$	$\frac{3}{2}^+$	$.230 \times 10^2$	β^+ 2.50, . . . ; γ .35	3.55	2.3860	
$_{11}Na^{22}$	0	-5563_1	$3/2^+ (211)$	$3/2^+ (211)$	3^+	$.814 \times 10^4$	β^+ .54, . . . ; γ 1.28; EC	2.84	1.7460	
$_{11}Na^{23}$	$-\frac{1}{2}$	-10229_1		$(1d_{5/2})^4$	$\frac{3}{2}^+$		**100**		2.2176	0.110
$_{11}Na^{24}$	−1	-9038_1		$5/2^+ (202)$	4^+	$.540 \times 10^5$	β^- 1.39, . . . ; γ 2.75, 1.37, . . .	5.51	1.6890	
$_{11}Na^{25}$	$-\frac{3}{2}$	-10045_1		$(1d_{5/2})^6$	$\frac{5}{2}^+$	$.600 \times 10^2$	β^- 3.8, 2.8, . . . ; γ .98, .58, . . .	3.83		
$_{11}Na^{26}$	−2	-8260_3		$1/2^+ (211)$		$.100 \times 10^1$	β^- 6.7, . . . ; γ 1.83, . . .	8.52		
$_{12}Mg^{22}$	1	-150_2	$(1d_{5/2})^4$	$(1d_{5/2})^2$	0^+	$.390 \times 10^1$	γ .74, .59	5.04		
$_{12}Mg^{23}$	$\frac{1}{2}$	-5875_1		$3/2^+ (211)$	$\frac{3}{2}^+$	$.120 \times 10^2$	β^+ 3.0, . . . ; γ .44	4.06		
$_{12}Mg^{24}$	0	-14958_1		$(1d_{5/2})^4$	0^+		**78.70**			
$_{12}Mg^{25}$	$-\frac{1}{2}$	-14161_1		$5/2^+ (202)$	$\frac{5}{2}^+$		**10.13**		−0.8553	0.220
$_{12}Mg^{26}$	−1	-17407_1		$(1d_{5/2})^6$	0^+		**11.17**			
$_{12}Mg^{27}$	$-\frac{3}{2}$	-15655_1		$1/2^+ (211)$	$\frac{1}{2}^+$	$.570 \times 10^3$	β^- 1.75, 1.59; γ .84, 1.01, . . .	2.61		
$_{12}Mg^{28}$	−2	-16125_1		$(2s_{1/2})^2$	0^+	$.767 \times 10^5$	β^- .45; γ .032, 1.35, . . .	1.84		
$_{13}Al^{24}$	1	100_2	$(1d_{5/2})^5$	$3/2^+ (211)$	(4^+)	$.210 \times 10^1$	β^+ 8.8, 4.5, . . . ; γ 1.37–7.1	14.03		
$_{13}Al^{25}$	$\frac{1}{2}$	-9588_1	or	$(1d_{5/2})^4$	$\frac{5}{2}^+$	$.720 \times 10^1$	β^+ 3.24, . . . ; γ .58–1.6	4.26		
$_{13}Al^{26}$	0	-13109_1	$5/2^+ (202)$	$5/2^+ (202)$	5^+	$.234 \times 10^{14}$	β^+ 1.16; EC; γ 1.83, 1.12, . . .	4.00		
$_{13}Al^{27}$	$-\frac{1}{2}$	-18461_1		$(1d_{5/2})^6$	$\frac{5}{2}^+$		**100**		3.6414	0.150
$_{13}Al^{28}$	−1	-18095_1		$1/2^+ (211)$	3^+	$.138 \times 10^3$	β^- 2.87; γ 1.78	4.63		

Note: An asterisk placed before the J^π values denotes disagreement between J^π and the model terms given. A dagger placed before the half-life indicates that a metastable state exists with a longer half-life than the ground state. The abbreviation EC denotes Electron Capture; SF denotes Spontaneous Fission.

(Continued)

Table of Nuclides (*continued*)

Nuclide	T_3	Mass excess $M - A$, μu	Prominent terms for ground state or low-lying level: Proton	Neutron	J^π	Half-life, sec	**Abundance**, percent or decay modes with energies, MeV	Total disintegration energy, MeV	Magnetic moment, nm	Quadrupole moment, barns
$_{13}Al^{29}$	$-\frac{3}{2}$	-19558_1	$(1d_{5/2})^5$ or	$(2s_{1/2})^2$		$.396 \times 10^3$	β^- 2.5, 1.4; γ 1.28, 2.43	3.68		
$_{13}Al^{30}$	-2	-18410_3	5/2+ (202)	$(1d_{3/2})^1$		$.330 \times 10^1$	β^- 5.05, . . . ; γ 2.26, 3.52	7.29		
$_{14}Si^{26}$	1	-7657_2	$(1d_{5/2})^6$	$(1d_{5/2})^4$	0+	$.200 \times 10^1$	β^+ 3.8, 2.9; γ .82, . . .	5.08		
$_{14}Si^{27}$	$\frac{1}{2}$	-13297_1		5/2+ (202)	$\frac{5}{2}$+	$.420 \times 10^1$	β^+ 3.8, 1.5; γ .84, 1.01	4.81		
$_{14}Si^{28}$	0	-23070_1		$(1d_{5/2})^6$	0+		**92.21**			
$_{14}Si^{29}$	$-\frac{1}{2}$	-23504_1		1/2+ (211)	$\frac{1}{2}$+		**4.70**		-0.5553	
$_{14}Si^{30}$	-1	-26237_1		$(2s_{1/2})^2$	0+		**3.09**			
$_{14}Si^{31}$	$-\frac{3}{2}$	-24651_1		$(1d_{3/2})^1$	$\frac{3}{2}$+	$.943 \times 10^4$	β^- 1.48, . . . ; γ 1.27	1.48		
$_{14}Si^{32}$	-2	-25980_2		$(1d_{3/2})^2$	0+	$.221 \times 10^{11}$	β^- .1	0.10		
$_{15}P^{28}$	1	-8220_3	$(2s_{1/2})^1$	$(1d_{5/2})^5$	+	.280	β^+ 11, ~8, . . . ; γ 1.78, 2.6–7.6	13.83		
$_{15}P^{29}$	$\frac{1}{2}$	-18192_1	or	$(1d_{5/2})^6$	$\frac{1}{2}$+	$.440 \times 10^1$	β^+ 3.95, . . . ; γ 1.28, 2.43	4.95		
$_{15}P^{30}$	0	-21683_1	1/2+ (211)	1/2+ (211)	1+	$.156 \times 10^3$	β^+ 3.3, . . . ; γ 2.24	4.24		
$_{15}P^{31}$	$-\frac{1}{2}$	-26235_1		$(2s_{1/2})^2$	$\frac{1}{2}$+		**100**		1.1317	
$_{15}P^{32}$	-1	-26091_1		$(1d_{3/2})^1$	1+	$.124 \times 10^7$	β^- 1.71	1.71	-0.2523	
$_{15}P^{33}$	$-\frac{3}{2}$	-28272_1		$(1d_{3/2})^2$	+	$.216 \times 10^7$	β^- .25	0.25		
$_{15}P^{34}$	-2	-26660_3		$(1d_{3/2})^3$	1+	$.124 \times 10^2$	β^- 5.1, 3.0; γ 2.1, 4.0	5.10		
$_{16}S^{30}$	1	-15127_2	$(2s_{1/2})^2$	$(1d_{5/2})^6$	0+	$.140 \times 10^1$	β^+ 4.42, 5.08; γ .67	6.11		
$_{16}S^{31}$	$\frac{1}{2}$	-20389_2		$(2s_{1/2})^1$	$\frac{1}{2}$+	$.260 \times 10^1$	β^+ 4.4, . . . ; γ 1.27	5.45		
$_{16}S^{32}$	0	-27926_0		$(2s_{1/2})^2$	0+		**95.0**			
$_{16}S^{33}$	$-\frac{1}{2}$	-28538_1		$(1d_{3/2})^1$	$\frac{3}{2}$+		**0.76**		0.6434	-0.055
$_{16}S^{34}$	-1	-32135_1		$(1d_{3/2})^2$	0+		**4.22**			
$_{16}S^{35}$	$-\frac{3}{2}$	-30969_1		$(1d_{3/2})^3$	$\frac{3}{2}$+	$.749 \times 10^7$	β^- .168	0.17	± 1.0350	0.040
$_{16}S^{36}$	-2	-32910_1		$(1d_{3/2})^4$	0+		**0.014**			
$_{16}S^{37}$	$-\frac{5}{2}$	-28990_2		$(1f_{7/2})^1$	($\frac{7}{2}$−)	$.306 \times 10^3$	β^- 1.6, 4.8; γ 3.1	4.76		
$_{16}S^{38}$	-3	-28770_3		$(1f_{7/2})^2$	0+	$.104 \times 10^5$	β^- 1.1, . . . ; γ 1.88	3.00		
$_{17}Cl^{32}$	1	-13760_3	$(1d_{3/2})^1$	$(2s_{1/2})^1$	(2)+	.310	β^+ 10, 8, . . . ; γ 2.2, 4.8, . . .	13.20		
$_{17}Cl^{33}$	$\frac{1}{2}$	-22560_2		$(2s_{1/2})^2$	$\frac{3}{2}$+	$.250 \times 10^1$	β^+ 4.5; γ 2.8	5.57		
$_{17}Cl^{34}$	0	-26250_1		$(1d_{3/2})^1$	0+	$.150 \times 10^1$	β^+ 4.5	5.48		
$_{17}Cl^{35}$	$-\frac{1}{2}$	-31149_1		$(1d_{3/2})^2$	$\frac{3}{2}$+		**75.53**		0.8218	-0.079
$_{17}Cl^{36}$	-1	-31691_1		$(1d_{3/2})^3$	2+	$.947 \times 10^{13}$	β^- .71; EC	0.71	1.2850	-0.017
$_{17}Cl^{37}$	$-\frac{3}{2}$	-34102_1		$(1d_{3/2})^4$	$\frac{3}{2}$+		**24.47**		0.6841	-0.062
$_{17}Cl^{38}$	-2	-31995_1		$(1f_{7/2})^1$	2−	$.224 \times 10^4$	β^- 4.8, 1.1, 2.8; γ 2.2, 1.6	4.92		
$_{17}Cl^{39}$	$-\frac{5}{2}$	-31992_2		$(1f_{7/2})^2$	($\frac{3}{2}$+)	$.330 \times 10^4$	β^- 1.91, 2.18, 3.43; γ 1.27, . . .	3.44		
$_{17}Cl^{40}$	-3	-29600_3		$(1f_{7/2})^3$		$.840 \times 10^2$	β^- 3.2, 7.5; γ 2.75, 1.46, 6.0	7.50		
$_{18}Ar^{35}$	$\frac{1}{2}$	-24746_2	$(1d_{3/2})^2$	$(1d_{3/2})^1$	$\frac{3}{2}$+	$.180 \times 10^1$	β^+ 4.96, . . . ; γ 1.19, 1.73	5.96		

[illegible]	$\frac{1}{2}$	[illegible]		$(1d_{3/2})$[illegible]	$\frac{3}{2}$	$.296 \times 10^{[illegible]}$	EC	0.81	± 1.0000	
$_{18}Ar^{38}$	-1	-37272_1		$(1d_{3/2})^4$	$0+$		**0.063**			
$_{18}Ar^{39}$	$-\frac{3}{2}$	-35683_1		$(1f_{7/2})^1$	$\frac{7}{2}-$	$.821 \times 10^{10}$	β^- .57	0.57		
$_{18}Ar^{40}$	-2	-37616_0		$(1f_{7/2})^2$	$0+$		**99.60**			
$_{18}Ar^{41}$	$-\frac{5}{2}$	-35500_1		$(1f_{7/2})^3$	$\frac{7}{2}-$	$.659 \times 10^4$	β^- 1.20, 2.49; γ 1.29	2.49		
$_{18}Ar^{42}$	-3	-36952_2		$(1f_{7/2})^4$	$0+$	$.110 \times 10^9$	β^-	0.60		
$_{19}K^{37}$	$\frac{1}{2}$	-26635_2	$(1d_{3/2})^3$	$(1d_{3/2})^2$	$\frac{3}{2}+$	$.120 \times 10^1$	β^+ 5.1	6.14		
$_{19}K^{38}$	0	-30903_2		$(1d_{3/2})^3$	$(3)+$	$.462 \times 10^3$	β^+ 2.7; γ 2.2	5.93		
$_{19}K^{39}$	$-\frac{1}{2}$	-36290_1		$(1d_{3/2})^4$	$\frac{3}{2}+$		**93.10**		0.3914	0.090
$_{19}K^{40}$	-1	-36000_1		$(1f_{7/2})^1$	$4-$	$.410 \times 10^{17}$	**0.0118**; β^- 1.32; EC; γ 1.46	$\begin{cases}1.32-\\1.50+\end{cases}$	-1.2980	-0.070
$_{19}K^{41}$	$-\frac{3}{2}$	-38168_1		$(1f_{7/2})^2$	$\frac{3}{2}+$		**6.88**		0.2148	± 0.110
$_{19}K^{42}$	-2	-37594_2		$(1f_{7/2})^3$	$2-$	$.446 \times 10^5$	β^- 3.53, 2.01; γ 1.52, . . .	3.52	-1.1400	
$_{19}K^{43}$	$-\frac{5}{2}$	-39270_2		$(1f_{7/2})^4$	$\frac{3}{2}+$	$.792 \times 10^5$	β^- .83, .46–1.82; γ .37, .61	1.82	± 0.1630	
$_{19}K^{44}$	-3	-37960_3		$(1f_{7/2})^5$	$(-)$	$.132 \times 10^4$	β^- 4.91, . . . ; γ 1.16, 2.1	6.10		
$_{19}K^{45}$	$-\frac{7}{2}$	-39320_3		$(1f_{7/2})^6$		$.120 \times 10^4$	β^-; γ .18, 1.7	4.18		
$_{19}K^{47}$	$-\frac{9}{2}$	-38910_3		$(1f_{7/2})^8$		$.180 \times 10^2$	β^- 4.1, 3.5, . . . ; γ 2.0, 2.6	6.10		
$_{20}Ca^{38}$	1	-23280_4	$(1d_{3/2})^4$	$(1d_{3/2})^2$	$0+$	.700	γ 3.5	7.10		
$_{20}Ca^{39}$	$\frac{1}{2}$	-29309_2		$(1d_{3/2})^3$	$\frac{3}{2}+$	.900	β^+ 5.5	6.50		
$_{20}Ca^{40}$	0	-37411_1		$(1d_{3/2})^4$	$0+$		**96.97**			
$_{20}Ca^{41}$	$-\frac{1}{2}$	-37725_1		$(1f_{7/2})^1$	$\frac{7}{2}-$	$.243 \times 10^{13}$	EC	0.41	-1.5950	
$_{20}Ca^{42}$	-1	-41375_1		$(1f_{7/2})^2$	$0+$		**0.64**			
$_{20}Ca^{43}$	$-\frac{3}{2}$	-41220_1		$(1f_{7/2})^3$	$\frac{7}{2}-$		**0.145**		-1.3170	
$_{20}Ca^{44}$	-2	-44510_1		$(1f_{7/2})^4$	$0+$		**2.06**			
$_{20}Ca^{45}$	$-\frac{5}{2}$	-43811_1		$(1f_{7/2})^5$	$\frac{7}{2}-$	$.143 \times 10^8$	β^- .25	0.25		
$_{20}Ca^{46}$	-3	-46311_1		$(1f_{7/2})^6$	$0+$		**0.0033**			
$_{20}Ca^{47}$	$-\frac{7}{2}$	-45462_1		$(1f_{7/2})^7$	$\frac{7}{2}-$	$.406 \times 10^6$	β^- .67, 1.98; γ 1.31, . . .	1.98		
$_{20}Ca^{48}$	-4	-47469_1		$(1f_{7/2})^8$	$0+$		**0.18**	0.29		
$_{20}Ca^{49}$	$-\frac{9}{2}$	-44325_2		$(2p_{3/2})^1$	$\frac{3}{2}-$	$.528 \times 10^3$	β^- 2.0, 1.0; γ 3.10, 4.05, 4.7	5.26		
$_{21}Sc^{40}$	1	-22430_3	$(1f_{7/2})^1$	$(1d_{3/2})^3$		.180	β^+ 9.2; γ 3.75	13.95		
$_{21}Sc^{41}$	$\frac{1}{2}$	-30753_2		$(1d_{3/2})^4$	$\frac{7}{2}-$	.550	β^+ 5.61	6.50		
$_{21}Sc^{42}$	0	-34505_2		$(1f_{7/2})^1$	$(0+)$	†.660	β^+ 5.53	6.40		
$_{21}Sc^{43}$	$-\frac{1}{2}$	-38835_1		$(1f_{7/2})^2$	$\frac{7}{2}-$	$.140 \times 10^5$	β^+ 1.19, .82; γ .37	2.22	4.5200	-0.050
$_{21}Sc^{44}$	-1	-40594_1		$(1f_{7/2})^3$	$2+$	†$.144 \times 10^5$	β^+ 1.47; EC; γ 1.16, .68–2.7	3.65	2.5600	0.140
$_{21}Sc^{45}$	$-\frac{3}{2}$	-44081_1		$(1f_{7/2})^4$	$\frac{7}{2}-$		**100**		4.7564	-0.220
$_{21}Sc^{46}$	-2	-44827_1		$(1f_{7/2})^5$	$4+$	$.726 \times 10^7$	β^- .36, . . . ; γ 1.12, .89, . . .	2.37	3.0300	0.120
$_{21}Sc^{47}$	$-\frac{5}{2}$	-47587_1		$(1f_{7/2})^6$		$.294 \times 10^6$	β^- .44, .60; γ .16	0.60	5.3100	-0.220
$_{21}Sc^{48}$	-3	-47779_1		$(1f_{7/2})^7$	$6+$	$.158 \times 10^6$	β^- .65, .48; γ 1.31, 1.04, .99	3.98		
$_{21}Sc^{49}$	$-\frac{7}{2}$	-49974_1		$(1f_{7/2})^8$	$(\frac{7}{2})-$	$.345 \times 10^4$	β^- 2.01, . . . ; γ 1.76	2.01		
$_{21}Sc^{50}$	-4	-48270_3		$(2p_{3/2})^1$		$.108 \times 10^3$	β^- 3.6; γ .52, 1.56, 1.12	6.47		
$_{22}Ti^{43}$	$\frac{1}{2}$	-31500_3	$(1f_{7/2})^2$	$(1f_{7/2})^1$		.400	β^+ 5.6	6.83		
$_{22}Ti^{44}$	0	-40428_2		$(1f_{7/2})^2$	$0+$	$.300 \times 10^{11}$	EC; γ .79, .70, . . .	0.16		

(Continued)

Table of Nuclides (*continued*)

Nuclide	T_3	Mass excess $M - A$, μu	Prominent terms for ground state or low-lying level: Proton	Neutron	J^π	Half-life, sec	**Abundance,** percent or decay modes with energies, MeV	Total disintegration energy, MeV	Magnetic moment, nm	Quadrupole moment, barns
$_{22}Ti^{45}$	$-\frac{1}{2}$	-41871_1	$(1f_{7/2})^2$	$(1f_{7/2})^3$	$\frac{7}{2}-$	$.111 \times 10^5$	β^+ 1.02; EC; γ	2.06		
$_{22}Ti^{46}$	-1	-47368_1		$(1f_{7/2})^4$	$0+$		**7.93**			
$_{22}Ti^{47}$	$-\frac{3}{2}$	-48231_1		$(1f_{7/2})^5$	$*\frac{5}{2}-$		**7.28**		-0.7884	
$_{22}Ti^{48}$	-2	-52049_1		$(1f_{7/2})^6$	$0+$		**73.94**			
$_{22}Ti^{49}$	$-\frac{5}{2}$	-52129_1		$(1f_{7/2})^7$	$\frac{7}{2}-$		**5.51**		-1.1040	
$_{22}Ti^{50}$	-3	-55214_1		$(1f_{7/2})^8$	$0+$		**5.34**			
$_{22}Ti^{51}$	$-\frac{7}{2}$	-53397_1		$(2p_{3/2})^1$	$(\frac{3}{2}-)$	$.348 \times 10^3$	β^- 2.13, 1.52; γ .32, .93, .61	2.46		
$_{23}V^{45}$	$\frac{1}{2}$		$(1f_{7/2})^3$	$(1f_{7/2})^2$		$.100 \times 10^1$	β^+			
$_{23}V^{46}$	0	-39786_1		$(1f_{7/2})^3$		.420	β^+ 6.05	7.06		
$_{23}V^{47}$	$-\frac{1}{2}$	-45101_1		$(1f_{7/2})^4$	$*(\frac{5}{2}-)$	$.192 \times 10^4$	β^+ 1.94; EC; γ 1.54, 1.87	2.92		
$_{23}V^{48}$	-1	-47741_1		$(1f_{7/2})^5$	$(4)+$	$.139 \times 10^7$	β^+ .70; EC; γ .99, 1.31, 2.25	4.01		
$_{23}V^{49}$	$-\frac{3}{2}$	-51477_1		$(1f_{7/2})^6$	$\frac{7}{2}-$	$.285 \times 10^8$	EC			
$_{23}V^{50}$	-2	-52836_1		$(1f_{7/2})^7$	$6+$	$.189 \times 10^{24}$	**0.24**; β^-; EC; γ .71, 1.59	1.03− / 2.21+	3.3470	
$_{23}V^{51}$	$-\frac{5}{2}$	-56038_1		$(1f_{7/2})^8$	$\frac{7}{2}-$		**99.76**		5.1480	0.270
$_{23}V^{52}$	-3	-55220_1		$(2p_{3/2})^1$	$(2)+$	$.226 \times 10^3$	β^- 2.7; γ 1.43	3.97		
$_{23}V^{53}$	$-\frac{7}{2}$	-56020_4		$(2p_{3/2})^2$	$(\frac{7}{2})-$	$.120 \times 10^3$	β^- 2.53; γ 1.01, . . .	3.10		
$_{23}V^{54}$	-4	-53280_4		$(2p_{3/2})^3$	$*0+$	$.550 \times 10^2$	β^- 3.3; γ .99, .84, 2.21	7.30		
$_{24}Cr^{46}$	1		$(1f_{7/2})^4$	$(1f_{7/2})^2$	$0+$	$.110 \times 10^1$	β^+			
$_{24}Cr^{48}$	0	-46240_3		$(1f_{7/2})^4$	$0+$	$.828 \times 10^5$	EC; γ .30, .12	1.40		
$_{24}Cr^{49}$	$-\frac{1}{2}$	-48729_2		$(1f_{7/2})^5$	$*(\frac{5}{2})-$	$.252 \times 10^4$	β^+ 1.54, 1.39, .73; γ .09, .06, .15	2.56		
$_{24}Cr^{50}$	-1	-53945_1		$(1f_{7/2})^6$	$0+$		**4.31**			
$_{24}Cr^{51}$	$-\frac{3}{2}$	-55231_1		$(1f_{7/2})^7$	$\frac{7}{2}-$	$.240 \times 10^7$	EC; γ .32	0.75		
$_{24}Cr^{52}$	-2	-59486_1		$(1f_{7/2})^8$	$0+$		**83.76**			
$_{24}Cr^{53}$	$-\frac{5}{2}$	-59347_1		$(2p_{3/2})^1$	$\frac{3}{2}-$		**9.55**		-0.4744	-0.030
$_{24}Cr^{54}$	-3	-61118_1		$(2p_{3/2})^2$	$0+$		**2.38**			
$_{24}Cr^{55}$	$-\frac{7}{2}$	-59167_1		$(2p_{3/2})^3$	$\frac{3}{2}-$	$.210 \times 10^3$	β^- 2.5	2.59		
$_{24}Cr^{56}$	-4	-59360_3		$(2p_{3/2})^4$	$0+$	$.354 \times 10^3$	β^- 1.5; γ .083, .026	1.61		
$_{25}Mn^{50}$	0	-45785_2	$(1f_{7/2})^5$	$(1f_{7/2})^5$	$0+$	†.290	β^+ 6.6	7.60		
$_{25}Mn^{51}$	$-\frac{1}{2}$	-51810_2		$(1f_{7/2})^6$	$*(\frac{5}{2}-)$	$.270 \times 10^4$	β^+ 2.2; γ .74, 1.17	3.19		
$_{25}Mn^{52}$	-1	-54432_1		$(1f_{7/2})^7$	$6+$	$.493 \times 10^6$	EC; β^+ .58; γ 1.43, .94, .74, . . .	4.71	± 3.0000	
$_{25}Mn^{53}$	$-\frac{3}{2}$	-58705_1		$(1f_{7/2})^8$	$\frac{7}{2}-$	$.300 \times 10^{14}$	EC	0.60	± 5.0500	
$_{25}Mn^{54}$	-2	-59638_1		$(2p_{3/2})^1$	$3+$	$.271 \times 10^8$	EC; γ .84	0.69	± 3.3000	
$_{25}Mn^{55}$	$-\frac{5}{2}$	-61949_1		$(2p_{3/2})^2$	$*\frac{5}{2}-$		**100**		3.4680	0.400
$_{25}Mn^{56}$	-3	-61089_1		$(2p_{3/2})^3$	$3+$	$.929 \times 10^4$	β^- 2.86, 1.05, .75; γ .84, 1.81, . . .	3.70	3.2400	
$_{25}Mn^{57}$	$-\frac{7}{2}$	-61700_3		$(2p_{3/2})^4$	$-$	$.102 \times 10^3$	β^- 2.6, 1.1; γ 1.22, .014, .137, . . .	2.70		
$_{25}Mn^{58}$	-4	-59740_4		$(1f_{5/2})^1$		$.660 \times 10^2$	β^-	6.50		

[illegible]	0	[illegible]	$(1f_{7/2})^6$	$(1f_{7/2})^6$	0^+	$.299 \times 10^5$	β^+ .80, . . . ; EC; γ .17, .380	2.37		
$_{26}Fe^{53}$	$-\frac{1}{2}$	-54428_2		$(1f_{7/2})^7$	$(\frac{7}{2})^-$	$.534 \times 10^3$	$\beta^+ \sim 2.8$, 1.6; γ .38, . . .	3.98		
$_{26}Fe^{54}$	-1	-60383_1		$(1f_{7/2})^8$	0^+		**5.82**			
$_{26}Fe^{55}$	$-\frac{3}{2}$	-61701_1		$(2p_{3/2})^1$	$\frac{3}{2}-$	$.852 \times 10^8$	EC	0.23		
$_{26}Fe^{56}$	-2	-65063_1		$(2p_{3/2})^2$	0^+		**91.66**			
$_{26}Fe^{57}$	$-\frac{5}{2}$	-64602_1		$(2p_{3/2})^3$	$*\frac{1}{2}-$		**2.19**		0.0905	
$_{26}Fe^{58}$	-3	-66718_1		$(2p_{3/2})^4$	0^+		**0.33**			
$_{26}Fe^{59}$	$-\frac{7}{2}$	-65122_1		$(2p_{3/2})^{-1}$	$\frac{3}{2}-$	$.389 \times 10^7$	β^- .46, .27, 1.56; γ 1.10, 1.29, . . .	1.57		
$_{26}Fe^{60}$	-4	-66036_2		$(1f_{5/2})^2$	0^+	$.300 \times 10^{13}$	β^- .13; γ .027	0.14		
$_{26}Fe^{61}$	$-\frac{9}{2}$	-63480_4		$(1f_{5/2})^3$		$.360 \times 10^3$	β^- 2.8; γ .29, . . .	3.80		
$_{27}Co^{54}$	0	-51525_1	$(1f_{7/2})^7$	$(1f_{7/2})^7$	0^+	.190	β^+ 7.3	8.25		
$_{27}Co^{55}$	$-\frac{1}{2}$	-57987_2		$(1f_{7/2})^8$		$.648 \times 10^5$	β^+ 1.51, 1.04, . . . ; EC; γ .93, . . .	3.46		
$_{27}Co^{56}$	-1	-60153_2		$(2p_{3/2})^1$	4^+	$.668 \times 10^7$	EC; β^+ 1.46, . . . ; γ .85, 1.24, . . .	4.57	±3.8500	
$_{27}Co^{57}$	$-\frac{3}{2}$	-63704_1		$(2p_{3/2})^2$	$\frac{7}{2}-$	$.231 \times 10^8$	EC; γ 1.22, .014, .137, . . .	3.24	±4.6500	
$_{27}Co^{58}$	-2	-64239_1		$(2p_{3/2})^3$	2^+	$.613 \times 10^7$	EC; β^+ .48, . . . ; γ .81, 1.65	{0.39− / 2.31+	±4.0600	
$_{27}Co^{59}$	$-\frac{5}{2}$	-66810_1		$(2p_{3/2})^4$	$\frac{7}{2}-$		**100**		4.6490	0.400
$_{27}Co^{60}$	-3	-66186_1		$(1f_{5/2})^1$	5^+	$.166 \times 10^9$	β^- .31, . . . ; γ 1.33, 1.17, . . .	2.82	3.8100	
$_{27}Co^{61}$	$-\frac{7}{2}$	-67560_2		$(1f_{5/2})^2$	$(\frac{7}{2})^-$	$.594 \times 10^4$	β^- 1.22; γ .068	1.29		
$_{27}Co^{62}$	-4	-66054_2		$(1f_{5/2})^3$	(5^+)	$.834 \times 10^3$	β^- 2.88, .88; γ 1.17, 1.47, 1.74, . . .	5.22		
$_{27}Co^{63}$	$-\frac{9}{2}$	-66470_3		$(1f_{5/2})^4$		$†.520 \times 10^2$	β^- 3.6	3.60		
$_{27}Co^{64}$	-5			$(1f_{5/2})^5$		$.468 \times 10^3$	β^-; γ			
$_{28}Ni^{56}$	0	-57884_2	$(1f_{7/2})^8$	$(1f_{7/2})^8$	0^+	$.527 \times 10^6$	EC; γ .16, .82, .76, .48, .27, . . .	2.11		
$_{28}Ni^{57}$	$-\frac{1}{2}$	-60231_2		$(2p_{3/2})^1$	$(\frac{3}{2}-)$	$.133 \times 10^6$	EC; β^+ .84, .71, . . . ; γ 1.37, . . .	3.24		
$_{28}Ni^{58}$	-1	-64658_1		$(2p_{3/2})^2$	0^+		**67.88**			
$_{28}Ni^{59}$	$-\frac{3}{2}$	-65657_1		$(2p_{3/2})^3$	$\frac{3}{2}-$	$.253 \times 10^{13}$	EC	1.07		
$_{28}Ni^{60}$	-2	-69213_1		$(2p_{3/2})^4$	0^+		**26.23**			
$_{28}Ni^{61}$	$-\frac{5}{2}$	-68944_1		$(2p_{3/2})^{-1}$	$\frac{3}{2}-$		**1.19**		±0.7500	
$_{28}Ni^{62}$	-3	-71658_1		$(1f_{5/2})^2$	0^+		**3.66**			
$_{28}Ni^{63}$	$-\frac{7}{2}$	-70336_1		$(2p_{3/2})^{-1}$	$(\frac{3}{2}-)$	$.290 \times 10^{10}$	β^- .067	0.07		
$_{28}Ni^{64}$	-4	-72042_1		$(1f_{5/2})^4$	0^+		**1.08**			
$_{28}Ni^{65}$	$-\frac{9}{2}$	-69928_1		$(1f_{5/2})^5$	$(\frac{5}{2}-)$	$.922 \times 10^4$	β^- 2.10, 6.10, . . . ; γ 1.49, 1.11, . . .	2.13		
$_{28}Ni^{66}$	-5	-70915_2		$(1f_{5/2})^6$	0^+	$.198 \times 10^6$	β^- .20	0.20		
$_{29}Cu^{58}$	0	-55459_1	$(2p_{3/2})^1$	$(2p_{3/2})^1$	$(+)$	$.320 \times 10^1$	β^+ 7.5, 4.6; γ 1.45, 2.9	8.57		
$_{29}Cu^{59}$	$-\frac{1}{2}$	-60504_2		$(2p_{3/2})^2$	$(\frac{3}{2})^-$	$.810 \times 10^2$	β^+ 3.78, . . . ; γ 1.30, .87, .46, .34	4.80		
$_{29}Cu^{60}$	-1	-62638_1		$(2p_{3/2})^3$	2^+	$.144 \times 10^4$	β^+ 2.00, 3.00, . . . ; EC; γ 1.33, . . .	6.13		
$_{29}Cu^{61}$	$-\frac{3}{2}$	-66543_1		$(2p_{3/2})^4$	$\frac{3}{2}-$	$.119 \times 10^5$	β^+ 1.21, . . . ; EC; γ .28, .66, . . .	2.24	2.1600	
$_{29}Cu^{62}$	-2	-67434_2		$(1f_{5/2})^1$	1^+	$.594 \times 10^3$	β^+ 2.91, . . . ; EC; γ	3.94		
$_{29}Cu^{63}$	$-\frac{5}{2}$	-70408_1		$(1f_{5/2})^2$	$\frac{3}{2}-$		**69.09**		2.2260	−0.180
$_{29}Cu^{64}$	-3	-70241_1		$(1f_{5/2})^3$	1^+	$.464 \times 10^5$	EC; β^- .57; β^+ .66; γ 1.34	{0.57− / 1.68+	−0.2160	
$_{29}Cu^{65}$	$-\frac{7}{2}$	-72214_1		$(1f_{5/2})^4$	$\frac{3}{2}-$		**30.91**		2.3850	−0.190
$_{29}Cu^{66}$	-4	-71129_1		$(1f_{5/2})^5$	1^+	$.306 \times 10^3$	β^- 2.63, 1.59, . . .; γ 1.04, .83	2.63	±0.2830	

(Continued)

Table of Nuclides *(continued)*

Nuclide	T_3	Mass excess $M - A$, μu	Prominent terms for ground state or low-lying level: Proton	Neutron	J^π	Half-life, sec	**Abundance,** percent or decay modes with energies, MeV	Total disintegration energy, MeV	Magnetic moment, nm	Quadrupole moment, barns
$_{29}Cu^{67}$	$-\frac{9}{2}$	-72241_2		$(1f_{5/2})^6$	$(\frac{3}{2}-)$	$.220 \times 10^6$	β^- .40, .48, .57; γ .182, .090, . . .	0.57		
$_{29}Cu^{68}$	-5	-70230_2		$(2p_{1/2})^1$		$.300 \times 10^2$	β^- 3.5, 2.7, 3.3; γ 1.08, .81, . . .	4.58		
$_{30}Zn^{60}$	0		$(2p_{3/2})^2$	$(2p_{3/2})^2$	$0+$					
$_{30}Zn^{61}$	$-\frac{1}{2}$	-60750_3		$(2p_{3/2})^3$	$(\frac{3}{2}-)$	$.890 \times 10^2$	β^+ 4.38, . . . ; γ .48, 1.64, .98, .69	5.40		
$_{30}Zn^{62}$	-1	-65620_2		$(2p_{3/2})^4$	$0+$	$.335 \times 10^5$	EC; β^+ .67, . . . ; γ .042, .59, . . .	1.69		
$_{30}Zn^{63}$	$-\frac{3}{2}$	-66794_1		$(2p_{3/2})^{-1}$	$\frac{3}{2}-$	$.228 \times 10^4$	β^+ 2.35, . . . ; EC; γ .67, .97, . . .	3.37		
$_{30}Zn^{64}$	-2	-70855_1		$(1f_{5/2})^2$	$0+$		**48.89**			
$_{30}Zn^{65}$	$-\frac{5}{2}$	-70766_1		$(1f_{5/2})^3$	$\frac{5}{2}-$	$.212 \times 10^8$	EC; β^+ .33; γ 1.11	1.35	0.7690	−0.026
$_{30}Zn^{66}$	-3	-73948_1		$(1f_{5/2})^4$	$0+$		**27.81**			
$_{30}Zn^{67}$	$-\frac{7}{2}$	-72855_2		$(1f_{5/2})^5$	$\frac{5}{2}-$		**4.11**		0.8757	0.170
$_{30}Zn^{68}$	-4	-75143_1		$(1f_{5/2})^6$	$0+$		**18.57**			
$_{30}Zn^{69}$	$-\frac{9}{2}$	-73459_1		$(2p_{1/2})^1$	$(\frac{1}{2}-)$	†$.330 \times 10^4$	β^- .91	0.90		
$_{30}Zn^{70}$	-5	-74666_1		$(2p_{1/2})^2$	$0+$		**0.62**			
$_{30}Zn^{71}$	$-\frac{11}{2}$	-72490_2		$(2p_{1/2})^{-1}$		†$.150 \times 10^3$	β^- 2.61, 2.1, . . . ; γ .51, . . .	2.61		
$_{30}Zn^{72}$	-6	-73157_1		$(1g_{9/2})^2$	$0+$	$.167 \times 10^6$	β^- .30, . . . ; γ .14, .19, .05	0.44		
$_{31}Ga^{63}$	$-\frac{1}{2}$	-60890_4	$(2p_{3/2})^3$	$(2p_{3/2})^4$		$.350 \times 10^2$		5.50		
$_{31}Ga^{64}$	-1	-63263_2		$(1f_{5/2})^1$		$.156 \times 10^3$	β^+ 6.0, 2.8, . . . ; γ .98, 3.3, . . .	7.07		
$_{31}Ga^{65}$	$-\frac{3}{2}$	-67267_2		$(1f_{5/2})^2$	$(\frac{3}{2}-)$	$.900 \times 10^3$	β^+ 2.11, 1.39, . . . ; EC; γ .12, . . .	3.26		
$_{31}Ga^{66}$	-2	-68393_1		$(2p_{3/2})^{-1}$	$0+$	$.342 \times 10^5$	β^+ 4.15, . . . ; EC; γ 1.04, 2.75, . . .	5.18		
$_{31}Ga^{67}$	$-\frac{5}{2}$	-71784_2		$(1f_{5/2})^4$	$\frac{3}{2}-$	$.281 \times 10^6$	EC; γ .092, .182, .30, .090–.87	1.00	1.8500	0.220
$_{31}Ga^{68}$	-3	-72008_1		$(1f_{5/2})^5$	$1+$	$.408 \times 10^4$	β^+ 1.89, . . . ; EC; γ 1.08, .81–1.88	2.92	±0.0117	±0.031
$_{31}Ga^{69}$	$-\frac{7}{2}$	-74426_1		$(1f_{5/2})^6$	$\frac{3}{2}-$		**60.4**		2.0160	0.190
$_{31}Ga^{70}$	-4	-73965_1		$(2p_{1/2})^1$	$1+$	$.126 \times 10^4$	β^- 1.65, . . . ; γ 1.04, .17, . . .	{1.66− / 0.65+		
$_{31}Ga^{71}$	$-\frac{9}{2}$	-75294_1		$(2p_{1/2})^2$	$\frac{3}{2}-$		**39.6**		2.5620	0.120
$_{31}Ga^{72}$	-5	-73628_1		$(1g_{9/2})^1$	$3-$	$.508 \times 10^5$	β^- .96, .66–3.16; γ .84, .69, . . .	4.00	−0.1322	0.590
$_{31}Ga^{73}$	$-\frac{11}{2}$	-74874_2		$(1g_{9/2})^2$		$.173 \times 10^5$	β^- 1.19, . . . ; γ .30, .74, . . .	1.55		
$_{31}Ga^{74}$	-6	-72810_2		$(1g_{9/2})^3$		$.480 \times 10^3$	β^- 2.45, . . . ; γ .60, 2.35, .38–3.4	5.60		
$_{31}Ga^{75}$	$-\frac{13}{2}$			$(1g_{9/2})^4$		$.120 \times 10^3$	β^- 3.3; γ .58			
$_{31}Ga^{76}$	-7			$(1g_{9/2})^5$		$.320 \times 10^2$	β^- ~6; γ .57, .96, 1.12			
$_{32}Ge^{65}$	$-\frac{1}{2}$	-60400_4	$(2p_{3/2})^4$	$(1f_{5/2})^1$		$.900 \times 10^2$	β^+ 3.7, . . . ; γ .67, 1.72	6.40		
$_{32}Ge^{66}$	-1	-65200_3		$(1f_{5/2})^2$	$0+$	$.864 \times 10^4$	β^+ 1.3, 2.0; EC; γ .38, .046, . . .	2.97		
$_{32}Ge^{67}$	$-\frac{3}{2}$	-67060_3		$(1f_{5/2})^3$		$.114 \times 10^4$	β^+ 3.2, 2.3, . . . ; EC; γ .17, .92, . . .	4.40		
$_{32}Ge^{68}$	-2	-71470_4		$(1f_{5/2})^4$	$0+$	$.242 \times 10^8$	EC	0.50		
$_{32}Ge^{69}$	$-\frac{5}{2}$	-72036		$(1f_{5/2})^5$		$.144 \times 10^6$	EC; β^+ 1.21, .61, . . . ; γ 1.12, . . .	2.23		

${}_{32}Ge^{71}$	$-\frac{7}{2}$	-75044_1		$(2p_{1/2})^1$	$\frac{1}{2}-$	$.950 \times 10^6$	EC	0.23	0.5460	
${}_{32}Ge^{72}$	-4	-77918_1		$(2p_{1/2})^2$	$0+$		**27.43**			
${}_{32}Ge^{73}$	$-\frac{9}{2}$	-76537_1		$(1g_{9/2})^1$	$\frac{9}{2}+$		**7.76**		-0.8792	-0.220
${}_{32}Ge^{74}$	-5	-78819_1		$(1g_{9/2})^2$	$0+$		**36.54**			
${}_{32}Ge^{75}$	$-\frac{11}{2}$	-77117_2		$(2p_{1/2})^{-1}$	$(\frac{1}{2}-)$	$.492 \times 10^4$	β^- 1.18, .92, . . . ; γ .27, .07–.63	1.20		
${}_{32}Ge^{76}$	-6	-78594_1		$(1g_{9/2})^4$	$0+$		**7.76**			
${}_{32}Ge^{77}$	$-\frac{13}{2}$	-76400_2		$(1g_{9/2})^5$	$*(\frac{7}{2}+)$	$.396 \times 10^5$	β^- 2.2, 1.38, . . . ; γ .22, .27, . . .	2.75		
${}_{32}Ge^{78}$	-7			$(1g_{9/2})^6$	$0+$	$.756 \times 10^4$	β^- .9	0.90		
${}_{33}As^{68}$	-1		$(1f_{5/2})^1$	$(1f_{5/2})^3$		$.400 \times 10^3$	β^+			
${}_{33}As^{69}$	$-\frac{3}{2}$	-67850_3	or	$(1f_{5/2})^4$		$.900 \times 10^3$	β^+ 2.9; γ .23	3.90		
${}_{33}As^{70}$	-2	-69054_2	$(2p_{3/2})^{-1}$	$(1f_{5/2})^5$		$.300 \times 10^4$	β^+ 1.4, 2.5; EC; γ 1.04, 2.0, . . .	6.24		
${}_{33}As^{71}$	$-\frac{5}{2}$	-72887_1		$(1f_{5/2})^6$	$\frac{5}{2}-$	$.223 \times 10^6$	EC; β^+ .81; γ .175, .023	2.01		
${}_{33}As^{72}$	-3	-73237_2		$(1g_{9/2})^1$	$2-$	$.936 \times 10^5$	β^+ 2.50, 3.34, . . . ; EC; γ .84, . . .	4.36		
${}_{33}As^{73}$	$-\frac{7}{2}$	-76139_2		$(2p_{1/2})^2$	$\frac{3}{2}-$	$.657 \times 10^7$	EC	0.37		
${}_{33}As^{74}$	-4	-76067_1		$(1g_{9/2})^1$	$2-$	$.156 \times 10^7$	EC; β^+ .90, . . . ; β^- 1.36, . . . ; γ .60, . . .	$\begin{cases}1.36^-\\2.56^+\end{cases}$		
${}_{33}As^{75}$	$-\frac{9}{2}$	-78403_1		$(1g_{9/2})^2$	$\frac{3}{2}-$		**100**		1.4390	0.290
${}_{33}As^{76}$	-5	-77603_2		$(1g_{9/2})^3$	$2-$	$.954 \times 10^5$	β^- 2.97, 2.41, . . . ; γ .56, 1.21, .66	$\begin{cases}2.97^-\\0.92^+\end{cases}$	-0.9050	
${}_{33}As^{77}$	$-\frac{11}{2}$	-79354_2		$(1g_{9/2})^4$	$\frac{3}{2}-$	$.140 \times 10^6$	β^- .68; γ .24, .52, .086, .160	0.68		
${}_{33}As^{78}$	-6	-78100_3		$(1g_{9/2})^5$	$(2-)$	$.546 \times 10^4$	β^- 4.1, 1.4; γ .62, .70, 1.31, . . .	4.27		
${}_{33}As^{79}$	$-\frac{13}{2}$	-79110_2		$(1g_{9/2})^6$	$(\frac{3}{2}-)$	$.540 \times 10^3$	β^- 2.2, 1.2–1.8; γ .36–.87	2.23		
${}_{33}As^{80}$	-7	-77030_3		$(1g_{9/2})^7$		$.150 \times 10^2$	β^- 6.0, 5.4, 3.0–4.5; γ .66, .8–2.35	6.00		
${}_{33}As^{81}$	$-\frac{15}{2}$			$(1g_{9/2})^8$		$.330 \times 10^2$	β^- 3.8	3.80		
${}_{33}As^{85}$	$-\frac{19}{2}$			$(2d_{5/2})^2$		.430	β^-			
${}_{34}Se^{70}$	-1		$(1f_{5/2})^2$	$(1f_{5/2})^4$	$0+$	$.264 \times 10^4$	β^+			
${}_{34}Se^{71}$	$-\frac{3}{2}$	-68160_3		$(1f_{5/2})^5$		$.300 \times 10^3$	β^+ 3.4; γ .16	4.40		
${}_{34}Se^{72}$	-2	-72590_4		$(1f_{5/2})^6$	$0+$	$.726 \times 10^6$	EC; γ .46	0.60		
${}_{34}Se^{73}$	$-\frac{5}{2}$	-73186_2		$(1g_{9/2})^1$	$(\frac{9}{2}+)$	$.256 \times 10^5$	β^+ 1.30, 1.7; γ .36, .066	2.75		
${}_{34}Se^{74}$	-3	-77524_1		$(2p_{1/2})^2$	$0+$		**0.87**			
${}_{34}Se^{75}$	$-\frac{7}{2}$	-77475_2		$(1g_{9/2})^1$	$*\frac{5}{2}+$	$.104 \times 10^8$	EC; γ .265, .136, .280, .024–.58	0.87		1.000
${}_{34}Se^{76}$	-4	-80793_1		$(1g_{9/2})^2$	$0+$		**9.02**			
${}_{34}Se^{77}$	$-\frac{9}{2}$	-80089_1		$(2p_{1/2})^{-1}$	$\frac{1}{2}-$		**7.58**		0.5340	
${}_{34}Se^{78}$	-5	-82686_1		$(1g_{9/2})^4$	$0+$		**23.52**			
${}_{34}Se^{79}$	$-\frac{11}{2}$	-81505_1		$(1g_{9/2})^5$	$*\frac{7}{2}+$	$.221 \times 10^{13}$	β^- .16	0.15	-1.0200	0.800
${}_{34}Se^{80}$	-6	-83472_1		$(1g_{9/2})^6$	$0+$		**49.82**			
${}_{34}Se^{81}$	$-\frac{13}{2}$	-82016_1		$(2p_{1/2})^{-1}$	$\frac{1}{2}-$	$†.108 \times 10^4$	β^- 1.6, . . . ; γ .28, . . .	1.58		
${}_{34}Se^{82}$	-7	-83293_1		$(1g_{9/2})^8$	$0+$		**9.19**			
${}_{34}Se^{83}$	$-\frac{15}{2}$			$(1g_{9/2})^9$	$(\frac{9}{2}+)$	$.150 \times 10^4$	β^- .45, 1.0, 1.7; γ .23–2.3	3.45		
${}_{34}Se^{84}$	-8			$(1g_{9/2})^{10}$	$0+$	$.180 \times 10^3$	β^-			
${}_{34}Se^{85}$	$-\frac{17}{2}$			$(2d_{5/2})^1$		$.390 \times 10^2$	β^-			

(Continued)

Table of Nuclides (*continued*)

Nuclide	T_3	Mass excess $M - A$, μu	Prominent terms for ground state or low-lying level: Proton	Neutron	J^π	Half-life, sec	**Abundance,** percent or decay modes with energies, MeV	Total disintegration energy, MeV	Magnetic moment, nm	Quadrupole moment, barns
${}_{35}Br^{74}$	-2	-70220_4	$(1f_{5/2})^3$	$(2p_{1/2})^1$		$<.252 \times 10^4$	β^+; γ .64	6.80		
${}_{35}Br^{75}$	$-\frac{5}{2}$	-74553_2	or	$(2p_{1/2})^2$		$.576 \times 10^4$	β^+ 1.72, 1.10, .65; EC; γ .285, .62	2.72		
${}_{35}Br^{76}$	-3	-75820_2	$(2p_{3/2})^{-1}$	$(2p_{1/2})^{-1}$	1^+	$.594 \times 10^5$	β^+ 3.58, . . . ; EC; γ .56, .65, . . .	4.63	±0.5480	±0.250
${}_{35}Br^{77}$	$-\frac{7}{2}$	-78624_1		$(1g_{9/2})^2$	$\frac{3}{2}^-$	$.209 \times 10^6$	EC; β^+ .34; γ .086–1.00	1.36		
${}_{35}Br^{78}$	-4	-78850_1		$(2p_{1/2})^{-1}$	1^+	$.390 \times 10^3$	β^+ 2.45, . . . ; γ .62	{0.70− {3.57+		
${}_{35}Br^{79}$	$-\frac{9}{2}$	-81670_1		$(1g_{9/2})^4$	$\frac{3}{2}^-$		**50.54**		2.1060	0.310
${}_{35}Br^{80}$	-5	-81464_1		$(2p_{1/2})^{-1}$	1^+	†$.108 \times 10^4$	β^- 2.00, 1.38; γ .62, . . .; EC; β^+ .87; γ .65	{2.01− {1.87+	±0.5140	±0.180
${}_{35}Br^{81}$	$-\frac{11}{2}$	-83708_1		$(1g_{9/2})^6$	$\frac{3}{2}^-$		**49.46**		2.2700	0.260
${}_{35}Br^{82}$	-6	-83198_1		$(1g_{9/2})^7$	5^-	$.127 \times 10^6$	β^- .44; γ .78, .55, .62, . . .	{3.09− {0.09+	±1.6260	±0.700
${}_{35}Br^{83}$	$-\frac{13}{2}$	-84832_2		$(1g_{9/2})^8$	$(\frac{3}{2}^-)$	$.864 \times 10^4$	β^- .94, . . . ; γ .51	0.97		
${}_{35}Br^{84}$	-7	-83450_2		$(1g_{9/2})^9$		$.192 \times 10^4$	β^- 4.7, 2.8; γ .88, 2.1, 1.9, . . .	4.70		
${}_{35}Br^{85}$	$-\frac{15}{2}$	-84470_3		$(1g_{9/2})^{10}$	$(\frac{3}{2}^-)$	$.180 \times 10^3$	β^- 2.5; γ	2.80		
${}_{35}Br^{86}$	-8	-81800_3		$(2d_{5/2})^1$		$.540 \times 10^2$	β^- 3, 5, 7.1; γ 1.6, 2.8	7.10		
${}_{35}Br^{87}$	$-\frac{17}{2}$			$(2d_{5/2})^2$		$.550 \times 10^2$	β^- 2.6, 8.0; γ 3.2, 5.4	8.00		
${}_{35}Br^{88}$	-9			$(2d_{5/2})^3$		$.160 \times 10^2$	β^-			
${}_{35}Br^{89}$	$-\frac{19}{2}$			$(2d_{5/2})^4$		$.450 \times 10^1$	β^-			
${}_{35}Br^{90}$	-10			$(2d_{5/2})^5$		$.160 \times 10^1$	β^-			
${}_{36}Kr^{74}$	-1	-66900_4	$(1f_{5/2})^4$	$(1f_{5/2})^6$	0^+	$.900 \times 10^3$	β^+ 3.1	4.10		
${}_{36}Kr^{75}$	$-\frac{3}{2}$	-69080_4		$(2p_{1/2})^1$		$.300 \times 10^3$		5.10		
${}_{36}Kr^{76}$	-2	-74530_4		$(2p_{1/2})^2$	0^+	$.533 \times 10^5$	EC; γ .040–.65	1.20		
${}_{36}Kr^{77}$	$-\frac{5}{2}$	-75520_2		$(1f_{5/2})^{-1}$	$\frac{5}{2}^-$	$.432 \times 10^4$	β^+ 1.86, . . . ; EC; γ .108, .131, . . .	2.89		
${}_{36}Kr^{78}$	-3	-79597_1		$(1g_{9/2})^2$	0^+		**0.35**			
${}_{36}Kr^{79}$	$-\frac{7}{2}$	-79932_1		$(2p_{1/2})^{-1}$	$\frac{1}{2}^-$	$.122 \times 10^6$	EC; β^+ .60, .34; γ .044, .261, . . .	1.62		
${}_{36}Kr^{80}$	-4	-83620_1		$(1g_{9/2})^4$	0^+		**2.27**			
${}_{36}Kr^{81}$	$-\frac{9}{2}$	-83390_1		$(1g_{9/2})^5$	$*\frac{7}{2}^+$	$.631 \times 10^{13}$	EC	0.30		
${}_{36}Kr^{82}$	-5	-86518_1		$(1g_{9/2})^6$	0^+		**11.56**			
${}_{36}Kr^{83}$	$-\frac{11}{2}$	-85868_1		$(1g_{9/2})^7$	$\frac{9}{2}^+$		**11.55**		−0.9700	0.230
${}_{36}Kr^{84}$	-6	-88496_1		$(1g_{9/2})^8$	0^+		**56.90**			
${}_{36}Kr^{85}$	$-\frac{13}{2}$	-87477_1		$(1g_{9/2})^9$	$\frac{9}{2}^+$	$.340 \times 10^9$	β^- .67, . . . ; γ .52	0.67	±1.0050	0.380
${}_{36}Kr^{86}$	-7	-89384_1		$(1g_{9/2})^{10}$	0^+		**17.37**			
${}_{36}Kr^{87}$	$-\frac{15}{2}$	-86635_2		$(2d_{5/2})^1$	$*(\frac{7}{2}^+)$	$.456 \times 10^4$	β^- 3.8, 1.3, 3.3; γ .40, 2.57, . . .	3.89		
${}_{36}Kr^{88}$	-8	-85730_3		$(2d_{5/2})^2$	0^+	$.101 \times 10^5$	β^- .52, 2.7, . . . ; γ 2.4, 1.9, .85	2.80		
${}_{36}Kr^{89}$	$-\frac{17}{2}$	-83400_3		$(2d_{5/2})^3$		$.192 \times 10^3$	β^- 4.0, ~2; γ .60, .22, .38–1.52	4.60		
${}_{36}Kr^{90}$	-9	-80280_3		$(2d_{5/2})^4$	0^+	$.330 \times 10^2$	β^- 2.8, . . . ; γ .120, .54, 1.11, 1.54	4.56		
				$(2d_{5/2})^5$		$.100 \times 10^2$	β^- 3.6, . . . ; γ			

$_{36}$Kr[illegible]	[illegible]			($1g_{7/2}$)[illegible]		[illegible]	β^-			
$_{36}Kr^{94}$	-11			$(1g_{7/2})^2$	0^+	$.100 \times 10^1$	β^-			
$_{36}Kr^{95}$	$-\frac{23}{2}$			$(1g_{7/2})^3$		Short	β^-			
$_{37}Rb^{79}$	$-\frac{5}{2}$		$(1f_{5/2})^5$	$(1g_{9/2})^2$	$(\frac{3}{2}^-)$	$.126 \times 10^4$	β^+; γ .15, .19			
$_{37}Rb^{80}$	-3	-78100_3	or	$(2p_{1/2})^{-1}$	1^+	$.340 \times 10^2$	β^+ 4.1; EC; γ .62	5.10		
$_{37}Rb^{81}$	$-\frac{7}{2}$	-80980_3	$(2p_{3/2})^{-1}$	$(1g_{9/2})^4$	$\frac{3}{2}^-$	$.169 \times 10^5$	EC; β^+ 1.03, . . . ; γ .19, .45, . . .	2.24	2.0500	
$_{37}Rb^{82}$	-4	-82041_2		$(2p_{1/2})^{-1}$	1^+	†$.750 \times 10^2$	β^+ 3.15, . . . ; γ .78, 1.4	4.17		
$_{37}Rb^{83}$	$-\frac{9}{2}$	-85270_4		$(1g_{9/2})^6$	$\frac{5}{2}^-$	$.717 \times 10^7$	EC; γ .52, . . .	0.60	1.4000	
$_{37}Rb^{84}$	-5	-85619_1		$(1g_{9/2})^7$	2^-	$.285 \times 10^7$	EC; β^+ .8, 1.6; γ .88, . . . ; β^- .90	$\begin{cases}0.89^-\\2.68^+\end{cases}$	-1.3200	
$_{37}Rb^{85}$	$-\frac{11}{2}$	-88200_1		$(1g_{9/2})^8$	$\frac{5}{2}^-$		**72.15**		1.3527	0.280
$_{37}Rb^{86}$	-6	-88807_1		$(1g_{9/2})^9$	2^-	$.162 \times 10^7$	β^- 1.77, .7, . . . ; γ 1.08, . . .	$\begin{cases}1.78^-\\0.54^+\end{cases}$	-1.6910	
$_{37}Rb^{87}$	$-\frac{13}{2}$	-90813_1		$(1g_{9/2})^{10}$	$\frac{3}{2}^-$	$.148 \times 10^{19}$	**27.85**; β^- .27	0.27	2.7506	0.140
$_{37}Rb^{88}$	-7	-88730_2		$(2d_{5/2})^1$	2^-	$.108 \times 10^4$	β^- 5.2, 3.3, 2; γ 1.85, .91, . . .	5.24		
$_{37}Rb^{89}$	$-\frac{15}{2}$	-88350_2		$(2d_{5/2})^2$		$.900 \times 10^3$	β^- 3.9, 2.8, . . .; γ 1.05, 1.26, . . .	3.92		
$_{37}Rb^{90}$	-8	-85180_3		$(2d_{5/2})^3$		$.174 \times 10^3$	β^- 6.6, 5.8, 2.2, . . .; γ .84, . . .	6.59		
$_{37}Rb^{91}$	$-\frac{17}{2}$	-83930_4		$(2d_{5/2})^4$		$.720 \times 10^2$	β^- 4.6; γ .095, .35	5.50		
$_{37}Rb^{92}$	-9	-80860_4		$(2d_{5/2})^5$		$.500 \times 10^1$	β^-	7.60		
$_{37}Rb^{93}$	$-\frac{19}{2}$			$(2d_{5/2})^6$		$.600 \times 10^1$	β^-			
$_{37}Rb^{94}$	-10			$(1g_{7/2})^1$		$.300 \times 10^1$	β^-			
$_{37}Rb^{95}$	$-\frac{21}{2}$			$(1g_{7/2})^2$		$<.250 \times 10^1$	β^-			
$_{38}Sr^{80}$	-2		$(1f_{5/2})^6$	$(1g_{9/2})^2$	0^+	$.612 \times 10^4$	EC; γ			
$_{38}Sr^{81}$	$-\frac{5}{2}$			$(2p_{1/2})^{-1}$	$(\frac{1}{2}^-)$	$.174 \times 10^4$	β^+			
$_{38}Sr^{82}$	-3	-81610_4		$(1g_{9/2})^4$	0^+	$.216 \times 10^7$	EC	0.40		
$_{38}Sr^{83}$	$-\frac{7}{2}$	-82800_4		$(1g_{9/2})^5$		$.119 \times 10^6$	EC; β^+ 1.15, .8, . . . ; γ .755, . . .	2.30		
$_{38}Sr^{84}$	-4	-86569_1		$(1g_{9/2})^6$	0^+		**0.56**			
$_{38}Sr^{85}$	$-\frac{9}{2}$	-87011_2		$(1g_{9/2})^7$	$(\frac{9}{2}^+)$	$.553 \times 10^7$	EC; γ .514	1.10		
$_{38}Sr^{86}$	-5	-90715_1		$(1g_{9/2})^8$	0^+		**9.86**			
$_{38}Sr^{87}$	$-\frac{11}{2}$	-91107_1		$(1g_{9/2})^9$	$\frac{9}{2}^+$		**7.02**		-1.0930	0.360
$_{38}Sr^{88}$	-6	-94359_1		$(1g_{9/2})^{10}$	0^+		**82.56**			
$_{38}Sr^{89}$	$-\frac{13}{2}$	-92558_1		$(2d_{5/2})^1$	$\frac{5}{2}^+$	$.436 \times 10^7$	β^- 1.46	1.46		
$_{38}Sr^{90}$	-7	-92253_1		$(2d_{5/2})^2$	0^+	$.884 \times 10^9$	β^- .54	0.54		
$_{38}Sr^{91}$	$-\frac{15}{2}$	-89839_2		$(2d_{5/2})^3$	$\frac{5}{2}^+$	$.349 \times 10^5$	β^- 1.09, 1.36, . . . ; γ .65–1.41	2.67		
$_{38}Sr^{92}$	-8	-89020_2		$(2d_{5/2})^4$	0^+	$.972 \times 10^4$	β^- .545, 1.5; γ 1.37, .44, .23	1.92		
$_{38}Sr^{93}$	$-\frac{17}{2}$	-85290_3		$(2d_{5/2})^5$		$.498 \times 10^3$	β^- 2.0, 3.0–4.8; γ .15–2.0	4.80		
$_{38}Sr^{94}$	-9	-84620_3		$(2d_{5/2})^6$	0^+	$.720 \times 10^2$	β^- 2.1; γ 1.42	3.45		
$_{38}Sr^{95}$	$-\frac{19}{2}$			$(1g_{7/2})^1$		$.480 \times 10^2$	β^- 2			
$_{39}Y^{82}$	-2		$(2p_{1/2})^1$	$(1g_{9/2})^3$		$.540 \times 10^3$	β^+			
$_{39}Y^{83}$	$-\frac{5}{2}$			$(1g_{9/2})^4$						
$_{39}Y^{84}$	-3	-79810_3		$(1g_{9/2})^5$		$.252 \times 10^4$	β^+ 2.5, 3.5, . . . ; γ .80, .98, . . .	6.30		
$_{39}Y^{85}$	$-\frac{7}{2}$	-83511_2		$(1g_{9/2})^6$		$.180 \times 10^5$	β^+ 2.2, 2.0, . . . ; EC; γ .23–2.5	3.26		

(Continued)

Table of Nuclides *(continued)*

Nuclide	T_3	Mass excess $M - A$, μu	Prominent terms for ground state or low-lying level: Proton	Neutron	J^π	Half-life, sec	**Abundance,** percent or decay modes with energies, MeV	Total disintegration energy, MeV	Magnetic moment, nm	Quadrupole moment, barns
$_{39}Y^{86}$	-4	-85054_2	$(2p_{1/2})^1$	$(1g_{9/2})^7$	$4-$	$.540 \times 10^5$	EC; β^+ 1.19, .6–3.1; γ 1.08, . . .	5.27		
$_{39}Y^{87}$	$-\frac{9}{2}$	-89260_3		$(1g_{9/2})^8$	$(\frac{1}{2}-)$	$.288 \times 10^6$	EC; β^+ .7; γ .48	1.72		
$_{39}Y^{88}$	-5	-90472_1		$(1g_{9/2})^9$	$4-$	$.933 \times 10^7$	EC; β^+ .78; γ 1.83, .90, . . .	3.62		
$_{39}Y^{89}$	$-\frac{11}{2}$	-94128_1		$(1g_{9/2})^{10}$	$\frac{1}{2}-$		**100**		-0.1373	
$_{39}Y^{90}$	-6	-92837_1		$(2d_{5/2})^1$	$2-$	$.231 \times 10^6$	β^- 2.27, . . . ; γ 1.75	2.29	-1.6300	
$_{39}Y^{91}$	$-\frac{13}{2}$	-92705_2		$(2d_{5/2})^2$	$\frac{1}{2}-$	$.510 \times 10^7$	β^- 1.55, . . . ; γ 1.21	1.54	± 0.1640	
$_{39}Y^{92}$	-7	-91074_2		$(2d_{5/2})^3$	$2-$	$.127 \times 10^5$	β^- 3.64, 1.32, . . . ; γ .932, 1.39, . . .	3.63		
$_{39}Y^{93}$	$-\frac{15}{2}$	-90448_2		$(2d_{5/2})^4$	$(\frac{1}{2}-)$	$.364 \times 10^5$	β^- 2.89, . . . ; γ .27, .94, .38–2.4	2.89		
$_{39}Y^{94}$	-8	-88320_3		$(2d_{5/2})^5$		$.120 \times 10^4$	β^- 5.0, . . . ; γ .92, .56, 1.13, . . .	5.00		
$_{39}Y^{95}$	$-\frac{17}{2}$	-87460_4		$(2d_{5/2})^6$		$.660 \times 10^3$	β^-	4.20		
$_{39}Y^{96}$	-9	-84310_4		$(1g_{7/2})^1$		$.138 \times 10^3$	β^- 3.5; γ .7, 1.0	6.90		
$_{40}Zr^{85}$	$-\frac{5}{2}$		$(2p_{1/2})^2$	$(1g_{9/2})^5$						
$_{40}Zr^{86}$	-3	-83770_4		$(1g_{9/2})^6$	$0+$	$.594 \times 10^5$	EC; γ .24	1.20		
$_{40}Zr^{87}$	$-\frac{7}{2}$	-85510_3		$(1g_{9/2})^7$		$.576 \times 10^4$	β^+ 2.10, . . . ; γ 1.2, . . .	3.50		
$_{40}Zr^{88}$	-4	-89940_4		$(1g_{9/2})^8$	$0+$	$.734 \times 10^7$	EC; γ .39	0.50		
$_{40}Zr^{89}$	$-\frac{9}{2}$	-91086_1		$(1g_{9/2})^9$	$(\frac{9}{2}+)$	$.282 \times 10^6$	EC; β^+ .90; γ 1.7, . . .	2.83		
$_{40}Zr^{90}$	-5	-95300_1		$(1g_{9/2})^{10}$	$0+$		**51.46**			
$_{40}Zr^{91}$	$-\frac{11}{2}$	-94358_1		$(2d_{5/2})^1$	$\frac{5}{2}+$		**11.23**		-1.3030	
$_{40}Zr^{92}$	-6	-94969_1		$(2d_{5/2})^2$	$0+$		**17.11**			
$_{40}Zr^{93}$	$-\frac{13}{2}$	-93550_1		$(2d_{5/2})^3$	$\frac{5}{2}+$	$.300 \times 10^{14}$	β^- .063, .034	0.06		
$_{40}Zr^{94}$	-7	-93686_1		$(2d_{5/2})^4$	$0+$		**17.40**			
$_{40}Zr^{95}$	$-\frac{15}{2}$	-91965_1		$(2d_{5/2})^5$	$(\frac{5}{2}+)$	$.562 \times 10^7$	β^- .40, .36, .89; γ .72, .76	1.12		
$_{40}Zr^{96}$	-8	-91714_1		$(2d_{5/2})^6$	$0+$		**2.80**	0.21		
$_{40}Zr^{97}$	$-\frac{17}{2}$	-89034_2		$(3s_{1/2})^1$	$\frac{1}{2}+$	$.612 \times 10^5$	β^- 1.91, . . . ; γ .5–2.6	2.67		
$_{40}Zr^{99}$	$-\frac{19}{2}$			$(1g_{7/2})^3$		$<.160 \times 10^1$	β^-			
$_{41}Nb^{89}$	$-\frac{7}{2}$	-86920_3	$(1g_{9/2})^1$	$(1g_{9/2})^8$		$.684 \times 10^4$	β^+ 2.9	3.88		
$_{41}Nb^{90}$	-4	-88741_2		$(1g_{9/2})^9$	$(+)$	$.526 \times 10^5$	β^+ 1.50, . . . ; γ 1.14, 2.32	6.11		
$_{41}Nb^{91}$	$-\frac{9}{2}$	-93140_2		$(1g_{9/2})^{10}$	$(\frac{9}{2}+)$	Long	EC	1.14		
$_{41}Nb^{92}$	-5	-92789_2		$(2d_{5/2})^1$		$.873 \times 10^6$	EC; γ .93, .89, 1.82	{0.37− {2.03+		
$_{41}Nb^{93}$	$-\frac{11}{2}$	-93618_1		$(2d_{5/2})^2$	$\frac{9}{2}+$		**100**		6.1670	-0.220
$_{41}Nb^{94}$	-6	-92697_2		$(2d_{5/2})^3$	$(6+)$	$.631 \times 10^{12}$	β^- .5, . . . ; γ .87, .70	{2.06− {0.92+		
$_{41}Nb^{95}$	$-\frac{13}{2}$	-93168_1		$(2d_{5/2})^4$		$.302 \times 10^7$	β^- .16, . . . ; γ .77	0.92		
$_{41}Nb^{96}$	-7	-91944_2		$(2d_{5/2})^5$		$.828 \times 10^5$	β^- .7, .4; γ .77, .56, 1.08, . . .	3.15		
$_{41}Nb^{97}$	$-\frac{15}{2}$	-91904_1		$(2d_{5/2})^6$	$(+)$	$.432 \times 10^4$	β^- 1.27, . . . ; γ .66	1.93		

[illegible]				[illegible]		[illegible] $\times 10$[illegible]	β^- 3.2, . . . ; γ .16, .26	3.10		
$_{41}Nb^{100}$	-9	-85980_4		$(1g_{7/2})^3$		†.180 $\times 10^3$	β^-; γ .53, .36, .45, .14–2.9	6.10		
$_{41}Nb^{101}$	$-\frac{19}{2}$			$(1g_{7/2})^4$		.600 $\times 10^2$	β^-			
$_{42}Mo^{90}$	-3	-86060_3	$(1g_{9/2})^2$	$(1g_{9/2})^8$	0^+	.205 $\times 10^5$	EC; β^+ 1.2; γ	2.50		
$_{42}Mo^{91}$	$-\frac{7}{2}$	-88350_2		$(1g_{9/2})^9$	$(\frac{9}{2}^+)$	.936 $\times 10^3$	β^+ 3.44; EC	4.46		
$_{42}Mo^{92}$	-4	-93189_1		$(1g_{9/2})^{10}$	0^+		**15.84**			
$_{42}Mo^{93}$	$-\frac{9}{2}$	-93170_2		$(2d_{5/2})^1$	$(\frac{5}{2})$	.300 $\times 10^{12}$	EC	0.42		
$_{42}Mo^{94}$	-5	-94909_1		$(2d_{5/2})^2$	0^+		**9.04**			
$_{42}Mo^{95}$	$-\frac{11}{2}$	-94161_1		$(2d_{5/2})^3$	$\frac{5}{2}^+$		**15.72**		-0.9135	
$_{42}Mo^{96}$	-6	-95326_1		$(2d_{5/2})^4$	0^+		**16.53**			
$_{42}Mo^{97}$	$-\frac{13}{2}$	-93978_1		$(2d_{5/2})^5$	$\frac{5}{2}^+$		**9.46**		-0.9327	
$_{42}Mo^{98}$	-7	-94591_1		$(2d_{5/2})^6$	0^+		**23.78**			
$_{42}Mo^{99}$	$-\frac{15}{2}$	-92280_2		$(3s_{1/2})^1$	$(\frac{1}{2}^+)$	.238 $\times 10^6$	β^- 1.23, .45, . . . ; γ .74, .041–.78	1.37		
$_{42}Mo^{100}$	-8	-92525_1		$(1g_{7/2})^2$	0^+		**9.63**			
$_{42}Mo^{101}$	$-\frac{17}{2}$	-89647_2		$(1g_{7/2})^3$		.876 $\times 10^3$	β^- 2.23, . . . ; γ 1.02, .59, 2.08, . . .	2.82		
$_{42}Mo^{102}$	-9	-89750_4		$(1g_{7/2})^4$	0^+	.660 $\times 10^3$	β^- 1.2	1.00		
$_{42}Mo^{104}$	-10			$(1g_{7/2})^6$	0^+	.960 $\times 10^2$	β^- 2.2, . . . ; γ .89, .36			
$_{42}Mo^{105}$	$-\frac{21}{2}$			$(1g_{7/2})^7$		.400 $\times 10^2$	β^-			
$_{43}Tc^{92}$	-3	-84540_3	$(1g_{9/2})^3$	$(1g_{9/2})^9$		.246 $\times 10^3$	β^+ 4.1; γ 1.54, .79, .33, .14, . . .	8.06		
$_{43}Tc^{93}$	$-\frac{7}{2}$	-89749_2		$(1g_{9/2})^{10}$	$(\frac{9}{2}^+)$	.972 $\times 10^4$	EC; β^+ .82, .6; γ 1.3, 1.5, .86, . . .	3.19		
$_{43}Tc^{94}$	-4	-90337_1		$(2d_{5/2})^1$	(2^+)	.173 $\times 10^5$	EC; β^+ ~1.7, . . . ; γ .87, .71, .85	4.26		
$_{43}Tc^{95}$	$-\frac{9}{2}$	-92380_2		$(2d_{5/2})^2$	$(\frac{9}{2}^+)$	†.720 $\times 10^5$	EC; γ .77, .84, .21–1.1	1.66		
$_{43}Tc^{96}$	-5	-92170_2		$(2d_{5/2})^3$		.372 $\times 10^6$	EC; γ .77, .84, .81, 1.12, . . .	{0.21⁻ 2.94⁺		
$_{43}Tc^{97}$	$-\frac{11}{2}$	-93660_4		$(2d_{5/2})^4$	$(^+)$	.821 $\times 10^{14}$	EC	0.30		
$_{43}Tc^{98}$	-6	-92890_3		$(2d_{5/2})^5$		.475 $\times 10^{14}$	β^- .3; γ .75, .66	{1.70⁻ 1.59⁺		
$_{43}Tc^{99}$	$-\frac{13}{2}$	-93751_1		$(2d_{5/2})^6$	$\frac{9}{2}^+$	.663 $\times 10^{13}$	β^- .29	0.29	5.6800	0.300
$_{43}Tc^{100}$	-7	-92160_2		$(1g_{7/2})^1$	1^+	.170 $\times 10^2$	β^- 3.37, 2.24, . . . ; γ .54, .59, . . .	{3.37⁻ 0.34⁺		
$_{43}Tc^{101}$	$-\frac{15}{2}$	-92674_2		$(1g_{7/2})^2$		.840 $\times 10^3$	β^- 1.32, 1.07; γ .31, .54, . . .	1.63		
$_{43}Tc^{102}$	-8	-90820_4		$(1g_{7/2})^3$		†.500 $\times 10^1$	β^- 4	4.50		
$_{43}Tc^{103}$	$-\frac{17}{2}$	-91170_3		$(1g_{7/2})^4$		.500 $\times 10^2$	β^- 2.2, 2.0; γ .135, .35, .215	2.35		
$_{43}Tc^{104}$	-9	-88290_3		$(1g_{7/2})^5$		.108 $\times 10^4$	β^- 2.4, . . . ; γ .31–4.8	5.85		
$_{43}Tc^{105}$	$-\frac{19}{2}$	-88670_3		$(1g_{7/2})^6$		.480 $\times 10^3$	β^- 3.4, 1.8; γ .11, . . .	3.40		
$_{44}Ru^{93}$	$-\frac{5}{2}$		$(1g_{9/2})^4$	$(1g_{9/2})^9$		.500 $\times 10^2$	β^+			
$_{44}Ru^{94}$	-3			$(1g_{9/2})^{10}$	0^+	.342 $\times 10^4$	EC; β^+; γ			
$_{44}Ru^{95}$	$-\frac{7}{2}$	-90199_2		$(2d_{5/2})^1$		.594 $\times 10^4$	EC; β^+ 1.0, 1.3, .7; γ .34, 1.1, . . .	2.03		
$_{44}Ru^{96}$	-4	-92402_1		$(2d_{5/2})^2$	0^+		**5.51**			
$_{44}Ru^{97}$	$-\frac{9}{2}$	-92370_4		$(2d_{5/2})^3$	$(\frac{5}{2}^+)$	.251 $\times 10^6$	EC; γ .22, .11–.57	1.20		
$_{44}Ru^{98}$	-5	-94711_1		$(2d_{5/2})^4$	0^+		**1.87**			
$_{44}Ru^{99}$	$-\frac{11}{2}$	-94064_1		$(2d_{5/2})^5$	$\frac{5}{2}^+$		**12.72**		-0.6300	
$_{44}Ru^{100}$	-6	-95782_1		$(2d_{5/2})^6$	0^+		**12.62**			

(*Continued*)

Table of Nuclides (*continued*)

Nuclide	T_3	Mass excess $M - A$, μu	Prominent terms for ground state or low-lying level: Proton	Neutron	J^π	Half-life, sec	**Abundance,** percent or decay modes with energies, MeV	Total disintegration energy, MeV	Magnetic moment, nm	Quadrupole moment, barns
$_{44}Ru^{101}$	$-\frac{13}{2}$	-94423_1	$(1g_{9/2})^4$	$(2d_{5/2})^{-1}$	$\frac{5}{2}+$		**17.07**		−0.6900	
$_{44}Ru^{102}$	-7	-95652_1		$(1g_{7/2})^2$	0+		**31.61**			
$_{44}Ru^{103}$	$-\frac{15}{2}$	-93694_2		$(2d_{5/2})^{-1}$	$(\frac{5}{2}+)$	$.346 \times 10^7$	β^- .21, 1.0, .71, . . . ; γ .50, . . .	0.74		
$_{44}Ru^{104}$	-8	-94570_1		$(1g_{7/2})^4$	0+		**18.58**			
$_{44}Ru^{105}$	$-\frac{17}{2}$	-92321_2		$(1g_{7/2})^5$		$.160 \times 10^5$	β^- 1.15, 1.08, 1.87, . . . ; γ .72, . . .	1.87		
$_{44}Ru^{106}$	-9	-92678_2		$(1g_{7/2})^6$	0+	$.316 \times 10^8$	β^- .04	0.04		
$_{44}Ru^{107}$	$-\frac{19}{2}$	-89870_3		$(1g_{7/2})^7$		$.252 \times 10^3$	β^- 3.2, 1.9–3.0; γ .19, . . .	3.15		
$_{44}Ru^{108}$	-10	-89900_2		$(1g_{7/2})^8$	0+	$.270 \times 10^3$	β^- 1.3, 1.2; γ 1.7	1.32		
$_{45}Rh^{96}$	-3		$(1g_{9/2})^5$	$(2d_{5/2})^1$		$.700 \times 10^3$				
$_{45}Rh^{97}$	$-\frac{7}{2}$	-88620_4	or	$(2d_{5/2})^2$		$.198 \times 10^4$	β^+ 1.8, 2.1, . . . ; EC; γ .08–2.5	3.49		
$_{45}Rh^{98}$	-4	-90200_3	$(2p_{1/2})^{-1}$	$(2d_{5/2})^3$		$.522 \times 10^3$	β^+ 2.5; EC; γ .66	4.20		
$_{45}Rh^{99}$	$-\frac{9}{2}$	-91810_2		$(2d_{5/2})^4$		$.138 \times 10^7$	EC; β^+ 1.03, . . . ; γ .35, .089	2.10		
$_{45}Rh^{100}$	-5	-91874_2		$(2d_{5/2})^5$	2−	$.756 \times 10^5$	EC; β^+ 2.61, . . . ; γ .54, .44, . . .	3.64		
$_{45}Rh^{101}$	$-\frac{11}{2}$	-93822_2		$(2d_{5/2})^6$	$(\frac{1}{2}-)$	$.160 \times 10^9$	EC; γ .195, .127	0.56		
$_{45}Rh^{102}$	-6	-93158_1		$(1g_{7/2})^1$	(−)	†$.178 \times 10^8$	EC; β^- 1.15, . . . ; β^+ 1.28, .81; γ .47, . . .	{1.15− 2.32+		
$_{45}Rh^{103}$	$-\frac{13}{2}$	-94489_1		$(1g_{7/2})^2$	$\frac{1}{2}-$		**100**		−0.0883	
$_{45}Rh^{104}$	-7	-93341_1		$(1g_{7/2})^3$	1+	†$.420 \times 10^2$	β^- 2.44, . . . ; γ .56, 1.24	2.47		
$_{45}Rh^{105}$	$-\frac{15}{2}$	-94329_2		$(1g_{7/2})^4$	$*(\frac{7}{2})+$	$.130 \times 10^6$	β^- .57, .25, . . . ; γ .31	0.57		
$_{45}Rh^{106}$	-8	-92721_2		$(1g_{7/2})^5$	1+	†$.300 \times 10^2$	β^- 3.53, . . . ; γ .51, .62, .7–3.4	3.54		
$_{45}Rh^{107}$	$-\frac{17}{2}$	-93247_2		$(1g_{7/2})^6$		$.130 \times 10^4$	β^- 1.2, .83–1.5; γ .31, . . .	1.51		
$_{45}Rh^{108}$	-9	-91300_3		$(1g_{7/2})^7$	1+	$.170 \times 10^2$	β^- 4.5, 3.5, 4.1, . . . ; γ .43, .62, . . .	4.50		
$_{45}Rh^{109}$	$-\frac{19}{2}$	-91360_4		$(1g_{7/2})^8$		†$.300 \times 10^2$	β^-; γ .49, .31	2.50		
$_{45}Rh^{110}$	-10	-88900_3		$(3s_{1/2})^1$		$.500 \times 10^1$	β^- 5.5, . . . ; γ .38	5.50		
$_{46}Pd^{98}$	-3		$(1g_{9/2})^6$	$(2d_{5/2})^2$	0+	$.102 \times 10^4$	β^+			
$_{46}Pd^{99}$	$-\frac{7}{2}$	-87730_3		$(2d_{5/2})^3$		$.132 \times 10^4$	β^+ 2.0, . . . ; γ .14, .28, .42, .67	3.80		
$_{46}Pd^{100}$	-4	-91230_4		$(2d_{5/2})^4$	0+	$.346 \times 10^6$	EC; γ .082, .073, .04–.31	0.60		
$_{46}Pd^{101}$	$-\frac{9}{2}$	-91930_2		$(1g_{7/2})^1$	$(\frac{7}{2}+)$	$.306 \times 10^5$	EC; β^+ .58; γ .59, .29, . . .	1.76		
$_{46}Pd^{102}$	-5	-94391_2		$(2d_{5/2})^6$	0+		**0.96**			
$_{46}Pd^{103}$	$-\frac{11}{2}$	-93893_2		$(1g_{7/2})^1$	$(\frac{7}{2}+)$	$.147 \times 10^7$	EC; γ .052–.36	0.56		
$_{46}Pd^{104}$	-6	-95989_2		$(1g_{7/2})^2$	0+		**10.97**			
$_{46}Pd^{105}$	$-\frac{13}{2}$	-94936_2		$(2d_{5/2})^{-1}$	$\frac{5}{2}+$		**22.23**		−0.6015	
$_{46}Pd^{106}$	-7	-96521_1		$(1g_{7/2})^4$	0+		**27.33**			
$_{46}Pd^{107}$	$-\frac{15}{2}$	-94868_1		$(2d_{5/2})^{-1}$	$(\frac{5}{2}+)$	$.221 \times 10^{15}$	β^- .035	0.04		
$_{46}Pd^{108}$	-8	-96109_1		$(1g_{7/2})^6$	0+		**26.71**			

$_{46}Pd^{111}$	$-\frac{19}{2}$	-92330_2		$(3s_{1/2})^1$		$\dagger.132 \times 10^4$	β^- 2.13, . . . ; γ	2.19		
$_{46}Pd^{112}$	-10	-92614_2		$(1h_{11/2})^2$	0^+	$.756 \times 10^5$	β^- .28; γ .018	0.30		
$_{46}Pd^{113}$	$-\frac{21}{2}$			$(3s_{1/2})^1$		$.900 \times 10^2$	β^-			
$_{46}Pd^{114}$	-11			$(1h_{11/2})^4$	0^+	$.144 \times 10^3$	β^-			
$_{46}Pd^{115}$	$-\frac{23}{2}$			$(1h_{11/2})^5$		$.450 \times 10^2$	β^-			
$_{47}Ag^{102}$	-4	-88700_4	$(1g_{9/2})^7$	$(2d_{5/2})^5$		$.780 \times 10^3$	EC; β^+ 2.2; γ .55, .72, .84–3.3	5.30		
$_{47}Ag^{103}$	$-\frac{9}{2}$	-91110_3	or	$(2d_{5/2})^6$	$*\frac{7}{2}^+$	$.396 \times 10^4$	EC; β^+ 1.3, . . . ; γ .11, .13, .15, . . .	2.59		
$_{47}Ag^{104}$	-5	-91404_2	$(2p_{1/2})^{-1}$	$(1g_{7/2})^1$	5^+	$.402 \times 10^4$	EC; β^+ .99; γ .56, .77, .94, . . .	4.27	4.0000	
$_{47}Ag^{105}$	$-\frac{11}{2}$	-93540_4		$(1g_{7/2})^2$	$\frac{1}{2}^-$	$.346 \times 10^7$	EC; γ .064, .34, .28, .09–1.1	1.30	$\pm$0.1010	
$_{47}Ag^{106}$	-6	-93339_1		$(1g_{7/2})^3$	1^+	$\dagger.144 \times 10^4$	β^+ 1.95, 1.45; EC; γ .51	{0.19− 2.96+	Large	
$_{47}Ag^{107}$	$-\frac{13}{2}$	-94906_1		$(1g_{7/2})^4$	$\frac{1}{2}^-$		**51.82**		−0.1135	
$_{47}Ag^{108}$	-7	-94051_1		$(1g_{7/2})^5$	1^+	$\dagger.144 \times 10^3$	β^- 1.65, . . . ; EC; β^+ .7; γ .63	{1.64− 1.92+	4.2000	
$_{47}Ag^{109}$	$-\frac{15}{2}$	-95244_1		$(1g_{7/2})^6$	$\frac{1}{2}^-$		**48.18**		−0.1305	
$_{47}Ag^{110}$	-8	-93905_1		$(1g_{7/2})^7$	1^+	$\dagger.240 \times 10^2$	β^- 2.87, . . . ; γ .66, . . .	{2.87− 0.87+		
$_{47}Ag^{111}$	$-\frac{17}{2}$	-94684_2		$(1g_{7/2})^8$	$\frac{1}{2}^-$	$.648 \times 10^6$	β^- 1.05, .71, . . . ; γ .34, .25	1.05	−0.1450	
$_{47}Ag^{112}$	-9	-92936_2		$(3s_{1/2})^1$	$*2^-$	$.115 \times 10^5$	β^- 4.05, . . . ; γ .62, 1.4, .69–3.28	4.01	$\pm$0.0540	
$_{47}Ag^{113}$	$-\frac{19}{2}$	-93444_2		$(1h_{11/2})^2$	$\frac{1}{2}^-$	$.191 \times 10^5$	β^- 2.0, . . . ; γ .31, .12–1.18	2.00	$\pm$0.1590	
$_{47}Ag^{114}$	-10	-91700_3		$(3s_{1/2})^1$		$.500 \times 10^1$	β^- 4.6, . . . ; γ .56	4.60		
$_{47}Ag^{115}$	$-\frac{21}{2}$	-91070_3		$(1h_{11/2})^4$	$*(\frac{7}{2}^+)$	$.126 \times 10^4$	β^- 1.1, 3.2, .7–3.0; γ .22, . . .	3.26		
$_{47}Ag^{116}$	-11	-88690_4		$(1h_{11/2})^5$		$.150 \times 10^3$	β^- 5.1, . . . ; γ 1.8, .5–2.6	6.10		
$_{47}Ag^{117}$	$-\frac{23}{2}$			$(1h_{11/2})^6$		$.660 \times 10^2$	β^-			
$_{48}Cd^{103}$	$-\frac{7}{2}$		$(1g_{9/2})^8$	$(2d_{5/2})^5$		$.600 \times 10^3$	β^+; γ .22, .62, .85			
$_{48}Cd^{104}$	-4	-90120_4		$(2d_{5/2})^6$	0^+	$.342 \times 10^4$	EC; γ .084, .067	1.20		
$_{48}Cd^{105}$	$-\frac{9}{2}$	-90530_4		$(1g_{7/2})^1$		$.330 \times 10^4$	EC; β^+ 1.69, .8; γ .025–2.32	2.80		
$_{48}Cd^{106}$	-5	-93537_1		$(1g_{7/2})^2$	0^+		**1.22**			
$_{48}Cd^{107}$	$-\frac{11}{2}$	-93385_1		$(2d_{5/2})^{-1}$	$\frac{5}{2}^+$	$.234 \times 10^5$	EC; β^+ .30; γ .093, .033–1.22	1.42	−0.6160	0.770
$_{48}Cd^{108}$	-6	-95813_1		$(1g_{7/2})^4$	0^+		**0.88**			
$_{48}Cd^{109}$	$-\frac{13}{2}$	-95072_1		$(2d_{5/2})^{-1}$	$\frac{5}{2}^+$	$.410 \times 10^8$	EC	0.16	−0.8290	0.780
$_{48}Cd^{110}$	-7	-96988_1		$(1g_{7/2})^6$	0^+		**12.39**			
$_{48}Cd^{111}$	$-\frac{15}{2}$	-95811_1		$(3s_{1/2})^1$	$\frac{1}{2}^+$		**12.75**		−0.5950	
$_{48}Cd^{112}$	-8	-97237_1		$(1g_{7/2})^8$	0^+		**24.07**			
$_{48}Cd^{113}$	$-\frac{17}{2}$	-95591_1		$(3s_{1/2})^1$	$\frac{1}{2}^+$		**12.26**	0.30	−0.6224	
$_{48}Cd^{114}$	-9	-96639_1		$(1h_{11/2})^2$	0^+		**28.86**			
$_{48}Cd^{115}$	$-\frac{19}{2}$	-94569_2		$(3s_{1/2})^1$	$(\frac{1}{2}^+)$	$\dagger.199 \times 10^6$	β^- 1.11; γ .52, . . .	1.45	−0.6470	
$_{48}Cd^{116}$	-10	-95238_1		$(1h_{11/2})^4$	0^+		**7.58**			
$_{48}Cd^{117}$	$-\frac{21}{2}$	-92761_2		$(1h_{11/2})^5$		$.100 \times 10^5$	β^- .67, 2.2, 2.0, 1.8; γ .3–1.6	2.52		
$_{48}Cd^{118}$	-11	-93030_4		$(1h_{11/2})^6$	0^+	$.300 \times 10^4$	β^- 1.8, 2.3; γ .42			
$_{48}Cd^{119}$	$-\frac{23}{2}$	-90260_3		$(1h_{11/2})^7$		$.570 \times 10^3$	β^-	3.50		

(Continued)

Table of Nuclides *(continued)*

Nuclide	T_3	Mass excess $M - A$, μu	Prominent terms for ground state or low-lying level: Proton	Neutron	J^π	Half-life, sec	**Abundance,** percent or decay modes with energies, MeV	Total disintegration energy, MeV	Magnetic moment, nm	Quadrupole moment, barns
$_{49}In^{106}$	-4	-86560_3	$(1g_{9/2})^9$	$(1g_{7/2})^1$		$.318 \times 10^3$	β^+ 3.1, 4.85; γ 1.65, 1.85, . . .	6.50		
$_{49}In^{107}$	$-\frac{9}{2}$	-89640_3		$(1g_{7/2})^2$		$.192 \times 10^4$	β^+ 2.3; EC; γ .22, .28–2.3	3.49		
$_{49}In^{108}$	-5	-90280_2		$(1g_{7/2})^3$		$.348 \times 10^4$	EC; β^+ 1.3; γ .24, .15, . . .	5.15		
$_{49}In^{109}$	$-\frac{11}{2}$	-92904_2		$(1g_{7/2})^4$	$\frac{9}{2}+$	$.155 \times 10^5$	EC; β^+ .80; γ .20, .63, . . .	2.02	5.5300	0.860
$_{49}In^{110}$	-6	-92769_2		$(1g_{7/2})^5$	$2+$	$†.396 \times 10^4$	β^+ 2.25; EC; γ .66, . . .	3.93		
$_{49}In^{111}$	$-\frac{13}{2}$	-94640_3		$(1g_{7/2})^6$	$\frac{9}{2}+$	$.243 \times 10^6$	EC; γ .247, .173, . . .	1.09	5.5300	0.850
$_{49}In^{112}$	-7	-94456_2		$(1g_{7/2})^7$	1^+	$†.840 \times 10^3$	β^- .66; EC; β^+ 1.6; γ .62, .71	{0.66− / 2.59+		
$_{49}In^{113}$	$-\frac{15}{2}$	-95911_1		$(1g_{7/2})^8$	$\frac{9}{2}+$		**4.28**		5.5230	0.820
$_{49}In^{114}$	-8	-95095_1		$(1g_{7/2})^{-1}$	1^+	$†.720 \times 10^2$	β^- 1.98, . . . ; EC; β^+ .4; γ 1.3, .2	{1.99− / 1.44+		
$_{49}In^{115}$	$-\frac{17}{2}$	-96129_1		$(1h_{11/2})^2$	$\frac{9}{2}+$	$.158 \times 10^{23}$	**95.72**; β^- .5	0.49	5.5340	0.830
$_{49}In^{116}$	-9	-94683_2		$(1g_{7/2})^{-1}$	$+$	$†.140 \times 10^2$	β^- 3.29; γ 1.3	3.33		
$_{49}In^{117}$	$-\frac{19}{2}$	-95466_2		$(1h_{11/2})^4$	$\frac{9}{2}+$	$†.270 \times 10^4$	β^- .74; γ .56, .16	1.47		
$_{49}In^{118}$	-10	-93890_3		$(1g_{7/2})^{-1}$	$1+$	$†.510 \times 10^1$	β^- 4.2, . . . ; γ 1.22	4.20		
$_{49}In^{119}$	$-\frac{21}{2}$	-94010_3		$(1h_{11/2})^6$		$†.120 \times 10^3$	β^- 1.6; γ .82	2.49		
$_{49}In^{120}$	-11	-92000_4		$(1h_{11/2})^7$		$.440 \times 10^2$	β^- 2.2; γ .73–1.18	5.40		
$_{49}In^{121}$	$-\frac{23}{2}$	-91910_4		$(1h_{11/2})^8$		$†.300 \times 10^2$	β^-; γ .94	3.60		
$_{49}In^{122}$	-12	-89400_3		$(1h_{11/2})^9$		$.750 \times 10^1$	β^- ~5; γ 1.14, 1.0	6.70		
$_{49}In^{123}$	$-\frac{25}{2}$	-89430_4		$(1h_{11/2})^{10}$		$†.100 \times 10^2$	β^-; γ 1.10	4.50		
$_{49}In^{124}$	-13	-86800_3		$(1h_{11/2})^{11}$		$.360 \times 10^1$	β^- 5.3; γ 1.13, .99, 3.21	7.40		
$_{50}Sn^{108}$	-4		$(1g_{9/2})^{10}$	$(1g_{7/2})^2$	0^+	$.540 \times 10^3$	EC			
$_{50}Sn^{109}$	$-\frac{9}{2}$			$(1g_{7/2})^3$		$.108 \times 10^4$	β^+ 1.6; γ .34, 1.12, .52, .89			
$_{50}Sn^{110}$	-5			$(1g_{7/2})^4$	0^+	$.144 \times 10^5$	EC; γ .283			
$_{50}Sn^{111}$	$-\frac{11}{2}$	-91940_3		$(1g_{7/2})^5$	$(\frac{7}{2}+)$	$.210 \times 10^4$	EC; β^+ 1.51	2.52		
$_{50}Sn^{112}$	-6	-95165_2		$(1g_{7/2})^6$	0^+		**0.96**			
$_{50}Sn^{113}$	$-\frac{13}{2}$	-94813_2		$(3s_{1/2})^1$	$(\frac{1}{2}+)$	$.102 \times 10^8$	EC; γ .255	1.02		
$_{50}Sn^{114}$	-7	-97227_1		$(1g_{7/2})^8$	0^+		**0.66**			
$_{50}Sn^{115}$	$-\frac{15}{2}$	-96654_1		$(3s_{1/2})^1$	$\frac{1}{2}+$		**0.35**		−0.9180	
$_{50}Sn^{116}$	-8	-98255_1		$(1h_{11/2})^2$	0^+		**14.30**			
$_{50}Sn^{117}$	$-\frac{17}{2}$	-97041_1		$(3s_{1/2})^1$	$\frac{1}{2}+$		**7.61**		−1.0000	
$_{50}Sn^{118}$	-9	-98394_1		$(1h_{11/2})^4$	0^+		**24.03**			
$_{50}Sn^{119}$	$-\frac{19}{2}$	-96686_1		$(3s_{1/2})^1$	$\frac{1}{2}+$		**8.58**		−1.0460	
$_{50}Sn^{120}$	-10	-97801_1		$(1h_{11/2})^6$	0^+		**32.85**			
$_{50}Sn^{121}$	$-\frac{21}{2}$	-95773_1		$(1h_{11/2})^7$		$†.972 \times 10^5$	β^- .38	0.38		
$_{50}Sn^{122}$	-11	-96558_1		$(1h_{11/2})^8$	0^+		**4.72**	[illegible]		

$_{50}Sn^{126}$	-13	-92360_4		$(1h_{11/2})^{12}$	0^+	$.300 \times 10^{13}$	β^-; γ .092, .07	0.30		
$_{50}Sn^{127}$	$-\frac{27}{2}$	-89740_4		$(2d_{3/2})^1$		$.756 \times 10^4$	β^-; γ 1.10, .82, .12–2.8	3.10		
$_{50}Sn^{128}$	-14	-89530_3		$(3s_{1/2})^2$	0^+	$.372 \times 10^4$	β^- .8, .7; γ .04–.57	1.30		
$_{50}Sn^{129}$	$-\frac{29}{2}$			$(2d_{3/2})^1$		$\dagger.372 \times 10^3$	β^-; γ 1.1–3.1			
$_{50}Sn^{130}$	-15			$(2d_{3/2})^2$	0^+	$.156 \times 10^3$	β^-			
$_{50}Sn^{131}$	$-\frac{31}{2}$			$(2d_{3/2})^3$		$<.120 \times 10^3$	β^-			
$_{50}Sn^{132}$	-16			$(2d_{3/2})^4$	0^+	$.132 \times 10^3$	β^-			
$_{51}Sb^{112}$	-5		$(1g_{7/2})^1$	$(1g_{7/2})^5$		$.540 \times 10^3$	β^+; γ 1.27			
$_{51}Sb^{113}$	$-\frac{11}{2}$	-90014_2	or	$(1g_{7/2})^6$		$.420 \times 10^3$	β^+ 2.42, 1.85; EC; γ .3–1.5	4.47		
$_{51}Sb^{114}$	-6	-90490_3	$(2d_{5/2})^1$	$(1g_{7/2})^7$		$.204 \times 10^3$	β^+ 4.0, 2.7; γ .9, 1.3	6.28		
$_{51}Sb^{115}$	$-\frac{13}{2}$	-93401_2		$(1g_{7/2})^8$	$(\frac{5}{2}^+)$	$.186 \times 10^4$	EC; β^+ 1.51; γ .5, .98, 1.24, . . .	3.03		
$_{51}Sb^{116}$	-7	-93370_2		$(1g_{7/2})^{-1}$	(2^+)	$\dagger.900 \times 10^3$	β^+ 2.4, 1.5; EC; γ 1.27, .9, 2.2	4.55		
$_{51}Sb^{117}$	$-\frac{15}{2}$	-95088_2		$(1h_{11/2})^2$	$(\frac{5}{2}^+)$	$.101 \times 10^5$	EC; β^+ .64; γ .16	1.82		
$_{51}Sb^{118}$	-8	-94426_1		$(1g_{7/2})^{-1}$	(6^+)	$.184 \times 10^5$	EC; γ 1.22, .25	3.70		
$_{51}Sb^{119}$	$-\frac{17}{2}$	-96065_2		$(1h_{11/2})^4$	$(\frac{5}{2})^+$	$.137 \times 10^6$	EC; γ .024	0.58		
$_{51}Sb^{120}$	-9	-94919_1		$(1g_{7/2})^{-1}$	1^+	$\dagger.984 \times 10^3$	β^+ 1.70, . . ; EC; γ 1.18	$\begin{cases} 0.99^- \\ 2.69^+ \end{cases}$		
$_{51}Sb^{121}$	$-\frac{19}{2}$	-96183_1		$(1h_{11/2})^6$	$\frac{5}{2}^+$		**57.25**		3.3590	-0.290
$_{51}Sb^{122}$	-10	-94817_1		$(1h_{11/2})^7$	2^-	$.242 \times 10^6$	β^- 1.4, . . . ; EC; β^+ .57; γ .56, . . .	$\begin{cases} 1.97^- \\ 1.62^+ \end{cases}$	-1.9000	0.690
$_{51}Sb^{123}$	$-\frac{21}{2}$	-95787_1		$(1h_{11/2})^8$	$\frac{7}{2}^+$		**42.75**		2.5470	-0.370
$_{51}Sb^{124}$	-11	-94027_1		$(1h_{11/2})^9$	3^-	$.520 \times 10^7$	β^- .61, . . . ; γ .60–2.1	2.92		
$_{51}Sb^{125}$	$-\frac{23}{2}$	-94768_1		$(1h_{11/2})^{10}$	$\frac{7}{2}^+$	$.852 \times 10^8$	β^- .30, .12, .61, . . . ; γ .43, .60, . . .	0.76		
$_{51}Sb^{126}$	-12	-92680_3		$(1h_{11/2})^{11}$		$.108 \times 10^7$	β^- 2.0, . . . ; γ .42, .67, .3–1.0	3.73		
$_{51}Sb^{127}$	$-\frac{25}{2}$	-93073_2		$(1h_{11/2})^{12}$		$.337 \times 10^6$	β^- 1.53, 1.1; γ .47, .25, .69, . . .	1.60		
$_{51}Sb^{128}$	-13	-90930_3		$(2d_{3/2})^1$		$.346 \times 10^5$	β^- 1.0–1.5; γ .31–.90	4.28		
$_{51}Sb^{129}$	$-\frac{27}{2}$	-90740_4		$(3s_{1/2})^2$		$.155 \times 10^5$	β^- 1.87, . . . ; γ .18–2.1	2.50		
$_{51}Sb^{130}$	-14	-87960_4		$(2d_{3/2})^1$		$.198 \times 10^4$	β^-; γ .19–.94	5.40		
$_{51}Sb^{131}$	$-\frac{29}{2}$			$(2d_{3/2})^2$		$.138 \times 10^4$	β^-			
$_{51}Sb^{132}$	-15			$(2d_{3/2})^3$		$.126 \times 10^3$	β^-			
$_{51}Sb^{133}$	$-\frac{31}{2}$			$(2d_{3/2})^4$		$.246 \times 10^3$	β^-			
$_{51}Sb^{134}$	-16			$(2f_{7/2})^1$		$.480 \times 10^2$	β^-			
$_{51}Sb^{135}$	$-\frac{33}{2}$			$(2f_{7/2})^2$		$<.240 \times 10^2$	β^-			
$_{52}Te^{114}$	-5		$(1g_{7/2})^2$	$(1g_{7/2})^6$	0^+	$.960 \times 10^3$	β^+			
$_{52}Te^{115}$	$-\frac{11}{2}$			$(1g_{7/2})^7$						
$_{52}Te^{116}$	-6	-91700_3		$(1g_{7/2})^8$	0^+	$.900 \times 10^4$	EC; β^+; γ	1.56		
$_{52}Te^{117}$	$-\frac{13}{2}$	-91330_2		$(3s_{1/2})^1$	$\frac{1}{2}$	$.366 \times 10^4$	EC; β^+ 1.74; γ .71–2.2	3.50		
$_{52}Te^{118}$	-7	-94100_4		$(1h_{11/2})^2$	0^+	$.518 \times 10^6$	EC	0.30		
$_{52}Te^{119}$	$-\frac{15}{2}$	-93602_2		$(3s_{1/2})^1$	$\frac{1}{2}^+$	$\dagger.576 \times 10^5$	EC; β^+ .63; γ .64, .70, . . .	2.29		
$_{52}Te^{120}$	-8	-95977_2		$(1h_{11/2})^4$	0^+		**0.089**			
$_{52}Te^{121}$	$-\frac{17}{2}$	-94801_2		$(3s_{1/2})^1$		$\dagger.147 \times 10^7$	EC, β^+; .57, .51, . . .	1.29		

(Continued)

Table of Nuclides (*continued*)

Nuclide	T_3	Mass excess $M - A$, μu	Prominent terms for ground state or low-lying level: Proton	Neutron	J^π	Half-life, sec	**Abundance,** percent or decay modes with energies, MeV	Total disintegration energy, MeV	Magnetic moment, nm	Quadrupole moment, barns
$_{52}Te^{122}$	-9	-96934_1	$(1g_{7/2})^2$	$(1h_{11/2})^6$	0+		**2.46**			
$_{52}Te^{123}$	$-\frac{19}{2}$	-95723_1		$(3s_{1/2})^1$	$\frac{1}{2}$+	$.379 \times 10^{21}$	**0.87**; EC	0.06	−0.7359	
$_{52}Te^{124}$	-10	-97158_1		$(1h_{11/2})^8$	0+		**4.61**			
$_{52}Te^{125}$	$-\frac{21}{2}$	-95582_1		$(3s_{1/2})^1$	$\frac{1}{2}$+		**6.99**		−0.8871	
$_{52}Te^{126}$	-11	-96678_1		$(1h_{11/2})^{10}$	0+		**18.71**			
$_{52}Te^{127}$	$-\frac{23}{2}$	-94791_1		$(2d_{3/2})^1$	($\frac{3}{2}$+)	†$.335 \times 10^5$	β^- .69, . . . ; γ .06–.42	0.69		
$_{52}Te^{128}$	-12	-95524_1		$(1h_{11/2})^{12}$	0+		**31.79**			
$_{52}Te^{129}$	$-\frac{25}{2}$	-93425_1		$(2d_{3/2})^1$	($\frac{3}{2}$+)	†$.402 \times 10^4$	β^- 1.45, 1.0; γ .027, .46, . . .	1.48		
$_{52}Te^{130}$	-13	-93762_1		$(3s_{1/2})^2$	0+		**34.48**			
$_{52}Te^{131}$	$-\frac{27}{2}$	-91425_2		$(2d_{3/2})^1$	($\frac{3}{2}$+)	†$.150 \times 10^4$	β^- 2.1, 1.7; γ .15, .45, . . .	2.28		
$_{52}Te^{132}$	-14	-91477_2		$(2d_{3/2})^2$	0+	$.281 \times 10^6$	β^- .22; γ .023, .053, . . .	0.51		
$_{52}Te^{133}$	$-\frac{29}{2}$			$(2d_{3/2})^3$		†$.120 \times 10^3$	β^- 1.3, 2.4; γ .6, 1.0, . . .			
$_{52}Te^{134}$	-15			$(2d_{3/2})^4$	0+	$.252 \times 10^4$	β^-; γ .030–.262			
$_{52}Te^{135}$	$-\frac{31}{2}$			$(2f_{7/2})^1$		$.600 \times 10^2$	β^-			
$_{53}I^{117}$	$-\frac{11}{2}$		$(1g_{7/2})^3$	$(1g_{7/2})^8$		$.600 \times 10^3$				
$_{53}I^{118}$	-6		or	$(3s_{1/2})^1$		$.100 \times 10^4$				
$_{53}I^{119}$	$-\frac{13}{2}$		$(2d_{5/2})^1$	$(1h_{11/2})^2$		$.108 \times 10^4$	β^+			
$_{53}I^{120}$	-7	-90180_4		$(3s_{1/2})^1$		$.504 \times 10^4$	β^+ 4.0	5.40		
$_{53}I^{121}$	$-\frac{15}{2}$	-92270_2		$(1h_{11/2})^4$		$.504 \times 10^4$	EC; β^+ 1.13; γ .21, .32, .27	2.36		
$_{53}I^{122}$	-8	-92489_2		$(3s_{1/2})^1$	+	$.210 \times 10^3$	β^+ 3.12, 2.56, . . . ; EC; γ .56, . . .	4.14		
$_{53}I^{123}$	$-\frac{17}{2}$	-94270_2		$(1h_{11/2})^6$	$\frac{5}{2}$+	$.468 \times 10^5$	EC; γ .159, . . .	1.40		
$_{53}I^{124}$	-9	-93754_2		$(1h_{11/2})^7$	2−	$.363 \times 10^6$	EC; β^+ 1.55, . . . ; γ .60, 1.7, . . .	{0.12− / 3.17+		
$_{53}I^{125}$	$-\frac{19}{2}$	-95422_1		$(1h_{11/2})^8$	$\frac{5}{2}$+	$.520 \times 10^7$	EC; γ .035	0.15	3.0000	−0.890
$_{53}I^{126}$	-10	-94369_1		$(1h_{11/2})^9$	2−	$.114 \times 10^7$	EC; β^- .38–1.25; β^+ 1.13, . . . ; γ .39, . . .	{1.25− / 2.15+		
$_{53}I^{127}$	$-\frac{21}{2}$	-95530_1		$(1h_{11/2})^{10}$	$\frac{5}{2}$+		**100**		2.8080	−0.790
$_{53}I^{128}$	-11	-94162_1		$(2d_{3/2})^1$	1+	$.150 \times 10^4$	β^- 2.12, 1.67, . . . ; EC; γ .45, . . .	{2.14− / 1.27+		
$_{53}I^{129}$	$-\frac{23}{2}$	-95013_1		$(1h_{11/2})^{12}$	$\frac{7}{2}$+	$.505 \times 10^{15}$	β^- .15; γ .04	0.19	2.6170	−0.550
$_{53}I^{130}$	-12	-93324_2		$(2d_{3/2})^1$	5	$.450 \times 10^5$	β^- .60, 1.02; γ .66, .53, .74, . . .	2.95		
$_{53}I^{131}$	$-\frac{25}{2}$	-93872_1		$(3s_{1/2})^2$	$\frac{7}{2}$+	$.695 \times 10^6$	β^- .61, .25–.81; γ .36, . . .	0.97	2.7400	−0.400
$_{53}I^{132}$	-13	-92019_1		$(2d_{3/2})^1$	4+	$.828 \times 10^4$	β^- 1.53, 1.16, . . . ; γ .67, .78, . . .	3.56	±3.0800	±0.080
$_{53}I^{133}$	$-\frac{27}{2}$	-92250_2		$(2d_{3/2})^2$	$\frac{7}{2}$+	$.756 \times 10^5$	β^- 1.4, ∼.5, . . . ; γ .53, .87, . . .	1.80	2.8400	−0.260
$_{53}I^{134}$	-14	-90150_2		$(2d_{3/2})^3$		$.318 \times 10^4$	β^- 2.4, 1.25, .5, 2.2; γ .85, .61, . . .	4.15		
$_{53}I^{135}$	$-\frac{29}{2}$	-89980_4		$(2d_{3/2})^4$	$\frac{7}{2}$+	$.241 \times 10^5$	β^- 1.0, .5, 1.4; γ 1.14, 1.28, . . .	2.80		
$_{53}I^{136}$	-15	-85260_2		$(2f_{7/2})^1$	(2−)	$.830 \times 10^2$	β^- 4.2, 4.4, 5.6, . . . ; γ 1.32	7.00		

$_{54}Xe^{121}$	$-\frac{13}{2}$	-88200	$(1g_{7/2})^4$	$(3s_{1/2})^1$		$.240 \times 10^4$	β^+ 2.8; EC; γ .096, .080, .132	3.79		
$_{54}Xe^{122}$	-7			$(1h_{11/2})^4$	0^+	$.684 \times 10^5$	EC; γ 1.5, .09, .24			
$_{54}Xe^{123}$	$-\frac{15}{2}$	-91270_4		$(3s_{1/2})^1$		$.666 \times 10^4$	EC; β^+ 1.5; γ .15	2.80		
$_{54}Xe^{124}$	-8	-93880_3		$(1h_{11/2})^6$	0^+		**0.096**			
$_{54}Xe^{125}$	$-\frac{17}{2}$	-93380_4		$(3s_{1/2})^1$	$(\frac{1}{2}^+)$	$.648 \times 10^5$	EC; γ .187, .056, .243, .096–.46	1.90		
$_{54}Xe^{126}$	-9	-95712_1		$(1h_{11/2})^8$	0^+		**0.090**			
$_{54}Xe^{127}$	$-\frac{19}{2}$	-94780_3		$(3s_{1/2})^1$	$(\frac{1}{2}^+)$	$.315 \times 10^7$	EC; γ .20, .17, .15, .06	0.70		
$_{54}Xe^{128}$	-10	-96460_1		$(1h_{11/2})^{10}$	0^+		**1.92**			
$_{54}Xe^{129}$	$-\frac{21}{2}$	-95216_1		$(3s_{1/2})^1$	$\frac{1}{2}^+$		**26.44**		-0.7768	
$_{54}Xe^{130}$	-11	-96491_1		$(1h_{11/2})^{12}$	0^+		**4.08**			
$_{54}Xe^{131}$	$-\frac{23}{2}$	-94914_1		$(2d_{3/2})^1$	$\frac{3}{2}^+$		**21.18**		0.6908	-0.120
$_{54}Xe^{132}$	-12	-95839_1		$(3s_{1/2})^2$	0^+		**26.89**			
$_{54}Xe^{133}$	$-\frac{25}{2}$	-94185_2		$(2d_{3/2})^1$	$\frac{3}{2}^+$	$.455 \times 10^6$	β^- .35, . . . ; γ .081, . . .	0.43		
$_{54}Xe^{134}$	-13	-94602_1		$(2d_{3/2})^2$	0^+		**10.44**			
$_{54}Xe^{135}$	$-\frac{27}{2}$	-92980_3		$(2d_{3/2})^3$	$(\frac{3}{2}^+)$	$.331 \times 10^5$	β^- .91, .55; γ .25, .61, . . .	1.16		
$_{54}Xe^{136}$	-14	-92779_1		$(2d_{3/2})^4$	0^+		**8.87**			
$_{54}Xe^{137}$	$-\frac{29}{2}$	-88900_3		$(2f_{7/2})^1$		$.234 \times 10^3$	β^- 4.2, 3.7; γ .46	4.04		
$_{54}Xe^{138}$	-15	-86190_4		$(2f_{7/2})^2$	0^+	$.840 \times 10^3$	β^- .214; γ .42, .51, 1.8, 2.0	2.80		
$_{54}Xe^{139}$	$-\frac{31}{2}$	-82160_3		$(2f_{7/2})^3$		$.410 \times 10^2$	β^- ~4.6; γ	4.60		
$_{54}Xe^{140}$	-16			$(2f_{7/2})^4$	0^+	$.160 \times 10^2$	β^-			
$_{54}Xe^{141}$	$-\frac{33}{2}$			$(2f_{7/2})^5$		$.200 \times 10^1$	β^-			
$_{54}Xe^{142}$	-17			$(2f_{7/2})^6$	0^+	$.150 \times 10^1$	β^-			
$_{54}Xe^{143}$	$-\frac{35}{2}$			$(2f_{7/2})^7$		$.100 \times 10^1$	β^-			
$_{54}Xe^{144}$	-18			$(2f_{7/2})^8$	0^+	$.100 \times 10^1$	β^-			
$_{55}Cs^{123}$	$-\frac{13}{2}$		$(1g_{7/2})^5$	$(1h_{11/2})^4$		$.480 \times 10^3$	β^+			
$_{55}Cs^{125}$	$-\frac{15}{2}$	-90090_4	$(2d_{5/2})^1$	$(1h_{11/2})^6$		$.270 \times 10^4$	EC; β^+ 2.05; γ .112	3.07		
$_{55}Cs^{126}$	-8	-90560_3	or	$(3s_{1/2})^1$	1^+	$.960 \times 10^2$	β^+ 3.8, . . . ; EC; γ .39	4.80		
$_{55}Cs^{127}$	$-\frac{17}{2}$	-92520_3	$1/2^+$ (420)	$(1h_{11/2})^8$	$\frac{1}{2}^+$	$.223 \times 10^5$	EC; β^+ .7, 1.06, . . . ; γ .41, . . .	2.10	1.4300	
$_{55}Cs^{128}$	-9	-92241_2		$(3s_{1/2})^1$	1^+	$.180 \times 10^3$	β^+ 2.9, 2.5, . . . ; EC; γ .13, . . .	3.93		
$_{55}Cs^{129}$	$-\frac{19}{2}$	-94040_4		$(1h_{11/2})^{10}$	$\frac{1}{2}^+$	$.112 \times 10^6$	EC; γ .040, .39, .37, .58, . . .	1.10	1.4790	
$_{55}Cs^{130}$	-10	-93280_2		$(3s_{1/2})^1$	1^+	$.180 \times 10^4$	EC; β^+ 1.97; β^- .44	$\begin{cases}0.44^-\\2.99^+\end{cases}$	± 1.4100	
$_{55}Cs^{131}$	$-\frac{21}{2}$	-94534_1		$(1h_{11/2})^{12}$	$\frac{5}{2}^+$	$.838 \times 10^6$	EC	0.36	3.5400	
$_{55}Cs^{132}$	-11	-93607_2		$(1h_{11/2})^{-1}$	2^-	$.562 \times 10^6$	EC; β^-; β^+ .4; γ .67, .46, .51–2.0	$\begin{cases}1.18^-\\2.08^+\end{cases}$	2.2200	
$_{55}Cs^{133}$	$-\frac{23}{2}$	-94645_2		$(3s_{1/2})^2$	$\frac{7}{2}^+$		**100**		2.5790	-0.003
$_{55}Cs^{134}$	-12	-93177_2		$(2d_{3/2})^1$	4^+	$.663 \times 10^8$	β^- .65, .09, .21–1.45; γ .60, .80, . . .	$\begin{cases}2.06^-\\1.33^+\end{cases}$	2.9900	
$_{55}Cs^{135}$	$-\frac{25}{2}$	-94230_3		$(2d_{3/2})^2$	$\frac{7}{2}^+$	$.631 \times 10^{14}$	β^- .21	0.21	2.7290	0.049
$_{55}Cs^{136}$	-13	-92660_2		$(1h_{11/2})^{-1}$	5^-	$.112 \times 10^7$	β^- .34, .66; γ 1.04, .83, . . .	2.83		
$_{55}Cs^{137}$	$-\frac{27}{2}$	-93230_2		$(2d_{3/2})^4$	$\frac{7}{2}^+$	$.947 \times 10^9$	β^- .51, 1.17	1.18	2.8380	0.050

(Continued)

Table of Nuclides (*continued*)

Nuclide	T_3	Mass excess $M - A$, μu	Prominent terms for ground state or low-lying level: Proton	Neutron	J^π	Half-life, sec	**Abundance,** percent or decay modes with energies, MeV	Total disintegration energy, MeV	Magnetic moment, nm	Quadrupole moment, barns
$_{55}$Cs^{138}	-14	-89200_4	$(1g_{7/2})^5$	$(2f_{7/2})^1$		$.193 \times 10^4$	β^- 3.40, . . . ; γ 1.43, 1.0, .46	5.40		
$_{55}$Cs^{139}	$-\frac{29}{2}$	-87100_3	$(2d_{5/2})^1$	$(2f_{7/2})^2$		$.570 \times 10^3$	β^- 4, ~3.4, ~2.7; γ 1.28, .63	4.00		
$_{55}$Cs^{140}	-15	-82890_4	or	$(2f_{7/2})^3$		$.660 \times 10^2$	β^- >4.4, . . . ; γ .59, .88–3.15	6.10		
$_{55}$Cs^{141}	$-\frac{31}{2}$		$1/2^+(420)$	$(2f_{7/2})^4$		$.240 \times 10^2$	β^-			
$_{55}$Cs^{142}	-16			$(2f_{7/2})^5$		$.230 \times 10^1$	β^-			
$_{55}$Cs^{143}	$-\frac{33}{2}$			$(2f_{7/2})^6$		$.200 \times 10^1$	β^-			
$_{55}$Cs^{144}	-17			$(2f_{7/2})^7$		Short	β^-			
$_{56}$Ba^{125}	$-\frac{13}{2}$		$(1g_{7/2})^6$	$(3s_{1/2})^1$						
$_{56}$Ba^{126}	-7			$(1h_{11/2})^6$	$0+$	$.582 \times 10^4$	EC; γ .27, .70			
$_{56}$Ba^{127}	$-\frac{15}{2}$	-88660_4		$(3s_{1/2})^1$		$.600 \times 10^3$	β^+	3.60		
$_{56}$Ba^{128}	-8	-91490_4		$(1h_{11/2})^8$	$0+$	$.207 \times 10^6$	EC; γ .27, . . .	0.70		
$_{56}$Ba^{129}	$-\frac{17}{2}$	-91410_4		$(3s_{1/2})^1$		$.900 \times 10^4$	EC; β^+ 1.43, . . . ; γ .18, .21, . . .	2.45		
$_{56}$Ba^{130}	-9	-93755_2		$(1h_{11/2})^{10}$	$0+$		**0.101**			
$_{56}$Ba^{131}	$-\frac{19}{2}$	-93284_2		$(3s_{1/2})^1$	$(\frac{1}{2}+)$	$.100 \times 10^7$	EC; γ .50, .122, .216, .055–1.03	1.16		
$_{56}$Ba^{132}	-10	-94880_3		$(1h_{11/2})^{12}$	$0+$		**0.097**			
$_{56}$Ba^{133}	$-\frac{21}{2}$	-94121_2		$(3s_{1/2})^1$	$(\frac{1}{2}+)$	$.227 \times 10^9$	EC; γ .081, .36, .30, .08–.38	0.49		
$_{56}$Ba^{134}	-11	-95388_2		$(3s_{1/2})^2$	$0+$		**2.42**			
$_{56}$Ba^{135}	$-\frac{23}{2}$	-94450_3		$(2d_{3/2})^1$	$\frac{3}{2}+$		**6.59**		0.8372	0.180
$_{56}$Ba^{136}	-12	-95700_2		$(2d_{3/2})^2$	$0+$		**7.81**			
$_{56}$Ba^{137}	$-\frac{25}{2}$	-94500_2		$(2d_{3/2})^3$	$\frac{3}{2}+$		**11.32**		0.9366	0.280
$_{56}$Ba^{138}	-13	-95000_2		$(2d_{3/2})^4$	$0+$		**71.66**			
$_{56}$Ba^{139}	$-\frac{27}{2}$	-91400_2		$(2f_{7/2})^1$		$.498 \times 10^4$	β^- 2.34, 2.17, . . . ; γ .166, 1.43, . . .	2.30		
$_{56}$Ba^{140}	-14	-89435_2		$(2f_{7/2})^2$	$0+$	$.111 \times 10^7$	β^- 1.02, .48; γ .54, .16, . . .	1.05		
$_{56}$Ba^{141}	$-\frac{29}{2}$	-85950_3		$(2f_{7/2})^3$		$.108 \times 10^4$	β^- 2.8, . . . ; γ .19, .12–1.6	3.00		
$_{56}$Ba^{142}	-15	-83650_3		$(2f_{7/2})^4$	$0+$	$.660 \times 10^3$	β^-; γ .26, .89, 1.20, .08, . . .	2.20		
$_{56}$Ba^{143}	$-\frac{31}{2}$			$(2f_{7/2})^5$		$.120 \times 10^2$	β^-			
$_{56}$Ba^{144}	-16			$(2f_{7/2})^6$	$0+$	Short	β^-			
$_{57}$La^{124}	-5		$(1g_{7/2})^7$	$(3s_{1/2})^1$		$.420 \times 10^3$				
$_{57}$La^{126}	-6		$(2d_{5/2})^1$	$(3s_{1/2})^1$		$.600 \times 10^2$	β^+; EC; γ .26			
$_{57}$La^{127}	$-\frac{13}{2}$		or	$(1h_{11/2})^6$						
$_{57}$La^{128}	-7		$1/2^+(420)$	$(3s_{1/2})^1$		$.276 \times 10^3$	β^+; EC; γ .28, . . .			
$_{57}$La^{129}	$-\frac{15}{2}$	-87110_4		$(1h_{11/2})^8$		$.600 \times 10^3$	β^+; EC; γ .28	4.00		
$_{57}$La^{130}	-8	-87740_4		$(3s_{1/2})^1$		$.540 \times 10^3$	β^+; EC; γ .36, . . .	5.60		
$_{57}$La^{131}	$-\frac{17}{2}$	-90110_2		$(1h_{11/2})^{10}$		$.366 \times 10^4$	EC; β^+ 1.42, 1.94, . . . ; γ .115, . . .	2.96		
$_{57}$La^{132}	-9	-89700_3		$(3s_{1/2})^1$	$0+$	$.151 \times 10^5$	β^+ 3.8; γ 1.0–3.3	4.82		
$_{57}$La^{133}	$-\frac{19}{2}$	-91760_3		$(1h_{11/2})^{12}$		$.144 \times 10^5$	EC; β^+ 1.2; γ .8	2.20		

								2.87+		
$_{57}La^{137}$	$-\frac{23}{2}$	-93960_4		$(2d_{3/2})^2$	$(\frac{7}{2}+)$	$.189 \times 10^{13}$	EC	0.50		
$_{57}La^{138}$	-12	-93090_2		$(1h_{11/2})^{-1}$	5−	$.347 \times 10^{19}$	**0.089**; EC; β^- .205; γ 1.4	1.02− 1.78+	3.7070	±0.800
$_{57}La^{139}$	$-\frac{25}{2}$	-93860_2		$(2d_{3/2})^4$	$\frac{7}{2}+$		**99.91**		2.7780	0.220
$_{57}La^{140}$	-13	-90562_2		$(2f_{7/2})^1$	3−	$.145 \times 10^6$	β^- 1.34, 1.10, . . . ; γ 1.6, .49, . . .	3.77		
$_{57}La^{141}$	$-\frac{27}{2}$	-89172_2		$(2f_{7/2})^2$		$.140 \times 10^5$	β^- 2.4, . . . ; γ 1.37	2.43		
$_{57}La^{142}$	-14	-86020_2		$(2f_{7/2})^3$	(2−)	$.504 \times 10^4$	β^- 2.1, 2.0, . . . ; γ .64, 2.41, . . .	4.51		
$_{57}La^{143}$	$-\frac{29}{2}$	-84130_2		$(2f_{7/2})^4$	$(\frac{7}{2}+)$	$.840 \times 10^3$	β^- 3.3; γ .63, .20–2.85	3.30		
$_{57}La^{144}$	-15	-80400_4		$(2f_{7/2})^5$		Short	β^-	5.60		
$_{58}Ce^{131}$	$-\frac{15}{2}$	-84500_3	$(1g_{7/2})^8$	$(3s_{1/2})^1$		$.180 \times 10^4$	β^+ 4.2	5.22		
$_{58}Ce^{132}$	-8	-88410_4		$(1h_{11/2})^{10}$	0+	$.151 \times 10^5$	β^+	1.20		
$_{58}Ce^{133}$	$-\frac{17}{2}$	-88750_4		$(3s_{1/2})^1$		$.227 \times 10^5$	EC; β^+ 1.3; γ 1.8	2.80		
$_{58}Ce^{134}$	-9	-91190_2		$(1h_{11/2})^{12}$	0+	$.259 \times 10^6$	EC	0.14		
$_{58}Ce^{135}$	$-\frac{19}{2}$	-90860_4		$(3s_{1/2})^1$		$.648 \times 10^5$	EC; β^+ .81; γ .09–.27	2.10		
$_{58}Ce^{136}$	-10	-92900_3		$(3s_{1/2})^2$	0+		**0.193**			
$_{58}Ce^{137}$	$-\frac{21}{2}$	-92670_4		$(2d_{3/2})^1$		$\dagger.324 \times 10^5$	EC; γ .010, .46	1.20		
$_{58}Ce^{138}$	-11	-94170_2		$(2d_{3/2})^2$	0+		**0.250**			
$_{58}Ce^{139}$	$-\frac{23}{2}$	-93570_2		$(2d_{3/2})^3$	$\frac{3}{2}+$	$.121 \times 10^8$	EC; γ .166	0.27		
$_{58}Ce^{140}$	-12	-94608_2		$(2d_{3/2})^4$	0+		**88.48**			
$_{58}Ce^{141}$	$-\frac{25}{2}$	-91781_2		$(2f_{7/2})^1$	$\frac{7}{2}-$	$.281 \times 10^7$	β^- .435, .58; γ .145	0.58	±0.9000	
$_{58}Ce^{142}$	-13	-90860_2		$(2f_{7/2})^2$	0+	$.158 \times 10^{24}$	**11.07**; α			
$_{58}Ce^{143}$	$-\frac{27}{2}$	-87673_2		$(2f_{7/2})^3$		$.119 \times 10^6$	β^- 1.09, 1.38, . . . ; γ .058, .29, . . .	1.45		
$_{58}Ce^{144}$	-14	-86409_2		$(2f_{7/2})^4$	0+	$.246 \times 10^8$	β^- .3, .19, . . . ; γ .034–.134	1.44		
$_{58}Ce^{145}$	$-\frac{29}{2}$	-82730_4		$(2f_{7/2})^5$		$.180 \times 10^3$	β^- 2.0	0.32		
$_{58}Ce^{146}$	-15	-81330_3		$(2f_{7/2})^6$	0+	$.840 \times 10^3$	β^- .7; γ .32, .05–.27	2.60		
$_{58}Ce^{147}$	$-\frac{31}{2}$			$(2f_{7/2})^7$		$.720 \times 10^2$	β^-	1.00		
$_{58}Ce^{148}$	-16			$(2f_{7/2})^8$	0+	$.420 \times 10^2$	β^-			
$_{59}Pr^{134}$	-8		$(2d_{5/2})^1$	$(3s_{1/2})^1$		$.360 \times 10^4$	γ 1.3, 2.2, .94			
$_{59}Pr^{135}$	$-\frac{17}{2}$		or	$(1h_{11/2})^{12}$		$.132 \times 10^4$	β^+ 2.5; γ .22, .08, .30			
$_{59}Pr^{136}$	-9		$(1g_{7/2})^{-1}$	$(3s_{1/2})^1$		$.420 \times 10^4$	β^+ 2.0; γ .17, .8, 1.1			
$_{59}Pr^{137}$	$-\frac{19}{2}$	-89640_4		$(3s_{1/2})^2$		$.540 \times 10^4$	EC; β^+ 1.7	2.82		
$_{59}Pr^{138}$	-10	-89540_3		$(2d_{3/2})^1$		$.720 \times 10^4$	EC; β^+ 1.4; γ .16–1.7	4.32		
$_{59}Pr^{139}$	$-\frac{21}{2}$	-91420_3		$(2d_{3/2})^2$		$.162 \times 10^5$	EC; β^+ 1.0; γ 1.3, 1.6	2.00		
$_{59}Pr^{140}$	-11	-90993_2		$(2d_{3/2})^3$	1+	$.204 \times 10^3$	β^+ 2.37, . . . ; EC; γ	3.37		
$_{59}Pr^{141}$	$-\frac{23}{2}$	-92404_2		$(2d_{3/2})^4$	$\frac{5}{2}+$		**100**		4.5000	−0.060
$_{59}Pr^{142}$	-12	-90022_2		$(2f_{7/2})^1$	2−	$.691 \times 10^5$	β^- 2.15, .58; γ 1.57	2.16− 0.78+	±0.2600	±0.030
$_{59}Pr^{143}$	$-\frac{25}{2}$	-89219_2		$(2f_{7/2})^2$	$\frac{7}{2}+$	$.118 \times 10^7$	β^- .93	0.93		
$_{59}Pr^{144}$	-13	-86752_2		$(2f_{7/2})^3$	0−	$.104 \times 10^4$	β^- 2.98, .8, . . . ; γ .69, 2.18, . . .	2.99		
$_{59}Pr^{145}$	$-\frac{27}{2}$	-85524_2		$(2f_{7/2})^4$	$(\frac{7}{2}+)$	$.212 \times 10^5$	β^- 1.80; γ .072–1.15	1.81		
$_{59}Pr^{146}$	-14	-82410_3		$(2f_{7/2})^5$	(2−)	$.144 \times 10^4$	β^- 3.7, 2.3; γ .46, 1.49, .75, . . .	4.20		
$_{59}Pr^{147}$	$-\frac{29}{2}$	-81200_4		$(2f_{7/2})^6$		$.720 \times 10^3$	β^-; γ .32–~1.7	2.50		

(Continued)

Table of Nuclides *(continued)*

Nuclide	T_3	Mass excess $M - A$, μu	Prominent terms for ground state or low-lying level: Proton	Neutron	J^π	Half-life, sec	**Abundance,** percent or decay modes with energies, MeV	Total disintegration energy, MeV	Magnetic moment, nm	Quadrupole moment, barns
$_{60}Nd^{138}$	-9		$(2d_{5/2})^2$	$(3s_{1/2})^2$	0^+	$.132 \times 10^4$	β^+ 2.4			
$_{60}Nd^{139}$	$-\frac{19}{2}$	-88420_4		$(2d_{3/2})^1$		$.187 \times 10^5$	EC; β^+ 3.3, . . . ; γ 1.3			
$_{60}Nd^{140}$	-10	-90670_4		$(2d_{3/2})^2$	0^+	$.285 \times 10^6$	EC; γ .11–.5	0.30		
$_{60}Nd^{141}$	$-\frac{21}{2}$	-90472_2		$(2d_{3/2})^3$	$\frac{3}{2}+$	$.900 \times 10^4$	EC; β^+ .78; γ 1.15, 1.30, . . .	1.80		
$_{60}Nd^{142}$	-11	-92337_2		$(2d_{3/2})^4$	0^+		**27.11**			
$_{60}Nd^{143}$	$-\frac{23}{2}$	-90221_2		$(2f_{7/2})^1$	$\frac{7}{2}-$		**12.17**		-1.1000	-0.600
$_{60}Nd^{144}$	-12	-89961_2		$(2f_{7/2})^2$	0^+	$.757 \times 10^{23}$	**23.95**; α	1.90		
$_{60}Nd^{145}$	$-\frac{25}{2}$	-87462_2		$(2f_{7/2})^3$	$\frac{7}{2}-$		**8.30**		-0.7100	-0.300
$_{60}Nd^{146}$	-13	-86914_2		$(2f_{7/2})^4$	0^+		**17.22**			
$_{60}Nd^{147}$	$-\frac{27}{2}$	-83926_2		$(2f_{7/2})^5$	$*\frac{5}{2}-$	$.959 \times 10^6$	β^- .82, .38, . . . ; γ .091, .53, . . .	0.90	± 0.5900	
$_{60}Nd^{148}$	-14	-83131_2		$(2f_{7/2})^6$	0^+		**5.73**			
$_{60}Nd^{149}$	$-\frac{29}{2}$	-79878_2		$(2f_{7/2})^7$	$*\frac{5}{2}$	$.648 \times 10^4$	β^- 1.42, 1.02, 1.13, . . . ; γ .21, . . .	1.67		
$_{60}Nd^{150}$	-15	-79085_2		$(2f_{7/2})^8$	0^+		**5.62**			
$_{60}Nd^{151}$	$-\frac{31}{2}$	-76230_3		$3/2^-$ (521)		$.720 \times 10^3$	β^- 1.93, 2.06, . . . ; γ .12, .26, . . .	2.40		
$_{61}Pm^{141}$	$-\frac{19}{2}$	-86590_3	$(2d_{5/2})^3$	$(2d_{3/2})^2$		$.132 \times 10^4$	β^+ 2.6	3.62		
$_{61}Pm^{142}$	-10	-87180_3	or	$(2d_{3/2})^3$	1^+	$.340 \times 10^2$	β^+ 3.8; EC; γ 1.57	4.80		
$_{61}Pm^{143}$	$-\frac{21}{2}$	-89010_3	$(1g_{7/2})^{-1}$	$(2d_{3/2})^4$		$.229 \times 10^8$	EC; γ .742	1.13		
$_{61}Pm^{144}$	-11	-87490_4		$(2f_{7/2})^1$	$(-)$	$.328 \times 10^8$	EC; γ .70, .62, .48	{0.48− {2.30+		
$_{61}Pm^{145}$	$-\frac{23}{2}$	-87309_2		$(2f_{7/2})^2$	$(\frac{5}{2}+)$	$.568 \times 10^9$	EC; α 2.2; γ .068, .073	{0.14+ {2.32α		
$_{61}Pm^{146}$	-12	-85368_2		$(2f_{7/2})^3$		$.138 \times 10^9$	EC; γ .45, .75; β^- .78; γ .75	{1.53− {1.44+		
$_{61}Pm^{147}$	$-\frac{25}{2}$	-84892_2		$(2f_{7/2})^4$	$\frac{7}{2}+$	$.852 \times 10^8$	β^- .23; γ .12	0.23	± 3.2000	± 0.700
$_{61}Pm^{148}$	-13	-82579_2		$(2f_{7/2})^5$	1^-	†$.467 \times 10^6$	β^- 2.46, 1.0, 1.9; γ .55, .91, . . .	2.45		
$_{61}Pm^{149}$	$-\frac{27}{2}$	-81670_2		$(2f_{7/2})^6$	$\frac{7}{2}+$	$.190 \times 10^6$	β^- 1.06, .78, . . . ; γ .28–.85	1.07		
$_{61}Pm^{150}$	-14	-79040_2		$(2f_{7/2})^7$	(1)	$.972 \times 10^4$	β^- 2.3, 1.8, . . . ; γ .33, 1.18, . . .	3.43		
$_{61}Pm^{151}$	$-\frac{29}{2}$	-78802_2		$(2f_{7/2})^8$	$\frac{5}{2}+$	$.101 \times 10^6$	β^- .85, 1.03, . . . ; γ .34, .10, . . .	1.19	± 1.8000	± 1.900
$_{61}Pm^{152}$	-15	-76490_4		$3/2^-$ (521)		$.360 \times 10^3$	β^- 2.2; γ .12, .24, 1.0	3.50		
$_{61}Pm^{153}$	$-\frac{31}{2}$	-75970_3		$(1h_{9/2})^2$		$.330 \times 10^3$	β^- 1.65; γ .125, .180	1.80		
$_{61}Pm^{154}$	-16			$3/2^-$ (521)		$.150 \times 10^3$	β^- 2.5			
$_{62}Sm^{141}$	$-\frac{17}{2}$		$(2d_{5/2})^4$	$(2d_{3/2})^1$		$.170 \times 10^7$	EC			
$_{62}Sm^{142}$	-9			$(2d_{3/2})^2$	0^+	$.432 \times 10^4$	EC; β^+ 1.0			
$_{62}Sm^{143}$	$-\frac{19}{2}$	-85450_2		$(2d_{3/2})^3$	$(\frac{3}{2}+)$	$.540 \times 10^3$	EC; β^+ 2.4	3.32		
$_{62}Sm^{144}$	-10	-88011_2		$(2d_{3/2})^4$	0^+		**3.09**			
$_{62}Sm^{145}$	$-\frac{21}{2}$	-86606_2		$(2f_{7/2})^1$		$.294 \times 10^8$	EC; γ .061, .48	0.65		

$_{62}Sm^{148}$	-12	-85209_2		$(2f_{7/2})^4$	0^+	$.379 \times 10^{21}$	**11.24**; α	2.00		
$_{62}Sm^{149}$	$-\frac{25}{2}$	-82820_2		$(2f_{7/2})^5$	$\frac{7}{2}^-$	$.126 \times 10^{23}$	**13.83**; α 1.84	1.90	−0.7500	±0.700
$_{62}Sm^{150}$	-13	-82724_2		$(2f_{7/2})^6$	0^+		**7.44**			
$_{62}Sm^{151}$	$-\frac{27}{2}$	-80081_2		$(2f_{7/2})^7$	$\frac{7}{2}^-$	$.284 \times 10^{10}$	β^- .076, . . . ; γ .022	0.08		
$_{62}Sm^{152}$	-14	-80244_2		$(2f_{7/2})^8$	0^+		**26.72**			
$_{62}Sm^{153}$	$-\frac{29}{2}$	-77898_2		$3/2^-(521)$	$\frac{3}{2}^-$	$.169 \times 10^{6}$	β^- .70, .64, . . . ; γ .103, .07, . . .	0.80	−0.0300	1.200
$_{62}Sm^{154}$	-15	-77718_2		$(1h_{9/2})^2$	0^+		**22.71**			
$_{62}Sm^{155}$	$-\frac{31}{2}$	-75299_2		$3/2^-(521)$	$\frac{3}{2}^-$	$.132 \times 10^{4}$	β^- 1.53, 1.39; γ .10, .25, .14	1.65		
$_{62}Sm^{156}$	-16	-74431_2		$(1h_{9/2})^4$	0^+	$.338 \times 10^{5}$	β^- .72, .43; γ .087, .20, . . .	0.72		
$_{62}Sm^{157}$	$-\frac{33}{2}$			$3/2^-(521)$		$.300 \times 10^{2}$	β^-; γ .57			
$_{63}Eu^{144}$	-9		$(2d_{5/2})^5$	$(2d_{3/2})^3$		$.108 \times 10^{4}$	β^+ 2.4			
$_{63}Eu^{145}$	$-\frac{19}{2}$	-83610_2	or	$(2d_{3/2})^4$		$.510 \times 10^{6}$	EC; β^+; γ .89, .64, .53	2.79		
$_{63}Eu^{146}$	-10	-82862_2	$5/2^+(413)$	$(2f_{7/2})^1$		$.397 \times 10^{6}$	EC; β^+ 1.5, . . . ; γ .74, .64, .15–2.9	3.86		
$_{63}Eu^{147}$	$-\frac{21}{2}$	-83200_3		$(2f_{7/2})^2$	$\frac{5}{2}^+$	$.207 \times 10^{7}$	EC; β^+; γ .12, .077, .20, . . . ; α 2.9	{1.80 {2.99α		
$_{63}Eu^{148}$	-11	-81890_2		$(2f_{7/2})^3$	$(-)$	$.467 \times 10^{7}$	EC; β^+ .92; γ .55, .63, .41, . . .	{0.01− {3.09+		
$_{63}Eu^{149}$	$-\frac{23}{2}$	-82000_4		$(2f_{7/2})^4$	$\frac{5}{2}^+$	$.916 \times 10^{7}$	EC; γ .28, .33, .023–.53	0.80		
$_{63}Eu^{150}$	-12	-80311_2		$(2f_{7/2})^5$	(4)	$.160 \times 10^{9}$	EC; γ .33, .44, .59–1.07	{1.01− {2.25+		
$_{63}Eu^{151}$	$-\frac{25}{2}$	-80162_2		$(2f_{7/2})^6$	$\frac{5}{2}^+$		**47.82**		3.4640	0.950
$_{63}Eu^{152}$	-13	-78251_2		$(2f_{7/2})^7$	3^-	$.410 \times 10^{9}$	EC; β^- 1.47, . . . ; β^+ .72, . . . ; γ .12, .34, . . .	{1.82− {1.86+	±1.9240	±2.600
$_{63}Eu^{153}$	$-\frac{27}{2}$	-78758_2		$(2f_{7/2})^8$	$\frac{5}{2}^+$		**52.18**		1.5300	2.420
$_{63}Eu^{154}$	-14	-76947_2		$3/2^-(521)$	*3^-	$.515 \times 10^{9}$	β^- .15–1.84; γ .123, 1.28, .72, . . .	1.98	±2.0000	
$_{63}Eu^{155}$	$-\frac{29}{2}$	-77070_2		$(1h_{9/2})^2$	$(\frac{5}{2}^+)$	$.568 \times 10^{8}$	β^- .14, .10–.24; γ .087, . . .	0.25		
$_{63}Eu^{156}$	-15	-75198_2		$3/2^-(521)$		$.130 \times 10^{7}$	β^- 2.44, 1.21, . . . ; γ .089, . . .	2.45		
$_{63}Eu^{157}$	$-\frac{31}{2}$	-74610_2		$(1h_{9/2})^4$		$.547 \times 10^{5}$	β^- 1.3, .53–.90; γ .42, .065, . . .	1.27		
$_{63}Eu^{158}$	-16	-72060_3		$3/2^-(521)$		$.276 \times 10^{4}$	β^- 1.5, 2.3; γ .08–1.2, . . .	3.50		
$_{63}Eu^{159}$	$-\frac{33}{2}$	-71160_3		$(1h_{9/2})^6$		$.114 \times 10^{4}$	β^- 2.2; γ .045, .176, . . .	2.30		
$_{63}Eu^{160}$	-17	-69000_3		$5/2^-(523)$		$.150 \times 10^{3}$	β^- 3.6	3.60		
$_{64}Gd^{145}$	$-\frac{17}{2}$		$(2d_{5/2})^6$	$(2d_{3/2})^3$		$.150 \times 10^{4}$	EC; β^+ 2.4; γ 1.75, 1.04, .80			
$_{64}Gd^{146}$	-9	-81680_4		$(2d_{3/2})^4$	0^+	$.415 \times 10^{7}$	EC; γ .115, .150	1.10		
$_{64}Gd^{147}$	$-\frac{19}{2}$	-80830_4		$(2f_{7/2})^1$		$.900 \times 10^{5}$	EC; γ .23, .40, .90, .37, . . .	2.20		
$_{64}Gd^{148}$	-10	-81899_2		$(2f_{7/2})^2$	0^+	$.268 \times 10^{10}$	α 3.18	3.27		
$_{64}Gd^{149}$	$-\frac{21}{2}$	-80700_3		$(2f_{7/2})^3$	$(\frac{7}{2}^-)$	$.778 \times 10^{6}$	EC; γ .107–.94; α 3.0	{1.22+ {3.08α		
$_{64}Gd^{150}$	-11	-81395_2		$(2f_{7/2})^4$	0^+	$.631 \times 10^{14}$	α 2.73	2.80		
$_{64}Gd^{151}$	$-\frac{23}{2}$	-79730_4		$(2f_{7/2})^5$		$.104 \times 10^{8}$	EC; γ .022, .175, .08–.35	0.40		
$_{64}Gd^{152}$	-12	-80206_2		$(2f_{7/2})^6$	0^+	$.347 \times 10^{22}$	**0.200**; α	2.24		
$_{64}Gd^{153}$	$-\frac{25}{2}$	-78497_2		$3/2^+(651)$	$\frac{3}{2}^+$	$.207 \times 10^{8}$	EC; γ .097, .103, .070, . . .	0.24		
$_{64}Gd^{154}$	-13	-79071_2		$(2f_{7/2})^8$	0^+		**2.15**			

(Continued)

Table of Nuclides *(continued)*

Nuclide	T_3	Mass excess $M - A$, μu	Prominent terms for ground state or low-lying level: Proton	Neutron	J^π	Half-life, sec	**Abundance,** percent or decay modes with energies, MeV	Total disintegration energy, MeV	Magnetic moment, nm	Quadrupole moment, barns
$_{64}Gd^{155}$	$-\frac{27}{2}$	-77336_2	$(2d_{5/2})^6$	$3/2^-(521)$	$\frac{3}{2}^-$		**14.73**		−0.2700	1.300
$_{64}Gd^{156}$	−14	-77825_2		$(1h_{9/2})^2$	0^+		**20.47**			
$_{64}Gd^{157}$	$-\frac{29}{2}$	-75975_2		$3/2^-(521)$	$\frac{3}{2}^-$		**15.68**		−0.3600	1.500
$_{64}Gd^{158}$	−15	-75822_2		$(1h_{9/2})^4$	0^+		**24.87**			
$_{64}Gd^{159}$	$-\frac{31}{2}$	-73632_2		$3/2^-(521)$	$\frac{3}{2}^-$	$.648 \times 10^5$	β^- .95, .89, . . . ; γ .058, .36, . . .	0.95		
$_{64}Gd^{160}$	−16	-72885_2		$(1h_{9/2})^6$	0^+		**21.90**			
$_{64}Gd^{161}$	$-\frac{33}{2}$	-70280_2		$5/2^-(523)$		$.222 \times 10^3$	β^- 1.6, . . . ; γ .057, .078–.53	2.00		
$_{64}Gd^{162}$	−17	-69120_4		$(1h_{9/2})^8$	0^+	$>.300 \times 10^8$	β^-; γ .041–1.39	1.00		
$_{65}Tb^{147}$	$-\frac{17}{2}$		$(1h_{11/2})^1$	$(2d_{3/2})^4$		$.144 \times 10^4$	β^+; γ .30, .14			
$_{65}Tb^{148}$	−9	-75870_3	$5/2^+(413)$	$(2f_{7/2})^1$		$.420 \times 10^4$	EC; β^+; γ .78, 1.12	5.62		
$_{65}Tb^{149}$	$-\frac{19}{2}$	-76650_2	or $3/2^+(411)$	$(2f_{7/2})^2$		$.148 \times 10^5$	EC; α 3.95; γ .17–.64	{3.77⁺ 4.06α		
$_{65}Tb^{150}$	−10	-76252_2		$(2f_{7/2})^3$		$.112 \times 10^5$	EC; γ .64, .51, .93	4.79		
$_{65}Tb^{151}$	$-\frac{21}{2}$	-76850_3		$(2f_{7/2})^4$		$.648 \times 10^5$	EC; α 3.44; γ .108, .18–1.3	{2.69⁺ 3.50α		
$_{65}Tb^{152}$	−11	-75720_3		$(2f_{7/2})^5$		$.648 \times 10^5$	β^+ 2.8, 1.8, . . . ; γ .34, .42, . . .	4.18		
$_{65}Tb^{153}$	$-\frac{23}{2}$	-76510_4		$(2f_{7/2})^6$	$(\frac{5}{2})$	$.225 \times 10^6$	EC; γ .088, .21, .11, .17, . . .	1.90		
$_{65}Tb^{154}$	−12	-75420_4		$3/2^+(651)$		$.756 \times 10^5$	EC; β^+ 2.7, . . . ; γ .12, .25, . . .	{0.21⁻ 3.40⁺		
$_{65}Tb^{155}$	$-\frac{25}{2}$	-76370_4		$(2f_{7/2})^8$		$.484 \times 10^6$	EC; γ .045, .087, .105, .160, . . .	0.90		
$_{65}Tb^{156}$	−13	-75250_4		$3/2^-(521)$	(3^-)	$.467 \times 10^6$	EC; γ .089, .53, .11–2.0	{0.76⁻ 2.40⁺		
$_{65}Tb^{157}$	$-\frac{27}{2}$	-75910_2		$(1h_{9/2})^2$		$.473 \times 10^{10}$	EC; γ .055	0.06		
$_{65}Tb^{158}$	−14	-74536_2		$3/2^-(521)$	(3^-)	$.300 \times 10^{11}$	EC; β^-; γ .08–1.19	{0.95⁻ 1.20⁺		
$_{65}Tb^{159}$	$-\frac{29}{2}$	-74649_2		$(1h_{9/2})^4$	$\frac{3}{2}^+$		**100**		±1.7000	
$_{65}Tb^{160}$	−15	-72854_2		$3/2^-(521)$	3^-	$.631 \times 10^7$	β^- .57, .87, .45, . . . ; γ .087–1.3	1.81		
$_{65}Tb^{161}$	$-\frac{31}{2}$	-72428_2		$(1h_{9/2})^6$	$\frac{3}{2}^+$	$.596 \times 10^6$	β^- .51, .58, .45; γ .049, .026, . . .	0.58		
$_{65}Tb^{162}$	−16	-70190_4		$5/2^-(523)$		$.720 \times 10^4$		2.80		
$_{65}Tb^{163}$	$-\frac{33}{2}$	-69440_2		$(1h_{9/2})^8$		$.252 \times 10^5$	β^-	1.68		
$_{65}Tb^{164}$	−17	-66720_4		$7/2^+(633)$		$.864 \times 10^5$	β^-	3.80		
$_{66}Dy^{149}$	$-\frac{17}{2}$		$(1h_{11/2})^2$	$(2f_{7/2})^1$		$.900 \times 10^3$	EC			
$_{66}Dy^{150}$	−9	-74410_4		$(2f_{7/2})^2$	0^+	$.432 \times 10^3$	β^+; α 4.3; γ .39	{1.71⁺ 4.35α		
$_{66}Dy^{151}$	$-\frac{19}{2}$	-73750_4		$(2f_{7/2})^3$		$.108 \times 10^4$	β^+; EC; α 4.06; γ .15	{2.88⁺ 4.18α		
								{0.42⁺		

							EC; α 3.5; γ .081, .100, .082–.54	3.58α		
$_{66}Dy^{154}$	−11	-75650_2		$(2f_{7/2})^6$	0^+	$.300 \times 10^{14}$	α 2.85			
$_{66}Dy^{155}$	$-\frac{23}{2}$	-74120_4		$3/2^+ (651)$		$.360 \times 10^5$	EC; β^+ .85, . . . ; γ .23, .090–1.67	2.93		
$_{66}Dy^{156}$	−12	-76070_3		$(2f_{7/2})^8$	0^+	$.631 \times 10^{22}$	**0.052**; α	2.10		
$_{66}Dy^{157}$	$-\frac{25}{2}$	-74730_4		$3/2^- (521)$		$.306 \times 10^5$	EC; γ .327, .083, .061, .144, . . .	2.81		
$_{66}Dy^{158}$	−13	-75551_2		$(1h_{9/2})^2$	0^+		**0.090**	1.10		
$_{66}Dy^{159}$	$-\frac{27}{2}$	-74241_2		$3/2^- (521)$	$(\frac{3}{2}^-)$	$.124 \times 10^8$	EC; γ .058, .36, .29, .20, . . .	0.38		
$_{66}Dy^{160}$	−14	-74798_2		$(1h_{9/2})^4$	0^+		**2.29**			
$_{66}Dy^{161}$	$-\frac{29}{2}$	-73055_2		$5/2^+ (642)$	$\frac{5}{2}^+$		**18.88**		±0.4200	±1.100
$_{66}Dy^{162}$	−15	-73197_2		$(1h_{9/2})^6$	0^+		**25.53**			
$_{66}Dy^{163}$	$-\frac{31}{2}$	-71245_2		$5/2^- (523)$	$\frac{5}{2}^-$		**24.97**		±0.5800	±1.300
$_{66}Dy^{164}$	−16	-70800_2		$(1h_{9/2})^8$	0^+		**28.18**			
$_{66}Dy^{165}$	$-\frac{33}{2}$	-68184_2		$7/2^+ (633)$	$\frac{7}{2}^+$	$.828 \times 10^4$	β^- 1.30, 1.20, . . . ; γ .094, .28–1.1	1.30		
$_{66}Dy^{166}$	−17	-67193_2		$(1h_{9/2})^{10}$	0^+	$.288 \times 10^6$	β^- .40, .48, .06; γ .083, . . .	0.48		
$_{66}Dy^{167}$	$-\frac{35}{2}$			$1/2^- (521)$		$.264 \times 10^3$	β^-			
$_{67}Ho^{151}$	$-\frac{17}{2}$		$(1h_{11/2})^3$	$(2f_{7/2})^2$		$†.360 \times 10^2$	α 4.51			
$_{67}Ho^{152}$	−9	-68440_3	or $7/2^- (523)$	$(2f_{7/2})^3$		$†.520 \times 10^2$	α 4.45	{6.37+ 4.50α		
$_{67}Ho^{153}$	$-\frac{19}{2}$	-69730_2		$(2f_{7/2})^4$		$.540 \times 10^3$	EC; α 3.92	{4.22+ 4.03α		
$_{67}Ho^{155}$	$-\frac{21}{2}$			$(2f_{7/2})^6$		$.276 \times 10^4$	β^+ 2.1, . . . ; γ .14			
$_{67}Ho^{156}$	−11			$3/2^+ (651)$		$.342 \times 10^4$	β^+ 1.8, . . . ; EC; γ .14, .27, . . .			
$_{67}Ho^{158}$	−12	-71210_2		$3/2^- (521)$		$†.690 \times 10^3$	β^+; γ	4.04		
$_{67}Ho^{159}$	$-\frac{25}{2}$	-72310_4		$(1h_{9/2})^2$		$.198 \times 10^4$	EC; γ .20–.30, . . .	1.80		
$_{67}Ho^{160}$	−13	-71260_2		$3/2^- (521)$	(5^+)	$†.168 \times 10^4$	EC; β^+ .57, . . . ; γ .73, .97, . . .	3.30		
$_{67}Ho^{161}$	$-\frac{27}{2}$	-72200_4		$(1h_{9/2})^4$	$\frac{7}{2}^-$	$.900 \times 10^4$	EC; γ .026, .078, .075, .044–.176	0.80		
$_{67}Ho^{162}$	−14	-70878_2		$5/2^- (523)$	1^+	$†.720 \times 10^3$	β^+ 1.14, . . . ; γ .76	{0.35− 2.16+		
$_{67}Ho^{163}$	$-\frac{29}{2}$	-71234_2		$(1h_{9/2})^6$		$>.300 \times 10^{11}$	EC	0.01		
$_{67}Ho^{164}$	−15	-69610_2		$5/2^- (523)$	1	$.222 \times 10^4$	β^- .99, .90; EC; γ .073, .09, . . .	{1.03− 1.11+		
$_{67}Ho^{165}$	$-\frac{31}{2}$	-69579_2		$(1h_{9/2})^8$	$\frac{7}{2}^-$		**100**		4.1000	3.000
$_{67}Ho^{166}$	−16	-67711_2		$7/2^+ (633)$	0^-	$†.979 \times 10^5$	β^- 1.84, 1.76, . . . ; γ .08, .14, . . .	1.85		
$_{67}Ho^{167}$	$-\frac{33}{2}$	-66870_3		$(1h_{9/2})^{10}$		$.108 \times 10^5$	β^- 1.0, 2.8; γ .35, .70	1.00		
$_{67}Ho^{168}$	−17	-64070_3		$1/2^- (521)$		$.180 \times 10^3$	β^- 2.0; γ .85	3.30		
$_{67}Ho^{169}$	$-\frac{35}{2}$	-63140_3		$(3p_{3/2})^2$		$.288 \times 10^3$	β^- 1.20, 1.95, . . . ; γ .76, .16–.92	2.10		
$_{67}Ho^{170}$	−18	-59930_3		$5/2^- (512)$		$.450 \times 10^2$	β^- ~3.1	4.20		
$_{68}Er^{152}$	−8		$(1h_{11/2})^4$	$(2f_{7/2})^2$	0^+	$.107 \times 10^2$	α 4.93; β^+			
$_{68}Er^{153}$	$-\frac{17}{2}$			$(2f_{7/2})^3$		$.360 \times 10^2$	α 4.80; β^+			
$_{68}Er^{154}$	−9	-67240_4		$(2f_{7/2})^4$	0^+	$.270 \times 10^3$	α 4.26	{2.33+ 4.26α		
$_{68}Er^{158}$	−11			$(2f_{7/2})^8$	0^+	$.900 \times 10^4$	β^+; γ			
$_{68}Er^{159}$	$-\frac{23}{2}$			$3/2^- (521)$		$.360 \times 10^4$	EC; γ .21, .05–.30			

(Continued)

Table of Nuclides *(continued)*

Nuclide	T_3	Mass excess $M - A$, μu	Prominent terms for ground state or low-lying level: Proton	Neutron	J^π	Half-life, sec	**Abundance,** percent or decay modes with energies, MeV	Total disintegration energy, MeV	Magnetic moment, nm	Quadrupole moment, barns
$_{68}Er^{160}$	-12		$(1h_{11/2})^4$	$(1h_{9/2})^2$	0^+	$.104 \times 10^6$	EC			
$_{68}Er^{161}$	$-\frac{25}{2}$	-70050_4		$3/2^-(521)$		$.112 \times 10^5$	EC; β^+ 1.21; γ .067, .211, .83, . . .	2.00		
$_{68}Er^{162}$	-13	-71260_2		$(1h_{9/2})^4$	0^+		**0.136**			
$_{68}Er^{163}$	$-\frac{27}{2}$	-69935_2		$5/2^-(523)$	$(\frac{5}{2}^-)$	$.450 \times 10^4$	EC; γ .43, 1.1	1.21		
$_{68}Er^{164}$	-14	-70713_2		$(1h_{9/2})^6$	0^+		**1.56**			
$_{68}Er^{165}$	$-\frac{29}{2}$	-69181_2		$5/2^-(523)$	$\frac{5}{2}^-$	$.371 \times 10^5$	EC	0.37		
$_{68}Er^{166}$	-15	-69693_2		$(1h_{9/2})^8$	0^+		**33.41**			
$_{68}Er^{167}$	$-\frac{31}{2}$	-67940_2		$7/2^+(633)$	$\frac{7}{2}^+$		**22.94**		-0.5600	2.800
$_{68}Er^{168}$	-16	-67617_2		$(1h_{9/2})^{10}$	0^+		**27.07**			
$_{68}Er^{169}$	$-\frac{33}{2}$	-65390_2		$1/2^-(521)$	$\frac{1}{2}^-$	$.812 \times 10^6$	β^- .34, . . . ; γ .008	0.34	0.5130	
$_{68}Er^{170}$	-17	-64440_2		$(3p_{3/2})^2$	0^+		**14.88**			
$_{68}Er^{171}$	$-\frac{35}{2}$	-61870_2		$5/2^-(512)$	$\frac{5}{2}^-$	$.270 \times 10^5$	β^- 1.06, .5–1.49; γ .112, .308, . . .	1.49	± 0.7000	± 2.400
$_{68}Er^{172}$	-18	-60670_2		$(3p_{3/2})^4$	0^+	$.176 \times 10^6$	β^- .28, .36, .9; γ .05, .41, . . .	0.89		
$_{69}Tm^{153}$	$-\frac{15}{2}$		$(1h_{11/2})^5$	$(2f_{7/2})^2$		$.158 \times 10^1$	α 5.11			
$_{69}Tm^{154}$	-8		or	$(2f_{7/2})^3$		$.310 \times 10^1$	α 5.04			
$_{69}Tm^{161}$	$-\frac{23}{2}$	-66270_4	$1/2^+(411)$	$(1h_{9/2})^2$		$.180 \times 10^4$	EC; γ .084, .172	3.52		
$_{69}Tm^{162}$	-12	-66010_3		$3/2^-(521)$		$.132 \times 10^4$	β^+ 3.8, 2.3, ~.9; EC; γ .102, . . .	4.89		
$_{69}Tm^{163}$	$-\frac{25}{2}$	-67498_2		$(1h_{9/2})^4$		$.720 \times 10^4$	EC; γ .104, .242, .022–.66	2.27		
$_{69}Tm^{164}$	-13	-66459_2		$5/2^-(523)$		$.120 \times 10^3$	β^+ 2.9, 1.3; γ .091, .21–.93	3.96		
$_{69}Tm^{165}$	$-\frac{27}{2}$	-67460_4		$(1h_{9/2})^6$		$.104 \times 10^6$	EC; γ .054, .243, .015–1.38	1.60		
$_{69}Tm^{166}$	-14	-66490_2		$5/2^+(642)$	2^+	$.277 \times 10^5$	EC; β^+ 1.9, 1.2; γ .08, .18, . . .	2.98	± 0.0500	± 4.600
$_{69}Tm^{167}$	$-\frac{29}{2}$	-66970_4		$(1h_{9/2})^8$	$\frac{1}{2}^+$	$.829 \times 10^6$	EC; γ .21, .057, .53	0.90		
$_{69}Tm^{168}$	-15	-65770_2		$7/2^+(633)$	(3^+)	$.734 \times 10^7$	EC; γ .8, .20, .080–1.64	{0.07− 1.72+		
$_{69}Tm^{169}$	$-\frac{31}{2}$	-65755_2		$(1h_{9/2})^{10}$	$\frac{1}{2}^+$		**100**		-0.2290	
$_{69}Tm^{170}$	-16	-63940_2		$1/2^-(521)$	1^-	$.108 \times 10^8$	β^- .96, .88; γ .084	{0.97− 0.46+	± 0.2400	± 0.570
$_{69}Tm^{171}$	$-\frac{33}{2}$	-63470_2		$(3p_{3/2})^2$	$\frac{1}{2}^+$	$.600 \times 10^8$	β^- .097, .03; γ .067	0.10	± 0.2300	
$_{69}Tm^{172}$	-17	-61620_2		$5/2^-(512)$	2^-	$.230 \times 10^6$	β^- 1.5, . . . ; γ .079, .18–1.09	1.88		
$_{69}Tm^{173}$	$-\frac{35}{2}$	-60520_2		$(3p_{3/2})^4$	$(\frac{1}{2}^+)$	$.295 \times 10^5$	β^- .92, .85, . . . ; γ .40, .47	1.32		
$_{69}Tm^{174}$	-18	-58030_3		$7/2^-(514)$		$.330 \times 10^3$	β^- 2.5	3.00		
$_{69}Tm^{175}$	$-\frac{37}{2}$	-56170_4		$(1i_{13/2})^2$		$.120 \times 10^4$	β^- 2.0; γ .51	2.50		
$_{69}Tm^{176}$	-19	-52810_4		$9/2^+(624)$		$.900 \times 10^2$	β^- 4.2	4.20		
$_{70}Yb^{154}$	-7		$(1h_{11/2})^6$	$(2f_{7/2})^2$	0^+	.390	α 5.48			
$_{70}Yb^{155}$	$-\frac{15}{2}$			$(2f_{7/2})^3$		$.165 \times 10^1$	α 5.21			
$_{70}Yb^{162}$	-11			$(1h_{9/2})^2$	0^+	$.140 \times 10^4$	EC; γ .041			
				$(1l\ \ )^4$	0^+	$.450 \times 10^4$	EC; β^+ 2.9, . . .			

				$(1h_{9/2})$…	0…	.194 × 10…	EC; γ .08	0.32		
$_{70}Yb^{167}$	$-\frac{27}{2}$	-64870_4		5/2− (523)		.108 × 10^4	EC; γ .106, .113, .026–.176	1.96		
$_{70}Yb^{168}$	−14	-65840_3		$(1h_{9/2})^8$	0+		**0.135**			
$_{70}Yb^{169}$	$-\frac{29}{2}$	-64470_4		7/2+ (633)	$\frac{7}{2}$+	.277 × 10^7	EC; γ .008, .109, .021–.309	1.20		
$_{70}Yb^{170}$	−15	-64980_2		$(1h_{9/2})^{10}$	0+		**3.03**			
$_{70}Yb^{171}$	$-\frac{31}{2}$	-63570_2		1/2− (521)	$\frac{1}{2}$−		**14.31**		0.4930	
$_{70}Yb^{172}$	−16	-63640_2		$(3p_{3/2})^2$	0+		**21.82**			
$_{70}Yb^{173}$	$-\frac{33}{2}$	-61940_2		5/2− (512)	$\frac{5}{2}$−		**16.13**		−0.6780	3.000
$_{70}Yb^{174}$	−17	-61260_2		$(3p_{3/2})^4$	0+		**31.84**			
$_{70}Yb^{175}$	$-\frac{35}{2}$	-58860_2		7/2− (514)		.363 × 10^6	β− .47, .073, . . . ; γ .40, .11, . . .	0.47		
$_{70}Yb^{176}$	−18	-57320_2		$(1i_{13/2})^2$	0+		**12.73**	0.02		
$_{70}Yb^{177}$	$-\frac{37}{2}$	-54590_2		9/2+ (624)	$\frac{9}{2}$+	.684 × 10^4	β− 1.38, . . . ; γ .15, .12, .11, . . .	1.38		
$_{71}Lu^{155}$	$-\frac{13}{2}$		7/2+ (404)	$(2f_{7/2})^2$		.700 × 10^{-1}	α 5.63			
$_{71}Lu^{156}$	−7			$(2f_{7/2})^3$		.230	α 5.54			
$_{71}Lu^{167}$	$-\frac{25}{2}$	-61610_4		$(1h_{9/2})^6$		.324 × 10^4	EC; γ .030, .24, .056–.40	3.04		
$_{71}Lu^{168}$	−13	-60910_4		5/2− (523)		.720 × 10^4	EC; γ .089	4.60		
$_{71}Lu^{169}$	$-\frac{27}{2}$	-62040_4		$(1h_{9/2})^8$		.130 × 10^6	EC; γ .087, .024, .063, .070–1.39	2.26		
$_{71}Lu^{170}$	−14	-61170_2		7/2+ (633)		.173 × 10^6	EC; β+ 1.8; γ .084, .193, . . .	3.55		
$_{71}Lu^{171}$	$-\frac{29}{2}$	-61860_4		$(1h_{9/2})^{10}$		.717 × 10^6	EC; γ .74, .076, .067, . . .	1.60		
$_{71}Lu^{172}$	−15	-60740_4		1/2− (521)	4−	.579 × 10^6	EC; γ .079, 1.09, .90, .091, . . .	2.70		
$_{71}Lu^{173}$	$-\frac{31}{2}$	-61200_2		$(3p_{3/2})^2$	$\frac{7}{2}$+	.442 × 10^8	EC; γ .079, .101, .273, .171	0.69		
$_{71}Lu^{174}$	−16	-59650_2		5/2− (512)		†Short	EC	1.50		
$_{71}Lu^{175}$	$-\frac{33}{2}$	-59360_2		$(3p_{3/2})^4$	$\frac{7}{2}$+		**97.41**		2.2300	5.600
$_{71}Lu^{176}$	−17	-57340_2		7/2− (514)	7−	.694 × 10^{18}	**2.59**; β− .42; γ .31, .20, .09	1.02	3.1800	8.000
$_{71}Lu^{177}$	$-\frac{35}{2}$	-56070_2		$(1i_{13/2})^2$	$\frac{7}{2}$+	†.588 × 10^6	β− .50, .18, . . . ; γ .208, .113, . . .	0.50	2.2400	5.400
$_{71}Lu^{178}$	−18	-53700_2		9/2+ (624)		.180 × 10^4	β− 2.3	2.25		
$_{71}Lu^{179}$	$-\frac{37}{2}$	-52530_3		$(1i_{13/2})^4$	($\frac{7}{2}$+)	.166 × 10^5	β− 1.35, 1.08; γ .22, .05	1.34		
$_{71}Lu^{180}$	−19	-49630_3		1/2− (510)		.150 × 10^3	β− 3.3	3.30		
$_{72}Hf^{157}$	$-\frac{13}{2}$		$(1h_{11/2})^8$	$(2f_{7/2})^3$		.120	α 5.68			
$_{72}Hf^{158}$	−7			$(2f_{7/2})^4$	0+	.300 × 10^1	α 5.27			
$_{72}Hf^{168}$	−12			$(1h_{9/2})^6$	0+	.132 × 10^4	EC; β+ 1.7; γ			
$_{72}Hf^{169}$	$-\frac{25}{2}$			5/2− (523)		.684 × 10^4	EC; β+ 2.4; γ			
$_{72}Hf^{170}$	−13			$(1h_{9/2})^8$	0+	.432 × 10^5	EC; β+; γ .12–.77			
$_{72}Hf^{171}$	$-\frac{27}{2}$			7/2+ (633)		.432 × 10^5	EC; γ .18, .12–1.07			
$_{72}Hf^{172}$	−14			$(1h_{9/2})^{10}$	0+	.160 × 10^9	EC; γ .123, .080			
$_{72}Hf^{173}$	$-\frac{29}{2}$			1/2− (521)	$\frac{1}{2}$−	.864 × 10^5	EC; γ .140, .124, .135, .163–1.2			
$_{72}Hf^{174}$	−15	-59640_2		$(3p_{3/2})^2$	0+	.136 × 10^{24}	**0.18**; α ~2.5	{0.01+ 2.56α		
$_{72}Hf^{175}$	$-\frac{31}{2}$	-58390_4		5/2− (512)	($\frac{5}{2}$−)	.605 × 10^7	EC; γ .343, .089, .113–.432	0.90		
$_{72}Hf^{176}$	−16	-58430_2		$(2p_{3/2})^4$	0+		**5.20**			
$_{72}Hf^{177}$	$-\frac{33}{2}$	-56600_2		7/2− (514)	$\frac{7}{2}$−		**18.50**		0.6100	3.000
$_{72}Hf^{178}$	−17	-56120_2		$(1i_{13/2})^2$	0+		**27.14**			
$_{72}Hf^{179}$	$-\frac{35}{2}$	-53970_2		9/2+ (624)	$\frac{9}{2}$+		**13.75**		−0.4700	3.000

(Continued)

Table of Nuclides *(continued)*

Nuclide	T_3	Mass excess $M - A$, μu	Prominent terms for ground state or low-lying level: Proton	Neutron	J^π	Half-life, sec	**Abundance,** percent or decay modes with energies, MeV	Total disintegration energy, MeV	Magnetic moment, nm	Quadrupole moment, barns
$_{72}Hf^{180}$	-18	-53180_3	$(1h_{11/2})^8$	$(1i_{13/2})^4$	0^+		**35.24**			
$_{72}Hf^{181}$	$-\frac{37}{2}$	-50895_2		$1/2^-$ (510)	$(\frac{1}{2}^-)$	$.389 \times 10^7$	β^- .41, . . . ; γ .48, .006–.70	1.02		
$_{72}Hf^{182}$	-19	-49300_3		$(1i_{13/2})^6$	0^+	$.284 \times 10^{15}$	β^- ~.5; γ .27	0.50		
$_{72}Hf^{183}$	$-\frac{39}{2}$	-46170_3		$3/2^-$ (512)		$.396 \times 10^4$	β^- 1.4	2.20		
$_{73}Ta^{172}$	-13		$7/2^+$ (404)	$7/2^+$ (633)		$.180 \times 10^4$	β^+			
$_{73}Ta^{173}$	$-\frac{27}{2}$			$(1h_{11/2})^{10}$		$.900 \times 10^4$	EC; γ .037–.181			
$_{73}Ta^{174}$	-14			$1/2^-$ (521)		$.468 \times 10^4$	β^+; γ .091–.35			
$_{73}Ta^{175}$	$-\frac{29}{2}$			$(3p_{3/2})^2$		$.396 \times 10^5$	EC; γ .082, .207, .267, .104, . . .			
$_{73}Ta^{176}$	-15			$5/2^-$ (512)	(1^-)	$.288 \times 10^5$	EC; γ .088, 1.00–2.08			
$_{73}Ta^{177}$	$-\frac{31}{2}$	-55350_2		$(3p_{3/2})^4$	$(\frac{7}{2}^+)$	$.199 \times 10^6$	EC; γ 1.13, .208, 1.058, . . .	1.17		
$_{73}Ta^{178}$	-16	-54070_3		$7/2^-$ (514)	(7^-)	$.792 \times 10^4$	EC; β^+; γ .332	1.91		
$_{73}Ta^{179}$	$-\frac{33}{2}$	-53840_2		$(1i_{13/2})^2$	$+$	$.500 \times 10^8$	EC	0.12		
$_{73}Ta^{180}$	-17	-52456_2		$9/2^+$ (624)			**0.0123**	{0.50− / 0.67+		
$_{73}Ta^{181}$	$-\frac{35}{2}$	-51993_2		$(1i_{13/2})^4$	$\frac{7}{2}^+$		**99.99**		2.3600	4.200
$_{73}Ta^{182}$	-18	-49833_2		$1/2^-$ (510)	$(-)$	$.994 \times 10^7$	β^- .51, . . . ; γ .10, 1.12, 1.22, . . .	1.74		
$_{73}Ta^{183}$	$-\frac{37}{2}$	-48530_2		$(1i_{13/2})^6$	$\frac{7}{2}^+$	$.432 \times 10^6$	β^- .61, . . . ; γ .046, .053, .108, . . .	1.07		
$_{73}Ta^{184}$	-19	-46020_2		$3/2^-$ (512)		$.313 \times 10^5$	β^- 1.19, 1.45–2.64; γ .40, .111, . . .	2.75		
$_{73}Ta^{185}$	$-\frac{39}{2}$	-44440_2		$(1i_{13/2})^8$		$.288 \times 10^4$	β^- 1.71, . . . ; γ .175, .10, .075, . . .	1.90		
$_{73}Ta^{186}$	-20	-41590_3		$3/2^-$ (512)		$.600 \times 10^3$	β^- 2.2; γ .20, .73, .12–1.1	3.70		
$_{74}W^{175}$	$-\frac{27}{2}$		$(1h_{11/2})^{10}$	$1/2^-$ (521)	$(\frac{1}{2}^-)$	$.540 \times 10^4$	β^+; γ			
$_{74}W^{176}$	-14			$(3p_{3/2})^2$	0^+	$.468 \times 10^4$	EC; γ .10, .03–.95			
$_{74}W^{177}$	$-\frac{29}{2}$			$5/2^-$ (512)		$.792 \times 10^4$	EC; γ ~.5, 1.2			
$_{74}W^{178}$	-15			$(3p_{3/2})^4$	0^+	$.190 \times 10^7$	EC; γ .093, 1.35			
$_{74}W^{179}$	$-\frac{31}{2}$			$7/2^-$ (514)	$(\frac{7}{2}^-)$	$.180 \times 10^4$	EC; γ .031			
$_{74}W^{180}$	-16	-53000_2		$(1i_{13/2})^2$	0^+		**0.14**			
$_{74}W^{181}$	$-\frac{33}{2}$	-51789_2		$9/2^+$ (624)	$\frac{9}{2}^+$	$.112 \times 10^8$	EC; γ .15, .14	0.19		
$_{74}W^{182}$	-17	-51699_2		$(1i_{13/2})^4$	0^+		**26.41**			
$_{74}W^{183}$	$-\frac{35}{2}$	-49676_2		$1/2^-$ (510)	$\frac{1}{2}^-$		**14.40**		0.1170	
$_{74}W^{184}$	-18	-48975_2		$(1i_{13/2})^6$	0^+		**30.64**			
$_{74}W^{185}$	$-\frac{37}{2}$	-46481_2		$3/2^-$ (512)	$\frac{3}{2}^-$	$.639 \times 10^7$	β^- .43, . . . ; γ .125	0.43		
$_{74}W^{186}$	-19	-45560_2		$(1i_{13/2})^8$	0^+		**28.41**			
$_{74}W^{187}$	$-\frac{39}{2}$	-42756_2		$3/2^-$ (512)	$\frac{3}{2}^-$	$.864 \times 10^5$	β^- .63, 1.33, .33; γ .69, .13, . . .	1.31		
$_{74}W^{188}$	-20	-41184_2		$(1i_{13/2})^{10}$	0^+	$.562 \times 10^7$	β^- .36, ~.07, . . . ; γ .29, . . .	0.43		
$_{74}W^{189}$	$-\frac{41}{2}$			$9/2^-$ (505)		$.660 \times 10^3$	β^- ~1.4			
$_{75}Re^{177}$	$-\frac{27}{2}$		$5/2^+$ (402)	$(3p_{3/2})^2$		$.102 \times 10^4$	β^+ 7.4			
$_{75}Re^{178}$	-14			$5/2^-$ (512)		$.900 \times 10^3$	β^+ 3.1; EC			

$_{75}Re^{180}$	−15			7/2⁻ (514)		$.720 \times 10^{[illegible]}$	β^+ 1.9	2.90		
$_{75}Re^{181}$	$-\frac{31}{2}$			$(1i_{13/2})^2$		$.720 \times 10^5$	EC; γ .020–1.54			
$_{75}Re^{182}$	−16	-48628_2		9/2⁺ (624)		$.230 \times 10^6$	EC; γ .020–1.44	2.86		
$_{75}Re^{183}$	$-\frac{33}{2}$	-48740_4		$(1i_{13/2})^4$	$\frac{5}{2}^+$	$.605 \times 10^7$	EC; γ .041–.41	0.90		
$_{75}Re^{184}$	−17	-47220_4		1/2⁻ (510)		$\dagger.328 \times 10^7$	EC; γ .90, .79, .097–.90	1.63		
$_{75}Re^{185}$	$-\frac{35}{2}$	-46941_2		$(1i_{13/2})^6$	$\frac{5}{2}^+$		**37.07**		3.1720	2.600
$_{75}Re^{186}$	−18	-44980_2		3/2⁻ (512)	1⁻	$.324 \times 10^6$	β^- 1.07, .93, . . . ; EC; γ .137, . . .	{1.07⁻ 0.54⁺	±1.7200	
$_{75}Re^{187}$	$-\frac{37}{2}$	-44167_2		$(1i_{13/2})^8$	$\frac{5}{2}^+$	$.126 \times 10^{19}$	**62.93**; β^- .0012	0.00	3.2040	2.600
$_{75}Re^{188}$	−19	-41647_2		3/2⁻ (512)	1⁻	$.612 \times 10^5$	β^- 2.12, 2.0, . . . ; γ .155, . . .	2.12	±1.7600	
$_{75}Re^{189}$	$-\frac{39}{2}$	-40630_2		$(1i_{13/2})^{10}$		$.828 \times 10^5$	β^- 1.0, .8, . . . ; γ .219, .150, . . .	1.00		
$_{75}Re^{190}$	−20	-38040_3		3/2⁻ (512)	(4)⁻	$.180 \times 10^3$	β^- 1.7, . . . ; γ .19, .57, .39, . . .	3.10		
$_{75}Re^{191}$	$-\frac{41}{2}$			$(1i_{13/2})^{12}$		$.600 \times 10^3$	β^- 1.8			
$_{76}Os^{181}$	$-\frac{29}{2}$		$(1h_{11/2})^{12}$	7/2⁻ (514)		$.138 \times 10^4$	EC; γ .167, .174			
$_{76}Os^{182}$	−15			$(1i_{13/2})^2$	0⁺	$.792 \times 10^5$	EC; γ .51, .18, .029–.37			
$_{76}Os^{183}$	$-\frac{31}{2}$			9/2⁺ (624)	$\frac{9}{2}^+$	$.432 \times 10^5$	EC; γ .38, .11, .15–1.44			
$_{76}Os^{184}$	−16	-47250_2		$(1i_{13/2})^4$	0⁺		**0.018**			
$_{76}Os^{185}$	$-\frac{33}{2}$	-45887_2		1/2⁻ (510)	$\frac{1}{2}^-$	$.812 \times 10^7$	EC; γ .65, .88, .87, .072–.75	0.98		
$_{76}Os^{186}$	−17	-46130_2		$(1i_{13/2})^6$	0⁺		**1.59**			
$_{76}Os^{187}$	$-\frac{35}{2}$	-44168_2		1/2⁻ (510)	$\frac{1}{2}^-$		**1.64**		0.0670	
$_{76}Os^{188}$	−18	-43919_2		$(1i_{13/2})^8$	0⁺		**13.3**			
$_{76}Os^{189}$	$-\frac{37}{2}$	-41700_2		3/2⁻ (512)	$\frac{3}{2}^-$		**16.1**		0.6566	0.800
$_{76}Os^{190}$	−19	-41370_2		$(1i_{13/2})^{10}$	0⁺		**26.4**			
$_{76}Os^{191}$	$-\frac{39}{2}$	-39030_2		9/2⁻ (505)	$(\frac{9}{2})^-$	$.130 \times 10^7$	β^- .14; γ	0.31		
$_{76}Os^{192}$	−20	-38550_2		$(1i_{13/2})^{12}$	0⁺		**41.0**			
$_{76}Os^{193}$	$-\frac{41}{2}$	-35773_2		$(3p_{1/2})^1$		$.115 \times 10^6$	β^- 1.13, . . . ; γ .139, .073, . . .	1.13		
$_{76}Os^{194}$	−21	-34771_2		$(1i_{13/2})^{14}$	0⁺	$.600 \times 10^8$	β^-; γ	0.10		
$_{76}Os^{195}$	$-\frac{43}{2}$	-32000_3		$(2f_{5/2})^1$		$.360 \times 10^3$	β^- 2	2.00		
$_{77}Ir^{182}$	−14		5/2⁺ (402)	7/2⁻ (514)		$.900 \times 10^3$	EC; β^+; γ			
$_{77}Ir^{183}$	$-\frac{29}{2}$		or	$(1i_{13/2})^2$		$.330 \times 10^4$	EC; γ .24, . . .			
$_{77}Ir^{184}$	−15		$(2d_{3/2})^1$	9/2⁺ (624)		$.115 \times 10^5$	EC; β^+; γ .27, 1.3, .39–4.3			
$_{77}Ir^{185}$	$-\frac{31}{2}$			$(1i_{13/2})^4$		$.540 \times 10^5$	EC; γ .037–.254			
$_{77}Ir^{186}$	−16	-42010_2		1/2⁻ (510)		$.540 \times 10^5$	EC; β^+ 1.92, . . . ; γ .07–1.7	3.83		
$_{77}Ir^{187}$	$-\frac{33}{2}$	-42440_4		$(1i_{13/2})^6$		$.432 \times 10^5$	EC; γ .025–.99	1.60		
$_{77}Ir^{188}$	−17	-40878_2		1/2⁻ (510)	2⁻	$.148 \times 10^6$	EC; β^+ 1.7, 1.2; γ .155, .63, . . .	2.83		
$_{77}Ir^{189}$	$-\frac{35}{2}$	-41090_4		$(1i_{13/2})^8$		$.115 \times 10^7$	EC; γ .070, .245, .031–.798	0.60		
$_{77}Ir^{190}$	−18	-39170_3		3/2⁻ (512)	(4)	$.104 \times 10^7$	EC; γ .19, .60, .56, .52, .2–1.3	{0.81⁻ 2.05⁺		
$_{77}Ir^{191}$	$-\frac{37}{2}$	-39360_2		$(1i_{13/2})^{10}$	$\frac{3}{2}^+$		**37.3**		0.1800	1.300
$_{77}Ir^{192}$	−19	-37300_2		3/2⁻ (512)	4⁻	$\dagger.639 \times 10^7$	β^- .67, .53, . . . ; EC; γ .32, .47, . . .	{1.45⁻ 1.17⁺		
$_{77}Ir^{193}$	$-\frac{39}{2}$	-36988_2		$(1i_{13/2})^{12}$	$\frac{3}{2}^+$		**62.7**		0.1800	1.200
$_{77}Ir^{194}$	−20	-34875_2		$(3p_{1/2})^1$	(1⁻)	$.684 \times 10^5$	β^- 2.24, 1.90, . . . ; γ .33, .29, .65	2.24		

(Continued)

Table of Nuclides (*continued*)

Nuclide	T_3	Mass excess $M - A$, μu	Prominent terms for ground state or low-lying level: Proton	Neutron	J^π	Half-life, sec	**Abundance,** percent or decay modes with energies, MeV	Total disintegration energy, MeV	Magnetic moment, nm	Quadrupole moment, barns
$_{77}Ir^{195}$	$-\frac{41}{2}$	-34110_3	$5/2^+ (402)$	$(1i_{13/2})^{14}$		$.151 \times 10^5$	β^- 1.1, .6, . . . ; γ .19, .29, . . .	1.00		
$_{77}Ir^{196}$	-21	-31750_4	or	$(2f_{5/2})^1$		$<.180 \times 10^5$	β^-	3.10		
$_{77}Ir^{197}$	$-\frac{43}{2}$	-30510_3	$(2d_{3/2})^1$	$(2f_{5/2})^2$		$.420 \times 10^3$	β^- 2.0, 1.5; γ .50	2.00		
$_{77}Ir^{198}$	-22	-27380_3		$(2f_{5/2})^3$		$.500 \times 10^2$	β^- 3.6; γ .78	4.40		
$_{78}Pt^{184}$	-14		$(2d_{3/2})^2$	$(1i_{13/2})^2$	$0+$	$.100 \times 10^5$				
$_{78}Pt^{186}$	-15			$(1i_{13/2})^4$	$0+$	$.900 \times 10^4$	EC			
$_{78}Pt^{187}$	$-\frac{31}{2}$			$1/2^- (510)$		$.700 \times 10^4$				
$_{78}Pt^{188}$	-16	-40330_2		$(1i_{13/2})^6$	$0+$	$.864 \times 10^6$	EC; γ .195, .187, .54, . . .	0.51		
$_{78}Pt^{189}$	$-\frac{33}{2}$	-39390_4		$1/2^- (510)$		$.392 \times 10^5$	EC; γ .25, .95–.15	1.58		
$_{78}Pt^{190}$	-17	-40050_2		$(1i_{13/2})^8$	$0+$	$.221 \times 10^{20}$	**0.0127**; α	3.25		
$_{78}Pt^{191}$	$-\frac{35}{2}$	-38550_4		$3/2^- (512)$	$(\frac{3}{2}-)$	$.259 \times 10^6$	EC; γ .54, .36, .41, . . .	0.80		
$_{78}Pt^{192}$	-18	-38850_2		$(1i_{13/2})^{10}$	$0+$		**0.78**; α	2.29		
$_{78}Pt^{193}$	$-\frac{37}{2}$	-36940_2		$(3p_{1/2})^1$		$<.160 \times 10^{11}$	EC	0.05		
$_{78}Pt^{194}$	-19	-37275_2		$(1i_{13/2})^{12}$	$0+$		**32.9**			
$_{78}Pt^{195}$	$-\frac{39}{2}$	-35187_2		$(3p_{1/2})^1$	$\frac{1}{2}-$		**33.8**		0.6060	
$_{78}Pt^{196}$	-20	-35033_2		$(1i_{13/2})^{14}$	$0+$		**25.3**			
$_{78}Pt^{197}$	$-\frac{41}{2}$	-32653_2		$(2f_{5/2})^1$	$*(\frac{3}{2}-)$	$.720 \times 10^5$	β^- .67, .48, . . . ; γ .077, .19, . . .	0.75		
$_{78}Pt^{198}$	-21	-32105_2		$(2f_{5/2})^2$	$0+$		**7.21**			
$_{78}Pt^{199}$	$-\frac{43}{2}$	-29420_2		$(2f_{5/2})^3$	$(\frac{5}{2}-)$	$.180 \times 10^4$	β^- 1.7, .7–1.6; γ .54, .075–.96	1.68		
$_{78}Pt^{200}$	-22	-28570_4		$(2f_{5/2})^4$	$0+$	$.414 \times 10^5$	β^-	0.70		
$_{78}Pt^{201}$	$-\frac{45}{2}$	-25230_3		$(2f_{5/2})^5$		$.150 \times 10^3$	β^- .90, 2.66, . . . ; γ 1.76, .23, . . .	2.66		
$_{79}Au^{186}$	-14		$(2d_{3/2})^3$	$9/2^+ (624)$		$.900 \times 10^3$	EC			
$_{79}Au^{187}$	$-\frac{29}{2}$		or	$(1i_{13/2})^4$		$.480 \times 10^3$				
$_{79}Au^{188}$	-15		$3/2^+ (402)$	$1/2^- (510)$		$.270 \times 10^3$	EC	5.20		
$_{79}Au^{189}$	$-\frac{31}{2}$			$(1i_{13/2})^6$		$.252 \times 10^4$	EC; γ .29, 1.4, . . .			
$_{79}Au^{190}$	-16	-35290_4		$1/2^- (510)$	1	$.234 \times 10^4$	EC; β^+; γ .295, .30–3.5	4.40	±0.0660	
$_{79}Au^{191}$	$-\frac{33}{2}$	-36450_4		$(1i_{13/2})^8$	$\frac{3}{2}+$	$.115 \times 10^5$	EC; γ .091, .048, .16, .13, . . .	1.95	±0.1370	
$_{79}Au^{192}$	-17	-35380_2		$(3p_{1/2})^1$	$1-$	$.173 \times 10^5$	EC; β^+ 2.22; γ .32, .29, .05–1.16	3.24	±0.0079	
$_{79}Au^{193}$	$-\frac{35}{2}$	-35760_4		$(1i_{13/2})^{10}$	$\frac{3}{2}+$	$.648 \times 10^5$	EC; γ .19, .11, .01–.49	1.10	±0.1390	
$_{79}Au^{194}$	-18	-34582_2		$(3p_{1/2})^1$	$1-$	$.140 \times 10^6$	EC; β^+ 1.16, 1.49; γ .33, .20, . . .	2.51	±0.0740	
$_{79}Au^{195}$	$-\frac{37}{2}$	-34949_2		$(1i_{13/2})^{12}$	$\frac{3}{2}+$	$.158 \times 10^8$	EC; γ .093, .03, .13	0.22	±0.1482	
$_{79}Au^{196}$	-19	-33445_2		$(3p_{1/2})^1$	$2-$	$.536 \times 10^6$	EC; β^- .26; γ .356, .333, .43	{0.68− 1.48+	±0.6300	
$_{79}Au^{197}$	$-\frac{39}{2}$	-33459_2		$(1i_{13/2})^4$	$\frac{3}{2}+$		**100**		0.1449	0.580
$_{79}Au^{198}$	-20	-31769_1		$(3p_{1/2})^1$	$2-$	$.233 \times 10^6$	β^- .96, .29, 1.37; γ .412, .674, . . .	{1.37− 0.31+	0.5800	
[illegible]	[illegible]	[illegible]		[illegible]	$\frac{3}{2}+$	$.272 \times 10^6$	β^- .30, .25, .46; γ .158, .208, . . .	0.46	0.2660	

$_{79}Au^{201}$	$-\frac{43}{2}$	-28080_3		$(2f_{5/2})^4$		$.132 \times 10^2$	β^- 1.5, . . . ; γ .55	1.50		
$_{79}Au^{202}$	-22	-25880_4		$(2f_{5/2})^5$		$.250 \times 10^2$	β^-	3.20		
$_{79}Au^{203}$	$-\frac{45}{2}$	-24870_4		$(2f_{5/2})^6$		$.550 \times 10^2$	β^- 1.9; γ .69	2.10		
$_{80}Hg^{187}$	$-\frac{27}{2}$		$(2d_{3/2})^4$	$(3p_{1/2})^1$		$.180 \times 10^3$	γ .18, .26, .40			
$_{80}Hg^{189}$	$-\frac{29}{2}$			$(3p_{1/2})^1$		$.600 \times 10^3$	EC; γ .029, .14, .22			
$_{80}Hg^{190}$	-15			$(1i_{13/2})^6$	0^+	$.120 \times 10^4$	EC; γ .14, .22, .03			
$_{80}Hg^{191}$	$-\frac{31}{2}$			$(3p_{1/2})^1$		$.342 \times 10^4$	EC; γ .253, .274			
$_{80}Hg^{192}$	-16	-33840_4		$(1i_{13/2})^8$	0^+	$.176 \times 10^5$	β^+ 1.2; γ .031, .272, .04–.44			
$_{80}Hg^{193}$	$-\frac{33}{2}$	-33250_4		$(3p_{1/2})^1$	$(\frac{1}{2}^-)$	†$.216 \times 10^5$	EC; γ .038, .187, .76	2.34		
$_{80}Hg^{194}$	-17	-34210_4		$(1i_{13/2})^{10}$	0^+	$.126 \times 10^8$	EC	0.40		
$_{80}Hg^{195}$	$-\frac{35}{2}$	-33380_4		$(3p_{1/2})^1$	$\frac{1}{2}^-$	†$.342 \times 10^5$	EC; γ .061, .18, .78, .20–1.17	1.50	0.5380	
$_{80}Hg^{196}$	-18	-34180_2		$(1i_{13/2})^{12}$	0^+		**0.146**			
$_{80}Hg^{197}$	$-\frac{37}{2}$	-32640_2		$(3p_{1/2})^1$	$\frac{1}{2}^-$	$.234 \times 10^6$	EC; γ .077, .191	0.76	0.5240	
$_{80}Hg^{198}$	-19	-33244_1		$(1i_{13/2})^{14}$	0^+		**10.02**			
$_{80}Hg^{199}$	$-\frac{39}{2}$	-31721_1		$(3p_{1/2})^1$	$\frac{1}{2}^-$		**16.84**		0.5027	
$_{80}Hg^{200}$	-20	-31673_1		$(2f_{5/2})^2$	0^+		**23.13**			
$_{80}Hg^{201}$	$-\frac{41}{2}$	-29692_1		$(2f_{5/2})^3$	$*\frac{3}{2}^-$		**13.22**		−0.5567	0.450
$_{80}Hg^{202}$	-21	-29358_1		$(2f_{5/2})^4$	0^+		**29.80**			
$_{80}Hg^{203}$	$-\frac{43}{2}$	-27120_1		$(2f_{5/2})^5$	$(\frac{5}{2}^-)$	$.406 \times 10^7$	β^- .21; γ .279	0.49	0.8400	±13.000
$_{80}Hg^{204}$	-22	-26505_1		$(2f_{5/2})^6$	0^+		**6.85**			
$_{80}Hg^{205}$	$-\frac{45}{2}$	-23790_3		$(3p_{1/2})^1$		$.312 \times 10^3$	β^- 1.6, 1.4; γ .20	1.65		
$_{80}Hg^{206}$	-23	-22487_2		$(3p_{1/2})^2$	0^+	$.450 \times 10^3$	β^-	1.31		
$_{81}Tl^{191}$	$-\frac{29}{2}$		$(3s_{1/2})^1$	$(1i_{13/2})^6$		$.600 \times 10^3$	EC			
$_{81}Tl^{192}$	-15			$(2f_{5/2})^1$	(2^-)	†$<.660 \times 10^3$	EC			
$_{81}Tl^{193}$	$-\frac{31}{2}$			$(1i_{13/2})^8$		$.138 \times 10^4$	EC; γ .24, .25, .26, .27–.33			
$_{81}Tl^{194}$	-16	-28430_4		$(2f_{5/2})^1$		$.198 \times 10^4$	EC; γ .43	5.40		
$_{81}Tl^{195}$	$-\frac{33}{2}$	-30160_4		$(1i_{13/2})^{10}$	$\frac{1}{2}^+$	$.432 \times 10^4$	EC; β^+ ~1.8; γ .037, .23–.88	3.00		
$_{81}Tl^{196}$	-17	-29240_3		$(2f_{5/2})^1$		$.648 \times 10^4$	EC; γ .425	4.60		
$_{81}Tl^{197}$	$-\frac{35}{2}$	-30280_3		$(1i_{13/2})^{12}$	$\frac{1}{2}^+$	$.101 \times 10^5$	EC; γ .152, .018–1.0	2.20		
$_{81}Tl^{198}$	-18	-29530_2		$(2f_{5/2})^1$	2^-	$.191 \times 10^5$	EC; β^+ 2.4, 2.1, . . . ; γ .412, . . .	3.46	±0.0020	
$_{81}Tl^{199}$	$-\frac{37}{2}$	-30540_3		$(1i_{13/2})^{14}$	$\frac{1}{2}^+$	$.266 \times 10^5$	EC; γ .208, .455, .158, .050–.492	1.10	1.5900	
$_{81}Tl^{200}$	-19	-29038_1		$(2f_{5/2})^1$	2^-	$.936 \times 10^5$	EC; β^+ 1.06, 1.44, . . . ; γ .37, . . .	2.45	±0.1500	
$_{81}Tl^{201}$	$-\frac{39}{2}$	-29250_2		$(2f_{5/2})^2$	$\frac{1}{2}^+$	$.263 \times 10^6$	EC; γ .167, .135, .031–.166	0.41	1.6000	
$_{81}Tl^{202}$	-20	-28050_2		$(2f_{5/2})^3$	2^-	$.104 \times 10^7$	EC; γ .44, .96, .52	1.22	±0.1500	
$_{81}Tl^{203}$	$-\frac{41}{2}$	-27647_1		$(2f_{5/2})^4$	$\frac{1}{2}^+$		**29.50**		1.6115	
$_{81}Tl^{204}$	-21	-26135_1		$(2f_{5/2})^5$	2^-	$.120 \times 10^9$	β^- .765; EC	$\begin{cases}0.76^-\\0.35^+\end{cases}$	±0.0890	
$_{81}Tl^{205}$	$-\frac{43}{2}$	-25558_1		$(2f_{5/2})^6$	$\frac{1}{2}^+$		**70.50**		1.6274	
$_{81}Tl^{206}$	-22	-23896_1		$(3p_{1/2})^1$	(0^-)	$.258 \times 10^3$	β^- 1.57	1.52		
$_{81}Tl^{207}$	$-\frac{45}{2}$	-22550_2		$(3p_{1/2})^2$	$(\frac{1}{2}^+)$	$.287 \times 10^3$	β^- 1.44; γ .89	1.44		
$_{81}Tl^{208}$	-23	-17987_1		$(2g_{9/2})^1$	5^+	$.186 \times 10^3$	β^- 1.80, .10–2.38; γ 2.61, .58, . . .	4.99		
$_{81}Tl^{209}$	$-\frac{47}{2}$	-14704_2		$(2g_{9/2})^2$		$.132 \times 10^3$	β^- 1.8; γ .12, .45, 1.56	3.93		
$_{81}Tl^{210}$	-24	-9946_2		$(2g_{9/2})^3$		$.780 \times 10^2$	β^- 1.91, .3, 2.3; γ .80, .30, . . .	5.47		

(Continued)

Table of Nuclides *(continued)*

Nuclide	T_3	Mass excess $M - A$, μu	Prominent terms for ground state or low-lying level: Proton	Neutron	J^π	Half-life, sec	**Abundance,** percent or decay modes with energies, MeV	Total disintegration energy, MeV	Magnetic moment, nm	Quadrupole moment, barns
$_{82}Pb^{194}$	-15		$(3s_{1/2})^2$	$(1i_{13/2})^8$	$0+$	$.660 \times 10^3$	γ .204			
$_{82}Pb^{195}$	$-\frac{31}{2}$			$(2f_{5/2})^1$		$.102 \times 10^4$	EC			
$_{82}Pb^{196}$	-16	-26200_4		$(1i_{13/2})^{10}$	$0+$	$.222 \times 10^4$	EC; γ .191, .240, .253, . . .	2.80		
$_{82}Pb^{198}$	-17	-27590_4		$(1i_{13/2})^{12}$	$0+$	$.864 \times 10^4$	EC; γ .290, .365, .031–.865	1.80		
$_{82}Pb^{199}$	$-\frac{35}{2}$	-27140_4		$(2f_{5/2})^1$	$(\frac{5}{2}-)$	$.540 \times 10^4$	EC; β^+ 2.8; γ .367, .27–1.13	4.20		
$_{82}Pb^{200}$	-18	-28030_4		$(1i_{13/2})^{14}$	$0+$	$.756 \times 10^5$	EC; γ .148, .142, .24, .27, . . .	0.90		
$_{82}Pb^{201}$	$-\frac{37}{2}$	-27140_4		$(2f_{5/2})^1$	$(\frac{5}{2}-)$	$.338 \times 10^5$	EC; β^+; γ .330, .13–1.10	2.00		
$_{82}Pb^{202}$	-19	-27997_2		$(2f_{5/2})^2$	$0+$	$.900 \times 10^{13}$	EC	0.05		
$_{82}Pb^{203}$	$-\frac{39}{2}$	-26771_2		$(2f_{5/2})^3$	$(\frac{5}{2}-)$	$.187 \times 10^6$	EC; γ .28, .40, .68	0.82		
$_{82}Pb^{204}$	-20	-26956_1		$(2f_{5/2})^4$	$0+$	$.442 \times 10^{25}$	**1.48**; α 2.6	1.97		
$_{82}Pb^{205}$	$-\frac{41}{2}$	-25520_1		$(2f_{5/2})^5$	$(\frac{5}{2}-)$	$.947 \times 10^{15}$	EC	0.04		
$_{82}Pb^{206}$	-21	-25532_1		$(2f_{5/2})^6$	$0+$		**23.6**			
$_{82}Pb^{207}$	$-\frac{43}{2}$	-24097_1		$(3p_{1/2})^1$	$\frac{1}{2}-$		**22.6**		0.5895	
$_{82}Pb^{208}$	-22	-23350_1		$(3p_{1/2})^2$	$0+$		**52.3**			
$_{82}Pb^{209}$	$-\frac{45}{2}$	-18918_2		$(2g_{9/2})^1$	$(\frac{9}{2}+)$	$.119 \times 10^5$	β^- .635	0.64		
$_{82}Pb^{210}$	-23	-15813_1		$(2g_{9/2})^2$	$0+$	$.694 \times 10^9$	β^- .015, .061; γ .047	0.06		
$_{82}Pb^{211}$	$-\frac{47}{2}$	-11258_2		$(2g_{9/2})^3$		$.217 \times 10^4$	β^- 1.39, .56, . . . ; γ .83, .41, . . .	1.34		
$_{82}Pb^{212}$	-24	-8095_2		$(2g_{9/2})^4$	$0+$	$.383 \times 10^5$	β^- .34, .58, . . . ; γ .239, .30, . . .	0.58		
$_{82}Pb^{213}$	$-\frac{49}{2}$	-3710_4		$(2g_{9/2})^5$		$.600 \times 10^3$	β^-	1.80		
$_{82}Pb^{214}$	-25	-234_2		$(2g_{9/2})^6$	$0+$	$.161 \times 10^4$	β^- .7, . . . ; γ .352, .295, .050–.259	1.01		
$_{83}Bi^{196}$	-15		$(1h_{9/2})^1$	$(2f_{5/2})^1$		$.420 \times 10^3$	EC; α			
$_{83}Bi^{199}$	$-\frac{33}{2}$	-21560_4		$(1i_{13/2})^{12}$	$\frac{9}{2}$	$.162 \times 10^4$	EC	5.20		
$_{83}Bi^{200}$	-17	-21060_4		$(2f_{5/2})^1$	7	$.210 \times 10^4$	EC; γ 1.03, .46	6.49		
$_{83}Bi^{201}$	$-\frac{35}{2}$	-22630_4		$(1i_{13/2})^{14}$	$\frac{9}{2}-$	$.648 \times 10^4$	EC	4.20		
$_{83}Bi^{202}$	-18	-22120_4		$(2f_{5/2})^1$	5	$.576 \times 10^4$	EC; γ .42, .96	5.50		
$_{83}Bi^{203}$	$-\frac{37}{2}$	-23350_2		$(2f_{5/2})^2$	$\frac{9}{2}-$	$.425 \times 10^5$	EC; β^+ 1.35, .73; α 4.85; γ	3.19+ / 4.85α	4.5900	-0.620
$_{83}Bi^{204}$	-19	-22190_4		$(2f_{5/2})^3$	$6+$	$.403 \times 10^5$	EC; γ .08, .38, .22, .91, . . .	4.40	4.2500	-0.400
$_{83}Bi^{205}$	$-\frac{39}{2}$	-22618_2		$(2f_{5/2})^4$	$\frac{9}{2}(-)$	$.132 \times 10^7$	EC; β^+ .98; γ .70, 1.77, . . .	2.70	5.5000	
$_{83}Bi^{206}$	-20	-21611_2		$(2f_{5/2})^5$	$6+$	$.539 \times 10^6$	EC; γ .80, .88, .18, .11–1.9	3.65	4.5600	-0.190
$_{83}Bi^{207}$	$-\frac{41}{2}$	-21562_1		$(2f_{5/2})^6$		$.125 \times 10^{10}$	EC; γ .57, 1.77, . . .	2.36		
$_{83}Bi^{208}$	-21	-20269_1		$(3p_{1/2})^1$	$(5+)$	$.117 \times 10^{14}$	EC; γ 2.62	2.87		
$_{83}Bi^{209}$	$-\frac{43}{2}$	-19606_1		$(3p_{1/2})^2$	$\frac{9}{2}-$		**100**		4.0800	-0.340
$_{83}Bi^{210}$	-22	-15879_1		$(2g_{9/2})^1$	$1-$	†$.432 \times 10^6$	β^- 1.16; α 4.7, . . .	1.16− / 5.04α	± 0.0442	± 0.130

$_{83}Bi^{213}$	$-\frac{47}{2}$	-5683_2		$(2g_{9/2})^4$		$.282 \times 10^4$	β^- 1.39, .96; γ .44; α 5.86	$\begin{cases}1.39^- \\ 5.98\alpha\end{cases}$		
$_{83}Bi^{214}$	-24	-1314_2		$(2g_{9/2})^5$		$.118 \times 10^4$	β^- .4–3.2; α 5.5; γ .61, 1.12, . . .	$\begin{cases}3.25^- \\ 5.62\alpha\end{cases}$		
$_{83}Bi^{215}$	$-\frac{49}{2}$	1830_3		$(2g_{9/2})^6$		$.480 \times 10^3$	β^-	2.24		
$_{84}Po^{192}$	-12		$(1h_{9/2})^2$	$(1i_{13/2})^4$	0^+	.500	α 6.58			
$_{84}Po^{193}$	$-\frac{25}{2}$			$(2f_{5/2})^1$		$.400 \times 10^1$	α 6.47			
$_{84}Po^{194}$	-13			$(1i_{13/2})^6$	0^+	$.130 \times 10^2$	α 6.38			
$_{84}Po^{195}$	$-\frac{27}{2}$			$(2f_{5/2})^1$		$.300 \times 10^2$	α 6.24			
$_{84}Po^{196}$	-14			$(1i_{13/2})^8$	0^+	$.114 \times 10^3$	α 6.14			
$_{84}Po^{197}$	$-\frac{29}{2}$			$(2f_{5/2})^1$		$.240 \times 10^3$	α 6.04			
$_{84}Po^{198}$	-15			$(1i_{13/2})^{10}$	0^+	$.420 \times 10^3$	α 5.93			
$_{84}Po^{199}$	$-\frac{31}{2}$			$(2f_{5/2})^1$		$.720 \times 10^3$	α 5.85			
$_{84}Po^{200}$	-16	-17180_4		$(1i_{13/2})^{12}$	0^+	$.600 \times 10^3$	α 5.77, 5.86	$\begin{cases}3.62^+ \\ 5.99\alpha\end{cases}$		
$_{84}Po^{201}$	$-\frac{33}{2}$	-16980_4		$(2f_{5/2})^1$	$*\frac{3}{2}$	$.108 \times 10^4$	EC; α 5.68, 5.57, 5.77	$\begin{cases}5.26^+ \\ 5.89\alpha\end{cases}$		
$_{84}Po^{202}$	-17	-18870_4		$(1i_{13/2})^{14}$	0^+	$.270 \times 10^4$	EC; α 5.58	$\begin{cases}3.03^+ \\ 5.70\alpha\end{cases}$		
$_{84}Po^{203}$	$-\frac{35}{2}$	-18530_4		$(2f_{5/2})^1$	$\frac{5}{2}$	$.270 \times 10^4$	EC; α 5.48	$\begin{cases}4.48^+ \\ 5.60\alpha\end{cases}$		
$_{84}Po^{204}$	-18	-19540_4		$(2f_{5/2})^2$	0^+	$.126 \times 10^5$	EC; α 5.37	$\begin{cases}2.47^+ \\ 5.49\alpha\end{cases}$		
$_{84}Po^{205}$	$-\frac{37}{2}$	-18800_4		$(2f_{5/2})^3$	$\frac{5}{2}^-$	$.648 \times 10^4$	EC; α 5.2	$\begin{cases}3.55^+ \\ 5.35\alpha\end{cases}$	0.2600	0.170
$_{84}Po^{206}$	-19	-19676_2		$(2f_{5/2})^4$	0^+	$.760 \times 10^6$	EC; α 5.22; γ .060, .083–1.32	$\begin{cases}1.80^+ \\ 5.33\alpha\end{cases}$		
$_{84}Po^{207}$	$-\frac{39}{2}$	-18442_2		$(2f_{5/2})^5$	$\frac{5}{2}^-$	$.223 \times 10^5$	EC; β^+ 1.14, . . . ; α 5.10; γ .10–2.06	$\begin{cases}2.91^+ \\ 5.33\alpha\end{cases}$	0.2700	0.280
$_{84}Po^{208}$	-20	-18757_2		$(2f_{5/2})^6$	0^+	$.915 \times 10^8$	α 5.11; γ .6, .28	$\begin{cases}1.41^+ \\ 5.21\alpha\end{cases}$		
$_{84}Po^{209}$	$-\frac{41}{2}$	-17574_2		$(3p_{1/2})^1$	$\frac{1}{2}^-$	$.325 \times 10^{10}$	α 4.88, . . . ; EC; γ .91, .26	$\begin{cases}1.89^+ \\ 4.98\alpha\end{cases}$		
$_{84}Po^{210}$	-21	-17124_1		$(3p_{1/2})^2$	0^+	$.120 \times 10^8$	α 5.30; γ .80	5.41		
$_{84}Po^{211}$	$-\frac{43}{2}$	-13343_1		$(2g_{9/2})^1$		†.520	α 7.44, . . . ; γ .89, .106	7.59		
$_{84}Po^{212}$	-22	-11134_1		$(2g_{9/2})^2$	0^+	$.300 \times 10^{-6}$	α 8.78	8.95		
$_{84}Po^{213}$	$-\frac{45}{2}$	-7175_2		$(2g_{9/2})^3$		$.400 \times 10^{-5}$	α 8.37	8.51		
$_{84}Po^{214}$	-23	-4799_1		$(2g_{9/2})^4$	0^+	$.164 \times 10^{-3}$	α 7.68	7.84		
$_{84}Po^{215}$	$-\frac{47}{2}$	-577_2		$(2g_{9/2})^5$		$.180 \times 10^{-2}$	α 7.36; β^-	$\begin{cases}0.71^- \\ 7.52\alpha\end{cases}$		
$_{84}Po^{216}$	-24	1922_2		$(2g_{9/2})^6$	0^+	.150	α 6.78	6.91		

(Continued)

Table of Nuclides *(continued)*

Nuclide	T_3	Mass excess $M - A$, μu	Prominent terms for ground state or low-lying level: Proton	Neutron	J^π	Half-life, sec	**Abundance,** percent or decay modes with energies, MeV	Total disintegration energy, MeV	Magnetic moment, nm	Quadrupole moment, barns
${}_{84}Po^{217}$	$-\frac{49}{2}$	6060_4	$(1h_{9/2})^2$	$(2g_{9/2})^7$		$<.100 \times 10^2$	α 6.54	1.31 6.67α		
${}_{84}Po^{218}$	-25	8930_2		$(2g_{9/2})^8$	0+	$.183 \times 10^3$	α 6.00; β^-	0.30− 6.11α		
${}_{85}At^{201}$	$-\frac{31}{2}$		$(1h_{9/2})^3$	$(1i_{13/2})^{12}$		$.900 \times 10^2$	α 6.35			
${}_{85}At^{202}$	-16	-10200_4		$(2f_{5/2})^1$		$.180 \times 10^3$	EC; α 6.13, 6.23	8.07+ 6.37α		
${}_{85}At^{203}$	$-\frac{33}{2}$	-12290_4		$(1i_{13/2})^{14}$		$.432 \times 10^3$	EC; α 6.09	5.82+ 6.22α		
${}_{85}At^{204}$	-17	-11940_4		$(2f_{5/2})^1$		$.540 \times 10^3$	EC; α 5.95	7.08+ 6.08α		
${}_{85}At^{205}$	$-\frac{35}{2}$	-13560_4		$(2f_{5/2})^2$		$.156 \times 10^4$	EC; α 5.90	4.88+ 6.03α		
${}_{85}At^{206}$	-18	-13210_4		$(2f_{5/2})^3$		$.174 \times 10^4$	EC; α 5.70–5.90	6.02+ 5.89α		
${}_{85}At^{207}$	$-\frac{37}{2}$	-14440_2		$(2f_{5/2})^4$		$.648 \times 10^4$	EC; α 5.75	3.73+ 5.88α		
${}_{85}At^{208}$	-19	-13390_4		$(2f_{5/2})^5$		$.576 \times 10^4$	EC; α 5.65; γ .66, 1.75, . . .	5.00+ 5.78α		
${}_{85}At^{209}$	$-\frac{39}{2}$	-13833_2		$(2f_{5/2})^6$	$(\frac{9}{2}-)$	$.198 \times 10^5$	EC; α 5.64; γ .195, .091, .55, .78	3.49+ 5.76α		
${}_{85}At^{210}$	-20	-12964_2		$(3p_{1/2})^1$		$.299 \times 10^5$	EC; α 5.36–5.52; γ .047, .25, . . .	3.88+ 5.63α		
${}_{85}At^{211}$	$-\frac{41}{2}$	-12538_1		$(3p_{1/2})^2$	$\frac{9}{2}-$	$.259 \times 10^5$	EC; α 5.86; γ .67, . . .	0.75+ 5.98α		
${}_{85}At^{212}$	-21	-9276_2		$(2g_{9/2})^1$		.310	α 7.66, 7.60; γ .06	1.73+ 7.81α		
${}_{85}At^{213}$	$-\frac{43}{2}$	-6930_3		$(2g_{9/2})^2$		$<.200 \times 10^1$	α 9.2	0.23+ 9.38α		
${}_{85}At^{214}$	-22	-3660_2		$(2g_{9/2})^3$		$<.500 \times 10^1$	α 8.78	0.90− 8.96α		
${}_{85}At^{215}$	$-\frac{45}{2}$	-1337_2		$(2g_{9/2})^4$		$.100 \times 10^{-3}$	α 8.00	8.16		
${}_{85}At^{216}$	-23	2411_2		$(2g_{9/2})^5$		$.300 \times 10^{-3}$	α 7.79	1.99− 7.95α		

$_{85}At^{218}$	-24	8607_2		$(2g_{9/2})^7$		$.130 \times 10^1$	α 6.70, 6.65	{2.80⁻ 6.92α
$_{85}At^{219}$	$-\frac{49}{2}$	11290_2		$(2g_{9/2})^8$		$.540 \times 10^2$	α 6.27; β^-	{1.69⁻ 6.40α
$_{86}Rn^{204}$	-16	-7700_4	$(1h_{9/2})^4$	$(1i_{13/2})^{14}$	0^+	$.180 \times 10^3$	α 6.28	{3.95⁺ 6.41α
$_{86}Rn^{206}$	-17	-9420_4		$(2f_{5/2})^2$	0^+	$.390 \times 10^3$	α 6.25; EC	{3.53⁺ 6.39α
$_{86}Rn^{207}$	$-\frac{35}{2}$	-9240_4		$(2f_{5/2})^3$		$.660 \times 10^3$	EC; α 6.12	{4.84⁺ 6.23α
$_{86}Rn^{208}$	-18	-10210_4		$(2f_{5/2})^4$	0^+	$.138 \times 10^4$	EC; α 6.14	{2.97⁺ 6.27α
$_{86}Rn^{209}$	$-\frac{37}{2}$	-9580_4		$(2f_{5/2})^5$		$.180 \times 10^4$	EC; α 6.04	{3.96⁺ 6.16α
$_{86}Rn^{210}$	-19	-10460_2		$(2f_{5/2})^6$	0^+	$.972 \times 10^4$	α 6.04; EC	{2.33⁺ 6.16α
$_{86}Rn^{211}$	$-\frac{39}{2}$	-9434_2		$(3p_{1/2})^1$		$.576 \times 10^5$	EC; α 5.78, 5.85, 5.61; γ .069, . . .	{2.89⁺ 5.97α
$_{86}Rn^{212}$	-20	-9293_2		$(3p_{1/2})^2$	0^+	$.150 \times 10^4$	α 6.26	6.39
$_{86}Rn^{215}$	$-\frac{43}{2}$	-1310_3		$(2g_{9/2})^3$		$<.600 \times 10^2$	α 8.6	{0.02⁺ 8.78α
$_{86}Rn^{216}$	-22	272_2		$(2g_{9/2})^4$	0^+	$.450 \times 10^{-4}$	α 8.04	8.20
$_{86}Rn^{217}$	$-\frac{45}{2}$	3896_2		$(2g_{9/2})^5$		$.500 \times 10^{-3}$	α 7.74	7.84
$_{86}Rn^{218}$	-23	5603_2		$(2g_{9/2})^6$	0^+	$.350 \times 10^{-1}$	α 7.13, 6.52; γ .61	7.26
$_{86}Rn^{219}$	$-\frac{47}{2}$	9481_2		$(2g_{9/2})^7$		$.400 \times 10^1$	α 6.81, 6.54, 6.41; γ .27, .40	{0.21⁻ 6.94α
$_{86}Rn^{220}$	-24	11401_2		$(2g_{9/2})^8$	0^+	$.560 \times 10^2$	α 6.29, 5.74; γ .54	6.41
$_{86}Rn^{221}$	$-\frac{49}{2}$	15230_4		$(2g_{9/2})^9$		$.150 \times 10^4$	β^-; α 6.0	{0.97⁻ 6.13α
$_{86}Rn^{222}$	-25	17531_2		$(2g_{9/2})^{10}$	0^+	$.330 \times 10^6$	α 5.49, 4.98, . . . ; γ .51	5.59
$_{86}Rn^{223}$	$-\frac{51}{2}$			$3/2^+$ (631)		$.258 \times 10^4$	β^-	
$_{86}Rn^{224}$	-26			$(1i_{11/2})^2$	0^+	$.684 \times 10^4$	β^-	
$_{87}Fr^{204}$	-15		$(1h_{9/2})^5$	$(2f_{5/2})^1$		$.200 \times 10^1$	α 7.02	
$_{87}Fr^{205}$	$-\frac{31}{2}$			$(1i_{13/2})^{14}$		$.370 \times 10^1$	α 6.91	
$_{87}Fr^{206}$	-16	-160_4		$(2f_{5/2})^1$		$.160 \times 10^2$	α 6.77	{8.62⁺ 6.93α
$_{87}Fr^{207}$	$-\frac{33}{2}$	-2270_4		$(2f_{5/2})^2$		$.190 \times 10^2$	α 6.77	{6.50⁺ 6.91α
$_{87}Fr^{208}$	-17	-2050_4		$(2f_{5/2})^3$		$.380 \times 10^2$	α 6.65	{7.59⁺ 6.79α
$_{87}Fr^{209}$	$-\frac{35}{2}$	-3680_4		$(2f_{5/2})^4$		$.550 \times 10^2$	α 6.65	{5.50⁺ 6.78α

(Continued)

Table of Nuclides *(continued)*

Nuclide	T_3	Mass excess $M - A$, μu	Prominent terms for ground state or low-lying level: Proton	Neutron	J^π	Half-life, sec	**Abundance,** percent or decay modes with energies, MeV	Total disintegration energy, MeV	Magnetic moment, nm	Quadrupole moment, barns
$_{87}Fr^{210}$	-18	-3430_4	$(1h_{9/2})^5$	$(2f_{5/2})^5$		$.159 \times 10^4$	α 6.55	6.55+ 6.68α		
$_{87}Fr^{211}$	$-\frac{37}{2}$	-4670_2		$(2f_{5/2})^6$		$.186 \times 10^3$	α 6.55	4.44+ 6.68α		
$_{87}Fr^{212}$	-19	-3770_4		$(3p_{1/2})^1$		$.114 \times 10^4$	EC; α 6.39, 6.41, 6.34	5.15+ 6.54α		
$_{87}Fr^{213}$	$-\frac{39}{2}$	-3816_2		$(3p_{1/2})^2$		$.340 \times 10^2$	α 6.77; β^+	2.10+ 6.91α		
$_{87}Fr^{217}$	$-\frac{43}{2}$	4750_3		$(2g_{9/2})^4$		$<.200 \times 10^1$	α 8.3	0.80+ 8.47α		
$_{87}Fr^{218}$	-22	7540_2		$(2g_{9/2})^5$		$<.500 \times 10^1$	α 7.85	0.34− 8.00α		
$_{87}Fr^{219}$	$-\frac{45}{2}$	9257_2		$(2g_{9/2})^6$		$.200 \times 10^{-1}$	α 7.30	7.44		
$_{87}Fr^{220}$	-23	12337_2		$(2g_{9/2})^7$		$.280 \times 10^2$	α 6.69	1.22− 6.82α		
$_{87}Fr^{221}$	$-\frac{47}{2}$	14183_2		$(2g_{9/2})^8$		$.288 \times 10^3$	α 6.33, 6.11; γ .22	0.27− 6.46α		
$_{87}Fr^{222}$	-24	17630_4		$(2g_{9/2})^9$		$.900 \times 10^3$	β^-; α	2.10− 5.98α		
$_{87}Fr^{223}$	$-\frac{49}{2}$	19736_2		$(2g_{9/2})^{10}$		$.132 \times 10^4$	α 5.34; β^- 1.15; γ .050, .080, . . .	1.15− 5.44α		
$_{87}Fr^{224}$	-25	23590_4		$3/2^+(631)$		$.120 \times 10^3$	β^-	3.10		
$_{88}Ra^{213}$	$-\frac{37}{2}$	420_4	$(1h_{9/2})^6$	$(3p_{1/2})^1$		$.162 \times 10^3$	α 6.90	3.95+ 6.90α		
$_{88}Ra^{219}$	$-\frac{43}{2}$	10050_3		$(2g_{9/2})^5$		$<.600 \times 10^2$	α 8.0	0.74+ 8.16α		
$_{88}Ra^{220}$	-22	11029_2		$(2g_{9/2})^6$	0+	$.200 \times 10^{-1}$	α 7.45, 6.90; γ .47	7.60		
$_{88}Ra^{221}$	$-\frac{45}{2}$	13892_2		$(2g_{9/2})^7$		$.300 \times 10^2$	α; γ .089, .150, .176, . . .	6.87		
$_{88}Ra^{222}$	-23	15376_2		$(2g_{9/2})^8$	0+	$.370 \times 10^2$	α 6.60, 6.75, 6.66; γ .33	6.68		
$_{88}Ra^{223}$	$-\frac{47}{2}$	18501_2		$1/2^+(640)$	$\frac{1}{2}$+	$.101 \times 10^7$	α 6.55, 6.23; γ .031–.45	5.98		
$_{88}Ra^{224}$	-24	20218_2		$(2g_{9/2})^{10}$	0+	$.315 \times 10^6$	α 5.71, 5.60, 5.53, . . . ; γ .24	5.79		
$_{88}Ra^{225}$	$-\frac{49}{2}$	23528_2		$3/2^+(631)$		$.128 \times 10^7$	β^- .32; γ .040	0.35		
$_{88}Ra^{226}$	-25	25360_2		$(1i_{11/2})^2$	0+	$.511 \times 10^{11}$	α 4.78, 4.99, . . . ; γ .187, . . .	4.87		
$_{88}Ra^{227}$	$-\frac{51}{2}$	29159_2		$5/2^+(633)$		$.246 \times 10^4$	β^- 1.30; γ .29, .50	1.31		
$_{88}Ra^{228}$	-26	31139_2		$(1i_{11/2})^4$	0+	$.180 \times 10^9$	β^- .055	0.06		
$_{88}Ra^{229}$	$-\frac{53}{2}$			$5/2^+(633)$		$<.300 \times 10^3$	β^-			
$_{88}Ra^{230}$	-27			$(1i_{11/2})^6$	0+	$.360 \times 10^4$	β^- 1.2			

$_{89}Ac^{222}$	-22	17760_2	or $3/2^+ (651)$	$(2g_{9/2})^7$		$.500 \times 10^1$	α 6.96	$\begin{cases} 2.22^+ \\ 7.10\alpha \end{cases}$		
$_{89}Ac^{223}$	$-\frac{45}{2}$	19144_2		$(2g_{9/2})^8$		$.132 \times 10^3$	α 6.64, 6.57, . . . ; EC; γ .01, . . .	$\begin{cases} 0.60^+ \\ 6.79\alpha \end{cases}$		
$_{89}Ac^{224}$	-23	21690_2		$1/2^+ (640)$		$.104 \times 10^5$	EC; α 6.17; γ .217, .133	$\begin{cases} 1.37^+ \\ 6.28\alpha \end{cases}$		
$_{89}Ac^{225}$	$-\frac{47}{2}$	23153_2		$(2g_{9/2})^{10}$		$.864 \times 10^6$	α 5.82, 5.78, 5.72; γ .037–.187	5.93		
$_{89}Ac^{226}$	-24	26160_3		$3/2^+ (631)$		$.104 \times 10^5$	β^- 1.2; EC; γ .068–.253	$\begin{cases} 1.17^- \\ 0.74^+ \end{cases}$		
$_{89}Ac^{227}$	$-\frac{49}{2}$	27753_2		$(1i_{11/2})^2$	$\frac{3}{2}^+$	$.669 \times 10^9$	β^- .043; α 4.94	$\begin{cases} 0.04^- \\ 5.00\alpha \end{cases}$	1.1000	1.700
$_{89}Ac^{228}$	-25	31080_2		$5/2^+ (633)$		$.221 \times 10^5$	β^- 1.11, .45–2.8; γ .058, .10, . . .	2.17		
$_{89}Ac^{229}$	$-\frac{51}{2}$	32800_4		$(1i_{11/2})^4$		$.396 \times 10^4$	β^-	1.10		
$_{89}Ac^{230}$	-26	36210_4		$5/2^+ (633)$		$<.600 \times 10^2$	β^- 2.2	2.90		
$_{89}Ac^{231}$	$-\frac{53}{2}$	38550_3		$(1i_{11/2})^6$		$.900 \times 10^3$	β^- 2.1; γ .18	2.10		
$_{90}Th^{223}$	$-\frac{43}{2}$	20920_3	$(1h_{9/2})^8$	$(2g_{9/2})^7$		.900	α 7.55	$\begin{cases} 1.65^+ \\ 7.71\alpha \end{cases}$		
$_{90}Th^{224}$	-22	21477_2		$(2g_{9/2})^8$	0^+	$.100 \times 10^1$	α 7.17, 6.90, . . . ; γ .18, .09, . . .	7.31		
$_{90}Th^{225}$	$-\frac{45}{2}$	23927_2		$1/2^+ (640)$		$.480 \times 10^3$	α 6.47, 6.30–6.79; EC; γ .32, . . .	$\begin{cases} 0.72^+ \\ 6.92\alpha \end{cases}$		
$_{90}Th^{226}$	-23	24901_2		$(2g_{9/2})^{10}$	0^+	$.186 \times 10^4$	α 6.33, 6.22, . . . ; γ 1.11, .13, . . .	6.45		
$_{90}Th^{227}$	$-\frac{47}{2}$	27706_2		$3/2^+ (631)$		$.157 \times 10^7$	α 5.98, 6.04, . . . ; γ .050, .087, . . .	6.15		
$_{90}Th^{228}$	-24	28750_2		$(1i_{11/2})^2$	0^+	$.603 \times 10^8$	α 5.42, 5.34, . . . ; γ .08, .21, . . .	5.52		
$_{90}Th^{229}$	$-\frac{49}{2}$	31652_2		$5/2^+ (633)$	$\frac{5}{2}^+$	$.230 \times 10^{12}$	α 4.85, 4.94, 5.02; γ .20, .15	5.14	0.3800	4.600
$_{90}Th^{230}$	-25	33087_2		$(1i_{11/2})^4$	0^+	$.240 \times 10^{13}$	α 4.62; γ .068, .14–.25	4.77		
$_{90}Th^{231}$	$-\frac{51}{2}$	36291_2		$5/2^+ (633)$		$.922 \times 10^5$	β^- .30, . . . ; γ .084, .017–.31	0.39		
$_{90}Th^{232}$	-26	38124_2		$(1i_{11/2})^6$	0^+	$.445 \times 10^{18}$	α 4.01, 3.95; γ .059; SF	4.08α		
$_{90}Th^{233}$	$-\frac{53}{2}$	41469_2		$7/2^- (743)$		$.133 \times 10^4$	β^- 1.23; γ .029–.90	1.25		
$_{90}Th^{234}$	-27	43583_2		$(1i_{11/2})^8$	0^+	$.208 \times 10^7$	β^- .19, .10; γ .092, .063, .029	0.27		
$_{90}Th^{235}$	$-\frac{55}{2}$			$1/2^+ (631)$		$<.300 \times 10^3$	β^-			
$_{91}Pa^{225}$	$-\frac{43}{2}$	26230_4	$5/2^- (523)$ or	$(2g_{9/2})^8$		$.200 \times 10^1$	α	$\begin{cases} 2.15^+ \\ 7.38\alpha \end{cases}$		
$_{91}Pa^{226}$	-22	27810_3	$1/2^- (530)$	$1/2^+ (640)$		$.108 \times 10^3$	α 6.81	$\begin{cases} 2.71^+ \\ 6.94\alpha \end{cases}$		
$_{91}Pa^{227}$	$-\frac{45}{2}$	28811_2		$(2g_{9/2})^{10}$		$.230 \times 10^4$	α 6.46, 6.41, 6.42; EC; γ .065, . . .	$\begin{cases} 1.03^+ \\ 6.58\alpha \end{cases}$		
$_{91}Pa^{228}$	-23	31010_2		$3/2^+ (631)$		$.792 \times 10^5$	EC; α 6.09, 5.85; γ .058–1.51	$\begin{cases} 2.10^+ \\ 6.26\alpha \end{cases}$		
$_{91}Pa^{229}$	$-\frac{47}{2}$	32022_2		$(1i_{11/2})^2$	$\frac{5}{2}$	$.130 \times 10^6$	EC; α 5.78, 5.67, 5.61; γ .09, . . .	$\begin{cases} 0.35 \\ 5.84\alpha \end{cases}$		

(Continued)

Table of Nuclides (*continued*)

Nuclide	T_3	Mass excess $M - A$, μu	Prominent terms for ground state or low-lying level: Proton	Neutron	J^π	Half-life, sec	**Abundance,** percent or decay modes with energies, MeV	Total disintegration energy, MeV	Magnetic moment, nm	Quadrupole moment, barns
$_{91}Pa^{230}$	-24	34433_2	$5/2^-$ (523) or	$5/2^+$ (633)		$.147 \times 10^7$	EC; β^- .41; β^+; α; γ .12, .053, . . .	0.46− 1.25+ 5.18		
$_{91}Pa^{231}$	$-\frac{49}{2}$	35877_2	$1/2^-$ (530)	$(1i_{11/2})^4$	$*\frac{3}{2}-$	$.103 \times 10^{13}$	α 5.00, 4.67–5.05; γ .29, . . .	5.53	±1.9800	
$_{91}Pa^{232}$	-25	38612_2		$5/2^+$ (633)		$.114 \times 10^6$	β^- .33; γ .047, .08–.47	1.35− 0.45+		
$_{91}Pa^{233}$	$-\frac{51}{2}$	40132_2		$(1i_{11/2})^6$	$*\frac{3}{2}-$	$.237 \times 10^7$	β^- .26, .15, .51; γ .31, . . .	0.57	3.4000	−3.000
$_{91}Pa^{234}$	-26	43298_2		$7/2^-$ (743)		$.240 \times 10^5$	β^- .5, . . . ; γ .04–1.7	2.23		
$_{91}Pa^{235}$	$-\frac{53}{2}$	45420_3		$(1i_{11/2})^8$		$.144 \times 10^4$	β^- 1.4	1.40		
$_{91}Pa^{237}$	$-\frac{55}{2}$	51080_2		$(1i_{11/2})^{10}$		$.234 \times 10^4$	β^- 2.30, 1.35, . . . ; γ .090, .91, . . .	2.30		
$_{92}U^{227}$	$-\frac{43}{2}$		$(1h_{9/2})^{10}$	$1/2^+$ (640)		$.780 \times 10^2$	α 6.8; EC			
$_{92}U^{228}$	-22	31387_2		$(2g_{9/2})^{10}$	0+	$.558 \times 10^3$	α 6.68, 6.59, . . . ; EC; γ	0.35+ 6.81α		
$_{92}U^{229}$	$-\frac{45}{2}$	33481_2		$3/2^+$ (631)		$.348 \times 10^4$	EC; α 6.36, 6.33, 6.30, . . .	1.36+ 6.47α		
$_{92}U^{230}$	-23	33937_2		$(1i_{11/2})^2$	0+	$.180 \times 10^7$	α 5.88, 5.81, 5.66; γ .078, .159, . . .	5.99		
$_{92}U^{231}$	$-\frac{47}{2}$	36270_2		$5/2^+$ (633)		$.363 \times 10^6$	EC; α 5.45; γ .018–.22	0.36+ 5.55α		
$_{92}U^{232}$	-24	37168_2		$(1i_{11/2})^4$	0+	$.227 \times 10^{10}$	α 5.32, 5.26, 5.13; γ .057, . . . ; SF	5.42α		
$_{92}U^{233}$	$-\frac{49}{2}$	39522_2		$5/2^+$ (633)	$\frac{5}{2}+$	$.511 \times 10^{13}$	α 4.82, 4.78, 4.73; γ .043, .054	4.91	0.5400	3.500
$_{92}U^{234}$	-25	40904_2		$(1i_{11/2})^6$	0+	$.783 \times 10^{13}$	**0.0057**; α 4.77, 4.72; γ .053, .118	4.86		
$_{92}U^{235}$	$-\frac{51}{2}$	43915_2		$7/2^-$ (743)	$\frac{7}{2}-$	$.225 \times 10^{17}$	**0.72**; SF; α 4.18–4.56; γ .195	4.68α	−0.3500	4.100
$_{92}U^{236}$	-26	45637_2		$(1i_{11/2})^8$	0+	$.754 \times 10^{15}$	α 4.50, . . . ; γ .05; SF	4.57α		
$_{92}U^{237}$	$-\frac{53}{2}$	48608_2		$1/2^+$ (631)		$.583 \times 10^6$	β^- .25; γ .060, .21, .026–.37	0.51		
$_{92}U^{238}$	-27	50770_2		$(1i_{11/2})^{10}$	0+	$.142 \times 10^{18}$	**99.27**; α 4.19; SF; γ .048	4.27α		
$_{92}U^{239}$	$-\frac{55}{2}$	54300_2		$5/2^+$ (622)		$.141 \times 10^4$	β^- 1.21; γ .074	1.28		
$_{92}U^{240}$	-28	56594_2		$(1i_{11/2})^{12}$	0+	$.508 \times 10^5$	β^- .36, . . . ; γ .044	0.48		
$_{93}Np^{231}$	$-\frac{45}{2}$	38280_2	$5/2^+$ (642)	$(1i_{11/2})^2$		$.300 \times 10^4$	EC; α 6.28	1.88+ 6.40α		
$_{93}Np^{232}$	-23	39860_4		$5/2^+$ (633)		$.800 \times 10^3$	EC; γ	2.51		
$_{93}Np^{233}$	$-\frac{47}{2}$	40670_2		$(1i_{11/2})^4$		$.210 \times 10^4$	EC; α 5.53	1.07+ 5.63α		
$_{93}Np^{234}$	-24	42860_3		$5/2^+$ (633)		$.380 \times 10^6$	EC; β^+ .8; γ .043–1.61	1.82+		
$_{93}Np^{235}$	$-\frac{49}{2}$	[illegible]		[illegible]		[illegible]	[illegible]	0.13+		

$_{93}Np^{236}$	-25	46624_2		$7/2^-(743)$		$.158 \times 10^{12}$	β^-	0.52 0.92+		
$_{93}Np^{237}$	$-\frac{51}{2}$	48056_2		$(1i_{11/2})^8$	$\frac{5}{2}+$	$.675 \times 10^{14}$	α 4.52–4.87; γ .087, .029–.20	4.96	5.0000	
$_{93}Np^{238}$	-26	50896_2		$1/2^+(631)$	2	$.181 \times 10^6$	β^- 1.24, .25, . . . ; γ .044, .99, . . .	1.29− 0.12+		
$_{93}Np^{239}$	$-\frac{53}{2}$	52924_2		$(1i_{11/2})^{10}$	$\frac{5}{2}+$	$.203 \times 10^6$	β^- .72, . . . ; γ .045–.355	0.72		
$_{93}Np^{240}$	-27	56080_2		$5/2^+(622)$		$.360 \times 10^4$	β^- .84; γ .56, .44, .085–1.16	2.05		
$_{93}Np^{241}$	$-\frac{55}{2}$	58200_3		$(1i_{11/2})^{12}$		$.960 \times 10^3$	β^- 1.36	1.36		
$_{94}Pu^{232}$	-22	41180_2	$(2f_{7/2})^2$	$(1i_{11/2})^2$	0+	$.216 \times 10^4$	EC; α 6.58	1.23+ 6.70α		
$_{94}Pu^{233}$	$-\frac{45}{2}$	42972_2		$5/2^+(633)$		$.120 \times 10^4$	EC; α 6.3	2.14+ 6.42α		
$_{94}Pu^{234}$	-23	43315_2		$(1i_{11/2})^4$	0+	$.324 \times 10^5$	EC; α 6.19; γ .047	0.43+ 6.31α		
$_{94}Pu^{235}$	$-\frac{47}{2}$	45270_2		$5/2^+(633)$		$.156 \times 10^4$	EC; α 5.85	1.13+ 5.96α		
$_{94}Pu^{236}$	-24	46071_2		$(1i_{11/2})^6$	0+	$.899 \times 10^8$	α 5.76, 5.72, . . . ; γ .047, . . . ; SF	5.87α		
$_{94}Pu^{237}$	$-\frac{49}{2}$	48298_2		$7/2^-(743)$	$\frac{7}{2}-$	$.394 \times 10^7$	EC; α 5.2–5.65; γ .03–.076	0.23+ 5.75α		
$_{94}Pu^{238}$	-25	49511_2		$(1i_{11/2})^8$	0+	$.281 \times 10^{10}$	α 5.49, 5.45, . . . ; γ .044, . . . ; SF	5.59α		
$_{94}Pu^{239}$	$-\frac{51}{2}$	52146_2		$1/2^+(631)$	$\frac{1}{2}+$	$.769 \times 10^{12}$	α 5.15, 5.13, . . . ; γ .013, . . . ; SF	5.24α	0.2100	
$_{94}Pu^{240}$	-26	53882_2		$(1i_{11/2})^{10}$	0+	$.213 \times 10^{12}$	α 5.16, 5.12, . . . ; γ .045, . . . ; SF	5.26α		
$_{94}Pu^{241}$	$-\frac{53}{2}$	56737_2		$5/2^+(622)$	$\frac{5}{2}+$	$.410 \times 10^9$	β^- .02; α 4.89, 4.85; γ .100, .145	0.02− 5.15α	−0.7300	5.600
$_{94}Pu^{242}$	-27	58725_2		$(1i_{11/2})^{12}$	0+	$.120 \times 10^{14}$	α 4.90, 4.86; γ .045; SF	4.99α		
$_{94}Pu^{243}$	$-\frac{55}{2}$	61972_2		$7/2^+(624)$		$.179 \times 10^5$	β^- .57, .49; γ .084, .042, . . .	0.57		
$_{94}Pu^{244}$	-28	64100_4		$(3d_{5/2})^2$	0+	$.240 \times 10^{16}$	α; SF	4.57α		
$_{94}Pu^{245}$	$-\frac{57}{2}$	67830_4		$9/2^-(734)$		$.364 \times 10^5$	β^-	1.40		
$_{94}Pu^{246}$	-29	70090_2		$(3d_{5/2})^4$	0	$.937 \times 10^6$	β^- .15, .33; γ .047, .027, .08, . . .	0.40		
$_{95}Am^{237}$	$-\frac{47}{2}$	49840_2	$5/2^-(523)$	$(1i_{11/2})^6$		$.470 \times 10^4$	EC; α 6.01	1.44+ 6.13α		
$_{95}Am^{238}$	-24	51940_4		$7/2^-(743)$		$.670 \times 10^4$	EC; γ .98, .58, .37, .95, 1.35	2.26		
$_{95}Am^{239}$	$-\frac{49}{2}$	53016_2		$(1i_{11/2})^8$		$.432 \times 10^5$	EC; α 5.77; γ .23, .28, .045–.49	0.81		
$_{95}Am^{240}$	-25	55280_4		$1/2^+(631)$		$.184 \times 10^6$	EC; γ 1.00, .90, 1.40, .043, .099	1.30		
$_{95}Am^{241}$	$-\frac{51}{2}$	56714_2		$(1i_{11/2})^{10}$	$\frac{5}{2}-$	$.145 \times 10^{11}$	α 5.48, 5.31–5.53; γ .060, . . . ; SF	5.64α	1.4000	4.900
$_{95}Am^{242}$	-26	59502_2		$7/2^+(624)$	1−	†$.576 \times 10^5$	β^- .63, . . . ; EC; α; γ .04	0.67− 0.72+ 5.59α	±0.3300	±2.800
$_{95}Am^{243}$	$-\frac{53}{2}$	61367_2		$(1i_{11/2})^{12}$	$\frac{5}{2}-$	$.241 \times 10^{12}$	α 5.27, 5.22, 5.17–5.34; γ .075, . . .	5.44	1.4000	4.900
$_{95}Am^{244}$	-27	64355_2		$7/2^+(624)$	6−	$.360 \times 10^5$	β^- .39; γ .043, .009, .15, .75, . . .	1.43− 0.20+		
$_{95}Am^{245}$	$-\frac{55}{2}$	66340_2		$(3d_{5/2})^2$		$.745 \times 10^4$	β^- .91; γ .036, .230, .255, . . .	0.90		
$_{95}Am^{246}$	-28	69660_2		$9/2^-(734)$		$.150 \times 10^4$	β^- 1.31, 1.60, 2.10; γ .035, .10, . . .	2.29		

(Continued)

Table of Nuclides *(continued)*

Nuclide	T_3	Mass excess $M - A$, μu	Prominent terms for ground state or low-lying level: Proton	Neutron	J^π	Half-life, sec	**Abundance,** percent or decay modes with energies, MeV	Total disintegration energy, MeV	Magnetic moment, nm	Quadrupole moment, barns
$_{96}Cm^{238}$	-23	53036_2	$(2f_{7/2})^4$	$(1i_{11/2})^6$	0^+	$.900 \times 10^4$	EC; α 6.52	1.03+ 6.63α		
$_{96}Cm^{239}$	$-\frac{47}{2}$	54880_4		$7/2^-$ (743)		$.100 \times 10^5$	EC; γ .188	1.73		
$_{96}Cm^{240}$	-24	55545_2		$(1i_{11/2})^8$	0^+	$.232 \times 10^7$	α 6.26, . . . ; SF	0.25+ 6.40α		
$_{96}Cm^{241}$	$-\frac{49}{2}$	57542_2		$1/2^+$ (631)	$\frac{1}{2}^+$	$.302 \times 10^7$	EC; α 5.95; γ .48, 1.45	0.77+ 6.19α		
$_{96}Cm^{242}$	-25	58788_2		$(1i_{11/2})^{10}$	0^+	$.141 \times 10^8$	α 6.11, 6.07, . . . ; γ .044, . . . ; SF	6.22α		
$_{96}Cm^{243}$	$-\frac{51}{2}$	61370_2		$5/2^+$ (622)		$.101 \times 10^{10}$	α 5.78, 5.74, . . . ; EC; γ .28, . . .	0.00+ 6.17α		
$_{96}Cm^{244}$	-26	62821_2		$(1i_{11/2})^{12}$	0^+	$.571 \times 10^9$	α 5.80, 5.76, . . . ; γ .043, . . . ; SF	5.90α		
$_{96}Cm^{245}$	$-\frac{53}{2}$	65371_2		$7/2^+$ (624)		$.294 \times 10^{12}$	α 5.36, 5.45; γ .173, .13	5.62		
$_{96}Cm^{246}$	-27	67202_2		$(3d_{5/2})^2$	0^+	$.173 \times 10^{12}$	α 5.37, . . . ; SF	5.47α		
$_{96}Cm^{247}$	$-\frac{55}{2}$	70280_4		$9/2^-$ (734)		$.527 \times 10^{15}$	α	0.02− 5.31α		
$_{96}Cm^{248}$	-28	72220_4		$(3d_{5/2})^4$	0^+	$.148 \times 10^{14}$	α 5.05; SF	5.14α		
$_{96}Cm^{249}$	$-\frac{57}{2}$	75810_3		$7/2^+$ (613)		$.390 \times 10^4$	β− .9	0.86		
$_{96}Cm^{250}$	-29			$(3d_{5/2})^6$	0	$.631 \times 10^{12}$	SF			
$_{97}Bk^{243}$	$-\frac{49}{2}$	62965_2	$3/2^-$ (521) or	$(1i_{11/2})^{10}$		$.162 \times 10^5$	α 6.55, 6.72, 6.20; γ .74, .84, . . .	1.49+ 6.84α		
$_{97}Bk^{244}$	-25	65170_4	$7/2^+$ (633)	$5/2^+$ (622)		$.158 \times 10^5$	EC; α 6.67; γ .20, .90, 1.06, . . .	2.19+ 6.79α		
$_{97}Bk^{245}$	$-\frac{51}{2}$	66272_2		$(1i_{11/2})^{12}$		$.428 \times 10^6$	EC; α 5.89–6.37; γ .25, .38, . . .	0.84 6.48α		
$_{97}Bk^{246}$	-26	68770_4		$7/2^+$ (624)		$.156 \times 10^6$	EC; γ .82, 1.09	0.00− 1.46+		
$_{97}Bk^{247}$	$-\frac{53}{2}$	70260_2		$(3d_{5/2})^2$		$.300 \times 10^{12}$	α 5.51, 5.61, 5.30; γ .084, .27; EC	0.00+ 5.85α		
$_{97}Bk^{248}$	-27	72960_2		$9/2^-$ (734)		$.828 \times 10^5$	β− .65; EC	0.65		
$_{97}Bk^{249}$	$-\frac{55}{2}$	74883_2		$(3d_{5/2})^4$		$.271 \times 10^8$	β− .125; γ .32; α 5.42, . . . ; SF	0.13 5.53α		
$_{97}Bk^{250}$	-28	78270_2		$7/2^+$ (613)		$.115 \times 10^5$	β− .72, 1.76, . . . ; γ	1.76		
$_{98}Cf^{244}$	-24	65969_2	$(2f_{7/2})^6$	$(1i_{11/2})^{10}$	0^+	$.150 \times 10^4$	α 7.17	0.75+ 7.29α		
$_{98}Cf^{245}$	$-\frac{49}{2}$	67905_2		$5/2^+$ (622)		$.264 \times 10^4$	EC; α 7.11	1.52+ 7.23α		
$_{98}Cf^{246}$	-25	[illegible]		[illegible]	0^+	[illegible]	[illegible]	[illegible]		

$_{98}$Cf[illegible]	−26	72262_2		$(3d_{5/2})^2$	0^+	$.302 \times 10^8$	α 6.26; SF	6.37α
$_{98}$Cf^{249}	$-\frac{53}{2}$	74749_2		$9/2^-$ (734)		$.114 \times 10^{11}$	α 5.81, 5.93, 6.20; γ .39, . . . ; SF	6.31α
$_{98}$Cf^{250}	−27	76384_2		$(3d_{5/2})^4$	0^+	$.316 \times 10^9$	α 6.02, 5.98; SF; γ .043	6.13α
$_{98}$Cf^{251}	$-\frac{55}{2}$	79260_4		$7/2^+$ (613)		$.250 \times 10^{11}$	α; γ .18	5.95α
$_{98}$Cf^{252}	−28	81500_4		$(3d_{5/2})^6$	0^+	$.805 \times 10^8$	α 6.11, 6.07; γ .043, 1.00; SF	6.22α
$_{98}$Cf^{253}	$-\frac{57}{2}$	85020_2		$11/2^-$ (725)		$.164 \times 10^7$	β^- .27	0.27
$_{98}$Cf^{254}	−29			$(2g_{7/2})^2$	0^+	$.518 \times 10^7$	SF	
$_{99}$Es^{245}	$-\frac{47}{2}$	71060_4	$7/2^+$ (633)	$(1i_{11/2})^{10}$		$.720 \times 10^2$	α 7.7	2.94^+ 7.79α
$_{99}$Es^{246}	−24	72430_4		$5/2^+$ (622)		$.438 \times 10^3$	α 7.35	3.41^+ 7.48α
$_{99}$Es^{248}	−25	75280_4		$7/2^+$ (624)		$.150 \times 10^4$	EC; α 6.87	2.81^+ 7.00α
$_{99}$Es^{249}	$-\frac{51}{2}$	76258_2		$(3d_{5/2})^2$		$.720 \times 10^4$	EC; α 6.76	1.41^+ 6.88α
$_{99}$Es^{250}	−26	78610_4		$9/2^-$ (734)		$.288 \times 10^5$	EC	2.07
$_{99}$Es^{251}	$-\frac{53}{2}$	79930_2		$(3d_{5/2})^4$		$.130 \times 10^6$	EC; α 6.48	0.63^+ 6.60α
$_{99}$Es^{252}	−27	82810_2		$7/2^+$ (613)		$.120 \times 10^8$	α 6.64	1.23^+ 6.76α
$_{99}$Es^{253}	$-\frac{55}{2}$	84730_2		$(3d_{5/2})^6$		$.173 \times 10^7$	α 6.63, . . . ; SF; γ .042, .051, . . .	6.75α
$_{99}$Es^{254}	−28	87900_2		$11/2^-$ (725)		$.415 \times 10^8$	α 6.42; γ .062	0.98^- 6.54α
$_{99}$Es^{255}	$-\frac{57}{2}$			$(2g_{7/2})^2$		$.207 \times 10^7$	β^-	
$_{99}$Es^{256}	−29			$9/2^+$ (615)		Short	β^-	
$_{100}$Fm^{248}	−24	77092_2	$(2f_{7/2})^8$	$(1i_{11/2})^{12}$	0^+	$.360 \times 10^2$	α	1.69^+ 7.94α
$_{100}$Fm^{249}	$-\frac{49}{2}$	79140_3		$7/2^+$ (624)		$.150 \times 10^3$	α 7.9	2.68^+ 8.04α
$_{100}$Fm^{250}	−25	79490_2		$(3d_{5/2})^2$	0^+	$.180 \times 10^4$	α 7.43	0.81^+ 7.56α
$_{100}$Fm^{251}	$-\frac{51}{2}$	81190_4		$9/2^-$ (734)		$.252 \times 10^5$	EC; α 6.89	1.17^+ 7.00α
$_{100}$Fm^{252}	−26	82562_2		$(3d_{5/2})^4$	0^+	$.828 \times 10^5$	α 7.04	7.17
$_{100}$Fm^{253}	$-\frac{53}{2}$	84930_2		$7/2^+$ (613)		$.390 \times 10^6$	EC; α 6.94	0.19^+ 7.06α
$_{100}$Fm^{254}	−27	86839_2		$(3d_{5/2})^6$	0	$.117 \times 10^5$	α 7.20, 7.16, 7.06; γ .041, . . . ; SF	7.31α
$_{100}$Fm^{255}	$-\frac{55}{2}$	89640_4		$11/2^-$ (725)		$.720 \times 10^5$	α 7.02, 6.96, . . . ; γ .058, . . . ; SF	7.25α
$_{100}$Fm^{256}	−28			$(2g_{7/2})^2$	0^+	$.972 \times 10^4$	SF	
$_{100}$Fm^{257}	$-\frac{57}{2}$			$9/2^+$ (615)		$.864 \times 10^6$	SF	
$_{101}$Md^{255}	$-\frac{53}{2}$	90550_2	$7/2^-$ (514)	$(3d_{5/2})^6$		$.180 \times 10^4$	EC; α 7.34	0.85^+ 7.46α
$_{101}$Md^{256}	−27			$11/2^-$ (725)		$.540 \times 10^4$	EC	

(*Continued*)

Table of Nuclides *(continued)*

Nuclide	T_3	Mass excess $M - A$, μu	Prominent terms for ground state or low-lying level: Proton	Neutron	J^π	Half-life, sec	**Abundance,** percent or decay modes with energies, MeV	Total disintegration energy, MeV	Magnetic moment, nm	Quadrupole moment, barns
$_{102}No^{254}$	-25	91140_3	$(3p_{3/2})^2$	$(3d_{5/2})^4$	0^+	$.300 \times 10^1$	α 8.8	1.55^+; 8.43α		
$_{102}No^{255}$	$-\frac{51}{2}$	92730_4		$7/2^+$ (613)		$.150 \times 10^2$	α 8.2	2.04^+; 8.34α		
$_{102}No^{256}$	-26			$(3d_{5/2})^6$	0	$.800 \times 10^1$	α; SF			
$_{103}Lw^{257}$	$-\frac{51}{2}$	98940_4	$1/2^-$ (521)	$(3d_{5/2})^6$		$.800 \times 10^1$	α 8.6	8.75α		

Name Index

*Subject Index**

* Page numbers appearing in italic type indicate the primary reference.

Adjusted Values of Physical Constants (mks)

Selected from *Physics Today*, February 1964; recommended by National Academy o Sciences – National Research Council.

CONSTANT	SYMBOL	VALUE
Speed of light in vacuum	c	2.997925×10^{8} m-sec^{-1}
Elementary charge	e	1.60210×10^{-19} coul
Avogadro constant	N_A	6.02252×10^{23} mole^{-1}
Electron rest mass	m_0	9.1091×10^{-31} kg
		$= 5.48597 \times 10^{-4}$ u
Proton rest mass	m_{p}	1.67252×10^{-27} kg
		$= 1.00727663$ u
Neutron rest mass	m_{n}	1.67482×10^{-27} kg
		$= 1.0086654$ u
Faraday constant	F	9.64870×10^{4} coul-mole^{-1}
Planck constant	h	6.6256×10^{-34} joule-sec
	$\hbar$	1.05450×10^{-34} joule-sec
Compton wavelength of electron	h/m_0c	2.42621×10^{-12} m
Compton wavelength of proton	$h/m_{\mathrm{p}}c$	1.32140×10^{-15} m
Gyromagnetic ratio of proton	γ	2.67519×10^{8} rad-m^{2}-sec^{-1}-Wb^{-}
	$\gamma/2\pi$	4.25770×10^{7} Hz-m^{2}-Wb^{-1}
(uncorrected for diamagnetism, H_2O)	γ'	2.67512×10^{8} rad-m^{2}-sec^{-1}-Wb^{-}
	$\gamma'/2\pi$	4.25759×10^{7} Hz-m^{2}-Wb^{-1}
Bohr magneton	μ_{B}	9.2732×10^{-24} joule-m^{2}-Wb^{-1}
Nuclear magneton	μ_{N}	5.0505×10^{-27} joule-m^{2}-Wb^{-1}
Proton moment	μ_{p}	1.41049×10^{-26} joule-m^{2}-Wb^{-1}
	$\mu_{\mathrm{p}}/\mu_{\mathrm{N}}$	2.79276
Boltzmann constant	k	1.38054×10^{-23} joule-°K^{-1}
Stefan-Boltzmann constant	σ	5.6697×10^{-8} W-m^{-2}-°K^{-4}
Gravitational constant	G	6.670×10^{-11} N-m^{2}-kg^{-2}